FROM VICTORIA.
        CHRISTMAS 1995.

Base Map

A general map of the region, showing the distribution of the broads in the river valleys. Note that the majority of them are located beside the R. Bure and its principal tributaries, the Ant and the Thurne, and that there are few broads in the Yare and Waveney valleys. Much of the Drained Marshland Area lies below mean high tide level, and would therefore be flooded were the rivers not embanked.

NORWICH

R. WENSUM

RIVER YARE

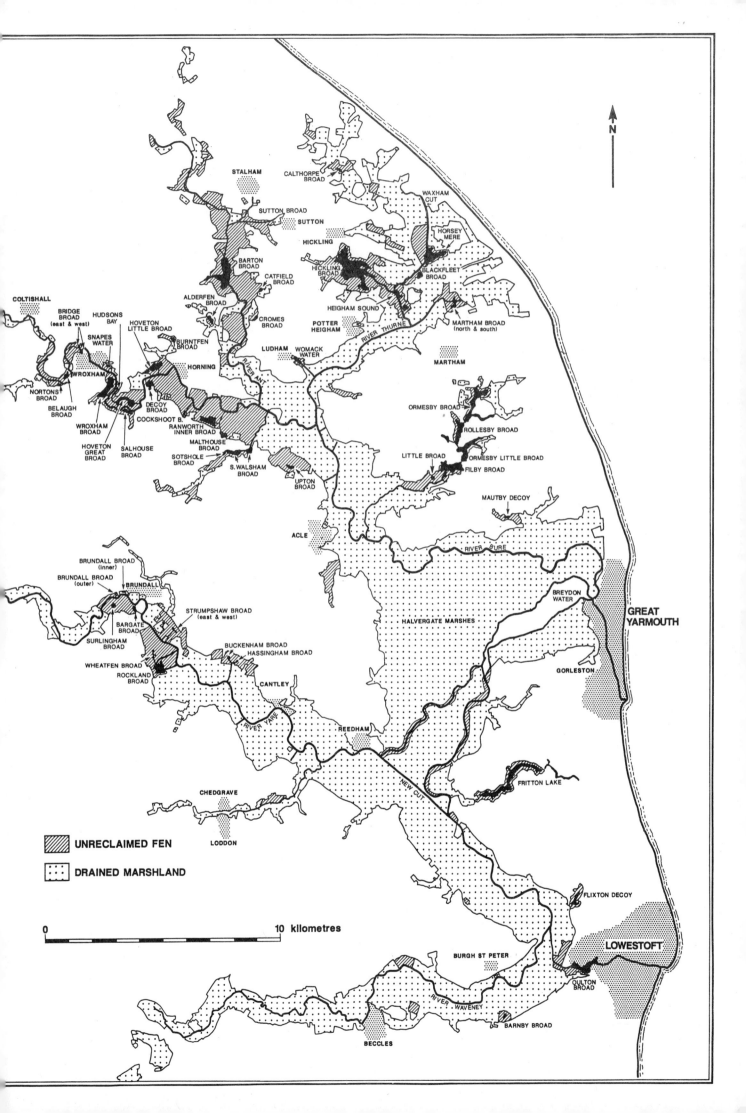

N

STALHAM
CALTHORPE BROAD
WAXHAM CUT
SUTTON BROAD
SUTTON
HICKLING
HORSEY MERE
BARTON BROAD
CATFIELD BROAD
HICKLING BROAD
BLACKFLEET BROAD
ALDERFEN BROAD
CROMES BROAD
HEIGHAM SOUND
COLTISHALL
BRIDGE BROAD (east & west)
HUDSONS BAY
HOVETON LITTLE BROAD
POTTER HEIGHAM
MARTHAM BROAD (north & south)
SNAPES WATER
BURNTFEN BROAD
HORNING
LUDHAM
WOMACK WATER
MARTHAM
WROXHAM
RIVER THURNE
RIVER ANT
ORMESBY BROAD
NORTONS BROAD
DECOY BROAD
ROLLESBY BROAD
BELAUGH BROAD
COCKSHOOT B.
WROXHAM BROAD
RANWORTH INNER BROAD
LITTLE BROAD
ORMESBY LITTLE BROAD
HOVETON GREAT BROAD
SALHOUSE BROAD
MALTHOUSE BROAD
FILBY BROAD
SOTSHOLE BROAD
S. WALSHAM BROAD
UPTON BROAD
MAUTBY DECOY
ACLE
RIVER BURE
BRUNDALL BROAD (inner)
BRUNDALL BROAD (outer)
BRUNDALL
BREYDON WATER
GREAT YARMOUTH
STRUMPSHAW BROAD (east & west)
BARGATE BROAD
SURLINGHAM BROAD
BUCKENHAM BROAD
HASSINGHAM BROAD
HALVERGATE MARSHES
WHEATFEN BROAD
ROCKLAND BROAD
CANTLEY
GORLESTON
RIVER YARE
REEDHAM
CHEDGRAVE
NEW CUT
FRITTON LAKE
LODDON
UNRECLAIMED FEN
DRAINED MARSHLAND
FLIXTON DECOY
0   10 kilometres
LOWESTOFT
BURGH ST PETER
OULTON BROAD
RIVER WAVENEY
BARNBY BROAD
BECCLES

*The Land Use, Ecology
and Conservation of*
BROADLAND

Frontispiece

Looking north-east towards Cold Harbour Farm from the top of Thurne Dyke Mill – 1984.

As will become apparent from Chapter 3, the waterway shown in the foreground (which now forms part of the R. Thurne) was originally occupied by the R. Ant. The latter flowed down the Hundred Dyke, whose relict embankments can be seen behind the cattle in the left middle distance, and after joining the watercourse shown in the photograph at a point just south of the farm buildings, discharged into the R. Bure at the place now known as Thurne Mouth. The R. Ant was subsequently diverted so that it joined the Bure at Ant Mouth, as it does today, whilst the R. Thurne underwent a current reversal. But it is not known whether this resulted from the natural silting up of its original sea outfall, or whether the latter was dammed or sluiced off deliberately.

The R. Thurne is only about 30m wide here, and the person at the tiller of the hired yacht is unintentionally presenting the other helmsmen with some interesting problems. Note that the motor cruiser on the right has had to go astern to avoid a collision.

Thurne Dyke Mill was built in 1820, and restored by Mr. R. D. Morse in the 1950s. It is now cared for by the Norfolk Windmills Trust, which opens it to the public in the summer months.

Photo: R. N. Flowers

The Land Use, Ecology and Conservation of
BROADLAND

Martin George

"Nature is always right, always just;
mistakes and errors arise from human beings".
GOETHE

PACKARD PUBLISHING LIMITED
CHICHESTER

THE LAND USE, ECOLOGY AND CONSERVATION OF BROADLAND

© **Martin George**

First published in **1992** by Packard Publishing Limited,
16 Lynch Down, Funtington, Chichester, West Sussex PO18 9LR.

*All rights reserved. No part of this publication may be
reproduced, stored in a retrieval system or transmitted
in any form or by any means, electronic, mechanical, photo-
copying, recording, or otherwise, without the prior written
permission of the publisher.*

ISBN 1 85341 047 0

A CIP catalogue record for this book is available
from the British Library.

Cover painting by Colin Burns; design by Cecil Smith.
This book was edited by Michael Packard and planned
by Cecil Smith, based on a 'house style' by Louise Burston.

Typesetting by Inforum Typesetting, Portsmouth, Hampshire;
colour reprographics arranged in Hong Kong by Fotographics Ltd.,
Princes Risborough, Buckinghamshire.
Printed and bound by Butler and Tanner Ltd., Frome, Somerset.

Contents

Illustrations

Figures

Tables

Acknowledgements

I have received an immense amount of help during the compilation of this book; indeed, it could not have been written without this. I would particularly like to thank the following persons for commenting on the drafts of specific sections:

Professor Brian Funnell (University of East Anglia) – Chapter 2 (Geology and physiography);

Dr David Dent (University of East Anglia) – Chapter 2 (Acid sulphate soils);

Paul Ashford (formerly an hydrologist on the staff of Anglian Water) – Chapter 3 (Water regime);

Keith Clarke (formerly General Manager of the East Anglian Water Company) and Dr David Burgess (National Rivers Authority) – Chapter 4 (Water supply);

Dr (now Professor) Brian Moss* (formerly at the University of East Anglia, but now at the University of Liverpool) – Chapter 5;

Dr Ros Boar* (University of East Anglia) – Chapter 6;

Dr Bryan Wheeler (University of Sheffield) – Chapter 7 (the plant ecology of the fens);

Dr Andy Foster (Nature Conservancy Council) – Chapter 7 (Lepidoptera);

Dr Garth Foster (Balfour-Browne Club) – Chapter 7 (Water beetles);

Dr Morris Gosling* (Ministry of Agriculture, Fisheries and Food) – Chapter 7 (Coypu);

John Goldsmith (Castle Museum, Norwich) – Chapter 7 (Deer);

Rob Driscoll* (Castle Museum, Norwich) – Chapter 8 (the ecology of the Drained Marshland Area);

Stephen Earl (Norfolk Windmills Trust) – Chapter 8 (Drainage mills);

Professor Tim O'Riordan (University of East Anglia) – Chapters 9 and 12;

Chris Groves (formerly the Rivers Manager of the Great Yarmouth Port and Haven Commissioners) – Chapter 11.

Although I have taken full account of the comments and criticisms made by these persons, I am wholly responsible for any errors or misconceptions which remain in these sections.

Amongst the innumerable other individuals who have provided me with assistance, I should like to express my special thanks to the following (listed alphabetically):

Stan Alden, Arthur Alsop, John Ash* and other staff of the National Rivers Authority, Bryan Ayers, Dr Chris Barringer, the late Michael Bell, Mike Blackburn, the late Tom Blofeld, Dr Laurie Boorman*, Dr John Bowers, Dr Christine Boyce (née Leuze), David Brewster, Jan Brooke, Don Buckingham and other staff of the Norfolk County Council, Ken Buckley, Dr David Burgess, John Buxton, David Cargill, Dr David Cartwright, Francis Cator, Aitken Clark, David Coleman, Dr Brian Coles*, the late Charles Collier, Bill Corbett, Barbara Cornford, Anne Cryer, Andrew Darby, Alan Davison, John Day, Dr Quentin Dresser, Peter Edrich, the late Dr Ted Ellis, Vincent Ellis, John Fielding, Herbert Grapes, John Habgood, John Hart, Dr John Harvey, Richard Hobbs, Rob Holman and other staff of the Broads Authority, Sam Hornor, Dr Tony Irwin, Dr Don Jefferies, Dr Clive Jermy, Dr K. Kristiansen, Bill Lacey, Professor Hugh Lamb*, Dr Joyce Lambert, Peter Lambley, Dr Rick Leah*, Andrew Lees, Stewart Linsell, Jane Madgwick, Keith McDougall, Dr John Murphy, Dr Peter Murphy, John O'Sullivan, Professor John Owen, Dr Peter Owens, Dr Tim Peet, Dr Geoff Phillips*, Tony Prater, Greg Pritchard, Dr David Pugh, the late Dr Derek Ranwell, Bryan Read, Dr John Rodwell, Francis Russell, Malcolm Rush, Ken Saul, Michael Seago, Magnus Sinclair, Les Street, Peter Tennant, Dr (now Professor) Colin Townsend, Desmond Truman, Keith Turner, Kerry Turner, Dr Chris Vincent*, Dr Susan Walker, Moira Warland, Dr Raymond Watson, Dr Sarah Webster, Dr Jonathan Wortley*, and, last but not least, Peter Wright and other colleagues in the East Anglian region of the Nature Conservancy Council. Those whose names are asterisked have kindly allowed me to reproduce figures or maps which have appeared in their published works.

My particular thanks are also due to David Court of Blakes Holidays Ltd., and Jimmy Hoseason of Hoseason's Holidays Ltd., who gave me permission to extract hitherto unpublished data from the archives of their boat-letting firms, and who provided me with information about the economics of the local holiday industry.

Additional thanks are extended to the following societies and publishing houses which gave permission to use figures and data from their journals: the British Ecological Society and Blackwell Scientific Publications Ltd., Oxford, the *Journal of Applied Ecology*; Akademie-Verlag, Berlin, the *Internationale Revue der gesamten Hydrobiologie*; Dr. W. Junk Publishers/Kluwer Academic Publishers, Dordrecht, *Hydrobiologia*; Elsevier Science Publishers, Amsterdam, the *Journal of Hydrology* and *Aquatic Botany*; the British Phycological Society and Academic Press Inc. (London) Ltd., the *British Phycological Journal*. References to the relevant papers are cited in the captions to the respective figures.

My daughter, Lucy, produced a fair copy of Chapter 11 for me, and Sue Holmes of the How Hill Residential Centre somehow found the time to re-type the remainder. I am deeply appreciative of their efforts, and also those of Sue Brodie of Presentation Graphics, who was responsible for the figures, Phillip Judge of the University of East Anglia, who produced the maps, and Richard Denyer and Dick Flowers, who supplied the majority of the black and white photographs, and Colin Burns, who very kindly allowed me to reproduce on the dust-jacket his oil painting of Horsey Mill. My wife, Barbara, proved a most adept and meticulous proof-reader, and I should also like to thank Cecil Smith of Evergreen Graphics, who was responsible for the book's layout, and Michael Packard of Packard Publishing Limited, who dealt with a seemingly endless number of queries and last-minute adjustments to the text with unfailing courtesy and understanding.

Virtually the entire book was drafted during the time that I was employed by the Nature Conservancy Council, and it consequently occupied much of my attention in the evenings and at weekends. I am most grateful for the forbearance shown by Barbara and our four children during that period.

Martin George

Introduction

The region popularly known as the Norfolk Broads, or Broadland, takes its name from a series of shallow lakes, now known to be flooded medieval peat workings, located beside the lower, tidally-influenced reaches of three of East Anglia's principal rivers. These are the Waveney in the south, the Yare and its tributaries the Chet and the Wensum in the centre, and the Bure and its tributaries the Ant and the Thurne in the north (see the end-papers base map). The Yare is joined by the Waveney at the south-western end of Breydon Water, a relic of an extensive estuary which existed in this part of the region in Romano-British times. After receiving the waters of the Bure, the Yare then discharges to the North Sea through a channel, known as the Haven, which has been deflected southwards by the progressive growth of the shingle spit on which the town of Great Yarmouth now stands. In all, there are over 170 kilometres of navigable, lock-free waterways in the region, and in the circumstances it is hardly surprising that it forms one of the most important centres for waterborne tourism and recreation in Britain. Over twelve and a half thousand vessels are licensed to use the waterways, and it has been estimated that about three quarters of a million visitors spend time afloat each year.

The broads, of which there are about 50, have very varied water regimes, some being physically isolated from the rivers, whereas others are in direct communication with the latter. They vary in size from the *c.* 140 hectare expanse of Hickling Broad, to relict pools with a water surface of a quarter of an hectare or less: none of them has a mean depth of more than about 4 metres, and the majority are much shallower than this. The rivers are wide and slow-moving, and are brackish in their lower reaches. They are bordered for much of their length by extensive tracts of drained marsh and unreclaimed fen, the latter displaying much ecological variability as a result of local differences in its hydrology and water chemistry, and variations in the way individual fens were exploited in the past as a source of peat for fuel, reed and saw-sedge for thatching, marsh hay, alder poles and other crops.

Because of the large size, close juxtaposition and varied nature of these areas of open water, marsh and fen, the region is of quite outstanding land-use and natural history interest. Indeed, although it has been subject to major environmental changes since the Second World War, notably as a result of the enrichment of the waterways by excessive quantities of nitrates and phosphates, and the ploughing up of much grass marshland, Broadland is still regarded by conservationists as one of the most important wetland systems in Britain. The region is also extremely attractive scenically, a fact formally recognized in recent legislation, which has afforded it a status comparable to that of a national park.

Not the least of Broadland's present interest lies in the fact that its ecology has been subject to intensive research over the past 15 years or so. Whilst much further work needs to be done, our understanding of the reasons why the region's principal habitats, notably the open water and reedswamp communities, have become degraded has developed sufficiently to enable conservation organizations such as the Broads Authority, Nature Conservancy Council (now English Nature) and Royal Society for the Protection of Birds to begin the task of restoring selected sites to the condition they were in 40 to 50 years ago.

The boundary of Broadland is defined differently in the numerous reports which have been produced about the region since the 1940s, the main variations being related to how much of the higher ground bordering the valley flood plains should be included, and whether the boundary should be drawn so as to encompass the formerly canalized sections of the rivers Bure, Ant and Waveney. In the following chapters these one-time navigations are mentioned, albeit briefly, but the region is otherwise defined as comprising only the flood plains of the tidal sections of the rivers, and in the case of the Thurne broads, their immediate catchment.

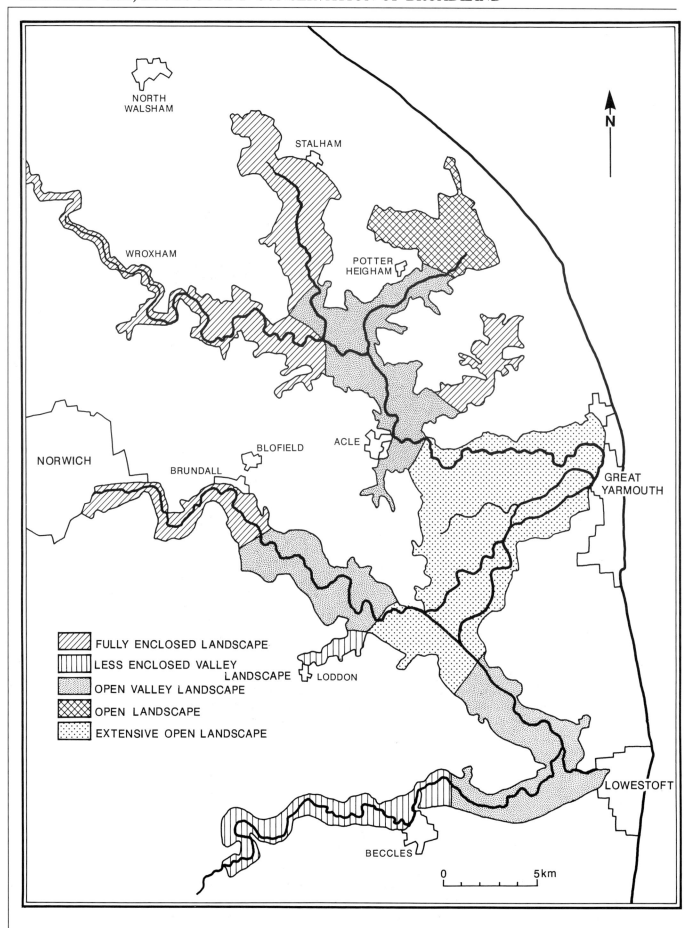

Map 1.1   The types of landscape found in Broadland.

Source: Broads Authority (1982b)

Chapter 1
Broadland's Scenery

Broadland's scenery has long formed an inspiration to painters, and excellent examples of their work, particularly that of John Crome and John Sell Cotman of the Norwich School, are on display at the Castle Museum, Norwich. Numerous writers, too, have sought to describe, often in very evocative terms, the region's quiet charm. Davies (1884), for example, noted that:

> Often times within the circle of your sight there is neither house nor man visible. A grey church tower, a windmill, or the dark-brown sail of a wherry in the distance breaks the sense of utter loneliness, but the scene is wild enough to enchain the imagination of many. Long miles of sinuous gleaming river, marshes gay with innumerable flowering plants, wide sheets of water bordered with swaying reeds, yachts or wherries, boats, fish, fowl, and rare birds and plants, and exquisite little bits to paint and sketch – these are the elements out of which a pleasant holiday may be made.

The region is described in the Hobhouse Report (Ministry of Town and Country Planning, 1947a) in rather similar terms:

> Slow rivers creep between its fields and fens. Wide shallow meres – the Broads themselves – lie along their courses, their edges merging into reed beds or waterlogged alder carrs. The bank of a dyke is an eminence whence you may see white or gaily coloured sails progressing mysteriously across a meadow; you will see also a few scattered woods, perhaps a derelict windmill or two, an immense stretch of sky, and sometimes, on the far horizon, a pale sliver of sand dunes marking the shore of the North Sea.

Similarly, Wentworth Day (1967) wrote of the Waveney valley:

> Quiet, peaceful, lit with beauty . . . it remains largely unspoiled, . . . you will see shining rivers, white sails gliding above green marshes, windmills standing immobile as forgotten sentinels, brown acres of reed where the bittern creeps, [and of the Acle and Halvergate marshes:]. . . . that immense prairie of fourteen thousand acres of green, dyke-seamed, river-bounded cattle marshes which run on and on under the high skies of summer and the pewter clouds of winter to the distant spires and faint marching roofs of Yarmouth.

Such descriptions are not merely lyrical; they pick out most of the salient features of the Broadland landscape. In a report compiled for the Countryside Commission in 1978, the most enduring of these is identified as land form: in particular, the flatness of the valley floors, and the slight, but nonetheless important elevation of the adjoining higher ground (Land Use Consultants, 1978). Reference is also made to the close association between the landscape of the region and the water, not only of the broads and rivers, but of the small dykes which help to break up what would otherwise be near-continuous expanses of marsh. Other principal elements in the landscape identified in the report include the woodlands, scrub and fen, the reedy 'edge' habitats beside the rivers and broads, the rough texture of the drained marshland, and the animals grazing thereon, and the human artifacts which serve the needs of settlement, transport, recreation and above all agriculture. Of the latter . . . "perhaps the most important are the windpumps which, though in varying states of disrepair, are not found in like numbers anywhere else in Britain".

Intrusive elements in the landscape listed by the authors include power lines, and in particular the extra-tall pylons near Haddiscoe and Thorpe, the "large and depressingly ugly" road bridge carrying the A143 across the New Cut at St. Olaves, the railways on their embankments across the marshes, and most dominating of all, the sugar beet factory at Cantley.

Three principal categories of landscape were recognized in the report and these were subsequently worked up by the Landscape Working Group of the Broads Authority (1982b) into a classification, of which the following is a summary:

A. *Enclosed Landscapes*

(i) Fully Enclosed. This includes many of the alder-fringed broads and rivers which are more or less enclosed by carr, fen or waterside trees; when viewed from a boat the landscape is often varied by visual contrasts between one side of the river and the other. Examples, include the upper parts of the Ant, Bure and Yare valleys, and the Ormesby, Rollesby, Filby area.
(ii) Less Enclosed. This is a larger-scale landscape than the last, but still displays a distinct valley form. Grazing marsh predominates, but poplars, willows or other trees, are prominent. The Upper Waveney and Chet valleys fall into this category.

B. *Open Valley Landscapes*

In these, the valleys are very wide, and relatively tree-less. Grazing marsh, with its livestock, dykes, field gates and windpumps predominates, and forms a marked visual contrast with the varied arable landscape of the rising land at the valley margin. Examples include the middle Bure, Ant, Thurne, Yare and Waveney valleys.

C. *Open Flat Landscapes.*

(i) Open. These are confined to the catchment of the R. Thurne, and consist of extensive sheets of open water, reed fen and grazing marsh; there are few trees, and windpumps form a very conspicuous feature of the landscape.
(ii) Extensive Open. These consist of vast expanses of flat, predominantly grazing marshland, with very few trees or buildings in sight. Windpumps are very conspicuous, and the upland margin is often so far distant as to be almost invisible. The sky is very significant in such open areas, which are located beside the lower reaches of the rivers Bure, Yare and Waveney.

The distribution of these landscape types is shown on Map 1.1.

Members of the Working Group responsible for drawing up this classification were only too well aware of the old adage that 'beauty is in the eye of the beholder', and that no two people would necessarily agree as to which parts of Broadland were scenically more attractive than the remainder. In order to reduce the element of subjectivity, they therefore decided to grade the different areas according to the extent to which they possessed features characteristic of the landscape type to which they belong. The four grades chosen were defined as follows:

Grade 1 – Land of exceptional Broads landscape significance, due to its land use and features associated with the particular landscape type.

Grade 2 – Land possessing typical features of the particular landscape type, but not as exceptionally valuable and outstanding as Grade 1 land.

Grade 3 – Land that lacks a positive and consistent Broads character. Mixed land uses and a number of intrusive features usually combine to reduce the traditional Broads quality of the landscape.

Grade 4 – Land with no positive Broads character.

On the basis of their survey, the Group decided that *c.* 9500 hectares (ha) were of Grade 1 landscape importance (see Map 1.2) of which *c.* 5500 ha consisted of woodland, fen and water, whilst the remainder was grass marshland in 1980/1, most of it unimproved.

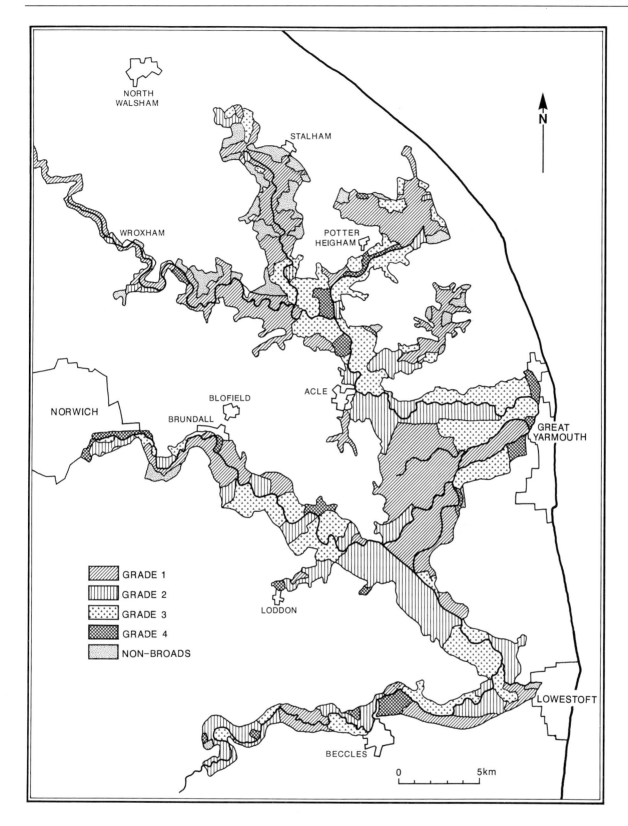

Map 1.2

Landscape quality in Broadland.

Source: Broads Authority (1982b)

A further 5000 ha were classified as being of Grade 2 importance, of which *c.* 4300 ha were grazing marsh, whilst 5000 ha and 1000 ha were classed as being of Grade 3 and 4 interest respectively. Almost all the Grade 3 land, and most of the Grade 4, was farmed, the rest being urbanized to a greater or lesser extent.

Even while the Working Group was finalizing its Report, farmers were busy ploughing up their grass marshes, and by the end of 1984, staff of the Broads Authority estimated that some 1750 ha of the area classified as being of Grade 1 or 2 landscape importance had been converted. The reasons for this, and the steps taken to halt the process are discussed in Chapters 9 and 13.

Table 2a   Geological strata in Broadland

Years (y) & millions of years (my)	Formations & deposits	Stages, Systems & Eras			
	Valley alluvium i.e. Upper Peat Upper Clay Middle Peat Lower Clay Lower Peat	Flandrian (= Post–Glacial)	HOLOCENE	QUATERNARY	CENOZOIC
11 000y		Devensian Glaciation	PLEISTOCENE		
		Ipswichian Interglacial			
130 000y		Wolstonian Glaciation			
		Hoxnian Interglacial			
	Lowestoft Till Corton Beds Cromer Till & Norwich Brickearth	Anglian Glaciation			
300 000y	Weybourne Crag Norwich Crag				
2my	London Clay Reading Beds		EOCENE		
65my	Chalk	Upper	CRETACEOUS		MESOZOIC
100my		(Lower)			
136my			(JURASSIC)		
195my			(TRIASSIC)		
225my			PERMIAN		PALAEOZOIC
280my			CARBONIFEROUS		
345my			(DEVONIAN)		
400my			SILURIAN		
440my			(ORDOVICIAN)		
530my			(CAMBRIAN)		
570my			PRECAMBRIAN		
4500my					

Note: Systems in parentheses are not mentioned in the text.

Source: Modified from Funnell (1976)

Chapter 2
The Geology, Physiography, Soils and Climate of Broadland

Geology

The sloping platform of Precambrian rocks which underlies Broadland at a depth of between 400 and 500 m, and which is variously known as the Anglo-Brabant Massif, or St. George's Land, lies at too great a depth to affect the physiography or water regime of the region directly. Nor too do the Silurian, Carboniferous and Permian strata (see Table 2a) which successively overlie the Precambrian Shield, and which are revealed in deep boreholes such as that sunk beside the Somerton to Horsey road for the Continental Oil Company in 1969. However, the 400 m deep layer of oozy sediment which was laid down in Cretaceous times on top of these older rocks, and which subsequently hardened to become what we call the Chalk formation, is of importance in a Broadland context for several reasons. Much of the water carried by the region's rivers is derived from its aquifers, and in addition, the Chalk has been widely exploited as a source of groundwater for domestic, agricultural and industrial purposes, and more recently for river-regulation schemes.

The water in the Chalk is generally of good quality, although the concentration of chloride ions in it increases from a mean of about 50 milligrams per litre (mg l^{-1}) to 500 mg l^{-1} or more near the coast, a figure in excess of the 200 mg l^{-1} recommended by the World Health Organisation (WHO) as the maximum for public water supply. A trial borehole at Lowestoft yielded water containing 3300 mg Cl$^-$ l^{-1} and even higher figures have been recorded further south. These high chloride waters are thought to be 'connate' (fossil) sea water trapped in the Chalk by impermeable clay strata laid down in Eocene times.

Most boreholes in the Chalk underlying Broadland yield water which contains considerably less nitrogen than the level of 11.3 mg l^{-1} NO$_3$–N* which is 'recommended' by the WHO as a maximum for supply purposes. For instance, samples taken from the Caistor St. Edmund and Colney bores between April 1980 and March 1981, had mean concentrations of 5.7 and 6.7 mg l^{-1} respectively, with a maximum of 8.4 mg l^{-1} at each site. However, nitrogen concentrations in water from the boreholes at the Thorpe St. Andrew pumping station at the foot of Harvey Lane are slightly in excess of the WHO

---

* Although limnologists usually refer to the amount of nitrogen in a water body in terms of the number of milligrams of nitrate nitrogen (NO$_3$–N) in it, nitrogen concentrations are often quoted as a function of the number of milligrams of nitrate present per litre. 22.58 per cent of the nitrate ion consists of nitrogen, and thus 50 mg nitrate per litre can also be expressed as 11.3 mg nitrate nitrogen per litre.

recommended level, varying between *c.* 12.5 and 13.3 mg l^{-1}, with a maximum of *c.* 14.7 mg l^{-1}, and this water is therefore blended with another source of supply before it is used.

Although the nitrogen levels in these and various other boreholes, including those at Aylsham and Lyng, are moderately high and slowly rising, nitrogen concentrations elsewhere in the region are not only very low, but stable (Bamfield, pers. comm.). The boreholes at East Ruston, for instance, yield water containing only about 0.23 mg NO_3–N, and the mean concentration at Strumpshaw is even less than this. These low figures are attributable to the fact that much of the water obtained at these and other sites in this part of Broadland has percolated through the iron-rich, Quaternary Crag deposits which overlie the Chalk here. Iron levels in the water are therefore high, and this favours the presence of de-nitrifying bacteria. Where, as at Caistor St. Edmund, Aylsham and Lyng, the Crag is either absent or poorly represented, the iron concentration in the water obtained from the Chalk aquifers is low, and nitrogen levels are much higher. As in other parts of Eastern England, the latter are also tending to rise, as a result of the more intensive farming methods now being practised in the area.

As the Chalk Sea retreated at the end of the Cretaceous period, some 100 million years ago, earth movements caused the pre-Mesozoic platform and the Chalk resting thereon to be tilted. It is for this reason, that the Chalk, (the upper horizons of which sometimes contain huge barrel-shaped flints known as 'paramoudras') lies at a depth of some 137 m at Great Yarmouth, but is exposed in the vicinity of Norwich and Wroxham, particularly in the river valleys.

The material we know as chalk was extensively worked from such outcrops in the past, some of the largest quarries being located on the south side of the Bure valley between Wroxham and Horstead. Here the chalk was loaded on to wherries and taken away via a series of canals connected with the river. Woodward (1881) notes that the workings went out of use in 1877, and the now overgrown pits, piles of over-burden, and silted-up waterways are known locally as 'Little Switzerland'. Huge quantities of chalk were also obtained in Thorpe Hamlet from quarries near the R. Wensum (one of which, 'The Nest', formed the site of the Norwich City football ground between 1908 and 1935), and also from opencast workings beside the R. Yare at Thorpe St. Andrew and Whitlingham (see Plate I). Chalk and flints were also extensively mined in and around Norwich, and it is thought that some of the resultant tunnels may date from medieval times (Atkin, 1983).

Some chalk was, in the absence of other rock, used as a foundation for roads and buildings, whilst during Victorian times, large quantities were taken in wherries downstream to the cement works at Berney Arms and Burgh Castle. But the remainder was burnt to form lime, a practice thought to have been introduced by the Romans (Alderton, pers. comm.). Some of the lime was employed in the tanning industry, and to make lime-mortar, but from the sixteenth century onwards, huge quantities were used to improve the productivity of farm land, particularly where the soils were derived from glacial tills which, on deposition, were deficient in calcium carbonate and therefore acidic, or which had become so as a result of subsequent leaching. According to Jones (1977), many kilns went out of use from the late nineteenth century onwards as a result of the competition afforded by the railways, which made it more economic to import lime from counties such as Derbyshire, than burn it locally. But the same worker notes that there were at one time kilns at Whitlingham, Reedham, Yarmouth, Acle Bridge, Barton Turf (beside Lime Kiln Dyke!), Stalham, Buxton (which would have been supplied by wherries using the Upper Bure (Coltishall to Aylsham) Navigation, Dilham and Coltishall (behind the Railway Inn). Kilns in recognizable condition survive at the two latter sites, and there are also two on the Crown Point Estate, close to the Whitlingham Picnic Site. One of these is an above-ground structure beside the road, and is in a ruinous condition, but the other (which is located some 75 m to the south) was, like most East Anglian kilns, built below ground level. All four of these kilns are on private property, and should not be visited without the landowner's permission. They should also be regarded as being structurally unsafe.

Most of the sites where chalk was quarried are now covered with talus and overgrown, and there are few exposures where its stratigraphy and fauna as described by

Peake and Hancock (1961) can be studied. However, provided permission is obtained, 'Weybourne Chalk' can be seen at Keswick in a partially-infilled pit owned by the Leicester Lime Company, while deposits of 'Beeston Chalk' are still being actively worked by the Frettenham Lime Company at Caistor St. Edmund.

Given the proximity of Broadland to the Hewett, Leman and other gas fields in the southern North Sea, it is hardly surprising that the region has attracted considerable attention from companies anxious to determine whether the older strata underlying it contain exploitable reserves of hydrocarbons. An exploration licence was granted to Cluff Oil over the Sea Palling, Somerton to Acle area in 1983 (XL 175), and this was renewed over a slightly smaller area in 1986 (EXL 076). Concessions over two other 10 by 10 kilometre squares embracing parts of north-east Broadland were granted to consortia headed by Trafalgar House Oil and Gas Ltd in 1986 (EXL 075) and 1988 (EXL 157).

For commercial reasons, the data obtained during petroleum exploratory work are not generally available, but it is understood that the deep borehole sunk beside the Horsey to Somerton road in 1969 failed to reveal any worthwhile oil or gas reserves.

Plate I

Crown Point Pit (Whitlingham) – *c.* **1900.**

This is one of several large disused quarries in the vicinity of what is now the Whitlingham Picnic Site, and was probably the last to be worked. The Upper Chalk which was exposed in it at the turn of the century was referrable to the 'mucronata zone', and was capped by fossiliferous Norwich Crag deposits. The working faces of the Pit are now covered by talus, and the whole site is very overgrown.

The mineral line shown in the photograph was used to convey chalk to wherries moored alongside the nearby R. Yare. The now-derelict quay headings where these vessels were loaded can still be seen at low tide, but are now located 6 m or so out into the river, as a consequence of bank erosion.

Photo: R.N. Flowers from a plate in Dutt (1903).

Despite this, a further borehole was put down by Trafalgar House a short distance south-west of Somerton Church in 1987. It, too, is alleged to have been 'dry'.

In addition to these 'wild-cat' boreholes, three seismic surveys have been carried out in Broadland using vibroseis vehicles. The first of these was done for Quintana Anglia Ltd. by the Compagnie Générale de Géophysique in 1981, and included areas around Hoveton, as well as North Walsham and Cromer. Rees Geophysical did a similar survey for Cluff Oil in the district around Blofield, Acle and Martham in 1984, and the Coltishall to Wroxham area was covered for Trafalgar House by Horizon Exploration in 1987.

East Anglia displays a fuller sequence of Quaternary deposits than any other part of the British Isles, and much of the classic work on the stratigraphy of this era was carried out in Broadland. During the early part of the period, the eastern parts of East Anglia were covered by a shallow sea, and a series of strata collectively known as the Norwich Crag, and consisting mainly of iron-rich sands, laminated clays and pebbly gravels, were laid down. The Crag deposits dip to the east and attain their maximum thickness of over 60 m at Oulton Broad and Caister. In some parts of Broadland, for instance at Lound, the Norwich Crag has been exploited as a source of water, but elsewhere, notably in the Hickling-Horsey area, its aquifers contain saline water.

In the east, the Norwich Crag is separated from the Chalk by the London Clay and the underlying Reading Beds, but in the west it directly overlies the eroded surface of the Chalk. Here characteristically there is a basal 'stone-bed' which consists of brown-stained flints, amongst which have been found the bones of mastodon, antelope, hyena, leopard and other vertebrates.

The Norwich Crag deposits were extensively worked in the past, some of the material being used for making bricks (as at Brundall, Coltishall and Reedham), or, if it contained above-average quantities of clay, tiles. But most of the pits mentioned by Woodward (1881), Reid (1882), Harmer (1902) and other Victorian geologists in their descriptions of the successional fauna of the Norwich Crag, have long since been grown over or filled in. Nevertheless, the classic sections at Bramerton (TG 295059) can still be seen and have been re-assessed by Funnell (1961). These, and other exposures of the Norwich Crag contain the shells of mussels, dog-whelks, periwinkles and other marine molluscs, not unlike those found today in coastal waters.

By examining the plant and animal remains found at differing horizons in the Norwich Crag, and in succeeding strata, such as the Weybourne Crag which outcrops near Wroxham (Cambridge, 1978), early workers were able to show that the climate varied considerably during the early Pleistocene; in addition they were able to point to changes in the shoreline and depth of the Crag Sea. Our understanding of the conditions which existed during the Pleistocene was improved still further following an examination of the pollen and foraminiferans found in sediment cores taken from boreholes put down during the 1950s at Ludham (West, 1961). This and subsequent work, notably on the fine series of exposures on the coast of north-east Norfolk and East Suffolk, has enabled West and his colleagues to trace the changes which have occurred from the onset of the Pleistocene, some 1.7 to 2 million years ago, up to the present time (Funnell & West, 1977; West, 1980).

Two separate ice advances occurred in the first or 'Anglian' glaciation. The 'Cromer Advance' commenced about 300 000 years ago, and was from a northerly direction. The 'North Sea Drift' which it deposited characteristically contains occasional igneous rock fragments of Scottish and Scandinavian origin, as well as much material transplanted from the North Sea Basin. On the coast, the North Sea Drift is known as the Cromer Till and contains numerous chalk fragments and flint. Inland, however, the deposits thought by most geologists to be contemporaneous with this Till, are collectively known as the Norwich Brickearth, and consist of a sandy-clay or greyish sandy-clay loam, often decalcified, and therefore acidic near the surface. In Broadland, the Brickearth varies in thickness from about 1 m at Ludham, to about 18 m at Panxworth.

The drifts laid down by the Cromer Advance are overlain on the coast of East Norfolk and Suffolk by a succession of beach deposits, piled up to a height of some 10 to 20 m above present sea level. Inland these 'Corton Beds' usually consist of false-bedded sands and gravels, often containing layers of peat or driftwood remains. Lenses of clay containing brackish-water foraminiferans, and the occurrence of marine mollusc shells in the sands, suggest that the beds were originally formed in estuarine channel and back-water environments, and were subsequently re-deposited (Funnell, *in litt.*).

Although there is general agreement that the Corton Beds are glacio-fluvial or glacio-marine in origin, and that they were laid down between the two ice advances of the Anglian Glaciation (West, 1961), there is disagreement amongst geologists as to the extent to which the climate ameliorated during this time. However the fact that these Beds contain a pollen record suggestive of a full or late glacial flora, and that ice-wedge casts occur in them, both at their type locality at Corton, and in a sand pit at Burgh Castle (Ranson, 1968), suggests that they were laid down in a permafrost environment.

Earlier workers believed that the Chalky Boulder Clay which covers much of East Anglia was laid down during separate glaciations. However it now seems possible that the Lowestoft and Gipping Tills, as they are known, were deposited more or less contemporaneously by the ice-sheets of the second, or Lowestoft Advance of the Anglian Glaciation. Evidence for this comes partly from the fact that the mechanical composition and minerology of geographically distinct exposures of the Till are remarkably uniform, and partly from the absence of terminal moraines, outwash fans and other surface features indicative of the Tills being laid down during separate glacial episodes.

Stone orientation and other studies (West & Donner, 1956) have shown that the main mass of ice approached from the west, picking up not only chalk, but fragments of Jurassic strata as it crossed West Norfolk. There is a thick belt of sand and gravel outwash along the western limit of the Norwich Brickearth, and it is believed by many geologists that the ice which laid down the latter, deflected the advancing Lowestoft ice-sheet to the south of Norwich. In any event, as this ice passed over Broadland it swung north-eastwards towards Flegg, meantime overriding the Corton Beds in many places.

The Chalky Boulder Clay laid down as this great mass of ice melted, covers not only much of the southern and eastern parts of Broadland, but substantial parts of the catchments of its rivers. The run-off from these areas tends to be calcium-rich, and this, together with the fact that the water in the rivers is in part derived from springs in the underlying Chalk, accounts for their high alkalinity and calcium content. The alkalinity of the R. Bure, for example, ranges between 3.5 and 4.5 milli-equivalents per litre (meq l^{-1}), whilst the R. Yare has a mean alkalinity of about 5 meq l^{-1} (Moss, pers. comm.).

To the north of the Wensum and Yare valleys, and closely associated with the Till laid down during the Lowestoft Advance is a complex series of intercalated, mainly unbedded, clays and loamy sands, collectively known as the Contorted Drift. Outwash sands and gravels deposited by the streams flowing from the ice are also of frequent occurrence.

As the ice melted, sub-glacial channelling took place, often to a considerable depth in the Chalk. Later, the channels were infilled with boulder clay, sandy outwash or silt, but their presence can lead to unexpected difficulties during the development of underground water resources, when boreholes may have to be extended to greater depths than intended to reach the chalk aquifers beneath (Funnell, 1976). Problems of this sort were encountered during the sinking of the boreholes for the Thorpe St. Andrew pumping station in the 1960s.

As the climate ameliorated and the Lowestoft ice-sheet retreated, water-filled hollows formed both on the surface of the Till, and along the course of some of the valleys eroded therein. Research on the stratigraphy and pollen record of the lacustrine deposits formed in such hollows has yielded information about the vegetational and faunistic changes which took place during the succeeding Hoxnian Interglacial. The classic site for such studies was at Hoxne, near Diss (West, 1956), but several other places, including South Elmham in the Waveney valley (West, 1961) have been examined subsequently. The pollen analyses have shown that tundra-like conditions gradually gave way to forests, dominated initially by birch, and later by oak; meantime, sea levels rose by approximately 20 m as a result of the partial melting of the polar ice-caps. Later during the Interglacial, the climate became gradually colder and the vegetational succession was reversed until tundra-like conditions once again developed (Birks, 1976).

Although the region was probably not ice-covered during the second, or Wolstonian Glaciation, the periglacial conditions which developed undoubtedly helped to mould the Broadland landscape. Furthermore, the proximity of ice-sheets is suggested by the occurrence of well-bedded gravels overlying the boulder clay; these may represent glacial outwash of this period.

Despite the suggestion that the Broadland river valleys follow the course of the buried river channels created at the end of the Lowestoft Advance, the lakes formed on the surface of the boulder clay during the succeeding Hoxnian Interglacial are unrelated to the present drainage system (Funnell, 1976). Accordingly, the latter must have developed afterwards, and probably towards the end of the Wolstonian Glaciation, some 130 000 year ago. Confirmation of this is afforded by the fact that in places the valleys contain sediments, sometimes in the form of river terraces, which were laid down during the warm period – the Ipswichian Interglacial – which followed this glaciation.

The plant and animal remains found in deposits formed during this Interglacial provide an insight into the climatic changes which occurred during this period, which lasted until about 70 000 years ago. Birks (1976) has pointed out that the occurrence of such southern species as the Montpellier Maple (*Acer monospessulanum*), Water Chestnut (*Trapa natans*) and Small Naiad (*Naias minor*), and the ability of Frogbit (*Hydrocharis morsus-ranae*) and Water Soldier (*Stratiotes aloides*) to set seed, indicates that the summers during this Interglacial were 2° to 3° C warmer than they are today. The mammalian fauna shows that during the latter half of the period, dense forest cover had given way to open heathlands, over which roamed horses, fallow deer and bison, together with the wolves, lions and other carnivores which preyed upon them. Hippopotamuses were present in Broadland, as in other parts of East Anglia during this Interglacial, though apparently absent during the preceding Hoxnian period.

The third or Devensian Glaciation, once again brought tundra-like conditions to East Anglia. However the ice cover did not extend as far south as Broadland and on two occasions the climate ameliorated sufficiently to permit the establishment of a light forest cover. During the first of these interstadials, which occurred some 60 000 years ago, a boreal forest containing spruce, pine and birch developed, whilst in the second, or Allerod Interstadial, open birch woodland, with an understorey containing juniper and a variety of tall herbs, covered the landscape (Birks, 1976).

It is clear from the work of Woodward, Reid and others that the sands, gravels and clays laid down during the successive glaciations of East Anglia were extensively worked in the past and many of Broadland's brickworks were dependent on nearby deposits of Norwich Brickearth (e.g. Barton Turf and How Hill) or Boulder Clay (e.g. Rockland St. Mary). Huge quantities of glacially-derived material were also used for claying light, sandy farm land, whilst the gravelly deposits were widely utilized as sources of hoggin for road making and similar purposes.

More recently, the fluvio-glacial sands and gravels flooring the Yare valley in the vicinity of Norwich have begun to be exploited by commercial interests. The embankment carrying the Cringleford by-pass across this valley is composed of 'fill' obtained from the 'broad' created on the campus of the University of East Anglia between 1973 and 1978, whilst planning permission was given in 1989 for the phased extraction of some 4.3 million tonnes of sand and gravel from beneath the Trowse and Thorpe marshes (see page 444).

Physiography

At the height of the last glaciation, some 18 000 years ago, about 5 per cent of the earth's total water inventory was in the form of ice on land, and the sea level was, in consequence, some 100 to 130 m lower than it is today (Lamb, 1972). Since then there has been a progressive, if somewhat irregular, moderation in the climate, and a corresponding return to the oceans of water from the melting ice-caps. This 'eustatic' rise in sea level has continued throughout the present Flandrian or post-glacial period, which commenced some 11 000 years ago. But during the past few millennia, the fluctuations in the general eustatic rise, have tended to be masked by 'isostatic' alterations in the configuration of the earth's crust caused by variations in loading during, and after, the Ice Ages. At the climax of the Anglian Glaciation, the 2650 m thick mantle of ice which covered Scandinavia would have produced a crustal depression of some 739 m, and even during the Devensian period, when the ice covering Scandinavia and Scotland was only about 1000 m thick, a crustal depression of over 300 m must have resulted. As these enormous masses of ice melted, and the load on the earth's crust was correspondingly reduced, updoming of the depressed areas took place. Simultaneously, the margins of the southern North Sea, including what is now Broadland, gradually subsided as a result of the compensatory movement of material beneath the earth's crust. That Broadland has been more markedly affected by post-glacial subsidence than many other parts of Britain is illustrated by the fact that the surface of the sediments laid down in the lower Yare valley between about 4000 and 5000 years ago now lies some 7 m below Ordnance Datum (OD), whereas the corresponding stratigraphic horizon in the Somerset Levels lies only about 1 m below OD (Coles, 1977).

Just how different land/sea levels were in early Flandrian times compared with today is illustrated by the fact that pieces of peat formed under fen conditions have been dredged up from a depth of between 32 and 52 m in the southern North Sea. Pollen counts indicate that this peat was formed between about 10 000 and 8000 years ago during the Pre-Boreal (Zone IV) and early Boreal (Zone V) periods, and that adjoining parts of what is now the sea bed were clothed with open birch woodland, and later pine forest. In 1931, the barbed prong of a mesolithic fish spear of Maglemose type was trawled up from a depth of about 35 m between the Leman and Ower banks, some 40 km north-east of Cromer, and subsequent pollen counts showed that the peat in which this was embedded dated from the transition between Zone V and Zone VI; i.e. about 8000 years ago (Jennings & Green 1965). As peat deposits more recent than this was apparently absent, the North Sea is thought to have been submerged during late Boreal times, some seven to eight thousand years ago.

Stratigraphical studies by Lambert and Jennings in the 1940s and 1950s, and by Coles in the 1970s, have demonstrated how different Broadland was in early Flandrian times, compared with today. Instead of being occupied by wide, almost flat expanses of alluvial marsh and fen, the valleys were deep set and had sloping, forest-covered margins, floored by coarse sands, or less frequently, clays or gravels. The original valley floors are often 10 m or more below the present marsh surface, but this is only apparent when the poor load-bearing properties of the alluvial 'fill' make it necessary to seek a firmer foundation for buildings, tidal defences and other structures. For instance, when strengthening the dam built across Cockshoot Dyke in 1982, it proved necessary to use tubular piles up to 15.5 m long in order to obtain a secure base in the valley floor.

The rivers, too, were very different in appearance. Not only did they discharge into an open embayment, unprotected by the spit of sand and shingle which was to form across its entrance later, but they had much steeper gradients, and were therefore much faster flowing than they are today. Borings show that the gravelly floor of the Ant valley lies 4.9 m below OD downstream of Wayford Bridge, but is 2.19 m deeper just upstream of Barton Broad (Jennings 1952). These points are *c.* 3 km apart, and this section of the R. Ant therefore fell by almost a metre per kilometre in early Flandrian times. Similarly, the sandy floor of the Yare valley lies 6.5 m below OD at Postwick, but is 3.5 m deeper near Surlingham Ferry, only *c.* 3.2 km downstream (Coles, 1977; Lambert & Jennings, 1960). This section of the Yare therefore had a gradient not dissimilar to that of the Ant upstream of Barton Broad. In contrast, the channel of the present-day R. Yare lies *c.* 3.5 m below OD at Trowse Bridge (May Gurney, pers. comm.), and at *c.* 6.0 m below OD just upstream of the new Yarmouth relief road bridge. These sites are *c.* 42 km apart, and therefore the channel now has a mean gradient of only about 6 cm per kilometre.

As the relative sea level rose, the rivers would have become subject to tidal influence, at first in their lowermost reaches, and later further upstream; simultaneously their flood plains would have progressively widened. Reedswamp and fen communities would have developed under these conditions, and the organic remains of these form the stratigraphical horizon known as the 'Lower Peat'. Although this usually consists of strongly compacted *Phragmites* peat throughout, Coles found that the *Phragmites* remains at Rockland are underlain by the 'brushwood' deposits formed when an area is clothed with Fen Carr*, whilst at Buckenham, a 30 to 40 cm thick layer of brushwood peat extends across much of the valley.

The Lower Peat is often absent further downstream, probably because it was eroded

---

* 'Carr' is the name given in East Anglia to wet woodland; it is usually dominated by Alder (*Alnus glutinosa*).

away subsequently by wave and tidal action. However, a sample taken from between 19.3 and 19.5 m below OD at the site of the former Breydon railway bridge (now occupied by the Yarmouth relief road bridge) was found in 1978 to contain the shells of *Hydrobia*, and the fruits of *Ruppia*, and must therefore have been laid down under brackish conditions. It was subsequently radio-carbon-dated to 7580 ± 90 years BP* (Murphy, pers. comm.).

Pollen counts from a 75 cm thick layer of compressed, silty peat obtained from a bore put down in the early 1950s in Ranworth Fen, 75 m south of the R. Bure, provide an insight into the conditions which existed in the middle sections of the valleys between nine and six thousand years ago (Jennings 1955). In the lowermost 25 cm, pine pollen is dominant, with that of birch also fairly abundant; hazel is significant but only occasional grains of oak, lime and other mixed deciduous forest species occur. This indicates that when this peat was formed, the land bordering the rivers was clothed with the pine-dominated forest characteristic of early Boreal (Zone V) times (*c.* 9000 to 8000 BP). The pollen record shows that the next 35 cm of the peat was formed in the late Boreal (*c.* 8000 to 7000 BP); pine was still dominant, birch had declined, but hazel had greatly increased. Elms, oaks and limes were present, but only in small numbers. The pollen of the upper 15 cm shows that alder had become dominant in place of the pine, whilst other mixed hardwoods, notably lime, had increased in quantity. Jennings concluded that this peat must have been laid down at the beginning of Atlantic times, some six and a half to seven thousand years ago.

At Strumpshaw Fen, the fossil channel of the River Yare is infilled with organic mud rather than peat. However pollen counts from the lowermost layers of this suggest that they date from Pre-Boreal (Zone IV) times as birch, rather than pine is dominant (Jennings, 1955). The horizons above show a progression towards the oak, elm, lime and alder forest of the Atlantic (Zone VII) period; however, the Boreal-Atlantic transition (at *c.* 7000 BP) occurs at 8.15 m below OD, some 3.5 m nearer the present-day surface than the corresponding horizon at Ranworth.

Research in southern Scandinavia, and in Somerset, suggests that eustasis caused a rise of relative sea level of between 22 and 26 m during the period 8700 to 4500 BP, and in Broadland, this change was marked by an extension of tidal influence further and further up the valleys. Ultimately, the fens bordering the rivers gave way to estuarine communities, and the 'Lower Peat' was overlain by a thickening layer of 'Lower Clay'.

Coles and Funnell (1981) have pointed out that in the early stages of this marine transgression, the sediments laid down in the open embayment now occupied by the Halvergate marsh 'triangle', consisted mainly of fine sand and silt, and that clay was only deposited where the conditions were more sheltered, for instance around the edges of the embayment, and up the valleys. The foraminiferan fauna found in these sediments is a predominantly estuarine one, being characterized by *Protelphidium anglicum*, *Elphidium magellanicum*, *E. excavatum* and *Ammonia beccarii*, but the fact that up to 5 per cent of the total population consists of marine species strongly suggests that near-maritime conditions occurred in the embayment at this time (Coles, 1977).

Although the thickness of the sediment layer increased in concert with the continued rise in the relative sea level, the development of more sheltered conditions in the embayment is indicated by the deposition of clay near its centre, rather than sand or silt. In addition, the foraminiferan fauna tends to lose its marine element, and develops into a community very similar to that found today in the intertidal flats of Breydon Water. That these estuarine mudflats were then progressively colonized by saltmarsh plants is indicated by the development of foraminiferan assemblages typical of low, and later high, level saltings. The former are characterized by *Jadammina macrescens*, *Trochammina inflata*, *Miliammina fusca*, *Haplophragomoides* sp., *Elphidium williamsoni* and small, thin-walled miloline foraminifers, whilst the latter are characterized by the first two species only.

Further up the valleys, the frequent presence of *Phragmites* remains beneath the clay suggests that extensive reed-beds developed in the flood plains of the rivers as the sea-level rose. Near the valley margins, these persisted throughout the transgression, probably as a result of freshwater run-off from the adjoining uplands. Elsewhere, however,

---

* BP – 'Before the Present' – the present being arbitrarily defined as 1950 AD.

conditions would have progressively become too saline even for *Phragmites*, and the reed-beds gave way to intertidal flats on which fine sediments, later to form clay, accreted. In some cases, for instance near the centre of the Yare valley at Buckenham, the clay rests directly on brushwood peat, with no sign of a *Phragmites* layer. This suggests either, that the alder-dominated fen woodland nearest the river was directly overwhelmed by tide-deposited sediment, or that if an intermediate reedswamp phase did occur, this was of very short duration. In either event, saltmarsh plants progressively colonized the accreting intertidal flats because the foraminiferan fauna of the sediments laid down in the valley shows the same succession as that beneath the Halvergate 'triangle', but without the marine species which occur in the latter's lowermost horizon.

Near the inland limits of the Lower Clay, an assemblage of brackish-water foraminiferans occurs which is very similar to that found in the sediment in the present-day channel of the Yare, near the upriver limit of saline water penetration. Similar findings were made in the Bure valley by Jennings (1955), who notes that brackish-water Foraminifera occur in the Lower Clay at Woodbastwick. But here, the abundance of chenopod pollen shows that saltmarsh communities were not far distant.

The Lower Clay is, as one would expect, thickest at the seaward end of the estuary, and at a borehole put down in 1977 near the site of the former Breydon railway bridge, was found to extend from −7.9 to −19.2 m OD (Rendel, Palmer and Tritton, 1977). In the vicinity of the Wheatacre and Norton Marshes, Coles found that the Lower Clay extends across the whole width of the valley, but is only 3 to 4 m thick, whilst further upriver, its lateral 'wings' become both narrower and thinner, ultimately disappearing at Strumpshaw. At its upstream limits at Brundall and Horning in the Yare and Bure valleys respectively, the Lower Clay is confined to the fossil river channels, whilst further up-valley still, it gives way to an organic mud. This is a freshwater deposit because Jennings found that near Decoy Broad it contains the shells of several molluscs of the genus *Pisidium*, as well as the fruits of an unidentified pondweed.

In general, the stratigraphy of the Lower Clay is similar in the Bure and Yare valleys. However, although its surface lies at a fairly constant depth of between 6.0 and 7.2 m below OD in the latter, it will be seen from Table 2b that this lies almost 3 m deeper in

Table 2b   The stratigraphy of the Lower Clay at various sites in Broadland

Location	Valley	Depth of surface of Lower Clay in metres below OD	Authority
Caister	–	6.5–7.2	Murphy, *in litt.*
Halvergate Marshes	–	7.2	Coles, 1977
Norton Marshes	Yare	6.8	Coles, 1977
Buckenham Marshes	Yare	6.0	Coles, 1977
Strumpshaw Fen	Yare	7.2	Lambert & Jennings, 1960
Acle Bridge	Bure	10.0	Green, 1961
Ranworth Fen	Bure	9.5	Lambert & Jennings, 1960
Woodbastwick Fen	Bure	9.9	Lambert & Jennings, 1960
Ludham Bridge	Ant	10.6	Green, 1961

the middle Bure and Ant valleys. No plausible explanation can be advanced to account for this curious anomaly.

The uppermost horizons of the Lower Clay characteristically contain *Phragmites* rhizomes, even in the Halvergate area, and this would suggest that after the transgression had passed its peak, the valley-edge fen communities began to spread outwards so as to colonize the extensive saltings which had developed in the central sections of the lower valleys; ultimately, freshwater peat-forming communities developed in the Halvergate marsh area itself. Such changes can, in part, be attributed to the fact that from about 5000 BP onwards, the rate at which the relative sea level was rising began to slacken.

But Coles and Funnell have also suggested that tidal action in the estuary declined about this time owing to the development of a shingle spit similar to the one on which Great Yarmouth stands today. In any event, the result was that the sediments laid down during the Transgression were progressively overlain by a thickening layer of 'Middle Peat'.

The stratigraphy shows that in the upper sections of the valleys, where little or no Lower Clay sediments were deposited, reed-beds gave way to alder-dominated woodland; this was probably similar to the community which is so widespread in the Bure and Ant valleys today. The brushwood peat which it formed typically contains twigs and rootlets, and fragments of bark; alder fruits and occasional sallow leaves also occur.

At Hickling, Barton and other up-valley sites, alder woodland persisted throughout the whole of the Middle Peat period. However, further down-valley, a softer, more fibrous deposit occurs, and this is thought to indicate that open (unbushed) fens predominated here. In the lowermost sections of the valleys, and in the Halvergate area, the Middle Peat consists of a dark brown structureless mass thought to have formed under freshwater lagoon-like conditions. Peat of this type was encountered in two of the boreholes sunk prior to the construction of the Caister by-pass, and was found to contain the fruits of a water crowfoot, a sedge, bramble, alder and bogbean (Murphy, *in litt.*).

Wetter conditions seem to have developed during the deposition of the Middle Peat since the remains of herbaceous fen plants tend to predominate in its upper horizons, particularly in the middle sections of the valleys. At Strumpshaw Fen, for example, the 1 to 2 m thick layer of brushwood peat resting on the sandy valley floor is overlain by mixed fen peat, which in places is up to 3 m deep. At Buckenham the middle and upper parts of the valley fill consist of a bright orange, hypnoid moss peat containing patches of *Sphagnum* or saw-sedge peat, rather than brushwood remains, whilst at down-valley sites like Barnby Fen, the stratigraphy of the Middle Peat is even more varied. The occurrence of thin layers of mud or marl in such deposits indicates that there were shallow, spring-fed pools in the valleys, especially near their margins (Lambert & Jennings, 1960).

Pollen counts made on core samples taken from the middle and upper sections of the Bure, Ant and Yare valleys confirm that a major climatic change took place during the period the Middle Peat was being formed. The lower two-thirds of the deposit was laid down during the warm, wet Atlantic period, since, although alder was the dominant species, other trees, particularly oak and lime were growing in the vicinity, though not necessarily in the fens. Alder pollen continues to be abundant in the remainder of the Middle Peat, but birch replaces lime, pine becomes more frequent, and beech appears for the first time. This combination of species is characteristic of the Transition Zone (VII–VIII), which occurred between about 2500 BP and 2000 BP (see Fig. 2A).

Dr. A. Jedrzejewski, formerly of the Botany School, Cambridge University, is known to have radiocarbon-dated a number of samples from the Middle Peat during the course of her studies in the early 1980s on the stratigraphy of the Waveney valley, but these have unfortunately not yet been published. However, radiocarbon dates are available for five specimens taken from Middle Peat deposits elsewhere in Broadland, and these are consistent with the timescale suggested by pollen analyses. Two samples from the Somerton Level – an oak located 2.65 m below OD and a birch at −2.25 m OD – were dated to 3540 ± 70 BP and 2770 ± 70 BP respectively (Dresser, *in litt.*), and although the other three samples were not stratigraphically controlled, they gave dates ranging from 4050 ± 110 BP (for a pine tree uncovered at How Hill in 1978), to 2760 ± 90 BP and 2650 ± 100 BP for two oak trunks dredged from the navigable channel across Hickling Broad in the mid-1970s.

The higher rainfall and consequently increased rate of run-off of the Transition Zone period caused the rivers to carve out deeper and wider channels for themselves, and increase their gradient. At Surlingham and other sites in the middle Yare valley, the fossil channel is incised into the Middle Peat only, but further downstream, for example near Reedham, it is cut right through the Middle Peat into the underlying Lower Clay. The river channels created at this time usually lie more or less directly beneath their modern counterparts, but Coles (1977) found that meander migration near Reedham has resulted in the present bed of the river being displaced by up to 80 m from the fossil channel (see Fig. 2B).

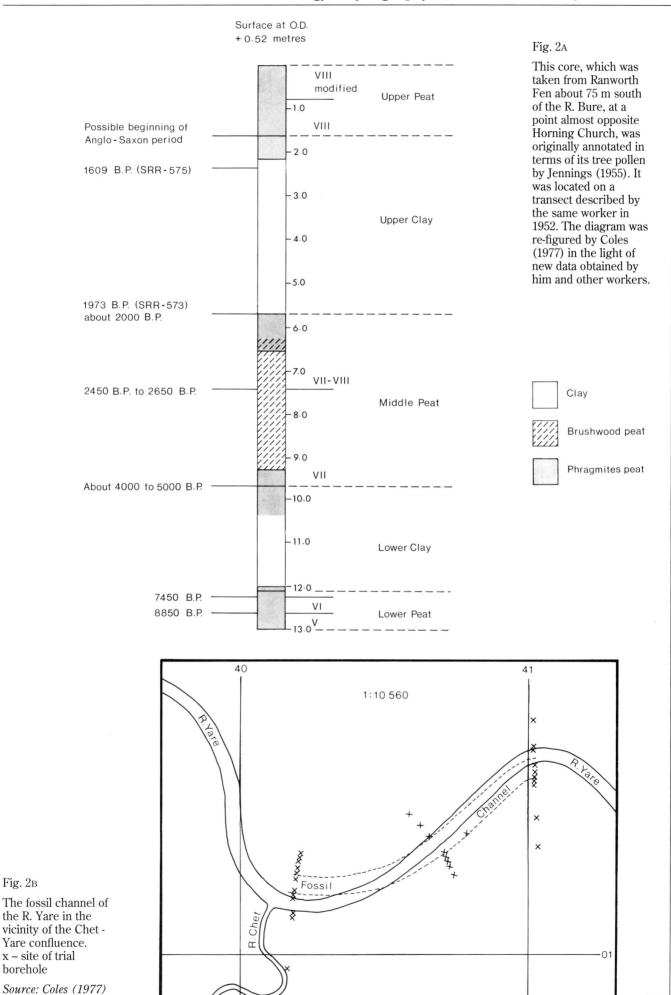

Surface at O.D. + 0.52 metres

VIII modified — Upper Peat

Possible beginning of Anglo-Saxon period — VIII

1609 B.P. (SRR-575)

Upper Clay

1973 B.P. (SRR-573) about 2000 B.P.

VII-VIII

2450 B.P. to 2650 B.P.

Middle Peat

VII

About 4000 to 5000 B.P.

Lower Clay

7450 B.P.

VI — Lower Peat

8850 B.P.

V

Fig. 2A

This core, which was taken from Ranworth Fen about 75 m south of the R. Bure, at a point almost opposite Horning Church, was originally annotated in terms of its tree pollen by Jennings (1955). It was located on a transect described by the same worker in 1952. The diagram was re-figured by Coles (1977) in the light of new data obtained by him and other workers.

☐ Clay

▨ Brushwood peat

▨ Phragmites peat

1:10 560

R. Yare

R. Chet

Channel

Fossil

Fig. 2B

The fossil channel of the R. Yare in the vicinity of the Chet-Yare confluence.
x – site of trial borehole

Source: Coles (1977)

Map 2.1

Eastern Broadland at the time of the Romano-British Transgression, i.e. between about 300 BC and 340 AD. The open estuary was known to the Romans as *Gariensis Ostium*.

Source: Based on data obtained by Coles (1977) and Lambert and Jennings (1960)

Borings in the Halvergate marsh 'triangle' have revealed that a 10 to 20 cm thick layer of brownish clay, containing brackish water foraminiferans, rests on the eroded surface of the Middle Peat. This estuarine deposit indicates that tidal action increased in the lower reaches of the rivers towards the close of the Middle Peat period, and Coles has suggested that the heavy fluvial flows carried by the rivers either found, or created, a breach in the shingle spit which had formed across the mouth of the estuary, and which, by analogy with the present spit, had probably deflected the mouth of the river Yare to the south. What the configuration of the lowermost reaches of the R. Bure was like at this time is not known. Indeed, at the moment there is nothing to show whether this river was discharging by a separate outfall to the north, as it did in early medieval times (see page 35), or whether it was sharing a common outfall with the R. Yare.

The estuarine episode did not last for long, since both at Halvergate and in adjoining down-valley sites, the clay abruptly gives way to coarse sandy strata, containing not only the shells of cockles and other marine molluscs, but microscopic grains of coal, almost certainly derived from the North Sea. Clearly the estuary had once again been converted into an open embayment (see Map 2.1), and Coles and Funnell attribute this to the

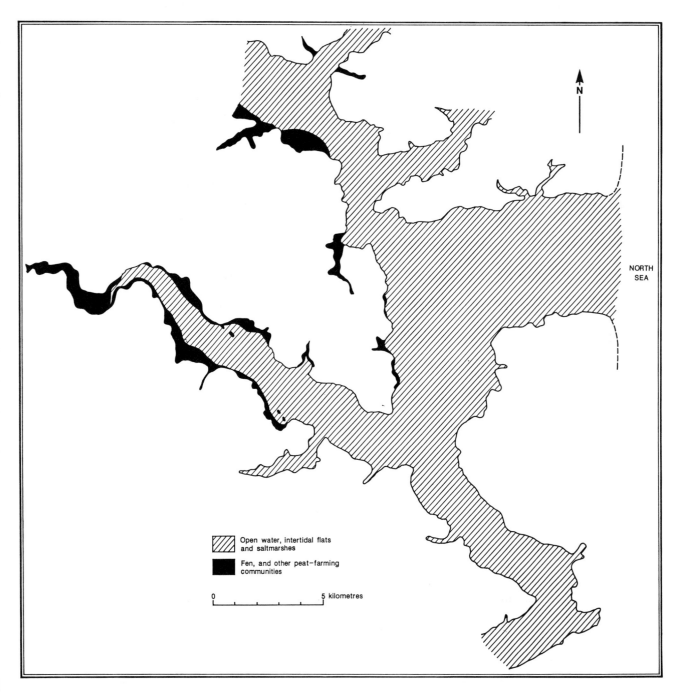

NORTH SEA

▨ Open water, intertidal flats and saltmarshes

■ Fen, and other peat-farming communities

0   5 kilometres

distintegration of the protective spit. It is not known for certain why this should have occurred, but Carr (1972), who has carried out much detailed research on another, comparable shingle spit on the East Coast – Orford Beach – has pointed out that as such a structure elongates and becomes increasingly attenuated, the hydraulic gradient between its river and seaward sides enlarges, and the time lag between high or low water between the two sides becomes greater. Under these circumstances, the spit will be particularly susceptible to increased seepage and overtopping during a surge, the very events most likely to culminate in a breach.

The greatly increased tidal action in the rivers which followed the destruction of the spit, together with the continuing rise in the relative sea level, marked the beginning of the Second Transgression, and the deposition in the valleys of a thickening layer of 'Upper Clay' sediments. Beneath what is now the Halvergate triangle, these are some 5.75 m thick, and display a gradation from coarse sands near the base to a blackish silt, which on exposure, is oxidized to an orange-brown colour on account of its high iron content.

In a study of the Foraminifera found in these deposits, Coles has shown that the estuarine species found in the clay layer laid down at the close of the Middle Peat period abruptly give way to a fauna typical of exposed intertidal sandflats. Later, as accretion continued, the fauna evolves into one characteristic of high-level mudflats; simultaneously, the percentage of marine species present falls.

In the lowermost sections of the Yare valley, for example at Limpenhoe, the Upper Clay sediments tend to be silty near the river, and finer-grained near the valley margins. But in the more sheltered conditions which must have prevailed further up-valley, they consist of a blue-grey 'buttery' clay up to 3 m thick near the river, but thinning out laterally, and penetrated by reed rhizomes near the valley margin. The foraminiferan fauna of the clay beside the river is usually dominated by species typical of intertidal flats, but nearer the upland edge, forms characteristic of low, and later high, level saltmarshes become more frequent.

At Rockland the clay forms a thin, reed-girt flange which finally tapers out some 500 m from the upland margin, whilst in the vicinity of Bargate Island, opposite Brundall, it extends for only about a third of the way across the flood plain. The presence of thin flanges of Upper Clay as far up-valley as Whitlingham shows that the Second Transgression was more extensive in its effects than the first. However the sediments in this area were laid down under freshwater, rather than brackish conditions, since Foraminifera are largely absent, whilst the oogonia of stoneworts (Charophyta) are frequently abundant.

The Transgression affected the tributary, as well as the main, valleys. Thin layers of clay occur just downstream of both Fritton Lake and Filby Broad, but in the Ant valley, the effects of the Transgression are stratigraphically much more apparent. At Ludham Bridge, for example, the clay stretches across almost the whole width of the valley, and for much of the way is over 6 m deep, whilst at Irstead, it wedges out on each side of the river for a distance of over 100 m. At the northern end of Barton Broad, the clay is represented by a small V marking the position of the former river channel, and only at Wayford Bridge, is it missing altogether. Here, the remains of reed and sedge directly overlie the brushwood deposits of the Middle Peat (Jennings, 1952).

The stratigraphy of the Upper Clay, together with the studies on its foraminiferan fauna (Coles, 1977; Coles & Funnell, 1981), make it possible to analyse the ecological changes which occurred in Broadland during the Second Transgression. In the Halvergate area, and at the seaward end of the valleys, where reedy, lagoon-like conditions had developed during the Middle Peat period, the partial breaching of the shingle spit and consequent increased tidal action, led to the destruction of the reedswamp communities by salt water, and their replacement by estuarine mudflats. Shortly afterwards, with the total disintegration of the spit, the whole area was transformed into an open, wave-swept embayment, and the mudflats were overlain by tide and current-borne sands and silts. Up-valley, the rising water-table and increased tidal action resulted in areas of alder woodland being replaced by reedswamp communities more tolerant of the brackish conditions. As salinities increased still further, these in turn were gradually converted into intertidal mudflats, but not before a layer of *Phragmites* remains up to about one metre thick had been sandwiched between the top of the Middle Peat and the base of the Upper Clay. A sample of this *Phragmites* peat taken in 1973 by Coles from just beneath the Upper Clay at Buckenham, a few metres from the river, gave a radiocarbon date of 1973 ± 50 BP, i.e. *c.* 23 BC.

The rising relative sea level, and the sheltered conditions, particularly up-valley, would have favoured a rapid rate of accretion, and the mudflats would soon have been colonized by saltmarsh plants. Evidence for this comes, not only from Coles' studies on the Foraminifera, but from the discovery of the seeds of Annual Seablite (*Suaeda maritima*) and Greater Sea-spurrey (*Spergularia marginata*) in Upper Clay sediments beneath the Caister by-pass (Murphy, pers. comm.), and from the increasing abundance of chenopod pollen towards the top of the Upper Clay in a borehole at Ranworth Fen (Jennings, 1952).

Where the water was only slightly brackish, with a mean depth of about 1.25 m or less, reed would have survived throughout the Transgression. In such situations, the deposition of tide, and fluvially-borne sediments in the reed-beds would have led to the formation of clay flanges penetrated throughout by *Phragmites* rhizomes, such as are found in the middle sections of the valleys. Minor, and relatively short-lived fluctuations in the rate at which land and sea levels were changing would have led to interlayering of the clays and peats, such as occurs in the Waveney valley near Beccles. But in the upper sections of the rivers, beyond the reach of normal tides and where the fens were regularly flooded by freshwater, and also near the valley margins, where there was a good supply of run-off from the adjoining uplands, reedswamp peat would have been laid down directly on top of the Middle Peat without any intervening Upper Clay sediments (see Map 2.1). Areas of continuous, more or less clay-free peat also occur as scattered 'islands' in the middle sections of the Yare valley, for example, at Buckenham; these probably mark the places where strong springs enabled fen vegetation to persist throughout the Transgression.

A sample of *Phragmites* peat taken by Coles from just beneath the thin (0.45 cm) flange of Upper Clay near Coldham Hall gave a radiocarbon date of 1609 ± 50 BP, i.e. *c.* 341 AD and this probably only shortly pre-dates the maximum inland extent of the Transgression. The latter seems to have been brought to a close at least partly because of the formation of the sand and shingle spit on which Yarmouth was to be founded a few centuries later. Although the physiography of this spit, and in particular its relationship with the bar, or 'Middle Ground' which is alleged to have developed at the mouth of the embayment (Green & Hutchinson, 1960) requires further study, it would have tended to reduce upriver tidal penetration as it extended further and further southwards. Salinities upstream would also have declined if, as work in Scandinavia and Holland suggests, a period of higher rainfall, and therefore increased run-off, commenced in about 400 AD. There may, in addition, have been a net lowering of the level of the sea relative to that of the land towards the end of the Transgression. This would have occurred if, as Tooley (1978) has claimed, the general rise in sea level which has taken place during the past eight or nine thousand years, has been punctuated by a series of temporary recessions, each lasting between 400 and 800 years. One such oscillation, known as Lytham IX, is thought to have culminated in about 350 AD, and to have caused a temporary fall in mean sea level of up to 0.8 m. If, during this period, the rate at which the land was sinking due to isostatic subsidence was less than this, there would have been a slight lowering of the relative sea level. But in any event, as Coles and Funnell (1981) have pointed out, "Whatever the precise combination of factors was, estuarine waters were largely excluded from all except the area of Breydon Water by about 1500 BP (450 AD)".

Further up-valley, the saltmarshes were gradually succeeded by reed-beds, as tidal influence and salinities declined. This took place as a result of the outwards spread both of the spring-fed islands of fen vegetation in the central sections of the Yare valley and elsewhere, and of the reed-dominated fens which occurred at the upriver limits of the Transgression. Eventually, peat started to accumulate across the whole width of the valleys just as it had after the First Transgression.

The *Phragmites* remains which comprise the lower layers of this 'Upper Peat' are succeeded by brushwood deposits in the middle Bure and Ant valleys, indicating that the reed-beds were later invaded by alder, oak and other woody species. A bog-oak uncovered in 1978 at How Hill was radiocarbon-dated to 1110 ± 90 BP (i.e. *c.* 840 AD), but unfortunately its exact position in relation to Ordnance Datum was not recorded.

In the middle Yare valley, the reed-beds gave way to *Glyceria maxima*-dominated fens, which in some cases were, in turn, invaded by trees and bushes. Both here and in the corresponding sections of the Bure and Ant valleys, about 2 m of peat has accumulated since the Upper Clay transgression. However, it is impossible to determine how much formed at the seaward ends of the valleys, as the organic deposits here have been subject to oxidation and wastage, following the embanking of the rivers and the draining of the adjoining land. Indeed, in many places, the Upper Peat has disappeared altogether, or has with time become incorporated in the soil derived from the silts and clays laid down during the Second Transgression. In the Halvergate triangle, peat probably did not accumulate at all, except along the valley margins, where a series of springs and seepage lines has enabled fen communities to persist right up to the present time.

Summary of Events

c. 8500 BP – *c.* 7500 BP	The once forested bed of the North Sea submerges as a consequence of a progressive rise in sea level relative to the land (i.e. eustasis and isostasis). Tidal influence begins to be apparent in the embayment into which the rivers discharged, with the consequent formation of the 'Lower Peat' in their lowermost reaches.
c. 7500 BP – *c.* 5000 BP	The relative sea level continues to rise, and a thickening layer of sandy, silty or clayey sediments, collectively known as the 'Lower Clay', is laid down under open estuarine conditions in the lower and middle sections of the valleys. Brackish and freshwater conditions prevail further upstream and lead to the formation of 'Lower Peat' in these areas.
c. 5000 BP – *c.* 2250 BP	A shingle spit forms across the mouth of the open embayment, deflecting the R. Yare southwards, and reducing tidal penetration, thus allowing fen vegetation to replace the estuarine communities which had existed previously. The 'Middle Peat' thus formed, consisted initially of the remains of open (i.e. unbushed) communities dominated by *Phragmites*, but in the middle and upper valleys these soon gave way to alder-dominated woodland, which formed brushwood peat. Towards the end of the period, rainfall, and therefore fluvial flows, increase, and these find, or create, a breach in the shingle spit, leading to increased tidal penetration, and the re-development of estuarine conditions in the lower valleys.
c. 2250 BP – *c.* 1610 BP	The shingle spit disintegrates (possibly as a result of a major storm surge), thus re-creating an open embayment. The increased tidal action in the valleys, allied to a continuing rise in relative sea level, leads to the deposition of a thick layer of 'Upper Clay' on top of the Middle Peat. Although the lower valleys were occupied by mudflats and saltings during this period, open fen communities predominated near the valley margins (owing to run-off from the higher ground bordering the latter) and in mid-valley. The Upper Clay sediments become thinner further upstream, and are absent from the upper sections of the valleys, where alder carr and other fen communities persisted throughout the Trangression. The latter reaches its maximum extent in about 1609 BP.
c. 1610 BP – *c.* 1000 BP	Tidal penetration up-valley progressively decreases, as a result of a combination of circumstances, including the development of a new shingle spit across the mouth of the embayment. Fen communities develop once again in the lower valleys, but the resultant 'Upper Peat' has subsequently wasted away following the embankment of the rivers, and the drainage of the adjoining marshland. Further up-valley, the Upper Peat directly overlies the Middle Peat formed previously.

c. 1000 BP – *c.* 30 BP (i.e. 1920 AD)	The town of Yarmouth develops from a small fishing settlement established on the shingle spit, and the peat laid down in the middle and upper sections of the valleys is exploited as a source of fuel. Between *c.* 1000 and *c.* 600 BP the excavations often extended through the Upper Clay into the Middle Peat and these relatively deep pits subsequently flooded to form the broads. Peat continued to be cut from extensive, shallow workings in the fens until about 1920 AD (see Chapters 4 & 7).

The soils

The soils of Broadland reflect its geological and physiographical history. Poorly drained marine clays and silts laid down during the Second Transgression predominate at the seaward ends of the valleys and are shown on the 1 : 100 000 Soil Map of Norfolk (1982) as Unit no. 813c. They were formerly mapped by the Soil Survey of England and Wales as the Waveney Series, but were subsequently re-classified as the Newchurch Series (calcareous clay), Wallasea Series (non-calcareous clay) and Wisbech Series (silt loam). In the Halvergate triangle and the seaward ends of the valleys, the sediments tend to be calcareous because of the large quantities of foraminiferan and other shell fragments within them, but further up-valley, they contain relatively little such material.

Near the upland margins, and further up the valleys, where fen communities persisted throughout the whole, or most of the Second Transgression, the soils are peaty and are shown as Unit no. 1024b on the 1 : 100 000 Soil Map. But both here, and elsewhere in the region, the soil pattern tends to be complex, and interlayers of peat, clay and sand occur, especially along the valley margins. Differential settlement is liable to occur when such areas are deep-drained. In addition, at some sites, such as Beccles Marsh, the shrinkage and wastage which results when peaty soils dry out following the lowering of the water-table may lead to gravelly sub-soils being brought to the surface by repeated cultivation.

Since the peaty soils of the uppermost sections of the valleys are derived from fresh-water fen communities which were rarely, if ever, flooded by saline water, they contain little pyrite (FeS_2) and consequently do not acidify dramatically when the water-table is lowered. In contrast, the soil parent materials of the rest of the region were either laid down during the saline or brackish conditions prevailing during the Second Transgression or, as in the Hickling-Horsey-Somerton area, have been subject over the centuries to repeated sea flooding. Such soils contain pyrite formed by the bacterial reduction of sulphates derived from the sea water. No problems arise if the water-table is maintained fairly near the surface, since the pyrite is stable under anaerobic conditions. However, if such soils are drained, the pyrite is oxidized to soluble iron and sulphuric acid (Dent, 1984). The reaction path is complex, and is promoted by the bacterium, *Thiobacillus ferroxidans*, but the end result can be summarized by the equation:

$$FeS_2 + 14Fe^{3+} \rightarrow 15\,Fe^{2+} + 2\,SO_4^{2-} + 16\,H^+$$

Provided there is plenty of calcium carbonate available, the acid is neutralized to form gypsum:

$$CaCO_3 + 2H^+ + SO_4^{2-} \rightarrow CaSO_4 + H_2O + CO_2$$

and the soluble iron is precipitated in the soil as ferric hydroxide (commonly known as 'ochre').

$$Fe^{2+} + \tfrac{1}{4}O_2 + H^2 \rightarrow Fe^{3+} + \tfrac{1}{2}H_2O$$

$$Fe^{3+} + 3H_2O \rightarrow Fe(OH)_3 + 3H^+$$

However, if there is insufficient calcium carbonate to neutralize the acidity, the pH value of the soil and drainage water falls to less than 4, and sometimes as low as 2. At pH values less than about 4, aluminium is soluble and toxic to plants. Thus, if the acidity develops within the rooting zone, the range of crops that can be grown on the marsh is restricted, and yields are reduced, particularly during dry spells when the crop is subject to water stress. Applications of lime can only bring about a limited and temporary amelioration of these problems, owing to the large quantities of pyrite sometimes present in the soil, and the fact that the acid horizon may lie at too great a depth to be reached by conventional methods of cultivation.

As roots cannot penetrate the acid layer, the shrinkage and fissuring which normally takes place in the sub-soil when wetlands are drained does not take place. Instead the soil remains 'unripe' – soft, unable to bear loads and very poorly drained. Such soils have to be treated very carefully during seed-bed preparation and harvesting, and can often only be used for 'improved' grass, or autumn-sown cereals. Another difficulty encountered with these soils is that the perforations in the corrugated PVC piping now commonly used to under-drain them tend to become blocked by ochre. In several cases, the entire under-drainage system can be rendered inoperative within a year of installation (Dent, pers. comm.).

In affected areas, the sloping ('battered') margins of the dykes characteristically exhibit a thin band of the yellow mineral jarosite $[KFe_3(SO_4)_2(OH)_6]$ which forms at pH values less than 3.0, and which marks the position of the top of the acid horizon in the adjoining marsh. Owing to the acidity, the dyke batters are often almost devoid of vegetation, and are consequently prone to slumping.

The principal environmental problems associated with these acid-sulphate soils, whether clays or peats, stem from the fact that when their drainage water is discharged into a chemically buffered dyke, the acidity is neutralized, and large quantities of ochre are produced. This turns the water a bright orange colour. But since much of the chemical is finely particulate, it tends to find its way down to the drainage pump, and thence into the river or broad. Although it slowly sediments out here, it is liable to be stirred up by passing boats, and carried further downstream. Moreover, the rest of the ochre is in the form of a colloidal suspension, and this too can discolour the water course for a considerable distance downstream of the pump.

In poorly buffered systems, flushes of severe acidity can occur, especially at the end of a drought. Calthorpe Broad has been affected in this way on several occasions since 1970, following the lowering of the water-table of the adjoining marshland (see page 512).

Although farmers have long been aware that certain soils in Broadland are liable to acidify if deep-drained, the extent of the area affected was not fully appreciated until 1980, when an Environmental Impact Assessment on the Yare Basin Flood Control Scheme was published (Environmental Resource Management & Trans Econ Ltd., 1980). Subsequently, a more detailed investigation of the phenomenon was carried out for the Broads Authority by the same partnership (ERM & TE, 1981; Dent, 1984). This involved an examination of paired soil profiles at each intersection of the 1 km grid within the Authority's Executive Area, samples being collected at depths of 30 to 40 cm, 60 to 70 cm and 100 to 110 cm from the surface. The data obtained from the 2200 samples processed is summarized in Map 2.2, and the extent to which the four principal soil types in the region are affected by potential acidity is summarized in Table 2c.

While these surveys were in progress, the Ministry of Agriculture, Fisheries and Food (MAFF) had set up a Study Group to consider the extent of the acid sulphate soil problem in East Anglia, the remedies available, and the implications for arterial drainage and conservation. The resultant report, entitled 'The management of acid fen and marsh soils in East Anglia', was completed in 1983 but, being destined for internal use only, was never published. Nevertheless, it is understood that the Group questioned the wisdom of lowering the water-table of acid soils, and recommended that the owners and occupiers of grass marshland in such areas be urged by the Agricultural Development and Advisory Service (ADAS) to maintain the *status quo*. The Ministry's staff had, in fact, already started to alert farmers to the problems posed by acid sulphate soils, and in a Technical Bulletin issued in 1981, ADAS had pointed out that the acidity produced when certain areas of peat marsh are drained cannot readily be corrected by liming (MAFF, 1981).

Given the fast-changing economic milieu in which farmers were having to operate from 1983 onwards, it is difficult to assess to what extent they were influenced by the Ministry's advice, and the data produced by the Broads Authority's consultants. Moreover, by the time this information had become available, many acid sulphate areas in the

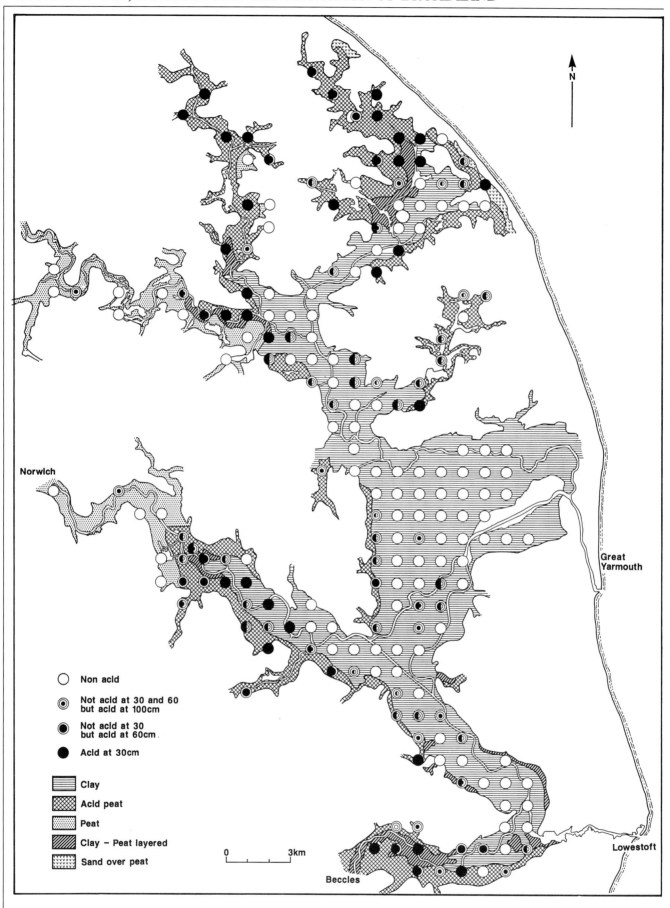

Map 2.2   The distribution of soils in Broadland which are liable to acidify if deep-drained. An acid soil is
                 defined here as one having a field or oxidized pH value of less than 4, or a pH of less than 3 after
                 peroxide treatment. Halved symbols represent differences between the duplicate samples which were
                 taken at each intersection of the grid.

                 Source: Environmental Resource Management Ltd. and Trans Econ Ltd. (1981)

Drained Marshland Area had already been put under the plough. The effects which this change of use had on the ecology and wildlife of the region are described in Chapters 8 and 9.

In 1985, it became known that some of the land in the Halvergate 'triangle' which had been deep-drained and put under the plough in the 1970s was producing poor crops, apparently as a result of waterlogging. Investigations showed that this was due to changes in soil structure caused by saline deflocculation. Previous research on marshes in Essex and North Kent which had been similarly affected had indicated that this is

Table 2c   Potential Acid Sulphate Soils in Broadland

Soil mapping unit				Estimated area – ha
C	–	Marine clays	A1	745
			A2	1788
			A3	1192
			N	10725
C/P	–	Interlayered peat and clay	A1	697
			A2	494
			A3	67
			N	67
AP	–	Acid peat	A1	3290
			A2	1768
			A3	1016
			N	NIL
P	–	Non-acid peat	(mostly in the form of narrow strips, and as fens which are not in agricultural use)	3126

Key: A1 – severe acid soil – oxidized pH less than 4 within 30 cm of the surface.
   A2 – non-acid topsoil, but severely acid within 60 cm of the surface.
   A3 – non-acid at 30 cm and at 60 cm, but severely acid within 1m of the surface.
   N – not acid sulphate – pH value 4 or more throughout the profile.

Source: Environmental Resource Management & Trans Econ Ltd (1981).

liable to occur some years after calcium-deficient, clay-based soils, such as those of the Wallasea Series, had been put under the plough, and that the process involves the leaching of soluble salts from the drainage water. Under these circumstances, the calcium and magnesium ions which are absorbed on to the clay particles, and which maintain the soil structural units in a stable condition, are replaced by sodium. This weakens the soil's cohesive strength, and clay particles are washed down through the soil by rainfall and re-deposited at depth as a thin slurry which often blocks the under-drains. As the calcium content of the soil falls, the ease with which sodium replaces the remaining calcium ions increases, and the process consequently tends to accelerate (Corbett, *in litt.*). The soil becomes increasingly subject to waterlogging as it loses its structure, and this problem is exacerbated if the farmer tries to cultivate the land, since the resultant smearing and compaction reduce its permeability still further. Remedial action is both difficult and expensive, and may involve the application of between 10 and 15 tonnes of gypsum per hectare if crop yields are to be restored to their former level (*Farmers' Weekly*, 1985), whilst for newly drained land in north Kent, the Soil Survey of England and Wales advocate the application of 50 tonnes of gypsum per hectare to a 2–3 m wide strip over each field drain, plus 5 to 12 tonnes ha^{-1} to the remainder of the marsh (Hazelden *et al.*, 1986).

In 1986, the Soil Survey was commissioned by the Ministry of Agriculture, Fisheries and Food (MAFF) to survey the distribution and extent of salt-affected soils in central Broadland, including the Halvergate triangle. The preliminary results indicate, as suspected, that most of the soils in the valleys are referable to the Waveney Series. They are characterized by gley horizons, and are non-calcareous in the uppermost 40 cm. The subsoil commonly consists of a silty clay loam, and is often calcareous to within 70 to 80 cm of the surface. Salinity and sodium levels in those areas known to be liable to deflocculate, are similar to those found by Hazelden *et al.* in north Kent but the Broadland soils appear to be more stable at depth (Soil Survey, 1987).

Climate

In common with other parts of East Anglia, Broadland has a slightly more continental climate than other parts of the British Isles, though maximum temperatures during the summer tend to be slightly lower, and minimum temperatures in the winter are marginally higher, than at places such as Cambridge, which are further away from the moderating influence of the North Sea (see Table 2d). This is not to say that extremes

Table 2d Average daily temperatures in Great Yarmouth during the period 1921–1950 (figures for Cambridge for the same period are given in parentheses for comparison)

Month	Maximum (°C)	Minimum (°C)
January	6.1 (6.7)	2.2 (0.6)
February	6.7 (7.8)	2.2 (0.6)
March	8.3 (10.6)	2.8 (1.7)
April	11.1 (13.3)	5.0 (3.9)
May	13.9 (17.2)	7.8 (6.1)
June	17.2 (20.0)	11.1 (9.4)
July	19.4 (22.2)	13.3 (11.7)
August	20.0 (21.7)	13.3 (11.1)
September	17.8 (19.4)	11.7 (9.4)
October	13.9 (14.4)	8.3 (6.1)
November	9.4 (10.0)	5.0 (3.3)
December	6.7 (7.2)	3.3 (1.7)
Annual Mean	12.8 (14.4)	7.2 (5.6)

Source: Ford & Lamb, 1976.

of temperature do not occur sometimes. During August 1921, for instance, the temperature in Norwich rose to 80°F (26.7°C) on twelve days, and the mean that month was 65.8°F (18.8°C), or 4.2°F (2.3°C) above the average (Preston, 1922). Temperatures during the summer of 1976 rose to similar, or even higher levels, and on only one of the first twelve days of July that year did the temperature fail to reach 80°F (Norgate, 1977). The region also experiences hard winters. Preston (1891 & 1895a) describes the prolonged cold spells which occurred in 1890/1 and 1894/5 (the latter lasting, with two short breaks, from 30 December until 5 March), and also provides summary data for eight other severe winters between 1788 and 1881. The early months of 1947 were also memorably cold. The temperature was continuously below freezing point for 333 hours in mid-February that year, and on the 25th. sank to −0.1°F (−17.9°C), the lowest for 35 years (Willis, 1948). The weather remained exceptionally cold until mid-March, but the temperature then rose by 20°F (11°C) in two days, producing an ultra-rapid thaw of the *c.* 1.2 m of snow which had fallen during the previous ten weeks, and consequent major fluvial flooding (see page 320).

The winter of 1962/3 was also exceptionally cold. Temperatures fell below freezing point on 23 December, and heavy snowfalls on 3 January, together with strong to gale force winds, resulted in drifting in many places. More snow fell during the ensuing weeks, and on 29 days during January, and 22 during February, the ground was snow-covered at Sprowston (Norwich), the corresponding figures for Gorleston, nearer the North Sea, being 8 and 14 days. The weather remained very cold until March 4, the mean temperatures at these two sites being as follows:

Table 2e   Maximum and minimum temperatures at Sprowston and Gorleston in 1953

		Mean Max. (A)	Mean Min. (B)	Mean of A & B	Diff. from average
January					
	Sprowston	0.8	−4.8	−2.0	−5.3
	Gorleston	1.1	−2.3	−0.6	−4.6
February					
	Sprowston	1.3	−4.8	−2.0	−5.3
	Gorleston	1.2	−2.0	−0.4	−4.6

Source: Meteorological Office (1963).

Hard winters, such as those of 1894/5, 1946/7 and 1962/3 have a pronounced effect on the birdlife of the region. Wildfowl populations are augmented by species such as Scaup, Smew and Goosander which do not commonly occur in Broadland, but against this must be set the fact that the freezing conditions exact a heavy toll, particularly on species which are small in size (e.g. Wren and Blue Tit), or dependent on either open water (e.g. Heron and Kingfisher) or easily probed mud (e.g. Redshank and, on Breydon Water, Dunlin).

Prolonged hard spells cause the broads, and eventually the rivers themselves, to freeze over, thus providing excellent skating (see Plate II). Emerson (1893) records that the ice

An ice yacht and skaters on Malthouse Broad – 1986.   Plate II

The broads are capable of providing excellent skating, and if the hard weather is particularly prolonged, as in the winter of 1962/3, one can skate for miles on the rivers. Such conditions were dreaded by wherrymen, since their vessels could be ice-bound for weeks at a time. In 1929, for instance, three wherries were stuck fast in Oulton Broad for a whole month (Clark, 1961).

Photo: R.N. Flowers/Countryside Commission

on Oulton Broad attained a thickness of 17 in (43 cm) during the winter of 1890/91, and according to Clark (1961) it was 7.5 in (19 cm) thick here in 1929. Similarly, Hickling Broad froze to a depth of 14 in (35.5 cm) in 1963, and 8 in (20 cm) in 1982 (Linsell, pers. comm.), this despite the fact that this site, like Oulton Broad, is slightly brackish, and therefore somewhat slower to freeze over than most other broads. Up to the turn of the century, ice from the broads and rivers was collected up with long-handled scoops, known as ice dydles, and transported by wherry to ice-houses, where it was stored until required for use as a refrigerant for fish and other perishable goods (Ellis, 1965c). In mild winters, when sufficient ice could not be obtained locally, it had to be imported from Scandinavia (Ashbourne, 1988). There were originally at least five ice-houses in Yarmouth and Gorleston (Asbourne, 1989), and there were others in Norwich (in Ice House Lane, off Bracondale), and beside the R. Yare near Surlingham Broad.

On the debit side, ice provides a hazard to navigation (see Plate III). Vessels built of glass reinforced plastic are particularly prone to damage if used on waters which are frozen over, and in January 1987 a freighter which became stuck between Reedham and Norwich pushed a piece of ice through the bottom of a moored cruiser when attempting to get on the move again. Posts marking the channels through sites such as Barton and Hickling Broads are also susceptible to damage by ice-floes, and it is not unknown for those in Breydon Water to be bodily up-rooted and washed away as the tide rises and falls.

The amount of bright sunshine at Norwich varies from about 50 hours in the months of December and January, to nearly 200 hours in May, June and July (see Table 2f), but

Table 2f The amount of sunshine at Sprowston, Norwich (30 year means)

Month	Sunshine hours
January	50.7
February	67.9
March	126.7
April	148.4
May	194.8
June	197.2
July	195.3
August	183.1
September	146.9
October	109.5
November	55.7
December	46.0

Source: Grove (1961).

Ice floes on the R. Yare at Limpenhoe – 1986.

Plate III

The rivers, as well as the broads, are liable to freeze over during prolonged periods of hard weather, and as they do so, they prove attractive to over-wintering wildfowl such as Scaup, Smew and Goosander. Ice floes such as those shown in the photograph form a hazard to navigation, vessels built of Glass Reinforced Plastic ('fibre-glass') being particularly prone to damage if used in such conditions. In addition, navigation aids on tidal waters, such as the posts marking the channel across Breydon Water, are liable to be uprooted and carried away by the ice.

Although Limpenhoe Marshes Mill, on the other side of the river, appears to be in a near-derelict condition, it is regarded by the Norfolk Windmills Trust as being restorable. However, it is not yet included on their 'protected' list (see Table 8d).

Photo: R.N. Flowers

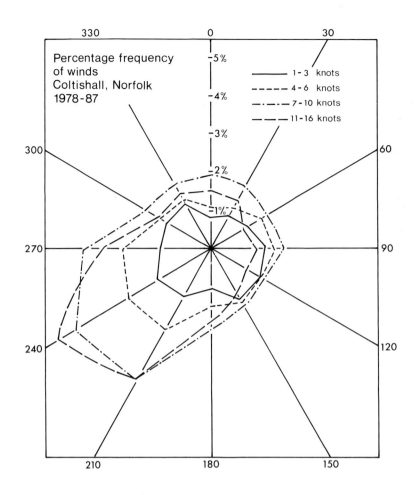

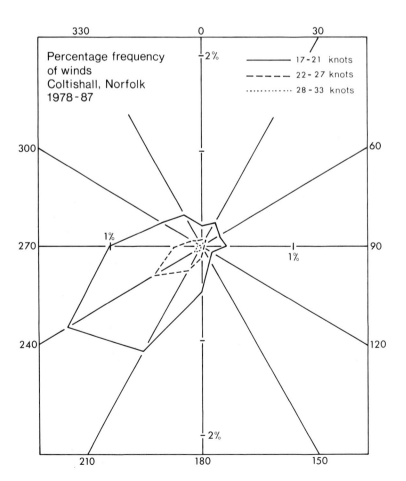

Fig. 2c

Percentage frequency of occurrence of winds in 30° sectors for speed classes from 1–3 to 28–33 knots (0.5–1.5 to 14.0–16.5 ms⁻¹). At higher wind speeds, the occurrence frequency is too small to be shown diagrammatically.

Source: Vincent (1988)

to the discomfiture of sun-worshippers, is somewhat less nearer the coast owing to the mists (known to Scots and north countrymen as 'haars') which drift in from the sea, particularly in late spring and early summer. These typically develop during periods of light, easterly winds, when the air is cooled by the sea to a temperature below its dew point, thus causing large-scale condensation, often accompanied by light drizzle, along the coast. Further inland, the cloud tends to dissipate as a result of the warming influence of the sun on the land, and it is for this reason that sites such as Wroxham can be basking in bright sunshine, when Hickling Broad and Horsey Mere, only a few miles to the east, are wreathed in thick mist.

The percentage frequencies of winds of differing directions and speeds of between 0 and 33 knots (16.5 metres per second (ms^{-1})) are diagrammatically illustrated in Fig. 2c. The data from which this figure is derived was collected at RAF Coltishall, some 21 km west of the coast at Horsey, and some of the light easterly winds recorded will have consisted of 'sea breezes'. These typically occur during anticyclonic conditions, when temperatures over the land significantly exceed those over the sea, thus generating a light inshore breeze, or, if the wind is already blowing from the east, an increase in its velocity. Winds of between 34 and 40 knots (17 to 20 ms^{-1}) only blew for a total of 25 hours during the 10-year period for which records were examined, and winds between 41 and 47 knots (20.5 to 23.5 ms^{-1}) only lasted for a total of 5 hours; all these gale-force winds blew from a south-westerly direction.

Broadland has been subjected to hurricane-force winds on at least three occasions during the past century. Preston (1985b) records the consequences of such an event on 24 March 1895, and notes that by mid-afternoon . . . "water was being blown out of the river (Yare) like dense clouds of smoke over the adjoining marsh, and the spray could be felt in my garden (at Brundall), sixty feet above it". Clouds of spray were also blown out of Surlingham and Rockland Broads, the effect being likened to that of two giant bonfires. Much damage was caused in the region; for instance, an entire plantation of larch trees was blown over at Strumpshaw, whilst the lead on the roof of Blofield Church was, in Preston's words "rolled up like parchment".

Unfortunately, the wind speeds attained locally were not measured, and the ferocity of the event cannot therefore be measured in relation to that of the hurricane of 2 January 1976, when a gust of 89 knots (44.5 ms^{-1}) was recorded in Norwich, 3000 council houses in the city being damaged as a result (Norgate, 1977). During the great storm of 16 October 1987, gusts of 71 knots (35.5 ms^{-1}) were recorded at Coltishall, and 79 knots (39.5 ms^{-1}) at Hemsby (Meteorological Office, 1987a), the mean wind speed between midnight and 1300 GMT at the latter locality being 45 knots (22.5 ms^{-1}) (Meteorological Office, 1987b). Although Broadland got off fairly lightly compared with Kent, Essex and East Suffolk, its trees did, as elsewhere, suffer much damage as a consequence of being still in leaf. Indeed, the work programme of the Rivers Commissioners* was disrupted during the winter of 1987/8 as a result of the need to remove scores of trees and branches which had fallen across the rivers.

Seasonal precipitation rates for several sites in Broadland, and in the catchments of its rivers, are given in Table 2g, and it will be seen that rainfall tends to be slightly less towards the east of the region. Evapo-transpiration rates are, as might be expected, high in the summer (Table 2h), the actual rates of loss being usually somewhat lower than the potential figures, as a consequence of the fact that the transpiration rate of farm crops and most plant communities decreases in concert with increases in the 'soil moisture deficit' (the latter being defined as the amount by which the field capacity of the soil has been reduced by growing plants). It will be noted from the Table that negative rainfall residuals commonly occur in the region during the summer months, a point of considerable importance to water resource planners, since such figures represent the amount by which the soil moisture deficit must be made good by subsequent rainfall, before any precipitation becomes available for groundwater recharge.

Meaned figures, such as those given in Table 2g, do, by definition, conceal variations

---

* The Committee of the Great Yarmouth Port and Haven Commissioners which, until its functions were assumed by the 'new' Broads Authority in 1989, was responsible for maintaining the rivers (but not Yarmouth Haven, Breydon Water and the lowermost reaches of the R. Bure) in a navigable condition. The work of this Committee is described in Chapter 11.

Table 2g   Seasonal precipitation (mm) as means for the period 1941 to 1970 at various sites (NGR in parentheses)

	E. Dereham (994132)	Tacolneston (137955)	Roydon Hall (093806)	N. Walsham (285305)	Ormesby (468152)	Sprowston (251123)	Burlingham (373101)	Gorleston (534037)
October	60	63	57	59	62	57	58	61
November	70	75	67	71	73	67	67	68
December	61	62	57	61	60	56	54	56
January	59	62	58	57	53	55	50	51
February	51	51	44	48	46	47	43	42
March	46	46	43	43	42	42	39	37
April	43	45	41	43	40	40	38	38
May	50	49	46	48	44	44	41	39
June	49	51	50	46	45	44	42	43
July	67	65	63	64	59	61	56	55
August	64	73	68	67	66	64	61	62
September	56	59	56	56	54	53	52	52
Annual Mean (mm)	676	701	650	663	644	630	601	604

Source: Records authenticated by the Meteorological Office, and made available through the courtesy of the AWA.

in the amount of precipitation which occur from year to year. For example, the annual reports of the Norfolk and Suffolk Local Land Drainage Committee show that the annual rainfall over the area covered by the Norwich Division of the Anglian Water Authority (AWA)* which embraced, *inter alia*, the catchments of all the Broadland rivers was nearly 40 per cent more in 1987/8 than the 1941 to 1970 mean of 629 mm. Conversely, rainfall between the beginning of April and the end of July 1976 was only 94 mm, instead of the mean figure for this period of 188 mm, though this deficiency was subsequently made up by above-average precipitation during the ensuing autumn and winter months.

Precipitation was even less during the drought year of 1921. Preston (1922) notes that only 14.81 in (376 mm) fell at Sprowston, while Geldeston, with 12.01 in (305 mm) received even less. In an account of the effects of this drought on plant and animal life, Bird (1922) observes that the reeds which fringe the broads are . . "this winter (1921/2) some 12 in (305 mm) shorter than after a normal season, and slender too in proportion". He goes on to record that Reedmace (*Typha*) too was dwarfed, and had died down early, while 'pin-rushes' (*Juncus* spp.) had hardly grown at all until August. He notes that birds, too, had been affected. For instance, very few Snipe had bred, almost certainly because the lowered water-table had allowed the surface of the marshes to become so hard that the young birds had been unable to feed successfully.

Cloudbursts sometimes occur in Broadland, as in other parts of Britain. But the 135 mm (5.42 in) recorded during the early hours of 1 August, 1972, at Costessey, just west of Norwich, was exceptional (Norgate, 1973). On this occasion, the rainfall was quite localized, and places only a few miles distant escaped the deluge altogether. This was far from being the case on 25 and 26 August, 1912, when between 4 and 6 inches (*c.* 100–150 mm) of rain fell in the catchments of all three main rivers. In

---

* This organization dropped the word 'Authority' from its title in 1983, in order to make itself more 'user-friendly'. But the abbreviation AWA is retained here in order to avoid confusion.

Broadland itself, 6.59 in (157 mm) was recorded at Ormesby, while an unprecedented 8.09 in (205 mm) fell at Brundall (Preston, 1913). The disastrous floods which ensued are described in Chapter 10.

Another extreme meteorological event occurred on 14 July, 1917, when a hailstorm devastated a swathe of country, half a mile wide, between East Ruston and Happisburgh (Bird, 1919). Orchards, hedgerow trees, and whole fields of cereals were stripped of foliage, windows were smashed in hundreds of houses, and a zinc chimney cowl at Stalham . . . "was pierced, as if by a gun shot". Many of the hailstones were as large as walnuts, but with jagged angles, and it is not altogether surprising that birds were observed to have been killed at Catfield and Hickling.

Table 2h   Precipitation, Evapo-transpiration and Residual precipitation (mm) at Barton Turf during the period 1956/7 to 1967/8

Water Year		Precipitation	Evapo-transpiration		Reisdual precipitation
			Potential	*Actual*	
1956/7	– winter (Oct–March)	305	95	94	211
	– summer (April–Sept.)	325	453	408	−83
1957/8	– winter	302	64	63	239
	– summer	357	396	387	−30
1958/9	– winter	241	63	63	178
	– summer	147	522	311	−164
1959/60	– winter	342	73	64	278
	– summer	331	440	389	−58
1960/1	– winter	413	75	75	338
	– summer	322	439	402	−80
1961/2	– winter	365	93	92	273
	– summer	278	438	389	−111
1962/3	– winter	258	83	83	175
	– summer	359	420	414	−55
1963/4	– winter	223	66	66	157
	– summer	261	466	383	−122
1964/5	– winter	315	97	94	221
	– summer	417	390	383	34
1965/6	– winter	336	99	98	238
	– summer	314	451	419	−105
1966/7	– winter	321	124	120	201
	– summer	255	470	368	−113
1967/8	– winter	310	124	121	189
	– summer	464	401	391	73
Average Water Year		630	529	473	157

Note: The land usage specification used by the Meteorological Office in making the above calculations was as follows: Riparian zone – 10%, woodland – 7%, heathland – 2%, urban – 1%, cereals – 32%, root crops – 30%, grass – 18%.

Source: East Suffolk and Norfolk River Authority, 1971.

Plate IV

Looking north-westwards from Postwick Grove – 1991.

The high ground bordering the R. Yare at Postwick Grove, about 4 miles downstream of Norwich Yacht Station, forms one of the best natural viewpoints in Broadland.

The outfall of the Whitlingham Sewage Treatment Works can be seen just to the left of the pontoon-mounted crane, while the piers for the bridge and viaduct which will carry the Norwich Southern Bypass across the Yare valley are under construction on the right of the photograph. Although the new bridge will provide a headroom of 11.7 m it will prevent sea-going yachts whose masts cannot be lowered from reaching the Port of Norwich.

Photo: R.N. Flowers

Chapter 3
The Water Regime and Other Physical Features of the Region

The Flood Plains

Apart from areas which have been made up and built on, for instance at Wroxham, Horning, Potter Heigham and Brundall, and some meadowland beside the North Walsham and Dilham Canal and the R. Bure between Belaugh and Coltishall, the land in the flood plains lies at or below high tide level, and would originally have been clothed with fen or, nearer the sea, saltmarsh vegetation. Over the centuries, much of this area was embanked and drained, so that it could be used for agriculture. These drained marshes may be on silt, clay or peat, and together cover some 18625 ha (Broads Consortium, 1971). They have traditionally been used as cattle pasturage, with a high water-table during the summer months, but between the mid-1960s and the mid-1980s, increasing numbers of owners found it necessary, in the face of changing economic circumstances, permanently to lower the water-table of the marshes so that they could grow cereals and other arable crops on them. By 1985, some 7500 ha, or c. 40 per cent of the Drained Marshland Area was being managed in this way.

Most of the remaining alluvial land is on peat, and has been left as unembanked, undrained fen. In some cases, this may have been because the land was considered too difficult to isolate hydrologically from the adjoining broads and rivers. However, landowners elsewhere seem to have been content to exploit their fens as a source of reed, 'sedge', marsh hay, peat and other produce, rather than try and bring them into agricultural use.

Although intensively managed up to the First World War, many of Broadland's fens are now undergoing natural succession, and are consequently clothed with sallow scrub or alder-dominated woodland, a community known locally as 'Fen Carr'. The figure of 7769 acres (3145 ha) quoted in the Report on Broadland (Nature Conservancy, 1965) is a substantial under-estimate of the amount of fen vegetation shown on the map which accompanies this document, and a survey showed that in 1980, there were 5255 ha of fen within the Broads Authority's executive boundary, of which 3014 ha were clothed with woody vegetation (Fuller, 1984*). A further 231 ha of fen lay outside the

---

* Fuller's figures relate to the area administered by the 'old' Broads Authority; this was responsible for the region between September 1978 and March 1989 (see Chapter 12). The area of responsibility of the present Authority (which took up its duties in April 1989) is slightly different – it does, for example, include more of the Upper Thurne catchment (see Maps 12.3 & 12.4).

Table 3a   The amount of fen (ha) in Broadland's main river valleys (after Fuller, 1984)

	Bure+	Ant	Thurne++	Yare+++	Waveney	Totals
Open unbushed fen*	440.6	436.2	558.2 (122.2)	623.7	182.6	2241.3 (2363.5)
Fen invaded by bushes & trees**	1367.5	677.2	159.0 (108.6)	553.5	257.0	3014.2 (3122.8)
Totals	1808.1	1113.4	717.2 (948.0)	1177.2	439.6	5255.5 (5486.3)

Notes:
*   Included under this heading are Fuller's Mown Fen, Herbaceous Fen, Cut reed and Reed fen categories.
**   Included under this heading are Fuller's Fen/carr and Carr categories.
+   Including the Muckfleet side-valley.
++   The figures in brackets relate to the areas of fen and carr in the Thurne catchment, which lay outside the Executive Area of the 'old' Broads Authority, but which are included within the jurisdiction of the present Authority.
+++   Including the Halvergate 'triangle'.

Authority's area of responsibility in the vicinity of Hickling and Calthorpe in the Upper Thurne catchment.

Despite being less ecologically diverse than they were in the past, the fens form one of the chief ecological and scenic attractions of the region. Many of them also serve as spillways, or 'washes', during times of flood. This function became more important as tidal penetration upstream increased as a consequence of the measures taken from Victorian times onwards to improve the navigability of the lower reaches of the rivers (see Chapter 11), and more recently, because of the greater 'flashiness' of the latter, following improvements to the drainage of the arable land which predominates in their catchments.

It will be seen from Table 3a that there is over twice as much unreclaimed fen beside the 'northern rivers' (i.e. the Bure, Ant and Thurne) as the southern. Furthermore, only two short sections of the R. Waveney are bordered by fen vegetation, whereas this adjoins the banks of the Ant for over half their total length (see Table 3b). All the rivers are embanked against flooding for much of their length, the proportions ranging from 41 per cent on the Ant, to 88 per cent on the Waveney.

Table 3b   The river margins – principal land uses

River	Total length of bank (m)	% Adjoined by meadowland or higher ground	% Adjoined by fen	% Embanked & adjoined by drained marshland	% Developed*
Bure	97 600	6	33	50	11
Ant	24 400	Nil	53	41	6
Thurne	19 200	Nil	10**	59	31***
Yare	70 400	3	21	71	5
Waveney	67 200	>1	3	88	8

Definitions:
R. Bure – Horstead Mill to confluence with R. Yare
R. Ant – Wayford Br. to Ant Mouth (excluding Barton Broad)
R. Thurne – Somerton Staithe to Thurne Mouth (excluding the Thurne broads)
R. Yare – Confluence with the R. Wensum to Berney Arms
R. Waveney – Geldeston Lock to the confluence with the R. Yare

NB Boat dykes and other waterways adjoining the main rivers are omitted.

*   There are minor inconsistencies between the figures given in this column, and those quoted by the Broads Authority (1982b), which were arrived at separately. This is probably due to differences in the criteria used to define 'development'.
**   Most of the fens in this valley are located beside the larger Thurne broads, rather than the river, and are therefore, by definition, excluded from this Table.
*** Almost all the 'development' beside the R. Thurne is in the vicinity of Potter Heigham, and consists of a line of bungalows on each side of the river, backed by drained marshland.

Apart from the Thurne, whose banks are lined for a considerable distance by bungalows, the river margins are remarkably free from residential or commercial development, the main centres for the letting, servicing and building of boats being at Wroxham (and its neighbour Hoveton on the north side of the R. Bure), Horning, Stalham, Potter Heigham, Brundall, Loddon, Oulton Broad and Beccles. Most of these settlements are located where the valley narrows (e.g. Wroxham and Potter Heigham), or where a meander brings a river near higher ground (e.g. Horning and Brundall). But not all such sites have been developed, and at Postwick Grove (just downstream of Norwich), Herringfleet and elsewhere, the valley margins are high and steep enough for panoramic views to be obtained across the wide expanses of fen and drained marsh bordering the rivers (see Plate IV).

Although the alluvial flood plains appear to be flat, there are in fact minor, and to a farmer and land drainage engineer, most important variations in their topography. The fens, for example, usually lie about a metre above Ordnance Datum, whereas most drained marshes are about half a metre below OD, mainly because of the wastage and shrinkage resulting from long-continued drainage. But there are variations in the micro-relief, even within a single area. For instance, parts of the great triangular block of marshland commonly, if somewhat inaccurately known as the 'Halvergate Marshes', lie at or only just below OD, whereas other parts are up to 0.8 m lower than this.

The rivers

(a) *Previous history*

Several of Broadland's rivers have altered course over the centuries as a result of natural processes, human intervention or both. For instance, some, or perhaps all, the water flowing down the Waveney was probably discharged at one time through what is now Lake Lothing, though this outfall was certainly blocked by the coastal sand and shingle deposits of Kirkley Ham by the late eighteenth century, when William Faden produced the first reliable map of the region. Indeed, the Waveney's confluence with the Yare at the head of Breydon Water may well have been established several centuries before then.

The former alignment of the lowermost reaches of the Bure is also somewhat uncertain, though it is generally agreed that this river originally discharged to the sea through a channel referred to in medieval documents as Grubb's Haven, or Cockle Water. This lay to the north of Yarmouth, and represented the relic of the aperture which formerly existed between the 'Middle Ground', a large sand-bank portrayed on an Elizabethan map purporting to show the extent of the Romano-British Transgression (Jennings & Green, 1965), and the higher ground in the vicinity of what is now Caister. As has been explained in Chapter 2, a shingle spit started to grow southwards from the latter towards the end of this Transgression, and this would have gradually narrowed the gap north of the 'Middle Ground', ultimately leaving the small outlet to the sea known as Cockle Water.

Doubts have recently been cast on this hypothesis by Lark (1990), who has pointed out that the alignment of the Bure downstream of Scare Gap does not look natural. In recognition of this, and the short distance separating Scare Gap from what is now Breydon Water, he has suggested that the Bure originally flowed across this section of the Romano-British estuary. Lark has also pointed out that the marshes between Three Mile House and the edge of Breydon Water are much lower in level than the neighbouring land. From this, he has deduced that Pickerell Holme, the stream which drains the area around Caister Castle, discharged into the Yare across the tidal flats bordering what is now Breydon Water, rather than into the Bure at Three Mile House, as it does today.

The principal flaw in Lark's hypothesis is that it fails to address how Cockle Water could have remained open to the sea, despite a continuing fall in the relative sea level from about 350 AD onwards, and the progressive southward growth of the Caister shingle spit. Following an assessment of land levels, he himself has pointed out, probably correctly, that the R. Yare at one time flowed directly out to sea across the site now occupied by St. Nicholas' Church. This was founded by Bishop Herbert in *c.* 1100, and therefore the spit must by then have grown a long way south of Cockle Water; indeed, it must have elongated sufficiently to deflect the R. Yare southwards along the alignment of the present-day Haven.

If, as seems certain, Cockle Water did at one time serve as the outfall of the Bure, Lark's hypothesis would, if correct, mean that the river must have changed course downstream of Scare Gap. This could have resulted either from human intervention, or natural processes and whilst the latter eventuality is possible, though unlikely, the river could not have been artificially diverted until the early twelfth century as the town of Yarmouth was not well established until then (Rutledge, 1990). Moreover, it seems inconceivable that the townsfolk would have been able to plan and execute such an ambitious project at such an early date.

In short, given the effects of long-shore drift, and the continuing southwards extension of the Caister shingle spit during the millennium following the end of the Romano-British Transgression, it seems most unlikely that Cockle Water would have remained open to the sea, had it not been serving as the outfall of the R. Bure throughout this period.

Rutledge notes that a description of the town in 1286 includes a reference to the existence of a harbour. This was almost certainly located at the northern end of what is now the Haven, but it is quite likely, given the relatively rapid rate at which the Yarmouth shingle spit is thought to have been extending southwards during this period, that the mouth of the river was difficult to navigate. This was certainly the case in the early fourteenth century, and led to a series of attempts being made between then and the mid-sixteenth century to create a satisfactory entrance to the Haven (see Chapter 11). If it was anything like as difficult for ships to get in and out of the Haven during the twelfth and thirteenth centuries as it was in the following 200 years, Cockle Water may well have served a useful role as an alternative harbour. It probably also enabled sea-going, as well as river, craft to gain access to the hinterland, the presence of a large religious establishment, St. Benet's Abbey, a few miles upstream, providing a direct impetus for this usage.

Despite being navigable for a time, Manship (1619) refers to . . . "the stopping of the sea from entering at the mouth of the Grubb's Haven", and later used the words "blocked off" to describe events taking place in 1346. Both phrases suggest that the channel was sealed off as a result of a deliberate act, rather than a natural process, and in the circumstances, it is tempting to suggest that those responsible were motivated by a desire to increase the amount of water flowing down what is now the Haven, thus helping to alleviate the difficulties which were by then being encountered in keeping the mouth of the latter open to shipping. This objective could have been attained by creating a new channel for the Bure from the western end of Cockle Water southwards to the point where the river currently discharges into the R. Yare, existing saltmarsh creeks being used whenever possible (see Maps 3.1 a & b). In the event, it continued to prove very difficult to maintain the mouth of the Haven in a navigable condition, and as we shall see in Chapter 11, the problem was not finally solved until some 220 years later.

Ships entering and leaving Grubb's Haven in the early fourteenth century would have passed quite close to Midsands Cross, the flinty plinth of which is today located incongruously within a modern housing estate, about 100 m east of the main coast road (A 149). Rye (c. 1962) believed that this Cross was constructed as a boundary marker in about 1300 or soon after, probably as a replacement for a less substantial structure erected in 1208 when Yarmouth was granted a Royal Charter. The Cross was almost certainly built near the seaward entrance to Grubb's Haven, and the fact that the present beach is now about half a mile away to the east, demonstrates very clearly just how much accretion has occurred on this stretch of coast since medieval times.

According to Rye, the centre of the Grubb's Haven channel was situated about a quarter of a mile north of Midsands Cross, and it is of interest that in 1961, when this area was being bulldozed prior to the construction of the present housing estate, the course of this channel was clearly visible in the form of a cockle-shell filled hollow (Driscoll, pers. comm.).

Because the area north of Midsands Cross has been landscaped and built upon, it is not at present possible to determine the exact location and width of Grubb's Haven. However, this information could readily be obtained by putting down some cores in the area. In addition, if such a study embraced the land to the west of the coast road, it would reveal whether, as the author suspects, the low-lying depression in Bure Park (part of which has been excavated as an ornamental lake) is a relic of the western end of Grubb's Haven.

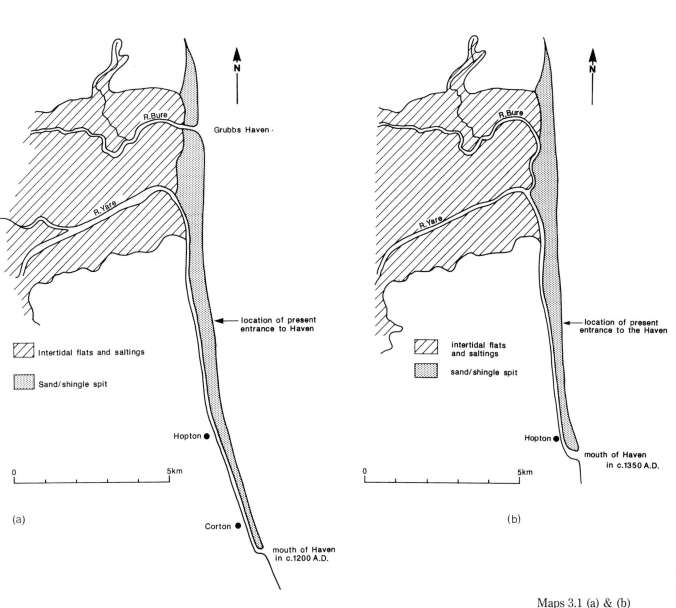

Maps 3.1 (a) & (b)

The outfalls of the rivers Yare and Bure prior to, and just after, the 'stopping up' of Grubb's Haven in 1346.

As will become apparent in Chapter 8, very little indeed is known about the ways in which the saltings and fens which formerly bordered the rivers were embanked and converted to grass marshland. Furthermore, the timescale involved is extremely uncertain, the most that can be said being that documentary evidence suggests that some areas may have been reclaimed by the fourteenth century, and that conversion was probably in full swing by the mid-sixteenth century.

Reclamation of the open estuary which formerly occupied the area immediately to the west of Yarmouth would have been difficult, and was accomplished in several stages, rather than all at once. Stratigraphical studies are needed to elucidate the exact sequence of events, and their timing, but it is the author's belief that the first marshland in the Yarmouth district to be embanked and reclaimed was that located to the north of the lowermost reaches of the R. Bure. This is because this area would have lain in the lee of the Caister shingle spit for longer than areas to the south, and would in consequence have had more time to accrete. As siltation of the intertidal flats proceeded, saltmarsh communities would have developed, and in time, the level of these would have risen sufficiently to make it possible to build an embankment separating the area being reclaimed from the remainder of the estuary.

If, as suggested, the marshes south-west of Caister were reclaimed fairly early on, this would imply that the precursor of Breydon Water originally encompassed the whole of

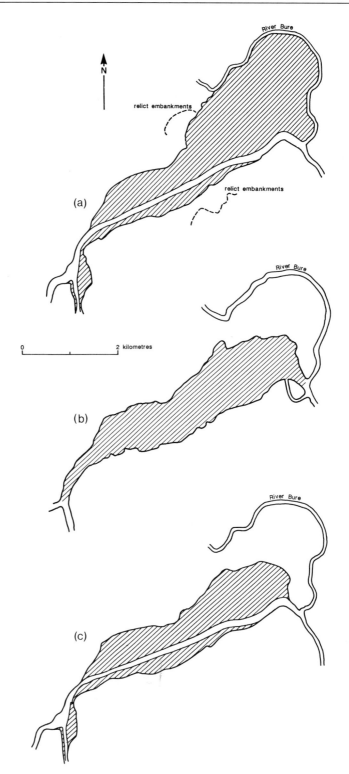

Maps 3.2 (a), (b) & (c)

Stages in the evolution of Breydon Water from the open estuary which existed in Romano-British times. Map (a), though speculative, is based on the alignment of relict sections of tidal embankment shown on early Ordnance Survey maps, whilst (b) is taken from William Faden's map. published in 1797. It will be noted that there are only minor differences between this, and (c), which portrays the present-day configuration of the relict estuary. (© Crown Copyright).

the area known as the 'Bure Loop' (see Map 3.2a). Evidence for this is provided by the fact that the County Series Ordnance Survey (OS) 6-inch maps of the area show an embankment running in a south-westerly direction from the northern margin of the 'Bure Loop', right through to the site of the now demolished Lockgate Farm. Sadly, most of this embankment was ploughed out during the 1960s and 1970s, but small sections of it are still visible on the ground.

The north-east corner of the present-day Breydon Water is accreting much faster than other parts of the relict estuary, and by analogy, it is believed that accretion in the north-eastern end of the Breydon 'precursor' (i.e. the area now known as the 'Bure Loop') would have been relatively rapid. Once the level of the land had risen sufficiently, its owners would, as in the area south-west of Caister, have found it possible to construct a new embankment so as to take in more of the estuary. If, as is thought, this was built on the alignment of Breydon's North Wall, it would have facilitated the conversion of the 'Bure

Loop' to grazing marshland. We do not know when this was done, but the new flood-wall had certainly been built by the end of the eighteenth century, as Faden's map portrays the boundaries of Breydon Water more or less as they are today (Maps 3.2 b & c).

It must be emphasized that numerous uncertainties remain about the above proposals, particularly in respect of the relationship between Cockle Water, the Caister shingle spit and the 'Middle Ground'. Detailed stratigraphical investigations are needed in this part of Broadland, and the ideas advanced will also need to be examined in relation to on-going studies on the history and archaeology of Yarmouth.

Although the R. Bure has probably been joined by a major tributary at Thurne Mouth since the last glaciation, there is evidence that much of the water discharged at this point was originally derived from the Ant catchment, rather than that of the R. Thurne. The latter once had an outfall to the sea between Winterton and Horsey, and its channel, crossing what is now the foreshore fronting the sand-dunes at Bramble Hill was scoured out when these were breached by the surge flood of 12 February, 1938 (see page 315); indeed, for at least two days afterwards, sea water continued to flow up this into the Thurne, even at low tide (EDP, 1938). The channel across the foreshore was again exposed by the great storm which produced the 1953 surge (Buxton, pers. comm.), but it was soon refilled by beach deposits, and it is impossible today to determine from the surface topography precisely where it was located. However, the lowermost reaches of the Thurne would have formed part of the boundary between the Hundreds of Happing and West Flegg, and since this today forms the dividing line between the Districts of North Norfolk and Great Yarmouth, the site of the former outfall can be pinpointed as being *c.* 750 m north of the present-day track from Winterton Ness to Somerton Holmes. Further to the east, the embanked course of the former river can still be clearly discerned from the B1159 coast road, crossing the marshes between West Somerton and Horsey to join the present-day R. Thurne at Dungeon Corner. The fact that the watercourse is bordered by widely-spaced embankments indicates, not only that this section of the river was at one time strongly tidal, but that the marshes in this part of Broadland were drained and brought into agricultural use before the Thurne lost its direct outfall to the sea.

It is not known when the Thurne started to flow southwards to the Bure, rather than northwards to the sea at Horsey, nor whether this current reversal resulted from the blockage of the outfall by the natural accretion of beach deposits, or whether this process was deliberately hastened, perhaps to reduce the risk of the hinterland being flooded. From time to time it has been claimed that a sluice was installed at the former mouth of the river, and rotten timbers, possibly representing the remains of this, are said to have been exposed on the beach in 1921. But in the absence of further information, timberwork in this very vulnerable spot seems more likely to have been the residue of past attempts to strengthen the sea defences. Cornford (1979) has pointed out that an Elizabethan map shows what appear to be two sets of sluice gates between Waxham and Winterton, and that one of these could mark the Thurne's former outfall. On the other hand, the configuration of the coastline portrayed on this map suggests that the symbols used were intended to represent sea defence works which had been erected at 'lows' in the dunes. Moreover, as Cornford herself has pointed out, the records of the Sea Breach Commissions formed from 1609 onwards (see page 314) make no mention of sluice gates. This suggests that if present in the first place, they were no longer functional, and that the Thurne had undergone a current reversal some time previously. The sea outfall had certainly been sealed off by 1794, since Faden's map (published in 1790, but surveyed in the first four years of that decade) shows a continuous line of dunes at this point, and marks the Hundred Stream as a 'dike' [*sic*] terminating a short distance to the west of these, with the Waxham to Winterton track in between.

The R. Ant formerly turned eastwards just south of Ludham Bridge, and flowed along the 'Hundred Dyke' (see Map 3.3) before joining what is now the R. Thurne at Cold Harbour (see Frontispiece). Evidence for this comes from the fact that the Hundred Dyke is bounded throughout its length by tall, widely spaced embankments, similar to those of the lower Thurne, but now functionless, and quite out of proportion to the diminutive ditch which follows this route today. In addition, it was the Hundred Dyke, rather than the lowermost section of the present-day R. Ant, which formed the boundary between the Hundreds of Happing and Tunstead, and which to this day forms the dividing line between the parishes of Horning and Ludham.

The Ant may have been diverted so that it discharged to the R. Bure at Ant Mouth when the Thurne underwent its current reversal; indeed, the new channel for the Ant may have been excavated to help bring this about. However, the diversion would have impeded access to the monastery on St. Benet's Holm which was in use from the early eleventh century, having been endowed by King Canute. This was the only religious house in England not to be dissolved by King Henry VIII (Snelling, 1971), but it is not known how long the site continued in use afterwards. The R. Ant is shown on Faden's map as joining the Bure at Ant Mouth, and the realignment of its lowermost reaches may have been carried out in a bid to improve the navigability of the river after the monastery on St. Benet's Holm had finally been abandoned, but before the end of the eighteenth century. An alternative, but much less likely suggestion, is that the new outfall channel for the Ant was dug when the Abbey was fortified in the mid-fourteenth century, since this would have ensured that the site was surrounded by water on all four sides, rather than three.

The course of the R. Ant has been extensively altered upstream, as well as downstream of Ludham Bridge. Barton Broad was originally a 'by-passed' site like Wroxham Broad, but the river was subsequently diverted so that it flowed through it, instead of just to the east. To achieve this, a new channel for the river had to be dug to the south of the broad (see Map 3.3), the place where this cut through the sands and gravels of the valley margin being known as Irstead Shoals. This diversion was almost certainly prompted primarily by a desire to improve the kavigability of the river, since it cut out its long meander through the fens to the south-east of the broad, thus making it much easier for trading vessels to reach the villages of Barton Turf, Neatishead and Irstead.

The Ant's meander across Reedham Marsh, between Irstead and Ludham Bridge, was also by-passed, and this too was almost certainly done in a bid to improve the navigability of the river. However, the work seems to have been carried out in two stages, since a short loop almost opposite How Hill is, like the river itself, shown as open water on the map accompanying the 1802 Enclosure Award for Ludham, and is referred to in the latter as the 'Old River'. This would suggest that it had been excavated fairly recently compared with the rest of the meander, which is not shown as open water, and which had therefore probably been abandoned and allowed to silt up a long time previously.

A fourth major diversion of the R. Ant was carried out between Barton Broad and Wayford Bridge. In this case, the new channel skirting the eastern margin of the valley is slightly longer than the original, suggesting that it may have been dug so as to create a single, and therefore more readily drained, block of marsh on the western side of the flood plain, rather than in an attempt to improve the navigability of the river. Since the latter is shown on its original course on Faden's map, but on its new alignment on the Stalham Enclosure Award of 1810, this diversion must have been carried out around the turn of that century. In contrast, the new channels to the east and south of Barton Broad, and to the east of Reedham Marsh were dug prior to 1794. But in each case it is the course of the old channels which marks the boundary between the parishes of Catfield, Irstead, and Ludham, and which in the past formed the dividing line between the Hundreds of Tunstead and Happing.

All told, some 4000 m of new channel have been dug for the R. Ant over the centuries, making it by far the most extensively altered waterway in the region. Nevertheless, considerable changes have taken place elsewhere, notably in the vicinity of the Thurne broads. Here, most if not all the works carried out were prompted by a desire to improve the drainage of the surrounding area, and, in contrast to the situation in the Ant valley, resulted in a loss of navigable water. Examples include the channels shown on Faden's map as linking Horsey Mere with the Hundred Stream, and Blackfleet Broad with the R. Thurne, both of which crossed land reclaimed for agriculture.

Very little information is available about the condition of the rivers prior to the nineteenth century, but they were certainly much narrower in Victorian times than they are today (see Chapter 11). In addition, given their gentle gradients, and their consequent tendency to silt up, their channels would have been relatively shallow, particularly at the margins. Some confirmation of this is provided by the frequent references in the Great Yarmouth Port and Haven Commissioners' archives to the need to dredge, dydle or 'draw' the latter. The channel profiles would have steepened as a result of the determined efforts made during the past 150 years or so to deepen the rivers, allied with increased tidal scouring, and the process will have accelerated from the 1930s onwards, as the numbers of motor craft using the waterways increased.

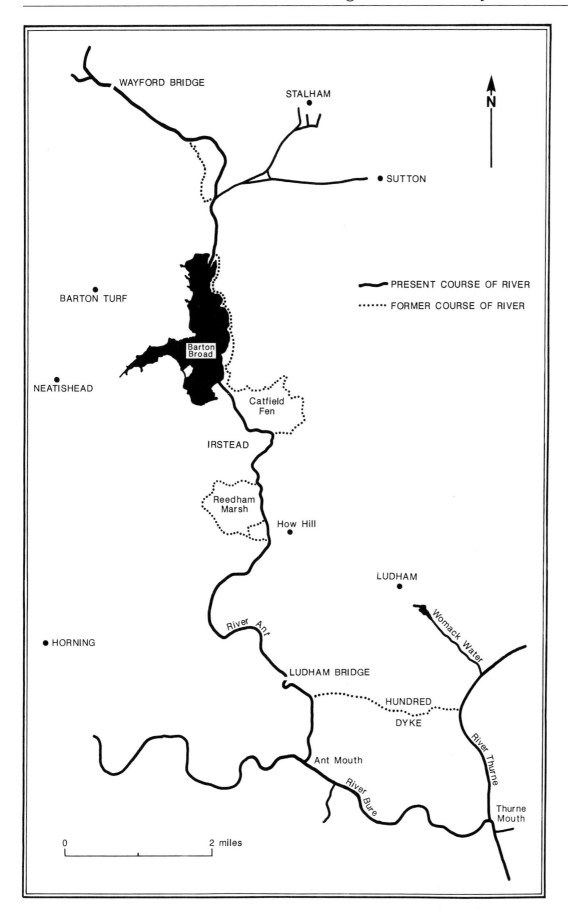

The course of the R. Ant has been extensively altered over the centuries. Note that after flowing through Catfield Fen and around Reedham Marsh, the river originally discharged to the R. Bure via the Hundred Dyke and the lowermost reaches of the R. Thurne, and not at Ant Mouth, as today.

Source: Jennings (1952)

Map 3.3

(b) *Present condition*

If one excludes the broads, the formerly canalized sections of the Bure and Waveney, and small channels such as Ranworth Dam, there are about 174 km of navigable waterway in the region (see Table 3c). The Bure and Waveney are between 25 and 40 m wide for much of their length, while the Yare is larger, being between 45 and 60 m wide between Berney Arms and Reedham, and not narrowing to 40 m until Bramerton. The Ant, the Thurne above Repps, the Bure and the Waveney upstream of Wroxham and Beccles respectively, and the New Cut, are all between 12 and 24 m wide, whilst Waxham Cut and the R. Chet are less than 12 m wide. Special efforts have been made since the 1820s to ensure that the R. Yare can accommodate sea-going vessels bound to and from the port of Norwich, and although shoals are liable to form here and there, particularly near Whitlingham, its central channel is almost everywhere at least 3 m deep at low tide. The R. Waveney up to Beccles is only slightly shallower than the Yare, and between St. Olaves and Burgh Castle is seldom less than 4.5 m deep at low tide, a figure 1.5 m or so greater than that quoted by Hamilton (1978). The Bure too, is generally 4 to 5 m deep as far upstream as Ant Mouth, but above this point, becomes progressively shallower, so that by Wroxham, its channel only has about 1.5 m of water in it; its tributaries, the Ant and the Thurne, are about 1.5 m and 1.8 m deep respectively (Groves, pers. comm.).

The catchments of Broadland's rivers are very large (see Table 3d); indeed, the Bure, Yare, Wensum and Waveney together drain a substantial part of East Anglia. Arable farming constitutes the predominant land use in the catchments of these rivers, a point of importance in relation to their water chemistry (see Chapter 5).

The rivers have very gentle gradients as they flow through Broadland, the figure commonly quoted being about 3 cm per kilometre. But their water regime is complicated by the tidal influence to which they are subject (see page 57), and also by differences in their rates of run-off (see Table 3e). These are due to variations in the permeability of the soil types which predominate in the catchments, those of the Bure being relatively permeable to rainfall, with an estimated annual infiltration rate of 143 mm (East Suffolk & Norfolk River Authority, 1971). Impermeable deposits of boulder clay occur more frequently in the catchment of the Yare, which therefore has an estimated mean infiltration rate of 94 mm per year, whilst soils derived from such strata

Table 3c   Lengths of navigable waterway in kilometres

Wensum	New Mills to confluence with R. Yare	4.8
Yare	Trowse Bridge to confluence with R. Wensum	1.6
Yare	Confluence with the R. Wensum to Berney Arms	35.2
Yare	Berney Arms to Haven Br., incl. Breydon Water	6.4
Chet	Loddon to R. Yare	5.6
New Cut		4.0
Waveney	Geldeston Lock to confluence with R. Yare	33.6
Bure	Horstead Mill to confluence with R. Yare	48.8
Ant	Honing Lock to Ant Mouth, incl. Barton Broad	13.2
Thurne	Somerton Staithe to Thurne Mouth	9.6
	Waxham Cut to R. Thurne, incl. Meadow Dyke and Heigham Sound	6.8
Yare	Haven Br. to the sea – not usable by hire craft	4.0
Total		173.6
Other navigable waterways (e.g. Oulton Dyke, Ranworth Dam & Fleet Dyke, but excluding the broads themselves)		16.4
Grand total		190.0

Source: Groves (*in litt.*)

Table 3d   The catchments of Broadland's rivers

Catchment	Sub-catchment	Gross Area (sq.km.)	
R. Bure	R. Bure	330.7	
	Spixworth Brook	61.5	
	N. Walsham & Dilham Canal	49.3	
	Tidal R. Bure and R. Ant	164.2	
	Tidal R. Bure and R. Thurne	271.7	
			877.4
R. Yare	R. Wensum	560.2	
	R. Tud	76.6	
	R. Yare	279.7	
	R. Tas	185.7	
	Tidal R. Yare (incl. estuary)	311.9	
			1414.1
R. Waveney	R. Waveney (upper)	152.7	
	R. Dove	199.9	
	R. Waveney (lower)	317.5	
	Tidal R. Waveney	218.6	
			888.7
		Sub total	3180.2
	Less Breydon Water and the saline sections of the rivers	5.5	
		Grand total	3174.7

Source: East Suffolk & Norfolk River Authority (1971)

Table 3e   Rates of catchment run-off

River	Gauging Station	Catchment-Area (sq km)	Period of observation	Mean Run-off (mm)	Maximum Run-off (mm) & year	Minimum Run-off (mm) & year
Bure	Horstead Mill	313.0	1974–1982	219.0	272.4–1981	164.5–1974
Ant	Honing Lock	49.3	1971–1982	191.1	221.5–1981	157.3–1973
Wensum	Costessey Mill	536.0	1971–1982	242.8	330.5–1979	140.7–1973
Tud	Costessey Park	73.2	1971–1982	145.8	198.8–1981	85.4–1973
Yare	Colney	231.8	1971–1982	183.0	245.7–1981	104.8–1973
Tas	Shotesham	146.5	1971–1982	145.6	226.2–1979	60.3–1973
Waveney	Needham	370.0	1971–1982	142.6	207.5–1981	45.8–1973

Source: Anglian Water Authority (in litt.)

predominate in the Waveney's catchment, which consequently has an average infiltration rate of only 43 mm per year. Being mainly surface fed, this river responds much more quickly to periods of drought or heavy rainfall than the Bure, which contains a relatively large groundwater component, and which therefore has a more stable annual flow regime. The mean discharge rates of the rivers are given in Table 3f.

The broads

(a) *Size and location*

Opinions vary as to which of the numerous pools and shallow lakes in the region should be termed broads. The Nature Conservancy (1965), for instance, considered that there were 42, whereas the Broads Consortium (1971) recognized 46 and the Broads Authority (1982e) 41. 50 sites are defined in the following account as broads, on the basis

Table 3f Mean discharge rates of the Broadland rivers

River and location	Measured(M) or estimated (E)	Mean discharge (m^3 sec^{-1})	Catchment area (sq. km.)
R. Bure – Horstead Mill	M	2.38	313.0
R. Bure – at confluence with R. Ant	E	3.2	—
R. Bure – at confluence with R. Yare	E	6.2	—
R. Ant – Honing Lock	M	0.32	49.3
R. Ant – at confluence with R. Bure	E	1.1	—
R. Thurne – at confluence with R. Bure	E	0.96	—
R. Wensum – Costessey Mill	M	4.22	536.0
R. Tud – Costessey Park	M	0.365	73.2
R. Yare – Colney	M	1.55	231.7
R. Tas – Shotesham	M	0.835	146.6
R. Yare – at entrance to Breydon Water	E	10.3	—
R. Waveney – Ellingham Mill	M	3.2	670.0
R. Waveney – at entrance to Breydon Water	E	2.7	—

Sources:
Measured values – East Suffolk & Norfolk River Authority (1971) & Anglian Water Authority (*in litt.*)
Estimates by Moss (1977) from data in the *Surface Water Year Book* and Supplement (1968).

that they are flooded peat pits of medieval age (see Table 3g). But in some cases what was once a single sheet of water has been partitioned into two, more or less separate sections (e.g. Ranworth and Malthouse Broads). Usually this has occurred naturally as a consequence of the progressive overgrowth of the site by reedswamp and fen vegetation; however, Bridge Broad was bisected when the Norwich to Wroxham railway line was built, whilst the Trinity Broads (the name sometimes given to the Ormesby, Rollesby, Filby group) are traversed by the causeways carrying the A149 and A1064 roads. Some of these sub-divided sites are of sufficient size to warrant a separate mention in the Table (e.g. South Walsham Inner and Outer Broads), but others (e.g. Strumpshaw East and West Broads) are so small that they have been listed as single entities.

It will be seen from the Table 3g, and the Base Map, that the broads are very unevenly distributed in the region, being far more numerous beside the northern rivers, than the southern. They range in size from small, relict pools to the *c.* 140 ha expanse of Hickling Broad. But only three other sites, Ormesby North and Barton Broads and Fritton Lake, possess more than 50 ha of open water, whilst 22 others cover less than 5 ha. According to the latest 1:2500 OS maps, the 50 broads listed in Table 3g have a combined water surface of 835.8 ha, but most sites are less than 2 m deep, the mean water depth being less than a metre in at least fifteen of them.

Gregory (1892) was the first to point out that apart from headwater sites such as Hickling Broad and Horsey Mere, the broads fall into two categories. 'Side-valley' sites such as Alderfen Broad, Flixton Decoy and the Trinity Broads are, as their name implies, situated in tributary valleys, unlike the 'by-passed' broads, which are located to one side of a main river. Down-valley sites such as Ranworth and Rockland Broads may lie a kilometre or more away from the latter, but by-passed sites further upstream are usually only separated from the river by a narrow, peaty baulk, often termed, somewhat misleadingly, a 'rond'; examples of such sites include Wroxham and Salhouse Broads.

Most of the broads are located within, or beside, large blocks of fen, but a few are bordered by drained marshland, and are embanked on one or more sides (e.g. Rockland and Oulton Broads). Hickling, Horsey, Blackfleet and the two Martham Broads, and their interconnecting dykes, are entirely surrounded by flood banks, and form a high level system into which water from the adjoining marshland is pumped for transmission seawards via the R. Thurne. Only at Barton, where the R. Ant has been diverted from its former course through Catfield Fen to the east (see Map 3.3) does a principal water-course actually flow through a broad. Gregory (1892) put it well when he wrote:

"Instead of the river (Bure) passing through the broads, it kept sullenly aloof of them; as we sailed down the river, there was broad to the left of us, broad to the right of us, broad in front of us, but by a series of ingenious twists and turns, it managed to wind through the whole lot of them, either eluding any direct contact with them, or by communicating only by a few narrow and overgrown passages".

There is far less open water in Broadland today than there was in Gregory's time. This is partly because the surface area of most of the broads has been considerably reduced as a consequence of the overgrowth of vegetation. 25-inch OS maps of the County Series show that the combined hectarage of the 50 sites listed in Table 3g was 1074.3, some 22 per cent greater than it is today, whilst in the mid-Victorian era, they together covered some 1227 ha. Some sites have, through marginal overgrowth, become extinct (e.g. Dilham Broad) or nearly so (e.g. Hedney's Bottom), whilst Sutton Broad and Womack Water would have suffered a similar fate, had not navigation channels across them been kept open by dredging. Other open waters have disappeared through the combined effects of overgrowth, and the lowering of the water-table following the drainage of the adjoining marshes. For instance, the open waters near Thurne, Ludham and Upton which are marked on Faden's map of 1797 had probably been drained by 1838, since they are not shown on the first One-inch Ordnance Survey map of this area, whilst Carleton and Barnby Old Broads, which appear on the latter, had disappeared by the 1880s when the first 6-inch OS maps of Broadland were published.

Another reason why there was more open water in the region at the time of Gregory's visit stems from the fact that peat continued to be dug from shallow excavations in the fens until the end of the nineteenth century. Once abandoned, the flooded workings or 'turf ponds' (see page 194) were rapidly overgrown by peat-forming plants, and in many cases have been infilled completely during the past 50 years or so.

The total hectarage of open water in the region declined progressively during the first half of the present century, reaching its lowest level in the early 1950s. Since then, it has tended to increase, partly as a result of the loss of marginal reedswamp from many broads through coypu grazing and regression (see Chapter 6), and partly because of the excavation here and there of new pools for sporting, conservation or amenity purposes. Maps and air photographs show that this trend has been particularly marked in the Ant valley, where at least 17 new flight ponds have been dug in the fens since the Second World War.

The names of extinct open waters, some of which probably orginated as a consequence of medieval peat digging, are given in Table 3h, while water-filled peat pits

Table 3h   Extinct open waters, some of which probably originated as peat workings

Name	NGR	Status
Barnby Old Broad	TM 490910	Peat pit shown as open water on 1847 tithe map, but extinct by 1882 when first OS 6-inch map was published
Carleton Broad	TG 347034	Peat pit shown as open water on 1839 tithe map, but extinct by 1881 (OS 25-inch first ed.)
Chapman's Broad	TG 426219	Formerly connected to Hickling Broad. Separated by 1838, and although alleged by Grantham (1868) to cover 19 ha, was extinct through drainage by 1881. May have been formed by the digging of clay as well as peat.
Dilham Broad	TG 343250	Peat pit covering 27 ha on 1838 tithe map. Now skirted by channel leading to Dilham Staithe.
Greenacres Broad	TG 372187	Peat pit shown on Indenture of 1903 (Boardman, pers.comm.) but not marked on OS maps.
Gage's Broad	TG 424233	These three sites are shown on a map of *c.* 1810 made when Hickling was enclosed, and they are also portrayed on Faden's map of 1797. Their origin is unknown, but they may have been low-lying areas in the marshes, rather than peat pits.
Hare Park Broad	TG 431228	
Wigg's Broad	TG 432245	
Thurne Broad	TG 400163	Shown (but not named) on Faden's map, but apparently extinct by 1838, since they are not shown on the first OS map. Their origin is obscure.
Ludham Broad	TG 403180	
Upton Old Broad	TG 408137	
5 unamed pools between East Somerton and Horsey	(approx) TG 490200 TG 482214 TG 475219 TG 462223 TG 464233	Shown on Faden's map, but not on OS map of 1838. Thought to have been low-lying areas in the marshes, rather than peat pits.

Table 3g The location, size and usage of the broads

Valley: Bure

Name	NGR	A	B (see key below)	C	D	Accessibility from main river system	Principal uses
Belaugh Broad	TG 293173	5	4.0	1.9	0.5	none	suction-dredged in 1987
Bridge Broad East &	TG 302182	5 (5)*	4.9	2.8	1.0	yes	boat moorings
Bridge Broad West	TG 301183				1.5	yes	general navigation
Burntfen Broad	TG 338188	6 (5)*	5.9	4.6	1.0	landlocked	–
Cockshoot Broad	TG 344155	12	5.1	5.3	1.0	dammed off in 1982	nature conservation: suction-dredged in 1982
Decoy Broad	TG 328168	9	9.3	10.0	1.5	none	nature conservation, scouting & angling
Filby Broad	TG 460134	47	47.0	41.9	2.0	landlocked	reservoir, angling & school sailing
Hoveton Great Broad	TG 317163	42(49)*	35.8	24.9	1.0	none	nature conservation
Hoveton Little Broad (Black Horse Broad & Pound End)	TG 332175	21(23)*	20.6	19.9	1.2	yes, (Easter–September)	general navigation & club sailing. Suction-dredged in 1990
Hudson's Bay	TG 314167	6	4.8	4.5	0.8	none	nature conservation
Little Broad	TG 450129	n/a	2.4	1.3	0.8	landlocked	–
Malthouse Broad (Ranworth Outer Broad)	TG 360148	11	10.9	11.1	1.5	yes	general navigation
Mautby Decoy	TG 483114	n/a	2.5	2.5	1.0	landlocked	angling
Norton's Broad (Cockle Broad)	TG 291169	2	1.0	0.7	0.8	landlocked	–
Ormesby Broad (north)	TG 467162	77	77.0	56.4	2.5	landlocked	reservoir & angling
Ormesby Little Broad	TG 465143	49	49.0	73.1	2.5	landlocked	reservoir & angling
Rollesby Broad (inc. Lily Broad)	TG 462141	39	39.2		2.5	landlocked	reservoir & angling
Ranworth (Inner) Broad	TG 353154	57	32.8	28.9	1.2	none	nature conservation & angling
Salhouse Broad (Great & Little)	TG 318158 & TG 314158	11(9)*	7.1	12.7	1.5	yes	general navigation (Gt. Broad only)
Snape's Water	TG 311175	3	2.8	2.5	0.5	none	–
Sotshole Broad (Ranworth Little Broad)	TG 359137	(5)*	1.3	1.3	0.5	landlocked	–
South Walsham Inner & Outer Broads	TG 365140 TG 372142	28(25)*	20.6	20.8	1.3	yes	general navigation
Upton Broad (Great & Little)	TG 389134	12	5.5(Gt.) 2.2(Lt.)	6.9	0.8	landlocked	angling
Wroxham Broad	TG 312168	32(37)*	32.4	34.4	1.3	yes	general navigation & club sailing
Totals:		479 + say 5 = 484	424.1	368.4			

Valley: Ant

Name	NGR	A	B	C	D	Accessibility from main river system	Principal uses
Alderfen Broad (Oliver Broad)	TG 354197	11(9)*	8.1	5.1	1.0	landlocked	nature conservation & angling
Barton Broad (inc. Turkey Broad)	TG 362213	115(93)*	104.9	77.3	1.5	yes	general navigation & nature conservation
Catfield Broad	TG 377208	(9)*	2.1	1.2	0.5	landlocked	–
Crome's Broad	TG 373197	6	5.3	4.3	0.8	landlocked	educational
Sutton Broad (inc. N. limb formerly known as Stalham Broad)	TG 375236	47 (Sutton B. only)	78.5	channels only	1.5	yes (channels only)	general navigation
Totals:		188	198.9	87.9			

Key:
A – Approximate hectarage of open water shown on Tithe Award maps, *c.* 1840
B – Hectarage of open water shown on the County Series OS 25″ maps, 1881–1938
C – Hectarage of open water shown on 1 : 2500 OS maps, 1971–1978
D – Approximate mean depth (m)

( )* – Hectarage figures based on acreages given by Grantham (1868) and quoted by Woodward (1881).

Valley: Thurne

Name	NGR	A	B	C	D	Accessibility from main river system	Principal uses
Blackfleet Broad	TG 445213	5	3.8	1.6	0.5	none	nature conservation
Calthorpe Broad	TG 410258	6	2.0	1.2	0.5	landlocked	nature conservation & research
Heigham Sound (inc. Duck Broad & the West Holes)	TG 435204	45 (234)*	43.3	34.4	1.3	yes	general navigation & nature conservation
Hickling Broad (inc. Heigham Corner & Whiteslea)	TG 415215	196	172.6	141.1	1.3	yes	general navigation, nature conservation & club sailing
Horsey Mere	TG 448222	44	48.6	32.8	1.5	yes	general navigation & nature conservation
Martham Broad North (Somerton Broad) & South	TG 459203 TG 459201	47	25.5	7.3 8.7	1.0 1.0	channel between N. & S. broads	nature conservation & angling
Womack Water	TG 395176	3(10)*	2.4	channels only	1.5	yes	general navigation
Totals:		346	298.2	227.1			

Valley: Yare

Name	NGR	A	B	C	D	Accessibility from main river system	Principal uses
Bargate Broad	TG 320076	(see under Surlingham B.)	4.8	(see under Surlingham B.)	1.5	yes	general navigation
Brundall Inner Broad	TG 319083	–	1.5	1.3	1.2	landlocked	Shown on 1839 Tithe map, and as a very small pool on the 1892 6in OS map. Probably enlarged during establishment of Brundall Gardens.
Brundall Outer Broad	TG 315083	–	–	0.5	1.2	none	Created as mooring basin for vessels visiting Brundall Gdns. Enlarged & suction-dredged in 1975
Buckenham & Hassingham Broads	TG 363055 TG 366053	11	6.7	4.6	2.0 0.5	landlocked	Buckenham B. suction-dredged in 1980
Rockland Broad	TG 332051	35(47)*	21.4	20.8	1.0	yes	general navigation
Strumpshaw Broad (East & West)	TG 340066	8(7)*	2.4	1.0	0.5	dammed off in 1978	nature conservation: suction-dredged in 1983
Surlingham Broad	TG 316077	29 (with Bargate B.) (42)*	6.3	14.4 (with Bargate B.)	0.5	yes, but too shallow	nature conservation
Wheatfen Broad	TG 330055	n/a	3.2	4.0	0.5	none	nature conservation
Totals:		83 + say 7 = 90	46.3	46.6			

Valley: Waveney

Name	NGR	A	B	C	D	Accessibility from main river system	Principal uses
Barnby Broad	TM 481906	11	3.8	2.5	0.5	landlocked	–
Flixton Decoy	TM 512955	7	6.9	7.0	0.5	landlocked	angling
Fritton Lake (Fritton Decoy)	TG 482005	66	61.9	60.7	2.5	landlocked	country park, angling & reservoir
Oulton Broad	TM 513925	35	34.2	35.6	1.3	yes	general navigation
Totals:		119	106.8	105.8			

Key:
A – Approximate hectarage of open water shown on Tithe Award maps, c. 1840
B – Hectarage of open water shown on the County Series OS 25″ maps, 1881–1938
C – Hectarage of open water shown on OS 1 : 2500 maps, 1971–1978
D – Approximate mean depth (m)

( )* – Hectarage figures based on acreages given by Grantham (1868) and quoted by Woodward (1881).

Summary of hectarages given in Table 3g

Valley	c.1840	1881–1938	1971–1978
Bure	484	424.1	368.4
Ant	188	198.9	87.9
Thurne	346	298.2	227.1
Yare	90	46.3	46.6
Waveney	119	106.8	105.8
Totals	1227 (estimated)	1074.3	835.8

thought to have been dug more recently, and various other water bodies in the region, are listed in Tables 3i and 3j respectively.

(b) *Water regime*

The hydrology of the side-valley broads is fairly simple, the majority being fed by small tributary streams (e.g. Burntfen and Flixton Decoy), whilst some probably possess springs as well. Apart from Sutton, Oulton and the two South Walsham Broads, all the side-valley sites, and some of the by-passed broads are separated from the main river system by sluices, installed to maintain a reasonable depth of water for supply or angling purposes, without interfering with the drainage of the adjoining marshland. Some of these sites have been isolated in this way for many years; for example, Muck Fleet, the channel draining the Trinity Broads, has been sluiced off from the R. Bure since 1884.

The water regime of the broads which are in open communication with the rivers is much more variable and complex. In some cases, the channel or channels connecting the site with the river are so wide that the water in it is replaced very frequently, especially if the system is subject to strong tidal action. Rockland Broad, for instance, is usually flushed once in every one and a half days, the maximum recorded time being once in 24 hours following a tidal surge, and the minimum, once in seven days during a period of sustained high fluvial flow (Darby, 1982). In contrast, sites such as Snape's Water, which are connected to the main river system by narrow, often heavily silted, dykes, and which are not fed by inflow streams or springs, have much longer retention times.

Two main difficulties confront hydrologists wishing to study the water regime of the broads: low current velocities, and a shortage of well-marked channel sections where flow rates can be measured. Ian Booker, one of the UEA team who investigated the nutrient regime of the R. Bure and its interconnected broads (Moss *et al.*, 1984), overcame these problems by using the dye tracer Rhodamine WT, to show that relatively rapid mixing of water masses takes place in sites such as Wroxham Broad, and that wind-induced currents, as well as tidal action are responsible for this. Booker calculated that Wroxham Broad has a retention time of about 4 weeks during dry spells in the summer, but that this decreases to 2 weeks in wet summers, and to one week in the winter. These figures represent mean flushing rates of about 4, 8 and 12 per cent a day

Table 3i   Other flooded peat workings

Name	NGR
Daisy Broad (site now occupied by boatyards and moorings)	TG 307177
Hedney's Bottom (now virtually extinct)	TG 370158
Mill Water Broad, plus other pools created in *c.* 1900 at the Lound Waterworks (16.0 ha)	TG 500010
Reedham Water (turf pond opposite How Hill) (4.1 ha)	TG 366188
Sprat's Water & Round Water	TM506917
Turf pond at Ranworth Flood (3.8 ha)	TG 371151
Turf pond in Woodbastwick Fen	TG 342164
Two 'pulk-holes' beside the R. Bure	TG 311159 & TG 321162

respectively. In contrast, Booker's tracer experiments and channel flow measurements suggest that Hoveton Great Broad has a theoretical replacement time of between 6 and 8 weeks; however, retention will be much greater during dry periods in the summer.

Hydrologically, the upper Thurne is probably the most complex system in Broadland. And yet, an understanding of its water regime, and in particular, the source, volume and nutrient concentration of the water in the Thurne broads is of vital importance in connection with the preparation of a nutrient budget for them. Holdway *et al.* (1978) and Moss and Leah (1982) note that water discharged into Horsey Mere by Brograve Mill and other land-drainage pumps during the winter is pushed up into Hickling Broad by tidal action in Heigham Sound, and that in the summer, when little water is being discharged by these pumps, the same mechanism causes an interchange of water between the Mere and the Broad (see Map 3.4). Watson (1981) in a detailed limnological study of the Thurne waterways, constructed a mathematical model of the system, based on its physical characteristics, and in particular the changes in water level in Hickling Broad, as measured by a tide recorder at Whiteslea Lodge.

Although the model was of the 'plug-flow' type (i.e. it was based on the assumption that when different water masses are moving along a waterway, they behave as separate entities, and do not intermingle), it recognized that the volume of drainage water pumped into the system would prevent an equal volume from downstream moving up

Table 3j   Other, miscellaneous open waters

Name	NGR	ha	Origin
Braydeston Pond	TG 334078	0.3	Created between 1892 and 1908, possibly as a borrow pit for the Brundall-Acle-Yarmouth line (which opened in 1883). Recently renovated
Breydon Water	TG 490070	*c.*380	Relict estuary
Brundall Gardens Lake	TG 084318	1.8	Created between 1892 and 1908 during the laying out of the riverside pleasure gardens at Brundall
Cantley Lagoons	TG 390030 & TG 390035	32.3	Settlement lagoons for sugar beet factory
Chedgrave Pit	TG 429013	0.7	Borrow pit for clay needed to repair tidal embankments
Hardley Flood	TM 380996	27.8	Flooded grazing marsh. Attempts to repair breaches in the embankment were abandoned in 1940
Martham Pits	TG 448195	0.3	Former brick pits which were later used as a source of clay for repairing the tidal embankments

Note:
Small pools are to be found in many other places. Some of these are relict duck decoys (e.g. as in Acle Decoy Carr – TG 190404). But most have been excavated relatively recently, either by wildfowling interests (e.g. the pool at Beccles Marsh – TM 433926) or for nature conservation (e.g. the new 'broads' on the Strumpshaw reserve – TG 331068) or amenity purposes (e.g. the ornamental lakes beside Tinker's Lane, Strumpshaw – TG 338073). A new 'broad' was excavated at How Hill by Peter Boardman in 1978/9 to provide a habitat for aquatic wildlife, and also serve as a stand-by reservoir (TG 371188).

into it; it was also refined to allow for the fact that once the water level in Hickling Broad had reached a height of about 37 cm OD, water entering the site would start to flood the fens bordering it. Thus a rise in level of, say, 10 cm will represent a greater input at higher, than lower, water levels.

The model was tested on chloride data obtained from various points upstream of Thurne Mouth, and then used to interpret some of the changes in nitrogen and phosphorus concentrations known to occur in the system. Watson concluded that during the winter Horsey Mere and Martham Broad receive large inflows, mainly from land drainage water, and that the system is therefore efficiently flushed, Horsey Mere and Martham Broads directly, and Hickling Broad by tide-induced mixing. During summer, however, inputs into the system are low, and a nett water loss, resulting from evapo-transpiration, is made good with water derived from the Bure. Moss (*in litt.*) on the other hand, whilst accepting that such back-flows probably occur during a drought, such as that of 1976, does not consider them to be significant in normal years.

The broads of the R. Thurne differ from the others, not only in the complexity of their hydrology, but in that they are slightly brackish. Victorian naturalists speculated freely about the cause of this phenomenon, one of the more novel suggestions (quoted by Innes, 1911) being . . . "the prevalence at times of dense sea fogs which cling to the reedbeds and leave a salt deposit". Another theory was that the drainage water

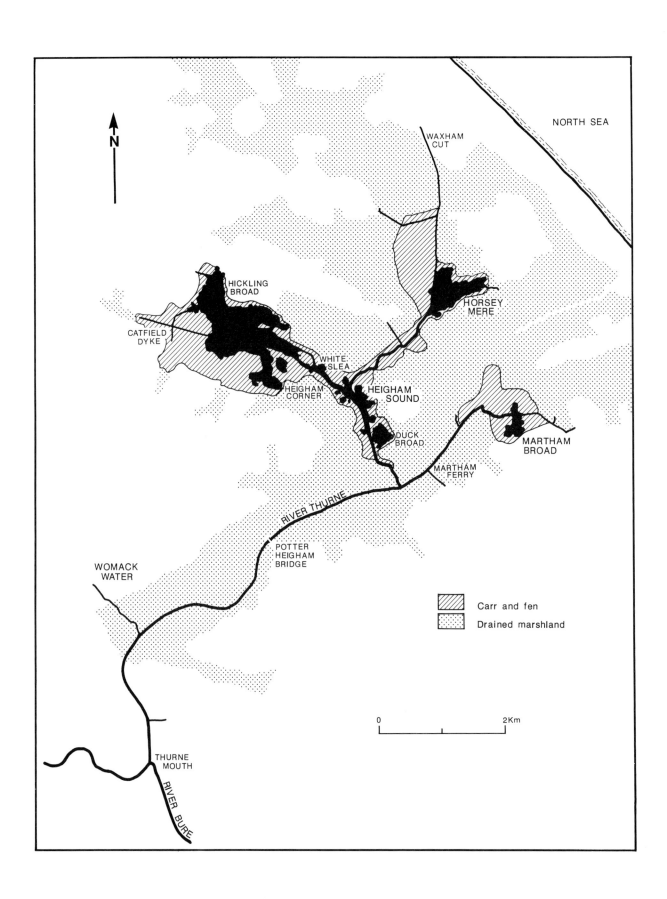

Map 3.4   The broads of the R. Thurne and their surroundings. The water regime of this part of the region is particularly complex, one of the reasons for this being that the system receives significant inputs from pumps draining the adjoining, low-lying agricultural land. The discharge from these is slightly brackish as a result of the proximity of the North Sea. The Thurne waterways are also responsive to changes in water level in the R. Bure. (© Crown Copyright)

discharged into these broads was contaminated by salt left in the soil by previous sea-floods. Others ascribed the salinity to tidal action, but in 1892, Lincoln Sutton proved this to be incorrect by showing that the R. Thurne became progressively less saline from Heigham Sound down to Thurne Mouth. This led Robert and Eustace Gurney to assert in 1907 that . . . "the high salinity (of the Thurne waterways) is due to the existence of salt springs in Horsey Mere, and probably also to a lesser extent in Hickling Broad". No evidence was provided to support this claim, and it was left to Marietta Pallis to investigate the problem scientifically. She concluded on the basis of chemical and stratigraphical studies that . . . 'there is a saltwater table in the Thurne district which is practically coincident with the level of the sea at low water, and which, moreover, contains most salt close to the sea" (Pallis 1911a).

More recently, Goldsworthy (1972) analysed samples of surface and sub-surface water collected in the catchment of Horsey Mere. She also examined the stratigraphy of the district, and found that the surface horizons consist of a layer of peat, some 2 m thick. This must correspond with the Upper Peat laid down after the end of the Second Marine Transgression, because beneath it Goldsworthy found a bluish clay, below which was a further organic layer, representing the Middle Peat.

A similar sequence of strata occurs on the foreshore near Horsey Gap, and on the basis of this, and her chemical analysis, Goldsworthy suggested that salt water from the sea percolates into the Upper Peat. In the past, relatively little salt infiltrated from this into the marsh dykes because the water in them was maintained at a high level. However, a reorganization of the Brograve Level drainage system by the Happisburgh to Winterton Internal Drainage Board (IDB) in the early 1950s had allowed the water-table to be lowered, and Goldsworthy suggested that this was resulting in more saline water reaching the arterial drainage system, and thus Horsey Mere via Brograve Mill and Waxham Cut. Although most of this was thought to be emanating from the Upper Peat, Goldsworthy observed that some of the dykes nearest the Brograve pumping station had been deepened to such an extent that saline water was entering them from the Middle Peat as well.

A dredger was used by the Rivers Commissioners to deepen Horsey Mere in 1969, and it has been suggested that this broke through the clay floor of this site, and allowed highly saline water in the Middle Peat to infiltrate it directly. The counter argument to this is that the surface of the Mere lies some 30 to 40 cm above mean sea level, and that the infiltration of sea water would therefore be prevented by the hydrostatic 'head'. However Watson (1981) has pointed out that the water-table of Horsey Holme, the higher ground on which the village of Horsey is located, may lie above that of the Mere, and that in this event, saline water in the Middle Peat could be entrained in any lateral seepage taking place between the Holme and the Mere.

Watson advanced this hypothesis, following a review of the data available in the literature about salinity levels in the Thurne system, from which he concluded that chloride levels in it are now higher than they were prior to the Second World War, particularly in Horsey Mere. Similar changes have occurred in the Martham Broads, the salinity of which in the 1970s hardly varied from a mean of about 1000 micrograms* per litre (μg l^{-1}), but which started to undergo wide fluctuations (with a maximum of 2000 μg l^{-1}) following the lowering of the water-table of the adjoining Somerton Level in 1979 (see Chapter 9).

(c) *Legal status and navigability*

Apart from Oulton Broad, which is vested in the Waveney District Council, and Rockland Broad, which was not allotted at the time of Enclosure (but which the Rockland St. Mary and Hellington Parish Council recently decided to try and establish legal title to, through 12 years of undisputed control, and a statutory declaration – EDP, 1988a), all the broads are privately owned. Many form parts of large estates, while nine, with a total water surface of some 368 ha, are owned or leased by the Norfolk Naturalists' Trust.

Some of the broads connected with the main river system are subject to well marked tidal rhythms, and therefore under Common Law, have public rights of navigation and fishing over them (Telling, 1980). In May 1908, two members of Norwich Angling Club who had refused to pay two shillings and sixpence (12p) for the privilege of fishing

---

* A microgram (μg) is one millionth (10^{-6}) of a gram. It is thus a thousandth of a milligram (mg).

in Rockland Broad the previous autumn, were summoned by Sir Charles Rich, the Lord of the Manor, for "unlawfully attempting to take and destroy fish in the Broad". However, the defence was able to show, not only that Rich could not prove title to the site, but that it was subject to tidal action. In the circumstances the magistrates had no hesitation in dismissing the case and awarding the defence 40 guineas costs (EDP, 1908). But difficulties have arisen from time to time in respect of sites where tidal fluctuations are less obvious than in the Yare valley. In 1892, for example, Mr. H. S. N. Micklethwait and his sporting tenant, W. E. Eyre, succeeded in obtaining an injunction restraining R. Vincent (the father of the renowned head-keeper of the Whiteslea Estate, Jim Vincent) from shooting or fishing over the northern part of Hickling Broad, although their attempt to prevent him taking a boat onto those parts of the site away from the marked channel failed. The case occupied 11 days in the Chancery Division, and turned partly on whether the Enclosure Commissioners had allotted the Broad in the Award for Hickling of 1808, the judge ruling that it had been included and that the sporting and fishing rights were therefore vested in Mr Micklethwait as owner. The other main issue raised in the case was whether the Broad was, or was not, subject to tidal action. Witnesses for the plaintiffs claimed that the water level in Candle Dyke only fluctuated by about three quarters of an inch (1.9 cm), even at spring tides, whereas those appearing for the defendant claimed that the fluctuations were greater than this. In the event, the judge preferred the evidence presented on behalf of the plaintiffs, and ruled accordingly. He did, nevertheless, accept that the public's right of access to the site was not restricted to the marked channel.

Although there is a local tradition that the plaintiff's witnesses were bribed to give perjured evidence (May, 1952), this seems unlikely. Gurney noted in 1911 that water levels in Hickling Broad only oscillated by about an inch (2.5 cm) and then only irregularly. But tidal action has certainly become more pronounced since then, and Holdway, Watson and Moss (1978) observe that the diurnal range is now about 4 cm, equivalent to three to four per cent of the volume of the site. In practice, the issue is somewhat academic, since the existence of a public right of navigation over the Broad is unlikely to be decided solely according to whether it is, or is not, subject to tidal action, but on the basis of claims that an easement has been created over the whole site as a result of its long continued use by pleasure craft.

That the navigability of Hickling Broad remains a sensitive local issue is well illustrated by a furore which developed in 1985 as a result of a suggestion by the Norfolk Naturalists' Trust and the Nature Conservancy Council (NCC) that Heigham Corner (an embayment at its south-eastern corner – see Plate 1) and three small pools off Heigham Sound (known as Duck Broad and the West Holes) should, in the interests of their birdlife, be closed to boat traffic. Although no one objected to the Trust erecting notices asking people not to take their boats onto Duck Broad and the West Holes (which are so shallow as to be unnavigable to anything larger than a dinghy), the idea that a physical barrier be placed across the entrance to Heigham Corner proved to be total anathema to the Hickling Parish Council, the Hickling Sailing Club and the Broads Society, even when the Trust offered to remove this during August and September.

In vain did the Trust and the NCC argue that the birdlife of the Hickling area is of national importance, that there was increasing evidence, albeit of an anecdotal nature, that this was being adversely affected by the heavy recreational use being made of the site, and that it was highly desirable to determine by means of a properly monitored experiment whether the problem could be alleviated by providing refuges, such as that proposed for Heigham Corner. The opponents of the scheme were adamant; there must be no physical impediment to boat movement on the site, even when, as the Trust proposed, this was for a trial, three-year period. In the event, the Trust decided not to pursue the proposals for the time being. However, the controversy which had arisen had brought into sharp focus the difficulties inherent in safeguarding wildlife on waters subject to rights of public navigation, and the inclusion in the *Norfolk and Suffolk Broads Act* 1988 of clauses (in Schedule 5) enabling the Authority . . . "for the purpose of nature conservation, to close to navigation any area at the edge of a waterway, or restrict navigation in any such area to specified classes of vessel", can be attributed to the saga which arose over the Heigham Corner closure proposal.

Certain sites in the Bure valley, including Hoveton Great, Decoy and Ranworth Broads (see Plate 2), have for many years been gated or chained off from the river to prevent boats being taken onto them. In most cases, the owners took this action originally to safeguard their shooting and fishing interests in the face of growing vandalism and trespass, following the development of Broadland as a centre for water-borne holidays. Hoveton Great Broad, for instance, was found by Rye (1884) to have been chained off from the river by the 1880s and this site had certainly been closed to public navigation by 1912 (Blofeld, pers. comm.). But the non-accessibility of this and other broads has been a contentious issue locally for many years (Rye, 1899). In 1885, the Divisional Court ruled that Wroxham Broad (see Plate V) was not subject to tidal action, and that the public did not therefore have a right to fish in it. A similar decision was reached in 1924, when four anglers were successfully prosecuted for refusing to pay the fee of two shillings and sixpence (about £2.50 at 1987 prices) per boat levied by the owner (EDP, 1924). The Rivers Commissioners' archives show that in the mid-nineteenth century, this Broad was only opened to the public for water frolics (or what would now be called regattas) on payment of a fee, and to this day, the Norfolk Broads Yacht Club, which leases the site from the Trafford Estates, is required to close both its entrances with chains or similar obstructions for not less than 24 hours during January or February each year in order to ensure that the public does not acquire an easement over it. Fees are still levied on those wishing to fish or moor their boats in this and several other broads (though the charges are often less in real terms than in 1924!), whilst mooring is banned altogether in South Walsham Inner Broad.

In 1925, the Broads Cruising Association, concerned by what it called . . . "the undefined and indefinite status of the public rights of access to various broads" appointed Lieut.-General Sir Edwin Alderson to discuss with the owners of such sites the extent to which increased public access could be permitted. His report (Rice, 1925) confirmed that the owners of Ranworth and Hoveton Little Broads would not agree to open them to public navigation, and that whilst Decoy and Hoveton Great Broads might be made available for sailing and rowing craft, the Cruising Association would have to meet the cost of wardening these sites, and prosecuting those who caused damage or annoyance. The owners also made it clear that they would reserve the right to close the broads again should the privileges given be abused. The Association possessed neither the powers, nor the resources, to give such undertakings, and no further action was taken. However in 1949, following the removal by a group of local boat hirers of the piles which, on the instructions of the landowner, were being driven in to prevent vessels being taken onto Hoveton Little Broad, a compromise was worked out by the late Anthony Buxton, whereby this site was closed during the winter months, but opened to boats between Easter and the second Saturday in September each year. Although the Norfolk and Suffolk Broads Yacht Owners Association negotiated the original access agreement, responsibility for implementing its provisions was assumed by the Rivers Commissioners in 1982 who, in turn, handed this on to the Broads Authority in 1989.*

Hoveton Great and Ranworth Broads have long been of great natural history interest, and in 1958 this was recognized by the Nature Conservancy by their inclusion within the Bure Marshes National Nature Reserve (NNR). Despite this, the owners of these broads, and the Conservancy, have from time to time come under pressure to make them available for public navigation. Although this has had to be resisted on the grounds that it would be damaging to nature conservation, interpretive facilities have been provided so that both sites can be seen and enjoyed by visitors without endangering their features of natural history interest. Of the three other broads included within this national nature reserve, Hudson's Bay is too shallow for anything larger than a rowing dinghy, Decoy Broad is much used by scouts and anglers, while the third site – Cockshoot Broad – has been experimentally mud-pumped by the Broads Authority and dammed off from the river in order to restore it to good ecological condition (see page 502).

Most of the 18 broads which are landlocked (see Table 3g) could not be connected with the main river system without major alterations being made to the drainage of the surrounding marshland, while a further 5 small sites, with a combined surface area of

---

* Following the suction-dredging of Hoveton Little Broad in 1990, the Broads Authority renegotiated the agreement with its present owner, Mr John Blofeld. Under this, the site is open to boats over Easter week, but is then closed, in the interests of breeding birds, until Whit Sunday. The barrier at the entrance to the Broad is then open until the last Saturday in October, before being closed for the winter months.

Plate V

Looking north-west over Wroxham Broad, with the western end of Hoveton Great Broad on the right – 1961.

Wroxham Broad is one of the most popular open-water sites in the region, and sailing boat races, organized by the Norfolk Broads Yacht Club (whose premises can be seen on the far side of the Broad) are regularly held on it. Like Hoveton Great Broad, it is a typical by-passed site, and the narrow 'baulk' of peat which formerly isolated it from the meandering R. Bure, can be seen clearly. Two channels were subsequently dug through this to allow boats to gain access to the flooded workings, and one of these – now the Broad's southern entrance – can be seen on the left.

Phase II waterweeds were still present in Hoveton Great Broad when this photograph was taken, but a comparison with Plate XII shows that this community was less well developed than in 1949. The marginal reedswamp had also started to regress.

The small broad known (somewhat misleadingly) as Hudson's Bay, can be made out in the right middle distance, and the villages of Hoveton and Wroxham (which would be coalescent were they not separated by the river) can be seen in the top left of the photograph.

Photo: Aerofilms Ltd.

some 10 ha, are less than a metre deep, and therefore too shallow for most pleasure craft, even if a right of access could be negotiated with their owners.

Those not familiar with the region are often taken aback to learn that only 13 sites (Bargate, Barton, Bridge, Hickling, Malthouse (see Plate VI), Oulton, Rockland, South Walsham Inner and Outer, Salhouse Great, Surlingham and Wroxham Broads, plus Heigham Sound, are available for all-the-year-round navigation. Two others, Sutton Broad and Womack Water, though navigable, are now little more than tributaries of the main rivers, while at Martham Broad boats have to keep to a central channel. Two other sites, Horsey Mere and Black Horse Broad (the main, eastern part of Hoveton Little Broad) are only open for the holiday season. In theory, these 18 sites have a combined water surface of some 450 ha; however, several of them have extensive shallows near their margins so the area usable by vessels drawing up to a metre or more is probably only about 400 ha.

This figure is small in comparison with the huge expanses of flooded gravel workings created during the past 20 or 30 years in the Thames valley, the Cotswold Water Park and elsewhere. Nevertheless, it must be remembered that the navigable broads are interconnected with some 190 km of lock-free waterways. If it is assumed that these have a mean channel width of 35 m, there is some 665* ha of water available for larger vessels, in addition to that in the broads themselves. It is the ability to explore, without impediment, such a varied and extensive system of waterways, together with the picturesque scenery of the region, which has made it so popular with the boat-borne holidaymaker.

Breydon Water

This relict estuary, which at high tide has a water surface area of some 877 ha, but which is left with a central channel only about 110 m wide as the tide retreats, has not shrunk in size during the past two or three centuries as have the great majority of the broads. However, its water regime has altered very considerably. The renowned Broadland naturalist, Arthur Patterson, noted in 1905 that the penetration of saltwater upriver had increased greatly during his lifetime, and that in the middle of the nineteenth century, the freshwater flowing downriver had, by half-ebb, largely displaced the saline water which had entered Breydon on the flood tide. But even by Patterson's time, the flats were 'growing up' and being colonized by glassworts (*Salicornia* spp.), and today the site is only filled with freshwater when the rivers Yare and Waveney are carrying very large fluvial flows.

The increased saltwater penetration is related to the steps taken from Victorian times onwards to improve the navigability of the Yare (see page 353), whilst the siltation to which Breydon is subject is mainly due to the large quantities of sediment which are carried downriver, some of which tends to settle out in it at high tide. Much of this is derived from the catchments of the Yare and Waveney, but the Bure probably also contributes since some of its outflow is carried up into Breydon on each flood tide. Until recently, a further source of sediment is thought to have been untreated sewage effluent, large volumes of which were discharged into the Haven and the lowermost reaches of the R. Bure. At least some of the suspended solids in this were probably deposited in the relict estuary after being carried upstream on the tide, but this problem will have been alleviated in 1987, when the AWA diverted much of the sewage generated in the Yarmouth area to a new sea outfall at Caister.

Although the speed at which the broads are filling up with sediment has been subject to considerable study during the past 15 years (see Chapter 5), no-one seems to have measured the overall rate of sedimentation in Breydon, and the claims made by Patterson, Dutt (1903) and others that 'wherries once sailed where there are now mudflats' must be regarded as anecdotal. Similarly, the assertion by Taylor (1871) that . . "Breydon has been silted up by four feet (1.2 m) within the last half century" needs to be viewed with caution. Ranwell *et al.* (1974), who introduced the Eelgrass, *Zostera noltii*, into the north-eastern corner of the site under controlled conditions, found that the surface of their experimental plots showed an overall tendency to erode by 2 to 3 cm during the two-year trial. However, no great significance can be attached to this finding, as they also discovered that the level of the mudflats can undergo rapid fluctuations; for

* The figure of 7000 acres (2834 ha) claimed by the Broads Consortium (1971) is an error.

Plate VI

Malthouse Broad from Ranworth Church tower – 1975.

This site, and Ranworth Broad (see colour Plate 2), formed a single sheet of open water in early Victorian times. However, by about 1890, this had become partially sub-divided as a result of the development of a triangular-shaped block of Swamp Carr: today, this is traversed by the walkway leading to the Ranworth Conservation Centre. Following the establishment of the Broadland holiday industry, the landowner at the time was faced with an increasing problem of vandalism and illicit shooting, and in response to this he put up a barrier across the remaining stretch of open water, so making it impossible for unauthorized persons to take their boats onto Ranworth Broad. But Malthouse Broad remained open to public navigation, and is today one of the most popular sites in the region.

Ranworth Church, too, with its fifteenth century painted screen and the illustrated manuscript known as the Sarum Antiphoner, is a major tourist attraction, and stunning views can be had from its tower. This photograph was taken looking south-east. The managed reed-beds which form Ranworth Flood (included within the Bure Marshes National Nature Reserve in 1981) can be made out in the middle distance, and on a clear day it would have been possible to see Great Yarmouth.

Photo: Peter Wakely/Nature Conservancy Council

example, in places the surface accreted by up to 3 cm during a gale.

Observations on the ground, confirmed by air photographs, show that accretion has raised the general level of flats at the Yarmouth end of Breydon well above that at its other, upstream end. Indeed, it has been estimated that the flats at the seaward end of the site are uncovered for about five-sixths of a tidal cycle, whereas those at the south-west end are only exposed for about one-sixth of the time (Street, pers. comm.). Breydon is highly unusual in this respect; in most estuaries, the intertidal flats tend to fall, rather than rise in level in a seawards direction.

Wave action in the estuary at high tide can be considerable, particularly when the wind is blowing from the north-east or south-west, and it is probably because of this that saltmarsh is confined to its north-east corner, and to two or three relatively sheltered sections of shore beside the North and South Walls. The main components of these marshes are Common Saltmarsh-grass (*Puccinellia maritima*), Common Scurvy-grass (*Cochlearia officinalis*), Sea Aster (*Aster tripolium*), Thrift (*Armeria maritima*), Sea Plantain (*Plantago maritima*), Sea Lavender (*Limonium vulgare*), Annual Seablite (*Suaeda maritima*), Greater Sea-spurrey, Sea Arrow grass (*Triglochin maritima*), Sea Purselane (*Halimione portulacoides*) and various glassworts. The saltmarshes at the seaward end of the estuary are extending outwards in several places, and glassworts and other pioneer species are also colonizing a bay near the Yarmouth end of the North Wall.

There are several good stands of Eelgrass in the estuary, notably on the flats north of the main river channel opposite Cobholm. Both *Zostera marina* and *Z. noltii* have been recorded recently (Baxter, 1988), the latter species so far distant from the site of Dr Ranwell's experimental introductions as to make it most unlikely that it is derived from them.

Tidal influence in the rivers and broads

All the rivers, and those broads which are in direct communication with them, are tidal in the sense that they respond to a greater or lesser extent, either to the tides themselves, or to meteorologically induced fluctuations in sea level, or both. Tidal influence is more pronounced in the Yare and Waveney, than in the Bure, because of the restricted channel capacity and convoluted alignment of the lowermost reaches of this river in relation to the large volumes of water stored in the numerous broads connected to it. In addition, the physical dimensions and configuration of the southern rivers are such that they can more readily 'resonate' to the rhythm of the tides, than can the Bure (Ashford, pers. comm.). At Norwich Yacht Station, *c.* 2 km downstream of the New Mills sluices, the mean range of the R. Wensum at spring tides is 0.6 m compared with the 1.9 m average rise and fall encountered at the mouth of the Haven, *c.* 47 km downstream. Similarly, at Beccles, *c.* 38.5 km from the sea, the tidal range of the Waveney is about 0.8 m at spring tides. These figures may not seem very large, but they mean that huge volumes of water move up and downriver during each tidal cycle. Flows in the Yare at Whitlingham, for example, were calculated by the AWA in 1973 to be in excess of 143 000 cubic metres per day ($m^3 d^{-1}$) for 95 per cent of the time (Stringer, *in litt.*).

In the past, the tidal, as well as the navigable, limit of the Waveney was at Geldeston. However, in 1967, the East Suffolk and Norfolk River Authority dredged and regraded the river, and created a by-pass channel around the derelict lock at this point, in an attempt to reduce the risk of the marshes upstream being flooded. As a result, tidal influence now extends as far up river as Ellingham Mill, though boats are prevented by a barrier from passing beyond Geldeston.

Anecdotal reports suggest that the Beccles to Geldeston area is more susceptible to flooding now than it was 20 years ago, and this has been linked with assertions that not only have the tidal embankments of the Waveney been allowed to fall into poor repair, but that the rate of run-off from the catchment has increased, thus making the river more 'flashy' than it was in the past. This could have resulted from a combination of events, including the improved channel capacity of the river between Geldeston and Ellingham, the widespread widening and straightening of its tributaries, and the steps taken by farmers to improve the field and under-drainage of the land within its catchment, so as to enhance its productivity.

Tidal influence in the Bure and its tributaries is, on average, about half that of the Yare and Waveney at corresponding distances from the sea. The tidal limits of this river and the Ant are at Horstead Mill and Honing Lock respectively, but true tidal rhythms

Fig. 3A

Tidal curves recorded simultaneously by the Anglian Water Authority at Great Yarmouth, and at six upriver sites: Rockland Staithe and Carrow Bridge on the Yare and Wensum respectively, Burgh St. Peter and Ellingham Mill on the Waveney, and Acle Bridge and Hoveton (Hudson's Bay) on the Bure. Note that tidal amplitudes are much less on the latter river, than on the Yare and Waveney. During the period of observation (April 16-23, 1980) a minor surge occurred, and the figure portrays the effects this had on water levels in different parts of the system.

Source: Anglian Water Authority (in litt.)

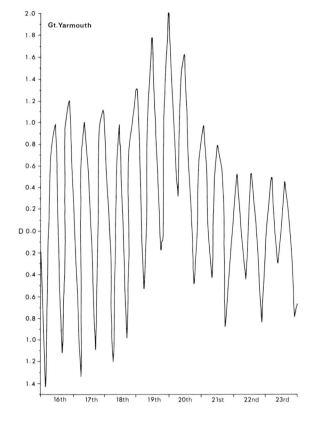

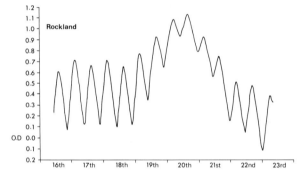

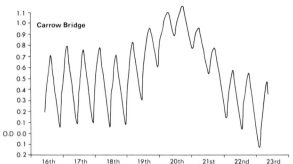

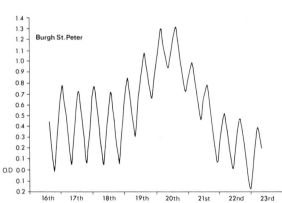

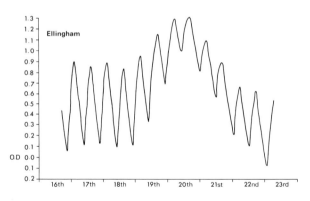

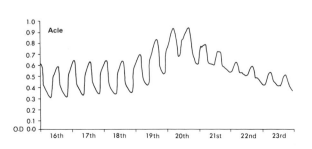

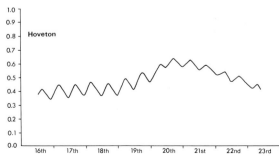

are masked at these points by water level fluctuations caused by other factors.

Tidal curves from different parts of the region vary somewhat in shape (Fig. 3A), those from the Bure and its tributaries having a particularly distinctive configuration (Fig. 3B). The time elapsing between a high and a low tide is usually greater on this river, than between low and high water (Gurney, 1911). However, the duration of the ebb and flood tide varies according to the amount of freshwater coming downriver, the ebb tending to be longer, and the flood shorter, the greater the fluvial flow.

During his study of the limnology of Hickling Broad, Watson (1981) found that its mean water level was 40 ± 5 cm above Mean Sea Level (= Ordnance Datum, Newlyn), whilst at Barton Broad, the average level was 2.5 cm higher than this. These measurements are consistent with estimates provided by the AWA, which indicate that in 1981, mean tide levels at Hudson's Bay, Rockland Broad and Beccles were about 0.46 m, 0.40 m and 0.375 m OD respectively, and also with figures obtained by Dr. J. Owens in 1928 (quoted in Davies, 1930), who simultaneously measured a spring tide at various places on the R. Bure (Fig. 3C) and showed that the greater the distances from the Haven, the higher the mean water level in relation to OD.

These phenomena are attributable to differences in the capacity of the river channels when they contain varying depths of water; the greater the depth and the larger the water cross-section, the more water that can be passed, and vice versa. When the tide is high at the entrance to the Haven, the water in the lowermost reaches of the rivers (which is, of course, at a level above that further upstream) is comparatively deep, and large quantities of tidal water can flow upriver with a relatively small river gradient. Conversely, on the ebb, the now shallower downriver reaches have a reduced channel capacity, and a rather larger gradient has to develop before the water can be discharged. As a consequence, the mean water level in the lower reaches of the rivers is maintained above that of the Haven. Further upriver, the differences between the channel capacity at high and low tide are of less importance owing to the large volumes of water in the broads, and the reduced tidal range. As a result, the difference in mean water level at localities upstream are less pronounced than in the lowermost reaches of the river (see Fig. 3C).

Fig. 3C

Tidal curves from the R. Bure and the lowermost reaches of the R. Yare, 23 February, 1928.

Source: Davies (1930)

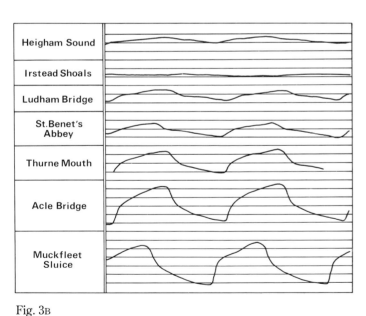

Fig. 3B

Tidal curves from various sites on the R. Bure and its tributaries. Each horizontal division represents 3 inches (7.6 cm).
Source: Gurney (1911)

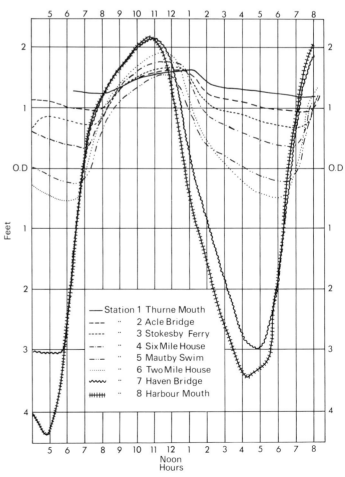

A further complication is that the direction of the tide-induced currents in the rivers does not change at the same time as the water attains its highest and lowest levels. At Reedham, for example, the gradients set up on the R. Yare during a tidal cycle cause the ebb to continue to run until the water downstream has attained the same level as that upstream. During this period, then, the water level will be rising at Reedham even though the tide is on the ebb. After a brief period of slack water, the gradient in the river will be reversed, and the tide will flow upstream on the flood until the water levels in the lower reaches of the river have fallen sufficiently to cause another gradient reversal, and a consequent change in the direction of the tidal current.

The relationship between current direction and water level is particularly noticeable, and important from the navigational point of view, in the R. Bure. The observant holiday-maker at Yarmouth Yacht Station is likely to be surprised, not so much by the fact that the river beside which he has moored his boat continues to ebb for about one and a quarter hours after the tide has started to flow up the R. Yare, (thus carrying water from the Bure up into Breydon Water), but that the water level in the Bure is rising, rather than falling, during this period. Conversely, water levels in the lower Bure start to fall long before the flood tide has ceased to run. At Stokesby, for example, the upstream flow continues for almost 2 hours after the water level has started to drop. Similarly, the ebb commences in Fleet dyke and Ranworth Dam while the sections of the R. Bure with which these waterways are united are still on the flood.

On all the rivers, the speed of the current varies, not only according to the state of the tide (springs or neaps), but the amount of freshwater coming downstream. Measurements made by P. Firstbrook, and quoted by Coles (1977) show that the ebb usually runs at about 0.8 metres per second (m sec $^{-1}$) at the eastern end of Breydon Water, while the flood here may reach a velocity of 1.0 m sec $^{-1}$. According to Hamilton (1978), spring tides at the Haven Bridge may attain a speed of 3 knots (1.5 m sec $^{-1}$) on the flood, and 3.5 knots (1.8 m sec $^{-1}$) on the ebb. He also notes that the flood can reach 5 to 6 knots (2.6 to 3.1 m sec $^{-1}$) in the lowermost reaches of the Bure, but that the speed quickly drops further upstream. The maximum velocity recorded by Gurney (1911) at Stokesby was only 0.39 m sec $^{-1}$, while at Ant Mouth and Ludham Bridge, speeds of 0.18 and 0.08 m sec $^{-1}$ respectively were noted.

The approximate tidal range at various localities, and the time at which high water occurs at each are as follows:

Place	Approx. time of high water after that at the entrance to the Haven (Gorleston)	mean range of Spring tides
Yarmouth Yacht Station	1 hr	1.7 m
Stokesby	2 hrs	0.5 m
Horning	3 hrs. 30 min.	0.2 m
Wroxham	4 hrs. 30 min.	0.1 m
Potter Heigham	4 hrs.	0.2 m
Burgh Castle	1 hr.	1.1 m
Buckenham Ferry	3 hrs. 30 min.	0.8 m
Rockland Broad	4 hrs.	0.6 m *
Brundall	4 hrs.	0.7 m
Norwich	4 hrs. 30 min.	0.7 m *
Haddiscoe	2 hrs. 30 min.	0.75 m *
Oulton Broad	3 hrs. 30 min.	0.7 m
Beccles	4 hrs.	0.6 m

NB. Low water at Yarmouth Yacht Station occurs about 7 hours after high water at the mouth of the Haven.

Sources: * Data supplied by AWA from their tide gauges. Other figures are approximate, and are derived from Hamilton (1978) and other guides and tide tables.

Works carried out in the mid-nineteenth century, and in particular, the replacement in the early 1850s of the old Haven Bridge with a new structure much less restrictive to water movement, the dredging of the Burgh Flats and the bar at the mouth of the Haven, and the steps taken to widen and increase the sectional area of the latter in the late 1860s (see Chapter 11), would have significantly increased tidal action in all the rivers, but especially in the Yare and Waveney. Anecdotal reports suggest that the trend was continuing at the turn of the century. Gurney (1911) for example, notes that . . . "There is a general consensus of opinion that the range and influence of the tides have been greatly extended by the dredging, in recent years, of Yarmouth Harbour and the Knoll".

The Haven itself is probably not quite so wide now as it was in the 1860s, but has a sectional area of at last 4000 sq. ft. (372 sq. m) (Read, *in litt.*). This is 25 per cent greater than it was in 1868, indicating that the Haven must have been deepened considerably since then in response to the increasing size of the sea-going vessels using it. Some confirmation of this is provided by the numerous references in the Port and Haven Commissioners' archives to the need to dredge the Haven, and the bar at its entrance. However, according to Read, the Haven has not had to be dredged comprehensively for about 25 years, though occasional shoals had to be removed until about 1979. This strongly suggests that the Haven is now self-scouring, and this was confirmed by the Port and Haven Commissioners in 1984, when they admitted that it was deepening by an average of 6 cm per year, with a maximum of 25 cm in two places. This can be attributed to the sediment disturbance caused by the numerous ships now using Yarmouth as a port (*c.* 400 000 tonnes per month in 1982/3 – Forbes, pers. comm.), and the fact that many of the larger vessels are now moved downriver on the ebb, rather than on the flood tide only as in the past.

The tendency for the Haven to deepen, rather than silt up, is viewed with alarm by environmentalists, since this will lead to increased tidal scouring in the lower reaches of the rivers, until the system once again reaches a state of equilibrium.

Owing to the dearth of pre-twentieth century tidal data for the rivers, it is impossible to quantify the changes which have occurred. Nevertheless, it is significant that Bacon, writing in 1844, records that it had been possible to improve the drainage of the marshes immediately downstream of Norwich owing to . . . "the more powerful reflux of the tide, in consequence of alterations at the mouth of Yarmouth harbour within the last fifteen or twenty years (i.e. in the 1820s); the ebb and flow of the tide being now felt as high as Norwich, which previously was not the case".

A trend towards increased tidal action in the rivers Yare and Waveney can also be detected from measurements made by Richard Taylor, who in 1826 surveyed the route for the New Cut for its designer, William Cubitt[*]. Taylor noted that the tidal range at Haddiscoe on 23 March that year was 10 inches (0.27 m). Dr. D. E. Cartwright of the Institute of Oceanographic Sciences (*in litt.*) has indicated that although the tides on that day were midway between springs and neaps, a figure approximating to 'mean springs' can be assumed since their range would have been increased by the proximity of the perigee (moon closest to earth) and the equinox. Analysis of the traces from the AWA's tide recorder at Haddiscoe show that the mean spring range here is now 0.75 m, suggesting that tidal action in the lower Waveney has increased very significantly during the past 160 years or so.

Taylor also observed that the tidal range at Reedham was 11 inches (0.29 m) on 3 March, 1826, a day when, according to Dr. Cartwright, the tides were at neaps. The AWA does not have a tide gauge at Reedham, but since the mean range at neaps at Haddiscoe is 0.55 m, and at Rockland Broad 0.45 m, it can be assumed that the neap range at Reedham is about 0.6 m. Here again, therefore, there is a suggestion that tidal action has increased considerably, although not quite to the extent indicated by the Haddiscoe figures.

A hint that saline penetration upstream, and therefore tidal influence, was much less marked in the mid-nineteenth century than it is today comes from an engineer's report which indicated that it would be possible to obtain . . . "at a proper state of the tide . . . an abundance of pure water" for Great Yarmouth, Southtown and Cobholm from the R. Waveney, at a point near to, or above Burgh Castle (Wickstead, 1845). Chemical data for this site is not available, but even at Burgh St. Peter, *c.* 15 km upstream, the minimum conductivity for the years 1975 to 1978 was 617 micromhos per cubic centimetre, which is well in excess of the EEC's guide level of 400 mhos cc $^{-1}$ for domestic consumption.

Bridge replacement has sometimes been held responsible for causing increased tidal

---

[*] Taylor's original drawings are in the possession of Arthur Alsop, who kindly allowed the author to inspect them.

action in the rivers. But when in 1928 Dr. J. Owens was commissioned by the Norfolk County Council to assess the effects of removing the Wey Bridge at Acle, and replacing it with a new and wider structure, he concluded on the basis of exhaustive measurements and calculations that this would not affect the tidal regime of the river appreciably, and that . . . "since the effects on the current velocities are likely to be negligible, there will be no increased erosion on the river banks" (Davies, 1930). Similarly, the construction of the present Haven Bridge at Yarmouth in 1930 is unlikely to have significantly affected the hydrology of Broadland, as it has a total aperture of 170 feet (52 m) (made up of a central span of 88 ft and two side spans of 41 ft each), whereas the Act of 1849 under which the bridge it replaced was built decreed that this should have a central, opening span of 50 ft, and two side spans of 65 ft each, giving a total aperture 10 ft (3.1 m) greater than the present structure.

But these arguments are not necessarily applicable elsewhere. For example, it is generally accepted that the historic, narrow-arched bridge at Potter Heigham (see Plate VII) restricts tidal penetration, and that the embankments upstream of it which protect the Hickling–Horsey–Martham area from flooding would be more likely to be over-topped or breached if it were to be removed. Conversely, it would be surprising if tidal action in the R. Ant did not increase slightly when Ludham Bridge, previously a notorious bottleneck for boat traffic, was replaced in 1960, and when the pillars supporting the swing bridge which once carried the Lowestoft–Yarmouth railway across the mouth of Breydon Water, were removed in 1962.

The near-disappearance of waterweeds from the rivers since the 1950s may have allowed tidal action to increase slightly, and so too may the erosion which has occurred during the same period, and which has led to a general widening of the rivers (see page 72). But many uncertainties remain. For instance, it is far from clear why the R. Waveney, which is five to six metres deep downstream of Somerleyton, should be self-scouring, whereas the lower reaches of the Yare tend to silt up, and have to be dredged periodically.

Changes in the level of the rivers relative to that of the land

Not only is tidal action in the rivers and broads greater than it was in early Victorian times, but sea, and therefore river, levels have also risen over the centuries. Evidence for this comes from the increasing susceptibility of Broadland's medieval peat pits to flooding (page 89) and the need to install pumps to drain the marshes in place of the gravity systems used at first (page 239). Similarly, some buildings, for example, Ranworth Old Hall, occupy sites so damp as to suggest that the water-table must have risen since they were built. But the cause of these higher water levels lies, not so much in the dredging, bridge renewal and other works carried out during the past one hundred and fifty years or so, as in a general, and long-continued lowering of the land level relative to that of the sea due to isostasis and eustasis (see Chapter 2). Valentin (1953) has demonstrated that this has occurred at a mean rate of about 1.6 mm per year in East Anglia during the past seven centuries, and confirmation of this has been forthcoming from the work of Funnell (1979) and Coles and Funnell (1981). On the basis of Valentin's figure, it would seem that mean water levels in Broadland's rivers are now about 24 cm higher now than they were in 1833.

The wastage and shrinkage which results from improved land drainage has also played a part. The 'Upper Peat' in the lower sections of the valleys has, as we have seen in the previous chapter, disappeared altogether, whilst even greater losses will have occurred further up-valley where peaty soils have been brought into agricultural use. Evidence for this comes from the fact that the scoop wheels fitted to many of the windpumps in the Drained Marshland Area had a maximum lift of about 4 ft 6 in (1.4 m) (Wailes, 1956), and for long periods would now be incapable of raising water from the ditches into the rivers. Soil shrinkage, allied to the general rise in mean water levels, may also account for anecdotal reports that in the 1920s, water in the Upton landspring dyke could still be discharged by gravity into the adjoining boat dyke, whereas today this would be quite impossible.

A conclusion somewhat different to that of Valentin was reached by Rendel, Palmer & Tritton (1977), who examined sequences of maximum tide levels recorded at Yarmouth

Potter Heigham Bridge – 1987.

Plate VII

One of the best known landmarks in the region, this bridge was built in stone in *c.* 1380, its brick parapets being added later. In addition to being very attractive aesthetically, it serves to restrict the amount of water passing upstream at times of flood, thus reducing the risk of the embankments bordering the upper Thurne and its broads being breached. The difficulties inherent in taking even quite small vessels through this bridge are demonstrated by the multicoloured streaks of paint on the inside of its central arch. Larger craft, including about 25% of the hire motor cruisers currently in use, cannot negotiate it at all, and are thus unable to reach the upper Thurne broads, a navigational constraint viewed differently by boat-letting interests and environmentalists!

For many years, the side arches were masked by boards helping to prevent the foundations of the bridge spreading outwards as a result of the heavy traffic passing over it. However, following the construction of the Potter Heigham bypass, and the imposition of a weight limit on the old bridge, it has been possible to remove these unsightly additions.

Photo: Richard Denyer

(1899 to 1953, and 1959 to 1976), and Lowestoft (1953 to 1976). They could find no evidence for a rise in mean sea levels from these records, but when they calculated ten-year running means from them in order to filter out the irregular fluctuations which are associated with annual values, they detected a general, albeit irregular, tendency for the values to fall prior to 1930, and to rise erratically thereafter, the total variation amounting to 0.2 m above or below the mean value.

Considerable doubt has been cast on Rendel, Palmer and Tritton's findings by Dr.

D. T. Pugh of the Institute of Oceanographical Sciences (Bidston Observatory), who has pointed out (*in litt.*) that the standard error band in the Lowestoft data is too large to infer any significant difference from zero. Similarly, Graff (1981) has shown that the Yarmouth tide records display such a high 'noise' level, that any trends in the order of 1 mm per year would be insignificant.

Surges

The water regime of the rivers and broads is affected not only by changes in mean sea level and tidal action, but by frequent minor and occasional major fluctuations in the level of the North Sea. These can be related to meteorological conditions, the best known example being the development of a 'surge' following a period of strong northerly or north-westerly winds. These funnel water southwards, thus raising mean sea levels in the western and southern shores of the North Sea for periods lasting from a few hours to a few days (Fig. 3D).

Water levels lower than normal can occur in Broadland from a 'negative' surge caused by strong southerly winds. But because of the shape of the North Sea basin, these never have such a marked effect on the sea level as do those of comparable force blowing from the opposite direction.

Fig. 3D

The weather chart at midnight on 1 February, 1953, showing the track of the 'low' which caused the sea flood.

Source: Lamb (1981)

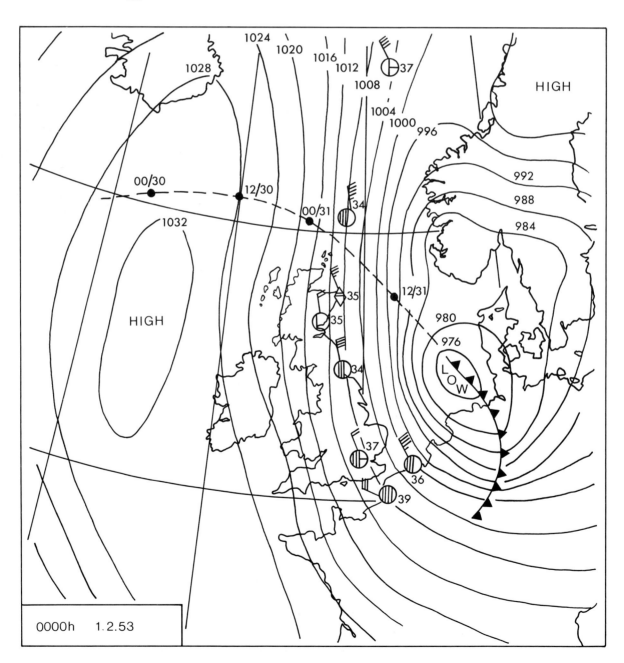

Water levels in the North Sea are also affected by changes in barometric pressure, mean tide levels being raised by about 1 cm for every one millibar fall in pressure, and vice versa (Grieve 1959). No one seems to have yet studied exactly how Broadland's water regime is influenced by such pressure changes or their importance in comparison with wind-generated events. However the low pressures associated with an intense depression of the type likely to produce a major surge will, by causing a rise in water levels, tend to accentuate its wind-generated effects.

A surge-induced rise in water level of 0.2 m in the rivers and broads is not uncommon during the autumn when there is little freshwater coming downstream, and it has been calculated that in the Bure upstream of Ant Mouth, and its associated broads, this is equivalent to the retention of an additional 260000 cubic metres, assuming a total water-surface area of 1.3 square kilometres (East Suffolk & Norfolk River Authority, 1971). Conversely, during a negative surge, tidal discharges are greater than normal, and unusually low water levels may be experienced, especially if the event is spread over several days. On 8 November 1970, the tide at Rockland Staithe fell to 0.34 m below OD (*c.* 0.74 m below the mean water level), with the result that many hectares of sediment were exposed in the adjoining broad (Ellis, 1970b).

The incidence of surges is a matter of vital concern to land-drainage engineers in the region because the higher-than-average water levels they produce can breach, either the

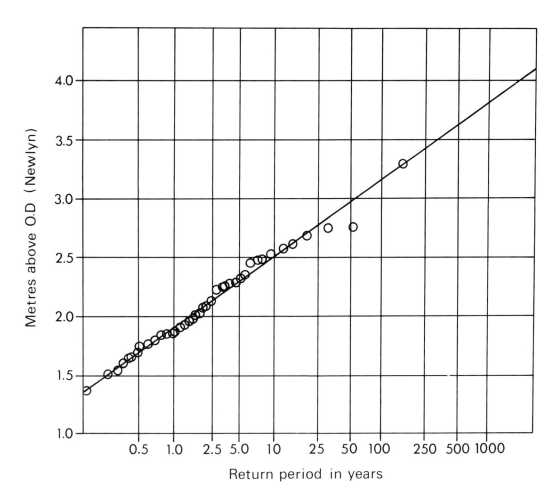

Fig. 3E

Annual maximum tide levels at Great Yarmouth, and their calculated return periods. According to this diagram, the surge-tide level attained in 1953 has a return period of about 175 years, but it is now thought that events of this magnitude are likely to recur much more frequently than this.

Source: Rendel, Palmer and Tritton (1977)

sand-dune defences between Happisburgh and Winterton, with consequent sea flooding, or the tidal embankments protecting the Drained Marshland Area (see Chapter 10). The frequency with which surges of differing magnitudes are likely to recur (i.e. the return period) was therefore calculated when the Yare Basin Flood Control Scheme was under study (Rendel, Palmer & Tritton, 1977) (see Fig. 3E). Since then, Lamb (1977, 1981 & 1982) has reviewed the factors which have contributed to sea flooding during historic times, and has concluded that in addition to alterations in relative land/sea-levels due to eustasis and isostasis, and cyclical changes in the strength of the tide-generating forces exerted by the sun and moon, there have been increases in the storminess of the North Sea owing to variations in the tracks and intensities of travelling cyclonic depressions. Lamb and Weiss (1979) have also demonstrated that the North Sea has been affected by more gales and severe gales since the early 1960s than during the 1940s and 1950s, and that the relative frequency of north-westerly winds has increased during the same period. As Rendel, Palmer & Tritton's predictions did not take account of these factors, but were based on tidal data collected since the turn of the present century, they almost certainly underestimated the height and number of surges likely to occur during the next few decades.

Salinities in the rivers

Data collected by P. Firstbrook, and quoted by Coles (1977) indicates that salt and fresh water is well mixed in the lowermost reaches of the R. Yare on the flood tide, but that stratification has frequently developed by the time the water has reached the southwestern end of Breydon Water. Further upstream, the water masses are almost always layered, but the distance upriver which the salt wedge from any particular tide penetrates is affected both by the height of the latter, and the amount of freshwater flowing downriver. Firstbrook recorded a complete tidal cycle at Cantley in September 1973, and found that on the evening tide the water nearest the bottom of the river attained a salinity of 11.1 parts per thousand* (2164 mg Cl$^-$ l^{-1}), while at the surface it was only about 4.2 parts per thousand (818 mg Cl$^-$ l^{-1}). Twelve hours later, the differences were much less at 7.7 parts per thousand near the bottom, and 6.6 parts per thousand at the surface (1502 and 1287 mg Cl$^-$ l^{-1} respectively). He also noted that water in the saline wedge sometimes continues to flow upstream for a short time after the fresh water near the surface has started to flow downriver on the ebb. The way in which the transition between the fresh and brackish water moves up and down river according to the state of the tide and the amount of fluvial flow is illustrated by the fact that the conductivity of the water in the R. Yare at Cantley rose above the normal level of *c.* 700 micromhos per cubic centimetre for about 650 hours in 1975, but for over 1000 hours during the drought year of 1976. Salinities at Buckenham during 1979 ranged between 45 and 560 mg l^{-1} of chloride, with a mean of 120 mg l^{-1} (AWA, 1981), but above this point, they are usually relatively stable.

Because fluvial flows in the R. Waveney are more variable than in the Yare, saltwater incursions are commoner, particularly in the summer. Periods when the conductivity was in excess of 1000 micromhos per cubic centimetre (approximating to 300 mg l^{-1} of chloride) at Burgh St. Peter totalled 1558 hours in 1975, but over 6900 hours in 1976 (Bell, *in litt.*).

The normal limit of saline penetration on the R. Bure is variously quoted as between 6.5 and 13 km upstream of Yarmouth Yacht Station, and in 1979 the salinity range at Horning was only 47 to 77 mg Cl$^-$ l^{-1}, with a mean of 55 mg Cl$^-$ l^{-1} (AWA, 1981). But saline incursions can and do occur in this river. For instance during a surge in March 1906, the salinity at Thurne Mouth rose to 906 grains per gallon (*c.* 13 000 mg Cl$^-$ l^{-1}) (Innes, 1911). Similarly, Clarke (1989) found that the water at Horning Church Bend still contained 4400 mg Cl$^-$ l^{-1} two days after a surge in February 1989, and that as a result it contained an assemblage of marine diatoms similar to those present in Lowestoft Harbour. On 13 October, 1981, chloride levels at Ludham Bridge and Irstead rose to 6000 and 1700 mg l^{-1} respectively due to the cumulative effect of surge conditions at Yarmouth on the two previous days. Even higher salinities occurred upriver as a result of another, more substantial surge on 24 and 25 November the same year, and on this occasion Barton Broad, which contained 780 mg l^{-1} chloride on 30 November, did not return to normal (annual mean – 156 mg l^{-1}) until the end of January 1982 (Bell, *in litt.*).

The ecology of the rivers and broads can be profoundly affected by major saltwater incursions. Nicholson (1896), for example, noted that countless dead fish and 'Mussels' (probably *Anodonta*) were floating on the surface of Heigham Sound and Candle Dyke

---

* Much confusion exists in the literature regarding the measurement of chloride and salinity levels. Sea water contains about 19 500 milligrams of chloride per litre (mg Cl$^-$ l^{-1}), and these are the units now commonly used by limnologists. However, salinity is often defined as the amount of salt (NaCl) contained in the water, and on this basis, pure sea water contains about 32 100 mg NaCl per litre. This can be expressed as 32.1 parts per thousand (‰) salinity. Earlier workers referred to salinity in terms of grains per gallon (where one grain per gallon was equivalent to 14.2 mg Cl$^-$ l^{-1}), but this unit is fortunately obsolete.

following a surge in May 1885. He added that the high salinities produced by this event had also killed fish in the R. Yare as far upstream as Coldham Hall, and damaged the vegetation growing on its banks.

Events of this nature are not particularly common as fish are able to detect the increasing salinity and move away from it by swimming upstream. However, following a surge at the end of February 1988, large numbers of fish, mainly one-year-old Roach and Bream, became trapped in an off-river mooring basin at Potter Heigham. Analyses showed that the water in this was between 65 and 75 per cent sea water (instead of the normal 5 per cent) and although some 20 000 fish were rescued and transferred to Somerton Dyke at the head of the Thurne, at least 100 000 fish are thought to have died, this despite the installation by the AWA of pumps to dilute the salinity of the water in the mooring basin (Crook, 1988).

Water supply

The susceptibility of the middle Bure to surge-induced saltwater incursions, and the fact that six weeks or more can elapse before the salinity returns to normality after such an event, has important implications for water resource engineers as well as ecologists, because much of the water used in and near Yarmouth was, until 1979, abstracted near Horning. When it was founded in 1853, the Great Yarmouth Waterworks Company drew its entire supply from the Ormesby, Rollesby, Filby group of broads. These hold about 3.2 million cubic metres of water, but owing to the need to avoid excessive drawdown, rather less than half of this can be exploited, the ascribed yield being 5 thousand cubic metres per day (tcmd) (East Suffolk & Norfolk River Authority, 1971). In response to increasing demand, the Company obtained powers in 1907 to abstract up to 6 million gallons per day (27.3 tcmd) from the Bure just downstream of Horning Church, and this intake came into use in 1914, the water being pumped to the Company's existing treatment works at Ormesby. The Company still takes water from the Trinity Broads, and until the early 1960s had to rely entirely on this source when salt concentrations in the river at Horning rose above the legal limit for abstraction of 20 grains of chlorine per gallon (286 mg Cl$^-$ l^{-1}), as it did, for instance, for several months during the drought years of 1921 and 1935.

In order to reduce its dependence on the Trinity Broads when its Horning intake became temporarily unusable, the East Anglian Water Company* (which was formed in 1962 by the amalgamation of the Yarmouth and Lowestoft Companies) obtained powers in 1964 to abstract from the Bure at Belaugh. Fishing and environmental interests are protected against any consequential increase in saltwater penetration upstream, as the amount of water which can be taken is linked to the fluvial flow as measured at Ingworth, being reduced in three stages from a maximum of 27 to 18 tcmd when the flow in the river drops to 0.385 cubic metres per second (cumecs) (East Suffolk & Norfolk River Authority, 1971). On such occasions, the Company maintains its supply by abstracting water from two boreholes located at its Belaugh works. The Horning intake has hardly been used since 1979, as the river at Belaugh does not contain such a large standing crop of phytoplankton, and water abstracted from it is therefore less costly to treat (Clarke, *in litt.*). Nevertheless, the Company has preserved at the Horning works two magnificent, diesel-powered pumps formerly used to convey water to the treatment plant at Ormesby.

During the late 1970s, it became apparent to the Company that it might not be able to meet the growing demand for water in the Yarmouth area, and at its request, the AWA agreed to take steps to regulate the river so that the Company could abstract more water from it without affecting other users. In the event, the demand in the Yarmouth area did not increase as much as had been predicted, and although two boreholes in the upper Bure catchment were sunk and test-pumped by the Authority, these have not yet had to be used for regulatory purposes. Nevertheless, they may prove useful in future, for instance during a severe drought.

The East Anglian Water Company has taken water from the R. Waveney since 1972, when it constructed an intake works at Shipmeadow, about 0.5 km upstream of Geldeston Lock. After being mixed with borehole water at the Company's works at Barsham, and treated, this is supplied to South Lowestoft and a substantial area in north

---

* Renamed the Suffolk Water Company in January 1991.

Suffolk. Initially, the Company was only licensed to abstract 1 million gallons per day (4.55 tcmd), but the Waveney is now capable of being regulated, five boreholes having been sunk in the catchment of its tributary, the R. Dove, in 1974. In 1976, the Company was granted a licence to abstract up to 3 million gallons per day (13.65 tcmd) from the Waveney and a further increase may eventually be possible, without the flow downstream of the Shipmeadow intake falling below 0.270 cumecs, the figure prescribed by the AWA as being necessary to safeguard downstream river users, and in particular, prevent excessive penetration of salt water upstream (AWA, 1981).

Lound is another site in Broadland used for water-supply purposes. In 1857, some former peat workings known as Mill Water Broad situated just up-valley from Fritton Lake, were developed as a source of supply by the Lowestoft Gas and Water Company, the increasing demand being met in *c.* 1900 by the excavation nearby of a series of ponds fed by springs. The site has been managed since 1962 by the East Anglian Water Company, which has preserved a pair of beam engines formerly used to pump water from one part of the works to another. The ascribed yield of the Lound pools is set at 8 tcmd in order to prevent saline infiltration into the aquifer through excessive drawdown, and a similar volume is drawn from Fritton Lake.

Although the East Anglian Water Company supplies most of Flegg, as well as large areas to the east and south of the R. Waveney, the privatized company known as Anglian Water Services* is responsible for the rest of Broadland, its predecessor, the Anglian Water Authority, having taken over the functions of the Norwich Corporation Water Undertaking on its formation in 1973. Norwich itself has always depended heavily on the Wensum; indeed, a pumping plant to supply piped water to the city was installed near New Mills in *c.* 1401, whilst in 1548, two "citizens and plumbers of London" entered into an agreement . . . "to build and set up a mill at or near New Mills to drive water through certain pipes of lead . . . to the Market Cross" (James *et al.*, 1945). Despite complaints as to its adequacy and efficiency, this undertaking remained in operation until 1794, when the Corporation entered into a new agreement involving the construction of a reservoir at Chapel Field. This arrangement, too, proved inadequate, but improvements followed the establishment of the City of Norwich Water Company in 1850. This undertaking was acquired by the Corporation in 1920, and between then and the mid-1940s, the quantity of water being abstracted from the Wensum rose from *c.* 900 million gallons to *c.* 1600 million gallons per year – the area of supply having increased from 3208 ha in 1850, to 6818 ha in 1878 and to 46 164 ha in 1945.

Until 1968, all the water required by Norwich and its suburbs continued to be drawn from the R. Wensum at a point immediately adjoining the Heigham Street waterworks. The reliable output is set at 38 tcmd, and although a further 20 tcmd can be taken under the abstraction licence, there is an obligation to leave a flow of 0.315 cumecs downstream of the intake. But the growing demand for water from the city and its suburbs made it necessary to exploit other sources during the 1960s, and boreholes were therefore sunk at Caistor St. Edmund, Thorpe St. Andrew and elsewhere; together these provide an additional 38 tcmd. After use, much of this water, plus that abstracted from the Wensum, is discharged by the Whitlingham sewage treatment works into the R. Yare, thus maintaining the fluvial flow of that river.

Concerned at the vulnerability of its existing intake to accidental pollution, the variable quality of the water in the river, and the consequent difficulty of treating it at certain times of the year, and the fact that there was only sufficient storage capacity at Heigham to supply the city for about a day in the event that a pollution incident made it necessary to close the intake temporarily, the AWA sought powers in 1984 to abstract from the Wensum at Costessey, instead of in the city. The Authority's scheme, which

---

* In common with other regional water authorities, the AWA was reorganized in 1989 under the terms of the *Water Act* 1989. Its water supply, sewerage and sewage disposal functions were assumed by Anglian Water Services, a new private company set up under the Act, whilst its water resources, pollution control, flood defence and fisheries management activities were taken over by another new organization, the National Rivers Authority. This is a non-departmental public body, sponsored by the Department of the Environment, and having policy links with the Welsh Office and the Ministry of Agriculture, Fisheries and Food. In some parts of the country, the National Rivers Authority acts as a navigation authority, but as will have become apparent from the footnote on page 29, this is not the case in Broadland. The National Rivers Authority, and all private water companies (and thus the East Anglian Water Company and Anglian Water Services) are required under Section 11 of the *Water Act*, 1989, to 'further the cause of conservation', insofar as this is compatible with their other duties and responsibilities.

had to be brought forward more quickly than originally intended as a result of a pollution problem at a nearby chemical factory (see page 156), involved storing the water in some disused gravel workings, prior to piping it to the Heigham Street works for treatment. This proposal had several advantages, not least the fact that it would greatly reduce the risk of the supply being disrupted in the event that the river became polluted. Even if there were such an incident and abstraction had to cease temporarily, the pits could be used as a stand-by source, sufficient for up to 7 days. In addition, the water taken from the river at Costessey would have time to settle out before it was piped to the Heigham Street works, thus making it much easier to treat.

Although the advantages of the scheme were widely appreciated, it was viewed with alarm by many conservationists and anglers, on the grounds that the reduced summer flows downstream of Costessey would adversely affect the lower reaches of the Wensum. However, it was pointed out at the subsequent public inquiry that the AWA would not be allowed to reduce the flow in the river below 0.514 cumecs as measured at Costessey Mill, and that in these circumstances, the ecology of the river would not be significantly affected. This claim was contested by Brian Moss and others, but in the event the Authority was granted permission to proceed, and work was completed in the autumn of 1987.

The rapidly increasing population of East Norfolk has made it necessary for the AWA, and more recently Anglian Water Services, to seek consent to sink additional boreholes, or maximize the use of its existing ones, and this has generated problems for conservationists at two sites in Broadland. A pumping station at East Ruston, which was refurbished in 1985, has since then been used at its designated capacity, thus lowering the water-table of the adjoining valley mire to the detriment of its flora and fauna (see Chapter 7). Similarly, the Royal Society for the Protection of Birds (RSPB) and the NCC became much concerned during the mid-1980s at the way the water regime of the Strumpshaw Fen nature reserve was being lowered, following the installation of new and more powerful machinery at an adjoining pumping station. In the light of representations, the Authority sank a new borehole into the Chalk some 800 m to the west of the latter, and this enables the Society to keep the water-table of the fens within its reserve at the required level, whilst allowing the Authority (and from 1989 onwards Anglian Water Services) to continue to abstract the water it needs for domestic supply from its own boreholes.

The amount of water required by farmers for spray irrigation has risen dramatically since the 1950s, and shows no signs of abating. Peak demand occurs during dry weather, and although water can be taken under licence from the Yare and Waveney at such times, owing to the huge, tide-induced flows in these rivers, the limit for direct abstraction from the Bure and its tributaries was reached in the early 1960s (O'Riordan, 1970). If additional quantities were taken, summer flows could well fall below the statutory minima set by the AWA to safeguard angling and environmental interests. Consequently, farmers in the northern part of the region who require water for spray irrigation, and who do not have licences of right under the *Water Resources Act* 1963, must provide their own storage reservoirs, to be filled in the winter when the rivers are carrying large fluvial flows. Alternatively, they can apply for a licence to sink a borehole so that they can abstract what they require from the groundwater resources of the region.

The ronds

Those responsible for reclaiming the saltings and fens which once bordered the rivers must have realized, either intuitively, or as a result of experience, that it was best to set the necessary embankments well back from the water's-edge, rather than immediately beside it. The shelf-like ronds (or 'rands') created in this way tend to be widest beside the lower, more strongly tidal reaches of the main rivers, suggesting that their primary function was to provide temporary storage space for water carried upstream on flood tides, and during surges. But the early reclaimers may also have realized that an embankment set back from the river would be stronger, more durable and easier to construct than one placed directly beside it, and that a wide rond would also reduce the amount of leakage through the new flood wall.

Because of their common origin, the surface of the rond and the adjoining marshland must originally have been at the same level in relation to Ordnance Datum. However, whilst the surface level of the ronds has tended to rise over the centuries, as a result of the continued deposition of river-borne silt on them, allied with the progressive rise in water levels due to eustasis, isostasis and other factors, the levels of the marshes have fallen owing to the shrinkage and wastage caused by improved drainage. As a result, ronds and marshes now lie at different levels.

When the embankments were first built, the rivers probably lay more or less equidistant between them. However, over the centuries, meander migration has carried the channels outwards on each curve, thus eroding the rond on that side. In many places, the outer rond has been completely worn away, and the river now lies directly against its embankment (see Table 3k). In general, the more pronounced the bend, the greater the length of rond which will have disappeared. But this relationship is affected by several

Table 3k   The lengths of main river with and without ronds

Type of river bank	Breydon Water		R. Yare* (Waveney confluence to Trowse Eye)		R. Waveney* (Yare confluence to Geldeston)		R. Bure* (Yarmouth to Ant Mouth)	
	L	R	L	R	L	R	L	R
Embankment and Rond	1.2	1.6	16.0	18.0	24.4	22.4	16.8	15.2
Embankment only**	4.4	2.8	8.0	8.0	2.8	4.4	4.8	9.6
Unembanked Fens (washes)	–	–	5.2	6.0	1.2	2.0	2.0†	0.4†
Other‡	0.4	1.6	5.2	2.4	2.0	1.6	3.2	1.6
Totals	6.0	6.0	34.4	34.4	30.4	30.4	26.8	26.8

Notes:
All lengths are in kilometres, and were measured along the centre-line of the rivers
L & R = Left and right banks, as seen when looking downstream.
* Tributaries, such as the rivers Chet, Ant and Thurne are not included
** Includes lengths of river bank where the ronds have been eroded away, and where, upstream, the embankments were built at the water's edge.
† Most of the fens associated with this river are located upstream of Ant Mouth, and are therefore not included in these figures
‡ Includes steel, masonry or concrete flood walls, and places where the river is bordered by higher ground not liable to flooding.
Source: Rendel, Palmer & Tritton (1977).

other factors, including the width and depth of the river, its mean velocity, the amount of boat traffic on it, and the distance between its embankments. The R. Bure, for example, is much more closely confined than are the Yare and Waveney and, in relation to its width, carries much more pleasure boat traffic. As a result, the erosion of its ronds has been relatively severe; indeed, they have been eroded away on both sides of the river in the vicinity of Three Mile House, and just upstream of Thurne Mouth.

The ronds of the R. Yare were originally wider than those of the Bure, but they have been completely worn away on the outside of most of the bends downstream of Brundall. This can be attributed primarily to the strong, tide-induced currents to which this river is subject, and the steps taken from the 1820s onwards to enable sea-going vessels to reach Norwich. The wash and 'draw' produced by these will have increased the rate of erosion, particularly between about 1920 and 1960 when the volume of commercial traffic was much greater than it is today.

The casual observer could be forgiven for concluding that erosion on the lower Waveney has been less marked than on the R. Yare since meander migration has only occasionally carried the river up to its embankments. But those responsible for building the latter set them a long way back from the water's edge. For instance, between Oulton Dyke and St. Olaves, where the river has a mean width of *c.* 40 m, the embankments are usually at least 120 m apart, and this increases to 300 m in the vicinity of Burgh Castle. Erosion in the lower reaches of the Waveney has in fact been extremely severe since the late 1970s, tidal scouring and boat wash having combined to produce a channel so steep-sided as to be physically unstable. Downstream of Oulton Dyke, the water is now usually at least 4 m deep at an equal distance from the edge of the rond, whilst the latter is frequently slightly undercut just below low tide mark. In the circumstances, it is hardly surprising that in several places, sections of rond 30 m or more long, and up to 8 m wide, have slumped into the river channel.

The ronds beside the lowermost reaches of the rivers, particularly those which are regularly grazed by cattle or ponies, are clothed with plant communities tolerant of periodic flooding by saltwater. These are typically dominated by mixtures of Sea Aster, Common Scurvy-grass, Sea Plantain, Greater Sea-spurrey and Common Saltmarsh-grass, but a number of brackish-water species also commonly occur, including Sea Milkwort (*Glaux maritima*), Mud Rush (*Juncus gerardi*) and Sea-Club (*Scirpus maritimus*). Particularly good examples of such communities are to be seen at Berney Arms and Mautby Marsh Farm, where there are several good stands of Sea Club-rush (*Juncus maritimus*), Sea Lavender and Sea Wormwood (*Artemisia maritima*). In the 1830s, Pedunculate Sea Purslane (*Halimione pedunculata*) occurred . . . "in damp saltmarshes at Cobholm and Runham in plenty" (Paget & Paget, 1834), and although this plant has not been recorded in the region since mid-Victorian times, it has recently been found growing in a brackish marsh in South Essex (Leach, 1988). The community in which it occurs here is not dissimilar to some of those found beside the lowermost reaches of Broadland's rivers, and since it is a plant which is both very easily overlooked, and erratic in its occurrence (Bennett, 1905), it could be rediscovered in the region one day.

Reed (*Phragmites australis*) is almost always present on the ronds beside the lower reaches of the rivers, doubtless because some of its biotypes are capable of tolerating salinities of up to 1.2 per cent (729 mg Cl⁻ 1⁻¹) (Ranwell, 1972). In the absence of grazing, it tends to suppress other salt-tolerant plants, and its stands become increasingly vigorous, and ultimately dominant, further upriver where the water is less brackish (see Plate 3).

With its towering stems (up to 2.5 m tall), the Marsh Sow-Thistle (*Sonchus palustris*) is easily the most distinctive plant found on reed-covered ronds. Apart from one or two introductions (it does, for example, occur in Woodwalton Fen, Cambridgeshire), this is now a Broadland 'special', having been known in the region since 1744, when it was recorded from Lothingland. It was considered a very rare species in the early years of the present century (Nicholson, 1914); moreover, some of the earlier records may be mis-identifications of the Field Milk-Thistle (*S. arvensis*). It is now much commoner, and more widely distributed, and Peter Lambley has suggested (*in litt.*) that this may be because the rivers are more frequently dredged than they were in the past; certainly, it is one of the first species to colonize bare mud.

Marsh Harriers sometimes nest on ronds which are wide and densely clothed with Reed, as are those beside the lower reaches of the R. Waveney, and if the growth of *Phragmites* is not too vigorous, they form an important breeding site for Redshank. Round and Campbell (1979) recorded a mean density of 15.1 nesting pairs per square kilometre on the ronds they examined, a figure not very dissimilar to the 22.5 pairs/km² found on high-level saltmarshes in the Ribble Estuary (Lancashire), and substantially greater than the 2.5 pairs/km² observed by Round and Campbell on wet grassland in Broadland's Drained Marshland Area.

In the past, the more vigorous stands of Reed growing on the ronds were regularly harvested, and this practice still occurs here and there, for instance near Stokesby and Somerleyton. However, the quality of the product has, as elsewhere in the region, tended to deteriorate recently (see page 219), and it has been suggested that this may be due to the fact that the drainage 'grips' which were dug to prevent water stagnating on the ronds, are no longer being maintained. Reed undoubtedly grows best on well-drained land (see page 212), and in an attempt to restore such conditions, the Broads Authority agreed in 1988 to grant-aid the digging of new drainage 'grips' on the ronds beside the Bure near Mautby.

The tidal embankments

Evidence is presented in Chapter 8 that some sections of Broadland's rivers had been embanked by the sixteenth century, if not before, and with the simple hand tools then available, those responsible would have been obliged to obtain the material they needed by excavating a ditch, usually known as a 'soke (or sock)-dyke', to the rear of the embankment they were constructing. All too often, this is set so close to the bank as to weaken its structural stability, and embankment failures, such as the one which occurred in 1967 near Whiteslea Lodge on the north side of Hickling Broad, sometimes result from the bank slumping back into the soke-dyke behind it.

A related problem stems from the fact that the material used in the construction of the original embankments was obtained on site, and consequently varies from a highly compressible peat, to a soft clay having a low resistance to shear stresses. Dredgings, or additional material from the soke-dyke subsequently dumped on top of a bank to raise and strengthen it have tended to displace these materials downwards, so that today they are often located at or near its base. In these circumstances, there is a real risk that if further material is placed on top of the embankment, its ability to withstand the lateral pressures generated by high water levels in the adjoining river or broad will be actually reduced rather than increased. This problem is compounded by the fact that many embankments are founded on silts and clays having a low bearing strength, and which are 10 m or more thick in places. Such banks are liable to collapse completely if too much material is placed on them too quickly during maintenance operations. Moreover, if breached, they may be very difficult, or even impossible, to repair by conventional methods. At Hassingham, for example, a 98 m-long gap torn in the left embankment of the Yare by a surge in 1968, had to be filled with steel sheet piling, supported by pairs of inclined piles driven at 4 m spacings down to the gravelly floor of the valley, *c.* 10 m below Ordnance Datum. In January 1976, a breach was made in the embankment immediately adjoining the repaired section, and this had to be made good in the same way. Together, these works cost some £173 000 at 1990 prices (Marsden, *in litt.*).

Bank erosion

Concern has been expressed on innumerable occasions about Broadland's bank erosion problem. As long ago as 1884 Christopher Davies remarked that . . . "One and a half acres was torn off the ronds (of the R. Yare) last summer by the swell from the steamers", and the amount of damage being caused to the banks by boat wash has undoubtedly increased dramatically since the 1930s, as a consequence of the change-over from sail to power-driven pleasure craft (see Table 11c). The effects of this have been greatly exacerbated by the losses of marginal reedswamp which have occurred during the same period. This community, which is described in Chapter 6, originally bordered the rivers for much of their length, and would have greatly reduced the amount of bank erosion resulting from boat wash, given the fact that 60 per cent of the energy contained in this is absorbed by a band of Reed only 2 m wide (Bonham, 1980). Unfortunately, for the reasons outlined in Chapter 6, marginal reedswamp is now poorly developed, or worse still, missing altogether, from long lengths of river bank (see Table 6a), and this will certainly have increased the rate at which they are eroding.

The disappearance of waterweeds from the rivers will have contributed to the bank erosion problem. The growth of these plants was formerly so luxuriant that much time and effort had to be spent cutting them back in order to keep the channels navigable (see page 345). But sufficient vegetation would have remained to dampen any wind-generated wave action before it reached the bank; in addition, the roots of the plants would have helped to stabilize the sediment, and thus prevent an over-steep profile developing. However, as the number of motorized pleasure craft using the rivers increased, the waterweeds would have suffered more and more damage from their threshing propellers, and this, combined with the inability of most species to tolerate the high turbidity levels now encountered almost everywhere in the region (see Chapter 5) has largely eliminated them; indeed, only two waterways – the upper Thurne (including Somerton Dyke), and the North Walsham and Dilham Canal – still possess a good growth of waterweeds throughout their length. The near absence of such plants from the other rivers will certainly have increased their susceptibility to over-deepening and bank erosion as a consequence of tidal scour, wind-generated wave action and boat wash.

Bank erosion is of no great concern to the land drainage engineer where a river is bordered by unreclaimed fen, since such land does not have to be protected against flooding. However, the situation is very different where drained marshland adjoins a river. Here, an accelerated rate of erosion will not only lead to increased rates of leakage through the tidal embankments, and a consequent rise in pumping costs but, much more serious, lead to the bank becoming so structurally weak that it will either collapse as a result of its 'toe' being undermined, or breach, usually during a high spring tide, or following a surge. Either way, serious flooding will occur. To prevent this happening, it will usually be necessary to pile the bank. Light-weight piling, made of timber and steel trench-sheeting, or timber alone is normally used beside the rivers Ant and Thurne, and other places where the water is relatively shallow; the average cost of piling of this type in 1988 was about £200 per metre run. But interlocked steel-sheet piles have to be employed in the deeper water downstream, and cost about £620 per metre in 1988 (Ash, pers. comm.).

Special problems are encountered on the R. Yare, where coasters negotiating the bends are apt to ram the banks and cause breaches in the piling; wave and tidal action subsequently cause wash-outs in the embankment behind. Repairs are both difficult and expensive, and compensation is therefore sought whenever possible from the culprits. In the 1950s, so many coasters were using the river, and so much damage was being caused, that the East Suffolk and Norfolk River Board found it worthwhile to employ a man to follow each ship up and down the river in an outboard dinghy, and report any collisions it had with the banks (Ellis, pers. comm.).

It is not known when land drainage interests first found it necessary to protect the tidal embankments against erosion, but the minutes of the Langley, Chedgrave and Toft Monks Board record that a short section of the embankment around Haddiscoe Island had to be piled in 1918. The average cost per foot run was £3 (equivalent to *c.* £217 per metre at 1990 prices), for timber piles 13 ft to 20 ft (4–6 m) long (Gaze, undated). The rotting piles upstream of Ludham Bridge, which today stand 3 m or more in front of the bank which they once protected, are thought to be of similar age. These, and many other lengths of old piling no longer serve any useful function and are having to be progressively replaced.

Most environmentalists appreciate the need to maintain the tidal embankments in good repair, and with some reservations, are prepared to accept the argument that it is in no one's interests for large expanses of marshland to become derelict owing to permanent flooding. They nonetheless deplore the fact that unless an alternative, cost-effective way of protecting the tidal embankments against erosion can be found (see Chapter 6), further long lengths of river bank will soon have to be piled if serious flooding is to be avoided. This type of 'canalization' eliminates a considerable amount of plant and animal life and, more importantly, greatly reduces the scenic appeal of the waterscape (see Plate 4). In addition, the water in a piled stretch of river remains in a troubled state for much longer after the passage of a motor vessel, than in a reach bordered by reedswamp (Payne & Hey, 1982). This is because the reeds dissipate much of the energy of the wave train, whereas piling reflects the waves back and forth across the river.

Despite the obvious importance of bank erosion to land drainage interests, and in particular the enormous costs which they incur when sections of river bank have to be piled, it is surprising that until recently, most of the information available about the rate at which it is occurring has been of an anecdotal nature. For instance, it has been claimed that a landing stage on the right bank of the R. Waveney, opposite Seven Mile House, has had to be shortened by *c.* 18 m since the 1930s in order to prevent it forming an obstruction to navigation (Marjoram, pers. comm.), and that the frontage of Decoy Staithe, Woodbastwick, retreated by *c.* 7 m between 1962 and 1982 (Dollman, pers. comm.).

One of the few rivers where the rate of erosion has actually been measured is the Chet. This was used by few boats until the later 1950s, when planning permission was granted for several new boat hire yards at Chedgrave and Loddon (see page 442). As a result, it became necessary for the Rivers Commissioners to dredge the river and remove various underwater obstructions. This, together with the fact that the river was clearly destined to be used by increasing numbers of motor cruisers caused great concern in land-drainage circles, as the weakness of the Chet's embankments and the difficulty of maintaining them in good order, had been demonstrated in 1940, when the East Norfolk Rivers Catchment Board had had to abandon its attempts to repair the breaches which had led to the creation of Hardley Flood. Anticipating trouble, staff of the East Suffolk and Norfolk River Authority installed markers, and found to their dismay that both banks of the river retreated, on average by 2 ft (0.6 m) between June 1965 and the end of 1967, and that a further 12 in (0.3 m) had been lost from each side by 1969 (Cotton 1969). If the river did indeed widen by 1.8 m between 1965 and 1969, the rate of bank erosion must have been very slow prior to the mid-1960s, as cartographical measurements included in a report by Payne and Hey (1982) indicate that the mean width of the river only increased by 2.7 m between 1883 and 1972.

It was, of course, only to be expected that a river seldom used previously by boats, and which is less than 40 ft (12 m) wide for much of its length, would be subject to rapid bank erosion, at least initially. Nevertheless, the likelihood that traffic on the Chet would increase – a prediction borne out by a 1976 boat census, which showed that it was being used by about 130 motor vessels a day during the peak holiday season – prompted the River Authority to embark on a programme of raising, strengthening and progressively piling its banks. This was continued by the AWA on its formation in 1973, and the Chet is now encased in piling for virtually the whole of its length.

Another place in Broadland where the past and present rates of erosion can be approximately compared is the Whitlingham Picnic Site. 12 marker posts were installed here by the South Norfolk District Council in February 1980, and by April 1982, it was found that the bank of the R. Yare had, on average, been cut back by 38 cm (Beckett, *in litt.*). Nearby is a derelict section of the quay heading alongside which wherries were moored whilst being loaded with chalk from the adjacent quarries. On average, this now stands 6 m in front of the river bank, and if it is assumed, firstly, that the latter was flush with the quay when it was last used, probably in about 1900 [Woodward (1881) notes that two chalk pits were still being worked here in the 1870s], and secondly that no attempt has been made subsequently to infill the growing gap between the quay heading and the bank, the mean rate of erosion during the past 84 years has been one metre every fourteen years. The fact that the bank has recently retreated by over a third of a metre in just over two years, shows that the rate of erosion here is much greater than it was in the past.

No firm conclusions regarding the rate of bank erosion elsewhere in the region can be drawn from the measurements made at these two sites, as both are atypical, the Chet for the reasons already given, and Whitlingham, because the banks of the Yare are gravelly here, rather than peaty or clayey, and are subject not only to boat wash, but to heavy recreational pressure. Moreover, although the AWA established 28 'key river' sections in the region in 1978 (7 on the Bure, 3 on the Ant, 2 on the Thurne, and 8 each on the Yare and Waveney), these were primarily designed to provide information on the changing configuration of the river channels, rather than their widths, and attempts by the author to use the data thus assembled to measure the amount of river widening which had taken place at these locations between 1978 and 1985 gave inconclusive results. However, Garrad and Hey (1988) who examined the same data set, have pointed out that it shows that the sectional areas of the rivers have certainly changed during this period, the amounts concerned varying between a net loss of over 7 square metres from the Bure at Dydler's Reach (near Decoy Staithe), and a net gain of over 3.5 square metres on the same river *c.* 800 m downstream of Acle Bridge. Measurements in the field by the same workers showed that the R. Bure widened by amounts varying between 0.0 and 1.78 m per year between 1981 and 1987.

Given the urgent need to obtain additional, and on-going information about the rates at which the rivers are widening [an objective referred to in Policy 22 of the Broads Plan (Broads Authority, 1987a)], it was decided in 1986 to establish a second series of sampling stations. 3 of these are on the Ant, 2 on the Thurne, 6 on the Bure, 7 on the Yare and 4 on the Waveney. The Broads Authority and the AWA also commissioned a specialist firm – Geosite Surveys – to carry out a preliminary solar scan of the rivers to see whether this technique could be used to measure their widths, and therefore, over time, their rates of erosion. Unfortunately, however, these experiments did not prove successful.

Prior to these initiatives, the Broads Authority and the Rivers Commissioners had commissioned Clive Doarks, a graduate of the University of East Anglia, to make a general assessment of the bank erosion problem by comparing the widths of the rivers Bure and Yare, and their tributaries, as shown on the 1:2500 maps produced by the Ordnance Survey between *c.* 1883 and 1976. Each river was divided up into a number of sections, and the mean amounts of bank retreat were measured in each. The results, which were incorporated in a report compiled for the Authority by Payne and Hey in 1982, show that both banks of the R. Bure between Belaugh and Ant Mouth – a distance of *c.* 12 miles – have retreated by an average of 4 m or more since the 1880s. Erosion has been even more severe between Ant Mouth and Caister, and on the lower reaches of the Thurne, where mean retreats of 4.5 and 4.4 m respectively have occurred, and in the middle and lowermost reaches of the R. Yare – where 5.6 and 5.8 m respectively have been lost. Thus some sections of the latter river have widened by over 11 m during the past 100 years.

Doarks also demonstrated that the rate of bank erosion has accelerated dramatically since the Second World War. In some places, the rivers widened by as little as 0.06 m every ten years between *c.* 1883 and 1946, and even in the two sections of river subject to the most rapid erosion today – the Yare between Claxton and Abbey Carr, Langley, and the Bure between Ant Mouth and Thurne Mouth – the maximum increase in width during this period was 1.2 m per ten years, with mean rates of 0.4 and 0.6 m respectively. In contrast, the mean, 10 yearly rate of river-width increase between Langley and Claxton was 2.4 m between 1946 and 1976, while the Bure widened even faster between Ant Mouth and Thurne Mouth – by an average of 2.8 m per 10 years between 1946 and 1963, and by 3.1 m per 10 years between 1963 and 1976.

Many reaches bordered by drained marshland have had to be piled, particularly on the outside of meanders, and this obviously reduces the rate at which the river widens; indeed, in places where both banks are protected in this way, widening will cease altogether so long as the piles are maintained in good condition. In contrast, where the rivers are bordered by fen vegetation, bank erosion has, in general, been allowed to continue unchecked (see Plate VIII). Evidence for this is provided by the alders growing beside the middle reaches of the Bure. Most of these germinated at the water's-edge, 40 years or more ago, but now stand 4 m or more in front of the continually retreating river bank.

Another indication of the rapid rate at which the middle Bure is eroding its banks is provided by the peaty baulks which separate Hoveton Great, Wroxham, Salhouse and Decoy Broads from the river, and which are much narrower now than they were even 20 years ago. A breach in the Salhouse baulk had to be repaired by the Rivers Commissioners with posts and wales in the early 1970s, and more recently, further sections of this baulk, and the one at Wroxham Broad have had to be quay-headed to prevent these Broads becoming mere embayments of the river.

Between 1979 and 1983, the Great Yarmouth Port and Haven Commissioners funded a research programme at the University of East Anglia (UEA) which led to the compilation by Dr Paul Garrad of a sediment budget for the Bure, and this has provided a further insight into the rate at which this river is currently eroding its banks (Garrad, 1987). For the purpose of this study, the river was divided into 12 sections, and the amount of sediment in the water in each was measured at regular intervals. A mathematical model of water movements into, and out of, each section was also constructed and cross-checked against measured values, and the rate of sediment deposition in adjoining broads was assessed by means of dated cores (see page 100). From the results obtained Garrad was able to demonstrate first, that broads in open connection with a river are, as had long been suspected, acting as sediment 'sinks' (for instance both Wroxham and Hoveton Great Broads each receive *c.* 1300 tonnes of material annually), and second that substantial quantities of inorganic matter in suspension are being passed downriver each year. On the assumption that the river-bed level remains constant (thus making it unnecessary to take account of the resuspension of bottom sediment which takes place during periods of high fluvial flow, and as a result of boat movements), and ignoring the not-inconsiderable volumes of sediment which are periodically removed when the river is dredged, Garrad argued that this inorganic material must be derived from the banks of the river. Measurements revealed that these have a mean inorganic content of 80 per cent, and a mean density of 1.3 tonnes per

cubic metre, and by assuming, firstly, that the banks are, on average, 2 m high and are retreating in parallel throughout, and secondly that piled stretches of bank can be ignored (since these will, by definition, be immune to erosion), Garrad was able to calculate from the amount of suspended sediment in the water, the annual loss of bank material, and therefore the rate of erosion, in each section. The most rapid rates of retreat were found to be occurring in the vicinity of Salhouse Broad, where each bank is being eroded at a rate of 5.57 ± 1.52 cm per year, and Horning (5.33 cm/yr), whilst the reaches between Wroxham and Horstead Mill are least susceptible, with a mean rate of bank retreat of 1.91 ± 0.52 cm per year. Garrad calculated that these rates of erosion would be approximately halved if no motor boats were using the river.

Air photographs taken between 1946 and 1980 indicate that each bank of the Bure between Horning and Ant Mouth is currently retreating, on average, by 4.8 cm per year, and this figure is remarkably consistent with Garrad's calculated rate of 4.5 cm/yr for the same stretch of river. The problem with mean figures such as these is that they tend to conceal the fact that bank erosion is occurring at some places at an even more alarming rate. For instance, the upstream entrance to Wroxham Broad was no less than 10.4 m wider in 1987 than it was in 1981 (Garrad & Hey, 1988a).

In an analysis of the factors affecting the stability of Broadland's river banks, Payne and Hey (1982) identify soil type, bank profile and type of marginal vegetation present (if any) as directly relevant, whilst water quality, the profile produced by dredging, trampling by anglers and others, and the burrowing activity of mammals [especially Water Voles (*Arvicola amphibius*)] are cited as factors which may indirectly affect the resistance of the bank to erosional forces, through their influence on the sheer strength of its soils.

Payne and Hey point out that the banks of the lowermost reaches of the rivers consist mainly of silts, as would be expected from the physiographic history of the valleys, but that clay and peat appear in the lower parts of the bank profile further upstream. The middle reaches of the rivers have a clay – peat – clay (or watery clay) sequence, the peaty layers becoming progressively thinner upriver. Near the navigable limits of the rivers, the banks possess a complex profile, with sands and gravels, and occasional sand lenses. The variety of substrates present is of great importance, as clay and silt have a much lower resistance to fluid shear forces than peat, and therefore erode comparatively quickly.

A certain amount of erosion is caused by moored craft. As these roll to and fro in the wash of passing vessels, their rubbing strakes abrade the bank, and ultimately produce characteristic crescent-shaped indentations in it (see Plate 5). But most of the erosion taking place in the region can, according to Payne and Hey, be attributed to less resistant strata in the bank being washed out below the waterline; the undercutting which occurs is then followed by the collapse of the resultant overhang. After a review of the relative importance of fluvial and tidal currents, and boat wash, as factors responsible for this type of erosion, it is concluded that the forces induced by the latter are much the most significant in the middle and upper reaches of the rivers, and that they are dependent on the speed of the vessel, its distance from the bank, and whether it is moving with, or against, the current. Tidal effects assume greater importance further downstream.

Much of the undercutting takes place along the line of the clay–peat interface, usually about 0.75 m below still water level, and is nearly always associated with the presence of water vole holes. This type of damage is caused by underwater pressure waves generated by propeller action rather than by surface waves. Attempts to measure pore-water pressure changes produced by the latter proved unsuccessful, but it is believed that as

Bank erosion on the R. Bure opposite the Ferry Inn, Horning – 1978.

Plate VIII

Although wind and boat-generated wave action is primarily responsible for this type of damage, trampling by anglers has exacerbated the problem here. Sections of river bank nearby have been quay-headed to stop further erosion, and a little further downriver, the Broads Authority has installed a number of platforms so that those wishing to fish can do so without still further reducing the amount of water's-edge vegetation.

Photo: Peter Wakely/Nature Conservancy Council

these waves break against the bank, air is momentarily trapped and compressed, producing miniature shock waves in the bank as it escapes. This tends to dislodge particles of soil from the bank, thus accelerating the rate at which it is eroding.

One of the assertions frequently voiced by those who know and love the region is that some of the boats currently in use produce a disproportionate amount of wash, and therefore bank erosion, relative to their size. Day launches are frequently singled out for criticism on the grounds that they tend to be beamy and relatively short on the water-line. Payne and Hey's data on the amount of wash generated by motor craft did not confirm these anecdotal comments; nor could it easily be reconciled with the results of Bonham (1980) and others who claim to have established a strong causative link. In view of the uncertainty, the Broads Authority decided in 1985 to commission a further series of trials aimed at clarifying the role of hull design and speed in relation to boat wash, and determining whether a reduction in the overall speed limit from, say, 7 mph to 5 mph, would significantly reduce the amount of bank erosion caused by boat wash. The results obtained from these experiments are described in Chapter 11.

Plate 1

An aerial view of part of the Hickling Broad National Nature Reserve – 1973.

The southern half of Hickling Broad, together with Heigham Corner (in the middle distance), Heigham Sound and the fens and marshes adjoining these water bodies, was acquired by Lord Lucas in 1909. The rest of the Broad was leased from a private landowner, and the whole area (which became known as the Whiteslea Estate) was managed as a sporting estate-cum-bird sanctuary, initially by Lord Lucas, and during the 1920s, 1930s and early 1940s by Lord Desborough. The land owned by the latter was purchased by the Norfolk Naturalists' Trust in 1945, and the remaining parts of the site were leased by the Trust the following year. The Nature Conservancy entered into nature reserve agreements over both the owned and the leased areas in 1957, and these were formally declared a National Nature Reserve the following year.

Responsibility for the day-to-day management of the reserve remains vested in the Trust, but the Nature Conservancy (and its successor from 1973 onwards, the Nature Conservancy Council) provides a substantial amount of financial help each year.

Although the aquatic plant and animal life of the Broad has been adversely affected by nutrient enrichment, the whole site remains of outstanding entomological and ornithological importance. This was recognized internationally when it was designated a Ramsar site in 1976.

Photo: John Hubbard / Nature Conservancy Council

Ranworth Broad, looking north from the tower of Ranworth Church – 1962.

Plate 2

Ranworth Dam, the waterway which links this site and Malthouse Broad with the R. Bure can be seen on the right, but the Ranworth Conservation Centre was not sited near its southern end until 1973.

Many of the fens on the far side of the Broad had already been invaded by trees and bushes by the early 1960s, but a narrow band of reedswamp still fringed the open water. This community has now almost completely disappeared, and large standing crops of algae now occur in the Broad, in place of the waterweeds which proliferated in it until about 50 years ago.

Photo: Martin George

Plate 3

Herringfleet Mill – 1974.

This is the only smock mill in the region which is in good condition; it is owned by Lord Somerleyton, who leases it to the Suffolk County Council. The difference between the river and dyke water levels has increased since the Mill last worked (probably in the early 1950s), and it no longer has sufficient 'lift' to fulfil its function of draining the adjoining marshes. Nevertheless, it is still capable of transferring water from one part of the dyke system to another, and on two or three advertised dates a year, County Council staff rig its canvas ('common') sails and, provided there is sufficient wind, lay on working demonstrations.

Wide, reed-covered 'ronds' form a very striking feature of the lower reaches of the R. Waveney. But its channel has very steeply shelving edges, and its banks are eroding rapidly, particularly at low tide. Suspended sediment, plus a large standing crop of phytoplankton, account for the brown colouration of the river water.

Photo: Martin George

Plate 4

Replacing steel sheet piling near Langley, on the R. Yare – 1984.

The National Rivers Authority has inherited from its predecessors a major backlog of essential repairs to Broadland's flood defences. In the lower reaches of the rivers, where the water is deep, steel sheet piling has to be used rather than timber or composite materials, and this is very expensive, particularly if, as here, derelict piling has to be removed before the new piles can be driven in. The average cost of such work in 1990 was in excess of £800 per metre, especially if heavy-gauge materials had to be used, as on bends.

It is rarely, if ever, possible to construct a new embankment to the rear of an existing one, owing to the poor load-bearing characteristics of the strata underlying the marshes. Consequently, once the rond has been eroded away, it is essential to protect the river bank with piling or some other material. If this is not done, the embankment will be undermined, and ultimately breached.

Photo: John Ash / National Rivers Authority

Plate 5

Crescent-shaped bank erosion on the R. Ant upstream of Barton Broad – 1962.

This form of erosion is caused by moored boats, which tend to roll to and fro in the wash of passing vessels, thus abrading the river banks. Although visually conspicuous, this type of erosion is of very local occurrence, and is of relatively minor importance, compared with the general wear and tear to which all Broadland's river banks are now subject.

Photo: Martin George

Plate 6

A peat excavation in Co. Wicklow, Eire – 1968.

Blanket bog peat is being exploited here, rather than fen peat, but similar techniques were probably adopted when the peat pits, which later flooded to form the broads, were being worked in medieval times. Simon George was just over a metre tall when this photograph was taken.

Photo: Martin George

Plate 7

Calthorpe Broad – 1975.

Steps have been taken by the NCC to alleviate the high acidities which occurred periodically in this site during the 1970s, and it is now one of the very few broads still supporting a Phase II, waterweed-dominated community. Water Soldier, Frogbit, Hornwort, Canadian Pondweed and several other plants occur, in addition to the luxuriant stand of Yellow Water-lily visible in the photograph, while 'wings' of Bogbean, and further away from the camera, Sweet Rush, can be seen spreading outwards from the edge of the Broad.

Between 1965 and 1985, Calthorpe Broad and some of its adjoining fens were used by the Ministry of Agriculture, Fisheries and Food for research on the ecology of Coypus, and the observation tower in the left background was built to facilitate these studies.

Photo: Derek Ratcliffe

Plate 8

Yellow Water-lilies growing beside the R. Bure near Horning Ferry – 1989.

Yellow Water-lilies are very tolerent of nutrient-rich conditions, and can also survive in quite turbid water. However, their floating leaves are highly susceptible to damage by threshing boat propellers, and they therefore only occur near the edges of busy waterways such as the R. Bure or, as here, in places which boats cannot get to. This particular group of lilies supports a colony of the Red-eyed Damselfly, a rather local species, the males of which are almost always associated with lily pads.

Hobbs' Mill, on the other side of the river, is currently being restored by the Norfolk Windmills Trust: it is to be fitted with sails shortly.

Photo: Simon George

Plate 9

An algal 'bloom' in Neatishead Dyke, off Barton Broad – 1975.

Phytoplankton 'blooms' such as this are normally caused by the development of a large standing crop of *Aphanizomenon*, *Anabaena*, *Microcystis* or some other blue-green alga. The species concerned possess gas vesicles, which enable them to regulate their buoyancy physiologically. Their consequent ability to move up and down in the water column has advantages in regard to nutrient uptake.

Fortunately, 'blooms' are fairly rare in Broadland, since although the species responsible are frequently present, especially in late summer, the particular circumstances which together favour such an occurrence (which include calm conditions, bright sunlight and a high concentration of nutrients in the water) only occasionally coincide.

Photo: Peter Stevens

Strumpshaw Broad (West) at low tide – 1962.

Plate 10

When this photograph was taken, both the east and west limbs of Strumpshaw Broad were still connected with the R. Yare by Fleet Dyke, and had been virtually filled up with tide-borne sediment. One of the first things that the RSPB did when they leased the site in 1974 was to dam off Fleet Dyke from the river, so as to prevent any further deposition of riverine silt in the east and west parts of the Broad. Both were later suction-dredged, and the water in them is now a metre or more deep.

As a result of heavy grazing by Coypus, there was virtually no reedswamp around the margins of Strumpshaw Broad in the 1960s and 1970s, the dominant plant in the adjoining fens being Reed Sweet-grass (*Glyceria maxima*). This was well able to withstand the tide-induced variations in water level to which the fens were subject when the photograph was taken; it was also little affected by Coypu grazing. Now that Coypus have been exterminated, Reed, Great Reedmace and other emergent species have re-colonized the margins of the Broad, whilst Reed Sweet-grass has become less common. This is partly because of the competition afforded by these species, and partly because the fens in this part of the reserve have been embanked by the RSPB, and are therefore no longer subject to tide-induced fluctuations in water level.

Photo: Martin George

Plate 11

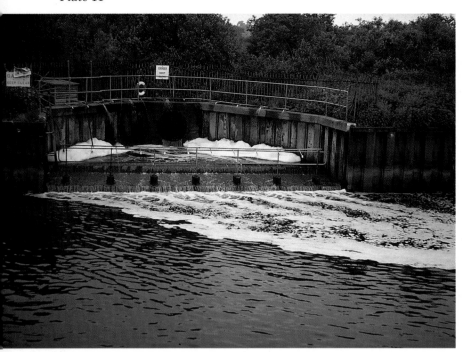

The outfall of the Whitlingham Sewage Treatment Works – 1979.

The Whitlingham Works receives the sewage from about 200 000 persons, and its outfall is by far the largest input of phosphorus to the R. Yare. Despite the large sums of money which have been spent on the Works since the 1950s, its final effluent is often discoloured, and of poor quality. Further improvements to the plant were started in 1990. But these will not include phosphorus-reduction equipment, since the capital and running costs of this would be very high on account of the large volumes of sewage passing through the Works each day.

Although jets of water are used to reduce foaming in the final effluent, it will be seen that these are only partially successful. Note that the effluent is being carried upstream on the flood tide, a phenomenon which those who go for a swim at the Whitlingham Picnic Site, about a mile upriver, appear not to be aware of.

Photo: Martin George

Plate 12   **Installing the first of two 'Lund Tubes' at Heigham Corner (Hickling Broad) – 1976.**

Each of these butyl rubber 'Tubes' was 20 m in diameter, and enabled observations to be made on the chemistry, phytoplankton and zooplankton of a large volume of water isolated from that in the Broad itself. Each 'Tube' comprised an inflatable flotation collar (on which the men are perched), from which hung down a weighted 'skirt', the bottom edge of which was embedded in the sediment. The circular shape of the Tube was maintained by anchors arranged around the outside, and these also served to prevent the structure being dislodged by high winds.

The experiments, which involved taking and analysing samples of water from the Broad itself, as well as from the Tubes, were far from trouble-free. Nevertheless, they yielded a great deal of information about the ecology of this nationally most important site, and the reasons why, in the late 1960s and early 1970s, it had 'switched' from a Phase II, waterweed-dominated community, to a Phase III, algal-dominated one.

Photo: Martin George

Plate 13

Feral Greylag Geese at Salhouse Great Broad – 1990.

Until about 15 years ago, most of Broadland's feral Greylag and Canada Geese were to be found in the Bure valley, particularly around Salhouse and Wroxham Broads. However, since then they have become much more numerous and widespread. As a result, the damage they cause to marginal reedswamp, fields of standing corn and, as here, grasslands near the water's edge, has greatly increased.

Both species can be shot between the beginning of September and the end of January, but shooting pressure alone is not proving sufficient to stabilize, let alone reduce, their numbers. Other measures, such as cannon netting them prior to removal elsewhere, could only be carried out under licence, and would undoubtedly prove extremely controversial, given the large numbers of holidaymakers who derive pleasure from seeing them around.

Photo: Martin George

Bank erosion at Salhouse Great Broad – 1976.

Plate 14

Patches of marginal reedswamp survived in this Broad until the mid-1960s, but this community had probably disappeared from this (the southern) edge of the site by the early 1950s, if not before.

This Broad is extremely popular with boat-borne holidaymakers, and also with picnic parties, who can walk down to it from a car park at Salhouse, provided by the Broads Authority. As a result, the grassland on this edge of the site is subject to heavy trampling pressure. It is also closely grazed, and fouled, by the numerous feral Greylag and Canada Greese which frequent the site. These birds have certainly contributed to the losses of marginal reedswamp from the rivers and broads; indeed, at this particular site, they occur in such large numbers, that they may have been primarily responsible.

Since this photograph was taken, the section of river bank nearest the camera has been quay-headed, the trees on the right having first been removed.

Photo: Martin George

Plate 15

Reedswamp regression in Heigham Sound – 1979.

Virtually all the Reed growing around the edges of this site is of the 'hover' variety, and the losses of marginal reedswamp have been correspondingly great (see Fig. 6E). The Lesser Reedmace in the foreground is displaying the clumped appearance which typically develops when this species is regressing.

Bulrush, the other primary colonizer of open water, has been even more seriously affected by regression than Lesser Reedmace, and is now only represented in Heigham Sound by a few scattered plants. Research on the reasons why these two species are disappearing is urgently needed, in order to complement the studies already carried out on the causes of Reed regression.

Photo: Martin George

Plate 16

The New Cut, looking south-eastwards towards its confluence with the R. Waveney – 1970.

The left (north-west) margin of this waterway has already had to be piled to afford Haddiscoe Island protection against flooding, and the relict stands of reedswamp visible beside the Reedham to Lowestoft railway line have disappeared since the photograph was taken.

The sides of the New Cut's channel are, like those of most of the rivers in the region, now very steeply shelving. Thus, even if Broadland's water quality problems were resolved, it is very doubtful whether reedswamp would be capable of forming a stand of sufficient width to cushion the bank against continued erosion by wind and boat-generated wave action. Re-profiling might be possible in certain locations, and is being carried out experimentally near Thurne Mouth. But to do this beside the New Cut, it would be necessary to move the railway, or drastically reduce the width of this navigable waterway, or both. In the circumstances, it seems inevitable that the right (south-east) bank of the Cut will shortly have to be piled.

Photo: Martin George

Chapter 4
The Origin
of the Broads

Although Samuel Woodward noted in 1834 that the boundary between the parishes of Barton Turf and Irstead was marked by a ridge across Barton Broad, and that the sharply defined edges of this, and the Broad itself suggested that peat had been worked from the site in the past, the sheer size of the lakes in the region, and their number, led scientists and laymen alike to assume until about 30 years ago that they had originated naturally. But there was little agreement as to exactly how and when they had been formed, and early geologists speculated freely, often on the flimsiest evidence. Grantham (1869) for example, thought that . . . "the broads, though freshwater lakes, are relics of the time when the whole of these valleys were submerged and in fact formed great estuaries", whilst Taylor (1872) erroneously asserted that . . . "most of the broads lie in hollows from which all the drift has been eroded away". A few years later, H. B. Woodward noted that the depth of alluvium in the valleys showed that they must have been submerged by the sea after they had formed, and that the development of peat-forming, freshwater communities in them could be attributed to the progressive south-ward growth of the Yarmouth shingle spit. He, like Samuel Woodward, considered it likely that Barton Broad, and perhaps Hickling Broad, were created by peat digging (Woodward, 1883), but perceptive as this observation was, its credibility was weakened by his belief that Ormesby Broad and Fritton Lake had been created artificially by the damming off of their valleys.

Blake (1890) suggested that broads in the tributary valleys were older than the others, and that they had not become infilled with alluvium owing to the formation of bars across their outlets. These ideas were later taken up by Reid (1913), who thought that the "small and sluggish" rivers were unable to fill up the wide estuaries formed by the post-glacial submergence; and that these . . . "were therefore silted up with tidal mud, and turned into irregular chains of lakes, separated by bars and sandbanks". He went on to propose that . . . "as soon as a bank became high enough for the growth of reed and sedges, the river mud was strained out, and only nearly clean water reached the lagoon behind".

Far-fetched as these ideas may seem today, they were taken up and developed by later workers, including Sainty (1949) and Jennings (1952), the latter concluding from strat-igraphical studies in the Bure and Ant valleys that the broads were initiated as a series of discontinuous, peaty hollows. In the case of the by-passed broads, these were said to be located beyond the limits of the estuarine clay laid down during the Romano-British Transgression, while the side-valley broads developed in tributary valleys whose mouths were blocked by the clay. Thereafter . . . "further isolation and deepening of the basins (of the broads) were brought about by resumed peat growth in the surrounding fenland after the sea had receded".

Hardly had this hypothesis been propounded by Jennings than Dr Joyce Lambert discovered that in the Yare valley and elsewhere the 'peaty hollows' had perpendicular walls. This and other features made it improbable in the extreme that the broads could have formed naturally, and a new and more thorough investigation was therefore commenced during the early 1950s by the two workers concerned. Soon afterwards, C. T. Smith, then at Cambridge University, embarked on a search for historical evidence that some, if not all the broads were, as Lambert and Jennings had begun to suspect, flooded medieval peat diggings. Meanwhile, Charles Green, an archaeological consultant to the then Ministry of Works, examined the size and distribution of the population of Broadland over the centuries, and with the help of J. N. Hutchinson, a civil engineer, analysed the evidence from a number of excavations in and around Great Yarmouth to determine what variations in relative land-sea levels had occurred during the past millennium. These latter studies were considered necessary as it seemed inconceivable that excavations 3 m or more deep could have been dug by hand in medieval times if water levels in the valleys were as high then as they are now.

The evidence produced as a result of the three interlinked investigations was published by the Royal Geographical Society in 1960, and showed conclusively that the broads are indeed flooded peat workings, the angular sides and perpendicular walls of which have been concealed by the overgrowth of marginal vegetation so as to give the lakes a natural appearance (Lambert & Jennings, 1960). In most cases, the flooded excavations are surrounded on all sides by peat, but at some sites, for instance Wroxham, Hoveton Little, Salhouse and South Walsham Broads, the latter was cut away right up to the edge of the valley. Each of these sites therefore has a shelving, gravelly margin nearest the upland, though perpendicular walls of peat occur on the other sides of the former excavation.

Each basin is typically floored by brushwood peat and is usually either gently sloping or almost flat; it hardly ever displays the concave surface which would be expected if the lake had been formed by natural processes. The peaty floor is overlaid by the sediments which have accumulated since the basin became flooded. However, at the base of these there is usually a layer, not of the *Phragmites* peat which would have formed if the broad had gradually filled with water, but of a mixture of mud and peat, probably representing the debris which accumulated on the floor of the pit as digging progressed.

In the majority of sites the floor of the basin lies between two and three metres below the present fen surface, but in the north-western corner of Decoy Broad, it lies at a depth of about four metres, whilst in the large, side-valley broads like the Ormesby, Rollesby and Filby group and Fritton Lake, where the peat was removed right down to the gravelly valley bottom, it is a metre or more deeper still. The basins of up-valley sites like Alderfen, Sutton and Calthorpe broads tend to be about 1.5 metres deep, or less.

The fact that most broads are situated either lateral to, or upstream of, the wedges of clay left by the Romano-British Transgression, suggests that the medieval peat diggers tried to avoid working in areas where they would encounter deep layers of clay. Where the latter did occur, for example in those broads dug in the middle sections of the Bure and Yare valleys, this would have formed a relatively thin sandwich between the Upper and Middle Peat, and would have been largely confined to the sides of the excavation nearest the river. Borings at such sites have shown that the walls of the basin are cut through the clay, and that lumps of the latter, apparently discarded and subsequently covered by lake sediments, lie on its floor.

When first formed, the straight edges and sharply-angled walls of the basins would have been very conspicuous, but over the centuries these features have been progressively obscured by marginal vegetation, and the exact boundaries of each basin can now only accurately be defined by close-spaced boring. But its approximate configuration can frequently be made out from ecological differences between the mature, species-rich communities which overlie the solid, unworked peat, and the Swamp Carr and other formations which characteristically develop in areas which were once open water. In addition, owing to the compaction of the underlying lake sediments, the surface level of these relatively recent communities tends to be 20 to 30 cm lower than that of areas from which peat has at sometime been removed. Good examples of this can be seen to the south of Hoveton Great Broad.

Elongated islands occur at several sites, including Decoy, Rockland, Surlingham and Barton Broads, and have been shown by borings to be steep-sided, and to display the same sequence of alluvial deposits as is found in the 'solid' fenland adjoining the basin. Similarly the peninsulars which jut out into the open water of many broads, and which in the past extended across the latter in the form of underwater ridges (see Plate IX), characteristically consist of solid peat, flanked on either side by the sediments which have accumulated in the basin.

A close study of maps, combined with evidence from air photographs and underwater soundings, has shown that these peninsulars and submerged ridges of peat usually traverse the broad in parallel lines. Lambert *et al.* have demonstrated that at sites like Surlingham Broad, where the 1839 Tithe map shows the whole site to be covered by

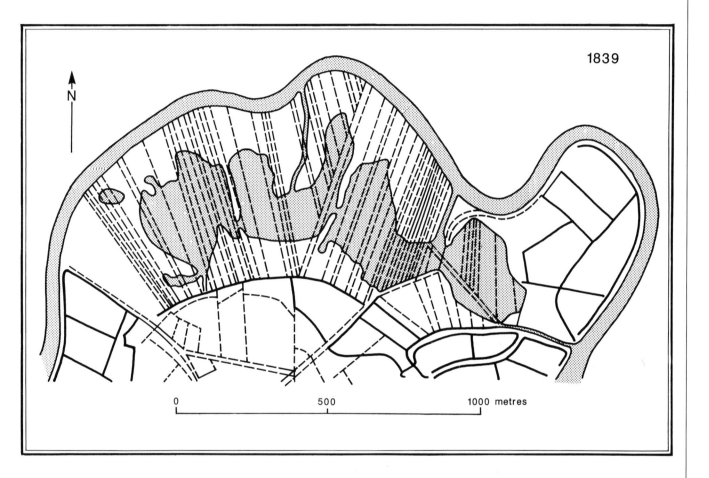

1839

0   500   1000 metres

close-set parcel lines (see Map 4.1), the peninsulars of solid peat not only closely follow the alignment of these lines, but lie within their limits.

Samuel Woodward's observation that the former boundary between Barton Turf and Irstead* parishes was marked by a ridge of peat across Barton Broad was found by Lambert and Jennings to apply also to Sutton Broad and Mill Water (upstream of Fritton Lake) where the boundaries between Stalham and Sutton, and Hopton and Lound respectively were demarcated in this way. In addition they observed that at Barton, the alignment of the peat ridges in what was once Irstead's half of the broad, differed from those in Barton Turf's. Until about 30 years ago, such ridges showed up as discontinuous lines of reedswamp. But these have now disappeared and the ridges themselves have been largely, if not wholly lost, as a consequence of erosion and dredging (see Plate X).

By analogy with present-day peat workings, such as those in the west of Ireland and Scotland, it is clear that the near-perpendicular walls of the basin of a broad represent

Map 4.1

Parcel lines on the 1839 tithe map for Surlingham. These almost certainly represent strip allocation of the area available for peat digging. Moreover, the fact that the parcel lines extend across areas of 'solid' fen which were never worked for peat, and which border what is now open water, indicates that the latter originated through peat digging.

Source: Lambert and Jennings (1960)

---

* Irstead was incorporated in the parish of Barton Turf in 1935.

Plate IX

Barton Broad, looking north – 1951.

The peninsulars and islets of reedswamp mark the position of the baulks of peat which in medieval times separated one excavation from another. These were submerged when the peat pits became permanently flooded, but the water overlying them was shallower than in the rest of the Broad, and they were therefore colonized by reedswamp species more quickly. Note that they are aligned at a different angle in the south of the Broad (which was included in the former parish of Irstead), than in the north, which has always formed part of the parish of Barton Turf.

Many of the fens in the photograph have not yet been invaded by trees and bushes. Marginal reedswamp communities are also very well developed, particularly on the left (west) side of the Broad, where they form a conspicuous 'wing' of vegetation.

Barton Broad was originally a by-passed site, the R. Ant being aligned on a circuitous route through the fens on its eastern side, as shown in Map 3.3. A new channel for the river was dug subsequently (a section of which can be seen, bottom right), and since then, it has flowed through the Broad, instead of round it. The date of this diversion is not known, but it was probably motivated by a desire to improve the Ant's navigability.

Photo: Aerofilms Ltd.

Barton Broad, looking north – 1979.   Plate X

Some of the ecological changes which have occurred at this site since the 1950s will be apparent if this photograph is compared with that reproduced in Plate IX. Most of the marginal reedswamp has disappeared, including many of the islets marking the position of the former peat baulks and in the near absence of this community, little, if any, new Tussock Fen is being formed. In addition, many of the fens bordering the Broad have been heavily invaded by trees and bushes, thus reducing the amount of 'open' fen in the area. Such terrain comprises an immensely diverse series of plant and animal communities, particularly in the Ant valley, and although representative examples survive here and there, it is most regrettable that so many areas have, through a lack of management, been lost over the past 30 to 40 years.

Research (described in Chapter 5) has shown that Barton Broad has been filling up with sediment at the rate of over a centimetre per year since the early 1970s. Much of the site is still a metre and a half or more deep, but its extreme southern end – Turkey Broad – (partly concealed by one of the aircraft's struts) was always its shallowest part, and is now only a few centimetres deep. As a result, it is now unusable by anything larger than a rowing dinghy. A similar fate will ultimately befall the remainder of the Broad, unless ways can be found of reducing the present high rate of sedimentation. One alternative would be to suction-dredge the site, thereby getting rid of the phosphorus-rich surface sediments, as well as increasing the depth of water. But this would be an extremely expensive undertaking.

Photo: Courtesy of the Norfolk County Council

the former working faces of the digging, whilst the steep-sided islands, peninsulars and submerged ridges are areas of undisturbed peat which for one reason or another were left unworked.

The baulks of untouched alluvium which separate the by-passed sites from the adjoining river (e.g. Wroxham and Salhouse Broads) would have been deliberately left to help prevent water seeping from the latter into the peat pits. Nevertheless, the primitive technology available would have made it extremely difficult to de-water excavations more than a few hundred square metres in extent, and it is believed that many of the ridges formerly visible in the larger broads represent baulks of peat which were intentionally left uncut in order to subdivide the basin into a series of

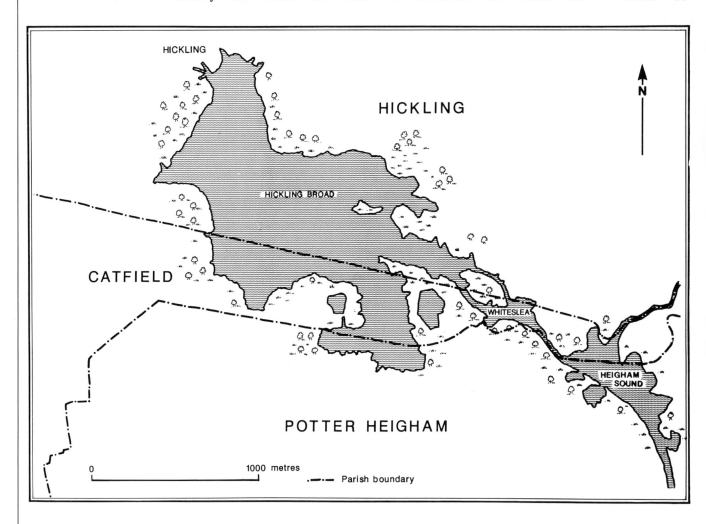

Map 4.2

The parish boundaries of Hickling, Catfield and Potter Heigham in the vicinity of Hickling Broad. These are aligned in such a way that the inhabitants of all three parishes would have been able to exploit the peat deposits which underlie the western end of the Broad and its adjoining fens, and also the clay which occurs in and around Heigham Sound.
(© Crown Copyright)

compartments. This would have made it much easier to keep those workings which were in active use pumped out, the remainder being allowed to flood temporarily. Today, several centuries later, the same technique is often used when large excavations, such as the new 'broad' at the University of East Anglia, and the mere at Holme Fen National Nature Reserve (Cambridgeshire), are being created. Only later, when the peat pits had become permanently flooded, would the baulks have been breached to enable boats to move freely from one part of the site to another.

Many of the smaller ridges would have marked the boundaries between adjoining strip holders, just as they do today in places where peat is still being dug by hand. Baulks such as these frequently serve as causeways as well as boundary markers, and striking evidence that they fulfilled this role in Broadland in medieval times has been obtained from the Surlingham, Wheatfen and Rockland area. Here, baulks have been found which show signs, not only of the compaction caused by frequent usage, perhaps by wheelbarrow traffic, but of the attempts made to improve the working surface by filling in the ruts with sand and gravel.

The fact that some ridges of solid peat are wider than others, and that 'islands' of unworked peat have been left here and there, for instance, to the south of Hoveton

Great Broad, is exactly what one would expect, given the vagaries of human affairs, both in relation to land ownership and individual endeavour.

Although clay seems in general to have been an unwanted by-product of peat excavation, large quantities are thought to have been extracted from the down river parts of Hickling Broad, Heigham Sound and Horsey Mere. Evidence for this is afforded by the presence of steep-sided blocks of undisturbed peat and clay at the edges of these broads. The islands in them, too, are formed of such residual blocks of solid alluvium.

To the west of Whiteslea, the clay thins and ultimately peters out, and the central and western parts of Hickling Broad are floored by brushwood peat and gravelly sand respectively. The boundaries of the parishes of Hickling, Catfield and Potter Heigham are aligned in such a way as to enable the inhabitants of each village to have had access to reserves of both brushwood peat and clay (see Map 4.2). It cannot be a coincidence that the peat-based southern limb of Hickling Broad is known to this day as Heigham Corner, whilst the extensive clay workings which now form Heigham Sound must surely have provided the raw material for the potteries known to have been in existence in the twelfth century, and which gave their name to the nearby village of Potter Heigham.

Once the excavation of peat and clay had ceased, each of the flooded workings would, as elsewhere, have served as a sump into which water from the adjoining fens tended to gravitate. But the Thurne broads differ from most other water bodies in the region in that embankments were later built around their margins to facilitate the drainage of the adjoining land. Subsequent wastage and shrinkage of the Upper Peat deposits which formerly covered much of the latter would have resulted in a general lowering of the land surface, ultimately making it necessary to introduce a system of pumped drainage for the marshes. Today, these lie at a level only just above that of the floor of the adjoining broads.

Although the stratigraphical evidence for the man-made origin of the broads is overwhelming, several interlinked questions arise immediately. Why, for example, were many of the pits dug to a depth of 2 to 3 metres or more, when deposits of surface peat could have been extracted from the nearby fens with much less difficulty and effort? Lambert, Jennings and Smith (1965) explain this as follows:

> The answer probably lies, at least in part, in the better combustible quality of the peat at the lower levels. Whereas the surface deposits consist predominantly of fairly fresh remains of reed and sedge, often with a somewhat muddy matrix, at the lower depths the compact, humified brushwood and fen peats were uncovered. Brushwood peat, when extracted in bulk, is of a close-set, cheesy consistency, lacking the fibrous coherence of the upper peats, but not impossibly difficult to handle; it has an obviously superior fuel value to the reed peat at the surface, and may well have provided economic returns well worth the extra effort in extraction. Moreover, in some areas, particular land-holders may have exhausted their own surface peats and been compelled on this count to dig deeper.

Confirmation of these textural differences has recently been afforded by Wheeler and Giller (1982c) who note that at Catfield Fen brushwood peat has a bulk density of 109 grams per litre, whilst most surface peats are in the 53 to 79 g l^{-1} range.

C. T. Smith's historical research, which involved an examination of account rolls, court rolls, deeds, leases, surveys, terriers and other documents, produced an abundance of evidence that there was an important turf industry in Broadland during the twelfth, thirteenth and fourteenth centuries. Most of the twelfth century references come from the Register of St. Benet's Abbey, which by the end of that century, had acquired rights in turbaries in 13 localities, all but two of which were in Broadland (Smith, 1960). Usually, the right to cut turf was one of several appurtenances related to the grant of arable land, but at Ludham and elsewhere, the turbaries are singled out for special mention.

References to turbaries, or the sale of turves, become increasingly numerous during the next two centuries, and it is significant that of the 20 places mentioned in documents relating to the thirteenth century, 15 are in parishes which now contain broads, or parts of broads; the corresponding figures for the fourteenth century are 29 and 25 (see Map 4.3). Parishes recorded as having turbaries, but which do not have a broad within their boundaries, for instance Waxham, Scratby and Rackheath, may well have held rights to cut turf elsewhere. For example, the Scratby turbaries held by Norwich Cathedral Priory may have been in what is now Hemsby's or Martham's share of Ormesby Broad. Despite these and other uncertainties concerning the location of individual turbaries, some of these early records are very specific. For example, a reference in 1209

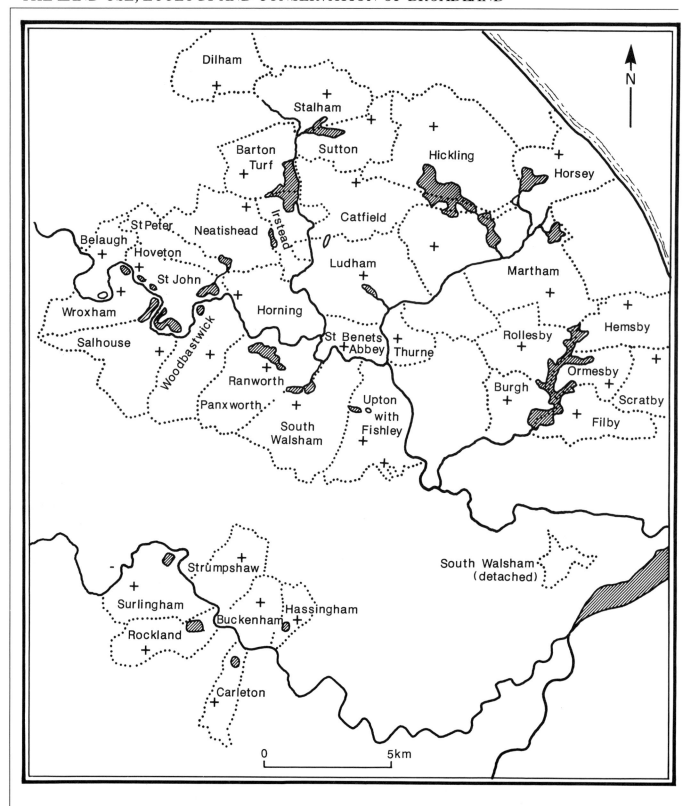

Map 4.3 The relationship between parish boundaries and broads in the Bure and Yare valleys. It will be seen that virtually every parish has all or part of a broad located within it, an indication that the peat pits were, whenever possible, located in such a way that people from several adjoining parishes had access to them. It is likely that each parish pit was originally separated from its neighbours by 'baulks' of unworked peat. Dilham originally had its own workings, but the broad which resulted when these were later flooded, became extinct during the last century.

Source: Smith (1960)

to 'Alderfen Pyttes' indicates, not only that peat digging was taking place, but that this was at the site now occupied by the broad of that name. Similarly, the sale of tree trunks from the turbary in the 'South Fen' at Martham in 1320–21 suggests that the cutting of turf there had reached down to the brushwood peat. Since the only fens lying to the south of Martham village are at the northern end of Ormesby Broad, it seems probable that the turbary in question now lies under the waters of this site.

Overall, the impression gained by Smith from the records he examined was that unlike the Fens, where superficial cutting on a large scale was accompanied by the alternate use of the same land as pasture, special, well-defined areas were set aside in Broadland for peat digging. Symptomatic of the importance of these turbaries to the local economy is the way the boundaries between different parishes are aligned so that their inhabitants had aceess to what is now a broad. Ormesby, Rollesby and Filby broads (Map 4.3) and Fritton Lake (Map 4.4) are particularly good examples of how turbaries were shared out amongst several adjoining parishes.

When, in 1960, it became generally known that Lambert and her co-workers believed the broads to be flooded medieval peat diggings, there was widespread incredulity, not least because of the huge size of these allegedly hand-dug excavations. On the basis that they originally had a total surface area of some 2611 acres (1057 ha), and had a mean depth of eight feet (2.4 m), Smith himself calculated that some 900 million cubic feet (25.5 million cu. m) of peat must have been removed. Many people found it difficult to believe that such an enormous quantity could have been needed, quite apart from the technical difficulties inherent in extracting it.

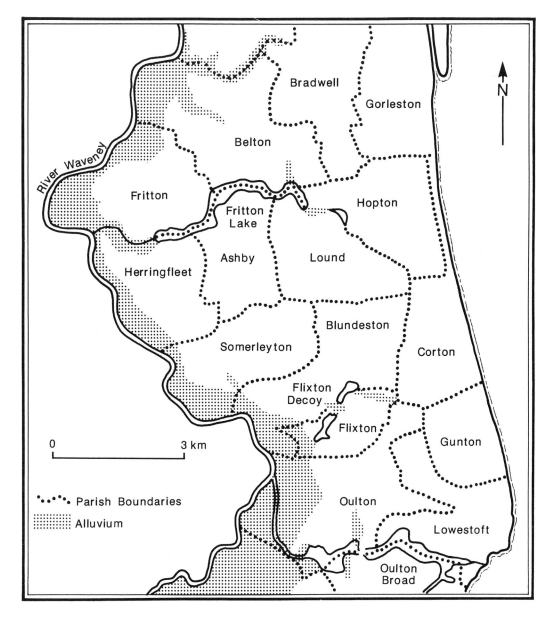

Map 4.4

The relationship between parish boundaries and broads in the Waveney valley. The peat pits which subsequently became flooded to form what is now one of the deepest broads, Fritton Lake, seem to have been shared out amongst no fewer than six parishes, whilst the workings now occupied by Flixton Decoy were probably created by persons living in Blundeston and Flixton.

Source: Smith (1960)

However, as Lambert, Jennings and Smith (1965) observed, there was probably a substantial demand for peat for fuel in medieval East Norfolk, in view of the fact that most of the forest which formerly covered the area had already been cleared by the time of the Domesday survey. By then, Norfolk and Suffolk were the most densely populated counties of England, whilst the Flegg and Happing Hundreds, in which the deepest broads – the Ormesby-Rollesby-Filby group – are to be found, were the most heavily settled parts of these counties. The demand for turf in these Hundreds would have been heavy and long sustained, as tax returns show that their population and wealth were still well above the average during the fourteenth century.

A considerable amount of turf would have been used by local people, but it was also exported to neighbouring towns. Particularly large quantities would have been required by Norwich, which between the eleventh and fourteenth centuries was one of the largest cities in the country, and by Yarmouth, whose tax assessment for 1334 was comparable to that of Norwich.

Lists of tolls levied in the fourteenth century include payments for consignments of turves delivered to these settlements by road and by water. Norwich Cathedral Priory used turf on a large scale, particularly in the kitchens, where as many as 400 000 turves were burnt each year during this period.

Documents examined by Smith confirm that some settlements were producing far more turf than their inhabitants would have needed for their own use. At South Walsham, for example, a series of account rolls of the second half of the thirteenth century reveal that the average annual sale of 200 000 turves a year yielded the Manor an income of £7 per year, whilst in one year in the fourteenth century the turbaries at Hoveton which belonged to the Abbott of St. Benet's produced 260 000 turves.

The revenue obtainable from the local turbaries was of very considerable importance to the local economy. For instance, turf sales generated a much larger income for the manor of South Walsham during the late thirteenth century than did sales of livestock, and in some years were worth more than the grain harvest.

In a few places, the amount paid in tithes on turf production is known. At Hemsby, for example, the tithes were worth an average of 15 shillings* a year in the late thirteenth and early fourteenth centuries, with a maximum of 23 shillings in 1294–5. Prices prevailing during this period were 1 shilling per 1000 turves, and on the assumption that the tithe represented a tenth of value of the crop, Smith calculated that about 150 000 turves were produced each year. Similar calculations suggest that the annual output at Oulton was as much as twice this during the same period.

According to Carrodus (1949) turves cut near Horning during the nineteenth century were 3 inches square, and some 2 to 3 feet long, and from this, and the dimensions of the peats being cut in the 1950s in Wigtownshire (*c.* 3½ × 2½ × 30 inches) Smith concluded that a turf in medieval Broadland probably contained about one quarter of a cubic foot (7084 cc) of peat. Using this figure he estimated that at Hemsby, an acre of fen would have been excavated to a depth of 3 m in 12 years, at the rate represented by the tithe levied on turf production at the end of the thirteenth and early fourteenth centuries. At Martham, a similar task would have occupied 16 years, whilst at South Walsham, the number of turves sold from the manor alone, would have created a 3 m deep excavation, covering an acre, in 8 to 9 years.

The recorded Domesday population of Broadland was 1215, and according to Smith, this can be regarded as an approximation to the number of families living in the area. The numbers increased substantially to the end of the thirteenth century, but fell rapidly between 1348 and 1377. On this basis, Smith estimated, probably conservatively, that some 1400 families lived in Broadland during medieval times. Assuming an average depth of 2 m for Hickling Broad and Horsey Mere, and 3 m for the remainder, and that each household needed 8000 turves per year, Smith concluded that all the broads could have been dug over a period of about 350 years.

Given the assumptions which Smith had to make when arriving at this estimate, it needs to be viewed with considerable discretion, especially as there is considerable doubt whether the becket commonly used in Broadland (see Plate XI) would have been

---

* Before decimal currency the main English coinage below a pound sterling consisted of the shilling (s) and the penny (d). Twenty shillings made a pound; twelve pennies a shilling. Methods of writing small sums varied, e.g., three shillings and four pence could be written as 3s 4d or 3/4. There are 100p in a pound, and thus the sum of 15 shillings (written as 15/-) was equivalent to 75p in decimal currency.

capable of yielding a turf two to three feet in length (see page 196). On the other hand, Smith based his estimate on the assumption that all the peat excavated from the broads was used by people living in the region. But in fact, as we have seen, very large quantities of peat were exported to Norwich and other neighbouring towns. Moreover, turf was probably used, not only as a domestic fuel, but in the making of salt, large quantities of which were needed annually because of the difficulties inherent in over-wintering live-stock in medieval times, and the consequent need to preserve meat. As Lambert, Jennings and Smith (1965) point out:

> . . . Domesday reveals a remarkable concentration of salt-pans in East Norfolk along the coast, in the lower valleys of the Bure and Yare and Waveney, and in the neighbourhood of what are now Ormesby-Rollesby-Filby Broads. Even though the salt industry yielded prime place to that of Lincolnshire in the later Middle Ages, salt-boiling must have used fuel on a large scale, and the only fuel available in large quantities was the turf of the Broadland valleys. Turf was preferred for the evaporation of salt in the medieval Low Countries, and in Lincolnshire the produce of some turbaries was reserved for use in the salt-pans, so that although there is no direct evidence of the use of peat in east Norfolk, there is a strong presumption that it was the fuel most used.

At first, the peat would have been dug from the fens in strips, just as it is today from the blanket bogs of Ireland and Scotland (see Plate 6); afterwards the turves would have been stacked above the excavation to dry, before being barrowed away. Plenty of evidence that peat was obtained in this way in Broadland was uncovered by Smith (1960). He notes, for example, that the tenants of the manor of Burgh were required in 1328 to dig in the turbaries for 14 days, or pay 14 pence in lieu, and that in 1328, one Henry Day, was paid two shillings and fourpence for digging peat for seven days at Hoveton St. John. Similarly the court roll of Moorhouse Manor in Hoveton includes a list of tenants who had been fined for digging turves in the lord's fen. Thomas Cullyng, for example, was fined two shillings for . . . "appropriating to himself the marsh of William atte Moor and he has dug and carried it away".

Although this and other references show that in some places peat continued to be dug by hand, at least up to the late fourteenth century, the workings elsewhere had by this time become flooded, making it necessary to obtain the peat by dredging rather than digging. Smith notes that the entries for 1320–1 and 1339–40 in the Martham account rolls distinguish between two separately costed activities – "the ferrying of fen (mora)" and "the making or scouring of turves from the fen". He also observed that the two processes are even more clearly defined in the account rolls for Bartonbury Hall (Barton Turf) which include the following entries:

Date	The making and sale of fen and turves	Price per last
1423	6s 8d for 8 lasts of fen taken and sold	10d
1431	12s 0d for 12 lasts of fen	12d
	13s 0d for 19½ lasts of fen	9d
1432	15 lasts, 2000 of fen taken with a dyday	8d
1433	4d for ½ last of fen taken with a dyday	8d
1434	2d for ¼ last of fen taken with a dyday	8d
1435	12s 5d for 18 lasts, 6500 of (turves)† fen taken with a dyday	
	and sold to the lord's men	8d
1438	4s 0d for 6 lasts of fen	8d
	2s 0d for 3½ lasts of fen, sufficient for the making of 4000 turves	
1439	4s 8d for 7 lasts of fen taken with a dyday	8d
1443	2s 0d for 3 lasts of fen taken with a dyday	8d
1444	6s 9d for 9 lasts of fen taken with a dyday	9d
1449	3s 8d for 5½ lasts of fen taken with a dyday	8d
	5s 0d for 5 lasts of fen taken with a (dyday)* laggyng in the several pond-water (sola) of the lord	12d
	6d for ½ last of fen taken similarly in the several pond-water of the lord at Chamberbyl	12d
1451	10s 0d for 12 lasts of fen taken on the several pond-water of the lord with laggyng	10d
	2s 3½d for 2½ lasts, 3000 of fen taken on the several pond-water of the lord, similarly with laggyng	10d
	20d for 2 lasts taken with laggyng on the pond-water of the lord	10d

† turves written, but crossed out and replaced by fen
* dyday written, but crossed out and replaced by laggyng
Source: Smith (1960)   *Note old coinage: s = shilling, d = penny*

Smith noted that a 'last' at Barton consisted of 10 000 pieces of fen, and cost between eight pence and one shilling to produce, whereas at Martham, Hemsby and South Walsham the same word had been used a century earlier to denote 10 000 turves, dug at a cost of between three shillings and four pence and nine shillings. He also drew attention to the entry for 1438 which shows that 3½ lasts of fen from the Barton workings were needed to make 4000 turves. But although he realized that a 'dyday' was the same as dydle, a long-handled scoop used until quite recently to remove mud and vegetation from Broadland's waterways, the full implication of the references to this tool in the literature did not become apparent until a Dutch colleague of his, Mr. J. Daams, pointed out that peat had originally been obtained for fuel in Holland by digging (*delven*) shallow excavations in the fens, but that in about 1500 his countrymen had started to dredge peat (*slagturven* or *moeren*) in the neighbourhood of the R. Vecht near Hilversum and elsewhere. This was done from a flat-bottomed barge or punt, using a long-handled tool (*baggerbeugel*) virtually identical to the dydle used in Broadland. Smith (1966) explains:

> The men who dredged the peat, or *trekkers*, also used straps around the waist, and attached to the *baggerbeugel*, in order to exert more force upon it. The peat was then brought to the balk, or *legakker*, on which a thick layer of reeds was spread. The peat was then raked, mixed with water and 'mashed' with an iron claw to form a homogeneous mass. This was then spread to a depth of 40 centimetres and allowed to drain. The peat was then pressed by means of wooden boards attached to the men's feet. After repeated treadings the surface of the compressed peat is scored, so that at a later stage during the drying process the peat shrinks and tends to crack along these lines. The turves were then cut with a long and sharp spade. Methods of this kind were still being used in 1930, and Mr. Daams has written that as a boy he sometimes went treading the peat with small boards tied to his feet. After drying the turves were then ready for loose stacking in piles to dry completely before being stored in airy, thatched wooden barns.

It seems highly likely that this method of winning peat (which is admirably interpreted in the Weerribben Nature Reserve Centre in North-west Overijssel) was practised in Broadland once the diggings had become flooded, and where there was a continuing demand for good quality fuel. However, it would have been a more laborious technique than direct digging, and in the deeper sites would only have been practicable around the margins of the flooded workings, and along the baulks left between them. The account rolls for Norwich Cathedral Priory show that the cost per 1000 turves from the Hemsby turbary (which was located at the north-eastern corner of Ormesby Broad) was about four shillings and four pence between 1294 and 1300, but increased to eight shillings and three pence in 1305–6, and to ten shillings and two pence in 1312–3, and Smith believes that this may have been due to the flooding of these workings at the turn of the century, and the consequent need to obtain peat by dredging, rather than digging.

In shallower sites, such as Barton Broad, peat could have been dredged from the floor, as well as the margins of the workings, but even here it would have been a laborious and time-consuming process. It is not known whether peat-dredging persisted into the sixteenth century, nor whether it finally succumbed as a result of the growing competition from other fuels, such as coal [known in Norwich in 1297 (Smith, 1960)] or faggots, or because of a shift back to the digging of peat, but from shallow excavations in the fens, rather than from the deeper pits which until the thirteenth century it had been customary to rely upon. What is certain is that most, if not all the old turbaries were flooded by the fifteenth century. Far more documents have survived from this period than from the fourteenth century, but despite this, there are very few references to turbaries in them. Furthermore, it is during the fifteenth century that places where turf diggings are known to have existed in the past begin to be referred to as 'water and

The type of peat-cutting tool traditionally used in Broadland (right), compared with the corresponding implements employed in Eire (centre) and the Shetland Islands (left).

Plate XI

The plain handles of the Irish and Shetland tools, and the presence on each of a 'step' to allow foot pressure to be used, give them a very different appearance to the Broadland implement. The Irish 'slane' was purchased in a Dublin ironmongers in 1970, but Shetland cutters can no longer be purchased new, this despite the large quantities of peat still being harvested annually on these islands.

Photo: Peter Scott

marsh', 'flasshes', or fisheries. At South Walsham, for example, Lambert, Jennings and Smith (1965) note that:

> . . . the first suggestion of the existence of a broad comes in 1315, by which time the turbaries had declined in value considerably from their heyday in the third quarter of the thirteenth century. By the end of the fourteenth century, turf production had ceased entirely, the reed-beds of the abbot of St. Benet's in South Walsham could not be cut because they were flooded with water, and the 'Flasshes' had appeared in a place which must represent roughly the south-east corner of South Walsham Broad.

Similarly, Smith (1960) points out that:

> . . . the St. Benet's turbaries in Irstead, Barton and Neatishead, mentioned together in a lease of the late thirteenth century, are represented in a lease of the sixteenth century by the fisheries of Burntfen, Irstead Fen and Barton Fen, which were worth 39s. 8d together with the fishery next to Wroxham Bridge and the eelset on the River Thurne. In thirteenth century records both these last fisheries are mentioned, but there is no sign of the first three. Again, one is left to presume that the valuable sixteenth century fisheries represented waters that covered the turbaries of the thirteenth.

Smith also notes that . . . "Divers parcells of Turffs and Watergrounds lying between Northern Bridge and Panxworth Bridge, abutting upon Broden" (Ranworth Little Broad) are referred to in a field book of 1566 relating to South Walsham, whilst 'Surlingham Broads' are mentioned in a lease of 1608. It was about this time that Simon Tobys paid 12d rent for three acres of fishing in 'Barton Broads'.

Saxton marked Fritton Lake and Ormesby-Rollesby-Filby Broads on his map of 1574, and Lambert, Jennings and Smith (1965) observe that a plan of Lothingland shows that Oulton Broad, Fritton Lake and Flixton Lake not only existed in 1584, but that they had outlines very similar to those of today.

Although it seems fairly certain from this and other evidence that most, if not all the broads were in existence by the beginning of the fifteenth century, and in many cases considerably earlier, Smith was unable to determine when peat digging commenced. He did, however, draw attention to several useful pointers. For example, the paucity of archaeological finds dating from the Anglo-Saxon period suggests that Broadland had a relatively sparse population at this time; Flegg, in particular, seems to have been largely uninhabited. But with the arrival of the Danes, initially in the form of spasmodic invasions, and in 865 AD with the first permanent settlement, the situation changed dramatically. Judging by the number of place names in the region with a Danish ending (see Map 4.5) and in particular the concentration of villages with the suffix 'by' in Flegg, Broadland was densely settled by these people, and by Domesday the size of its population and its relative wealth had greatly increased. This would have resulted in more and more of the land bordering the valleys being cleared of its forest cover, so that it could be brought into agricultural use, and also created a demand for peat as an alternative fuel to wood, both for domestic purposes, and for the making of salt. It cannot be a coincidence that the fens in Flegg, the wealthiest and most densely populated parts of the region in medieval times, have been almost totally cut away, and that their place has been taken by some of the largest and deepest broads.

In the absence of hard factual evidence, it is only possible to speculate as to who first started to dig peat in Broadland. The practice may, of course, have been initiated by the local people in response to their need for fuel. However, it seems much more likely to have been introduced by the Danish settlers, who would have been thoroughly conversant with the custom in their native land; indeed there is ample evidence that peat has been cut in Denmark since 500 BC (Kristiansen, *in litt.*).

One of the main problems which had to be faced by Lambert and her colleagues when they were developing what seemed in the late 1950s a novel, and potentially very contentious hypothesis, was that water levels in the valleys today would make it difficult, if not impossible, to excavate peat by hand to a depth of three metres or more below the fen surface. They therefore sought evidence that the water-table in the valleys was lower at the time the broads were being dug, probably between about 900 and 1350 AD, than it is today. Since water levels in the rivers are closely related both then and now, to those of the sea, Charles Green began an investigation of the height in relation to Ordnance Datum (OD) at which various artifacts at and near Great Yarmouth had been found. These included the buried hulks of two ships, a slipway, the foundations of the town wall and other buildings, a possible Anglo-Saxon cemetery at Runham Vauxhall, and an

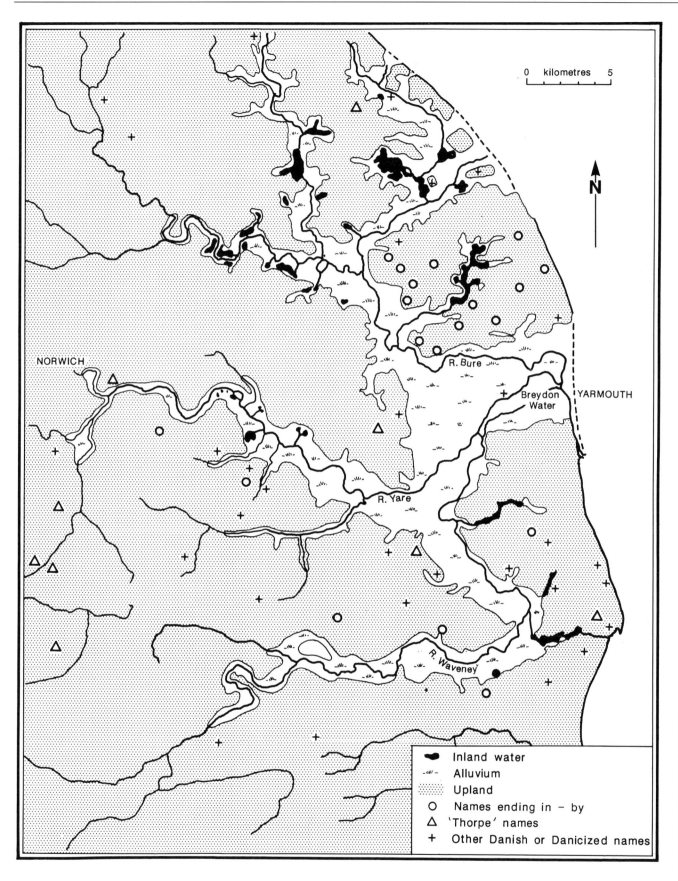

Danish settlements in Broadland and neighbouring parts of East Norfolk. The concentration of place names ending in 'by' on the 'island' of Flegg (e.g. Filby, Mautby and Clippesby) is very striking, and strongly suggests that this area was only lightly settled prior to the arrival of the Danes. 'Thorpe' (which, like the ending 'by', means a small settlement in Danish) is also frequent, either on its own (e.g. Thorpe St. Andrew), or as a suffix (e.g. Calthorpe). Hickling and Horning are examples of Danicized names, whilst those with a suffix 'ton' (e.g. Somerleyton) are hybrids.

Map 4.5

Source: Green and Hutchinson (1960)

eleven century occupation surface at Ashtree Farm, about a mile west of the borough council boundary. Taken together these suggested that the land level relative to the sea was between 0.8 and 1.5 m higher in early medieval times than it is today. This figure corresponds fairly well with the levels deduced at other sites in Britain, and with the estimate, based on work by Valentin (1953) elsewhere in East Anglia, that submergence at Great Yarmouth has occurred at a mean rate of about 1.6 mm a year during the past seven centuries or so.

Some confirmation of the rate at which relative land and sea levels have altered during the past two centuries was obtained during the examination of a mid-seventeenth century well at Great Yarmouth. When constructed this must have drawn its supply from the layer of fresh water, now about 0.3 m deep, which floats on top of the saline groundwater underlying the spit. The fact that the paved base of this well now lies some 0.6 m below the surface of the saline water strongly suggests that the relative land level has risen by slightly more than this during the past 200 years or so*.

A very different conclusion was reached about the past levels of land and sea as a result of investigations carried out in 1954, during the construction of a system of culverts for conveying coolant water to and from the South Denes power station at Yarmouth (Green & Hutchinson, 1960 & 1965). Of particular significance was the discovery of numerous shells of the acorn barnacle *Semibalanus balanoides* (formerly known as *Balanus balanoides*), attached to stones and thirteenth century pottery fragments lying on top of what was thought to have once been part of a beach. This took the form of a 6 to 7 foot (*c.* 2 m) deep hollow, some 200 feet (60 m) wide, and about 1740 feet (530 m) long, similar to the 'lows' often to be seen today in the intertidal zone of sandy beaches in East Norfolk. Much of the surface of this barnacle-strewn low lay about 4 m below OD, but at one end it descended to − 5.3 m OD. On the assumption that the tidal range in the thirteenth century was about the same as it is now, Green and Hutchinson argued that since this species of barnacle never settles below the level of mean low water of spring tides, which today is 0.95 m below OD, the sea level, relative to that of the land, must have been 4.35 m lower in the thirteenth century than it is now.

Above the barnacle-covered stones and pottery, and filling the low on which the latter had been deposited, was a layer of silty sand, whose surface lay 3 m or more below OD. Within this, there were numerous pottery fragments, including those of a decorated ware made in Western France in the latter part of the thirteenth century. As none of the shards was waterworn, it was claimed that the silt in which they were embedded must have been deposited during this period, probably during or just after the great flood of 1287.

Lying on the surface of the silt was a layer of mussel shells (*Mytilus edulis*), scattered amongst which were the remains of its principal predator, the dog whelk (*Nucella lapillus*). Unlike mussels, which often occur sublittorally, as well as on the shore, dog whelks are exclusively intertidal. Hence their presence did, according to Green and Hutchinson, support their assertion that the silt layer was in the intertidal zone at the end of the thirteenth century. Given that its surface lies 3 m or more below OD, and that the present level of high water mark of ordinary spring tides is 0.95 m above OD, they concluded that . . . "a change in relative land and sea level of at least 13 ft (3.95 m) has taken place" (Green & Hutchinson, 1965). If this claim is correct, it would imply that the relative sea level has risen during the past 700 years at a mean rate of about 0.57 cm per year. This is over three and a half times the normally accepted figure, and must therefore be viewed with great circumspection. Akeroyd (1972) in particular, has warned against . . . "the pitfalls involved in a too ready and uncritical acceptance of the evidence for apparent changes in relative land and sea level which has been derived from the archaeological and historical remains around the coasts of Southern Britain".

Green and Hutchinson's claims can, in fact, be questioned on several grounds. Firstly, were the barnacle shells correctly identified as those of *B. balanoides*, rather than one of the closely related species, such as *B. crenatus* which occur in the sublittoral,

---

* Much attention has recently been focused on the changes in relative land-sea levels which have taken place during the past century or so as a consequence of their relevance to 'Global Warming'. According to Boorman *et al.* (1989), the consensus of opinion is that the mean sea level has risen by some 10 to 15 cm over the past 100 years as a result of eustasis, and that South-East England is currently sinking relative to the sea by some 3 mm per year as a consequence of isostatic adjustment. But data summarized by Shennan (1989) suggests that the latter figure is a substantial over-estimate, and that the current rate of isostatic subsidence in Broadland lies between 0.7 and 2 mm per year.

rather than the intertidal zone? In this event, of course, it would not be possible to use the colony as evidence for a change in land and sea levels. In fact, the original identification was made by no less an authority than the late Ted Ellis and, somewhat unnecessarily in the circumstances, it has subsequently been verified by the author, who has inspected material taken from the culvert excavations and preserved in the Castle Museum, Norwich.

Second, did the barnacles settle on the stones and pottery fragments after these had been deposited in the place where they were discovered, or did colonization take place elsewhere, perhaps further up the beach? In this event, the stones and shards with their attached barnacles could have subsequently been washed away, and re-deposited in the sublittoral zone, thus giving a false impression of the changes which have occurred in relative land and sea levels during the past 7 centuries. Green and Hutchinson themselves were convinced that the colony had formed *in situ*, in particular: . . . "the larger pebbles carrying the shells are not scattered throughout the layer, as would have been the case if they had been derived from a colony elsewhere".

In the early 1980s work commenced on Yarmouth's sewerage system, prior to the construction of a new sea outfall at Caister, and the resultant excavations have enabled archaeologists to examine fresh sections through the spit on which the town is built. According to Lambley (*in litt.*), a layer of large cobble flints, together with the shells of oysters (*Ostrea edulis*), whelks (*Buccinum undatum*) and a few cockles (*Cerastoderma edule*) was found at a depth of 5.5 to 6.0 m below OD in a shaft sunk in 1981 near the Haven Bridge. Above and below the flint and shell horizon were pottery fragments dating from the fifteenth and the thirteenth to the fourteenth centuries respectively, indicating that it was formed, almost certainly artificially, about a century later than the layers of barnacle-covered stones and mussels described by Green and Hutchinson. Many of the oyster shells had been colonized by *Semibalanus balanoides*, and by the bryozoans *Conopeum reticulum*, *C. seurati* and *Electra crustulenta*, all three of which are listed by Ryland (1974) as being intertidal species. However, it was significant that four out of 36 shell-valves collected and examined subsequently by Lambley had been colonized by barnacles on both sides whilst six were encrusted by bryozoans on each surface. This shows that the shells must have shifted, either as a result of human interference, or through wave or tidal action, after they had been colonized on one side. Although this could have occurred whilst they were lying among the cobble flints, it is more likely that the shells were colonized elsewhere and subsequently re-deposited. Alternatively they could have been collected up and dumped amongst the cobbles to form a hardened surface for use in connection with the loading and unloading of vessels. Given these uncertainties the flint and shell layer cannot safely be used as evidence that the intertidal zone was 4 to 5 metres lower in relation to OD in the fourteenth century than it is today.

Until now, attention has tended to focus on the changes in relative land and sea levels which have occurred at Yarmouth during the past two millennia, rather than on what happened to water levels in the rivers, particularly between about 1100 and 1300, when peat digging was at its height. An insight into this has recently resulted from archaeological excavations carried out in 1979 and 1981 in the vicinity of Whitefriars, the site of the port of Norwich during the eleventh century (Ayers & Murphy, 1983; Ayers, in prep.). Ships seem to have been loaded and unloaded on a gently sloping beach here, rather than beside a jetty, and although the contemporary mean water level could not be precisely determined, it is unlikely that this was more than about 1 m below OD (Ayers, *in litt.*). A figure of between two and three metres below OD would have been expected had the sea level at Yarmouth been some 4 to 5 metres lower then than it is today.

It is worth recalling that the reason why Lambert and her colleagues decided to investigate the changes in relative land and sea levels which have occurred during the past millennium was their desire to prove that peat could have been dug in the valleys to a depth of 3 m or more below the present fen surface. As Lambert and Jennings (1960) put it:

> The sheer size and depth of the basins point either to more favourable conditions for the deep digging of peat at some time in the past than at the present day in the East Norfolk valleys, or else to the unlikely engineering in early historical times of effective methods for preventing continual flooding while the pits were being worked.

Two questions arise immediately. To what extent is the theory of the artificial origin of the broads dependent on the mean water-table being significantly lower than it is today, or put more simply, could peat have been dug to the observed depth if water levels were only, say, about a metre lower than they are today? Second, if mean water levels in the rivers were at one time as low as has been suggested, this would certainly have affected the ecology of the adjoining fens. Are such effects apparent in their stratigraphy? Taking the latter point first, if the mean levels of the rivers fell for any length of time, the peat deposits in the valleys would have tended to dry out and shrink. Simultaneously, there would have been changes in the fen flora, with birch and oak becoming commoner at the expense of moisture-loving species such as alder. The greater the drop in the mean water levels, the larger the hydraulic gradient across the valley alluvium, and the more the peat would have been subject to wastage. Similarly, the more prolonged the period when the peat at the surface was drying out, the greater the effect on the fen flora. The resultant changes in the stratigraphy would probably have been most obvious in the upper sections of the valleys, because further down-stream, the clay flanges deposited during the Second (Romano-British) Transgression, might have tended to form a water-proof barrier between the river and the springs and seepage lines on the valley margin, thus favouring the continuation of waterlogged conditions in the intervening fens.

Centuries later, when mean water levels in the valleys started to rise again, alder would gradually have regained its former prominence in the fen communities, and the dried out and wasted peat at the surface would have been overlaid by fresh deposits, formed under the waterlogged conditions. Now wasted peat layers do occur, both in the Bure and the Yare valleys. But these are always found at the top of the Upper Peat, and not as a sandwich within it. They must therefore have formed quite recently, rather than during the period, seven centuries or more ago, when the broads were being dug. Moreover the stratigraphy provides no evidence that the fen flora changed from a wet to a dry fascies and back again, although in the middle or lower sections of the valleys it often displays a well marked break, marking the period when the alder-woodland beside the rivers was suddenly overwhelmed by a rapidly rising water-table, following the breaching of the Yarmouth shingle spit at the onset of the Second Transgression (see page 16). In short, the stratigraphy of the valley alluvium does not support the assertion that mean water levels in the rivers fell after the end of the Second Transgression, until they were some 4 m lower in 1200 than they are today. Indeed, the relative levels of the clay laid down during the Second Transgression and the peat formed subsequently, suggests that since that event, the fen surface has never been more than a metre or so lower than it is now. In other words, the relationship between the mean water-table in the rivers and the level of the adjoining fens has varied little over the centuries, the rate of peat accrual keeping pace with the gradual rise in relative sea, and therefore river, levels which has occurred since the late thirteenth century. Some support for this comes from recent studies in the Ant valley, which have shown that since the Romano-British Transgression, about 1 m of peat has accumulated in those parts of Catfield Fen which appear never to have been exploited as a source of fuel (Wheeler & Giller, 1982). Although the rise in the water-table which has taken place subsequently is unlikely to have been at a uniform rate, there is no break in the peat stratigraphy as would have occurred had mean levels in the valleys been 3 to 4 m lower during the early medieval period than they are today.

With hindsight, it seems likely that Lambert and her co-workers laid too much stress on the difficulties involved in keeping the medieval peat pits free of water. This would have found its way into them as a result of lateral seepage, rainfall, and extra large floods, but some sort of baling technique would probably have proved effective, pro-vided the diggings were fairly small, and were kept isolated from their neighbours by baulks. Until about 50 years ago, most peat workings in the Somerset Levels were de-watered by 'ladle and gantry' (see Fig. 4A), and although there is no evidence that this device was ever used in Broadland, it would be surprising if a similar one was not developed to meet local needs.

Lambert and Jennings (1960) themselves admit that peat is not nearly so pervious to water as one might expect, particularly in its deeper, more compressed horizons; and provided the pits were not filled with water every time the adjoining fens were flooded – and this could have been prevented by building a low embankment around the workings – there seems no reason why it could not have been dug to a depth of 3 m or more, even if the water-table was quite near the surface. Nevertheless, the fact that the floor of

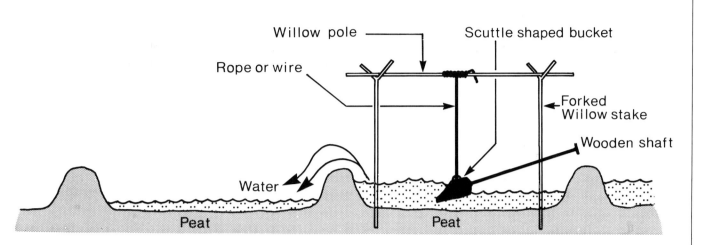

The 'ladle and gantry' method of removing water from a flooded peat pit, as formerly employed in the Somerset Levels. Anecdotal reports indicate that in the hands of an experienced operator, the bucket could be swung to and fro about 20 times a minute, thus removing about 2400 gallons an hour. As the water level in the peat pit fell, the rope suspending the bucket could be lengthened.

Fig. 4A

Source: Williams (in litt.)

many broads lies at a depth of 3 to 4 m, even though substantial thicknesses of good quality brushwood peat commonly lie below this level, suggests that the difficulty of keeping the workings free of water limited the depth to which they could be dug.

Lambert, Jennings and Smith (1965) have pointed out that . . . "the clay wedge (between the peat pits and the river) was still intact and formed an effective barrier at the time when the pits were made", and it is probably no coincidence that sites such as Sutton and Calthorpe Broads which are located upriver of the clay flanges laid down during the Second Transgression are much shallower than those further down-valley. The deepest pits of all, such as the Ormesby-Rollesby-Filby group are separated from the main rivers by thick layers of clay, and lie in side valleys whose tributary streams could have been diverted away from the peat workings fairly easily. Both here, and at other sites, water draining off the adjoining uplands could have been diverted around the peat pits with catchwater drains, similar in function to the land-spring dykes still used today in the Drained Marshland Area. Early maps suggest that such drains did indeed exist at Snape's Water and elsewhere (Smith, 1960), and although they can now seldom, if ever, be seen on the ground, this does not mean that they never existed, given the rapidity with which they would have been occluded by secondary peat, once they had fallen into disuse following the abandonment of the nearby workings.

Although measures were doubtless taken to prevent the peat pits becoming permanently flooded, periodic catastrophes, such as the great surge of 1287, would have profoundly affected the industry. In a review of the incidence of severe sea floods on the East Coast during the past two millennia, Lamb (1981) has concluded that there was a maximum occurrence of them in or about the thirteenth century, and that this coincided with the end of a run of several centuries, when the climate was of above average warmth. In the circumstances, it is possibly significant that the productivity of the South Walsham turbaries underwent a marked decline between 1285 and 1290 (Smith, 1960).

The risk of the pits becoming permanently flooded was probably increased, not only by periodic surges, but by a rise in the height of the water-table in the valleys, caused by greater fluvial flows as the weather conditions deteriorated. Lamb (1965) notes that there was a particularly high frequency of wet autumns between about 1300 and 1320. In addition, the relative sea level may, as Lambert and her co-workers have suggested, have started to rise from about 1200 onwards, as a consequence of continuing eustasis and renewed isostasis. Finally, Lamb (1981) has pointed to the fact that tide-generating forces combined to give maximum tidal ranges in the years 3500 BC, 1900 BC, 250 BC and 1433 AD, and it seems likely that the higher-than-average water levels which occurred in the latter year would have flooded any pits which were still being worked 'dry' at this time. Thereafter, peat was probably only obtainable in the region by dredging the deeper workings, or from relatively shallow excavations in the fens; these are described in Chapter 7.

Chapter 5
The Limnology of Broadland

Some general principles

The plant and animal ecology of a water body is heavily dependent on the chemistry of the water reaching it. Compounds of sodium, potassium, calcium, magnesium and iron are all required by plants, but are normally present in water in such large quantities that they rarely limit their growth and production. Nitrogen compounds, on the other hand are relatively scarce, but being soluble, are readily leached from the soil by rainfall, ultimately to find their way into a lake through its inflow streams. Some organisms, too, can fix atmospheric nitrogen, and thus contribute to the amount of nitrogen available to aquatic communities. In most water bodies, therefore, more nitrogen and other nutrients are present than are required by the plants growing in them, and their productivity is regulated by the amount of phosphorus available. This is the scarcest of the elements essential for plant growth, and may enter a lake in the form of inorganic ions (PO_4^{3-}, $H_2PO_4^-$ and HPO_4^{2-}) and organic compounds, and within the tissues of living and dead organisms. Together these sources constitute the 'total phosphorus load' reaching the site. This is conventionally measured in grams per square metre per year (g P $m^{-2}yr^{-1}$) or, as a function of the area of the site, in kilograms per hectare, whilst the size of a phosphorus source is usually given in kilograms per day or year. Only part of the total phosphorus load is immediately available to growing plants (as 'soluble reactive phosphorus'), but some of the remainder may become so through microbial activity.

For satisfactory growth, all aquatic plants, be they waterweeds* or algae, require nitrogen and phosphorus to be available in the proportion of about 10 to 1 by weight. But since nitrogen is normally present in most water bodies in quantities greater than this, plant growth in them is said to be 'phosphorus-limited'. Conversely, if, as sometimes happens, plant productivity is restricted by a shortage of phosphorus or silicon, the ecosystem is said to be phosphorus or silicon-limited.

Each year, some of the nutrients reaching a lake are carried away by its outflow stream (a process known for convenience as 'wash-out'); the rate of loss being dependent on the site's 'flushing rate', the number of times the water in it is completely replaced each year. The 'retention time' of a lake is therefore directly related to its flushing rate. The remaining nutrients reaching the lake are utilized by waterweeds or algae which, on

---

* 'Waterweed' is used here rather than 'aquatic macrophyte': both terms may be defined as water plants belonging to the Characeae (stoneworts), Bryophyta (mosses and liverworts), Pteridophyta (ferns and horsetails) and Spermatophyta (seed-bearing plants). The English and Latin names used in this and subsequent chapters in respect of the two latter groups are those employed by Clapham, Tutin & Moore (1989).

dying, fall to the bottom, carrying their nutrients with them. Each year, therefore, a proportion of the phosphorus reaching a lake becomes incorporated within its sediment. By taking samples of this from different levels, dating them, usually by radio-isotope techniques, and measuring the amount of phosphorus within each, it is possible to calculate how much phosphorus was incorporated within the sediment, and therefore to estimate the site's total phosphorus loading, at different periods in the past. Provided one knows how deep the lake was, and can estimate the flushing rate at the time, the mean total phosphorus concentration in the water (usually measured in micrograms of phosphorus per litre (μg P l^{-1}) can be calculated. This is a direct measure of the lake's fertility, and by determining how this has altered over the years, an insight into the limnological changes undergone by the lake during its history can be obtained. Additional information about its past ecology can be assembled by identifying and counting the siliceous walls (or more correctly the frustules) of diatoms preserved in datable levels in its sediment, and by examining the shells of molluscs and ostracods, sponge spicules and other animal remains contained in it.

During the past fifteen years, these techniques had been used to such effect by Brian Moss and his colleagues at the School of Environmental Sciences, University of East Anglia (UEA), that our understanding of what the broads were like in the past and the reasons why their ecology has altered so profoundly since the Second World War, has been transformed. So far, dated sediment cores from Barton, Alderfen, Upton, Hickling, Strumpshaw, Hoveton Great, Cockshoot, South Walsham and Belaugh Broads have been examined, but although the stratigraphy of several other sites is being investigated, the results are unlikely significantly to alter the team's principal findings.

Lead[210], the isotope mainly used to date the sediment cores taken from the broads, occurs naturally in the earth's crust as a radionuclide formed during the decay of Uranium[238]. Owing to its fairly short half-life (22.26 yrs), it can only be used to date sediments laid down during the past one hundred and fifty years or so; as with other radio-isotopes, the dates it provides become less accurate with the increasing age of the sediment. Some of the cores taken from Barton Broad were also dated by the Caesium[137] method. This isotope first appeared in the atmosphere in the early 1950s as a consequence of nuclear weapons testing, and although it provides a useful check on the rate of deposition during the last 35 years, it cannot be used on sediments older than this. Because of these technical limitations, the rate of sedimentation in a broad during the first few hundred years of its existence has to be estimated from the amount of material deposited in it between the assumed date of its initial flooding, usually taken as 1400 AD, and the earliest radio-isotope dating available.

In addition to this stratigraphical research, the present-day water chemistry and biology of the region have been subject to intensive study, special efforts having been made to work out the inter-relationships between waterweeds, epiphytic and planktonic algae, zooplankton, benthic invertebrates and fish, and the ways in which these communities are affected by increasing nutrient levels. Such research is difficult and time-consuming, not least because of the seasonal fluctuations which plankton undergoes, both in species composition and total biomass, and the consequent need to count numerous samples under the microscope. Limnological projects costing over £849 000 at 1990 prices have been carried out at UEA since 1974 (see Table 5a). Very large, but unquantified, sums have also been spent by the AWA during this period on in-house surveys and research into Broadland's water quality problems.

The total size of the phytoplankton crop is normally assessed by extracting samples with acetone and measuring the amount of chlorophyll in them spectrophotometrically, the results being expressed in micrograms of chlorophyll *a* per litre (μg Ch^a l^{-1}). The quantity of phytoplankton in the water is also sometimes estimated by measuring the turbidity of the latter with a secchi disc. But it needs to be borne in mind that the transparency of the water can also be reduced by dissolved organic material, and by sediment stirred up by passing motor craft, or fluvial floods. Conversely, phytoplankton does not have time to develop in a watercourse in which there is a moderate current. Such conditions prevail in all the Broadland rivers upstream of their navigable limits; indeed, anecdotal evidence suggests that as a result of enrichment, waterweeds are now growing more luxuriantly in the Bure, Yare and Waveney upstream of Horstead, Trowse and Ellingham Mill than in the past. Further downstream, both in these rivers and in the North Walsham and Dilham Canal, the flow rate is sufficiently reduced by

Table 5a   A summary of the main limnological research projects commissioned from the University of East Anglia between 1974 and 1987

Project title and ref. no. in Research Register	Outside bodies funding	Approx Cost (up to April '88)	Approx Cost at 1990 prices	Duration	Personnel Involved	Publications Resulting
Nutrient and sedimentation studies in Barton Broad (A/104)	AWA GYPHC Commonwealth Scholarship Fund	£300 £300 £3000	£13285	1974–1977	B. Moss and P.L. Osborne	Osborne & Moss (1977), Osborne (1978), Osborne (1981), Osborne & Phillips (1978), Moss (1980)
Physiological ecology of *Prymnesium parvum* in Broadland (A/302)	NERC	£16640	£61410	1974–1977	B. Moss, P.A. Holdway and R. Watson	Holdway, Watson & Moss (1978), Holdway (1979)
Causes of macrophyte decline in the Thurne Broads (D/001)	NCC and NERC studentship	£14120 £1000	£55800	1974–1977	G.L. Phillips, B. Moss and D. Eminson	Phillips (1976), Phillips, Eminson & Moss (1977), Eminson (1978), Eminson & Moss (1980), Eminson & Phillips (1978)
Experimental studies at Hickling and Brundall Broads (A/007 and A/008)	NCC	£67080	£169315	1976–1979	B. Moss, R.T. Leah and D.E. Forrest	Moss (1978), Moss & Leah (1982), Moss, Leah & Clough (1979), Moss, Leah and Forrest (1978), Leah, Moss & Forrest (1978), Leah, Moss & Forrest (1980)
Limnology of Hoveton Great Broad (A/105)	NCC (HF3/03/133)	£23079	£43540	1978–1981	M. Timms, B. Moss and B. Santer	Moss & Timms (1982), Timms & Moss (1984)
The limnology of the R. Bure and its broads (A/010)	DoE AWA	£60000 £30000	£151780	1979–1982	B. Moss, I. Booker, H. Balls K. Manson	Moss et al. (1982), Moss et al. (1984)
Fish – zooplankton studies in Alderfen Broad (E/101)	NERC and SERC studentships	£19500 £10000	£30280 £12375	1979–1983 1985–1988	C.R. Townsend, I.J. Winfield, M. Cryer, G. Peirson and M. Pernow	Winfield et al. (1983), Cryer et al. (1986), Peirson et al. (1984)
Regulatory mechanisms and their relevance to the management of the Norfolk broads (A/001)	Broads Authority Soap and Detergent Industry Assoc.	£48720 £30000	£111320	1982–1985	B. Moss, H. Balls and K. Irvine	Balls et al. (1985), Moss et al. (1985), Balls et al. (1989) Irvine et al. (1989)
Deterioration and restoration of freshwater ecosystems	Broads Authority Soap and Detergent Industry Assoc. NCC (HF3/03/338) AWA	£33000 £30000 £11000 £14000	£108930	1986–1989	B. Moss, K. Irvine and J. Stansfield	Moss et al. (1989) Stansfield et al (1989)
Phosphorus dynamics at the mud/water interface	NCC (HF3/03/350)	£15100	£18700	1987–1989	R. Jackson and G.L. Phillips	
Monitoring the changes the ecology and water chemistry of the Rivers Bure and Ant resulting from phosphorus reduction (contributions to AWA's costs)	Broads Authority NCC (HF3/03/341)	£28500 £30000	£72415	1986–1991	AWA staff	

tidal back-up to allow phytoplankton to develop. Moss *et al.* (1982), for instance, have pointed out that 2 or 3 generations of algae could develop during the *c.* 5.4 days which they estimate it takes for water in the R. Bure to flow between Coltishall and Thurne Mouth (assuming a total water volume of *c.* 1.4×10^6 cubic metres in the river between these points and a mean discharge rate of 3.0 cubic metres per second) and that a large standing crop of phytoplankton could therefore be expected to develop provided a plentiful supply of nutrients was available. The productivity of the phytoplankton is even greater in the broads themselves, because these have much longer retention times than the rivers.

Experience in other countries, subsequently confirmed in Broadland, has shown that the proportion of nutrients derived from 'point' sources such as sewage treatment works and livestock units, and background or 'diffuse' sources in the catchment, such as fertilizer residues in land drainage water, varies from river to river and site to site. A further complication is that the amounts of nutrients from different sources varies seasonally. For instance, run-off of nitrates from farm land is concentrated in the autumn and winter months, when it accounts for *c.* 90 per cent of the total load, whereas discharges of treated sewage, which are responsible for about 30 per cent of the mean annual nitrate load in most rivers, vary little from one month to another (House of Lords, 1989). Thus, to return a lake to the condition it was in, say 50 years ago, it is necessary closely to monitor its biological and water chemistry, so that a profit and loss account, or 'budget' can be compiled to show where the nutrients are coming from, and their subsequent fate. Special attention must be given to the inputs of phosphorus, as these are relatively easy to bring under control chemically, on account of the insolubility of most phosphorus compounds. Nitrogen removal, on the other hand, is difficult and very expensive because of the high solubility of nitrates. Moreover, even if the concentration of the latter reaching an ecologically important site could somehow be reduced to an acceptable level (and this would be quite impracticable in Broadland given the huge quantities of nitrogen emanating from the agricultural land in the catchments of the rivers), certain algae capable of 'fixing' atmospheric nitrogen would proliferate unless phosphorus levels were also controlled.

Iron, another plant nutrient, occurs naturally in such huge quantities (for example, Osborne and Moss (1977) calculated that Barton Broad receives 459.3 g Fe m^{-2} yr^{-1}, almost all of it from natural sources) that it would be quite impossible to limit the productivity of algal populations by removing this element from the water, whilst only two groups of algae are responsive to varying silicon levels.

In common with many other lakes and rivers in the 'developed' countries, Broadland's waterways receive much of their phosphorus from human excreta. Each of us generates between 1.3 and 1.5 g of the element each day (Jenkins & Lockett, 1943), to which must be added about 1.2 g P d^{-1} as a result of our use of detergents (Ministry of Technology, 1970). The performance of different treatment works varies greatly, but in some cases the phosphorus loading of the raw sewage may only be reduced by about 40 per cent before it is discharged to a watercourse, usually at a concentration of about 10000 µg l^{-1}. Additional contributions come from septic tank overflows, and phosphorus-rich discharges are also made by certain industrial concerns, and by many of the intensive livestock units which have been established in the river catchments since the Second World War. Since a pig and a cow respectively produce about 11 and 20 times as much phosphorus per day as a human being (Cooke, 1976), the slurry produced by such a unit is highly enriched; indeed, a dairy unit of 200 cows produces as much phosphorus as there is in the untreated sewage from a town of 4000 people. Consequently, if pig or cattle slurry is allowed to escape into a nearby ditch, either by accident or design, or if it is applied to land in excessive quantities, or under such conditions (for example, immediately after heavy rain) that it is washed into the field drains, the amount of phosphorus in the receiving watercourse will increase dramatically. If, as is often the case, this is a dyke in the Drained Marshland Area, the aquatic fauna and flora of this will be destroyed near the point of entry. However, by the time the polluted water reaches a stream or river, the sediment in the dyke system will have taken up much of the phosphorus, and its nutrient-enriching effect will be slight in comparison with that of sewage treatment works, whose effluents are normally discharged directly into principal watercourses. There are exceptions to this; for instance, the R. Waveney was badly polluted during the late 1970s and early 1980s by slurry discharged from piggeries in its catchment. In addition, it needs to be borne in mind that a pig produces about 500 kg of organic matter a year, and a cow four times as much, compared with the *c.* 43 kg generated each year by a human being (Cooke, 1976). As a result, the slurry from a livestock unit has a very high Biochemical Oxygen Demand (usually about 20000 mg l^{-1}) and Suspended Solid Content (*c.* 100000 mg l^{-1}). Even if fish and other forms of wildlife do not succumb as a consequence of a lack of oxygen in the water (EIFAC, 1973), they are likely to do so on account of the presence in it of nitrites, which are poisonous to invertebrates and fish (EIFAC, 1984) and ammonia. This too is toxic to fish when in the un-ionized state (NH_3) as distinct from the ionized form (NH_4), the proportion of the former being greater in alkaline water bodies such as those found in Broadland, than in rivers and lakes having a lower pH (EIFAC, 1970; Hasan & MacIntosh, 1986). To summarize: slurry is liable, not only to increase the nutrient levels in a watercourse, but cause oxygen depletion, the death of fish and plants, the impoverishment of the invertebrate fauna, and unpleasant smells (Richardson, 1976).

Phosphorus applied as a fertilizer to farm land 'locks' well to the mineral-based soils which predominate in the catchments of the Broadland rivers, and although the element tends to be leached if the land is waterlogged or peaty (Cooke, 1974), phosphatic fertilizers do not contribute much to the total phosphorus load in the rivers. Nevertheless, the phosphorus derived from septic tanks and fertilizers, plus small quantities eroded from the catchments (a process which has probably accelerated as a consequence of the steps taken since the Second World War to improve the drainage of the arable land therein) together make up a 'background' total phosphorus concentration. On the basis of the nutrient budgets which have been compiled for the rivers Bure, Ant and Thurne, and other data, it has been estimated by Moss (1983) that these background sources currently contribute about 50 µg P l^{-1} (range 32–72) and this is consistent with the estimates made for other fertile, mixed-agricultural catchments (Omernik, 1976).

Not all the phosphorus available for the growth of phytoplankton in the broads is derived immediately from external sources, some of it being generated internally by release from the sediments. Classic studies by Vollenweider (1969) and others have demonstrated that provided the surface layers of the sediment are maintained in an oxidized state, the great majority of the phosphorus reaching the latter remains chemically bonded to it, and thus unavailable to algae. However, if the sediment surface becomes temporarily anaerobic as a result of the deposition on it of large quantities of organic material (usually in the form of phytoplankton 'fall-out', or leaf-fall from a dense growth of waterweeds), soluble reactive phosphorus is liberated into the water column, and is quickly taken up by algae (see Fig. 5A.).

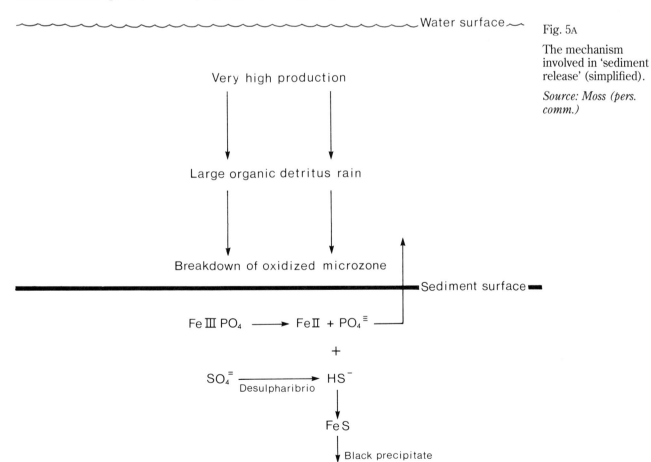

Fig. 5A

The mechanism involved in 'sediment release' (simplified).

Source: Moss (pers. comm.)

As will become apparent later in this Chapter, most of the broads have been receiving large quantities of phosphorus from external sources for 40 years or more, and since the majority of them have fairly long retention times, their sediment contains huge amounts of this element. In theory, this will remain *in situ*, provided the sediment surface remains in its normal oxidized state. Thus, if steps are taken to eliminate external phosphorus inputs, for instance by diverting water from the catchment so that it flows around the site, instead of through it, algal production will soon be reduced to such an extent that the fall-out of dead and dying material will not be sufficient to render the sediment surface anaerobic and trigger a release of phosphorus. In practice, things are rather different! It is rarely possible to reduce phosphorus inputs sufficiently to prevent occasional outbursts of algal growth, particularly in the spring, and when these phytoplankters die and fall to the bottom, sediment release is likely to occur for a time, so increasing the productivity of the site, and thus the chances that even more phosphorus will come out of the sediment a little later. In addition, evidence has begun to emerge during the past few years that phosphorus release can take place when the sediment surface of the broads is temporarily disturbed. This could result from the turbulence produced by powered craft, wave action (but in shallow water only), and the liberation of bubbles of methane from the mud, all of which could result in anoxic sediment from a few centimetres below the surface being brought into contact with the water column. In this event, phosphorus release would take place until the newly-exposed sediment was oxidized. Bioturbation (i.e. the disturbance produced by invertebrates such as midge larvae burrowing in the mud) may also be having the same effect.

If it is confirmed that sediment release occurs in the broads as a result of the disturbance of the mud surface, phosphorus recycling within a site could, in theory, continue for many years, even though the external supply to it had been drastically curtailed, or even eliminated altogether. Indeed, the only losses of phosphorus from the system would be in the form of 'wash-out' downstream, mainly of dead and dying plant and animal matter. The slower the flushing rate, and the greater the amount of phosphorus which had accumulated in the sediment, the longer re-cycling could occur. This is of profound importance in relation to the steps which will need to be taken to restore the broads to the condition they were in at the turn of the century, since it implies that unless some way can be found of preventing re-cycling, perhaps by reducing the amounts of phosphorus being released from the sediment at certain critical times of the year, it will be necessary, not only to reduce external inputs as much as possible, but to remove the phosphorus-rich layers of sediment from each site with a suction dredger. Although this has been done at several small broads during the past 15 years (see Chapter 13), the technique is very costly; in addition, it often proves difficult to find a suitable dumping ground for the dredged material. In the light of these circumstances, and in particular the uncertainties over the exact mechanisms by which phosphorus is released from the sediment, the NCC decided in 1987 to commission an in-depth investigation of the phenomenon (see page 145).

Since Broadland's principal rivers are fed by springs in the Chalk, and drain catchments in which Chalky Boulder Clay predominates, the water in them is very calcareous. The alkalinity of the Bure, for example, ranges between 3.5 and 4.5 milliequivalents per litre (meq l^{-1}), whilst the R. Yare has a mean alkalinity of about 5 meq l^{-1}, a figure well over five times as great as that typical of waters in the Lake District. The large inputs of calcium and other major ions ensure that the water is well buffered, and the pH consequently varies only slightly about its mean of about 7.8 – again a sharp contrast with the situation in the Lake District where the photosynthetic activity of populations of algae, small in comparison with those of Broadland, may induce the pH to rise to 10 or even 11. But the high alkalinity of the rivers and broads does lead to the deposition of marl. This results from the fact that when aquatic plants (including algae) are actively photosynthesizing in such water, the uptake of carbon dioxide causes the pH to increase temporarily to 8 or more during the late afternoon. In these circumstances, the solubility product of calcium carbonate (and also magnesium carbonate) is exceeded and marl is deposited. This gives the sediments laid down in the broads during the first 500 years or so of their existence a characteristic creamy hue, though this tends to be masked in the deposits formed more recently owing to the presence in them of blackish or dark brown sulphides and organic material as well as marl.

The sediment in the rivers and broads contains sufficient marl to have made it worthwhile in the nineteenth century to use it in the manufacture of cement. Dredgings from Oulton Broad and the lowermost reaches of the rivers were allowed to dry out, and then roasted at factories at Burgh Castle and Berney Arms to form cement clinker. This was then ground up by millstones powered in tandem with the wind-powered drainage mill at the latter site (Wailes, 1956).

The rivers and broads in their pristine (Phase I) state

When first formed, the broads would have been quite different in their appearance, and their ecology, from today. Phosphorus inputs in the form of sewage would have been relatively small since most people, both in the country and the towns, probably used earth closets; indeed, there is evidence (Campbell, 1983) that throughout most of the thirteenth century, and early fourteenth century, 'night soil' formed an important fertilizer on demesnes located within a 5-mile radius of Norwich, which at that time had a population of about 18 000. The lowermost sediments of Barton Broad contain about 0.5 mg of phosphorus per gram, equivalent to the retention in the sediment of 0.08 g of total phosphorus per square metre per year (Table 5b). Assuming that this represents

Table 5b   Past phosphorus budgets for Barton Broad.

Year	Retention of phosphorus in sediment $g\,P\,m^{-2}\,yr^{-1}$	Calculated total P loading $g\,P\,m^{-2}\,yr^{-1}$	Calculated $[m_w]$ $\mu g\,P\,l^{-1}$	Loading from sewage effluent $g\,P\,m^{-2}\,yr^{-1}$	Loading from land drainage $g\,P\,m^{-2}\,yr^{-1}$	Partial sewage $[m_w]$ $\mu g\,P\,l^{-1}$	Partial $[m_w]$ land drainage $\mu g\,P\,l^{-1}$
1800	.08	0.4	13.3	0	0.4	0	13.3
1900	.31	1.55	52				
1920	.43	2.15	72				
1940	.71	3.55	119				
1974			329*	2.15	1.40	72	47
1976		10.83*	361	8.6*	2.23*	287	74

* Measured by Osborne (1978)   *Source:* Moss (1980)

about 20 per cent of the phosphorus reaching the site, a retention rate similar to that encountered today, it can be calculated that prior to 1800, the broad had a total phosphorus loading of about 0.4 g m^{-2} yr $^{-1}$, and that the mean concentration of total phosphorus in the water was therefore only 13.3 µg l^{-1}, a level of fertility of one twenty-seventh of the mean of about 360 µg P l^{-1} recorded in this site in the mid-1970s. Data obtained from cores taken from Belaugh, Hoveton Great and Cockshoot Broads indicate that during the early nineteenth century, the mean total phosphorus levels in these sites, and therefore in the R. Bure, with which they are connected, were similar at this time to those of Barton Broad (Moss, pers. comm.).

Although the rivers would have carried moderate amounts of nitrogen, the high calcium carbonate content of the water would have ensured, not only that marl was deposited in the rivers and broads, but that such phosphorus, iron, manganese and other potential nutrients as were derived from the catchments, were converted to insoluble compounds, thus making them unavailable to algae. In their pristine state, therefore, the broads resembled the 'marl lakes' which occur today on chalk or limestone, or on fluvial-glacial deposits derived from these rocks, the best examples in Britain being Malham Tarn in North Yorkshire, and the Durness Lochs in the Highland Region of Scotland (Morgan & Britton, 1977). Stoneworts and low-growing waterweeds such as the Reddish Pondweed (*Potamogeton alpinus*) and the bladderwort, *Utricularia intermedia*, which favour relatively infertile water, but which, unlike algae, can take up the phosphorus they require from the sediment, would have predominated, whilst judging from the fossil diatoms recovered from cores, epiphytic and bottom-living algae were scarce, and phytoplankton virtually absent. The water would therefore have been crystal clear. But from the abundance of molluscan shells in the sediments laid down during the first few hundred years of their existence, it is apparent that the broads contained a considerable wealth of invertebrate life. Confirmation that the water was moderately productive biologically is afforded by references in the literature to the importance to the local economy of the region's fisheries, and the steps taken from the fifteenth century onwards to safeguard them (see page 449).

Comparatively little organic material would have been produced each year as a result of the decay of the low-growing waterweeds of Phase I and it is not, therefore, suprising that dated cores have shown that the mean sedimentation rate at Alderfen Broad prior to about 1854 was only *c.* 0.05 cm yr^{-1}. Until about 1800, the northern, southern and western parts of Barton Broad were filling up with sediment at a similar rate, and even less (0.008 to 0.023 cm yr^{-1}) was accumulating near the centre of this site. The mean deposition rate at Hickling Broad was 0.03 cm yr^{-1} up to the 1950s (Moss, 1978), and until the middle of the nineteenth century, only 0.07 cm was laid down in Belaugh Broad each year (Moss, pers. comm.).

The marl-rich sediments of Upton Broad, which until 1935-7 accumulated at a mean rate of 0.07 cm yr^{-1}, are highly unusual in that their upper 10 to 15 cm are stained green by a colonial blue-green alga, *Aphanothece stagnina*. This occurs, both in its normal free-living form, and in the faecal pellets of chironomid larvae. Sediments very similar to this have been recorded from Mud Lake, Florida, and Dr. J. Lund (*in litt.*) believed that they are a form of sapropel.

Unfortunately, none of the broads still possesses a true Phase I flora, though elements of this survive at Upton, Martham North and South, and Blackfleet Broads. Fairly heavy growths of charophytes (mainly *Chara hispida*, but with occasional plants of *C. aspera*, *C. contraria* and *C. globularia*), regularly occur at the three latter sites, while the continued presence in Martham Broad of *Nitellopsis obtusa* – a nationally rare stonewort now confined to the Upper Thurne broads – was confirmed by Mrs. J. A. Moore as recently as 1988. But all three sites also contain a number of nutrient-tolerant plants, notably Fennel-leaved Pondweed (*Potamogeton pectinatus*) and Canadian Pondweed (*Elodea canadensis*).

Upton Broad, with a mean total phosphorus concentration of 30 µg l^{-1}, is atypical, in

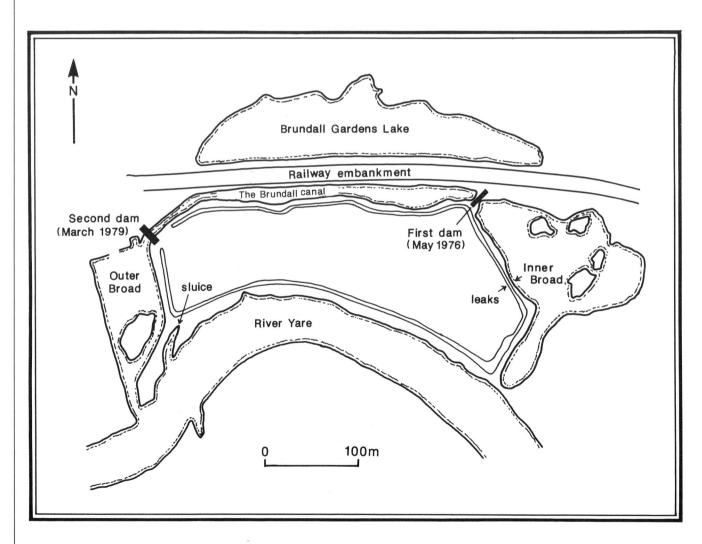

Map 5.1   The Brundall experimental site.

Source: Moss and Leah (1980)

that its flora is dominated by the Holly-leaved Naiad (*Najas marina*), another national rarity, which was not known in Britain until it was found in Hickling Broad and Heigham Sound in 1883 (Bennett, 1883 & 1884), and in Martham Broad in 1885 (Bennett, 1910). It was observed in Upton Broad by Dr Joyce Lambert in 1949, and was subsequently recorded in abundance in Barton and Black Horse Broads, and as a single plant in Alderfen Broad (Barry & Jermy, 1953). Although it may have been deliberately introduced into one or two of these localities, its appearance in Blackfleet Broad in 1977 – a site which had been subject to a thorough, but unsuccessful search for it 9 years previously – suggests that it is being transported by wildfowl from one part of the region to another.

Brundall Gardens Lake (see Map 5.1), with a mean total phosphorus concentration of 45.7 μg l^{-1}, and a nitrate nitrogen level of 1.08 mg l^{-1} (compared with *c.* 14 mg l^{-1} in the nearby River Yare) is almost as infertile as Upton Broad. Like the latter, it is hydrologically isolated from the main river system, but was excavated, not by medieval peat diggers, but between 1892 and 1908 during the creation of riverside pleasure gardens at Brundall. It receives water from a small catchment in which chalk-free sands and gravels predominate.

Mean total phosphorus concentrations in Martham North Broad were about 50 μg l^{-1} in the mid-1970s (Moss *et al.*, 1979), but have subsequently fallen to about 20 μg l^{-1} (Moss, pers. comm.). This is probably due to the precipitation of most of the phosphorus reaching the site as ferric phosphate, and can be related to the conversion of much of the adjoining grass marshland to arable in 1979, and a consequent increase in the amount of ochre (ferric hydroxide) being discharged into Somerton Dyke, just upstream of the Broad, by the West Somerton land drainage pump (see page 310). It will be interesting to see whether the reduced phosphorus concentrations in the Broad lead to a gradual increase in the abundance of stoneworts and Holly-leaved Naiad in it, and a corresponding reduction in the status of the nutrient-demanding components of its waterweed flora.

Phase II

The onset of the second phase in the ecological history of the rivers and broads was marked by a gradual rise in their nutrient loading, and their colonization by plants such as Horned Pondweed (*Zanichellia palustris*), Stiff-leaved Water-crowfoot (*Ranunculus circinatus*), Hornwort (*Ceratophyllum demersum*), Water Soldier (*Stratiotes aloides*), Greater Bladderwort (*Utricularia vulgaris*), Yellow Water-lily (*Nuphar lutea*), White Water-lily (*Nymphaea alba*), and in the Thurne broads particularly, the Spiked and Whorled Water-milfoils (*Myriophyllum spicatum* and *M. verticillatum*) and Fennel-leaved Pondweed. These nutrient-demanding species had a competitive advantage over the waterweeds of Phase I, since they were more robust. In addition, being taller, and therefore better able to reach up towards the light, they would have been less affected by the periphyton (epiphytic algae) which, stratigraphic studies show, began to grow on them as nutrient levels increased. At Hickling Broad, for example, the tall stems of *Myriophyllum* enabled it to withstand the growth of periphyton much more readily than could the low-growing *Najas* and *Chara*-dominated communities which had existed at this site previously (Phillips *et al.*, 1977).

The progressive enrichment of the rivers can, in part, be attributed to the increasing efficiency of farming methods. Symptomatic of the changing attitude towards the industry were the Enclosure Awards made from the 1790s onwards, and the reports written by William Marshall (1787), Arthur Young (1804) and others on the state of agriculture in the region. The Sheep-Corn Husbandry which had been practised during the late Middle Ages and sixteenth century over much of the land in the catchments of the rivers Bure, Ant, Thurne and Wensum was gradually superseded from the late seventeenth century onwards by new rotations, crops, methods of stock raising and land tenure (Allison, 1957). Moreover, many of the heathlands and common grazings in the Sheep-Corn region which had by long tradition been used as pasturage during the summer months, were limed, fertilized and brought under the plough. The conversion of these grasslands to arable would have greatly increased the rate at which nitrogen in the soil was mineralized, and thus augmented nitrate concentrations in the rivers. The changes brought about by ploughing were probably increased by liming, as this would have

Fig. 5B

The occurrence of epiphytic and planktonic diatoms in Barton Broad at various times between *c.* 1780 and 1975. Numbers are expressed as functions of the annual sedimentation rate of frustrules, and dates were obtained by Lead[210] and Caesium[137] methods.

Source: Phillips, Eminson and Moss (1977)

raised the pH of the soil, thus providing more favourable conditions for the microbial populations involved in nitrogen mineralization, than would have existed otherwise. Nitrogen, and to a lesser extent, phosphorus concentrations in the rivers would also have tended to increase as the drainage of Broadland's reclaimed marshland was improved, firstly by the replacement of windpumps by steam engines, and later, by the installation of diesel and electrically-powered machinery (see page 253).

Sediment cores show that the mean total phosphorus loading of Barton Broad increased from 1.55 gm^{-2} yr^{-1} in 1900, to 2.15 gm^{-2} yr^{-1} in 1920. From these figures it can be calculated that the mean total phosphorus concentration in the water increased from 52×72 µg P l^{-1} during this period (Table 5b). By analogy with Martham North and South Broads, which were of comparable fertility in the mid-1970s (Holdway *et al.,* 1978), it would seem that in the early years of the present century, Barton Broad possessed crystal clear water, with a luxuriant growth of Spiked Water-milfoil, Stiff-leaved Water-Crowfoot, Greater Bladderwort, White Water-lily, Hornwort and various pondweeds, and it is pleasing to find that all these species (plus Water Soldier, which does not occur in the Thurne broads as a result of this species' intolerance of brackish water – Driscoll, pers. comm.), were recorded by Pallis (1911b) in her description of the flora of the Ant valley broads.

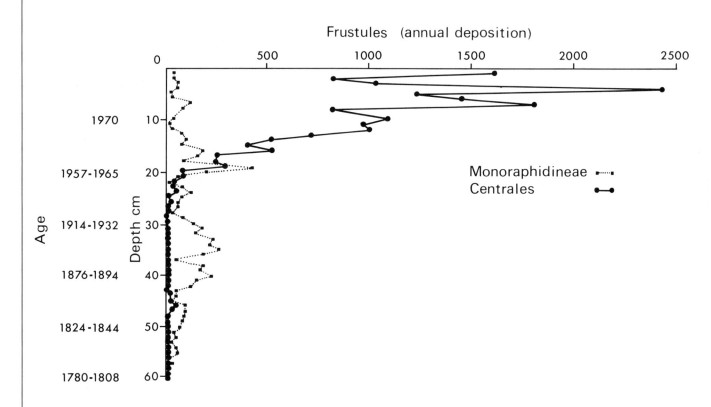

Sediment counts show that epiphytic diatoms became much commoner in Barton Broad between 1910 and 1950 (Fig. 5B), largely as a result of the increasing abundance of Monoraphidinean species, mainly *Cocconeis placentula* and *Achnanthes* sp., non-planktonic Fragilarians, and various Biraphidinean genera, such as *Cymbella* and *Gomphonema* which move freely, either over sediment surfaces, or epiphytic communities.

Nutrient enrichment began to affect the ecology of the waters of the Bure and Yare valleys at about the same time as the R. Ant and Barton Broad, but proceeded somewhat faster. There is evidence that the transition from Phase I to Phase II occurred in the Bure broads between 1850 and 1890 (Moss, pers. comm.), whilst in the Yare valley, algal remains, probably of *Vaucheria*, occur in sediment laid down in Strumpshaw Broad after about 1800, suggesting that its original, *Chara*-dominated, Phase I communities were beginning to be blanketed by filamentous algae by then (Fig. 5c). Monoraphidinean diatoms became much more numerous at about the same time, and there was also a more modest build-up in the numbers of other epiphytic diatoms, including various Biraphidineans and Fragilarians commonly associated with stable bottom deposits, submerged waterweeds and the bases of reeds. Evidence for a marked change in the ecology of this site in about 1912 comes from cores, which show that the greyish marl which was laid down early on abruptly gives way to a blackish-brown, sulphide-rich sediment at about this time. In contrast, the latter is absent from Hassingham Broad which was, with Buckenham Broad, according to OS maps, sluiced off from the river at some time between 1838 and 1908.

The relatively rapid enrichment of the R. Yare can be related to the increasing quantities of untreated sewage which Norwich was discharging to its tributary, the Wensum, in the early years of the nineteenth century. Although some of the phosphorus generated by the inhabitants of the city would doubtless have been retained in the sub-soil as a result of the use of earth closets or cess pits (the contents of which would have been dumped on the local midden), significant quantities would have been contained in the raw sewage which, until 1868, was discharged through a series of open gulleys ('cockies') directly into the Wensum. Since this river was being used as a source of water for Norwich (it is known to have served this function since the beginning of the nineteenth century – Mackley, 1984), there were periodic outbreaks of disease in the city, not least a serious cholera epidemic in 1830. Despite protests by the 'memorialists', a

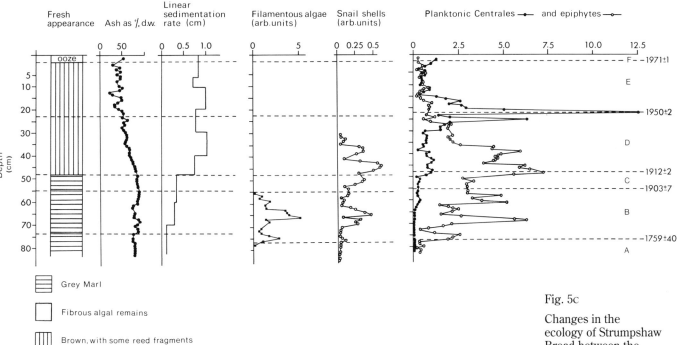

Fig. 5c

Changes in the ecology of Strumpshaw Broad between the mid-eighteenth century and the early 1970s, as revealed by sediment coring. Note in particular the increasing abundance of epiphytic algae between *c.* 1910 and 1950. Sedimentation rates rose rapidly from the turn of the century onwards, but will have undergone a dramatic decline, following the damming off of the Broad from the R. Yare in 1978.

Source: Moss (1979)

pressure group who argued that sewage should continue to be returned to the land within the city, an enquiry by the General Board of Health in 1850 led to the Corporation being served with an injunction restraining it from continuing to discharge untreated sewage to the river. Sir Joseph Bazalgette was engaged as a consultant and, by 1870, over 60 miles of main sewers had been built to his plans. Beam engines at Trowse were used to pump the sewage to Kirby Bedon where, with cartloads of cesspit contents collected in the city, it was discharged into an open channel, still to be seen today, leading to a newly established Sewage Farm at Whitlingham. Although some of the phosphorus reaching this would have been retained in the soil, the run-off from it would probably have been fairly nutrient-rich. In addition, so much groundwater found its way into the three miles of low-level sewers serving those parts of the city nearest the Wensum (Gorton & Davies, n.d.) that even though the Trowse pumps were worked for much of the time at about twice their designed capacity (stated to be 2½ million gallons per day (mg d^{-1}) – Norwich Corporation, 1963), discharges of diluted, but untreated, sewage had to made direct to the river at Trowse each time the flow reaching the pumps was augmented by rainwater run-off (EDP, 1909).

Attempts to cure the infiltration problem in *c.* 1880 proved unsuccessful and Bazalgette's low-level system was abandoned, and replaced with new sewers nearer the surface. Sewage was forced along these by Shone ejectors supplied with air by compressors installed at New Mills. Meantime, steps were taken to clear away the numerous middens which had hitherto been in use in the city (EDP, 1909).

The population of the city had risen to 104 000 by 1893, but only about a third of these were using the 4100 water closets then in use (Moss, 1979), many of the remainder continuing to have to make do with earth closets. Much of the nutrient load generated by the city would not therefore have found its way directly into the river. Nevertheless, by the early 1900s, about 1500 properties were being connected to the city's sewerage system each year, with the inevitable result that, as a contemporary account put it, the Sewage Farm . . . "sent it into the river in about the same condition as that in which it was received on the land" (EDP, 1909).

During 1908 and 1909, the city's sewerage system was extended, and a new pumping station (powered by gas instead of steam) built at Trowse, to convey the sewage through a 36-inch rising main to Travis tanks newly installed at the Sewage Farm. These allowed solids and detritus to settle out before the sewage was distributed around the latter, but the volume of nutrient-rich liquor released into the river continued to increase.

This profoundly affected the ecology, both of the river itself, and the broads connected with it. A core taken from Strumpshaw Broad, *c.* 9 km downstream of Whitlingham, shows that epiphytic diatoms were becoming increasingly numerous during this period. Moreover, Pallis (1911b) notes that Fennel-leaved Pondweed, Horned Pondweed, Whorled Water-milfoil, Hornwort and the alga *Enteromorpha intestinalis* – all species characteristic of a Phase II flora – were abundant in the Yare valley broads at this time, whereas stoneworts (which are typical of Phase I) were rare.

Further improvements were made to the sewage disposal system in 1914, but despite these, the river was grossly polluted in 1923, with reports of 'evil smells', and of severe de-oxygenation (20 per cent saturation) at Brundall (Moss, 1979). This can be attributed to the increasing population of the city, the continuing replacement of privies by flush toilets, and the resultant inability of the pumps at Trowse to cope with the flows reaching the Works every time the sewage was augmented by rain-water. The effects of this on the stratigraphy of Strumpshaw Broad were particularly marked shortly before, during and immediately after the Second World War (see Fig. 5C), doubtless because by then the Works were both obsolete, and hopelessly overloaded.

By examining the literature relating to the past and present distribution of aquatic plants in the broads, Jackson (1978 & 1981) has been able to date the change-over from Phase I to Phase II in other parts of the region. In the Ant valley broads, for instance, charophytes and species such as *Potamogeton alpinus*, *Utricularia intermedia* and *U. minor* which are characteristic of fairly infertile water, were recorded as present up to the beginning of the present century, but not after. *P. alpinus* also occurred in the Bure broads up to the same period, and although no written proof could be found that stoneworts once occurred here, their remains are abundant in sediments laid down prior to about 1900 in Wroxham and Hoveton Great Broads and other sites (Moss, pers. comm.). The phosphorus enrichment of the Ant and Bure during the mid-nineteenth century is, like that of the Yare, attributable to an increase in the number of people living in their catchments and the steps taken to provide main sewerage in some of the larger settlements, notably North Walsham and Aylsham. According to Moss (pers. comm.), the population of the latter remained roughly constant between 1086 and 1791 (varying between 810 in 1691 and 1320 in 1721), but had more than doubled to 2741 by 1851. An outbreak of cholera in the 1830s suggests that crude sewage was, as at Norwich, being discharged direct to the river, and in 1851, a committee set up by the Church authorities to report on the town's drainage system found . . . "a highly unsatisfactory state of affairs with numerous uncovered cesspools, open drains, and dung heaps in some of the most densely populated parts". The *Rivers Pollution Act* 1876, made it an offence to discharge untreated sewage into a watercourse, and arrangements were therefore made to collect it up and dump it on land to the south-east of the town; appropriately enough, this area is marked on OS maps as 'The Mucklands'. A sewage treatment works was built on the site in the early 1950s.

Jackson's literature search, and Moss' stratigraphical findings both suggest that a

Phase I, stonewort-dominated flora persisted longer in the Thurne broads, than in sites directly linked with the rivers Bure, Ant and Yare. Hickling Broad, in particular, was renowned for its charophytes, and by the turn of the century, *Nitellopsis obtusa*, plus ten different species of *Chara*, and a hybrid, had been recorded (Moore & Greene, 1983). Six of these were still present in 1960 (Phillips, 1963), but by then were growing in association with Greater Bladderwort, Fennel-leaved Pondweed, Spiked Water-milfoil and other species typical of the Phase II flora of the Thurne broads. Charophytes virtually disappeared from Hickling Broad in the early 1970s, but four species, *Chara aspera, C. hispida, C. globularis* and *Nitellopsis obtusa*, re-appeared in the site in the 1980s (Jackson, 1983: Kennison, 1984, 1985a & 1986c). Some of the material collected by Gary Kennison from Hickling Broad and Horsey Mere in 1987 has been tentatively identified by Mrs. J. A. Moore of the British Museum (Natural History) as *C. intermedia*. If this record is confirmed, it will be the first time this species has been found in Britain.

Jackson notes that several plants not previously recorded from the Thurne broads, including Canadian Pondweed, Water Crowfoot (*Ranunculus trichophyllus*), the Flat-stalked, Perfoliate and Hair-like Pondweeds (*Potamogeton friesii, P. perfoliatus* and *P. trichoides*) and the moss, *Fontinalis antipyretica*, appeared in them during the early 1930s. Such species are fairly tolerant of enriched conditions, and on decay produce a more bulky residue than stoneworts. Their arrival can be correlated with an abrupt increase in the amount of organic material in the sediment of Hickling Broad, dated by Moss to the mid-1930s, thus confirming that the transition between Phase I and II took place at this site about this time (Fig. 5D).

Despite various vicissitudes (see page 512), a fairly large number of Phase II plants

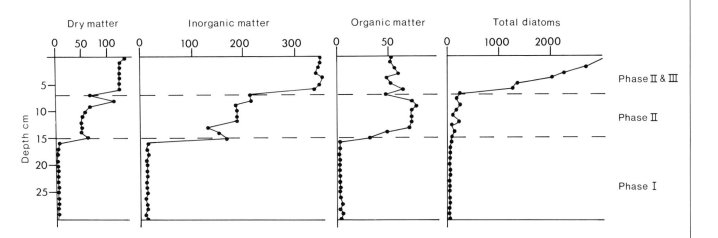

still occur in Calthorpe Broad (see Plate 7), species of particular note including Small Bur-reed (*Sparganium minimum*), Flowering Rush (*Butomus umbellatus*), Frogbit (*Hydrocharis morsus-ranae*), Water Soldier, Greater Bladderwort, and Grassy Pondweed (*Potamogeton obtusifolius*). Hornwort, Canadian Pondweed and one or two other species characteristic of Phase II have reappeared in Alderfen, Cockshoot, Crome's and Strumpshaw Broads as a consequence of remedial management, but elsewhere the waterweed flora is either wholly absent, or grossly impoverished, consisting mainly of Yellow Water-lily in the broads of the Bure, Ant, Yare and Waveney valleys, and Mare's-tail (*Hippuris vulgaris*), Spiked Water-milfoil, and Fennel-leaved Pondweed in the slightly brackish waterways associated with the R. Thurne. *Nuphar* is specially characteristic of well-flushed sites such as Rockland Broad, and Hudson's Bay, but despite its tolerance of high nutrient levels, this species has become noticeably less common in some of its off-river strongholds, like Salhouse Little and Hoveton Great Broads, since the early 1970s. Of the three Phase II species still found fairly commonly in the Thurne Broads, Mare's-tail is a robust, emergent species, which tends to be avoided by boat users, apprehensive lest its stems become entwined around their propellers; its stands have increased somewhat in size since the late-1970s, presumably because of the higher nutrient levels in the water and the sediment (see page 133). Of the other two Phase II species still found in the Thurne broads, *Myriophyllum spicatum* is

Fig. 5D

The sedimentation rates of dry, inorganic and organic matter, and of total diatoms, in Hickling Broad, at different stages in its ecological history.

Source: Moss (1978)

slightly more tolerant of turbid conditions than *Potamogeton pectinatus*, as its long stems can carry its leaves up to the surface. On the other hand, this makes it more susceptible to mechanical damage by boat propellers (Phillips, 1976).

In the rivers, elements of a Phase II flora persist in the Bure near Coltishall, and in the Ant and Waveney upstream of Wayford and Beccles bridges respectively, whilst in the Yare, Arrow-head (*Sagittaria sagittifolia*) and two or three other species occur upstream of the Whitlingham sewage works outfall, especially in the old course of the river by Thorpe Green, and above Trowse Eye. A more luxuriant and diverse Phase II flora still occurs in Waxham Cut upstream of the Brograve pumping station, and in Somerton Dyke. In the latter, the marginal reedswamp is bordered by dense stands of Yellow Water-lily and Fennel-leaved Pondweed, plus an abundance of two other pondweeds, namely *Potamogeton lucens* and *P. perfoliatus*, and their hybrid, *P. x salicifolius*. Further downstream, the only species tolerant of the highly enriched and turbid water in the rivers is the Yellow Water-lily, and even this is so susceptible to mechanical damage by boat propellers that, as in the navigable broads, it is mainly confined to small embayments, where the water is too shallow for powered craft (see Plate 8). Waterweeds are totally absent from the lower, more strongly tidal, reaches of the principal rivers.

None of the broads or stretches of river where Phase II waterweeds persist displays the great floristic diversity which Jackson has demonstrated must have existed in the past. In addition, many of the open-water sites are land-locked, or isolated from one another by long sections of river which are virtually devoid of waterweeds, and whose benthic invertebrate fauna is grossly impoverished. This is in marked contrast to the situation which existed a century or so ago, when, according to a multiplicity of records, the entire waterway system literally teemed with plant and animal life. For instance, when the Rivers Commissioners carried out their annual inspection in 1854, they noted that the Yare between Whitlingham and Buckenham was . . . "encumbered by weeds, particularly near Postwick, where they extended right across the river", whilst on the R. Bure between Mill Lane and Wroxham, . . . "weed formed a considerable obstruction, reaching half way across in several places" (YPH, 1884)*. It is not always clear whether the Commissioners were referring to submerged or emergent species, but the references in their report to the need to 'draw' certain reaches probably indicates the presence of the former, whilst the mention of . . . "rushes growing nearly in mid-river at Coldham Hall" must surely indicate the latter.

Confirmation of the high biological productivity of Broadland's waterways in the nineteenth century is afforded by the references made by Lubbock (1843), Southwell (1887), Davies (1884), Suffling (1892) and others to the immense catches of fish obtainable during this period. No real attempt seems to have been made to enforce the regulations until the 1870s (see page 449) and the nets in use were often of such a fine mesh that large numbers of fry were caught. The rivers were also regularly poached, often by night, and Dutt (1903) notes that . . . "bushels of Roach *(Rutilus rutilus)*, Bream *(Abramis brama)* and Rudd *(Scardinius erythrophthalmus)* (incidentally a species characteristic of clear, weedy water now rarely found in the region) were left to rot on the river banks, or cast on the land for manure, because no one would buy them". Anglers, too, were rewarded with catches which seem prodigious by today's standards. An article which appeared in *The Field* in July 1858, refers to 22 stone (138.6 kg) being landed by a man and a boy in a boat after a day's fishing, whilst 12 stone (75.6 kg) was regarded as a 'normal take' during this period (Moss *et al.*, 1979).

An indication of the condition of the R. Bure in the 1880s is given by Rye (1884) who, after referring to the extreme clarity of the water at Acle, notes that it was . . . "simply filled with shoals of fish, but nothing very big, but dodging in and out of the great waving masses of green weed".

In an account of Broadland's fisheries, and the ways in which these have been affected by increasing enrichment and boating pressure, Moss *et al.* (1979) conclude that the abundant supply of weed provided plenty of cover and spawning habitat for fish, and that the waterways remained a paradise for anglers until the 1920s, and in some places, much later. Nevertheless, in 1884, Christopher Davies prophesied that "The rivers and broads will never be so prolific of fish as they once were, because of the great diminution

---

* The archives of the Great Yarmouth Port and Haven Commission, and ite predecessors, are available for inspection in the Norfolk Record Office. They are indexed under the letters 'YPH'.

of breeding and feeding grounds caused by the drainage of the marshes. Hundreds of acres which were wet and splashy enough to enable the fish to roam over them are now firm soil; and it need scarcely be said that this diminution of feeding ground must lessen the stock and size of fish."

The heavy weed growth, and large populations of fish, strongly suggest the presence of a rich and varied benthic invertebrate fauna, and ample evidence for this is provided by papers published in the *Transactions of the Norfolk and Norwich Naturalists' Society* and other journals in the early years of the present century. To take but three examples: Hurrell (1927) recorded from the region all but one of the British species of freshwater bryozoans, whilst Charles Soar, writing in 1905, notes that of the 150 species of water mite (Hydrachnida) known to occur in Britain at that time, 71 had been recorded in Broadland. Similarly, Balfour-Browne (1905) listed no less than 117 different hydradephagid and lamellicorn water beetles from the northern river valleys alone. Although some of these insects were found in marsh dykes and areas of wet fen, rather than in the broads and rivers themselves, most water beetles are carnivorous, and their abundance in Broadland at the turn of the century serves to confirm that there was a wealth of other invertebrate life present and also, by implication, that their habitats were free of pollution.

Symptomatic of the value placed on the region by naturalists was a suggestion by W. A. Nicholson, one time Honorary Secretary of the Norfolk and Norwich Naturalists Society, that a wherry should be converted for use as a floating laboratory in order to facilitate research on aquatic plants and animals, and in particular on rarities such as *Najas* and *Stratiotes* (Nicholson, 1985). This proposal was put into effect in 1903, with the establishment of laboratories in a house beside Sutton Broad, known as Longmoor Point (Nicholson, 1904: Gurney & Gurney, 1908). This undoubtedly acted as stimulus to limnological studies in the region, and a number of individuals, including Balfour-Browne and Robert Gurney, worked at the laboratory until it closed at the outbreak of the First World War.

Contemporary accounts by ornithologists such as Stephenson (1866, 1870 & 1890), Turner (1924) and Riviere (1930) show that waterfowl, as well as aquatic invertebrates, were vastly more numerous in Broadland in the nineteenth century than they are today. Despite the loss of such breeding species as Crane, Ruff, Black Tern and Spoonbill as a result of a combination of improved drainage, and the Victorians' obsession with collecting (see page 450), ducks, geese, and waders occured in such numbers that many local people were able to make a living out of wildfowling during the winter months. Southwell (1879) notes that prior to 1848, 200 ducks were caught daily "for weeks on end" in one of the decoys at Fritton Lake, and that it was not uncommon for three times that number to be caught in a single day. At another decoy beside the same Broad, 13 421 duck were caught between 1862/3 and 1876/7. But wildfowl populations may well have been in decline by then, since Southwell notes that the decoys which once existed at Flixton, Mautby, Ranworth, Ormesby and Decoy Broads, and in Acle Decoy Carr, were derelict. This can be attributed mainly to drainage and other forms of habitat destruction, but Baker (1985) has pointed out that the increasing popularity of shooting, especially with the introduction of breech loading in the 1850s, would have destroyed the quietude essential if a decoy was to be worked successfully.

Phase III

(a) Waterweeds and phytoplankton

Most of the open waters in the region are now in this Phase, whose onset is characterized by a substantial loss of diversity in the benthic invertebrate fauna, an accelerated rate of sediment deposition (and associated changes in the proportions of organic and inorganic material in this), a large increase in the amount of phytoplankton in the water, and by the impoverishment, reduction in biomass, and eventual disappearance of the waterweed flora. At many sites, species such as Hornwort, Water Soldier and Spiked Water-milfoil which are capable of rapidly propagating themselves vegetatively, and which can take up nutrients from the water as well as from the sediment, proliferated towards the end of Phase II to the extent that they crowded out other, slightly slower-growing species, before they in turn succumbed, often quite abruptly. In Wheatfen

Broad, for instance, where the late Ted Ellis recorded 23 different waterweeds in the thirties, Hornwort had become the dominant plant by the late 1940s but had virtually disappeared ten years later (Ellis, 1935 & 1958). In 1963, the same species was growing so luxuriantly in Alderfen Broad that the Norfolk Naturalists Trust sought advice from the author concerning the practicability of using a weed-cutting machine to prevent the site becoming completely choked. And yet, a mere five years later, this and other waterweeds had almost totally disappeared. Similarly, Lambert (1965) notes that Water Soldier was abundant in Hoveton Great Broad in 1947, but was completely absent six years later (see Plate XII).

| Plate XII | **Looking south-eastwards over Hoveton Great and Salhouse Broads – 1949.** |

Note the well-developed marginal reedswamp and extensive stands of Phase II waterweeds in Hoveton Great Broad. Both communities are now virtually absent from it, though attempts are currently being made to provide conditions favouring the re-establishment of waterweeds in this and other broads (see Chapter 13). The preponderance of sailing craft on the R. Bure and Salhouse Great Broad provides another marked contrast with the present-day situation.

Salhouse Little Broad can be seen on the right, with two sailing craft near its entrance.

Photo: J.K. St. Joseph, University of Cambridge
© Crown Copyright/MoD; reproduced with the permission of the Controller of HMSO.

A major reduction in the biomass and diversity of the waterweed flora of Horsey Mere, Heigham Sound and Hickling Broad occurred in the early 1970s. At the latter site, for example, Morgan (1972) recorded 12 taxa in 1968, including an abundance of *Zannichellia palustris*, *Utricularia* sp., *Myriophyllum* sp., *Chara* spp., *Cladophora* sp. and the water moss, *Fontinalis antipyretica*, whereas ten years later the flora was restricted to . . . "isolated beds of *Potamogeton pectinatus*, *Hippuris vulgaris* and *Myriophyllum spicatum*, with scraps of *Chara vulgaris* and *Najas marina*" (Moss & Leah, 1982).

The near-total elimination of waterweeds from the rivers and most of the broads was associated with a marked increase in the turbidity of the water, and during the 1960s and early 1970s, before the effects of enrichment were fully understood, it was fre-

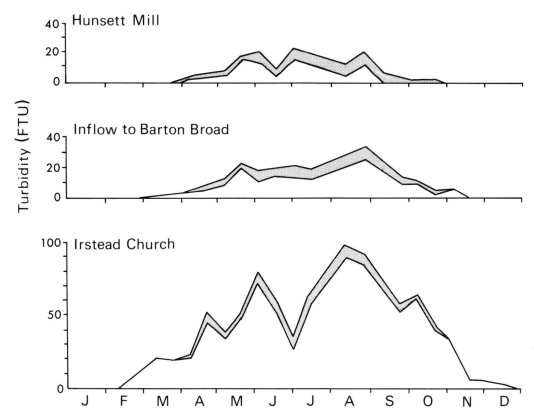

Fig. 5E

The turbidity (in Formazin Turbidity Units) of the R. Ant, as measured at three sites in 1979. The shaded areas represent the amount of turbidity predicted (by means of modelling) to have resulted from boat movements.

Source: Hilton and Phillips (1982)

quently claimed that this was due to the stirring up of sediment by passing motor boats. Some support for this hypothesis came from the work of Yousef (1974) who found that the turbidity of shallow lakes can be increased by boating activity by an amount dependent on the nature of the sediment, the engine-power of the vessel, and the depth of the water. In addition, a 'wake' of stirred-up mud behind moving craft can frequently be seen on air photographs of the shallower broads.

These views were challenged by Moss (1977) who found that highly significant correlations exist in Broadland between the opacity of the water, and the amount of phytoplankton in it. He concluded that although boats do stir up the sediment, especially in narrow, heavily used rivers, this does not contribute significantly to the sustained turbidity. This was subsequently confirmed by Hilton and Phillips (1982), who found that boat-induced turbidity only represents a small proportion of the total turbidity of the R. Ant for much of the holiday season (see Fig. 5E). But Hilton and Phillips' claim that turbidity in the Ant returns to background levels within five and a half hours of the cessation of boat movements has recently been challenged by Garrad and Hey (1988b), who have demonstrated that fine particles of sediment stirred up by passing vessels remain in suspension well into the following day, and that this significantly increases the opacity of the water. This finding is used by Garrad and Hey to support their contention that speed limits need to be lowered if conditions conducive to the re-establishment of waterweeds in the rivers are to be restored.

Although the relative importance of phytoplankton and suspended sediment as causes of the turbidity of the narrower and most heavily used rivers remains a subject of some dispute, there is absolutely no doubt that the presence of large standing crops of phytoplankton is the factor primarily responsible for the opacity of the broads. Maximum chlorophyll *a* levels at many sites frequently exceed 300 µg l^{-1}; indeed, figures as high as 600 µg l^{-1} were recorded by Osborne (1978) in Barton Broad, prior to the commencement of the R. Ant nutrient-reduction programme. 'Floaters' such as the duckweeds (*Lemna* spp.) might have been expected to be unaffected by such turbidities, and thus to have grown vigorously in still, sheltered waters, but they do not seem able to compete very effectively with the phytoplankton, especially when nitrogen is in short supply. It is probably because of this, that they are normally absent from broads which are in a Phase III condition.

Summarizing the work which he, and other limnologists have carried out in the region since the early 1970s, Moss (1983) distinguishes three patterns of phytoplankton production. Firstly, the Thurne broads, and the lowermost reaches of the three main rivers, have a flora dominated by brackish-water species, and lack the freshwater diatom genera commonly found elsewhere in the region. The second pattern is related to flushing rates. In the upstream sections of the rivers, the phytoplankton consists mainly of centric (radially symmetrical) diatoms, such as *Stephanodiscus hantzschii, Cyclotella meneghiniana*, and *Coscinodiscus lacustris*, together with an assemblage of very small algae known for convenience as µm flagellates; though very numerous, these usually contribute little in terms of biomass. Centric diatoms also predominate in well-flushed sites such as Wroxham, Salhouse and Barton Broads, but the species named above are joined by substantial populations of the genus *Melosira* in the summer. In the lower reaches of the rivers, and in broads which have longer residence times, the spring diatom growth is a mixture of centric and pennate (bilaterally symmetrical) diatoms, such as *Synedra* spp. and *Diatoma elongatum*. These also predominate in the poorly-flushed Hickling Broad.

The third pattern of phytoplankton production is also linked with residence time, and concerns the occurrence of blue-green algae (*Cyanophyta*). These form an insignificant part of the phytoplankton in well-flushed broads in the upper and middle reaches of the rivers, and in the lowermost section of the Yare, no matter how fertile the water. However large populations, mainly of *Oscillatoria* – a filamentous species – develop in the lower Bure, and in its less well-flushed broads, (e.g. Ranworth), whilst colonial blue-green algae such as *Aphanothece, Coelosphaerium* and *Merismopaedia* develop in sites with even longer residence times. Heterocyst-bearing, blue-green algae (e.g. *Anabaena, Anabaenopsis* and *Aphanizomenon*) which are capable of fixing atmospheric nitrogen, form large population densities in poorly-flushed broads (e.g. South Walsham Inner) which receive only small inputs of nitrate-containing water during the summer. Although these species only form a small proportion of the total algal population, their presence occasionally becomes apparent as a result of their ability to form surface 'blooms' (see Plate 9).

Microcystis aeruginosa, another member of the Cyanophyta, occurs in a number of sites, particularly in high summer, and in both 1989 and 1990, its population increased dramatically in several parts of the region. When this alga dies, it releases toxins into the water which are harmful to mammals (Bishop, *et al.*, 1959), and following incidents at several sites in the Midlands, notably Rutland Water (Northamptonshire) where several dogs and sheep died in 1989 as a result of drinking toxin-containing water, public warnings were issued by the National Rivers Authority. These advised persons temporarily to keep their dogs and other livestock away from certain reservoirs, lakes and rivers, and not to fish, swim, paddle or practise water sports on them. The sites in Broadland affected in this way in 1989 were Fritton Lake, and Filby, South Walsham and Barton Broads, while in 1990, warnings were issued in respect of Fritton Lake, and Filby, Rollesby, South Walsham, Ranworth, Decoy, Salhouse and Hoveton Great Broads.

Once the phytoplankton of Phase III has become firmly established, its productivity can be very high. In the heavily enriched R. Yare and its interconnected broads, for example, each millilitre may contain 50 000 frustules of the dominant diatom, *Cyclotella meneghiniana*, representing a standing crop of at least 10^7 frustrules per cubic centimetre. But algal productivity is restricted if the water is very shallow. Prior to being dammed off from the R. Yare in 1978, the two Strumpshaw broads had become so heavily silted (see Plate 10) that diatom production in them was substantially less than it had been in the early 1950s (Moss, 1979).

(b) Zooplankton

Rotifers and copepods are the main components of the zooplankton in Phase III sites, their numbers building up slowly during the spring, remaining high during most of the summer, before declining to almost nil during the late autumn. Cladocerans normally only occur in significant numbers in the spring. But Timms and Moss (1984), who investigated the ecology of two sites interconnected with the R. Bure, one of which – Hoveton Great Broad – is almost devoid of waterweeds, while the other – Hudson's Bay – possesses a luxuriant stand of Yellow Water-lilies, found that cladocerans persist throughout the summer in the latter as a consequence of being able to avoid being predated by fish by taking refuge amongst the plants during daylight hours, only moving out to feed at night when the fish cannot see them. Later in the season, when the lilies die back, the numbers of cladocerans decline.

The dominant rotifers are usually *Brachionus calyciflorus*, *Keratella cochlearis*, *Filinia longiseta* and *Polyarthra vulgaris*, all of which filter-feed on small algae, detrital particles and bacteria, and *Asplancha* sp., which feeds on other rotifers and larger algae. But different species tend to predominate in consecutive seasons, and the size of the population can also fluctuate on a week-to-week basis. Rotifers are generally too small to be subject to heavy predation by fish, but they suffer heavy mortality if large numbers of cladocerans are present as the latter compete more effectively for food supplies; in addition, some species, notably *Polythemus pediculus*, feed on rotifers. In the absence of cladocerans, rotifers tend to become more numerous. But even then, they exercise little control on the growth of phytoplankton, since they are only capable of feeding on the smaller components of this; they also filter water very slowly.

The predominant copepods in most sites are various species of *Cyclops*, notably *C. vernalis var. americanus*, and in the Thurne broads, *Eurytemora affinis*. They are relatively fast moving, and this affords them some protection against fish. However, most species feed on rotifers, rather than phytoplankton, and they therefore have little effect on the latter.

The cladocerans are represented by several species which are 1.5 mm long or more, notably *Simocephalus vetulus* (4.0 mm), *Daphnia hyalina* (1.7 mm) and *D. longispina (2.0 mm)*, whilst two other, smaller (*c.* 0.6 mm) species, namely *Bosmina longirostris* and *Pleuroxus aduncus* are also often abundant. Although these animals tend to avoid blue-green algae, they feed voraciously on diatoms and other phytoplankters, and Timms and Moss were able to show that the clear-water conditions which develop in Hudson's Bay during June, July and early August (when chlorophyll *a* concentrations are often less than 10 µg l^{-1}) could be attributed to the heavy grazing pressure exerted on the phytoplankton by these animals. But the cladocerans, and in particular the larger, and therefore visually more conspicuous forms, are themselves subject to heavy predation by fish unless they can take refuge amongst waterweeds during daylight hours. In the absence of such shelter, as at Hoveton Great Broad, their population is reduced in size; in addition, it tends to be dominated by smaller species, such as *Bosmina longirostris*, which are less easily seen by fish, but which exercise much less control on the phytoplankton than do the larger forms. It is for this reason that algal productivity in Hoveton Great Broad is much greater than in Hudson's Bay, chlorophyll *a* concentrations in the former being between 50 and 100 µg l^{-1} during the summer months.

The importance of this in regard to the steps which need to be taken to restore Broadland's waterways to a Phase II condition will become apparent in Chapter 13.

(c) The benthic invertebrate fauna

The switch from Phase II to Phase III had a dramatic effect on the benthic fauna of Broadland's waterways, since many of the leeches, snails, aquatic insects and other invertebrates which comprise it are dependent on waterweeds, either because they are permanently attached to them (as are, for example, many bryozoans), or because they provide them with food or shelter. In his description of the fauna of Wheatfen Broad when it was still in a Phase II state, Ellis (1934) recorded 20 different gastropods (7 prosobranchs, 13 pulmonates and 5 lamellibranchs). However, during a sweep-net survey carried out at this site between December 1976 and April 1977, only 1 prosobranch (*Valvata cristata*), 4 pulmonates (*Planorbis vortex*, *P. contortus*, *Segmentina complanata* and *Potamopyrgus jenkinsi*) and one bivalve (*Pisidium* sp.) were found, despite a careful search in 13 different sampling stations (Driscoll, 1982a). Strumpshaw, Surlingham and Rockland Broads were also examined, but only 45 different macro-invertebrates were recorded, many of them as single specimens.

If naturalists who knew and worked in Broadland around the turn of the century could return today, they would be quite horrified by the changes which have occurred. For instance, *Lophopus crystallinus*, a bryozoan which is now a national rarity (Mundy, 1980), was recorded by Hurrell (1911) from the Brundall to Surlingham area in such quantity that a single haul . . . "would have filled an ordinary-sized pail". Hurrell recorded six other bryozoan species from the same locality and would have been appalled to learn that Driscoll could find no bryozoans at all here, and that only one species, *Electra crustulenta*, is known to survive in the R. Yare, and then only in its lower reaches.

The benthic fauna of most Phase III broads consists almost entirely of tubificid (Oligochaeta) worms and chironomid larvae, and is thus grossly impoverished compared with that typical of Phase II. However, this is due, not so much to nutrient enrichment *per se*, as to the lack of underwater structure. At Alderfen Broad for example, Mason and Bryant (1974) found a much greater variety of benthic invertebrates in the marginal reedswamp, than in the then weedless open water of this site. Similarly, Moss and Timms (1982) note that benthic invertebrates were both slightly more numerous, and more diverse (15 taxa) in Hudson's Bay, as a result of the presence therein of an abundance of Yellow Water-lilies, than in Hoveton Great Broad, where this and other waterweeds are now largely absent (8 taxa). But most of the additional taxa recorded from Hudson's Bay were represented by very small numbers of individuals, the fauna being dominated here, as in other sites in the Bure valley by the Harlequin-fly (*Chironomus plumosus*), and the tubificids, *Limnodrilus hoffmeisteri* and *Potamothrix hammoniensis*.

Few invertebrate groups leave a datable fossil record. However, by counting the numbers of snail shells in samples taken from layers of sediment whose age had been determined by radio-isotope techniques, Moss has been able to confirm that there was a dramatic decline in their status at the beginning of Phase III. At Strumpshaw Broad, for example (see Fig. 5c), snail numbers increased fairly steadily during the post-1800 enrichment, and peaked in the early years of the present century. Thereafter, they declined rapidly, and virtually disappeared with the onset of Phase III in the mid-1940s.

(d) Sedimentation

Another symptom of the progression from Phase II to Phase III is an increase in the rate of sedimentation. At Barton Broad, for example, only between 1 and 3 mm of sediment were laid down each year from about 1400 until 1950. However during the 1950s, about 5 mm were deposited each year, and the rate doubled during the 1960s and averaged 12.8 mm yr^{-1} during the 1970s (Moss, 1980). Similarly, until Belaugh Broad was mud-pumped in 1987, about 17.5 mm were being deposited in it each year, whereas the rate was less than half this in the 1860s, and only c 0.7 mm yr^{-1} in the eighteenth century (Moss, pers. comm.).

The increased rate of sedimentation in the region can be attributed to several factors. More material is being generated within the broads themselves, (or 'autochthonously') as a result of the break-up of marginal reedswamp vegetation, and more importantly, by the fall-out of dead and dying phytoplankton, and the deposition of marl – the latter formed as a consequence of the photosynthetic activity of algae, rather than waterweeds as in the past. In addition, more 'allochthonous', or externally generated material is finding its way into the broads as a result of catchment erosion, now speeded up by the measures taken to improve the drainage of farm land. Run-off is much quicker now than it was in the 1950s, and this will have increased the amount of sediment carried downstream and deposited in the broads, especially after heavy rainfall. Evidence for this comes from radio-caesium measurements made on cores taken from Barton Broad (Moss, 1980). Although Cs^{137} would have been deposited uniformly in the catchment, the mineral particles to which it is bonded would, on being eroded from the latter, have tended to be deposited at the northern end of Barton Broad, rather than in its central and southern sections. It is thus significant that sediment cores taken from the northern end of this site were found to have accumulated between 200 and 230 picrocuries of

Cs^{137} per gram, whereas those from the south contained 70 picrocuries per gram or less.

The rate of sedimentation will also have increased as a result of the land-use changes which have occurred in Broadland itself since the 1960s. Research by Moss (1978), for example, has shown that when Hickling Broad switched from a Phase I/II to a Phase III flora in the early 1970s, there was not only a decrease in the organic fraction of the sediment, due to the disappearance of the waterweeds, but a rise in its inorganic content (see Fig. 5D). This can be attributed to increases in the amount of clay, silt, and ochre being discharged by land drainage pumps in the Upper Thurne catchment, following the conversion of grass marshland in the Brograve Level and elsewhere to arable (see page 306). Last, but not least, the wash generated by powered vessels, together with the abrasion caused by moored craft, will have greatly increased the amount of material being eroded from the river banks (see page 75).

The relative importance of these different sediment sources was investigated between 1979 and 1983 by Paul Garrad, who was then working at the School of Environmental Sciences of the University of East Anglia. Some of his results have yet to be published but, as we have seen in Chapter 3, he has already produced evidence that the increased rate of sedimentation in the broads can be attributed primarily to catchment erosion.

When the broads and rivers were still in a Phase II condition, much of the allochthonous material derived from the catchments would have been checked in its progress downstream by the heavy growths of waterweeds, ultimately to be anchored in the river bed by their roots. But the near-disappearance of these plants has made it more likely that such material will be carried by fluvial currents or tidal action into off-river broads, fen dykes or mooring basins, and deposited therein. In effect, these water bodies are now acting as settlement lagoons, both for the autochthonous material generated within, and for river-borne sediments. Moss *et al.* (1984) have found that the rate of sedimentation is faster (5.3 cm yr^{-1}) at the western end of Hoveton Great Broad than in the east (1.09 cm yr^{-1}) owing to the predominantly west to east fluvial flow through this site, and the restricted water circulation which occurs elsewhere within it. Similarly, the two-way, tide-induced flows which took place between Ranworth and Cockshoot Broads, prior to the latter being suction-dredged and dammed off in 1982, would have significantly increased the rate of sedimentation in both of them.

At many sites, particularly those regularly tide-flushed because of their connection with the main river system (e.g. Hoveton Little and Rockland Broads) or which originated as relatively shallow peat workings (e.g. Alderfen Broad) sedimentation has reached a stage where the water is a metre or less deep; indeed in some places, for instance, Salhouse Little and Surlingham Broads, the water is even shallower. This is not a new phenomenon as Pallis noted as long ago as 1911, that . . . "The smaller broads of the Bure may in extreme cases be silted up to within six inches [15 cm] of the surface of the water".

Although filamentous algae and diatoms often occur on the sediment surface of broads, turf ponds and fen dykes in which the water is as shallow as this, waterweeds are usually either absent altogether from such sites, or, as Pallis pointed out, represented by only "a few plants" of Yellow and White Water-lily. The reasons for this are not understood, but a lack of light, due to the presence of phytoplankton in the water, is most unlikely to be responsible given its extreme shallowness. However, the finely divided, and therefore physically unstable nature of the surface sediments may well make it difficult for waterweeds to establish themselves.

(e) Nutrient regime

By calculating the annual mean total phosphorus concentration, 35 μg l^{-1}, of four broads (Martham North and South, Blackfleet and Upton) in which diverse populations of waterweeds still occur, and comparing this with estimates of the amount of phosphorus likely to be used by the plants, Phillips (1976) suggested that the switch from Phase II to Phase III occurred once the annual mean concentration of total phosphorus in the water exceeded about 100 μg l^{-1}, and subsequent studies by Moss and others lent general support to this hypothesis. Apart from the four sites mentioned above, and possibly Calthorpe Broad (whose nutrient regime has not been investigated but which, as we have already seen, still possesses a fairly diverse Phase II flora), all the broads now support large standing crops of phytoplankton and have mean total phosphorus concentrations greater than 100 µg l⁻¹. They may therefore be classed as Phase III sites, even though one or two species of waterweeds characteristic of Phase II may still be growing in them. Although they all fall within Vollenweider's (1969) 'hyper-eutrophic' category, it will be seen from Fig. 5F that the mean total phosphorus concentrations of different sites varies considerably, the Yare broads being much more heavily enriched than those of the Thurne.

The amount of nitrogen, as well as phosphorus, is much greater in the rivers and broads now than it was in the past. Nitrate nitrogen (NO_3-N)* levels in the Bure at Horning, for instance, have risen from just over 1 mg l⁻¹ in the 1940s, to over 4.5 mg l⁻¹

---

* See footnote at the beginning of Chapter 2.

Fig. 5F

Mean annual total phosphorus concentrations in various sites in Broadland and elsewhere, and their relationships to the nutrient enrichment categories defined by Vollenweider (1969).

Source: Moss and Leah (1980)

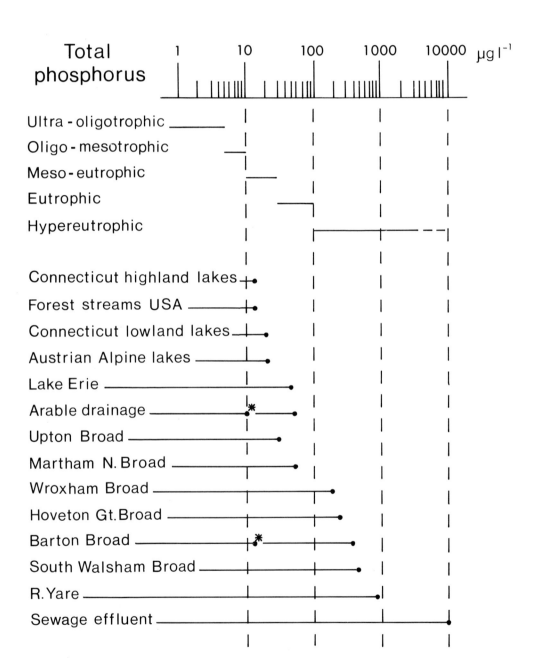

* Total phosphorus concentrations in c.1800

in the 1980s (Moss *et al.*, 1984), while in the Wensum at Costessey Mill, and the Yare at Colney Bridge, they average 5.0 mg l^{-1} (Leah *et al.*, 1980). This figure rises to 8.2 mg l^{-1} at Brundall, just downstream of the Whitlingham sewage outfall, but in general the high nitrate nitrogen concentrations in the rivers are due, not so much to the increasing quantities of treated sewage effluent being discharged into them, as to the efforts made by agriculturalists to raise the productivity of farm land within the river catchments. The ploughing up of grasslands, both within Broadland itself, and further up-valley, will have greatly increased the rate at which nitrogen is being mineralized from organic matter in the soil. In addition, given the huge reserves of nitrogen in the latter – arable land typically contains between 3000 and 6000 kilograms of nitrogen per hectare (House of Lords, 1989), compared with about 7000 kg N ha^{-1} under grass (Payne, 1986), the regular ploughing and cultivation of land in the river catchments ensures a continuing annual loss of large quantities of nitrogen through mineralization, especially as these management activities are normally carried out in the early autumn, when soil temperatures are still relatively high. It is also suspected, though not proved, that the enormous improvements brought about in the standard of field drainage since the Second World War will, by accelerating the rate of run-off, have increased the proportion of nitrates finding their way into the Broadland rivers, rather than percolating into the ground, and thence the aquifers in the underlying Chalk. Nevertheless, nitrate concentrations in the latter are generally far higher than in the rivers.

Fertilizer usage, which in the United Kingdom as a whole rose from 576 300 tonnes in 1965, to 1 470 000 tonnes in 1983 (Barfield, 1985) may also have contributed to the problem, although the widespread belief that there is a direct relationship between increasing applications of fertilizer and elevated losses of nitrate to ground and surface waters has been shown to be incorrect. However, the amount of nitrogen lost from cultivated land as a consequence of mineralization is topped up each year from the proportion of the applied nitrogen which has escaped uptake by the crop. The position is complicated by the fact that the amount of nitrogen leached from the soil immediately following an application of fertilizer has been shown by investigators (e.g. Cooke, 1974: Henin, 1986: Young, 1986) to vary according to a number of factors, the losses being particularly high in the winter months, and from bare soil. They are also greater from sandy soils than from clay-based ones.

In the rivers during the winter months, and in the up-river broads throughout the season, there is more than enough nitrogen in the water to sustain the populations of algae growing therein, and their productivity is thus limited by the availability of phosphorus. But further downstream nitrate nitrogen concentrations in the rivers and broads tend to fall as a consequence of uptake by algae, and bacterial de-nitrification. As a result, the phytoplankton in Barton and Hickling Broads, and in sites in the Bure valley which have a low flushing rate, frequently shows signs of nitrogen deficiency during the summer months (Watson & Osborne, 1979: Moss, 1981: Moss *et al.*, 1984).

Concentrations of ammonium nitrogen (NH$_4$-N) are generally low, averaging less than 1 mg l^{-1} in most sites. But concentrations much higher than this have been recorded from the Thurne broads, and this is thought by Watson (1981) to be due to de-nitrification being prevented by the low pH of the water pumped into these sites from the dykes of the adjoining marshes, many of which have been converted to arable since the mid-1960s (see page 272).

The relationship between Phase II and Phase III

When work on the limnology of Broadland commenced in the mid-1970s, it was generally assumed that the switch from Phase II to Phase III was a relatively simple process, and that it could be attributed to the increased phosphorus loading of the rivers. This was known to have risen as a consequence of the burgeoning number of people living in their catchments, and the steps taken after the Second World War to provide more and more towns and villages with main drainage. As each new sewage works was commissioned, so phosphorus levels would have risen, the problem being compounded during the 1950s by the introduction of phosphate-based detergents, which by 1970 had increased the amount of phosphorus in the raw sewage reaching the treatment plants by about 85 per cent (Ministry of Technology, 1970). It was also realized that the effects of enrichment would have been accentuated by the increasing quantities of water being abstracted from the rivers for domestic consumption and spray irrigation, since this would have reduced the rate of fluvial flushing during the summer months.

The amount of phosphorus in the waterways will also have increased as a result of the growth of Broadland's boat-borne holiday industry, though not to the extent sometimes claimed, since the number of people afloat at any one time has always been quite small in relation to the size of the population living in the catchments of the rivers. The introduction by the East Suffolk and Norfolk River Authority in 1971 of by-laws prohibiting the discharge of foul sewage (but not water used for washing) into the waterways by any boat, other than sailing cruisers and trading vessels on the R. Yare, meant in effect that it had to be stored aboard, and periodically pumped ashore into public sewers. This virtually cured a major aesthetic problem which had developed as the leisure use of the waterways increased, namely the all-too-obvious presence in them of human faeces and contraceptives, particularly in heavily used waters such as Salhouse and Malthouse Broads. But the by-laws did rather less than might be expected to alleviate the nutrient-enrichment problem, since instead of excreta being distributed untreated throughout the system from numerous small outlets, it is now released into the waterways through a small number of fixed points, representing the effluent outfalls of sewage treatment works. As we have seen earlier, the latter only reduce the phosphorus concentration of crude sewage by about 40 per cent (unless thay have been provided with specialized equipment), and consequently much of the phosphorus from boats continues to find its way into the waterways.

It has sometimes been claimed that one of the symptoms of enrichment – the progressive loss of waterweeds – has been hastened in the rivers and more heavily used broads by the change-over from sail to power-driven craft which took place from the 1930s onwards (see page 365), and the consequent increase in the amount of damage suffered by the plants from threshing boat propellers. In an anecdotal account of the natural history of Barton Broad, Gane (1976a) notes that the growth of waterweeds in it progressively declined during the 1930s, but recovered during the war when the Broad was closed to boat traffic. Large areas were, according to Gane, still overgrown in 1949, although by then the Rivers Commissioners had reopened the channels across the site, and begun an extensive programme of weed-cutting. The latter activity would not, of itself, have contributed significantly to the loss of waterweeds, since during the summer months, these quickly produce new shoots after being cut. But it can be argued that if the latter were continually being damaged as a result of the passage of motor craft along the cleared waterways, the plants would have been weakened, and may ultimately have succumbed, thus ensuring that more nutrients were available for phytoplankton production than would otherwise have been the case. In general, this seems unlikely as recent research at Woodbastwick (see page 139) has shown that waterweeds are surprisingly resilient to repeated mechanical damage. But in any event, the absence of waterweeds from sites such as Ranworth Broad, which are closed to all but rowing boats, indicates that the rivers and navigable broads would have undergone the switch from Phase II to Phase III as a result of increasing enrichment, even if no powered craft had been using them.

The initial hypothesis was that progressive nutrient enrichment, such as has occurred in Broadland since the Second World War, leads to the direct suppression of waterweeds as a result of the proliferation of phytoplankton, and the consequent reduction in the amount of light available for the germination and growth of the higher plants. But on the basis of field and laboratory experiments, and a review of the findings of limnologists elsewhere, Phillips *et al.* (1977) and Eminson and Phillips (1978) suggested that this is an over-simplification of a more complex set of changes, and that epiphytes and filamentous algae play a much more important part in bringing about these changes than had hitherto been thought. From work elsewhere, for example by Hogetsu *et al.* (1960) and Wetzel and Manny (1972), it is strongly suspected that in normal circumstances, the growth of phytoplankton is inhibited by organic secretions produced by waterweeds. The algal epiphytes which colonize these plants must, on the other hand, be tolerant of these substances, and from their work in Broadland, Phillips *et al.* suggested that as the water becomes more fertile, the epiphytes become increasingly numerous. This, plus the development of extensive stands of *Spirogyra*, *Oedogonium* and other filamentous algae, themselves often colonized by epiphytes, reduces the light available to the waterweeds, and thus their performance. If, as seems possible, this limits their ability to produce the inhibitory secretions, planktonic algae would become commoner, thus increasing the turbidity of the water, and making it even more difficult for the waterweeds to obtain sufficient light for germination and growth.

Field and laboratory studies strongly support this hypothesis. Cores taken from Barton and Strumpshaw Broads, for example, show that epiphytic diatoms proliferated long before planktonic forms started to become more numerous (Figs. 5B & C). At Barton Broad, the main build-up in the number of planktonic Centrales did not start until the mid-1950s, and although this was responsible for the final demise of the waterweed flora of this site, large quantities of periphyton had been growing on this since the 1870s as a result of the increasing enrichment. At Hickling Broad, waterweeds underwent a major decline in the early 1970s, before the phytoplankton-induced turbidity of the water had increased to a point where there was insufficient light for them. However, when allowance was made for the growth of periphyton on the plants, it was found that their failure to grow could indeed be attributed to lack of light.

Subsequent studies have demonstrated that the relationships, both within, and between the plant and animal communities of Phase II and Phase III are even more complex and subtle than was apparent from the work of Phillips *et al*. In particular it has been found that self-regulatory mechanisms exist which buffer the effects of external changes, such as the progressive enrichment of a Phase II community and it is now thought that Phases II and III are alternative, albeit relatively stable, communities at high nutrient concentrations. One of these buffering mechanisms, namely the heavy predation to which cladocerans are subject in the absence of waterweeds, and the consequent tendency for a Phase III community to remain in this state once the switch from Phase II has occurred, has already been referred to, and others have been unravelled as a result of the studies described in the following pages.

The R. Yare and its interconnected broads

A nutrient budget has not yet been compiled for the R. Yare, but Leah *et al*. (1980) note that nitrate levels in it are very high (up to 14 mg NO_3-N l^{-1} in the winter), because of the large, predominantly arable catchments of the Yare itself, and its major tributary, the Wensum. Phosphorus levels, too, are exceptionally high, especially in summer when the concentration of both total, and soluble reactive, phosphorus in the river can exceed 2000 µg l^{-1}, with a yearly mean of about 850 µg l^{-1}. These figures can be attributed mainly to the discharge from the Whitlingham sewage treatment works, the mean flows from which rose from about 5.25 mg d^{-1} (23.9 Ml d^{-1}) in 1951, to *c*. 8 mg d^{-1} (36.4 Ml d^{-1}) in 1963, as a consequence of extensions to Norwich's sewerage system as the population of the city and its suburbs expanded, and a general increase in the amount of water used for domestic and trade purposes (Norwich Corporation, 1963). Since then, the mean throughput of the Works has increased still further, and amounted to 49.7 Ml d^{-1} between April 1978 and March 1980 (Jones, in litt.).

The works have been modernized and substantially extended since 1951 (about £4 million having been spent on capital works between 1951 and 1981 – Jones, in litt.), but although the solids content and biochemical oxygen demand of the effluent improved, this is still of a very variable quality (see Plate 11), largely because the incoming sewage contains a variety of trade wastes which can upset, or even inhibit, the biological processes on which the efficiency of the plant ultimately depends.

The consequent risk of the R. Yare becoming seriously polluted was, until 1987, increased by the fact that the Trowse pumping station was incapable of dealing with the huge volumes of diluted sewage which it receives following heavy rainfall over the city. Under these conditions, which occur on average about four times a year, effluent had to be discharged direct to the river at Trowse, and on several occasions, notably 1981, this caused severe oxygen depletion in the river, and consequent fish kills. The likelihood of such events occurring in future was greatly reduced as a result of the construction in 1987 of storm tanks beside the pumping station capable of holding temporarily some 8000 cubic metres of water. Work started on major extensions to the Whitlingham Works in 1990, and when these come into use, a further improvement in the conditions of the R. Yare should result.

The Sewage Farm continued in active use until 1971, when parts of it were sold off to a neighbouring estate. However, the remaining land was retained so that sludge from the digesters at the Whitlingham works can be settled out on it.

The moderate fluvial flows in the river, even in summer, its arable catchment and the large volumes of treated sewage effluent discharged into it, notably from the Whitlingham works, combine to ensure that at no time is there a shortage in it of the key nutrients – phosphorus, inorganic nitrogen and, for diatoms, silicates. As a result, phytoplankton production in the river and its interconnected broads (e.g. Rockland) is limited by tide-induced wash-out, rather than by nutrient availability (Leah *et al.*, 1980).

Brundall Inner and Outer Broads

An early insight into the complex relationships between phytoplankton, zooplankton, fish and waterweeds, and the ways in which these are affected by the nutrient regime, resulted from experiments carried out for the NCC at Brundall Inner and Outer Broads between 1976 and 1978 (Leah, Moss & Forrest, 1980). Both these sites had been mud-pumped by their owner in 1975, and the NCC's original intention had been to dam off the Inner Broad so that comparisons could be made between a site which was isolated from a nutrient source – in this case the R. Yare – and another which remained in communication with it. In this way it was hoped to determine whether a Broad could be restored to a Phase II condition by removing the phosphorus-rich sediment from it, and thereafter reducing nutrient inputs to it by physical isolation.

Early on in the experiment, it became apparent that owing to leaks in the peaty walls of the Inner Broad, nutrient-rich water was continuing to reach it in considerable quantities, despite the dam which had been built to isolate it from the Outer Broad (see Map 5.1). As a result its water chemistry remained almost identical to that of the Outer Broad, which remained in open communication with the river, and which was therefore serving as a control to the experiment. Phytoplankton production on the other hand, was able to build up to a higher level in the Inner than the Outer Broad, owing to the lower flushing rate of the former. In both broads, populations of the diatoms *Cyclotella meneghiniana*, *Stephanodiscus hantzschii* and *Synedra* spp. were found to develop in the late winter and early spring, followed by a more diverse community of Chrysophyta, micrometre (μm) flagellates*, Cryptophyta and Chlorophyta.

The two broads remained in similar condition for the first few months of 1977, but to everyone's surprise, the water in the Inner Broad underwent a dramatic increase in clarity in the early summer. Investigation showed that whereas Chlorophyll *a* concentrations of up to 483 μg l^{-1} had been recorded in this site in the autumn of 1976, these had fallen to less than 10 μg l^{-1} by late May. These changes were found to be due to the development in the Inner Broad of a zooplankton population dominated by *Daphnia longispina* and *Bosmina longirostris*, both of which were feeding voraciously on the phytoplankton. In contrast, the zooplankton in the Outer Broad continued to be dominated by rotifers and copepods; *Daphnia* was virtually absent, and fewer than 100 adult *Bosmina* were present per litre compared with up to 900 per litre in the Inner Broad.

These differences in the plankton were related by Leah *et al.* to the fact that the fish populations of the Inner and Outer Broads were very dissimilar. Roach, Bream and Ruffe (*Gymnocephalus cernua*) all of which have plankton-feeding young, were present in the latter as a result of being able to swim freely into the site from the river, and were visually selecting the slower moving cladocerans, rather than the rotifers and copepods. This was reducing the grazing pressure on the phytoplankton, whose population was therefore increasing in size in the nutrient-rich water. In contrast, the fish which had been trapped in the Inner Broad when this was dammed off were subject to heavy predation by Cormorants, particularly a bird with a damaged wing which was resident here between October 1976 and June 1977. The net result was that the biomass of the fish populations in the Inner Broad had been reduced to between 4 and 12 kg (live weight) per hectare by December 1977, whereas in the Outer Broad it was estimated to be about 250 kg ha^{-1}.

Waterweeds were virtually absent from both broads in 1976, but the improved light regime in the Inner Broad the following summer led to the development in it of a continuous bottom cover of *Cladophora*, with moderate amounts of Fennel-leaved

---

* A miscellaneous group of very small (1 to 5 μm diameter) organisms from several taxonomic groups which are not identifiable without individual culturing; examination under an electron microscope is also frequently necessary.

Pondweed and Horned Pondweed, plus occasional plants of nine other species. By September, the water surface was largely covered by the duckweed, *Lemna minor*, with smaller amounts of *L. polyrhiza*.

A large-standing crop of phytoplankton developed in the Inner Broad in the spring of 1978, but although this was periodically decimated by grazing cladocerans, their effect was not so decisive as in 1977, as they were increasingly affected by fish predation. Shoals of fry were observed in August, and it was clear that the fish which had survived the Cormorant predation the previous year, had reproduced. Waterweeds, including *Lemna minor* and a pondweed appeared in the early summer, but did not survive, and were replaced by *Enteromorpha* and a straggly charophyte identified as *Nitella flexilis*.

Although the growth of waterweeds in the Inner Broad was nothing like so luxuriant in 1978 as it was the previous year, surveys revealed that its benthic invertebrate fauna was much more varied and numerous than that of the Outer Broad, where waterweeds were virtually absent.

In a renewed attempt to prevent nutrient-rich water from the river entering the Inner Broad, the NCC arranged for a second dam to be built in March 1979 (see Map 5.1). This was partially successful, since total phosphorus levels in the Inner Broad and the 'Canal' fell in relation to those of the Outer Broad. However, concentrations remained high enough in the Inner Broad to sustain a phytoplankton population similar to that in the Outer (Fig. 5G). As in 1978, there were frequent oscillations in the amount of

Fig. 5G

Total planktonic diatoms at the Brundall Experimental Site in 1978/9.

Source: Moss and Leah (1980)

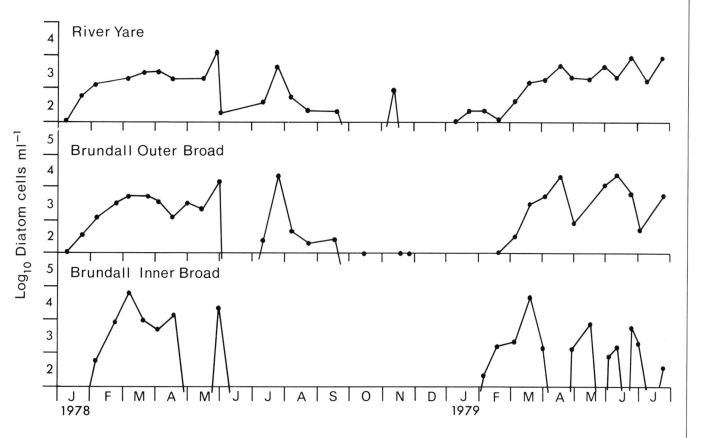

phytoplankton in the Inner Broad, due to the build-up of large populations of *Daphnia longispina*, and other cladocerans, and their subsequent collapse owing to predation by fish. Shoals of Perch (*Perca fluviatilis*) and Roach were seen in June, confirming that the fish populations of the site were continuing to recover.

In mid-summer, a population of the large, colonial nitrogen-fixing blue-green alga, *Aphanizomenon flos-aquae* developed in the Inner Broad. The appearance of this species, which is not readily taken by zooplankters, was thought to be due to the combined effects of heavy grazing pressure on the phytoplankton, and the fact that the second dam was limiting the ingress of nutrient-rich water from the river, and thus the renewal of the nitrogen used up by the growth of diatoms earlier in the season.

The R. Ant and Barton Broad

Hornwort, Water Soldier, White Water-lily and other Phase II waterweeds were abundant in Barton Broad in the late 1940s (Gane, 1976), but Osborne and Moss (1977) have pointed out that the presence in the sediment formed at this time of fairly large numbers of *Cocconeis placentula* and other epiphytic diatoms shows that the plants were thickly covered with periphyton, and therefore growing in moderately enriched water. In the early 1950s, a new sewage treatment works was opened at Stalham, about 3 km upstream of Barton Broad, and because of this, and the enlargement of the North Walsham plant, nutrient levels in the river and Broad rose rapidly. This caused a massive increase in the amount of phytoplankton, greater turbidity, and the consequent suppression of the waterweeds, which by 1968, if not before, were totally absent. This in turn led to a decline in the epiphytic diatom flora, which now consists mainly of various Monoraphidineans and Biraphidineans commonly associated with marginal reedswamp; numerous Fragilarians also occur during the winter months, both on the reed bases, and on the sediment surface.

The capacity of the two principal sewage treatment works in the Ant valley

Date	North Walsham Max. capacity (litres per day)	Date	Stalham Max. capacity (ld^{-1})
1924	318 000		
		1950	141 000
1953	1 114 700		
1963	2 548 000		
		1971	955 500
		1976	1 774 500

Source: Osborne & Moss (1977)

By the early 1960s, the phytoplankton was dominated between April and June by *Cyclotella meneghiniana*, *Stephenodiscus hanzschii*, *Melosira* spp., *Asterionella formosa*, *Ankistrodesmus falcatus* and *Cryptomonas* spp. but since 1974 these have been joined by *Synedra acus* and *Scenedesmus* spp. between April and June (Osborne & Moss, 1977). Algal production, both in the river and Barton Broad, reaches a maximum in the spring and early summer, but in the winter is only about a fifth as large, because of the greater volumes of water passing downriver, the shorter day length and the lower mean temperature. The water in the Broad itself is completely replaced about 25 times a year, a flushing rate much greater than that of most other broads.

Conditions in Barton Broad during the summer are more suitable for blue-green algae than diatoms, owing to the relatively long retention time, and dense growths of the filamentous phytoplankter, *Oscillatoria*, frequently develop, to be carried down-river towards Ant Mouth. As nitrate levels fall, through algal uptake and de-nitrification, nitrogen fixers such as *Aphanizomenon flos-aquae* may appear, and on several occasions during the 1970s, this formed a 'bloom' in Neatishead Dyke and other sheltered spots. Although nitrate nitrogen is usually undetectable in the Broad from April until September, abnormally high discharges in the R. Ant in the spring of 1981 led to significant quantities of nitrogen being present in the Broad until late July. This was probably why diatoms and green algae predominated in it much longer that year than usual (Phillips, 1984).

The Ant was the first river in Broadland for which a nutrient budget was compiled (Osborne & Moss, 1977), and following the publication of further work on the palaeolimnology of Barton Broad (Moss, 1980), this was revised and updated by Osborne (1981). It was concluded that Barton Broad was receiving a mean total phosphorus load of 10.83 gm^{-2} yr^{-1} in the mid-1970s. Of this, 2.23 g P m^{-2} yr^{-1} was thought to be coming from land drainage, and 7.07 g P m^{-2} yr^{-1} from sewage effluent; the remaining 1.53 g P m^{-2} yr^{-1} was being released from the Broad's sediments. A mean of 8.65 g P m^{-2} yr^{-1} was being washed downriver each year, showing that 2.18 g P m^{-2} yr^{-1} or *c.* 20 per cent of the total annual load was being retained in the sediment each year. But for the Broad and river as a whole, the net retention rate was much greater, as much of the phosphorus coming from the Stalham sewage treatment works was, at the time the research was being carried out, being incorporated in the sediment just below its outfall. In the absence of waterweeds, which would have helped to stabilize this deposit, some of it was being washed from here downstream, and entrained in a tongue of black, phosphorus-rich organic material which, dated cores have shown, has been creeping southwards across the Broad since the 1920s, and which now occupies much of its northern half.

In 1977, it was decided to try and restore Barton Broad to a Phase II condition by reducing phosphorus inputs to it, and details of these management experiments are given in Chapter 13.

Alderfen Broad

By the late 1970s, sufficient was known about the Yare, Ant and Thurne broads to enable limnologists to advance the general hypothesis that catchment run-off does not contain enough phosphorus to trigger the shift from Phase II to Phase III, and that this will only occur if a site is enriched by sewage effluent, farm wastes or other sources. Alderfen Broad, which was converted to a Phase III state in the mid-1960s, appeared to form an exception to this rule since the tributary of the R. Ant which flows through it was thought not to receive the effluent from a sewage treatment works.

Phillips (1977), who studied Alderfen's ecology and water chemistry, found that its inflow stream had a mean total phosphorus concentration of 220 µg l^{-1} and that the annual loading of the Broad was therefore about 0.77 g P m^{-2}. Since it has a surface area of 4.7 ha, it was receiving about 36.19 kg of phosphorus per hectare per year, which, given the fact that its inflow stream drains a catchment of 330 ha, meant that 0.11 kg P ha^{-1} yr^{-1} was emanating from the latter.

Later work, involving an examination of sediment cores taken from the Broad, and an assessment of the amount of phosphorus contained in streams draining arable land elsewhere in the region, suggested that only between 22 and 26 per cent of the phosphorus reaching the site could be derived from the farm land in the catchment of its inflow stream, and that the remainder must therefore be coming from some other source (Moss *et al.*, 1979). Air photographs and maps showed that a number of houses had been built in the village of Workhouse Common since the Second World War, and that 13 of these were located near, or beside the inflow stream less than a kilometre upstream of the Broad. Since main sewerage was not available, these houses had been provided with septic tanks, the overflows from which were able to reach the stream. Assuming that 45 persons live in the houses, that each excretes 0.5 kg P yr^{-1}, and generates a further 0.4 kg P yr^{-1} as a consequence of using phosphate- based detergents, Moss *et al.* calculated that the septic tanks of the 13 houses will collectively receive some 42 kg P yr^{-1}. If all this found its way into the broad, its phosphorus loading would amount to 0.89 g P m^{-2} per year from this source alone. However, they considered it unlikely that much more than half would in practice reach the site, and by making this assumption they balanced its phosphorus budget on the basis that *c.* 0.20 g P m^{-2} yr^{-1} originates from farmland in the catchment, and that the remaining 0.57 g P m^{-2} yr^{-1} was coming from Workhouse Common.

It was subsequently discovered that effluent from a small sewage treatment works is discharged into the inflow stream of the Broad, indicating that rather less phosphorus is emanating from the septic tanks in Workhouse Common than had been thought previously.

The results obtained from the Alderfen experiments were used by conservationists to devise a method of reducing phosphorus inputs to the Broad, and it now seems to be oscillating between a Phase III and a Phase II state (see page 499).

Hickling Broad, Heigham Sound and Horsey Mere

The switch to Phase III occurred in most broads in the early 1950s, and in some cases before, and few can therefore remember sites such as Barton and Wroxham Broads when dense masses of waterweed still grew in them. But the larger Thurne broads retained a Phase I/II flora similar to that still found in Martham and Blackfleet Broads until the late 1960s, and many can therefore vividly recall them when they still possessed a seemingly endless variety of waterweeds, molluscs, crustaceans, aquatic insects and fish, all fully visible in the beautiful, crystal-clear water.

During the summer of 1969, the larger Thurne broads suffered a major fish kill. This started in Horsey Mere, but soon spread to Hickling Broad and Heigham Sound, and later to the upper reaches of the R. Thurne. In each case the water became turbid, and assumed a brownish hue immediately before the kill. It was estimated (Bowler, 1971) that, all told, about 200000 Pike (*Esox lucius*), Perch, Bream, Roach, Rudd and Eels (*Anguilla anguilla*) perished, and although this figure cannot be substantiated, a contemporary report indicates that 7.5 tons of fish had been collected up from the "dykes and adjoining areas" of the Hickling reserve (Sankey, *in litt.*). Investigations by staff of the East Suffolk and Norfolk River Authority eliminated diurnal changes in dissolved oxygen, salinity fluctuations and 'pollution' as possible causes of the mortality, and the Authority therefore re-stocked Hickling Broad with some 36000 fish (mainly Bream). It is doubtful whether these survived for long, as there was another fish kill in 1970, and further research showed that the mortalities were due to the release of ichthyotoxins by one of the constituents of the phytoplankton, *Prymnesium parvum*. This is a small (up to 15 mm long) biflagellate, belonging to the Haptophyta, which is tolerant of a wide range of salinities (euryhaline) (Bowler, 1971: Holdway *et al.*, 1978).

Apart from Mare's-tail which, perhaps because of its robust and emergent growth form, is relatively tolerant of turbid water, the waterweed flora of Hickling Broad, Heigham Sound and Horsey Mere had been virtually eliminated by 1974, and this in turn, led to a decline in the numbers of birds dependent on these plants for food. For instance, unpublished data provided by the British Trust for Ornithology shows that the average numbers of Tufted Duck and Pochard on Hickling Broad between September and March decreased respectively from 160 and 66 during the period 1950 to 1956 inclusive, to 31 and 46 between 1975 and 1979. Similarly, the number of Mute Swans on this site fell from about 320, mainly non-breeders, in 1961, to 22 in 1979 (Taylor, 1979). The numbers of Coot overwintering on Hickling Broad has undergone a similar decline. Gurney (1901) notes that in February 1901 there were about 3000 of these birds on the site, of which 910 were shot in a single day, and indications that the numbers remained high during the 1920s and 1930s are afforded by a note in the possession of Mr. and Mrs. J. Tallowin of Marsh Farm, Hickling, in which Jim Vincent (headkeeper of the Whiteslea Estate from 1908 until 1944) records that 1175 were shot on the Broad on 18 February 1927. In addition, out of 2057 accounted for during the winter of 1933/4 (Long, 1936), no fewer than 1213 were shot on 10 February 1934 (Vincent, 1980). Reports by Jim Vincent's successor, Ted Piggin, show that about 2000 Coot over-wintered on the Broad in 1964 and 1965. But there was a dramatic decline following the conversion of the site into a Phase III condition, and the consequent loss of waterweeds from it, and the mean total winter population of this species between 1975/6 and 1979/80 was only 93 birds (Linsell, pers. comm.).

Greatly concerned by what had happened to the Hickling and Horsey reserves, both of which had been cherished by bird lovers and naturalists for 60 years or more, and puzzled that they exhibited many of the symptoms of nutrient enrichment despite the fact that sewage works effluent is not discharged directly into either, the NCC decided to commission a major programme of research into the causes of the changes taking place, and the ways in which they might be reversed. The work was carried out under the direction of Dr Brian Moss between 1976 and 1979, and involved the installation in the southern limb of Hickling Broad (Heigham Corner) of two 20m-diameter reservoirs, known as 'Lund Tubes' (see Plate 12). These enabled comparisons to be made between the changes taking place in the ecology of the Broad itself, and those occurring in bodies of water physically isolated from it.

In their report to the NCC (Moss & Leah, 1980) and their subsequent publications (Moss, 1978: Moss, Leah & Forrest, 1978: Moss, Leah & Clough, 1979: Leah, Moss & Forrest 1978: Leah, Moss & Forrest, 1980: Moss & Leah, 1982) Moss and his co-workers note that the phytoplankton of Hickling Broad falls into three distinct phases. Between May and October, dense populations of the gelatinous, colonial blue-green alga *Aphanothece* sp. predominate, together with substantial numbers of *Coelosphaerium* sp., *Lyngbya contorta*, *Anabaenopsis elenkinii* and *Merismopaedia glauca* (Fig. 5H). For much of this period, little exchange of water occurs between the Broad and the sites downriver of it, with the result that nitrate levels fall, owing to de-nitrification and algal

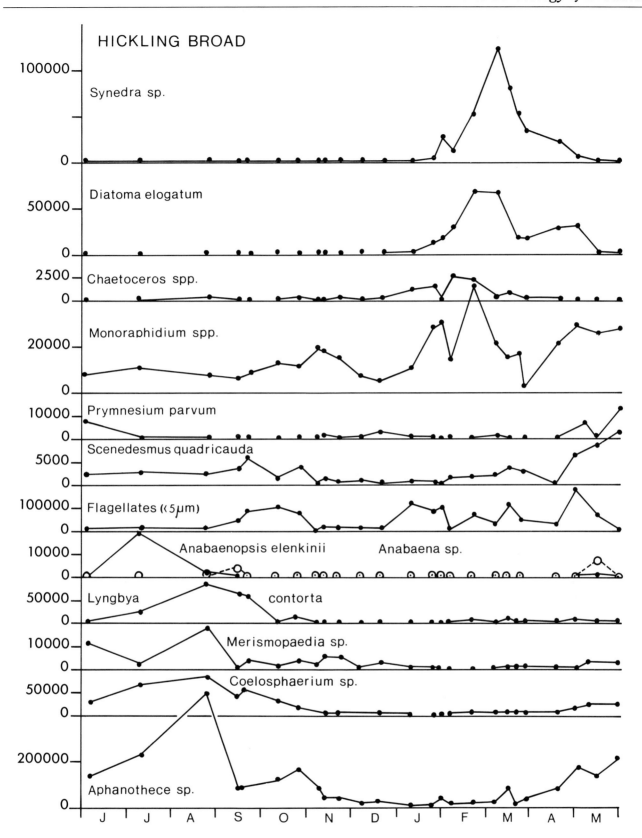

Changes in the phytoplankton community of Hickling Broad in 1976/7. Numbers are expressed as
cells per millilitre in the case of *Synedra*, *Diatoma*, *Chaetoceros*, *Prymnesium* and small flagellates, or
as filaments per millilitre (*Anabaenopsis*, *Anabaena* and *Lyngbya*), coenobia per millilitre
(*Scenedesmus*) or colonies per millilitre (*Merismopaedia*, *Coelosphaerium* and *Aphanothece*).

Fig. 5H

Source: Leah et al. *(1978)*

uptake. The flushing rate increases between November and January as a consequence of the higher rainfall, and the larger inputs of drainage water from the adjoining farm land. Nitrogen levels rise, but the algal population declines because of wash-out, and reduced growth rates in the shorter days. In January, *Monoraphidium* spp., Chaetoceros spp. and members of the Chlorococcales begin to increase in number, and there is simultaneously a very large increase in the populations of the diatoms *Synedra* sp. and *Diatoma elongatum*; in March 1977, for example, counts showed that there were respectively 120 000 and 70 000 cells of these species per millilitre. But silicate levels soon fall to a level when they start to limit the productivity of the diatoms, and although by May, some nitrate, and occasionally some ammonium ions remain, the population of *Aphanothece* has re-established its dominance.

These observations were made in 1976/7, but in the ensuing years the phytoplankton population was found to follow the same basic pattern although there were variations in its size, and the proportions of the species present.

When Moss and his co-workers examined the zooplankton of Hickling Broad, they found that instead of being dominated by large cladocerans such as *Simocephalus vetulus* and *Eurycercus lamellatus*, together with species of *Ceriodaphnia*, *Daphnia*, *Chydorus*, *Lynceus*, *Pleuroxus* and *Polyphemus*, as described by Gurney (1904 and 1965), it is very sparse and species-poor. Cladocerans are virtually absent, and for much of the year, the only zooplankter present is the calanoid copepod, *Eurytemora*, and this is never particularly numerous, even during the summer months. Since this species is, in any event, only capable of ingesting small particulate matter, it exercises a negligible degree of control over the growth of phytoplankton.

Copepod-dominated communities of this type characteristically develop as a result of heavy predation, and it was subsequently discovered that the *Eurytemora* is under pressure from a large population of the brackish water shrimp, *Neomysis integer*. This is capable of moving fast enough to avoid being caught in a conventional plankton net, and it was not realized just how numerous it is in the Broad until mid-water trawls were used in connection with a fishery survey.

The sedimentary benthos of Hickling Broad proved to be as impoverished as its zooplankton. Chironomid larvae predominate, and although tubificid worms and Tanypodinae larvae (Diptera) are present, albeit in limited numbers, crustaceans, molluscs and other organisms are either very rare or absent altogether.

The Lund Tube experiments were far from trouble-free. It proved difficult to prevent birds alighting on the floatation collars supporting the walls of the tubes, thus enriching the water within with their droppings, and this problem was not finally solved until May 1979, when the Tubes were completely enclosed by nets supported on steel posts. In addition, both Tubes were breached by a storm in January 1979, and could not be reinstated for several months.

Despite these set-backs, a number of interesting points emerged. Plants of *Potamogeton pectinatus* appeared in the Tubes shortly after they were installed, and despite the high turbidity of the water, caused by the large crop of phytoplankton in it, continued to grow quite well. In contrast, waterweeds outside the Tubes performed poorly, even though the water in the Broad at the time contained a smaller crop of phytoplankton, and was therefore less turbid than the water in the Tubes. On examination, these 'outside' plants proved to be thickly encrusted by epiphytes, whilst those growing within the Tubes had virtually none. Clearly, therefore, the performance of the 'outside' plants was being constrained by a lack of light, caused by the growth of epiphytes on them, rather than by the amount of phytoplankton in the water. But why were the epiphytes growing so much better outside the Tubes, than in? The explanation was that most of the inorganic nitrogen available in the Tubes had been used up by algae earlier in the season. Since the supply could not be replenished from the Broad, and since the nitrogen in gull droppings is in the form of organic compounds and ammonium salts which are readily de-nitrified on the sediment surface, the growth of epiphytes and phytoplankton in the Tubes was being limited by a shortage of nitrogen. Confirmation of this came not only from the negligible amounts of inorganic nitrogen in the water (Fig. 5J), but from the predominance of carotenoid pigments in the phytoplankton, which gave it an orange hue. Ultimately populations of the nitrogen-fixing blue-green alga, *Anabaenopsis*, appeared in the Tubes, but these were never as large as might have been expected. In contrast, the *Potamogeton* plants, being rooted, were able to take up nitrogen from the sediment in the Tubes, and were therefore unaffected by its near-absence from the water in the latter.

In the Broad itself, inorganic nitrogen derived from land-drainage water continued to be available until later in the season (Fig. 5J), with the result that phytoplankton and periphyton continued to grow in it for longer than in the Tubes. Even in the Broad, however, algal production eventually became nitrogen-limited.

Another interesting point to emerge from the experiments was that diatom populations similar to those which develop in the Broad each spring, never appeared in the Tubes. Instead, a very large population of *Aphanothece* persisted through the year. Moss and Leah attributed this to the lack of flushing in the Tubes, and the fact that this buoyant and very gelatinous species does not sink to the sediment, as most phytoplankters do when nutrient-limited. This, and the inability of *Eurytemora* to ingest *Aphanothece*, has important implications for the future management of the Thurne broads (see page 510).

As a result of their investigations, Moss and his team concluded that the major ecological changes which occurred in Hickling Broad and Horsey Mere in the late 1960s and early 1970s can be related to two interlinked factors: the increasing nutrient enrichment of these waters, and the Prymnesium-induced fish kills.

Taking these points in turn, surveys have shown that if allowance is made for the differing capacities of the six pumps which drain the land bordering Hickling Broad and Horsey Mere, the mean total phosphorus content of the water emanating from these

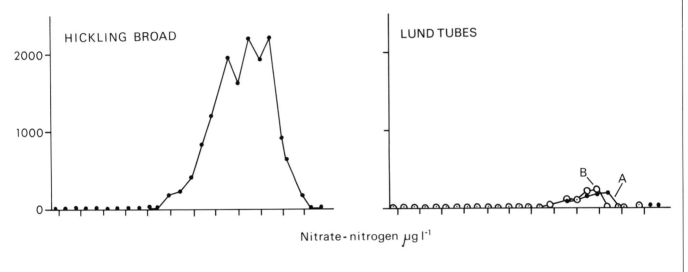

Nitrate-nitrogen μg l⁻¹

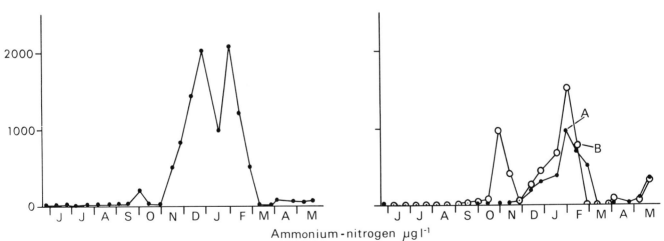

Ammonium-nitrogen μg l⁻¹

Changes in the concentrations of dissolved nitrate-nitrogen and ammonium-nitrogen in Hickling Broad and the Lund Tubes in 1976/7.

Fig. 5J

Source: Leah et al. (1978)

Table 5c The supply of phosphorus to Hickling Broad from the catchment area by pumped water (g P l⁻¹) Mean (± SD, n = 10) October–March

	74/75	75/76	76/77	77/78	78/79
Catfield	97 ± 41	54 ± 30	103 ± 52		113.6 ± 37
Stubb Mill (old and new)/Eastfield	70.6 ± 22	74 ± 74			48
Horsey Mill	80.4 ± 48	59 ± 18			64 ± 31
Brograve	41 ± 18	67 ± 54			51 ± 3
Winter mean weighted for relative contributions of the pumps	54	66	(58.4)*	(58.4)*	55.2
Minimum winter levels recorded in Hickling Broad	131	81	53	59	40**

* Estimated from means over whole period.
** Probably low because of freezing and subsequent ice melt.
Source: Moss & Leah (1982).

during the winter months is between 54 and 66 µg l⁻¹ (Table 5c). Similar concentrations occurred in the Broads themselves during the winter and early spring of 1977, 1978 and 1979, suggesting that they were completely flushed by land-drainage water, at least once during each of these years. In 1975 and 1976, however, the total phosphorus levels in Hickling Broad remained higher than predicted, suggesting that the site was incompletely flushed during 1974/5 and the very dry winter of 1975/6.

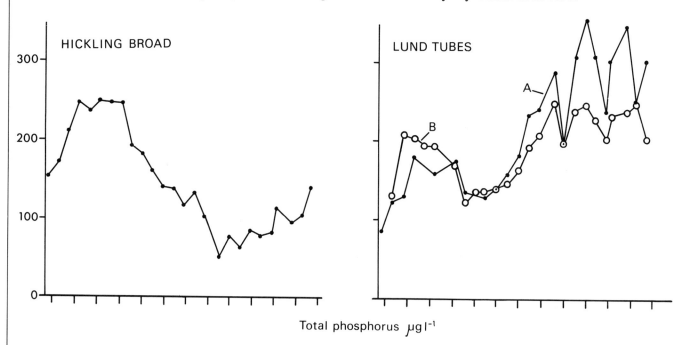

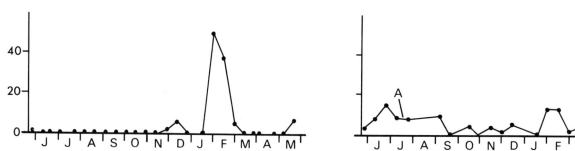

Fig. 5ᴋ   Changes in the concentrations of total phosphorus and soluble reactive phosphorus in Hickling Broad and the Lund Tubes in 1976/7.

Source: Leah et al. *(1978)*

Although land-drainage water seemed to be the main source of the phosphorus reaching Hickling Broad during the winter months, total phosphorus levels in it proved to be three and five times greater later in the season (Fig. 5K), despite the fact that little 'new', phosphorus-rich water enters the Broad, either from the pumps, or from downstream in a normal year. Indeed samples taken progressively downriver from the Broad usually show a declining gradient in total phosphorus values.

But what then was the source of the phosphorus? The answer lay in the roost of Black-headed Gulls which had been established in the site for many years, and which had been increasing in size, especially since the Second World War (Fig. 5L). Unlike the coots, swans and other waterfowl resident on the Broad, which merely re-circulate nutrients already in the ecosystem, the gulls were feeding in the countryside, before flying in to roost on the site, thus introducing nutrients into it from outside its catchment. Droppings from the roost are deposited on the sediment surface, where they decompose as water temperatures rise in the spring, thus releasing phosphorus at the very time when it is most needed by the burgeoning phytoplankton population. From the daily phosphorus excretion of each bird (*c.* 38 mg), the estimated amount of time it spends roosting on the Broad each day (16 hours), the number of 'gull-nights' each year, the volume of Hickling Broad and Horsey Mere (2×10^5 cubic metres) and the amount of mixing which is thought to occur between the two sites, Moss and Leah calculated the amount of phosphorus likely to have been contributed by the birds. Addition of this value to that derived from the incoming land-drainage water, enabled them to predict the total phosphorus levels likely to be attained in Hickling Broad during the summer months.

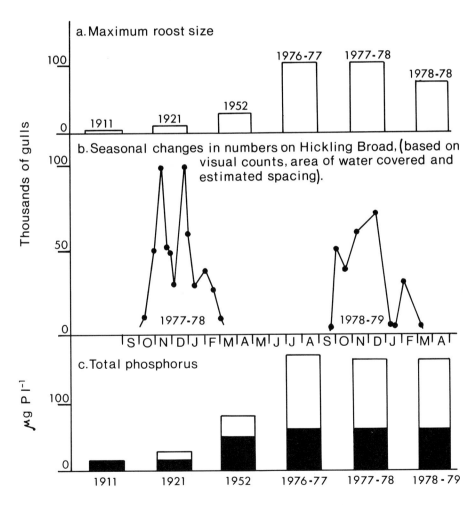

Changes in the population of Black-headed Gulls roosting on Hickling Broad, and their calculated effects on the maximum concentrations of phosphorus in the water. The blacked-in parts of the histograms in (c) represent the concentrations of phosphorus thought to have been derived from catchment area drainage, and the clear parts the amounts contributed by gulls.

Fig. 5L

Source: Moss and Leah (1982)

Table 5d   Gull contributions to total phosphorus concentrations in Hickling Broad
(All values in µg P l⁻¹)

Year	Winter minimum concentration	Addition from gulls	Concentration corrected for mixing with Horsey Mere	Total predicted	Maximum recorded
1975	131	?	–	–	312
1976	81	?	–	–	245
1977	53	164[1]	135	188	169
1978	59	110[2]	90.5	149.5	162
1979	40	103[3]	84.8	124.8 (140)[4]	160

1. Leah *et al.* (1978).
2. 6.34×10^6 gull-nights, 38 mg P/24 hr excretion for 16 hr, mean depth of Broad 1.2 m.
3. 5.93×10^6 gull-nights, other parameters as for 1978.
4. Figure in brackets is based on the concentration of P in land drainage water entering the Broad and not on the winter minimum of 40 µg, which is probably unrepresentatively low owing to the temporary effects of ice-melt in February 1979.

Source: Moss & Leah (1982).

Table 5d shows that the calculated figures are fairly close to those actually observed, though the former tend to be smaller, either because the number of gull-nights has been underestimated, or because the predictions do not allow for the phosphorus-rich droppings deposited by the large number of starlings which roost in the reedbeds around the Broad during the winter months. In addition, no allowance was made for the fact that nutrient-rich water from downstream is backed up into the Broad by surge-tides, particularly during dry seasons, when for prolonged periods, virtually no water is discharged into the Broad by land drainage pumps (Watson, 1981).

Although 1969 was the first year that a fish kill in the R. Thurne and its broads was attributed with certainty to toxins released by *Prymnesium*, mortalities are recorded in the literature as having occurred in these waters in 1894, 1914, 1922, 1925 (when a contemporary report blamed the . . . "noxious products of decay and fermentation" generated by *Cladophora* at the end of the season – EDP 1925), 1934, 1954, 1965, 1966, and 1967, and Bowler (1971) has suggested that *Prymnesium* may have been responsible for some at least of these incidents. Since 1969, ichthyotoxins produced by the alga have killed fish in the Hickling-Horsey area in 1970, 1973, 1975 and every year between 1980 and 1987 (but not in 1988), and in Oulton Broad in 1980 (Wortley, *in litt.*). Fortunately, none of these mortalities has been anything like so large as in 1969, and this has been attributed (Alden, pers comm.) to the fact that in that year only, the initial outbreak was in Horsey Mere. Ichthyotoxins were subsequently carried down Meadow Dyke into Heigham Sound, thus trapping a very large number of fish in Hickling Broad. These were subsequently killed by toxins released from the large *Prymnesium* population which developed in this site a little later in the summer.

The actual number of fish killed each year by *Prymnesium* outbreaks is a contentious issue. According to the AWA, only about 300 per year died from this cause from the mid-1970s onwards, and this figure is claimed to have dropped to about 50 in 1986 and 1987. However, many anglers hotly dispute these figures, on the grounds that most dead fish sink to the bottom, and that the annual mortalities quoted by the AWA are, as a consequence, gross underestimates. What does seem certain is that fish such as Pike and mature Bream which live solitarily, are particularly liable to be killed during a *Prymnesium* outbreak. In contrast, shoaling species such as Roach and small Bream, appear to be adept at detecting the toxins in the water and taking avoiding action. Indeed, on one occasion in 1985, *c.* 900 lb (409 kg) of eels were caught at Potter Heigham whilst moving downstream following a *Prymnesium* outbreak in Hickling Broad (Wortley, pers. comm.).

Research carried out at UEA during the mid-1970s by Holdway, Watson and Moss (1978), and consequently continued by Watson while employed by the AWA, has been aimed at finding out why the *Prymnesium* population periodically increases in size, and why toxins are released on some occasions but not on others. Cell counts of between 10^4 and 10^5 per millilitre seem to be necessary for the production of sufficient toxin to kill fish, but the relationship between the size of the population and the amount of ichthyotoxin produced is by no means straightforward. It is, for example, possible to have relatively high cell counts with no detectable toxins in the water, or large quantities of ichthyotoxins produced by relatively small numbers of algae. Thus, cell counts as high as 800 000 per millilitre were recorded at Womack Water in 1973, and yet no fish mortalities occurred, whereas in 1979, Bream and Pike were killed in Heigham Sound, even though the maximum *Prymnesium* cell count at the time was only 31 000 ml $^{-1}$.

Holdway *et al.* found that *Prymnesium* is intolerant of water whose chloride concentration is less than about 600 mg l^{-1}, and it is for this reason that the alga is more or less confined to the Thurne waterways, Oulton Broad and certain brackish dykes, only occurring elsewhere in the region occasionally, and in small numbers. But contrary to what was thought at first, any increase which may have taken place in the salinity of the Thurne broads during the 1950s and 1960s (see page 49), is unlikely to have directly affected the status of *Prymnesium* in them (Watson, pers. comm.).

During their work on the relationship between nutrient enrichment, *Prymnesium* production and the release of toxins, Holdway *et al.* discovered that the alga is present in the Thurne broads all the time, but is inhibited by quite moderate ammonium levels. During the proliferation of diatoms in the early spring, the ammonium ions are used up preferentially to the nitrate ions. Consequently, when, a little later in the season, diatom production becomes limited, usually because of a shortage of silicates, ammonium levels may have dropped sufficiently to allow the *Prymnesium* cells to proliferate rapidly, making use of the nitrates still available in the water. Although in these circumstances, *Prymnesium* has a competitive advantage over other algae, its cell membranes will break down, with consequent release of toxins, if its population subsequently becomes phosphorus-limited. The greater the *Prymnesium* cell count, and the shorter the period over which phosphate-limitation occurs, the larger the release of ichthyotoxins. This mechanism explains why fish kills have not been recorded from Womack Water, despite the large *Prymnesium* population frequently found in this site. Sufficient phosphate-rich effluent is discharged into it from the Ludham sewage treatment works to ensure that the *Prymnesium* is never phosphorus-limited to the extent that it starts to liberate toxins. In contrast, it is possible that nitrogen released during the dredging of sediments containing high concentrations of ammonium nitrogen may have been at least partly responsible for the build-up in the populations of *Prymnesium* which took place from 1969 onwards in the larger Thurne broads, and in Oulton Broad in 1980.

In order to understand the role of *Prymnesium* in regard to the 'switch' to Phase III, it is necessary to bear in mind that the ecology of Hickling Broad would have been completely different when its zooplankton was dominated by cladocerans, as described by Gurney (1965) and others (see Fig. 5M). Although these animals would have been

Fig. 5M

Relationships within the ecosystem of Hickling Broad prior to the changes of the late 1960s.

Source: Moss and Leah (1982)

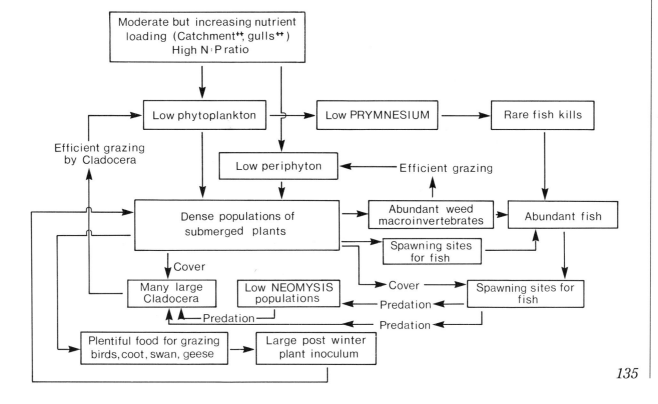

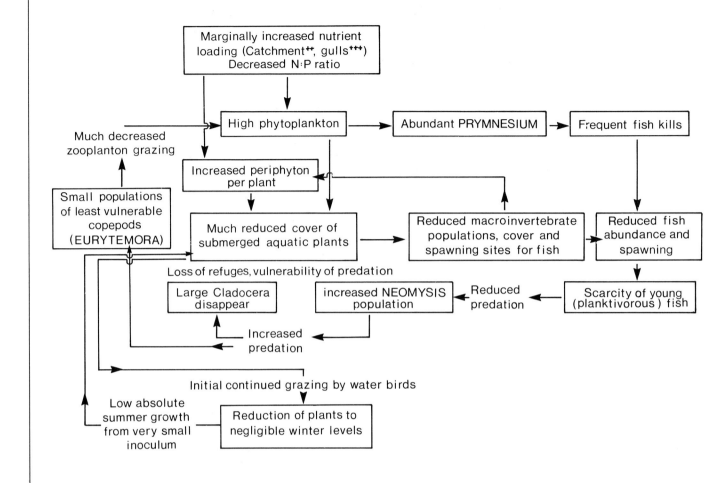

Fig. 5N

Relationships within the ecosystem of Hickling Broad during the 1970s and 1980s.

Source: Moss and Leah (1982)

subject to heavy predation, both by fish and *Neomysis*, they would, by analogy with the situation which exists today at Hudson's Bay (see page 117), have been able to seek shelter during daylight hours in the luxuriant stands of waterweeds which occurred in the site prior to the 'switch', moving out into the open water at night to graze on any planktonic diatoms which developed. This would have ensured that the clarity of the water was maintained, thus providing optimum conditions for the growth of water-weeds. It also affords an explanation for the near-absence of diatom remains from the sediment laid down in Hickling Broad prior to the late 1960s (Moss, 1978).

The fish kills which *Prymnesium* caused in the larger Thurne broads in 1969 and later years, removed one of the main constraints on the population of *Neomysis* (see Fig. 5N). This therefore increased in size, thus excercising much greater pressure on the cladocerans, and at the same time favouring the latter's replacement by the faster-moving, and therefore less readily caught, *Eurytemora*. The inability of this copepod to ingest the larger algae, and gelatinous species such as *Aphanothece*, together with the decline in the cladoceran population, allowed phytoplankters to take advantage of the increasing quantities of phosphorus reaching the site, mainly from the colony of roosting Black-headed Gulls. This also caused the periphyton to proliferate rapidly, which in conjunction with the turbidity produced by the phytoplankton, tended to suppress the growth of waterweeds. This in turn meant that more nutrients were available to the populations of algae, whose size therefore increased still further.

Two other factors helped to precipitate the near-demise of the waterweeds. First the decline in their productivity was probably not immediately matched by a corresponding reduction in the number of Coot and other herbivorous waterfowl. As a result, those waterweeds and over-wintering propagules which did survive would have been subject to intense grazing pressure until the numbers of birds fell back into equilibrium with the amount of food available. The effect of this would have been to reduce the amount of waterweed 'inoculum' available in the spring, thus lessening still further the chance that these plants would compete effectively with the algae.

Second, the relatively slow rate at which Hickling Broad and Horsey Mere are flushed in most years favours a large carry-over of *Aphanothece* during the winter months. Counts of ten to twenty thousand colonies per millilitre were often obtained by Moss *et al.* during the winter, and they point out that in the spring, this large inoculum, together with a surge in diatom production, results in a rapid increase in the turbidity of the water at the very time when the seeds and propagules of waterweeds require plenty of light.

Since work on the NCC's contract ceased, the condition of Hickling Broad has tended to improve. The summer populations of *Aphanothece* have not built up to the levels attained in previous years, and Spiked Water-milfoil and Fennel-leaved Pond-weed have become increasingly common away from the main boating channel. Holly-leaved Naiad, too, has reappeared in some of its former haunts, and *Nitellopsis obtusa* – a species which no longer occurs anywhere else in Britain apart from Martham North Broad – was found in both 1988 and 1989.

Doubtless because of the progressive re-colonization of the Broad by waterweeds, the number of Mute Swans overwintering on it had increasd to 46 by 1983 (Taylor, 1984). The Warden's reports indicate that the numbers of Pochard and Tufted Duck overwintering on the reserve have also tended to rise during the 1980s (see Table 5e), particularly on sites such as Duck Broad (off Heigham Sound) where the growth of waterweeds has been particularly prolific. However, neither species is yet as numerous as it was in the 1950s and 1960s, when 100 Pochard and 225 Tufted Duck were "regularly" present on the reserve (Wildfowl Trust, 1963).

Table 5e   The mean numbers of Pochard and Tufted Duck overwintering on the Hickling Broad NNR (October–March: 1975–1987)

	75/6	*76/7*	*77/8*	*78/9**	*79/80*	*80/1*	*81/2*	*82/3*	*83/4*	*84/5*	*85/6*	*86/7*
Pochard	93	27	40	41	28	31	28	59	37	59	67	192†
Tufted Duck	50	37	17	52	49	64	57	67	99	110	68	163†

* March count only.
† Most of these birds were on Duck Broad.
Source: Linsell (pers. comm.).

The improvement in the condition of Hickling Broad during the 1980s can be attributed firstly to a decline in the size of the winter gull roost on it (peak numbers of which were *c.* 50 000 in 1982/3 and *c.* 40 000 in 1981/2 and 1983/4), and secondly to the higher flushing rates which have tended to occur in early summer, and the consequent increased availability of nitrogen; this has favoured the continued growth of diatoms rather than the development of large standing crops of *Aphanothece*. But heartening as these improvements are to naturalists, they may not be maintained, particularly if gull numbers start to rise again, and if the flushing rate in the winter and early spring declines. The latter would favour a large carry-over of *Aphanothece*, a rapid build-up in its summer population, and the consequent suppression of waterweeds, a trend which would, for the reasons already given, be reinforced if phosphorus inputs from the gull roost were increasing at the same time.

The R. Bure and its broads

A major programme of research, funded jointly by the Anglian Water Authority and the Department of the Environment, was carried out between 1979 and 1982 under the supervision of Dr. Moss on the hydrology, ecology and water chemistry of the R. Bure and its broads. In summary, the objects were to assess the extent to which these water bodies are subject to enrichment, construct a nutrient budget, and ascertain the pattern of sediment movement and deposition in the system.

The results have not yet been fully published, but Moss (pers. comm.) has indicated that the river and its broads are flushed out with water high in nitrogen during the

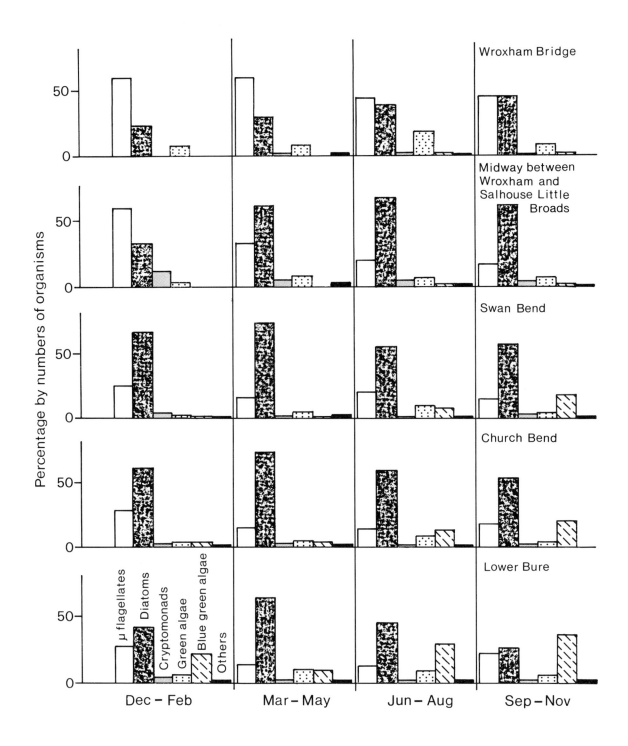

Fig. 5P(i)

Seasonal variations in
the phytoplankton of
the R. Bure.

*Source: Moss et al.
(1982)*

winter. The system begins to stagnate in the spring, and by late summer has subdivided, usually in the vicinity of Horning Church, into up and downriver sections. In the latter, total phosphorus reaches a high level (mean *c.* 250 µg l^{-1}) and the phytoplankton, which is nitrogen-limited, is dominated for much of the year by blue-green algae (Fig. 5P).

The upriver section is marginally less hypereutrophic (with a mean total phosphorus concentration of about 200 µg l^{-1} above the outfall of the Belaugh sewage treatment works, and *c.* 250 µg l^{-1} just below, dropping through sediment uptake to less than 200 µg l^{-1} in the broads) because it receives a continuous inflow of 'new' water from the catchment. As a result the phytoplankton in sites such as Wroxham Broad continues to be dominated by diatoms throughout the summer, its productivity limited by wash-out, rather than by nutrient availability. Centric species such as *Cyclotella*, *Stephanodiscus* and *Melosira* tend to predominate in the diatom flora of the upper and middle reaches of the river, and in well-flushed sites such as Wroxham and Salhouse Broads, but pennate forms such as *Synedra* and *Diatoma* become increasingly abundant downriver. In addition, the phytoplankton of Hoveton Great Broad tends to resemble that of the broads further downstream owing to its relatively long retention time.

Summary figures for total phosphorus, nitrate nitrogen, silicate silicon and chlorophyll *a* for ten broads interconnected with the R. Bure are given in Fig. 5R, and Moss estimates that about 75 per cent of the phosphorus in these broads and the river itself, is derived from sewage effluent. The implications of this for conservation are discussed in Chapter 13.

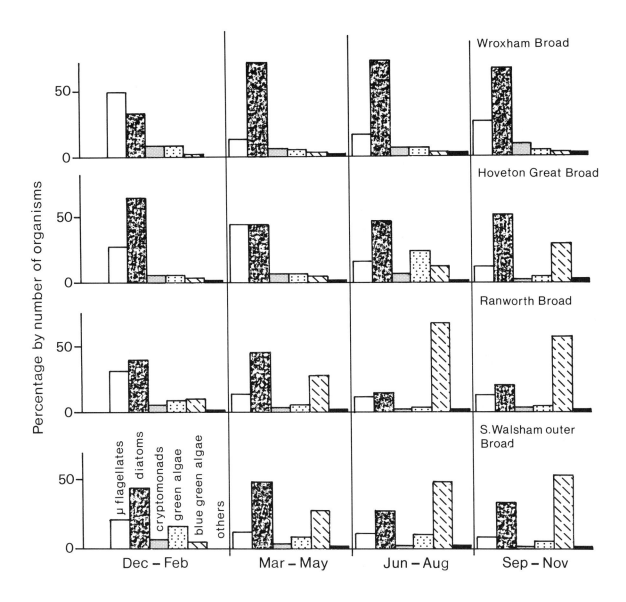

The Woodbastwick pond experiments

The site-related research described in the foregoing sections had pointed to the existence of ecological mechanisms which tend to maintain the dominance of Phase II waterweed communities in the face of increasing enrichment and, conversely, ensure that once the switch has occurred, phytoplankton continues to predominate, even though the phosphorus concentration has fallen below 100 µg l⁻¹. In view of the measures being taken to reduce phosphorus inputs to the R. Ant, and increasing uncertainty as to whether these would, of themselves, be sufficient to switch Barton Broad back to a Phase II condition, it was obviously desirable to obtain as much information as possible about these buffering mechanisms, and how they might be overcome. The need for such experiments was accentuated by the desirability of extending the phosphorus reduction programme to include the R. Bure, a nutrient budget for which had been produced by Moss under his contract with the DoE and AWA.

Fig. 5P(ii)

Seasonal variations in the phytoplankton of broads in the Bure valley.

Source: Moss et al. (1982)

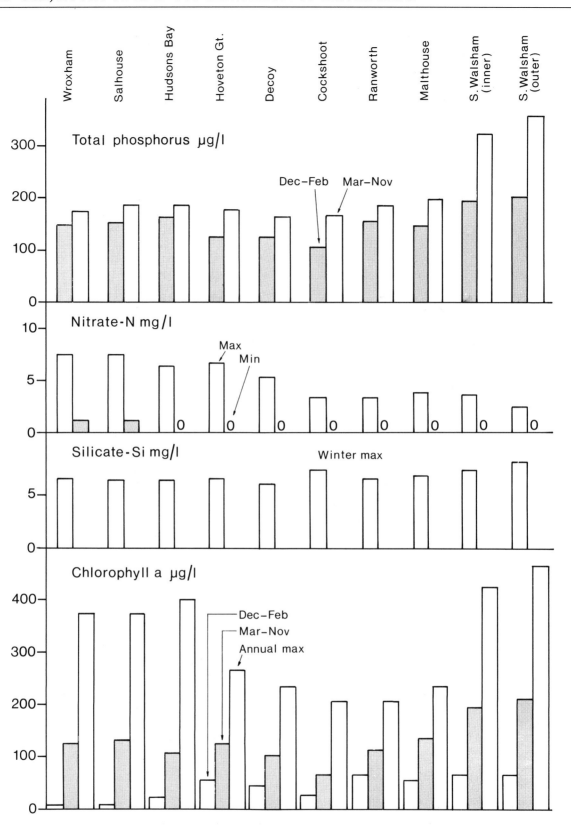

Fig. 5R

The water chemistry
of various broads in
the Bure valley – 1978
to 1981.

*Source: Moss et al.
(1982)*

It was impossible to make a controlled study of these mechanisms in the broads
themselves, and one of the dykes at Woodbastwick Fen which had been mud-pumped
by the NCC and subsequently re-colonized by Phase II waterweeds, was therefore sub-
divided by dams into a series of 19 ponds, each about 10 m long, 3 m wide and 1 m deep
(Balls, Moss & Irvine, 1985 & 1989). Fish were removed from all the ponds by electro-
fishing, and the diversity of the weed growth in 10 of them (the 'plant' ponds) was
increased by the addition of Water Soldier plants. 2 ponds were used as controls, and
the remaining 7 were cleared of aquatic vegetation. To keep them in this condition, it

proved necessary to rake out re-growing plants at frequent intervals throughout the season, an indication that waterweeds are much more resistant to mechanical damage than had been previously realized.

Since the main objective was to determine the response of plant and animal communities to different degrees of phosphorus enrichment, it was decided to eliminate the effects of varying nitrogen levels by maintaining in each pond a uniform nitrate nitrogen concentration of about 1 mg l⁻¹ by regular additions of a nitrate donor (calcium, and later ammonium nitrate). But the amount of phosphorus added (in the form of NaH_2PO_4 and Na_2HPO_4) to each pond was adjusted, the object being to obtain a series of fish-free ponds with and without waterweeds, having phosphorus concentrations ranging from 0 to 250 µg l⁻¹. In the event, it proved virtually impossible, even in the cleared ponds, to maintain phosphorus levels in the water greater than about 100 µg l⁻¹ for any length of time. Moreover, in the first year of the experiment (1982), the phytoplankton chlorophyll *a* concentrations never attained the values commonly encountered in broads in a Phase III condition.

In the plant ponds, this was due, in part, to the take-up of nutrients by the waterweeds. In addition, much of the nitrogen added to the ponds seems to have been denitrified by bacteria, or taken up by the sediment. But the most important finding from the 1982 experiments was that the grazing of phytoplankton by zooplankters, notably large cladocerans, does, as indicated by Timms and Moss (1984) constitute one of the chief mechanisms preventing the switch from Phase II to Phase III. It was also found that in the absence of fish, grazing zooplankters could, as in Brundall Inner Broad in 1977, prevent the development of large populations of algae, even if no waterweeds were present.

The ponds were subject to a similar nutrient regime in 1983 to that used in 1982. However, a known biomass of fish (mainly Roach, Carp (*Cyprinus carpio*) and Perch) were introduced into some of the ponds, any Pike which had gained entry to the latter during the winter floods, having first been removed by electro-fishing (Irvine *et al.*, 1989). As expected, the plant ponds into which fish were added, did not develop a large standing crop of phytoplankton, because the zooplankters were able to take refuge amongst the waterweeds during the daytime. However, the fish succumbed fairly quickly, probably because the plants depleted the supply of oxygen in the confined waters of the ponds.

In the cleared ponds, the numbers of *Daphnia* were reduced as a consequence of predation by fish, the greater the biomass of the latter, the greater the reduction in the *Daphnia* population. Other changes in the zooplankton also occurred including an increase in the number of calanoid copepods, and in particular, *Eudiaptomus*. This has a similar size range to that of *Daphnia*, but is capable of much quicker movements, and is therefore better able to avoid being predated by fish. *Bosmina longirostris* also became more numerous, but this cladoceran, being only about 0.5 mm long is, like the calanoid copepods, a much less efficient phytoplankton grazer than *Daphnia*.

As a result of the reduced grazing pressure exerted by the zooplankters, phytoplankton production, though variable, was much greater in the cleared ponds than in those containing waterweeds, and in one case, the chlorophyll *a* concentration rose to 159 µg l⁻¹, a figure comparable to that commonly encountered in broads which are in a Phase III condition.

For the final year of the project, 1984, it was decided to try and find out whether a high nutrient loading would, in the presence of fish, cause a pond which contained both Phase II waterweeds and open water to switch to Phase III, or whether the buffering mechanisms associated with the plants were sufficiently robust to prevent this happening. In the event, the results obtained were, for a variety of reasons, inconclusive. Nevertheless, sufficient data were gathered during the three-year experiment, and from the investigations at Barton, Brundall, Hickling and the Bure valley broads described above, to enable Moss and his colleagues to suggest that a Phase II plant-dominated community is buffered against change by several different mechanisms. One of these concerns the protection which waterweeds afford large cladocerans against fish and other predators during daytime. But some evidence was found at Woodbastwick that this mechanism may be reinforced by the partial de-oxygenation of the water in dense weed-beds, and the consequent avoidance of such areas by fish. The Woodbastwick experiments also showed that aquatic plants are capable of utilizing very large quantities of nutrients, thus depriving the algae of the latter, whilst the waterweed's ability to secrete chemicals inimical to the growth of phytoplankton – in the way demonstrated by Wetzel and Manny (1972) and others – would also help the plants to maintain the *status quo*.

But just as a plant-dominated community is buffered against change, so too is a phytoplankton-dominated one, once it is established. This can be attributed to several factors. Firstly, phytoplankton starts to grow and multiply early in the spring, when the waterweeds are still dormant. Consequently, if there are relatively few grazing zooplankters present (often because these have been subject to heavy predation by fish, owing to the absence of plants amongst which they can seek refuge during the daytime), the algae can take advantage of the plentiful supply of nutrients, and develop into a large summer population. Secondly, the grazing pressure exerted by fish on the zooplankton in the absence of waterweeds tends to produce a community dominated by copepods, rotifers and small cladocerans; these exercise little control on the phytoplankton. Thirdly, the dense standing crop of phytoplankton will, by increasing the turbidity, restrict, or even inhibit the growth of waterweeds, reduce seed production, and lead to the formation of small, poorly-endowed vegetative propagules. The inoculum for the following year will thus be small, and the plants may ultimately succumb altogether.

Last but not least, large, slow-growing phytoplankters may appear in nutrient-rich sites which are subject to a slow rate of flushing. The blue-green alga *Oscillatoria*, for example, tends to predominate in South Walsham Inner and Outer broads during the summer months, whilst reference has already been made to the occurrence of *Aphanothece* in Hickling Broad. Such species are too large to be ingested by most zooplankters, and are avoided by others, and may therefore be very persistent once established as a result of a switch from Phase II to Phase III.

The causes of the switch from Phase II to Phase III

Clear evidence emerged from the Woodbastwick pond experiments that an enriched water body can sustain either a Phase II or a Phase III community, and that each is relatively stable as a result of being buffered against external changes. The question therefore arises as to why Broadland's Phase II communities should almost everywhere have switched to their present Phase III state.

By far the most likely factor responsible is the failure of one of the mechanisms maintaining the stability of the Phase II communities. Most of these, for example, nutrient competition and the secretion of chemicals inimical to phytoplankton, result from the presence of the plants themselves, and cannnot therefore have contributed to their demise, unless these had first succumbed. But although it has been suggested at various times that Broadland's waterweeds may have been adversely affected by excessive grazing by Coypu (*Myocaster coypus*) or waterfowl, or by herbicide run-off, there is no evidence that this has occurred, save on a very local scale.

The only known external buffering mechanism which could have been affected, albeit perhaps only temporarily, concerns the phytoplankton-grazing zooplankton which find refuge amongst the plant-beds from fish and other predators. A loss of these, even for a year of two, might have been sufficient to allow a phytoplankton build-up, and take-over. The problem, then, was retrospectively to identify an environmental change which might have reduced the population of large cladocerans sufficiently to have allowed this to happen. Moss identified three possibilities:

(1) the poisoning of the cladocerans by the chemicals used in anti-fouling paints;
(2) a change in the fish population, resulting in the presence of a large number of small, zooplankton-feeding fish;
(3) a temporary reduction in the cladoceran population as a consequence of the presence of pesticides or their residues in the rivers and broads.

The first of these suggestions seemed most unlikely, not least because sites such as Alderfen Broad, which are not accessible to pleasure cruisers, and which do not receive water used by the latter, lost their waterweeds at much the same time as broads open to public navigation.

As will become apparent in the following sections, the fish population in the region has certainly changed during the past 50 years or so. But on balance, Moss considered it unlikely that predation by fish on the zooplankton has increased sufficiently to account for the widespread shift to Phase III. On the other hand, the outbreak of *Prymnesium* poisoning which occurred in the larger Thurne broads in 1969 did, as we have seen, almost certainly cause these sites to undergo the switch.

Much greater uncertainty surrounded the third possibility identified by Moss, and in the autumn of 1985 he initiated a research programme, funded jointly by the Broads Authority, the Soap and Detergent Industry Association, the NCC and the AWA, aimed at determining whether the sediment laid down in the broads during the 1950s and early 1960s contains organochlorine residues in sufficient quantity to suggest that the switch from a Phase II to a Phase III flora was triggered by a temporary reduction in the size of the cladoceran population attributable to the presence of these toxic substances in the water. Since this would necessitate the taking of sediment cores from selected broads it was decided to analyse these, not only for pesticide residues, but for the remains of cladocerans, the object being to see whether the populations of these zooplankters underwent changes in species composition analogous to those known, from studies described earlier in this chapter, to be occurring today. The feeding efficiencies of different species of cladocerans on phytoplankton, and of recently hatched Roach and Bream on zooplankton, would also be examined by Dr Moss and his associates, and it was arranged that they would, in addition, investigate under controlled conditions whether the numbers of large cladocerans in a broad can be increased artificially, and if so, the relative effectiveness of the various types of 'refuge' tried out. Finally, the UEA team undertook to continue to monitor the ecology and water chemistry of Cockshoot and Alderfen Broads in view of the changes which were still occurring at these sites.

The western end of Hoveton Great Broad was chosen for the artificial refuge experiments, and during the winter of 1985/6, 1050 bundles of brushwood cut from the adjoining fens (see Plate XIII), were anchored in the sediment by poles at three separate

Plate XIII

Preparing brushwood 'refuges' for zooplankton in Hoveton Great Broad – 1986.

The bundles of alder twigs were attached to stakes – seen here on the right – and groups of these were then driven into the sediment of the Broad.

Photo: Peter Wakely/ Nature Conservancy Council

places at densities of 50, 100, and 200 bundles per 100 metres square. In addition, artifacts were constructed of curtains of 12 mm mesh plastic netting, and also of 1 m lengths of buoyant, 10 mm diameter polypropylene rope, tied at 5 cm intervals onto wire mesh bases anchored to the bottom of the broad, to determine whether these provided a more, or less, effective refuge for cladocerans than the brushwood bundles. The experiments were augmented in April 1987 by the installation in the Broad of four small (2 m x 2 m), fish-proof cages. These were used to check that cladocerans, and in particular *Daphnia*, are capable, when feeding on the phytoplankton prevalent in the site, of surviving and reproducing successfully.

Data (summarized by Moss *et al.*,1988a) obtained from monitoring the artificial refuges during 1986 indicated that significantly larger populations of *Daphnia hyalina*, a species known from previous studies by UEA personnel to be a very efficient grazer of phytoplankton, were present during the summer months in the twiggy bundles and the netting curtain refuges, than in the open water of the Broad. However, this trend was not apparent in either 1987 or 1988, when none of the refuges contained greater densities of *Daphnia* than the open water (Moss, pers. comm.). There are a number of possible explanations for this. For instance, fish (and in particular, Perch) may 'learn' that more food is available in and around the refuges than elsewhere. Another possibility is that the slime produced by the epiphytic algae and tube-living chironomid larvae which colonize the refuges after they have been in the water for a few months, may render them unattractive to zooplankers. Either way, it does not seem likely that the provision of artificial refuges in a Phase III broad will be a practicable way of converting it back into a Phase II condition.

Samples from six sediment cores were examined for cladoceran remains, three of these having been taken from Hoveton Great Broad, two from Upton Broad and one from Martham South Broad. Most of the remains proved to be referable to *Bosmina* and various members of the Chydoridae, rather than large-bodied grazers such as *Daphnia* and *Sida* (Moss *et al.*, 1988b). This was not unexpected, as other workers have shown that the bodies of these and other genera are not well preserved in sediment. Nevertheless, it meant that Dr Moss and his associates were obliged to infer changes in the *Daphnia* population from those observed in the fossil record of other species. Despite this, and certain anomalies (for instance the occurrence in Phase I sediments of species known to favour turbid water), the investigations revealed clear differences between the cladoceran populations of Phases II and III, particularly in Hoveton Great Broad. Clear-water species such as *Alona guttata* and *Camptocercus rectirostris* predominate in sediments laid down in this site during Phase II, but thereafter give way to a population dominated by *Chydorus sphaericus* and *Alona rectangula*, both of which are known to favour turbid conditions. In addition, the proportion of *Bosmina*, a species characteristic of nutrient-enriched water, rose steadily in the cladoceran population from the end of Phase II onwards. The total numbers of this species also increased, reflecting the growing productivity of this Broad.

The hypothesis that pesticides might have triggered the switch from Phase II to Phase III was tested by analysing sediment samples from the cores taken from Martham South and Upton Broads, and two of those from Hoveton Great Broad. Analyses were made for Dieldrin (HEOD) – which is a degradation product of Aldrin, as well as being a pesticide *per se* – Polychlorinated Biphenyls (PCBs), the derivatives of DDT, namely DDE and TDE, and Lindane. However, the latter was not detected in any of the samples tested, probably because it is more soluble than the others, and breaks down more quickly (Moss *et al.*, 1988b; Stansfield *et al.*, 1989).

PCBs were encountered in all the sediment samples tested, including those laid down before these chemicals were first formulated in the early 1950s. This may reflect the burrowing activities of benthic invertebrates, which could have carried PCBs into the deeper sediment layers. Alternatively, the samples may have been contaminated, either during collection, or in the short time they were stored before they were analysed. But in any case, no firm conclusions can be drawn from the PCB data.

In contrast, the analyses for both Dieldrin and the degeneration products of DDT yielded very interesting and suggestive results. Large and circumscribed peaks of TDE (0.20 and 1.99 mg kg^{-1}) were found in late Phase II/early Phase III sediments in both the Hoveton Great Broad cores analysed, while significant concentrations of Dieldrin (0.10 to 0.29 mg kg^{-1}) were present in the sediment laid down in this site towards the end of Phase II, and during the early part of Phase III. Dieldrin was present hin much smaller quantities (0.01 to 0.60 mg kg $^{-1}$) in the Upton and Martham South Broad cores, while DDE was absent from the latter, and only present in one of the Upton cores; TDE was absent from both these sites.

These results are what one might expect, given the locations in the region of the three broads investigated. Hoveton Great Broad is in open communication with the river Bure which, because of its large, predominantly arable catchment, is more likely to have been contaminated with pesticides than either Upton Broad, which is isolated from the main river system, or Martham South Broad, in whose catchment grass marsh predominated until the late 1970s. In the circumstances, Dr Moss and his associates concluded that whilst one cannot retrospectively be certain that pesticide pollution was the cause of the switch from Phase II to Phase III, their hypothesis is 'not unreasonable'.

Sediment release

It had become increasingly clear from the experiments carried out in the past 15 years that the phenomenon of sediment release is of fundamental importance in relation to the nutrient enrichment problem, but that the processes involved were imperfectly understood, at least insofar as Broadland's shallow waters were concerned. In particular, given the very high cost of suction-dredging broads, it was essential to find out whether sedimentary phosphorus can in some way be prevented from escaping into the water column, so obviating the need to resort to this form of management.

Useful data, as yet unpublished, had already been assembled by Dr David Wilkinson on the subject during the course of his studies at the University of East Anglia for a PhD, and the NCC and the AWA therefore decided to follow this up by commissioning a research programme aimed at developing a way of measuring the amount of dissolved phosphorus in the sediment, so enabling its potential release rate to be calculated. In addition, it was agreed that sediment cores should be collected from Barton Broad and the R. Ant (and other sites, if time permitted), and that the release rate from these should be measured in the laboratory, using a flow-through system.

It was arranged that Dr Ros Jackson would be employed to carry out the research under the supervision of Dr Geoff Phillips of the AWA, and she started work in 1987. Unfortunately, a number of technical and other difficulties were encountered during the initial stages of the project. Nevertheless, in a preliminary report on it, dated November 1988, Dr Phillips informed the Broads Research Advisory Panel that the work had demonstrated that:
  a) Phosphorus release occurs during much of the year, and is not restricted to a brief period in June and July, as previously thought;
  b) The amount of phosphorus release varies considerably in different broads – the phenomenon also occurs in river sediments;
  c) The rate of release appears to be controlled by two principal factors: the phosphorus concentration in the pore water, and the amount of ferrous iron in the sediment;
  d) Burrowing invertebrates, particularly large Chironomid larvae, cause considerable enhancement of the release rate.

It was originally intended that the project would run for two years only, but it was subsequently agreed that Dr Jackson's contract should be extended in view of the importance of her work in relation to the management decisions which will have to be taken by the 'new' Broads Authority.

Avian botulism

Avian botulism, or Western Duck Disease, is well known in the United States, where its aetiology was worked out during the 1920s and 1930s, and it has been recognized in several parts of Western Europe, including the Coto Doñana (Spain) during the past 20 years or so (Smith, 1975). Its occurrence in Broadland was first suspected in 1969, and finally confirmed during a major outbreak in the unusually warm summer of 1975 (Borland et al. 1977); it was diagnosed in several other parts of the United Kingdom the same year (Lloyd et al., 1976).

Avian botulism is caused by the ingestion by birds of a neuro-toxin produced in the presence of rotting vegetable and animal matter by a spore-producing bacterium, *Clostridium botulinum*. The toxin induces paralysis of the bird's wing muscles, and later its legs and neck, and death usually results from respiratory failure, drowning, exposure, or as a result of the bird's inability to feed or drink. *Clostridium botulinum* is characteristically found in anaerobic sediments, and the occurrence of avian botulism in Broadland can therefore be related to the rapid rate of organic sedimentation in the region; thus the disease is another symptom of the nutrient-enrichment problem.

Signs of the 1975 outbreak were first noted at the end of June, the numbers of dead and dying birds reaching a peak in mid-August; deaths continued sporadically until the end of September. At first the mortalities were confined to broads in the middle Bure valley, but dying birds were later seen at Breydon Water, and at Hickling, Martham, Ormesby, Calthorpe, Wheatfen and other sites. Species affected included Mute Swan, Canada Goose, Mallard, Pochard, Coot, Common Tern, Black-headed Gull, Wood Sandpiper and many others. It is thought that avian botulism was particularly rife in 1975 because of the low water levels and above-average temperatures experienced in the region that summer. The warmth of the water and the surface sediments would have provided the bacterium with ideal conditions in which to multiply, and at the same time made it more likely that birds dabbling in the shallows would imbibe the toxin thus produced.

Centres where affected birds could be treated and rehabilitated were set up by the NCC, Royal Society for the Prevention of Cruelty to Animals (RSPCA) and private individuals, and it was found best to administer copious quantities of freshwater to the birds in order to dilute and flush out the toxin within their digestive tracts. Of 139 swans, ducks and coots treated by one individual in this way, about a third were cured and released, whilst the RSPCA claimed a 75 per cent success rate for birds showing the early symptoms of poisoning (NCC, 1976).

Borland *et al.* (1977) note that all but two of 45 sediment samples they collected from different parts of the region in 1979 contained *Clostridium*, and that three different types of the bacterium – B, C and E – were present. These were respectively demonstrated in 28, 23, and 27 of the 45 sediment samples analysed (Table 5f). Although most mortalities occur amongst water-loving birds, young Pheasants were affected on an estate a few miles from Broadland in July 1976 (Borland, 1976).

Table 5f   Avian botulism and *Clostridium botulinum* in Broadland in 1975

Name of site	Waterfowl mortality suggestive of botulism	Types of Cl.botulinum demonstrated in 45 mud samples**
Alderfen Broad	–	B(1), E(2)
Barton Broad	+	BE(1), CE(1), E(1)
Breydon Water	+	. . . . . .
R. Bure, nr. Horning	+*	C(1)
Calthorpe Broad	–	B(1), BE(1)
Cockshoot Broad	+	BCE(2)
Heigham Sound	–	BCE(1)
Hickling Broad	+	BE(1), CE(1), E(1)
Hickling Broad (Rush Hills)	+*	C(1), CE(1)
Horsey Mere	–	BE(1), None(1)
Hoveton Gt. Broad	+	C(1), E(1)
Hoveton Little Broad	+	. . . . . .
Malthouse Broad	+	BC(1), CE(1)
Martham Broad	+	BC(1), BCE(1), BE(2)
Ormesby Broad	+	B(1), BE(2)
Ranworth Broad	+*	BC(2), C(1)
Rockland Broad	–	BCE(1)
Rollesby Broad	–	BE(1)
Salhouse Broad	+	C(1)
S. Walsham Broad	–	B(1), BCE(1)
Strumpshaw Broad	–	B(1), BCE(1)
Upton Broad	–	B(1), C(1)
Wheatfen Broad	–	B(1), BCE(1)
Wroxham Broad	+	CE(1)

* Botulism confirmed by laboratory diagnosis.
** Numbers of mud samples given in parentheses.
Source: Borland *et al.*, 1977.

The 1975 outbreak is believed to have caused the deaths of several thousand birds (Borland *et al.*, 1977) and further large numbers died the following year. Subsequent mortalities have been on a much smaller scale, but *Clostridium* is now so widespread in the region that further outbreaks will almost certainly occur whenever there is a prolonged spell of warm weather during the summer months.

Although the severity of an outbreak can be limited if the corpses of infected birds are collected up and burnt, it will never be possible to find more than a small proportion of the birds which die during such an event, given the difficulty of the terrain. Moreover, even if the nutrient loading of all the rivers and broads was reduced – thus bringing about a decline in the rate of organic sedimentation – there are so many expanses of relatively shallow water in the region that the bacterium would almost certainly persist in it. Probably the best hope would lie in removing the sediment from ornithologically important sites with a suction dredger, thus eliminating the causative bacterium. Since the depth of water would be increased, the likelihood of the site being re-contaminated by infected birds flying in from areas where the bacterium was still rife would be simultaneously reduced.

The fisheries

Although lists of the fish found in Broadland have been produced periodically, the earliest being that compiled by Sir Thomas Browne in the seventeenth century (Nicholson, 1900), no real attempt was made by AWA to assess the size and extent of the fisheries until the mid-1970s; this despite the region's popularity amongst anglers, and the large number of permits issued annually (see page 378). However, prompted by uncertainties concerning the effects of *Prymnesium* on fish stocks, the increasingly strident, if unsubstantiated, assertions by anglers that their sport was declining as a consequence of the heavy boat traffic, and the anxieties of conservationists who felt that far too little was known about the relationships between fish, invertebrates, water plants and phytoplankton in Broadland's nutrient-enriched environment, the AWA's fisheries scientists embarked on an ambitious programme of survey and monitoring in 1977 (see Plate XIV).

Several problems had to be overcome, including the need to avoid obstructing boat traffic, and developing a suitable catching technique, as it was thought that the soft sediments in the rivers and broads would preclude the use of seine nets. In the event it was soon found that these could be employed successfully to catch fish with a fork length of *c.* 80 mm or more, and from February 1979, nets of this type have been worked from a pontoon, rather than from the shore, so as to avoid trampling and thus damaging the marginal vegetation (AWA, 1979a).

By September 1981, nearly 200 sites had been sampled. Special attention was given to the rivers Ant and Thurne, and their associated broads, but several sites in the middle Bure valley were also examined, including Wroxham, Salhouse and Malthouse Broads. Work on the R. Bure was carried out in conjunction with David Jordan of the School of Biological Sciences, UEA, who under the supervision of Dr Colin Townsend, studied the movements of fish between that river and Malthouse Broad at different times of the year.

The AWA's surveys have shown that marked seasonal variations in the distribution of fish occur in Broadland. For instance, during the summer months, Barton Broad holds a mixed population (Fig. 5s (i)) dominated numerically by Ruffe, but by Common Bream by weight. Small Roach are numerous, and other species present include Eels , Perch, Gudgeon (*Gobio gobio*), Flounder (*Platichthys flesus*), Pike and Roach/Bream hybrids. But most of the fish leave the Broad in the winter, and tend to congregate in boat dykes and other off-river sites (Fig. 5s (ii)). It is suspected that many move downriver into the R. Bure but this has not yet been proved.

Similar changes in distribution occur in the R. Thurne and its broads. 13 of the 44 sites sampled in these waters during the winter of 1980/81 had no fish at all, and the population was found to be strongly aggregated. Many fish congregate in yacht basins and off-river dykes, but shoals, particularly of Common Bream, also occur at certain points in the main river. These can provide the angler with good sport; for instance, 10 Bream, together weighing nearly 40 lb (18 kg) were caught by Mr Reg Wiles between Martham and Potter Heigham in February 1982 (EDP, 1982).

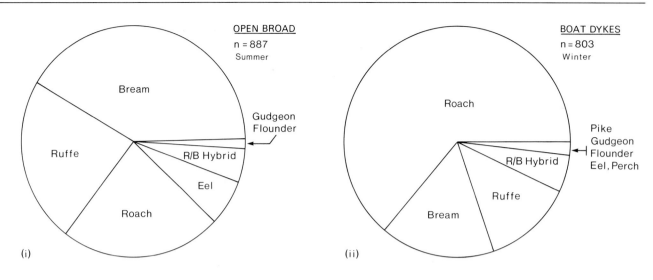

OPEN BROAD
n = 887
Summer

(i)

BOAT DYKES
n = 803
Winter

(ii)

Fig. 5s (i) & (ii)

The species of fish caught in the open water of Barton Broad in the summer of 1979, and in boat dykes off the main Broad the following winter.

Source: Anglian Water Authority (1979b)

Plate XIV

A fishery survey in progress on Wroxham Broad – 1984.

Prior to 1977, when the Anglian Water Authority embarked on a systematic survey of Broadland's fish populations, the information available about them was of a fragmentary and anecdotal nature. This was highly unsatisfactory, given the importance of fish in the Broadland ecosystem, and the large number of anglers who practise their sport in the region. Seine nets, as in this photograph, are now used regularly to monitor the fish populations in all five main rivers, plus several broads.

Photo: National Rivers Authority

The frequency of occurrences of the eleven species and one hybrid caught in the 44 sites sampled in the Thurne system by the AWA was as follows:

Roach	22	Pike	3
Common Bream	7	3–spined Stickleback	
Roach/Bream hybrids	6	(*Gasterosteus aculeatus*)	5
Perch	3	Common Goby	
Flounder	13	(*Pomatoschistus microps*)	2
Eel	2	Smelt (*Osmerus eperlanus*)	10
Rudd	2	Ruffe	2

In the summer, the population is much more evenly distributed, and of 62 sites sampled in 1980, only two were fishless. However, the same species occur as in the winter.

The marked differences between the winter and summer fish populations of the R. Thurne are illustrated by the following figures:

	Summer 1980	*Winter 1980/81*
Max. fish density recorded (nos. per sq.m)	2.1	36.6
Max. fish biomass recorded (grams per sq.m)	3.3	1787.7

The trigger for the onset of these and similar migrations which occur elsewhere in Broadland is almost certainly a change in water temperature, probably in the form of a sudden drop, rather than the occurrence of a specific temperature. Similarly, a rise in water temperatures probably triggers the dispersion of fish into the open water of the broads in the spring (AWA, 1982).

The AWA's surveys have shown that Roach is usually the most abundant species in Broadland, and dominates in terms of community biomass (Fig. 5T). But at many sites, there is a marked lack of older fish, most being in the 2 year age class, with a length of 90 to 120 mm (Fig. 5U). This may, in part be attributed to the poor recruitment to the population which occurred in Broadland, as in other parts of lowland Britain during the mid-1970s. But although young Roach feed on micro-organisms, notably cladocerans, which are normally abundant in the broads and rivers, they favour molluscs and other macro-invertebrates, as they mature. It has been suspected for some time that the scarcity of older Roach in many Broadland waters may be related to the near-absence of such animals in many parts of the region (but not the Thurne broads where the species is sustained by the large population of the shrimp, *Neomysis integer*), and some confirmation of this was provided in 1981, when the AWA discovered that Wroxham Broad

Fig. 5T

(i) The species of fish caught in the R. Ant in 1979, and (ii) the R. Thurne in January and February 1981.

Source: Anglian Water Authority (1979b & NSRD FSR 5/81)

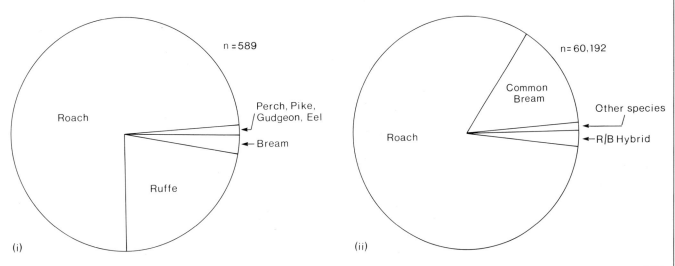

(i)

n = 589

Roach

Ruffe

Perch, Pike, Gudgeon, Eel

Bream

(ii)

n = 60,192

Common Bream

Roach

Other species

R/B Hybrid

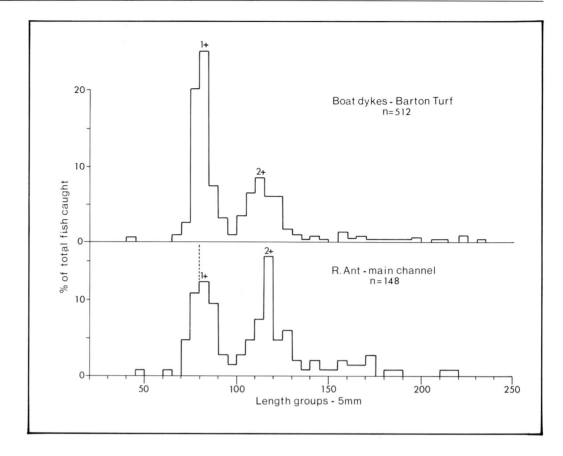

Fig. 5u

Length-frequency histograms of the Roach caught in the R. Ant in 1979.

Source: Anglian Water Authority (1979b)

contains fairly large numbers of older, larger Roach during the summer months, whereas in Salhouse Broad, the population is dominated by young fish (see Figs. 5v (i) & (ii)). It is thought that this may be related to the fact that the macro-invertebrate fauna of the former site is fairly diverse, with approximately 20 species or groups, including eight different Gastropods, whilst that of Salhouse Broad is comparatively impoverished (AWA, 1981).

The situation is complicated, first by uncertainties concerning the extent to which Roach are susceptible to predation by Pike – Peirson *et al.* (1984) believing that they and other fish, such as Perch, are less easily caught in dense weed-beds than in sites in a Phase III condition – and second by behavioural differences between the various age classes. The AWA's surveys of the R. Thurne showed that older Roach have a marked tendency to congregate together in certain favoured off-river localities during the winter. If these fish stay together when they move out into the main river in the spring, this could affect the results and interpretation of the surveys carried out during the summer. There is, in addition, some evidence that Roach tend to move further downriver as they grow older, and it is possible that their reluctance to move back upstream may account in part for the small numbers of larger fish found in mid-valley sites such as Barton Broad.

Cryer *et al.* (1986) have demonstrated that the Roach in Alderfen Broad spawn between mid and late May before waterweeds have had time to develop, and that the females lay their eggs on roots hanging down in the water from trees and herbaceous plants growing around the margin of the site. Good recruitment to the population took place on several occasions, suggesting that the loss of waterweeds from broads which have undergone the switch from Phase II to Phase III may not have directly affected the ability of this species to reproduce successfully in them.

Most workers (e.g. Linfield, 1980) have found that Roach populations contain a few, very strong year classes, and that the years in between are represented by relatively small numbers of fish, or none at all. However, Cryer *et al.* (1986) have demonstrated that the Roach population in Alderfen Broad exhibits a regular alternation of year classes, representing a sequence of good and poor years for recruitment. Their experiments indicate that when fry are abundant, they exercise a heavy grazing pressure on the cladocerans, whose density and mean length are correspondingly low during the summer months.

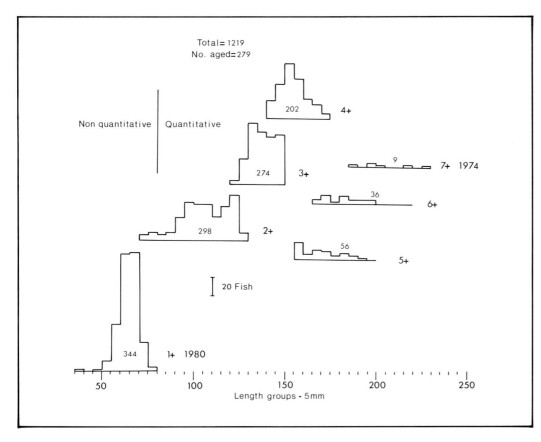

Fig. 5v(i)

The year-class structure of the Roach in Wroxham Broad in June/July 1981.

Source: Anglian Water Authority, NSRD FSR 6/81

The shortage of food available for the fish which will breed the following year reduces their fecundity, with the result that recruitment from the May spawning is poor. The predation pressure exercised by fry on the cladocerans during the ensuing months is relatively slight, and their density and mean size therefore remain fairly large compared with the previous year. This provides the older Roach with an adequate supply of food,

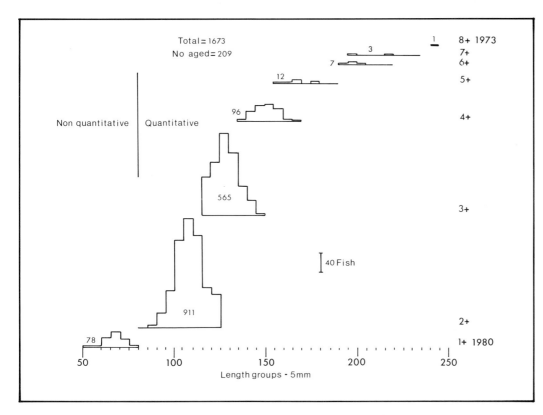

Fig. 5v(ii)

The year-class structure of the Roach in Salhouse Broad in June/July 1981.

Source: Anglian Water Authority, NSRD FSR 6/81

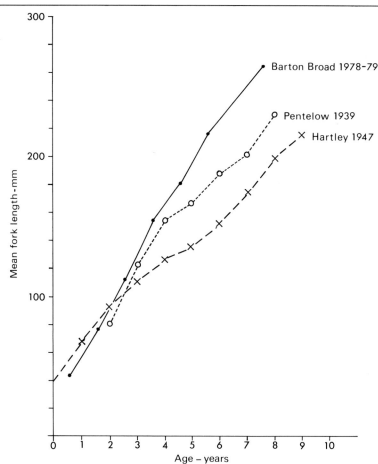

Fig. 5w

Growth rates of the
Roach in Broadland,
1939 to 1979.

*Source: Anglian Water
Authority (1979b)*

their fecundity is enhanced, and they breed successfully the following year, so re-starting
the 2-year cycle.

Cryer *et al.* have pointed out that the conditions in Alderfen Broad are unusual in
several respects, and that the conversion of the site to a Phase II condition (see page
499) may ultimately lead to an improvement in the macro-invertebrate fauna. This
would allow the Roach to survive to a greater age and size, and would probably break
the 2-year cycle of good and poor years for recruitment.

Although the AWA's surveys suggest that the growth rate of Roach in the region is, in
general, well above average (Fig. 5w) up to 20 per cent of the specimens taken from

Fig. 5x

The year-class
structure of the
Common Bream in the
R. Thurne in January/
February 1981.

*Source: Anglian Water
Authority, NSRD FSR
5/81*

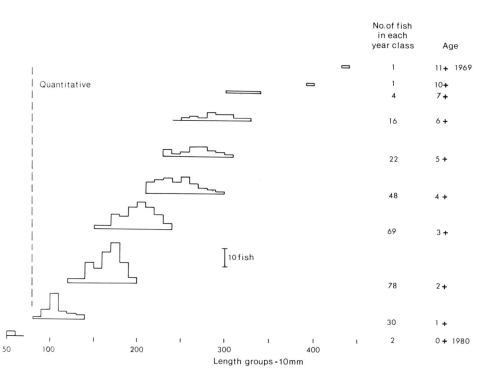

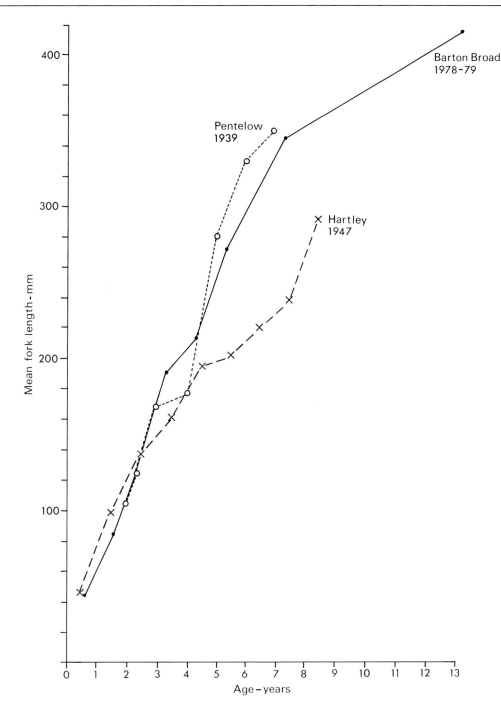

Fig. 5Y

Growth rates of the Bream in Broadland, 1939 to 1979.

Source: Anglian Water Authority (1979b)

some of their sample sites had open lesions, probably caused by bacterial infections induced by stress. In contrast, Common Bream form a healthy, well-balanced population, with a good representation of older fish (Fig. 5x). Unlike Perch and Rudd, which prefer clear, weedy water, and which in consequence are now only present in the region in small numbers, Common Bream are tolerant of turbid conditions and feed almost exclusively on chironomid larvae, tubificid worms and other benthic invertebrates. That the availability of such creatures has not altered greatly during the past 40 years, is suggested by the current growth rate of Bream in Barton Broad, which is as high as that recorded by Pentelow in 1939, and greater than that noted by Hartley in 1947 (Fig. 5Y).

The presence of very young (*c*. 80 mm long) Bream in the publicly navigable broads suggest that this species, like Roach, may be able to breed in them, despite the disturbance. On the other hand, large numbers of both species regularly congregate in off-river sites such as Hoveton Great Broad at spawning time, and such waters probably form an important breeding refuge for these, and perhaps other species.

Interesting insights into the relationships between under-yearling Bream and Roach in the region were obtained by Winfield *et al.* (1983). They confirmed the conclusion reached by other workers, including Brian Moss, that both species find copepods more difficult to catch in the plankton than cladocerans which, with some exceptions (e.g. *Bosmina longirostris*), are larger and relatively slow-moving. However, young Bream, with their protrusible mouths, find it somewhat easier to capture cladocerans, than do Roach of comparable age. Thus if both copepods and cladocerans are present in the plankton, young Roach exert a greater grazing pressure on the latter, than young Bream. A further finding by Winfield *et al.* was that non-planktonic cladocerans (mainly the sediment-living *Chydorus sphaericus*), form an important part of the diet of young Bream. This may be related to the latter's preference for feeding near the bottom, a behaviour pattern characteristic of older specimens.

The absence of quantitative data about Broadland's fish populations prior to the mid-1970s makes it impossible accurately to assess the effects on them of the switch from Phase II to Phase III. However, anecdotal reports by Davies (1884) and others around the turn of the century (when the broads and rivers were still in a Phase II condition) contrast strongly with the present position, as illustrated by the Fish Biomass map which AWA has prepared from the survey data it collected between 1980 and 1984 (AWA, 1985). Only one site in the region, Oulton Broad, is given a Class A rating, indicating that it had a mean biomass of 20 ± 2 grams of fish per square metre (gm^{-2}), although three other broads, together with the R. Thurne and the upper tidal reaches of the Yare and Wensum are categorized as Class B, with a mean biomass of between 10 ± 2 and 20 ± 2 gm^{-2}. Hickling Broad and the R. Bure are given a Class C rating (5 ± 1 to 10 ± 2 gm^{-2} while Horsey Mere, Heigham Sound and the rivers Yare and Waveney are included in Category D, since they had a mean biomass of less than 5 gm^{-2}.

The switch back from Phase III to Phase II could be expected on ecological grounds to have a beneficial effect on the fisheries because of the associated improvement in the benthic invertebrate fauna. Some evidence for this is provided by research at Alderfen Broad by Peirson *et al.* (1984). They have demonstrated that when this site was in a Phase III condition, its fish population was dominated by young Roach, with smaller numbers of Bream, Pike and Tench (*Tinca tinca*), but that a more balanced community developed after the recolonization of the site by waterweeds in 1981 (see page 499). This increase in equitability involved the reappearance of Ruffe and Perch, and an increase in the number and size of Tench (as witnessed by the catching in June 1990 of a specimen weighing 3.3 kg), whilst Roach and Bream became less important in the community.

Mute Swans and angling

In Broadland, as elsewhere, considerable concern was expressed by conservationists from the mid-1960s onwards about the numbers of Mute Swans dying as a result of the activities of anglers. It had, of course, long been appreciated that these birds, in common with Coot, Great-crested Grebes, feral geese and other waterfowl, were at risk as a consequence of becoming entangled with fishing line, and it was suspected that this problem had been exacerbated by the introduction in the late 1950s of nylon, monofilament line, discarded or 'snagged' lengths of which persist for much longer than those made of cotton, silk or flax. However, nationally, the number of ringed birds recorded as having died between 1966 and 1978 as a result of becoming entangled with fishing line, or through predation, or collisions with overhead power lines and other obstructions, was very small compared with the number of corpses for which no cause of death could be given (NCC, 1981).

Evidence that Mute Swans were dying from lead poisoning was first obtained in 1973 from the R. Trent, and subsequent surveys, summarized by the NCC (1981), showed that between 75 and 90 per cent of the total swan mortalities here and elsewhere could be ascribed to this cause, a finding confirmed by subsequent, more detailed research, such as that by Sears (1988) in the Thames valley. Angling, rather than shooting, was incriminated because the majority of the gizzards examined contained 'split-shot' (and in a few cases ledger weights), rather than shot-gun pellets. The latter were only found very occasionally, and then mainly in birds frequenting sites subject to heavy shooting pressure. In seeking to pin the blame on others, some angling correspondents, for example Dyson (1982), claimed that the lead killing the swans was emanating from the exhaust of petrol-engined vessels. However, the wide variation in blood-lead levels found in swans frequenting the same section of navigable river, together with the presence of split-shot pellets in most of the gizzards examined, rendered such assertions totally untenable.

According to Mathiasson (1973) the daily food requirement of an adult swan is about 4 kg of wet vegetable matter, the birds normally feeding mainly on waterweeds. In the absence of such plants (as in much of Broadland), the birds will graze on the marginal reedswamp, or emerge from the water to feed on the river banks or nearby marshland (where they display a partiality for improved grass). Whatever their diet, the food is ground down in the gizzard with the help of grit or fine gravel, picked up by the bird while it is feeding. If split-shot pellets are inadvertently swallowed, these too are retained in the gizzard, the lead being broken down and absorbed by the epithelium of the gut. This affects the bird's neuro-muscular system, the most obvious external manifestation of this being a tendency in the later stages for the lower third of the neck to be supported against the back, instead of being held upright. Internally the food tends to become impacted in the gizzard and oesophagus, the kidneys and liver are damaged, and the bird becomes increasingly anaemic and emaciated, until death ensues.

Len Baker, who founded the Swan Rescue Service at Sparham, Norfolk, in 1977, has claimed that 72 per cent of the 630 Mute Swan deaths he recorded in 1982 (not all in Broadland) could be attributed to angling (including swallowing split-shot, or fish hooks, or becoming entangled in discarded nylon line), 18 per cent to collisions with overhead power lines, 5 per cent to shooting (mainly farmers protecting their crops) and 5 per cent to vandalism (crossbows, air rifles, etc.). Baker (1983) also pointed out that the mean weight of the adult Mute Swans resident in Broadland was about 17 lb (7.7 kg), compared with the normal weight of *c.* 26 lb (11.8 kg), and attributed this to the birds getting out of condition during the summer months as a result of feeding on scraps of bread and other 'junk' food thrown to them by holidaymakers. In contrast, swans from upstream of Coltishall and Norwich, where the rivers contain an abundance of waterweeds, are of near-normal weight, and have a much higher breeding success rate, than those resident in the navigable sections of the same rivers (Baker, pers. comm.).

The hypothesis developed in the early 1980s, therefore, was that when searching for their preferred diet of waterweeds, swans in Broadland were very likely to swallow discarded split-shot lying on or near the sediment surface. The birds were also at risk when they emerged from the water to graze on the river banks, since anglers tended to spill split-shot on these when making up their tackle. The swans were already in poor condition because of their unnatural diet, and this probably made them even more susceptible to lead poisoning than would otherwise have been the case.

Despite the relatively large numbers of Mute Swans which were dying from lead poisoning, censuses organized by the British Trust for Ornithology in 1955, 1961, 1978 and 1983 showed that the numbers of pairs breeding or holding territories in East Norfolk had been rising fairly steadily. The figures for these years were 107, 101, 134, and 163 respectively (Taylor, 1984). The main breeding areas however, had changed. Whereas in 1955 and 1961 the majority of Mute Swans in East Norfolk bred beside the broads and the rivers Bure and Yare, the highest concentrations observed in 1978 and 1983 were in the Halvergate triangle, according to Taylor, and in the marshland adjoining the R. Waveney.

Although in these circumstances, the lead poisoning of swans had to be seen more as an animal-welfare than a nature-conservation problem, a great deal of public concern was expressed on the issue following the publication of the NCC's report in 1981. Some of the measures advocated in this, notably the collection of discarded line, hooks and lead weights were implemented at places such as Wroxham, Oulton Broad, Potter Heigham and Norwich where above-average numbers of swans with high blood-lead levels had been found by the Swan Rescue Service. In addition, fishermen came under strong pressure to adhere to a Code of Practice, published by the Norfolk & Suffolk Anglers Consultative Committee in 1982. But despite this, a minority of anglers continued to practise their sport in a way guaranteed to offend bird-lovers. For instance in September 1984, a 110 m stretch of the R. Wensum near Carrow Bridge, which had been cleared of fishermen's debris 2 years previously, yielded no less than 390 m of line, 42 hooks and 759 pieces of split-lead shot (EDP, 1984).

Spill-proof dispensers for lead shot were introduced in 1983, and it was arranged that the latter would no longer be marketed loose, or in spillage-prone containers. Meanwhile, in the expectation that the use of lead by anglers would sooner or later be banned, a number of tackle manufacturers developed non-toxic substitutes. These were tested in

1984, and in March 1985, following a meeting between representatives of nature conservation and angling interests, and the manufacturers of the alternative products, the NCC decided to recommend the Secretary of State for the Environment to introduce legislation banning, from January 1987 onwards, the sale and use of split-lead weights (except dust shot for which no satisfactory alternative had yet been developed), and ledger weights of 2 oz (57 g) or less.

The Government broadly accepted this recommendation, and in January 1987 it promulgated an Order under the *Control of Pollution Act* 1974 making it illegal to import, or supply to anglers, lead weights of less than 1 oz (28.4 g), apart from dust shot of up to 0.06 g. The Government also urged regional water authorities to introduce by-laws banning the use of lead, and despite opposition from angling organizations, who felt that such regulations would be unenforceable, the AWA decided to impose such by-laws with effect from July 1987. Conservationists welcomed this measure on the grounds that if anglers complied with it, the number of swans dying from lead poisoning was likely to be dramatically reduced.

Unfortunately, injuries and deaths continue to occur as a result of discarded tackle, the problem being worst at sites popular with anglers, such as Rollesby Broad. Baker and Milson (1988) claim that . . . "every swan that lands (here) and stays awhile dies of either hookings or lead poisoning", and in an impassioned plea for a more caring attitude by anglers have called for the use of barbless hooks, and the development of bio-degradable fishing line. They also ask that the edges of heavily fished waters are gritted (so as to reduce the risk of swans picking up lead discarded in the past), that heavy penalties be imposed on litter louts, that water birds should not be fed from boats, that fishing rods should never be left unattended, and that the new lead laws be more stringently enforced. Evidence that the last of these pleas has not fallen on deaf ears is provided by the fact that an angler who was prosecuted by the AWA for using a lead weight on the R. Thurne at Potter Heigham in June 1988 was fined £20, and it is understood that legal proceedings are being taken against other alleged offenders by the AWA's successor, the National Rivers Authority.

Pollution by mercury and tin compounds

During the early 1980s, a major controversy developed as a result of the discovery that a chemical factory in Norwich owned by May and Baker Ltd. (now Rhône Poulenc) had caused a serious pollution problem in Broadland. This first came to light in 1982 when a surface water lagoon near the works was found to have been contaminated by a variety of chemicals, including very high (130 mg kg^{-1} dry wt) levels of mercury. It subsequently became known that the chalk groundwater in the vicinity of the factory had been polluted, most obviously by bromides, and that as a result, two boreholes at AWA's Heigham Street waterworks, which is located about three quarters of a mile away, had been rendered unusable. The R. Wensum, from which the AWA abstracts large quantities of water for treatment at its adjoining works, was fortunately not affected, but the Authority decided that it would not be possible, as intended, to use the chalk aquifers underlying this part of Norwich as an alternative source of supply, in the event that the river was temporarily polluted as a result of an accident at May and Baker's factory, or on the nearby Norwich Ring Road. Instead, it would be obliged to seek powers to move its river water intake upstream to Costessey. This, plus the discovery that the sediment in the R. Yare and its interlinked broads was heavily contaminated by mercury, caused a public outcry.

The Costessey project lies outside the scope of this book, as it concerns a section of the Wensum well to the east of Broadland, as previously defined. Suffice therefore to say that after a public inquiry, during the course of which environmentalists and anglers expressed concern lest the ecology of the river between Costessey and Heigham Street be adversely affected on account of the reduced flow rates, AWA was given the necessary powers to move its abstraction point upstream, and store the water temporarily in Costessey Pits, prior to piping it to its works in Norwich (see page 68).

The pollution of the R. Yare by mercury can be attributed to the fact that between 1964 and c. 1984, the effluent discharged by May and Baker's factory contained significant quantities of this heavy metal, principally in the form of its halides, with copper as a co-pollutant, and that this was being carried via the Norwich sewerage system to the

Whitlingham treatment works. Aware of this, and alarmed by the poor condition of May and Baker's effluent-handling facilities in the early 1980s, the Friends of the Earth had a sample of eels caught in the Yare some 10 km downstream of Whitlingham analysed in 1985. They were found to contain, on average, 0.57 mg of mercury per kilogram (Lees, 1985), a figure subsequently confirmed independently by the AWA. This was a matter of the utmost concern to environmentalists, since under certain conditions, notably in the presence of a plentiful supply of anoxic organic matter, mercury is liable to be transformed by enzyme action into monomethyl mercury. This is water-soluble, very toxic, and prone to bioaccumulate in fish and other forms of wildlife. The relevant EEC Directive indicates that fish sold for human consumption must not contain more than 0.3 mg of mercury per kilogram, and the AWA therefore invited the MAFF to decide whether the sale of eels caught in the Yare should be temporarily banned. In the event, the Department ruled that this was unnecessary. However, preliminary surveys by the AWA indicated that despite the measures taken by May and Baker to reduce the amount of mercury in its effluent (which are reflected in the fact that the mean concentration of this metal in the Whitlingham outfall declined from 0.02 mg l^{-1} in 1976, to between 0.1 and 0.2 µg l^{-1} in the mid-1980s), the pollution of the river was sufficiently serious to warrant a full-scale investigation. Accordingly, the Authority commissioned the Department of Civil Engineering of Imperial College, London, to determine the distribution and quantity of mercury in the sediment, and develop a mathematical model so that predictions could be made of its future behaviour. It was subsequently decided to focus the main investigation on the 20 km stretch of river between Thorpe and Langley, and on Bargate and Rockland Broads.

The survey showed, as expected, that mercuric compounds in the Whitlingham effluent are quickly removed from the water column and incorporated in the sediment. This contained significant quantities of mercury for a distance of some 6 km downstream of the works, the mean concentrations ranging from 0.81 mg kg^{-1} at a point 1.4 km upstream of the outfall, to 11.9 mg kg^{-1} at two sites 2.1 and 3.4 km downstream of it. Mean concentrations in Bargate and Rockland Broads were 7.35 and 7.42 mg kg^{-1} respectively, and the highest individual sample, 32.9 mg kg^{-1}, was encountered 6 km downstream of the Whitlingham works. These figures are the highest recorded for any river in Britain, the mean sediment concentration being between 2 and 30 times the normal background level of 0.4 mg kg^{-1}. The mean concentrations of copper and cadmium in the sediment were also found to be elevated, being between one and four, and two and ten times the published background levels respectively (Imperial College, 1987).

On the basis of the trade-waste data which May and Baker was required to make available to Norwich Corporation, and from 1973 onwards to the AWA, and from its regular monitoring carried out from 1976 onwards, it was calculated that 13 027 kg of mercury had been discharged by the factory since it first started manufacturing chemicals containing this metal in 1964. Records kept of the performance of the Whitlingham works since 1976 suggested that 62 per cent of this would, on average, have been removed on treatment, leaving 4950 kg to be accounted for. On the basis of information supplied by the Port and Haven Commissioners, 1061 kg of this is thought to have been removed in the form of dredgings, while the results of the field survey suggest that a further 1535 kg has been retained in the sediment. The remainder is believed to have been transported downriver and out to sea as soluble mercury.

The depth of the contaminated layer of sediment varies considerably, the dominant accumulations being located in the top 10 cm in the vicinity of the Whitlingham outfall, and at a depth of 10 to 30 cm further downriver. It was thought that this could have resulted partly from variations in the rate at which fresh sediment is deposited in different sections of the river, and partly from disturbance by boating and dredging activities. In either event, it appears likely that little further transportation of contaminated sediments downstream will occur, and that average mercury concentrations in the study area will gradually decline as a consequence of the continued deposition of fresh sediment. Evidence in support of this was forthcoming in October 1989, when 21 eels taken by the National Rivers Authority from various sites in the R. Yare were found to contain, on average, 0.28 mg of mercury per kilogram, the maximum concentration encountered being 0.59 mg Hg kg^{-1} (Crook, *in litt.*).

Methyl mercury levels in the river are variable, ranging from less than 0.07 µg kg^{-1}

upstream of the Whitlingham outfall, to 13.2 and 10.6 µg kg $^{-1}$ 0.5 and 3.5 km downstream of it respectively. Concentrations of between 4 and 13 µg kg $^{-1}$ were found in Rockland Broad, and of 6.4 to 8.4 µg kg $^{-1}$ in Bargate Broad. Although these figures are not unduly high, 0.1 per cent of the inorganic mercury present in a site is converted to methyl mercury each year (Jenelov & Asell, 1975). Given this, and the large quantities of mercury remaining in the sediment of the R. Yare, methylation, and the attendant risk to wildlife, is likely to continue for a long time.

In the mid-1970s, antifouling paints based on organo-tin compounds, notably tributyl tin (TBT), replaced the copper-based formulations previously in use in the region. Although these proved much more effective and long-lasting, research in the early 1980s by staff based at MAFF's Fisheries Laboratory at Burnham-on-Crouch showed that they are leached from boat hulls at concentrations which damage shellfish and other marine organisms in enclosed tidal waters. Despite the introduction of regulations reducing the percentage organo-tin content of paints destined for retail sale, surveys showed that the water quality target set by the Government for TBT (20 nanograms*per litre) were still being exceeded, not only in estuaries such as the Crouch, but in Broadland (Anon, 1986a).

In view of the possibility that such concentrations were having adverse ecological effects, the AWA commissioned research studies on the quantity and distribution of organo-tin compounds in the region, and their impact, if any, on phytoplankton and zooplankton. In addition, the Government made an Order in July 1987 banning their future use both in Broadland and elsewhere. As a result, copper-based anti-fouling paints, which are thought to be relatively innocuous from the ecological point of view are once again in widespread use in the region.

The fauna and flora of the lower reaches of the rivers

Most of the limnological research carried out in the region since the mid-1970s has been focused on the broads, and the rivers and streams with which they are connected, and the lowermost reaches of the three principal rivers and Breydon Water, have in comparison tended to be somewhat neglected by ecologists. However, in 1976 the NCC commissioned Robert Driscoll to survey the rivers Bure and Yare downstream of St. Benets and Surlingham Ferry respectively in order to collect up-to-date information about the distribution and status of their aquatic fauna and flora, and compare the results with those obtained by previous workers from the same areas. Special attention was given to the work of Robert Gurney who, between 1904 and 1929, published a number of papers about these rivers, and in particular their crustacean fauna.

Gurney observed that the varying salinity of the water, and the strong tidal currents, make conditions very difficult for animal life in the lowermost reaches of the rivers, and that their fauna is correspondingly specialized. Gurney also noticed a relationship between invertebrates and waterweeds, pointing out that . . . "there is a good deal of *Potamogeton* and other weeds . . . in sheltered places upstream of Stokesby", and that the invertebrate fauna here was much more varied than that further downstream where weeds were largely absent. In making this comment, he was foreshadowing the results of recent research which has demonstrated that diverse communities of benthic invertebrates are heavily dependent on the presence of underwater 'structure', in the form of a firm bottom substrate or a dense growth of waterweeds, or both.

During the course of his survey Driscoll (1985c) made 84 site visits, which yielded 503 records of live aquatic vertebrates and invertebrates, 60 records of dead molluscs and 158 records of aquatic plants. In addition, 28 species of aquatic invertebrates were found in fen dykes near Wheatfen Broad. The survey revealed, as expected, that many of the groups recorded by earlier workers are very poorly represented today. For instance, Gurney (1904, 1907, 1911 and 1929) listed 31 species of copepods from the R. Bure between Acle Bridge and Yarmouth, including "enormous numbers" of *Tachidius littoralis*. Driscoll's collections of this group were not identified to species level, but he notes that it was only represented by small numbers of individuals, and that it was totally absent from 12 of the 15 sites he sampled between these two places.

---

* A nanogram equals one thousand millionth (10^{-9}) of a gram.

Although the weed and bottom-living faunas once found in the lower reaches of the rivers have largely disappeared, Driscoll found that many of the attached, brackish-water species recorded by Gurney and others are still present. The acorn barnacle, *Balanus improvisus*, for example, is still abundant on piling between St. Benet's and Yarmouth, and was also found by Driscoll at three of his six sampling points downstream of Reedham. Below Three Mile House on the Bure, and Seven Mile House on the Yare, this barnacle has been joined by *Elminius modestus*, an Australian species which first appeared in this country during the last War, and which has since colonized much of our coastline. Another interesting crustacean, *Corophium lacustre*, is an amphipod long thought to be confined in Britain to the slightly brackish waters of the Thurne broads, and the lower reaches of the region's three principal rivers, but which has recently been reported from a site in Hampshire. Driscoll recorded it in 1977 from piling between Ant Mouth and Mautby Marsh Farm on the Bure, and from Brundall, Seven Mile House and Six Mile House on the Yare.

Another species which Driscoll found to be still common on piling, particularly between Ant Mouth and Mautby Marsh Farm on the Bure, and at Strumpshaw, the Beauchamp Arms Inn and Seven Mile House on the Yare, is the brackish-water hydroid *Cordylophora caspia* (formerly known as *C. lacustris*). The sponge, *Ephydatia fluviatilis*, too, occurs on wooden piling at several places between Brundall and the Beauchamp Arms Inn. Crustaceans noted by Gurney, and still present, usually on piling, include *Heteronais ? gurneyi*, *Neomysis integer* and *Leptocheirus pilosus*, but Driscoll was unable to find many of the other species known to have occurred in the past. In contrast, *Gammarus duebeni* and *G. zaddachi*, both of which are brackish-water species, were still present, the latter being very widely distributed and abundant downriver from Ant Mouth and Langley Dyke on the Bure and Yare respectively.

The AWA carried out several surveys of the invertebrate fauna of the Yare between Trowse and Reedham during the 1980s, the main object being to see whether the effluent being discharged from the Whitlingham sewage treatment works is having an adverse effect on the ecology of the river. Many of the localities sampled by the Authority, were not examined by Driscoll, and vice versa, and this, plus the fact that a trawl and colonization samplers were used, rather than the hand-nets employed by Driscoll, makes it difficult to compare the results. However, in general, and not unexpectedly, a greater range of species was recorded by the AWA at the small number of sites (e.g. Surlingham) which had also been sampled by Driscoll. Furthermore, whilst the total number of taxa recorded from the river by the AWA is not greatly dissimilar to that noted by Driscoll, there are considerable imbalances between the different groups. For instance, the AWA recorded 12 molluscs and 7 crustaceans, whereas Driscoll's figures for these phyla were 4 and 15 respectively. But both sets of data show that the faunistic diversity does, as Gurney pointed out, decline downstream of Cantley as a result of the increasing salinity.

The AWA surveys served to confirm, as expected, that the benthic fauna of the Yare is much richer where the bottom sediments are firm, than where there are deep accumulations of soft mud (Matthews, *in litt.*). It is perhaps because of this, rather than pollution *per se*, that the Authority recorded 35 different species on colonization samplers upstream of the Whitlingham outfall in 1981, compared with only 26 downstream of it. Corresponding figures in 1987, using a trawl instead of colonization samplers, were 15 and 11.

Until recently our knowledge of the invertebrate fauna of Breydon Water was heavily dependent on the work of earlier naturalists, notably Arthur Patterson and Robert Gurney. The former recorded a wide variety of molluscs from the site, including the bivalves *Mytilus edulis*, *Cerastoderma edule*, *Tellina baltica*, *Scrobicularia plana* and *Mya arenaria*, and the gastropods *Littorina littorea*, *Hydrobia ulvae* and *Nucella lapillus*. Gurney noted in 1929 that the beds of *Zostera* (probably *Z. marina*) had a very rich fauna in which *Halicyclops magniceps* was the dominant copepod, with numerous ostracods, and immense numbers of the small mollusc, *Potamopyrgus jenkinsi*. Other invertebrates recorded from the site include the rag-worm *Nereis diversicolor*, *Corophium volutator*, *Idothea linearis* and *I. viridis*, *Palaemon squilla*, *Gammarus duebeni*, *Jaera marina* and the copepod *Eurytemora hirundoides*. According to Ellis (1965), the saltings bordering Breydon, and the brackish marsh communities characteristic of the ronds beside the lowermost reaches of the rivers Yare and Waveney, also form the locality of the rare mollusc, *Assiminea grayana*, a species which, like *Potamopyrgus jenkinsi*, is very tolerant of varying salinities.

Following its decision to establish a new nature reserve near Berney Arms (see page 455), the RSPB commissioned A.J. Baxter, a graduate at UEA, to investigate the relationship between Breydon's invertebrate fauna, and the birds which occur on the site itself, and the adjoining marshland. Two sampling areas, together covering *c.* 180 ha, were chosen, one ('A') being centred on the North Flats about midway along the relict estuary, while the other ('B') was located nearer its eastern end (between Ship and Five Stake Drains). 'A' was at a lower level than 'B' and 80 per cent of it was submerged less than three hours after low water, whereas 'B' was exposed for most of the time. The sediment was fairly similar in the two areas, but there was more carbon in 'A' than 'B', and the former contained almost twice as much water. *Zostera marina* was present in Site 'B', but not at 'A', and the abundance of the small gastropod *Hydrobia ulvae* at 'B', and its near absence from 'A', can be related to this difference.

The benthic fauna was sampled by taking 20 cores from each area, and these together yielded 22 taxa. Several of these, for example the amphipod crustacean, *Corophium volutator*, and the tube-living worm, *Capitella capitata*, were only present in small numbers, but the mean densities (per square metre) of the more abundant taxa were as follows:

	Site 'A'	Site 'B'
Oligochaetes (not identified by species)	33 778	
Polychaetes		
Nereis diversicolor	5182	775
Manayunkia aestuarina	3817	29 680
Pygospio elegans	4500	7687
Streblospio shrubsolii	86	743
Eteone longa-flava	90	
Molluscs		
Macoma baltica	3425 (mainly spat)	3906
Hydrobia ulvae	3 individuals only	1989
Retusa obtusa	Nil	612
Cerastoderma edule	*c.* 110	

Breydon has long been renowned for the richness and variety of its birdlife. Wildfowl resident during the winter months include Wigeon, Mallard, Pintail, Shoveler, Tufted Duck, Pochard, Goldeneye, Scaup and Shelduck, and small parties of geese (White-fronted, Pink-footed, Brent, Bean and sometimes Barnacle) also occur. Waders too, are plentiful, and include Grey Plover, Curlew Sandpiper, Dunlin (*c.* 4500 in 1975), Red-shank (*c.* 1000 in 1975), Black-tailed and Bar-tailed Godwit, Curlew, and Whimbrel. Spoonbill, Avocet (11 in 1975) and Black Tern occur on passage almost every year, and the site is regularly visited by parties of Twite, Lapland Bunting and Snow Bunting, the latter often in quite large numbers (O'Riordan, 1976b). Terek Sandpiper and Greater Yellowlegs were recorded in 1975 as 'firsts for Norfolk', while other rarities seen on Breydon during the past 30 to 40 years include American Golden Plover (in 1976), Caspian and Gull-billed Terns, Little Egret, Purple and Night Herons, Black Stork, American Wigeon, Ring-necked Duck, Greater Sand Plover, White-rumped and Pectoral Sandpipers, Wilson's Phalarope and a succession of Broad-billed Sandpipers (Allard, 1988).

Populations of Eel and Smelt are commercially exploited in Breydon, and in October 1987, the AWA carried out a fisheries survey, using an otter trawl. Ten, mainly brackish-water species were caught, their occurrence at the five sites sampled, being as follows:

Species	Occurrence	Total nos.*
Flounder (*Platichthys flesus*)	5	242
Common Goby (*Pomatoschistus microps*)	5	134
Smelt (*Osmerus eperlanus*	4	68
Eelpout (Viviparous Blenny) (*Zoarces viviparus*)	3	8
Whiting (*Merlangius merlangus*)	3	58
Pogge (Hooknose) (*Agonus cataphractus*)	2	32
Sprat (*Sprattus sprattus*)	2	8
Sole (*Solea solea*)	2	5
Sea Snail (*Liparis liparis*)	1	2
Eel (*Anguilla anguilla*)	1	1

* Note. No great significance should be attached to these figures, as several of the species listed (e.g. Eels) are not readily caught in an otter trawl.

Feral waterfowl

Large numbers of Greylag and Canada Geese occur in Broadland, and a third species, the Egyptian Goose – which despite its English name is more closely related to a Shelduck than a goose – is also likely to be seen on or near the waterways. The introduction of Greylags to the region is usually attributed to the late Col. H. J. Cator who, in 1935, brought back to his estate at Ranworth a pair of birds injured on the Solway. These bred for the first time in 1938, and the progeny reared in this and subsequent years were allowed to fly off (F. Cator, pers. comm.). The resultant stock shows no signs of in-breeding, and it would thus seem likely that their numbers have been augmented, either by occasional migrant wild birds which decided to stay on, or by escapees or releases from the wildfowl collections of other landowners.

Owen and Salmon (1988) suggest that there were about 300 feral Greylags in Broadland in the 1960s, but this is probably an under-estimate, based on the numbers of birds seen congregated at sites such as St. Benet's, Horning and Salhouse and Wroxham Broads, rather than in the whole region (see Plate 13). Anecdotal reports suggest that the population may have declined slightly in the mid-1970s as a result of outbreaks of avian botulism, but the numbers of birds increased dramatically during the 1980s, and a flock of 650 was counted on Salhouse Broad in 1985 (Salmon *et al.*, 1987). Comprehensive data are quite difficult to obtain, as although the main concentrations of birds still occur in the middle Bure valley, virtually the entire region has now been colonized. A survey by A. J. Prater and others in 1989 gave a total of 2537 birds, made up of 1149 adults, 732 juveniles, and 206 un-aged birds (Prater, pers. comm.). But even these figures understate the total population in the region, as no attempt was made to count the birds known to occur on Oulton Broad and the R. Waveney upstream of Haddiscoe or, apart from the R. Chet and Hardley Flood, the Yare up-valley of Reedham.

Using data derived from 35 areas in the British Isles where feral Greylags occur, Owen and Salmon have estimated that their numbers are increasing at a rate of about 13 per cent per year, and there is no reason to believe that the Broadland population is any different. This is an alarming prospect since, being gregarious, the birds close-graze and foul recreational grasslands in the vicinity of the rivers and broads. More serious from the ecological point-of-view, they constitute one of the reasons why reedswamp is regressing (see Chapter 6). They also cause much agricultural damage, particularly to crops of cereals shortly before they are due to be harvested.

Although the Greylag is listed as a quarry species in the *Wildlife and Countryside Act 1981*, and can therefore be shot in Broadland from the first of September until the thirty-first of January, only about 250 birds are accounted for in this way each year. This is probably not sufficient to maintain the population at its present level, let alone reduce it (Prater, pers. comm.). Because of the damage caused by the birds, landowners already shoot more than they need for culinary purposes, and the position is not helped by Section 6(2) of the Act, since this makes it illegal to sell geese which have been shot. This removes one of the incentives which wildfowlers might otherwise have had to shoot more birds. Other possible control measures, such as netting the birds when they are moulting, or using narcotizing agents, would have to be done under licence, and would certainly prove highly controversial, not least among holidaymakers who derive much pleasure from seeing (and feeding!) the birds at sites such as Salhouse Broad. Egg-pricking, which would also have to be done under licence, has not proved an effective method of holding the numbers of feral geese in check (Owen *et al.*, 1986). In any event, it would be extremely difficult to apply in Broadland as the nests are often sited in dense, jungle-like fen terrain, where they are difficult to locate.

It is not known when Canada Geese first colonized the rivers and broads. Stevenson (1890) mentions that 100 to 150 free-winged birds were present on the Gunton Estate in north Norfolk in the 1890s, and there was almost certainly a flock on Holkham Lake at this time also. Occasional birds are likely to have spread out southwards from these sites, but as late as 1953, there were still only 725 birds in the whole of East Anglia and Essex (Owen *et al.*, 1986). Since then, their numbers have increased dramatically, and Prater's 1989 census (which covered the same areas as for the Greylags) indicated that there were at least 742 Canada Geese in Broadland, comprising 576 adults, 109 juveniles and 57 un-aged birds (Prater, pers. comm.).

According to Owen *et al.*, the feral population of Canada Geese in Britain is currently increasing at a rate of about 8 per cent per year, and although this goose, like the Greylag, is a quarry species, insufficient numbers are currently being shot in the region, even to stabilize the population, let alone reduce it.

Free-flying flocks of Egyptian Geese were established at Holkham, Beeston and other estates in North Norfolk in the early eighteenth century (Owen *et al.*, 1986), and it is likely that the Broadland birds are derived from these. Their numbers remained quite small during the 1960s and 1970s, but have certainly increased markedly since then; indeed, Prater recorded 98 adults and 25 juveniles in 1989.

Chapter 6
The Marginal Reedswamp Communities

The emergent water's-edge vegetation which comprises reedswamp is of great environmental importance in Broadland. Not only does it form the ecological link between waterweed and fen communities, but it provides a habitat for a wide variety of birds and animals. Great Crested Grebe, Coot, Moorhen, Reed and Sedge Warblers, and in more secluded waters, Pochard, breed in it, Roach and other fish use it as a spawning ground, while its invertebrate fauna includes the Rush Wainscot moth (*Archanara algae*) as well as several other Broadland 'specials'. Reedswamp is also of importance aesthetically. Most people would agree that a reed-fringed stretch of river is scenically much more attractive than one whose banks have been piled, and on the broads, too, a band of reedswamp forms a welcome visual contrast between the open water, and the trees and bushes which now commonly grow on the adjoining fens.

Last, but not least, reedswamp plays a vital role in flood protection, as its principal component beside the rivers, *Phragmites*, has a pronounced cushioning effect on the wave action generated by wind and boats. Bonham (1980) has shown from experiments on the R. Thames that 60 per cent of the energy of boat wash is dissipated by a stand of Reed 2 metres wide, and that bank erosion above the water line is negligible in such circumstances.

Although Broadland's reedswamps may contain a number of different emergent plants, *Phragmites* is by far the commonest. The seeds of this species will not germinate in water more than about 1 cm deep (Haslam, 1973), and consequently Reed growing in the marginal reedswamp must have originated as a result of the vegetative propagation of plants growing in the water or sediment nearby, or in the adjoining fen or bank-edge vegetation. Crook, Boar and Moss (1983), who have studied the *Phragmites* growing beside the broads, have pointed out that it occurs as two distinct growth forms. In each, the aerial shoots are borne on vertical rhizomes, but in 'littoral-reed', the horizontal rhizomes from which the latter are budded off are embedded in the sediment, whereas those of 'hover-reed' are immersed in the water. Littoral-reed, being securely anchored in the sediment forms a physically stable community, unlike hover-reed which typically consists of a floating or semi-floating raft of roots and rhizomes, some 0.5 m thick, sections of which are liable to break adrift and float away as a result of wave or tidal action. It would appear that hover-reed is structurally similar to the *plav* which occupies much of the Danube delta (Pallis, 1916), but it never forms such a thick mattress in the broads, nor are the aerial shoots anything like so tall and robust.

The *Phragmites*-dominated reedswamps beside the rivers have not been studied in such detail as those found around the margins of the broads, but all the stands so far examined have been referable to either the floating or sediment-rooted growth forms.

The marginal reedswamp of the rivers

Little is known about the communities which bordered the rivers in medieval times, but *Phragmites* is likely to have predominated beside their middle and upper reaches in view of its ability to grow in low-nutrient water (Newbold & Palmer, 1979). Further downstream, the rivers would have been bordered by saltmarsh until they were embanked, but later, as tidal action, and therefore salinities, decreased as a consequence of the southwards growth of the Yarmouth shingle spit, Reed would have spread further downstream until even Breydon Water was fringed by it.

The gently sloping margins of the river channels would have favoured the growth of a wide band of littoral-reed. However, an indication that hover-reed was also present is provided by the frequent references in the navigation authority's archives to the need to dredge and 'draw' the rivers (see Chapter 11) and also by an official notice issued by Norwich Corporation in 1741, which enjoined riparian owners to . . . "cut their banks and draw their hoves (*sic*) and weeds".

During Victorian times, the band of reedswamp would have tended to become narrower as the margins of the river channels steepened as a consequence of the combined effects of dredging and greater tidal scouring. Meanwhile, Bulrush (*Schoenoplectus lacustris*) and Lesser Reedmace (*Typha angustifolia*), both of which are rather less tolerant of low-nutrient water than *Phragmites* (Newbold & Palmer, 1979) were probably becoming increasingly abundant in the community as a result of the progressive enrichment of the rivers taking place during this period. Early photographs confirm that all three species were present beside certain reaches of the rivers at the turn of the century.

The mid-nineteenth century dredging of the bar at the mouth of the Haven and the channel across the Burgh Flats to facilitate the commercial use of the R. Yare (see Chapter 11), allowed saline water to penetrate further upstream than in the previous few centuries, and this would have led to the continuing regression of the reedswamp beside the lowermost reaches of the three principal rivers. Paterson (1905) remarks that the reedy fringes of Breydon Water, which had previously been much favoured by wildfowlers as cover, had disappeared by the turn of the century, and there can be little doubt that this was due to the increasing salinity.

Further upstream, a vigorous growth of reedswamp persisted at the water's edge, particularly where the rivers were bordered by undrained, reed-dominated fens, and by ronds from which cattle and sheep had been excluded so that the stands of *Phragmites* growing thereon could be harvested, as are those beside the R. Waveney at Somerleyton and the R. Bure at Stokesby today. However, early photographs suggest that many sections of the rivers were bordered in late Victorian times by Yellow Iris (*Iris pseudoacorus*) and various sedges (*Carex* spp.) rather than by Reed. This may have been due to the practice of allowing livestock to graze the embankments and ronds, since similar, reed-free communities exist today just downstream of St. Benet's Abbey, and a few other places where farmers continue to allow their cattle to graze the ronds, despite the risk of them being injured by the broken glass, plastic bags and other litter dumped on the river banks by anglers and boat-borne visitors.

Schoenoplectus and *Typha* were frequent components of the reedswamp bordering the rivers until the 1940s, but the former species is now rare, apart from a good stand beside Somerton Dyke, adjacent to Martham South Broad, and scattered patches alongside the R. Waveney between Beccles and Burgh St. Peter. Lesser Reedmace, too, is relatively uncommon, and if present at all, usually forms mixed stands with Reed; occasionally it grows on its own, as beside the R. Bure near St. Benet's.

It is not altogether clear why these species are so much less common now than they were in the period up to the Second World War, but neither is as tolerant of hypereutrophic conditions as *Phragmites* (Wheeler, pers. comm.). In addition, as the river channel profiles steepened as a result of boat wash and increased tidal scouring, both species would have been confined to a narrowing band of water's-edge habitat as a consequence of their inability to grow in water more than about 1.5 m deep. When growing under such conditions, the plants would have been more susceptible to physical damage and being up-rooted than are wider stands. Moreover, in some places the banks are near perpendicular, or even undercut, and in the latter event, it is impossible for *Schoenoplectus*, *Typha* or the sediment-rooted form of *Phragmites* to grow at all.

Payne and Hey (1982) have pointed out that, provided tide-induced variations in the water level are minimal, the floating form of Reed can occur beside the rivers, even though the latter have very steeply shelving margins. But although this growth form can withstand a limited amount of boat wash, it is liable to produce hovers, and ultimately break up altogether if struck by large numbers of high amplitude waves of short duration, such as are now generated in the rivers by holiday craft during the summer months. It is probably because of this that hover-reed is now poorly developed, or missing altogether from many of the places where it used to occur; further downsteam, it is absent as a consequence of the inability of this growth form to tolerate the tide-induced fluctuations in water level which occur in the lower reaches of all three of the main rivers.

There can be little doubt that the rate of bank erosion increases once a section of river bank has lost its fringing band of reedswamp, but 'before and after' measurements of this process have yet to be made. In the lower reaches of the rivers, the edges of the ronds are probably provided with a degree of protection at high tide, on account of the well-rooted 'fen' reed growing thereon, but at low tide their steeply sloping edges are totally unprotected against boat wash and tidal scour.

In addition to channel erosion and undercutting, several other factors are contributing to the loss of marginal reedswamp from the rivers; these include shading by trees and

Table 6a   The distribution of marginal reedswamp beside the rivers

River	Total length of undeveloped bank	Areas bordered by fen				Areas bordered by drained marsh					
		Length (m)	% con-tinuous reed	% discon-tinuous reed	% ± no reed	Length (m)	% con-tinuous reed	% discon-tinuous reed	% ± no reed	% piled with wood composite etc.	% piled with steel
Bure (Wroxham Br. to Yarmouth)	71 398	21 088	13	14	73	50 310	17	28	27	8	20
Ant (excl. Barton Broad)	21 438	11 445	12	23	65	9 993	36	19	17	27	1
Thurne (Dungeon Corner to Thurnemouth)	12 997	Nil	–	–	–	12 997*	59	18	10	13	Nil
Yare (confluence with R. Wensum to Berney Arms)	69 470	15 931	Nil	4	96	55 539	27	16	27	13	17

* Excluding lengths of bank bordered by bungalows.

Source: Compiled from data collected by R. Driscoll and M. Jackson in 1977. Unfortunately this survey did not extend to the R. Waveney.

bushes growing near the water's-edge (a problem mainly confined to sections of river bordered by unreclaimed fen); grazing by waterfowl; and physical damage to the reed shoots by vessels being driven into, or too close to, the bank. The angler's habit of trampling and cutting the vegetation growing at the water's-edge in order to improve a 'swim' is also liable to increase the rate at which reedswamp is regressing locally (see Plate XV). To combat this problem the Broads Authority has provided small fishing platforms at one or two places, notably on the right bank of the river Bure just downstream of Horning Ferry. However, care has to be taken in the siting of such structures as they can form a hazard to passing vessels.

It will be seen from Table 6a that continuous stands of Reed are now absent from many lengths of river bank, particularly where these are bordered by fen vegetation; indeed, the Yare between Surlingham and Rockland is almost devoid of this community. In contrast, one of the best examples of littoral reedswamp in the northern river system is to be seen between Dydler's Mill and the entrance to Hoveton Little Broad – a section of the Bure bordered by fen vegetation. Despite this and similar anomalies, reedswamp tends to be better developed where the rivers are bounded by drained marshland, than by fen, and although the criteria used in distinguishing between continuous and discontinuous stands of this community are highly subjective, it would appear that Reed is better developed beside the Thurne, than the Bure, Ant or Yare. Data on the status of reedswamp in the Waveney valley are not available, but casual observations suggest that most sections of this river are still reed-clad.

Once a stretch of river has lost its fringing reedswamp, from whatever cause, or combination of causes, re-invasion of the open water will not take place, even under ideal conditions, unless one or other of the component species of the community is growing on or near the bank, and can extend its rhizomes outwards. However, all too often any reed plants growing thereon have already succumbed as a result of the shade cast by overhanging trees, excessive trampling or grazing by cattle, Coypu or waterfowl. The Rivers Commissioners' practice of using the edges of the fens, or less frequently, the ronds, as a dumping ground for dredgings contributed to the problem as these are rich in nutrients, and are consequently soon colonized by a rampant growth of Stinging Nettles (*Urtica dioica*), Great Hairy Willow-herb (*Epilobium hirsutum*) and other coarse species. These tend to suppress any remaining reed plants. In addition, the piles of spoil, once dry, prevent Reed growing in the adjoining fens from spreading outwards towards the rivers, and thus recolonizing their margins.

The AWA and its successor, the National Rivers Authority, is well aware of the wave-cushioning role of marginal stands of Reed and the fact that once a river bank has been over-steepened by boat wash, it will not be able to fulfill this function owing to the inability of its littoral growth form to grow in water more than about 1.5 m deep, and the susceptibility of hover-reed to damage by wave and tidal action. Accordingly, the Authority has carried out several management experiments aimed at finding ways of re-profiling an eroded bank artificially, and re-establishing Reed on it, thus saving the very high cost of piling the affected section. The first such trial was executed in 1977 on a *c.* 100 m section of the right bank of the R. Thurne near Coldharbour, but was abortive owing to the premature collapse of the bund which was providing temporary protection to the reeds planted on the freshly re-profiled channel margin.

The next experiment, carried out in 1981, was located near South Walsham pump on the right bank of the Bure, and was modelled on a suggestion by A.J. Bonham when he was working temporarily at the Hydraulics Research Station at Wallingford (Bonham, 1980). Old car tyres were used to protect two 30 m long sections of the rapidly eroding river bank against wave action, and the area behind these was back-filled to encourage the growth of Reed. Again, the experiment was not wholly successful, mainly because of the breaching of the membrane placed between the tyres and the bank, and the consequent wash-out of some of the back-fill material. In addition, owing to technical difficulties encountered during the installation of the tyres, they were set rather too high; as a result they are exposed at low tide and look even more unsightly than conventional piling.

Further experiments were carried out during the winter of 1985/6 near Thurne Mouth. In the first, sheet piling was driven underwater to a level such that it was only uncovered at dead low water. The piling was then back-filled with clay, and reed rhizomes laid on top; these were held in place by a 2 m wide band of a proprietary, asphalt-based matting, Enkamat A20 (Fig. 6A). Although the Reed grew quite well

Plate XV

Fishing in the R. Bure, near Acle Bridge – 1990.

Reed is intolerant of trampling and cutting during the summer months, and anglers are undoubtedly contributing to the losses of marginal reedwamp, albeit unintentionally and in strictly localized areas. Other factors, notably the shade cast by trees and bushes growing at the water's-edge, undercutting by boat wash, and grazing by waterfowl, are much more important reasons for the disappearance of this community from many river reaches. In addition, research has shown that it is performing poorly because of an imbalance between the amounts of nitrogen and potassium in the water.

Photo: R.N. Flowers

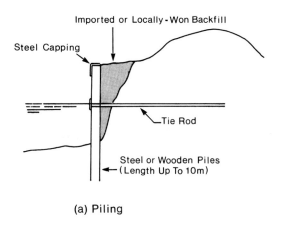

(a) Piling

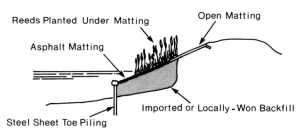

(b) Toe Piling and Asphalt Matting

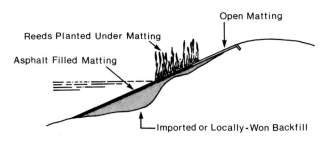

(c) Asphalt Matting Laid to Graded Bank

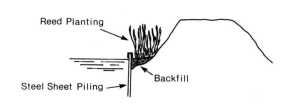

(d) Low Level Piling

Fig. 6A

Four different methods of river bank protection currently being practised in Broadland by the National Rivers Authority.

Source: National Rivers Authority (Anglian Division)

through this, it was heavily grazed by feral geese, and it proved necessary to protect it with wire netting.

In the second experimental site near Thurne Mouth, the whole of the channel margin was regraded, an underwater operation which proved difficult to accomplish. The new surface was then covered by reed rhizomes, over which was laid Ankamat matting. Again, it proved necessary to protect the reed shoots with wire netting, but they have grown reasonably well, especially at and above mean water level. A variation of this technique, involving the use of an experimental matting supplied by MMG and Tarmac Ltd., was employed successfully on the left bank of the R. Ant at Chapelfield Marsh in February 1987.

Wire mesh mattresses have been tried out on the left bank of the Bure at Mautby and opposite South Walsham pump, but these cannot be used below water, and they do not form a substitute for piling. Nevertheless, reed growth through them has been very good. Another trial, involving the laying of three-dimensional plastic webbing on a re-profiled section of the bank of the Bure near Upton Mill, was carried out in April 1986. However, this proved unsuccessful, as the material proved difficult to install, and the backfill between the grids tended to wash out.

As part of their continuing efforts to find an environmentally 'friendly' substitute for conventional piling, the AWA decided in 1989 to carry out a full-scale trial of Armorflex-180 on a re-profiled section of the right (south) bank of the R. Bure, about three-quarters of a mile upstream of the Eurocentre at Great Yarmouth. Over 4200 square metres of this material (which consists of cable-tied cellular concrete blocks made up into flexible mats) were laid on Nicolon F300, a woven geotextile which, like Armorflex-180, is marketed by MMG Civil Engineering Systems, and it is hoped that the spaces between the cellular blocks will in due course be colonized by *Phragmites* and other species.

The National Rivers Authority intends to carry out further experiments with proprietary products during the next few years, and it has been arranged that the performance of reed transplants at these, and the experimental sites referred to above, will be monitored by staff of the Broads Authority.

The marginal reedswamps of the broads

(a) Historical

Emergent plants would have been quick to colonize the margins of the medieval peat pits once these had become permanently flooded. However, the width of the reedswamp fringe would have varied according to whether the broad had gently sloping edges as a result of occupying a working which had been dug right up to the valley margin, or whether it had near-perpendicular walls as a consequence of the peat pit having been bordered, on flooding, by unworked alluvial deposits. The Trinity Broads, and Fritton Lake fall into the former category, and would, like the rivers, have been bordered by a fairly wide band of emergent vegetation. In contrast, the edges of sites such as Decoy and Surlingham Broads, which are bounded on all sides by unreclaimed fen, would have shelved so precipitously that any marginal reedswamp present would, at least initially, have been confined to a relatively narrow band. Sites such as Wroxham Broad, whose southern and western margins were gently sloping but whose other walls were near-perpendicular would have been bordered respectively by wide and narrow bands of reedswamp. This community would also have been present on any islands and baulks of peat left behind by the peat cutters, since the water here would have been relatively shallow. However, elsewhere the water would have been far too deep to permit the colonization of emergent species.

The species composition of the reedswamp during this early period, which at most sites lasted for at least 400 years, is likely to have been rather different to that prevailing today, in view of the low concentrations of nutrients in the water. Stratigraphical studies (Jennings, 1952; Lambert & Jennings, 1960) have shown that peat produced by Saw-sedge (*Cladium mariscus*) occurs here and there around the edges of the workings now occupied by Barton, Ranworth, Buckenham, Wheatfen and Upton Broads, and it would therefore seem that this species predominated initially in at least some of the reedswamp communities which colonized these, and perhaps other sites. But the ability of *Phragmites* to grow in low-nutrient water meant that it was at least as well able as *Cladium* to tolerate the conditions which prevailed in the broads prior to *c.* 1800, and cores confirm that at many sites it was the principal component of the reedswamp soon after the peat diggings were flooded. In addition, any *Cladium* peat is almost always overlain by *Phragmites* remains, showing that Reed succeeded Saw-sedge where this was the initial colonizer.

From about 1800 onwards, the ecology of the reedswamp of the broads was affected, first by a rise in nutrient concentrations in the water, which led to the progressive disappearance from most sites of *Cladium*, and the increasing abundance of *Schoenoplectus* and *Typha*, and second by continued sedimentation, which resulted in more and more sites becoming shallow enough to allow emergent plants to colonize the open water. Pallis (1911b) notes that the first species to do this in the Ant valley broads was *Schoenoplectus*, and early photographs, suggest that it fulfilled a similar role in other broads. This can be attributed partly to the ability of this species to grow in slightly deeper water than either *Phragmites* or *Typha*, and partly to its greater resistance to exposure (Hutchinson, 1975). Lesser Reedmace followed once sedimentation had reduced the mean water depth to about 1.5 m, and this was later joined by Reed to form communities containing varying proportions of the three species, and referable to an Association known to phytosociologists as the *Schoenoplecto-Phragmitetum*. A brief explanation of this form of nomenclature is given in the next Chapter.

Confirmation that *Typha* normally preceded *Phragmites* in the succession which occurred in the Bure, Ant, Thurne and Waveney valley broads is afforded by old photographs which often show a well-marked band of Lesser Reedmace between the open water and the reed-fringed margins of the site. In addition, stratigraphic cores show that in broads in the Bure valley which have become partly overgrown (and where the vegetation has therefore formed over deep accumulations of sediment), the *Phragmites* peat is usually underlain by a thin layer of *Typha* rhizomes, amongst which are scattered patches of *Schoenoplectus* remains (Lambert & Jennings, 1951).

Just how prolific the growth of Bulrushes in the broads was at the turn of the century is illustrated, not only by old photographs (see Plate XVI), but by a transect across Barton Broad (see Plate XVII), one of the first such diagrams ever to be published

Plate XVI

Alderfen Broad – 1917.

Note the abundance of the true Bulrush (whose stems and flowers show up best as reflections in the water) and Lesser Reedmace. The leaves of a water-lily, probably *Nymphaea alba*, can be seen in the reedswamp to the left.

Early descriptions of the region often refer to the difficulty of rowing across some of the shallower broads, and this photograph provides the explanation!

Photo: Robert Gurney

(Pallis, 1911b). In addition, Weaver (1908) points out that Bulrushes rendered many broads almost impossible to row across during this period.

Bulrushes (which were known locally as 'bolder') were regularly harvested in the past, long-handled scythes being used to cut the plants well below the water surface during the summer months. Weaver records that after being dried and bundled, they were made up into rush matting or chair seats, or, if mixed with Lesser Reedmace ('gladden'), into 'frail' baskets or braided horse collars, the wiry stems of Bog-rush (*Schoenus nigricans*) being used to stitch up these products (Bird, 1919). There were probably several small factories thus engaged during the late nineteenth and early twentieth centuries, the 'mat factory' beside Buckenham Wood, which was in business between the two world wars, being a typical example. When founded in the 1930s, the rush-weaving business conducted by Waveney Apple Growers of Aldeby, relied heavily on Bulrushes harvested from the broads, but the firm now has to obtain all the materials it needs from Holland (see Plate XVIII).

Making rush matting – 1989.   Plate XVIII

Only one firm, Waveney Apple Growers of Aldeby, near Burgh St. Peter, is currently engaged in this traditional trade, and it is obliged to import the bulrushes it needs from Holland, as this species is now rare in Broadland.

After being steeped, the bulrushes are woven into 4 in (10 cm) wide braids. Six of these are then stitched together, and these in turn are made up into a mat of the required size. Bulrushes are also used by the firm to manufacture log and dog baskets.

Photo: R.N. Flowers

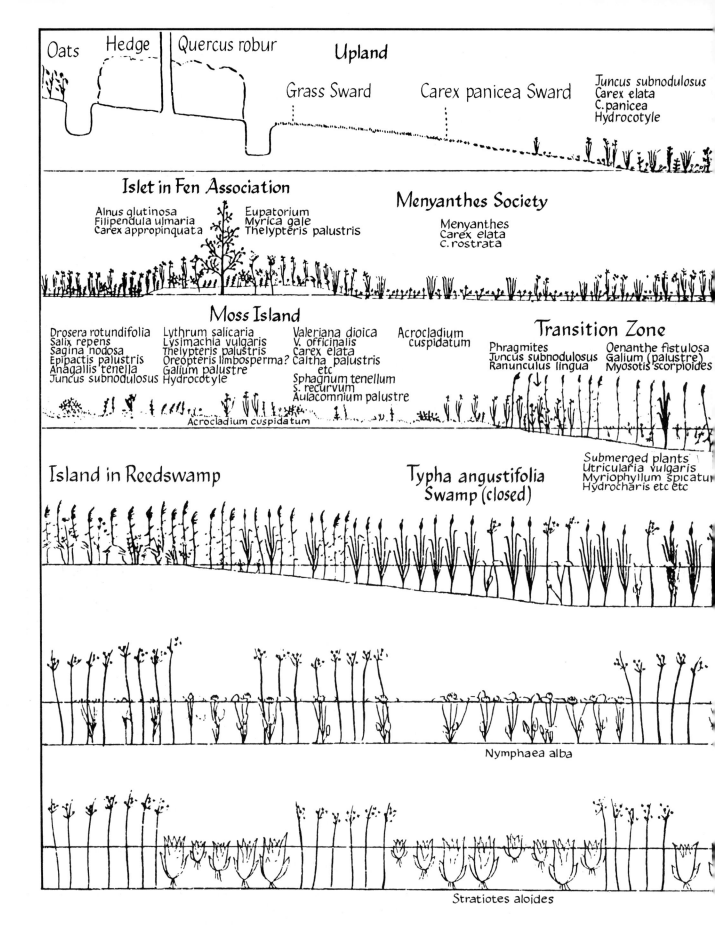

Plate XVII

The plant communities of Barton Broad and the fens to the west as they were in the early 1900s.

This transect, which has a horizontal scale of about 1 : 200, and a vertical scale of *c.* 1 : 150, forms one of the illustrations in an account of Broadland's wetland communities by Marietta Pallis; this was included by Tansley in his 'Types of British Vegetation', published in 1911. It is not only one of the earliest known attempts to portray the zoning of plant communities, but provides us with a valuable insight into what Barton Broad and its adjoining fens looked like at the turn of the century. In re-drawing the diagram, the opportunity has been taken to up-date the plant names in use in Pallis' time. Her inclusion of the fern *Lastrea montana* (known today as *Oreopteris limbosperma*) amongst the plants she found on 'Moss Island' may have been an error.

Note that the true Bulrush was the first emergent species to colonize the open water of the Broad,

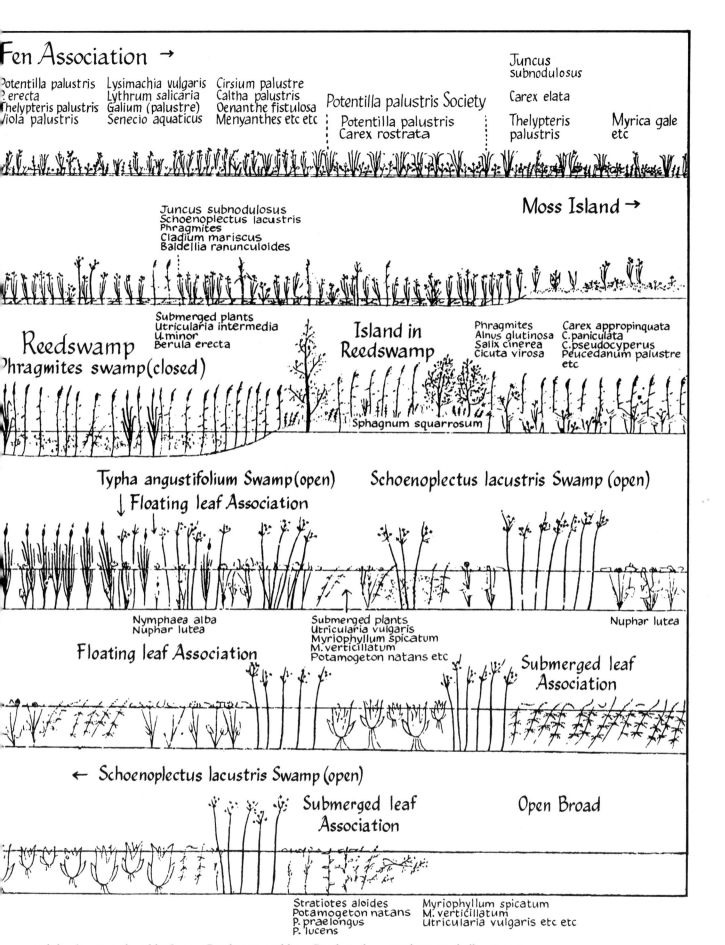

Fen Association →

Potentilla palustris   Lysimachia vulgaris   Cirsium palustre
P. erecta   Lythrum salicaria   Caltha palustris
Thelypteris palustris   Galium (palustre)   Oenanthe fistulosa
Viola palustris   Senecio aquaticus   Menyanthes etc etc

Juncus subnodulosus

Carex elata

Potentilla palustris Society
   Potentilla palustris
   Carex rostrata

Thelypteris palustris

Myrica gale etc

Moss Island →

Juncus subnodulosus
Schoenoplectus lacustris
Phragmites
Cladium mariscus
Baldellia ranunculoides

Submerged plants
Utricularia intermedia
U. minor
Berula erecta

Reedswamp
Phragmites swamp (closed)

Island in Reedswamp

Phragmites   Carex appropinquata
Alnus glutinosa   C. paniculata
Salix cinerea   C. pseudocyperus
Cicuta virosa   Peucedanum palustre
   etc

Sphagnum squarrosum

Typha angustifolium Swamp (open)   Schoenoplectus lacustris Swamp (open)
↓ Floating leaf Association

Nymphaea alba
Nuphar lutea

Submerged plants
Utricularia vulgaris
Myriophyllum spicatum
M. verticillatum
Potamogeton natans etc

Nuphar lutea

Floating leaf Association

Submerged leaf Association

← Schoenoplectus lacustris Swamp (open)

Submerged leaf Association

Open Broad

Stratiotes aloides   Myriophyllum spicatum
Potamogeton natans   M. verticillatum
P. praelongus   Utricularia vulgaris etc etc
P. lucens

and that it was replaced by Lesser Reedmace, and later Reed, as the water became shallower as a consequence of continued sedimentation. Examples of this succession are now extremely rare in the region.

The waterweeds observed by Pallis include Water Soldier (which at the time had only been known in Britain for about 25 years), Greater Bladderwort, the Spiked and Whorled Water-milfoils, the pondweeds *Potamogeton natans, P. praelongus* and *P. lucens* and White Water-lily (known in Pallis' day as *Castalia alba*). These Phase II plants succumbed during the 1950s as a result of nutrient enrichment, and attempts to get Water Soldier, Yellow Water-lily and various other species re-established in the site have so far proved unavailing.

Pallis' diagram was re-lettered by Cecil Smith

Plate XIX

A view from the north-western corner of Ranworth Broad – 1949.

This site, together with Cockshoot Broad and the adjoining fens, had just been donated to the Norfolk Naturalists' Trust by Col. H.J. Cator; it was subsequently included within the Bure Marshes National Nature Reserve under an agreement between the Trust and the Nature Conservancy Council.

Before the Broad became a nature reserve, it was regularly shot over, H.M. King George VI being a regular participant. One of the former butts can be seen just to the left of the boat.

The reedswamp in the middle distance consists solely of Lesser Reedmace. However, another photograph taken the same day shows that Saw-sedge was still common around the margins of this Broad in the late 1940s. Both these species, and also Reed, regressed during the ensuing 10 to 15 years, and there is now no reedswamp left in the site.

Photo: Courtesy of The Times

(b) Reedswamps in the broads in the post-1940 period

Reedswamps in which Saw-sedge predominates – a community known to phyto-sociologists as the *Cladietum marisci* – are now absent altogether from the highly enriched Yare valley broads, and in the broads of the Bure and Ant valleys are, at best, represented by only a few saw-sedge plants. This community is, however, still quite well developed around the margins of Upton Broad, a site in which nutrient levels have, as we have seen in the previous chapter, remained fairly low. It is also abundant in some of the turf ponds at Catfield Fen which are isolated from riverine influence, and where the input of nutrients is therefore fairly small. Cores show that *Cladium* was the first emergent species to colonize these sites, and today it grows so robustly and

The western end of Salhouse Great Broad – 1959.   Plate XX

Reedswamp is still well developed around the margins of the Broad, and Yellow Water-lilies are abundant. But air and ground photographs show that both communities had been virtually eliminated from this site by the mid-1960s.

The alders behind the yacht are growing on the peaty 'baulk' which formerly separated the Broad from the R. Bure. This section of the baulk has now been largely eroded away, mainly as a result of boat wash, and timber piles and wales have had to be installed in order to prevent the Broad becoming a mere embayment of the river.

Photo: Hallam Ashley

produces so much litter that few other plants can compete with it (Wheeler, 1980a: Wheeler & Giller, 1982a).

Despite their abundance at the turn of the century, Bulrushes had largely disappeared from the by-passed broads of the Bure valley by the late 1940s, as Lambert (1951) refers to the presence of their rhizomes, rather than the living plants. They are now rare almost everywhere, being confined to small isolated patches, for example beside Rollesby Broad and Heigham Sound. At Barton, the species survives as a small stand, re-introduced at the northern end of the site by the late Frank Tubbs in the early 1970s.

Photographs show that *Typha*, like *Schoenoplectus*, was much commoner in the early 1940s than it is today (see Plate XIX). Small stands still occur here and there, for instance in the Trinity Broads, but the species now rarely appears to be growing out into the open water in its guise as a primary colonizer. It does, however, still form mixed communities with Reed, particularly beside the Thurne broads, Fritton Lake and Upton Broad, and in the turf ponds at Catfield Fen which overlie clay (Wheeler & Giller, 1982). In the past, these mixed stands were regularly harvested, but thatchers tended to use them as a 'fill-in', or on the roofs of barns and outbuildings, where a fine quality appearance was not essential.

The progressive disappearance of *Schoenoplectus* and *Typha* from most broads in the region during the 1950s (see Plate XX) was certainly hastened, and perhaps even caused by the attentions of grazing Coypu, whose numbers were increasing rapidly

Plate XXI

Looking south from Whiteslea Lodge, Hickling, across the reedswamp and fen communities bordering the northern end of Heigham Sound – 1978.

Much of the reedswamp visible in this photograph is of the 'hover' type, and has regressed to a considerable extent over the past 25 years or so. In particular, the stands of Reed are not nearly so tall as they used to be. In 1978, the wind dislodged the bushed-up area just to the right of the sailing craft, and blew it sideways until it completely blocked the main channel (Deep Dyke) linking Heigham Sound and Hickling Broad. By dint of much effort, it was towed back to the site from whence it had come, and 'moored' in position with posts driven into the sediment.

The tree hide used in connection with the Water Trail on this national nature reserve is located in Whiteslea Wood, shown here in the middle distance. A traditional Hickling punt, formerly used for wildfowling, is moored in the dyke on the left. It was from this type of vessel that one of the best known classes of sailing craft in the region – the Norfolk Punt – evolved. The other vessel in the foreground is of a Scandinavian design.

Photo: Peter Wakely/Nature Conservancy Council

during this period, and which relish the succulent rhizomes and leaf bases of these species, as well as those of *Cladium* (Ellis, 1963). But given the success of the control campaign (see Chapter 7), it is very doubtful whether the Coypu population was large enough from the mid-1980s onwards to account for the failure of Bulrush or Lesser Reedmace to re-establish themselves, and this is more likely to be due to changes in water quality, or other environmental factors, combined with a dearth of viable propagules.

Although *Schoenoplectus* and *Typha* were at one time abundant around the margins of most, if not all, the broads of the Bure, Ant, Thurne and Waveney valleys, air and ground photographs, and the ecological descriptions of Pallis, Lambert and others show that the reedswamp of these sites consisted mainly of *Phragmites*, often in extensive stands. Most of the 8.5 ha of reedswamp present in Hoveton Great Broad in 1946 (Boorman, Fuller & Boar, 1979) consisted of Reed (Blofeld, pers. comm.), and this was regularly harvested, either from a boat or, in shallower water, by men in waders. The majority of the thatching reed cut on the Hickling Broad reserve prior to the early 1960s was obtained in the same way (Hickling Management Committee minutes). Such communities have significantly regressed, or even disappeared, from many broads during the past 20 to 30 years, and it is therefore impossible to determine the relative amounts of littoral and hover-reed which formerly occurred in them. However, Crook, Boar and Moss (1983), who examined 13 broads which still had some *Phragmites* growing around their margins, found that both growth forms occurred in 7 sites, whilst 2 broads had littoral-reed only and 4 hover-reed only. They demonstrated that the latter is regressing at a faster rate than littoral-reed. In addition, the hovers it produces seem to be larger than in the past. In 1978, for example, several floating masses of vegetation, whose windage had been increased by invading bushes and trees, became detached from the *Phragmites*-dominated reedswamp growing around the margins of the Thurne broads (see Plate XXI). One of these temporarily blocked the channel (Deep Dyke) which links Hickling Broad with Heigham Sound, another drifted downstream and became lodged under Potter Heigham Bridge, whilst a third floated out from Martham North Broad, and blocked Somerton Dyke.

Until the 1950s, many broads still possessed semi-floating islands of reedswamp, and at least two sites – Alderfen and Hoveton Great Broads – these were inhabited by colonies of nesting Black-headed Gulls (Gurney, 1920). Turner (1924) notes that 2000 of these birds were breeding at the latter site in 1904, but that the numbers had subsequently dwindled, allegedly because of predation by otters. Though smaller, the Alderfen colony survived for longer – with 350 pairs in 1963 – but breeding did not take place here after 1968, by which time the reedswamp islands on which the birds built their nests had virtually disappeared.

Numerous other birds besides Black-headed Gulls occur in marginal reedswamp, particularly if this is well developed. In a survey of the Trinity Broads, (where the reedswamp is still 15 m or more wide in many places) Ken Saul and Rob Andrews recorded the following species:

Species	No. of breeding pairs	
	1983	1984
Little Grebe	2	–
Great Crested Grebe	33	28
Shoveler	6	6
Pochard	48	46
Tufted Duck	45	36
Water Rail	2	–
Moorhen	9	16
Coot	35	41
Sedge Warbler	86	74
Reed Warbler	62	81
Reed Bunting	29	50

Since there are *c.* 12.25 miles of reedswamp around the margins of these broads (Brewster, pers. comm.), Reed and Sedge Warblers had mean breeding densities of *c.* 6 and 6.5 pairs per mile respectively. Pochard numbers, with a maximum of 6 breeding pairs per mile at Ormesby Broad, were also high but were significantly less on Rollesby and Filby Broads, owing to the relative scarcity of the food plant, *Potamogeton pectinatus*, favoured by this species, and the disturbance caused by the sailing craft using these sites.

(c) The succession from reedswamp to fen in the Bure, Ant, Thurne and Waveney valleys

Ecologists such as Pallis, and Lambert, who studied the ecology of various sites in the Bure and Ant valleys before, and just after, the Second World War, have demonstrated how reedswamp communities referrable to the *Schoenoplecto-Phragmitetum*, which had developed over sediments laid down in the broads, succeeded to fen. They found that Reed tended to retain its dominance if such a community was regularly mown during the winter months, and under these conditions, the raft of peat on which the plants were growing merely increased in thickness, until the community became physically stable, and only subject to occasional flooding. However, in the absence of interference, the semi-floating raft of reedswamp was progressively colonized by Tussock Sedge (*Carex paniculata*) so as to form a highly characteristic community known as Tussock Fen (see Plate XXII). Lesser Pond-sedge (*C. acutiformis*) was frequently present in this, and at some sites, for instance around the west side of Hoveton Great Broad, became locally dominant.

Sadly, hardly any examples of the succession from reedswamp to Tussock Fen are now to be found owing to the near-total absence of the primary colonizers of open water – Bulrush and Lesser Reedmace – from most broads in the region. However, patches of degenerating Tussock Fen can be seen here and there, and these are almost always backed by Swamp Carr, the alder-dominated community which in time developed from it (see Chapter 7).

A quite different type of succession occurs over solid, unworked peat deposits, such as are found around the margins of the Trinity Broads. Here, most of the *Phragmites*-dominated reedswamp is of the littoral type, and being firmly rooted in the sediment is much more stable physically than are the rafts of vegetation formed over what was once open water. Consequently, in the absence of human interference, it is quickly colonized by Sallows (*Salix* spp.), Alder and other woody species to produce what Lambert (1951) termed 'Fen Carr'.

Two other types of succession involving the *Schoenoplecto-Phragmitetum* can be distinguished. In the Thurne broads, it gives way to a nutrient-poor fen community characterized by the presence of Bog-rush, Carnation-grass (*Carex panicea*) and Parsley Water-Dropwort (*Oenanthe lachenalii*), and tolerant of fluctuations in the salinity (Wheeler & Giller, 1982), whilst at Sutton Broad, a species-rich Association, known as the *Cicuto-Phragmitetum* (see page 204) developed during the early years of the present century. Although this community is still represented at this site, it is no longer being formed as the heavy boat traffic to and from Stalham and Sutton has virtually eliminated the reedswamp growing on the channel margins.

(d) Reedswamp succession in the Yare valley broads

Although most reedswamps in Broadland are referable to the *Schoenoplecto-Phragmitetum*, a different type of community occurs in association with the *Glyceria maxima*-dominated fens of the Yare valley. In the early years of the present century, the reedswamp around the margins of broads in this part of the region was dominated by Reed Canary-grass (*Phalaris arundinacea*) (Pallis, 1911b). However, this had been replaced by *Phragmites* by the 1940s (Lambert, 1946 & 1947), and Ellis (*in litt.*) attributed this to the fact that the fens and reedswamps in the valley were by then no longer being mown regularly in the summer months, a form of management which would have favoured *Glyceria* and *Phalaris*, while tending to suppress *Phragmites*.

As a result of her investigations into the relationships between *Glyceria* and *Phragmites*, Lambert concluded that the latter predominates in the reedswamp bordering the waterways in the Yare valley because it is better able to withstand tidal scouring than the semi-floating rafts of vegetation formed by the *Glyceria*, pieces of which tend to break adrift and float away as 'hovers' as a consequence of wind and wave action. The rafts of *Glyceria* also tend to be underlain by the rhizomes of *Phragmites*, indicating that the latter usually precedes the former in the succession from open water to fen.

There is no evidence that the relationship between the two species has been affected by the progressive enrichment of the R. Yare and the broads connected with it; indeed, Buttery and Lambert (1965) demonstrated, *inter alia*, that the differences in their distribution could not be correlated with any limitation in major nutrients. However, they

**Tussock Fen on the Woodbastwick part of the Bure Marshes National Nature Reserve –
c. 1960.**

Plate XXII

This community is founded on a thin raft of rhizomes formed by the primary colonizers of open water, namely Bulrush and Lesser Reedmace, and it therefore typically occurs near the edges of broads and other open water sites created by peat digging. It is usually underlain by several metres of soft sediment, and in consequence is very unstable and dangerous to walk on. The Tussock Fen in this photograph is being colonized by sallows and alders, and will soon develop into 'Swamp Carr'.

Very little new Tussock Fen is currently developing in the region owing to the near-absence of the primary colonizers of open water. In addition, many examples of this community have disappeared over the past 20 years or so, probably because of the disintegration of the rhizomatous mat on which it is founded. Good examples of this community are therefore now rare in Broadland.

Most of the tussocks in this photograph are of the Greater Tussock-sedge (*Carex paniculata*), but clumps of the Tufted Sedge (*C. elata*) can be seen in the foreground.

Photo: John Markham

found that phosphorus levels were elevated near the margins of the fens, probably as a result of the deposition of silt.

Since these investigations were carried out, the relationship between the two species has been complicated by the build-up and subsequent decline of the Coypu population. These animals are very partial to *Phragmites* rhizomes, whereas swards of *Glyceria* are merely lightly grazed. During the late 1950s (when the numbers of Coypu were rapidly increasing), this difference led to *Glyceria* taking over some of the niches previously occupied in the Yare valley by *Phragmites*. This was especially noticeable at Strumpshaw and Surlingham Broads, which were directly bordered by *Glyceria* during the 1960s and early 1970s, instead of by the narrow edging of Reed which had existed 20 years previously.

Phragmites has re-colonized the margins of both these broads since the late 1970s, almost certainly because the grazing pressure exerted on this species by Coypus eased, and later ceased, as a consequence of the steps taken to exterminate these animals during this period. This is probably also responsible for the re-appearance around the Yare broads and waterways of Great Reedmace (*Typha latifolia*) and Sweet Flag (*Acorus calamus*), both of which were almost eliminated by Coypus when their numbers were at a peak in the late 1950s and early 1960s.

Reedswamp regression

During the 1960s it became apparent that Reed, as well as Bulrush and Lesser Reedmace, was fast disappearing from many of the broads in the Bure and Ant valleys, and a preliminary investigation commissioned by the NCC from the Institute of Terrestrial Ecology (ITE) and involving an examination of maps and air photographs, confirmed the gravity of the situation. At Hoveton Great Broad, (see Fig. 6B) for instance, the 8.5 ha of *Phragmites*-reedswamp present in 1946 had declined to *c.* 4.7 ha by 1958 and to *c.* 0.7 ha by 1963 (Boorman, *in litt.*), whilst at Ranworth Inner Broad, the corresponding figures were *c.* 4.05 ha in 1953 and *c.* 0.45 ha in 1958 (Boorman, Sheail & Fuller, 1977).

A study of the rate and extent of reed regression in other broads was obviously called for, and this was carried out for the NCC by ITE in 1978 (Boorman, Fuller & Boar, 1979). Sixteen sites were selected, and in each, the boundaries of the open water, reedswamp and fen were plotted from first and second editions of the 1:10560 (6-inch) maps, and from vertical air photographs flown at various dates between 1946 and 1978. The results obtained for three of the broads examined are reproduced as Figs. 6C, 6D and 6E, whilst overall changes in the distribution of open water and reedswamp between 1880 and 1977 for all 18 sites investigated in 1977 and 1978 are summarized in Tables 6b and 6c.

It was found that prior to 1946, the trend at most sites was for the reedswamp to

Table 6b Changes in the hectarage of open water and reedswamp for 18 broads

Year	Water	Reedswamp	Total
1880s	625	217	842
1905	582	244	826
1946	554	121	675
1977	618	47	665

Source: Boorman, Fuller and Boar (1979)

Table 6c Overall changes in the status of reedswamp calculated for 18 broads on a broad by broad basis Figures are in hectares

Period	Reedswamp Advance (Loss of Open Water)	Reedswamp Regression (Gain in Open Water)	Reedswamp to Fen/Carr
1880–1905	54.1	10.8	18.5
1905–1946	34.3	6.6	150.8
1946–1977	3.3	67.2	13.6

Source: Boorman, Fuller and Boar (1979)

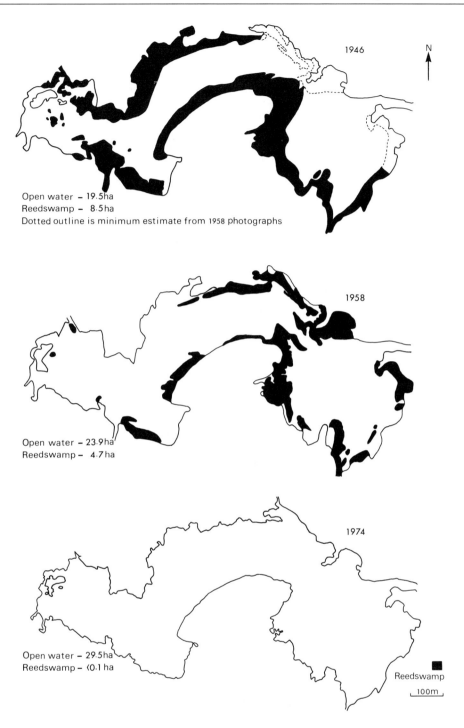

Open water – 19.5ha
Reedswamp – 8.5ha
Dotted outline is minimum estimate from 1958 photographs

1946

N

1958

Open water – 23.9ha
Reedswamp – 4.7ha

1974

Open water – 29.5ha
Reedswamp – <0.1 ha

Reedswamp

100m

Fig. 6B

Changes in the amount
of reedswamp in
Hoveton Great Broad
between 1949 and
1974.

*Source: Boorman,
Sheail and Fuller
(1977)*

advance into the open water. However, some regression occurred between 1880 and 1905 at Ormesby Broad, Heigham Sound, the inner part of Hoveton Little Broad (Pound End), and probably South Walsham Broad, and at Alderfen, Hassingham and Rockland Broads between 1905 and 1946. Until 1905, the overall rate of reedswamp advance exceeded that at which it was being 'lost' as a result of succession to fen and carr, but after that year the position was reversed.

From 1946 onwards, reedswamp retreated at all the sites studied except Hickling Broad; the succession from reedswamp to fen was also halted. The dramatic losses found to have occurred at Ranworth and Hoveton Great Broads during the 1950s were paralleled at other sites in the Bure and Ant valleys (see Plate 14), and also at Hassingham Broad. At Rockland Broad, gains and losses were in equilibrium between 1946 and 1958, but thereafter losses predominated, and by 1968 the amount of open water had increased to what it had been in 1881. Reedswamp loss in the remaining broads, most of which are partly or wholly floored by clay or gravel, rather than peat, was found to have been less; in addition, at many of these sites, the process started later.

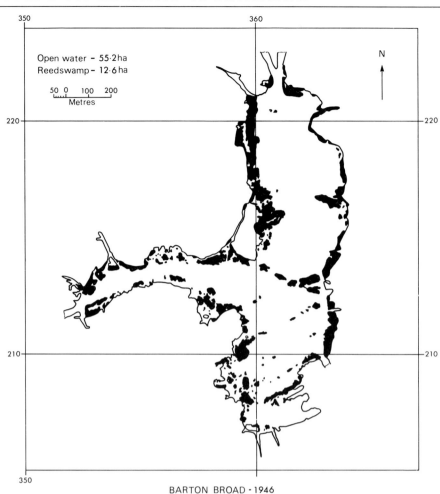

Fig. 6c

The amount of reedswamp in Barton Broad in 1946, 1958 and 1971.

Source: Boorman, Fuller and Boar (1979)

BARTON BROAD - 1946

At Filby Broad and Fritton Lake, for example, the decline did not commence until after 1958, whilst at Rollesby Broad it did not start until 1970.

Because the observed changes had taken place in the past – in some cases up to a century ago – it was impossible to determine their cause with certainty. Nevertheless, in a paper summarizing the results of their earlier studies, and incorporating data obtained from subsequent research, Boorman and Fuller (1981) suggested that the factor mainly responsible for reed regression in the broads from about 1950 onwards was grazing by Coypu. They pointed out that even if *Phragmites* only formed 27 per cent of the diet of these animals, they were sufficiently numerous prior to the population crash of 1962/3 (see page 231) to account for the losses which occurred during the 1950s and early 1960s. They also argued that in view of the known sensitivity of Reed to bud-removal from the rhizomes (Haslam, 1969) Coypu could have caused the observed changes, even if only a small (6.6 per cent) proportion of their diet during this period had consisted of the buds and young shoots of this species.

Anecdotal support for Boorman and Fuller's hypothesis comes from contemporary observations by Ted Ellis and other naturalists, who noted that marginal reedswamps were being widely damaged by marauding Coypu during the 1950s and early 1960s (Ellis,1963; Davis, 1963; Lambert, 1965).

Like many other water-loving plants, Reed has a system of lacunae in its stems and rhizomes enabling it to translocate oxygen to its roots, and Boorman and Fuller suggested that if its aerial shoots are damaged by Coypu or waterfowl, particularly at or below water level, this might reduce the root's tolerance of the anaerobic conditions found in the sediment of the broads, thus prejudicing the plant's ability to survive. Boorman and Fuller also pointed out that the progressive loss of waterweeds from broads in the Bure, Ant and Yare valleys during the 1950s would have forced Mute Swans, Coot, Greylag and Canada Geese increasingly to turn their attention to reedswamp as an alternative source of food. As this, in turn, started to disappear, the birds would have concentrated on the remaining patches, thus accelerating the rate at

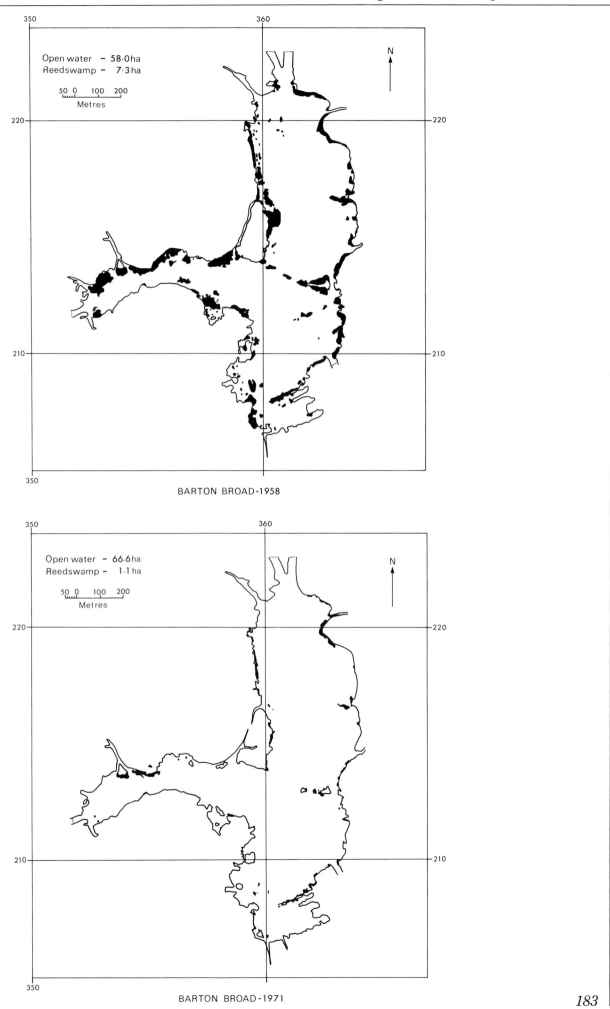

350   360

Open water – 58·0 ha
Reedswamp – 7·3 ha

50 0   100   200
Metres

N

220   220

210   210

350

BARTON BROAD-1958

350   360

Open water – 66·6 ha
Reedswamp – 1·1 ha

50 0   100   200
Metres

N

220   220

210   210

350

BARTON BROAD-1971

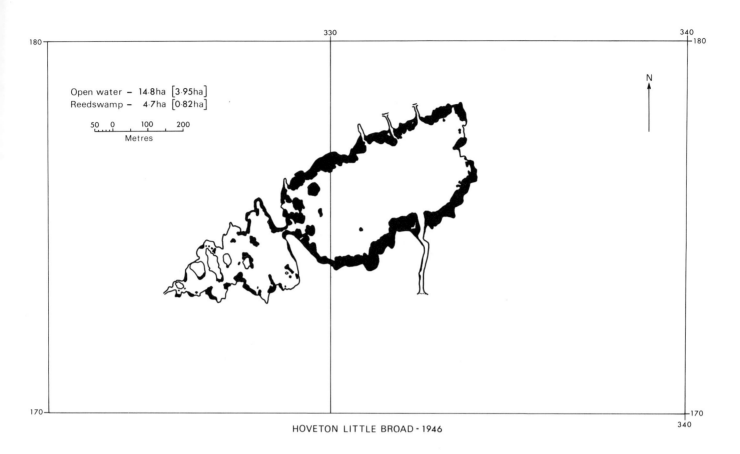

Open water – 14·8ha [3·95ha]
Reedswamp – 4·7ha [0·82ha]

50   0   100   200
Metres

HOVETON LITTLE BROAD - 1946

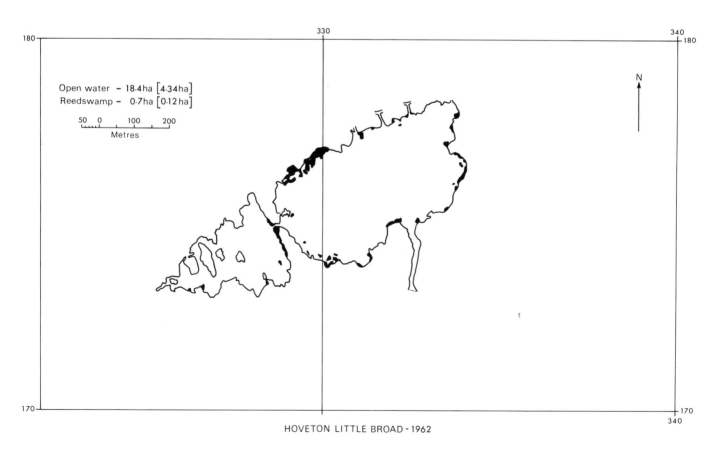

Open water – 18·4ha [4·34ha]
Reedswamp – 0·7ha [0·12ha]

50   0   100   200
Metres

HOVETON LITTLE BROAD - 1962

Fig. 6D   The amount of reedswamp in Hoveton Little Broad in 1946, 1962 and 1977. The figures in parentheses refer to Pound End.

Source: Boorman, Fuller and Boar (1979)

which these were regressing. Observations by the author since 1980 have confirmed that this retreat has certainly occurred at Wroxham Broad, and good examples of the stepped effect produced when waterfowl graze on *Phragmites* reedswamp, can be seen here and at other sites in the Bure and Ant valleys where the main concentrations of Greylag and Canada Geese occur.

Boorman and Fuller left a number of questions unanswered. Why, for example, did reedswamp apparently regress at Ormesby Broad, Pound End and Heigham Sound between 1880 and 1905, long before Coypu and Greylag Geese were naturalized in the region? Similarly, Coypu and feral geese are most unlikely to have been sufficiently numerous prior to 1946 to account for the losses of reedswamp which occurred at Alderfen, Hassingham and Rockland Broads between 1905 and that year. It was also difficult to understand why reedswamp should have regressed rapidly at Heigham Sound between 1946 and 1977, whereas at Hickling Broad nearby, gains and losses remained more or less in equilibrium during this period. Above all, given the relatively small numbers of Coypu left in the region by the late 1960s why was the reedswamp failing to regenerate in broads such as Rockland, which, until very recently, were not frequented by large numbers of feral geese? Indeed, far from recovering at this and other sites, it was actually continuing to regress.

To answer these and other questions, the Broads Authority decided in 1979 to commission from the University of East Anglia a 3-year study of the causes of reedswamp regression, and the ways in which this could be alleviated. Work started in 1980, and involved an investigation of a number of physiological and mechanical factors which, it was thought, might be responsible.

Within the latter category, ample confirmation was found that Coypu and waterfowl graze on reed shoots (Crook, Boar & Moss, 1983). But although netted enclosures were set up at various sites so that the performance of the reed plants inside and outside these

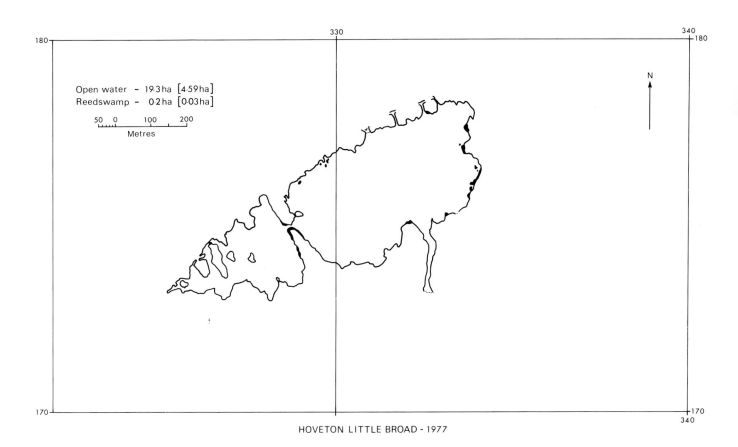

Open water – 19.3 ha [4.59 ha]
Reedswamp – 0.2 ha [0.03 ha]

HOVETON LITTLE BROAD - 1977

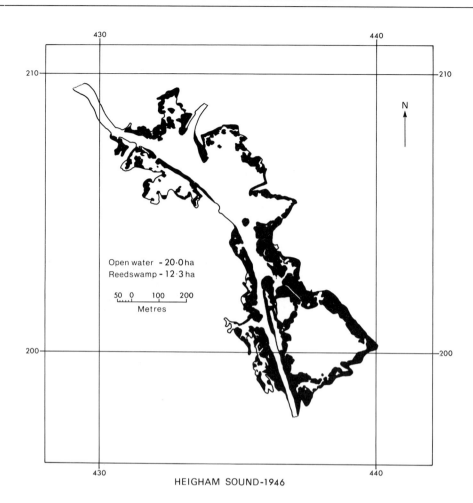

Fig. 6E

The amount of reedswamp in Heigham Sound in 1946, 1963 and 1977.

Source: Boorman, Fuller and Boar (1979)

Open water - 20·0 ha
Reedswamp - 12·3 ha

50 0   100   200
Metres

HEIGHAM SOUND-1946

could be compared under controlled conditions, direct evidence of grazing damage was only found at one site – Hickling Broad in 1981. It was concluded that although grazing may be preventing the regeneration of Reed at certain sites, particularly where, as Boorman and Fuller had suggested, large numbers of waterfowl are feeding on relatively small relict stands of reedswamp, grazing was not responsible for the widespread failure of Reed to regenerate. Nor was any relationship found between regression and the damage caused by the stem-boring larvae of the Rush, Brown-veined and Fenn's Wainscot moths (*Archanara algae, A. dissoluta* and *Photedes brevilinea*) which in some years (e.g. 1980) are present in a high proportion of the shoots of some stands of Reed.

In order to determine whether particular genotypes of Reed are dying out, perhaps as a result of their proneness to disease, or their inability to adapt as successfully as others to the man, or naturally-induced changes taking place in the region, seeds collected from a number of regression and non-regression sites were germinated in a glasshouse under carefully controlled conditions. These experiments demonstrated that there is, as expected, a wide range of different reed biotypes in Broadland, but that there is no association between seedling vigour and the rate at which regression is occurring; indeed, some of the fastest growing young plants originated from seed collected at sites subject to particularly rapid regression. Similarly, measurements of reed plants in the wild failed to reveal a link between their growth and biomass, and the rate of regression; for instance, some of the highest and lowest shoot densities were recorded at sites which had undergone very little regression. But shoot height was found to be positively correlated with regression, indicating that the Reed was growing vigorously at sites where this was occurring. The implications were clear; regression could not be attributed to either disease, or a loss of vigour as a consequence of genetic effects.

Boorman and Fuller's suggestion that *Phragmites* was unable to grow satisfactorily in the anoxic sediment formed in the broads as a consequence of nutrient enrichment, was not accepted by Crook, Boar and Moss, not least because of the well-documented ability of this species to tolerate such conditions. Despite their reservations, they measured the oxygen saturation levels, redox potential and sulphide levels at various depths

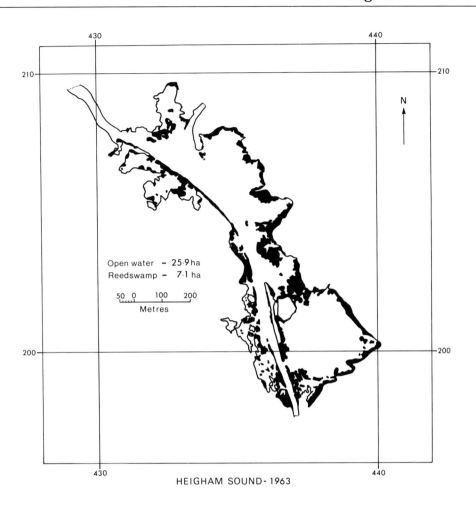

Open water – 25·9 ha
Reedswamp – 7·1 ha

HEIGHAM SOUND - 1963

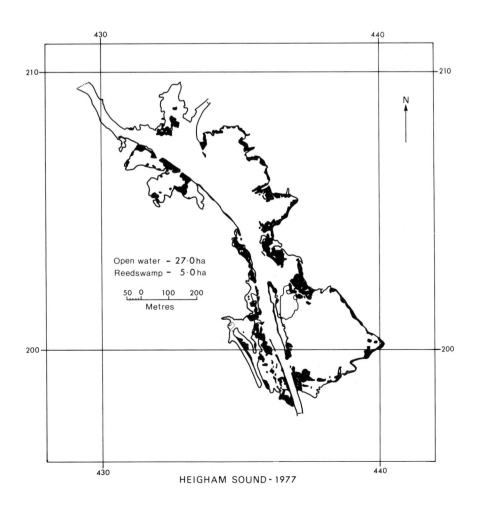

Open water – 27·0 ha
Reedswamp – 5·0 ha

HEIGHAM SOUND - 1977

at regression and non-regression sites, and found, as expected, that there were no significant differences. Indeed, many of the sites which supported the most vigorous growth of Reed, and which had not regressed, were those with the deepest and most anoxic sediment.

Nitrogen levels in the rivers and broads have, as we have seen in the previous chapter, increased markedly since the Second World War, and Crook, Boar and Moss carried out a number of experiments, both in the field and the laboratory, to determine whether there is any relationship betwen this, and reedswamp loss. In doing so, they had in mind that Klotzli (1973) had demonstrated, through studies on enriched lakes in Switzerland, that reed plants growing in nitrogen-rich water have stems which contain relatively more soft, parenchymatous tissue, and less sclerenchyma (woody fibres) than normal. Crook *et al.* failed to demonstrate any correspondence between stem strength and percentage regression in Broadland. However, they found positive correlations between the amount of nitrate nitrogen in the water, increased shoot growth, the nitrogen content of the reed leaves and percentage regression, indicating that reeds suffer the greatest losses when they are apparently growing most vigorously – in the most nitrogen-rich sites (Crook & Boar, 1984; Crook, Boar & Moss, 1983; Boar & Crook, 1985).

Glasshouse studies, involving the growth of seedlings supplied with four different

Fig. 6F

Changes in the distribution of littoral and hover-reed at Hickling Broad between 1946 and 1977.

Source: Crook, Boar and Moss (1983)

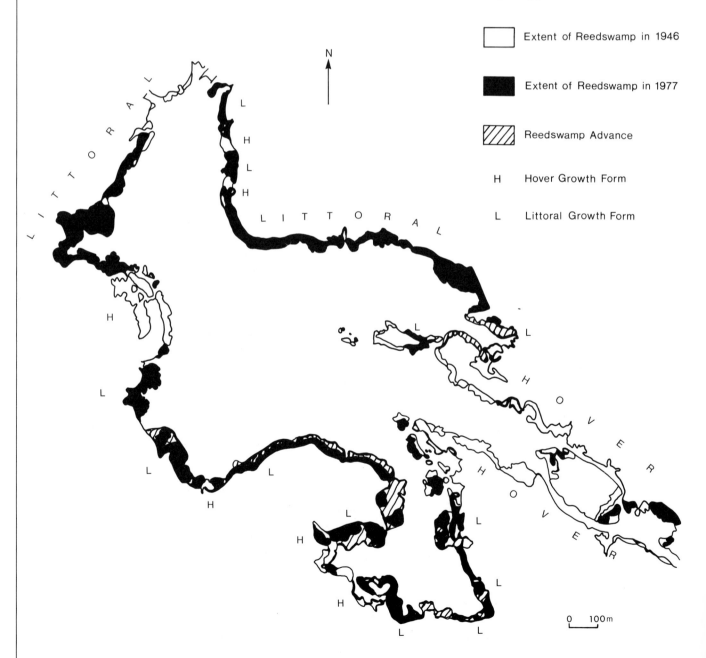

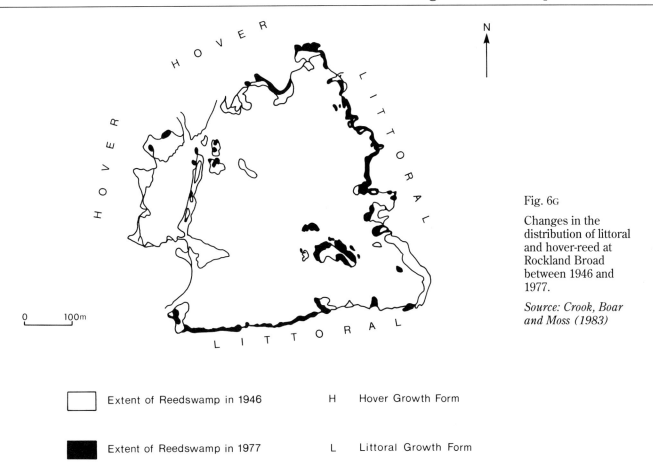

Fig. 6G

Changes in the distribution of littoral and hover-reed at Rockland Broad between 1946 and 1977.

Source: Crook, Boar and Moss (1983)

☐ Extent of Reedswamp in 1946	H Hover Growth Form
■ Extent of Reedswamp in 1977	L Littoral Growth Form

concentrations of nitrate (as the sodium salt) showed that the number of shoots, the above-ground biomass and the total biomass all increased as the nitrogen concentration rose. Perhaps most significantly of all, the above-ground biomass increased proportionately more than the below-ground biomass, a discovery consistent with the well-documented fact that similar changes occur when large quantities of nitrogen are applied to cereals and other grasses (Russell, 1973). This finding prompted Crook *et al.* to suggest that the increasing concentrations of nitrogen in the rivers and broads may be causing the *Phragmites* plants to produce a top-heavy growth, thus making them more vulnerable to wind and wave action than would be the case had they been growing in water containing less nitrogen.

Strong support for this hypothesis was obtained when Crook *et al.* examined the distribution of littoral and hover-reed in 13 broads, and plotted the results on maps showing how much regression had occurred since 1946. It was at once apparent (see, for example, Figs. 6F and 6G) that regression had been much more pronouncd on shores fronted by floating stands of Reed, than on those where the sediment-rooted growth form predominated (see Plate 15). Subsequent measurements taken at points on the maps equivalent to *c.* 50 m spacings along the present outer edge of the reedswamp confirmed that a much higher (84.3 per cent) proportion of the hover-reed sites had regressed than the littoral ones (23.8 per cent).

Further investigations (Boar, Crook & Moss, 1984), involving a comparison of the below and above-ground dry weight biomass of stands of hover and littoral-reed growing side by side at Hickling Broad, indicated that littoral-reed has 25 per cent more rhizome biomass per unit area than hover-reed. This difference is due to the fact that the latter only has a quarter as much horizontal rhizome as littoral-reed. The different ratios between above and below-ground biomass in the two growth forms is further illustrated by the greater weight of vertical rhizomes in hover-reed plants, suggesting that these make a greater investment in the organs responsible for the production of the above-ground biomass, than do littoral plants.

Boar *et al.* also demonstrated from growth experiments in the greenhouse that the ratio between nitrogen (N) and potassium (K) has a marked effect on the amount of sclerenchyma found in both the shoots and rhizomes of reeds, the percentage fibre content being significantly lower when N is high and K low, than when the ratio is balanced at either high or moderate concentrations. Measurements of the shoot strength were consistent with this finding, since shoots growing under the high-N, high-K treatment were found to be more resistant to breakage than those grown under high-N, low-K conditions.

These results support the hypothesis that when growing in the high nitrogen levels now commonplace in Broadland, hover-reed is structurally less able to withstand the physical stresses produced by wind and wave action than is littoral-reed, and that as a consequence, it is regressing more quickly.

Although Boar *et al.* were unable to detect any differences between hover-reed and littoral-reed in their resistance to bending stresses, continental workers, notably Sukopp *et al.* (1975) and Raghi-Atri and Bornkamm (1980), have demonstrated that increasing nitrogen and phosphorus concentrations in the water reduce the width of the outer ring of sclerenchyma in reed stems, and thus their mechanical strength.

In their report, Crook, Boar and Moss (1983) review the ways in which the reed regression problem might be ameliorated. There is no cheap way of removing nitrates from the rivers and broads chemically, and it is extremely doubtful whether nitrogen run-off from the catchments could be significantly reduced. However, if the waterways were returned to a Phase II condition, waterweeds would take up a lot of nitrogen and keep it 'locked up' during the reed growing season; in addition, the bacteria growing on the plants would convert nitrates to gaseous nitrogen, which would escape to the atmosphere (Moss, 1984).

Crook *et al.* point out that the edges of a broad would need to be protected by barriers if it is to be re-colonized by reedswamp. In addition, for sites still in a Phase III condition, and which are therefore devoid of waterweeds palatable to waterfowl, it may be necessary to reduce the numbers of Greylag Geese, Coot and other grazing birds, or physically exclude them with nets, until the reedswamp fringe has become firmly established. They felt that the aim should be to establish hover-reed beside the broads since its tendency to grow outwards would probably be more or less balanced by natural erosion. But they considered that this type of reed growth would not survive beside the rivers owing to the amount of boat wash, and that the aim here should therefore be to re-establish littoral-reed.

These objectives will be very difficult to achieve in practice. The fens bordering the broads are so heavily shaded by trees that these will have to be cut back before reed can be successfully reintroduced at the water's-edge. In addition, the near-perpendicular or even under-cut margins of many sections of river will, as has been done experimentally at Thurne Mouth, have to be re-profiled before littoral-reed can be re-established in sites from which it has been lost (see Plate 16). Nevertheless, given the vital importance of reedswamp in the region, it is essential that ways be found of implementing the recommendations put forward by Crook *et al.*

Another aspect of the reedswamp regression problem which urgently requires investigation concerns the reasons why *Schoenoplectus* and *Typha* have, despite the elimination of the Coypu population, shown no signs of re-establishing themselves beside the rivers and broads. Given the prime importance of these species as the initial colonizers of open water, as demonstrated by Joyce Lambert's classic investigations, it would appear essential that research on the best ways of getting these species re-established, should be commenced as soon as possible. Indeed, it is arguable that undue emphasis has been placed during the past few years on the reasons for the losses of *Phragmites* from the reedswamp community and that its other principal components have not received the attention they deserve.

Chapter 7
The Natural History of the Fens, Past and Present

The terminology used in Britain to describe wetlands has long been confused, largely because different workers have tended to use classifications which are inconsistent with those adopted by others. Tansley (1949) applies the term 'fen' to peat-forming vegetation growing in sites where the water-table is close to ground level, and where the water is neutral or alkaline, and reserves the word 'marsh' for communities growing in water-logged, mineral soils. But this distinction is not particularly apt in Broadland where the land commonly referred to as marsh has been drained so that it is no longer water-logged. In addition, many of the marshes in the region are founded on peat, rather than mineral soils.

Although it is convenient to apply the general term 'fen' to peat-forming vegetation growing in sites where the water-table is not artificially controlled (as distinct from 'marsh', which in Broadland may be defined as land whose water-table can be adjusted, usually by pumping), the more detailed nomenclature developed by Goode (1972), Goode and Ratcliffe (1977) and Wheeler (1975 & 1980a, b & c) has been adopted in the following account. According to this, most of the undrained peatlands in the region are 'flood plain mires', since they are subject to periodic flooding by a slow-moving river. But Smallburgh Fen, which is located beside a minor tributary of the R. Ant, and East Ruston Common, on another branch of the same river, but just outside the strict confines of Broadland, are 'valley mires' because they have developed along the slopes and floors of smallish valleys, and receive their supply of water from marginal springs and seepage lines.

Two main types of vegetation can be differentiated in Broadland's flood plain mires. First, there are the reedswamp communities, in which the muddy or peaty substratum in which the plants are growing is covered by water up to about 2 m deep. These are confined to former turf ponds and the edges of the rivers and broads and have been described in the previous Chapter. Second, there are the true fens. In these, the summer water-table is at, or a few centimetres below, the surface of the peat, while in the winter, the latter is often covered by up to 20 cm of river water, particularly in the valleys of the Bure, Yare and Waveney, which carry large fluvial flows at this time of year. There are nearly 5500 ha of fen vegetation in Broadland today; the relative amounts in the five main river valleys are shown in Table 3a on page 34.

Since the principal rivers drain catchments in which soils derived from chalky boulder clay predominate, the fens adjoining their middle and lower reaches are irrigated by base-rich water (with a pH range of 5.5 to 8.0), and in consequence contain communities characteristic of such conditions. These together constitute what is technically

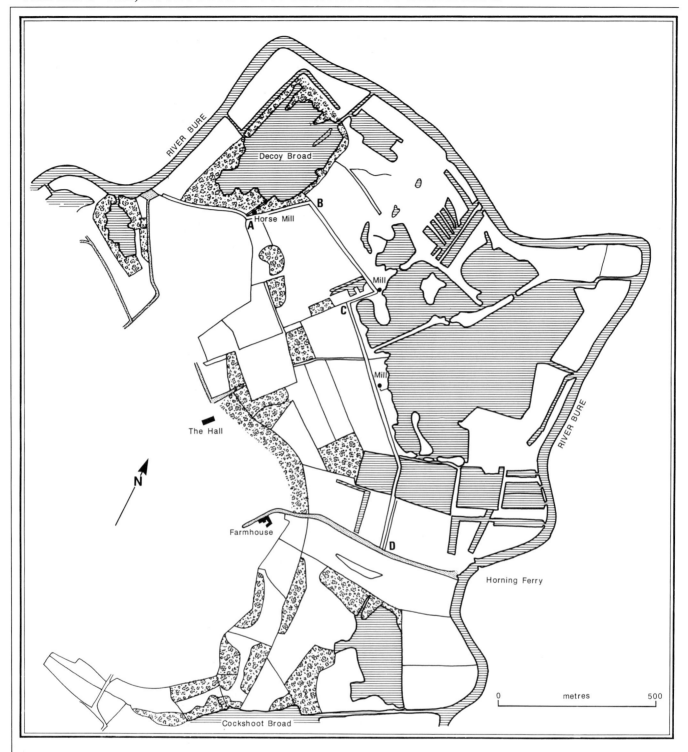

Map 7.1   A map, dated 1845, of part of the Woodbastwick Estate. The dyke marked ABCD was at one time embanked, and the two wind-powered drainage mills shown beside this waterway would have been used to try and lower the water-table of the fens nearest the valley margin. Later, a 'horse-mill' was installed at A, near the southern corner of Decoy Broad. However, it is doubtful whether this was any more effective than the windpumps, and it is believed that the attempts to drain part of the site had been abandoned by the turn of the century.

Source: Archives of the Woodbastwick Estate

known as a 'Rich-fen' system, as distinct from a 'Poor-fen' one. But the differences between the two categories are not always clear-cut, especially in the valleys of the rivers Ant and Thurne, whose catchments consist, in part, of calcium-deficient sands and gravels.

Most fens in Broadland can be loosely defined as 'unreclaimed', in the sense that they have never been isolated hydrologically from the adjoining rivers and broads. But it is convenient to include in this category areas which have at some time in the past been embanked and drained, but which have subsequently been allowed to revert. Strumpshaw 'Fen' was an embanked grazing marsh until the windpumps and sluices by which it was once drained, were destroyed by the great fluvial flood of 1912. Similarly, the southern half of Woodbastwick Fen is shown on an estate map of 1845 as being embanked and drained by windmills (see Map 7.1), but is not differentiated in this way on the 1885 OS 25-inch map. The first 1-inch OS map shows that several areas beside the R. Ant which are now fen, were in 1838 drained grazing marsh, including a large block of land north of Barton Broad, marked on old maps as 'Barton Marsh' and formerly drained by two windpumps. Likewise, Reedham Marsh, much of which was allotted as a 'Poor's Firing' in the 1802 Enclosure Award for Ludham, was later drained and used as cattle pasturage, as witnessed by the presence of old gate posts in several places. But in about 1932, the windpump (Turf Fen Mill) which drained the marsh fell into disuse, and the site reverted to reed-dominated fen.

The plant communities of sites such as Reedham Marsh and Strumpshaw Fen which were once in agricultural use, but which have not been drained and grazed for 70 years or more, are often indistinguishable from those of adjoining fens which have never been isolated hydrologically from the river system. However, areas which have fallen into disuse more recently, such as the Hoveton Marshes, which were last cattle-grazed between 1942 and 1949 (Blofeld, pers. comm.), and the derelict marshes between the Whitlingham sewage treatment works and the R. Yare, exhibit intermediate stages in the progression back to fen vegetation.

In a few almost inaccessible places, for example in parts of Larkbush, south of Hoveton Great Broad, the fens may have developed more or less directly from the vegetation growing in the middle and upper sections of the valleys at the end of the Second (Romano-British) Transgression. The antiquity of such communities is indicated by the much larger number of woody species present than in nearby areas which, though superficially similar, were open water or unbushed fen up to about 100 years ago, and which have not therefore had time to develop such a diverse flora. Such successional communities are, in fact much more typical; indeed, the vast majority of Broadland's fens have at some time in the past been subject to human exploitation. Some sites were, and in some cases still are, mown regularly for Reed, Saw-sedge, Marsh Hay or 'Litter', or used as rough pasturage for cattle, or for the production of alder poles, firewood and other materials, whilst others were cut over for peat, before being abandoned, and allowed to develop into 'secondary' communities, themselves often exploited as a source of fen produce. These forms of management produced a landscape quite different from that of today. Trees and bushes were scarce, and the scenery was therefore much less closely confined than it is now. The extensive views obtainable a hundred years or so ago can best be appreciated from the photographs taken of the fens by Emerson, Payne Jennings and others (Middleton, 1978).

The exploitation of the fens for such a wide range of crops also resulted in considerable ecological variation between adjoining compartments, and the different communities would have together comprised a mosaic of great biological richness. Although large areas of fen have now succeeded to scrub and alder woodland, and are therefore relatively homogenous, the remaining areas are still remarkably diverse ecologically. In part, this can be attributed to a continuation of many of the forms of management traditional to the area, albeit on a limited scale. But many areas, though now abandoned, are at a stage in the succession when they still show signs of the way they were managed in the past.

There is also much variation in the species density (i.e. the number of species present per unit area) of the different communities, some being virtual monocultures of Reed, Saw-sedge and other herbaceous plants, whilst others have up to 58 species per 100-metre square. The mean species density of 261 samples collected by Wheeler and Giller (1982a) was 22.1 per 100 m square. Two of the species involved, Crested Buckler-fern

Table 7a Vascular plants of the fens which occur nationally in fewer than 100 ten kilometre squares

Name	No. of grid squares	Distribution in Broadland
Crested Buckler-fern (*Dryopteris cristata*)	9	See p. 209
Marsh Fern (*Thelypteris palustris*)	98	Abundant in mixed fen and in alder carr in the Bure and Ant valleys. Occasional elsewhere.
Marsh Pea (*Lathyrus palustris*)	15	See p. 208
Cowbane (*Cicuta virosa*)	29	Locally common beside turf ponds and dykes. Co-dominant with *Sium latifolium* and *Ranunculus lingua* beside Sutton Broad.
Water Parsnip (*Sium latfolium*)	97	Abundant beside Sutton Broad; occasional elsewhere
Milk Parsley (*Peucedanum palustre*)	23	Very common in mixed fen and alder carr, expecially in the Bure, Ant and Thurne valleys
Round-leaved Wintergreen (*Pyrola rotundifolia*)	41	See p. 209
Marsh Sow-Thistle (*Sonchus palustris*)	17	See pp. 71 and 207
Fen Pondweed (*Potamogeton coloratus*)	44	Turf ponds in the Ant valley
Fen Orchid (*Liparis loeselii*)	1	See p. 207. The dune form of this species (var. ovata) occurs in S. Wales
Narrow-leaved Marsh Orchid (*Dactylorhiza traunsteineri*)	18	Occasional in the Ant valley
Fibrous Tussock-sedge (*Carex appropinquata*)	20	Frequent in the Bure and Ant valleys; occasional elsewhere.

Note: Several other uncommon species, e.g. *Stratiotes aloides* and *Potamogeton friesii* occur in fen dykes.

(*Dryopteris cristata*) and Fen Orchid (*Liparis loeselii*), are listed in the Red Data Book (Perring & Farrell, 1983) while 10 others occur in fewer than 100 ten-kilometre squares (Table 7a).

Until recently, the factors responsible for determining the distribution of the different communities found in the fens were imperfectly understood. However, studies by Wheeler (1978) and Wheeler and Giller (1982a) on the Ant Valley fens – ecologically the most diverse Rich-fen system in the region – have yielded evidence that this is determined by environmental constraints, reinforced by management rather than the other way round. Nonetheless, it is clear that the communities and species which are rarest, and which conservationists are thus particularly anxious to safeguard, are re-stricted to habitats which owe both their origin (peat cutting) and their maintenance (mowing) to human usage.

Peat digging

For centuries it would have been customary for local people to obtain the peat they needed for fuel from shallow excavations in the nearby fens, and it seems likely that the practice developed when the deeper pits became permanently flooded to form broads. In most cases, the workings were not taken below the top of the clay laid down during the Second Transgression, and the floor of such pits was therefore only about 1.5 m below the present fen surface. However, stratigraphical studies indicate that some of the older excavations in the Catfield area, and perhaps elsewhere, were slightly (*c.* 50 cm) deeper than this, thus enabling the brushwood peat formed prior to the Transgression to be exploited (Wheeler & Giller, 1982a).

The importance of peat digging in the local economy is reflected in the fact that land was specifically allotted for this purpose in many Enclosure Awards. At Upton-with-Fishley, for instance, an area of *c.* 36 ha is referred to as 'Turf Land', and is shown on the Tithe Apportionment Map of 1841 as being divided up into some 70 rectilinear 'doles' labelled 'water'. At both Hickling and Horning, each cottager was permitted to cut 3000 turves per year from the parish fens, whilst at East Ruston, each common-right holder was allowed to take up to 5000 turves a year (Bird, 1909). The prime purpose of such Awards was to ensure that people living locally had access to a source of fuel.

However, a great deal of peat was cut for sale in nearby villages and towns. In addition, considerable quantities were exported to other parts of East Anglia during the nineteenth century (Carrodus, 1949).

According to Bird, a man could cut 20 turves a minute under favourable conditions, and some fens were extensively exploited. For example *c.* 40 per cent of the Catfield Fen area is marked with 'swamp' symbols on the 1885 6-inch OS map, mostly in a rectilinear format (see Map 7.2), and Wheeler and Giller's stratigraphical investigations have confirmed Lambert's (1965) suspicion that these mark the position of former peat workings, known locally as 'turf ponds'. The fact that these are not shown on Faden's map of 1797 does not mean that none existed at this time, since there is some doubt as to how accurately he mapped areas of open water (Barringer, 1973).

Wheeler has argued that the diversion of the R. Ant so that it flowed through Barton Broad would have had the incidental (though not necessarily planned) benefit of making it easier to dig peat from the fens to the east and south-east. However, it is not altogether certain that all such excavations were in fact worked 'dry'. Even if peat cutting was only practised during the summer months [as on East Ruston Common where it was only

Map 7.2

The distribution of swamp vegetation (marking the position of shallow peat diggings), fen, rough grassland and woodland in the Catfield area, as revealed by the symbols used on a 6″ Ordnance Survey map, dated 1885.

Source: Wheeler and Giller (1982c)

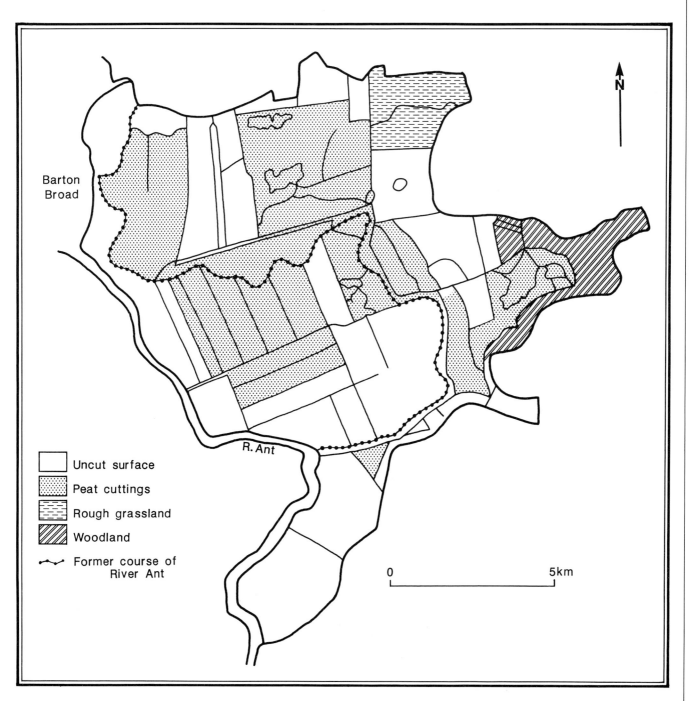

permitted between 8 May and 15 July – Bird (1909)], water levels in the main river valleys would seldom have been more than about 30 cm below the fen surface. Consequently, pumping or baling would have been necessary to counteract the effects of seepage and rainfall, if the peat was to be removed down to a depth of about 1.5 m with a becket. There is no evidence that windpumps were used to drain any excavations, and although it would have been possible to bale out the smaller workings, difficulty would have been experienced in keeping the larger pits free of water by this means. In the circumstances, it is possible that once the superficial deposits had been removed with a becket, some of the larger and deeper excavations were worked by the dredging technique described in Chapter 4. This was almost certainly used to remove peat from certain broads once these had become permanently flooded, and it would be surprising if the custom lapsed completely during the ensuing centuries. It is also significant that the Dutch chose to dredge, rather than dig, peat from sites very similar to our turf ponds. According to Verhoeven (*in litt.*), they continued this practice right up to the 1930s, the sods so produced measuring about 30 x 10 x 10 cm.

Suffling (1891) notes that turves were known in Broadland as 'hovers', and were 4 inches (9.2 cm) square, and about 2 feet (61 cm) long. Each square foot yielded 9 hovers, and since they sold for a shilling per hundred, an acre would produce 392 thousand, worth £196. The dimensions quoted by Suffling are compatible with those of Gurney (1923) who noted that the sods being cut at Wicken Fen, Cambridgeshire, were 15 x 5.5 x 3 inches when fresh, and about 9 x 3.5 x 2.5 inches when dry and ready for collection. In contrast, Carrodus (1949) states that the turves cut from the pits near Horning in the late nineteenth century were between 24 and 36 inches long. But the flattened shaft of the type of becket used in Broadland (see Plate XI) was only *c.* 18 inches (45 cm) long by 4 inches (10 cm) wide, and it would be difficult, if not impossible, to cut a 36-inch long turf with such an implement. In the circumstances, it seems likely that the length measurement quoted by Carrodus is erroneous.

Woodbastwick Fen is another site which was intensively worked for peat in the past, and the fact that flooded workings are shown here on Faden's map indicates this was in progress in the mid to late eighteenth century. Of the 232 ha shown on an 1845 Estate Map (reproduced as Map 7.1), 64 ha is marked as open water, and peat was still being obtained from here after this map was produced, as a handwritten note in its margin records that a Mr Shippen had been authorized in 1856 to cut 20 000 turves a year from a fen near the north-east corner of Decoy Broad, and a further 14 000 turves per annum from a site opposite the Ferry Inn, Horning.

Turf ponds as yet unfilled with 'secondary' peat are to be found in several places (see Table 3j) and given the rapid rate at which the succession back to fen takes place once digging ceases, these must have been created relatively recently. 'Reedham Water', for example, is not marked on the 6-inch OS map of 1907, and the workings here must therefore have become flooded after that date. It is not known exactly when peat excavation finally ceased in the region. However, according to John Beales, Chairman of the Hickling Parish Council, peat dug from a fen at Long Gore was being sold in the village by the late Mr William Turner until about 1906, and he went on cutting it from here for his own use until the 1920s.

Being only about 1.5 m deep, most turf ponds would have quickly been colonized by Lesser Reedmace and other peat-forming species, and the majority have subsequently been completely occluded by the fresh peat formed by such communities. Indeed, in many cases, the only signs that a fen has been exploited as a source of peat are lines of bushes or trees along the edge of the former turf pond, and a slight lowering of their surface relief compared with adjoining unworked areas. However, Jennings (1952) showed by means of trial borings through former turf ponds at Woodbastwick ('Broadwaters') that the secondary peat above is separated from the uncut deposits below by a thin (*c.* 3 cm) layer of lake mud containing the shells of freshwater molluscs. This sediment represents the remains of the aquatic plants and animals which occurred in the flooded workings before they were infilled by fresh peat.

The exact rate at which infilling took place cannot be determined owing to uncertainties regarding the age of each turf pond. It is also necessary to distinguish between the mass and the volume of the peat; Reed and Lesser Reedmace, in particular, produce a loose matt of entwined rhizomes having a low mass, but occupying a considerable volume. Nevertheless, according to Gunn (1864), derelict workings in the Ant valley were subject to a rate of peat 'growth' of a foot (30.5 cm) in 20 years – a high rate, but one compatible with an estimate (by turf cutters) of twenty inches (51 cm) in sixteen years from the fens at Isleham (Babbington, 1860). In contrast, the mean rate of accumulation in those parts of Catfield Fen which have never been exploited as a source of peat has only been about 0.75 mm per year during the past 2000 years (Wheeler & Giller, 1982a).

Dutt (1906) points out that the will-o'-the-wisp, or what was known locally as the 'lantern-man' (or Hob-o'-Lantern) was frequently sighted prior to the 'growing-up' (infilling) of many of the pools in the fens, but that by the turn of the century, this phenomenon was rarely observed. This is puzzling, given the large quantities of methane released when sediment in the dykes and relict turf ponds is stirred up, and the likelihood that this is contaminated, as in the past, by traces of spontaneously combustible P_4 vapour or Diphosphine (P_2H_4). Could the infrequency with which the 'lantern-man' is seen today be attributable, not only to the reduced amount of open water, but the limited number of people who visit the fens at night, compared with times past, when men would have frequently been working in them until the light failed?

Marsh Hay and other crops

In addition to peat, the fens were extensively exploited as a source of firewood, Saw-sedge and Reed for thatching (see page 212), and a variety of other crops. Of the latter, perhaps the most important was Marsh Hay, a mixture of herbaceous species in which various fen grasses, notably the Purple Small-reed (*Calamagrostis canescens*) and the rush *Juncus subnodulosus* predominated. This was commonly cut and swathed between May and October, and when dry was boated off the fens and stacked, ready to be fed to livestock.

Although Marsh Hay was harvested from some fens year after year, other areas were left uncut for a time (Ellis, pers. comm.), and this would have helped to maintain a diversity of communities. Much of the Marsh Hay was used locally, but some was processed into chaff, either at permanent installations, such as . . . "the large unsightly building near the (Hickling) Pleasure Boat Inn" mentioned by Turner (1922), or by movable rigs powered by traction engines. Either way, the chaff was bagged, and dispatched by rail to London to serve as a food for the cab and bus horses. During the First World War it is alleged to have been sent over to France for our cavalry.

'Litter' is a variant of Marsh Hay in which coarser species predominate. Small quantities are still cut in mid-summer at Ranworth Flood and elsewhere, but whilst in the past, it was mainly used as a cattle bedding (Boardman, 1940), it is now much more frequently employed to protect clamps, and nursery-grown plants against frost.

'Sheath' (sometimes known as 'shoof-stuff') consists of a mixture of taller growing species than is commonly contained in Litter; in addition, it is not cut until late summer. It is used as an alternative to Saw-sedge for ridging thatched roofs.

Although the vast majority of the Reed harvested from the fens has always been used for thatching, paper was made from it by several firms during the First World War on account of the difficulty of obtaining suitable fibres (Cowan & Sons, 1920). Renewed interest in the use of reeds for paper-making was taken during the early 1930s, but experiments carried out at the Imperial Institute showed that the material produced would not be competitive with that made from esparto (EDP, 1936).

The fen dykes

Because of the soft, waterlogged terrain, it was impossible to use horse-drawn carts to collect up the Marsh Hay, Litter, Reed, Saw-sedge and other crops, and dykes were therefore dug so that they could be transported away by boat, either to the landward margin of the fen, or to the nearby river or broad, and thence to a convenient staithe. The flat-bottomed, clinker-built 'reed lighters' used for this purpose came in three sizes: half, three-quarter and whole-load vessels. The latter were about 25 feet (7.6 m) long, with a beam of 8 to 9 feet (2.4 to 2.7 m) and were capable of carrying two cart-loads of reed (Bolingbroke, 1965).

Many fens have a very extensive system of dykes. For instance there were originally *c.* 21 km of dyke in the 65 ha of fen around Upton Broad, though *c.* 6 km of these were abandoned at the end of the last century (Hobbs, *in litt.*). Similarly, the 379 ha of fen within the Bure Marshes National Nature Reserve are criss-crossed by over 18 miles (29 km) of dykes, each being about 5.5 m wide, and 1.2 m deep (see Plate XXIII). To create a system of this size would have necessitated the excavation by hand of over 190 000 cu m of peat, no mean task, even if phased over a period of many years. But it pales into insignificance when compared with the vast amounts of peat dug for fuel, over 480 000 cu m having been removed from Woodbastwick Fen alone prior to 1845.

The age of Broadland's fen dykes is seldom known. However, maps show that about

Plate XXIII

A fenland dyke in the Woodbastwick part of the Bure Marshes National Nature Reserve – 1978.

Ten Water Soldier plants were introduced into this dyke in 1972, and by 1978, when this photograph was taken, the species had become the dominant waterweed. For reasons not yet understood, it is now much less common in this particular waterway. Nevertheless, dykes such as this form an immensely important refuge for the aquatic plants and animals once found in the broads and rivers.

Photo: Peter Wakely/Nature Conservancy Council

half those at Woodbastwick were in existence by 1845, and that the remainder were dug between then and 1907.

To maintain the dykes in a navigable condition, mud and vegetation were removed from them annually with dydles and cromes, and each was periodically 'bottomfied' (see page 259). Ecologically, these forms of management would have been beneficial, as they ensured that the dykes did not fill up with sediment, to the detriment of their aquatic plant and animal life. However, because of a combination of circumstances, including the nutrient enrichment of the rivers (and therefore the fen dykes which are linked with them), long-continued neglect (consequent upon the abandonment of many mowing fens during and after the First World War), and the deposition in them of large quantities of sediment by tidal and fluvial action, most dyke systems are now in a very degraded state. Indeed, in many cases, waterweeds are either absent altogether, or represented by scattered patches of Yellow Water-lily only. The dykes of Woodbastwick and Strumpshaw Fens, and the internal parts of Catfield Fen are exceptional, in that they possess a rich and varied aquatic fauna and flora, as a result of having been isolated hydrologically from the adjoining, nutrient-enriched rivers (see Chapter 13).

The two former sites have a waterweed flora dominated by species such as Hornwort, the pondweeds *Potamogeton natans* and *P. friesii*, Greater Bladderwort, Horned Pondweed, Canadian Pondweed and Water Soldier – the latter deliberately re-introduced. This mixture of species is similar to the Phase II community which develops in broads subject to moderate nutrient enrichment (see Chapter 6).

Following a study of the flora and water chemistry of dykes in the Catfield Fen complex, Wheeler and Giller (1982b) identified by information analysis three principal categories (or 'noda'*) of aquatic vegetation here. The *Elodea-Potamogeton crispus* and *Ceratophyllum–Stratiotes* 'noda' normally occur near the upland margin, the former being restricted to dykes which have been cut into mineral soils (rather than peat), and where there is some inflow of nitrogen-rich water from the adjoining agricultural land. The third 'nodum' occurs in the central sections of the fen complex, and usually consists of almost pure stands of its characterizing species, Greater Bladderwort.

The management of the fen vegetation in the past

The regular mowing of hundreds of hectares of fen vegetation, the removal of the crops by boat, and the maintenance of the dyke system, would have kept large numbers of men employed. However, many of those who left to fight for their country in the First World War never returned, and because of this, and a decline in the demand for some crops, particularly Marsh Hay [there were over 13 000 horse cab-drivers in London in 1900, but only 700 by 1918 (Hamer, 1982)], the number of men working on the fens never regained its former level. As a result, large areas became subject, often for the first time for many centuries, to the effects of unchecked natural succession, and in consequence began to be invaded by Sallows and other woody species. Nevertheless, a few landowners continued to manage their fens in the customary way. For instance, during the 1930s, Lord Desborough employed on his 290 ha Hickling Estate, seven full-time marshmen, three or four part-time reed-cutters, plus a headkeeper (the legendary Jim Vincent), and two under-keepers (Linsell, pers. comm.).

Many of those still working on the fens left at the outbreak of the Second World War, and most of the areas still being mown at this time were abandoned, at least temporarily. Fortunately, there has been a strong and continuing demand from thatchers for Reed and Saw-sedge since the War, and these crops continue to be harvested in many places.

The plant ecology of the fens

(a) Introduction

The first description of Broadland's principal fen communities, compiled by Marietta Pallis as long ago as 1911, assumed that the whole complex system of open water,

---

* The term 'nodum' is used by phytosociologists to denote a unit of vegetation whose rank and status has not yet been determined.

reedswamp, fen and carr had evolved by relatively simple ecological processes. This in turn was based on the belief, then current, that the broads were formed naturally as a result of differential sedimentation in an extensively branched estuary formed by post-glacial submergence (see Chapter 4).

In 1935, the inimitable Ted Ellis published a description of the ecology of the fens around his home near Wheatfen Broad, and this prompted Joyce Lambert to make a detailed study of the distribution of Reed-grass (*Glyceria maxima*) in this part of the Yare valley, and its role in the succession. Her results were published in 1946, and the following year she extended her research to the Bure valley. Here, with the assistance of the physiographer J. N. Jennings, she showed how the distribution of the principal communities present is related to the stratigraphy of the valley deposits. In particular, the successions which develop over lake sediments were differentiated from those over solid, unworked deposits of peat. In the former, physically unstable communities typically dominated by Tussock Sedge, but sometimes containing an abundance of Lesser Pond-sedge or Saw-sedge, develop over the thin raft of rhizomes formed by the pioneer Lesser Reedmace and Reed plants. Later, the tops of the *C. paniculata* tussocks are colonized by woody species, and as the community increases in weight, a 'pool and tussock' formation is created; this ultimately develops into alder-dominated 'Swamp Carr' (see Plate XXIV) (Lambert, 1951; Lambert & Jennings, 1951).

Lambert and Jennings pointed out that the communities which develop over un-worked peat are always firmer underfoot than those overlying lake sediments, and do not show the slight surface subsidence frequently exhibited by the latter. In most places, too, these 'solid' communities have been managed as a source of Reed, Saw-sedge, and other fen crops. However where the succession has been allowed to take place unhindered, the resultant Fen Carr tends, because of its greater age, to contain a greater range of species than Swamp Carr.

Lambert's research, like that of most other British wetland ecologists prior to about 1960, was aimed primarily at improving our understanding of the hydrosere – the succession from open water to woodland – rather than to a systematic description of the plant communities. More recent work, notably that of Wheeler (1975, 1978 and 1980a, b & c), Wheeler and Giller (1982a) and Giller and Wheeler (1986a & b and 1988) has favoured a somewhat different approach, namely to define and name the communities present, and only to seek an explanation for their occurrence, and the manner in which they have been affected by management, after this descriptive phase has been completed. During the past 10 years, special attention has been given to the Ant valley because, as Wheeler (1978) puts it: "it supports the greatest number of different plant communities (and probably species as well) including some absent or poorly developed in the other valleys; it presents the richest and most extensive development of many of them; it retains large tracts of herbaceous fen (cf. the Bure valley) as considerable areas are still regularly mown for reed and sedge; and partly related to this, it provides the only remaining sites for several plant communities and species that were once more widespread in Broadland."

Wheeler and Giller found that the biological richness of the Ant valley fens was dependent, not only on their past and present management, but on their water regime. The fluvial flows in the Ant are quite small relative to the width of its flood plain, and the communities nearer the margin of the latter are therefore only occasionally flooded by river water. In the circumstances, their hydrology reflects the quality of the water reaching them from the adjoining uplands, rather than that of the river itself. Since in some places, both in this valley, and that of the R. Thurne, the uplands are founded on calcium-deficient glacial sands and gravels, calcium levels decline markedly near the landward margin of the fens. On the north side of Sutton Broad, for example, Wheeler and Giller found that in July 1981, there were about 100 and 110 mg of calcium per litre in the peat water for a distance of about 130 m from the navigable channel, but that the concentration decreased markedly during the next 10 m, and that for the remaining 30 m of the transect, there were only 55 to 770 mg of calcium per litre.

Nitrogen and phosphorus levels in the peat water of many of the communities which occur at Catfield Fen were below detection limits, and were not therefore studied by Wheeler and Giller. However, on the south side of Sutton Broad, riverine influence is indicated by the fact that total nitrogen and phosphorus levels decline with increasing distance from the navigable channel. This is reflected both in the varying performance

Swamp Carr to the south of Hoveton Great Broad – *c.* **1964.**

Plate XXIV

This community develops as a result of the invasion of Tussock Fen by trees and bushes (mainly alders and sallows). As the weight of these increases, the thin raft of rhizomes on which the community is founded, tends to be unevenly depressed, thus producing a characteristic 'pool and tussock' appearance. Seedlings of a variety of species, including woody plants, frequently become established on the tops of the sedge tussocks, and Common Valerian can be seen growing on the one on the right.

Good examples of Swamp Carr are much less common than they were in the 1960s and virtually none is currently being formed in the region.

Photo: Bruce Forman

of seedlings of Great Hairy Willow-herb grown experimentally on peat taken from the fens at different distances from the channel (Table 7b), and in their ecology. Species-poor reedbeds, typical of enriched conditions, extend for a distance of 100m or more from the channel, but give way to much more diverse communities nearer the valley margin.

Table 7b Mean dry weight of *Epilobium hirsutum* shoots grown from seed for 2 months at 20°C on waterlogged peats from Sutton Broad

Origin of peat	Weight (g)
Alongside river (167 m from fen edge)	3.24
Reed-bed (100 m)	2.48
Carex lasiocarpa vegetation (7 m)	0.16

Source: Al-Dosary, M.M. (unpublished). Quoted in Wheeler & Giller (1982a).

The extent to which the fens are influenced by the chemistry of the river water varies from site to site. In the Ant valley, the effects are greater where swamp communities have invaded the open water of a broad, as at Sutton, and where the fens are traversed by dykes connected with the river, than at sites which are bordered by 'solid' unworked deposits of peat. Flooding, and the consequent deposition of silt, tends to be greater in the Bure valley, and since this river contains relatively high levels of nitrogen and phosphorus, many of the adjoining fens have been invaded by coarse, nutrient-demanding species such as Great Hairy Willow-herb, Stinging Nettle and Wild Angelica (*Angelica sylvestris*). The effects of enrichment are even more marked in the Yare valley fens, since these lie adjacent to a river which carries even larger concentrations of nitrogen and phosphorus than the Bure, and which is, in addition, more strongly tidal. At the other end of the scale, some fens, such as those around Upton Broad, are hydrologically isolated from the rivers and are thus unaffected by their nutrient regime.

The chemistry of the interstitial water in the peat of Catfield Fen varies considerably, both with depth, and according to the nature of the underlying deposits. In most of the samples examined, calcium, magnesium and sodium levels decline near the surface, whilst potassium increases, probably because of the release of this element by senescent plant material, and the concentrating effect of living vegetation. Almost all the cations measured were present in greater quantities in sites overlying the clay deposited in and beside the former channel of the R. Ant during the Second Transgression than over peat, and investigations confirmed that this stratigraphic difference has a significant effect on the ecology of the fens.

The occurrence here and there in Broadland of 'Poor-fen' communities, usually containing much *Sphagnum*, was remarked upon by Pallis as early as 1911, and in a recent study Giller and Wheeler (1988) have pointed out that these *Sphagnum* areas occur in two quite distinct situations; as marginal stands adjoining mineral substrate of low base status (such as those bordering the Ant valley), and as 'islands' in the midst of fens over deep peat, well separated from the margins, and surrounded by species-rich communities. Cation and pH levels in the *Sphagnum* areas are much lower than those of adjoining communities, because of their vertical isolation from the base-rich river water, and the activity of the moss itself. Wheeler and Giller found that *Sphagnum* hummocks under a canopy of birch contained only 25 to 26 mg of calcium per litre, whereas mean calcium levels in the interstitial water of alder-carr peat beside Barton Broad were 145 mg l^{-1}. The *Sphagnum* areas also had the lowest pH with a range of 5.2 to 5.9, whereas in other communities, the pH of the peat water was between 6.4 and 6.9; in contrast the pH of the R. Ant and Barton Broad was 8.0 and 7.7 respectively.

Although cation concentrations are often significantly lower below *Sphagnum* areas than beneath other communities nearby, suggesting that the progressive development of oligotrophic conditions (which may loosely be defined as calcium depletion) may be conducive to *Sphagnum* invasion, this is not always the case. For instance, the raft of *Sphagnum* in the 'Heater Swamp' (the triangular-shaped island at the northern end of Barton Broad) is underlain by watery sediments rich in cations, and having a high pH.

In addition to studying the chemistry of the fens, Wheeler and Giller measured the variations of water level relative to the peat surface which occur in different plant communities at Catfield. These, too, were found to have an effect on the ecology. For instance, the largest fluctuations (up to 39.8 cm) in water level were observed at sites near the river and broad, doubtless because the communities here can drain more freely at times of low water, than those further away. In the latter, the range of variation was up to 10 cm less than near the river, and the water level only rarely fell below the surface, and then only to a limited extent. The *Sphagnum* communities once again formed an exception, the range of fluctuation being as little as 5 cm, much less than in adjoining non-*Sphagnum* communities. Experiments showed that this difference was mainly attributable to the ability of the *Sphagnum* to swell and contract; indeed during the summer of 1981 the surface of the *Sphagnum* peat at one site near Irstead fell by 17 cm as water levels in the fen declined.

The fact that most fens in the region are located in the flood plains of the main rivers ensures that such fluctuations in the water-table are of a temporary nature. Indeed, the situation in Broadland is quite different from other parts of lowland Britain, where numerous fens have been damaged over the past 30 to 40 years as a consequence of a lowering of the water-table caused by improved land drainage, or ground or surface-water abstraction. However, there are some exceptions to this generalization, East Ruston Common being an example of a site adversely affected by groundwater abstraction, whilst the fens around Calthorpe Broad, and near Long Gore, are drying out as a result of steps taken by the Happisburgh to Winterton Internal Drainage Board and local farmers to lower the water-table of the marshland which adjoins these sites.

(b) The phytosociological approach

The descriptions given by Wheeler (1978 & 1980a, b & c) and Wheeler and Giller (1982a) of Broadland's fens, and their relationships with other 'Rich-fen' sites in Britain and North-West Europe, are related, not to the dominant-based hierarchies beloved of British ecologists, but to the phytosociological concepts which have been used for many years by continental workers. Information Analysis and other statistical techniques have been used to produce from data obtained in the field a series of classes, each distinguished by a number of 'characterizing' plants. These, and other species in the class are given a weighting according to their occurrence, rather than their size or dominance in the community. In explaining the reasons for this choice, which frequently involves putting stands with different dominants into a single Association. Wheeler points out that the pattern of dominance is not necessarily a natural phenomenon in fens, but may have been caused by the way the communities have been managed. In addition, the results obtained from his Information Analysis show that the presence of a particular dominant, such as Reed, Saw-sedge or Bog Myrtle (*Myrica gale*) does not exert an over-riding influence on the composition of the community.

Whenever possible Wheeler has placed the units of vegetation which he distinguished in Broadland within the hierarchies established by continental workers. For instance many of the region's alder-dominated communities have obvious affinities with the Association known to European ecologists as the *Osmundo-Alnetum*, and have therefore been included within this category.

Other communities found in Broadland have not been described by continental workers, but were considered by Wheeler to be sufficiently distinct to warrant designation as new Associations. In some cases, these were so floristically diverse, and so widely distributed, that Wheeler found it necessary to divide them into sub-associations, each distinguished by one or more characterizing species. His *Peucedano-Phragmitetum*, for example had to be split into seven sub-associations, several of which in turn had to be divided into 'varieties'. Communities containing only a few species, or only one, are defined by their dominants, and are known as sociations or societies respectively. But some of Broadland's communities have such a varied composition, or have such a restricted distribution, that Wheeler felt that it would be unwise to assign them to a particular vegetation unit; these have therefore been left as *ad hoc* or 'undifferentiated' communities until more information can be obtained about their status.

In his account of the 'Rich-fen' systems of England and Wales, Wheeler (1980a, b & c) recognizes 30 separate communities, and groups these into 8 Alliances. 17 communities could be defined sufficiently clearly to warrant being termed Associations, and the fact that 14 of these, together with 7 of the principal undifferentiated communities, occur in Broadland (see Table 7c) shows how ecologically diverse the region is, as well as how important it is in a British context.

Table 7c   Synopsis of the Rich-fen systems found in Broadland

Alliance	*Association*
PHRAGMITION	*Schoenoplecto – Phragmitetum* (*Scirpo – Phragmitetum*)
	Cladietum marisci
	Cicuto – Phragmitetum
MAGNOCARICION	*Caricetum elatae*
	Caricetum paniculatae
	Potentillo – Caricetum rostratae
	Angelico – Phargmitetum
	Peucedano – Phragmitetum (see Table 7d)
	Phragmites australis dominated communities
	Cladium mariscus dominated communities
	Glyceria maxima dominated communities
CARICION DAVALLIANAE	*Schoeno – Juncetum subnodulosi*
JUNCO (SUBULIFLORI) MOLINION	*Cirsio – Molinietum*
CALTHION PALUSTRIS	*Fen-meadow communities*
FILIPENDULION	*Epilobium hirsutum – Filipendula ulmaria* community
	Phragmites – Urtica dioica community
SALICION CINEREAE	*Myricetum gale*
	Betulo – Dryopteridetum cristatae
	Betulo – Myricetum
	Salix cinerea carr
ALNION GLUTINOSAE	*Osmundo – Alnetum*

(c) The vegetation of the flood plain mires

Seven of Wheeler's 8 Rich-fen Alliances occur in Broadland's flood plain mires, the eighth, the CARICION DAVALLIANAE, being represented only at Smallburgh Fen, one of the region's two valley mires. Woody vegetation predominates in 2 of the 7 Alliances, and a third, the PHRAGMITION, comprises the reedswamp vegetation described in the previous Chapter, together with an Association intermediate in character between reedswamp and fen, known as the *Cicuto-Phragmitetum*. This is particularly well developed beside the channels traversing Sutton Broad, and is characterized by an abundance of Cyperus Sedge (*Carex pseudocyperus*), Cowbane (*Cicuta virosa*), Greater Spearwort (*Ranunculus lingua*), Water Parsnip (*Sium latifolia*), Bulrush, Lesser Reedmace and the terrestrial form of the Yellow Water-lily, as well as Reed. Floristically, this Association is of considerable interest, since several of its component species are nationally rare, or are declining elsewhere in Britain. It is also very attractive in appearance, especially when the Greater Spearwort is flowering.

Five out of the six Associations placed by Wheeler in the MAGNACARICION Alliance occur in Broadland. Of these, the *Caricetum elatae* is mainly confined to the edges of turf ponds and fen dykes. Its characterizing species is the Tufted Sedge (*Carex elata*), but other plants growing with this include Cuckoo Flower (*Cardamine pratense*), Pennywort (*Hydrocotyle vulgaris*), Purple Loosestrife (*Lythrum salicaria*), Marsh Willow-herb (*Epilobium palustre*), Water Mint (*Mentha aquatica*), and saplings of Alder and Common Sallow (*Salix cinerea*).

The same species occur in the second Association of the MAGNACARICION, the *Caricetum paniculatae* (see Plate XXIV), often as epiphytes on the tussocks of the sedge which give this community its name, and which frequently attain a height of a metre or more. As the *C. paniculata* plants are rooted in a thin raft of peat overlying lake sediments which may at some sites be 3 m or more deep, those botanists foolhardy enough to venture into this community risk, at best, a highly unpleasant mud bath. The less intrepid will find it easier, and much safer, to use the Ranworth or Hoveton Great Broad walkways, both of which traverse areas where various stages in the succession from Tussock Fen to Swamp Carr can be seen.

As we have seen in the previous chapter, Tussock Fen is no longer being formed around the broads, owing to the absence from most of them of the primary colonizers of open water, Bulrush and Lesser Reedmace. Furthermore, many of the existing stands of this community are either being overgrown and smothered by Great Hairy Willow-herb and other coarse, nutrient-demanding species, as on the western side of Barton Broad, or are degenerating altogether. At Cockshoot and Hoveton Great Broads, for example, former islands of Tussock Fen and Swamp Carr are now represented only by dead and dying alders, the sedge tussocks which originally surrounded and partly supported the latter having disappeared altogether. The demise of Broadland's Tussock Fen communities is most regrettable, since they were much more extensively developed, and floristically diverse, than similar communities found elsewhere in Britain, for instance at Sweatmere in Shropshire.

The next Association of the MAGNACARICION, the *Potentillo-Caricetum rostratae*, contains several species intolerant of calcium bicarbonate and other bases, and is therefore often referred to as 'Poor-fen' by ecologists. Stands of this Association are rare in Broadland, being confined to the western extremity of the Hickling reserve, and other valley-margin sites receiving calcium-deficient water from the Norwich Brickearth and other leached deposits. Its characterizing species are Bottle Sedge (*Carex rostrata*), Bogbean (*Menyanthes trifoliata*), Cotton-grass (*Eriophorum angustifolium*) and Marsh Cinquefoil (*Potentilla palustris*), but in Broadland it is usually dominated either by the latter, or Soft Rush (*Juncus effusus*). Reed, though usually present, tends to be depauperate, particularly at sites where the dissolved calcium level and pH are low, while Milk Parsley (*Peucedanum palustre*), a nationally rare umbellifer whose autecology has been described by Harvey and Meredith (1981), is also a common constituent of this Association. Other species which may occur in it include Great Water Dock (*Rumex hydrolapathum*), Water Parsnip and the bog-moss, *Sphagnum squarrosum*, whilst Marsh St. John's-wort (*Hypericum elodes*), White Sedge (*Carex curta*) and other plants are to be found on fens not subject to disturbance.

The *Angelico-Phragmitetum* is a rather ill-defined Association which usually develops on fens which were previously mown for Reed, or cattle-grazed, but which have subsequently been abandoned. It contains a number of coarse, nutrient-demanding species, and for this reason is particularly common in the Yare valley. Its characterizing species are Wild Angelica, Reed, Hemp Agrimony (*Eupatorium cannabinum*), Purple Loosestrife and Great Hairy Willow-herb, but it is normally dominated by Reed, or Reed-grass, or less frequently by Reed Canary-grass or Tussock Sedge.

Although the next Association, the *Peucedano-Phragmitetum*, is known from Wicken and Woodwalton Fens in Cambridgeshire, and from one or two other sites in Somerset and East Yorkshire, it is far more extensively developed in Broadland than elsewhere in Britain; indeed most of the herbaceous vegetation of the region's flood plain mires falls within this category. Its characterizing species are Milk Parsley, Reed, Saw-sedge, Purple Small-reed, Yellow Loosestrife, Marsh Bedstraw (*Galium palustre*), Hemp Agrimony (*Lysimachia vulgaris*) and the Blunt-flowered Rush, *Juncus subnodulosus*. Although floristically very variable, the communities within this Association tend to be dominated either by Reed, Saw-sedge or, in the drier areas, Purple Small-reed.

Seven out of the eight sub-associations recognized by Wheeler (1980a, b & c) in the *Peucedano-Phragmitetum* occur in Broadland, and a simplified description of each is provided in Table 7d. In general, these sub-associations are best developed in the Ant valley fens, where they often occur in close proximity to other communities. As a consequence, the visiting ecologist is confronted by a fascinating, if somewhat bewildering, series of communities, ranging from stands referable to the *Cicuto-Phragmitetum* near the river, to species-rich swards of one or more of the sub-associations of the *Peucedano-Phragmitetum* in one direction, and to valley-margin communities of the *Potentillo-Caricetum rostratae* in another; at one place, these in turn grade naturally into *Calluna* and *Ulex*-dominated heathland.

Of all the communities found in Broadland's fens, the richest floristically is the *Peucedano-Phragmitetum Caricetosum*, and it is by no means unusual to find in its stands over 50 different species per ten metre square. Plants of particular note include the Grass-of-Parnassus (*Parnassia palustris*), Narrow-leaved Marsh Orchid (*Dactylorhiza*

Table 7d   Sub-associations within the Peucedano-Phragmitetum

Sub-association	Characterization	Summary description and Requirements	Distribution in Broadland
1. *Typicum*	Negative (i.e. absence of species differential for other groups).	Rather species-poor vegetation with a core of the Association's characterizing plants, plus occasional *Carex appropinquata, Menyanthes trifoliata, Stellaria palustris, Valeriana dioica, Schoenus nigricans,* and on drier sites, *Molinia caerulea, Thelypteris palustris* is sometimes abundant, particularly in places where bushes have become established.	Widespread in former mowing fens, e.g. Woodbastwick Fen.
2. *Myricetosum*	*Myrica gale, Thelypteris palustris* and a general prominence of *Salix* and other bushes.	A species-poor unit, usually dominated by *Cladium* or *Calamagrostis canescens,* rather than *Phragmites.* Is mainly confined to areas of solid, uncut peat and gradually develops into the *Myricetum gale* Association.	Frequent, especially in the Bure and Ant valleys. Often in small patches alongside dykes, or in overgrown saw-sedge beds. Frequently situated near stands of the Schoenetosum sub-association, from which it probably develops.
3. *Arrhenatheretosum*	*Arrhenatherium elatius, Cirsium arvense, Phalaris arundinacea, Polygonum amphibium* and *Stachys palustris.*	Degraded communities of fens subject to drying out. Usually dominated by *Calamagrostis canescens* or *Phalaris,* sometimes with some *Phragmites,* and often colonized by *Rubus* or *Pteridium.* Floristically variable.	Rare. Often occurs on peaty river banks. Best developed near Wayford Bridge.
4. *Glycerietosum*	Best defined by two overlapping species groups: a) *Lathyrus palustris, Solanum dulcemara* and *Thalictrum flavum;* b) *Carex paniculata, Epilobium hirsutum* and *Glyceria maxima.*	Floristically very variable, but typically dominated by *Phragmites. Glyceria maxima, Carex riparia* and *Epilobium hirsutum* are often abundant, and *Phararis* frequently occurs in patches. A community of nutrient-enriched situations.	Virtually confined to the Yare valley fens, but also develops in long-abandoned marshland, both here and in the Waveney valley.
5. *Cicutosum*	*Cicuta virosa, Carex pseudocyperus, Ranunculus lingua, Sium latifolia* and *Typha angustifolia.*	Many of the stands in this group have affinities with the Cicuto-Phragmitetum, and are probably developing into the Caricetosum sub-association. *Carex lasiocarpa* is often abundant, with *C. dioecia, C. appropinquata, Pedicularis palustris* and the moss, *Acrocladium giganteum. Menyanthes* and/or *Potentilla palustris* may predominate locally, and *Phragmites* is almost always abundant. Requires shallow, above-surface, water-table, but low-nutrient water and restricted water movement.	Peat-filled turf-ponds in the Ant Valley, such as those near Sutton Broad.
6. *Schoenetosum*	*Schoenus nigricans, Carex panicea, Oenanthe lachenalii,* and the absence of differentials for the *Caricetosum* sub-association.	Usually extensive, but rather species-poor areas of mowing fen, dominated by *Cladium* or less usually *Phragmites.* Has affinities with the valley fens of the Schoeno-Juncetum subnodulosi Association. In typical form, is confined to areas of solid, uncut peat with a periodically low summer water-table. A nutrient-poor community which is tolerant of a wide salinity range.	Widespread and extensive in the Ant and Thurne valleys, e.g. Saw-sedge beds beside Hickling Broad and Horsey Mere.
7. *Caricetosum*	*Carex diandra, C. lasiocarpa, C. approprinquata, Caltha palustris, Cirsium dissectum, Epipactis palustris, Pedicularis palustris, Valeiana dioica* the mosses *Acrocladium giganteum* and *Bryum pseudotriquetrum* and the liverwort *Riccardia pinguis.*	Many of the stands in this sub-association are very species-rich, and contain a host of rare and local species, including *Liparis loeselii, Carex limosa* and *Dactylorhiza traunsteineri.* The wetter versions of this community contain *Baldellia ranunculoides, Hottonia palustris, Potamogeton coloratus* and *Utricularia* spp. Appears intolerant of low summer water levels; base-rich, but perhaps with some impoverishment of elevated surfaces. Fairly nutrient-poor, and intolerant of raised salinity levels.	Occurs over former peat-pits, but is rare. Is found mainly in the Ant valley, but also at two sites in the Bure valley.

traunsteineri), Great Sundew (*Drosera anglica*), and Bog Pimpernel (*Anagallis tenella*), while the Lesser Water-Plaintain (*Baldellia ranunculoides*), Water Violet (*Hottonia palustris*), Fen Pondweed (*Potamogeton coloratus*) and three species of Bladderwort, *Utricularia vulgaris*, *U. intermedia* and *U. minor*, occur in damp hollows and former turf ponds.

Bryophytes are an important feature of the *Peucedano-Phragmitetum Caricetosum* and frequently form moss 'carpets'. Typical species include *Acrocladium cuspidatum*, *A. cordifolium*, *A. giganteum*, *Campylium stellatum*, *C. elodes*, *Drepanocladus revolvens*, *D. vernicosus*, *Mnium pseudopunctatum*, *Mn. seligeri*, *Scorpium scorpioiodes*, *Fissidens adianthoides* and *Riccardia pinguis*. 25 different mosses and liverworts, including several large patches of the nationally rare *Cinclidium stygium*, have been recorded by Francis Rose and Peter Lambley from fens in the Ant valley.

The rarest flowering plant found in the *Peucedano-Phragmitetum Caricetosum*, and indeed in the whole of Broadland, is the Fen Orchid (see Plate 17), a species included on Schedule 8 of the *Wildlife and Countryside Act*, and which is thereby afforded special protection. Crompton (1977), who investigated the former distribution of the fenland form of this plant (as distinct from var. *ovata*, which occurs in dune-slacks in South Wales) found that it has been recorded from 16 sites in East Anglia, of which 9 are in Broadland. Most of these areas have been overgrown by scrub as a result of lack of management or drainage, or both, and the species is now confined to two principal colonies in the Ant valley, and to one or two other sites elsewhere in Broadland. In some years, for instance 1971, 1973 and 1979, over 100 flowering spikes have been counted in its main colonies, but in dry seasons, few if any of the plants produce blooms.

Liparis sometimes occurs as an epiphyte on *Carex appropinquata* tussocks, together with Pennywort, Red Rattle (*Pedicularis palustris*), Bog-rush and other species, but more usually it grows in a carpet of mosses. Such communities are highly susceptible to damage by trampling, and because of this, and the fact that *Liparis* is very inconspicuous, even when in flower, a great deal of damage can unwittingly be caused by those wishing to see or photograph it. For this reason, the exact localities where this very rare and endangered orchid occurs cannot be disclosed.

None of the other sub-associations of the *Peucedano-Phragmitetum* is as floristically rich as the *P.P. Caricetosum*. Nevertheless, the *P.P. Schoenetosum* is an important community from the economic point of view, as many of the commercial saw-sedge beds in the region are referable to it. Wheeler and Giller note that at Catfield the peat underlying it is deficient in nitrogen and phosphorus, and that the slightly raised surface, and rather solid character of the peat, means that the summer water-table is lower than in most other fen communities. Because of this, and the high redox potential of the peat surface, Purple Moor-grass (*Molinia caerulea*) and Bog Myrtle are almost always abundant in this sub-association, as well as Bog-rush, its characterizing species. It is tolerant of a wide range of salinities, and as a consequence is well developed around the Thurne broads, Parsley Water-Dropwort (*Oenanthe lachenalii*) being more prominent here than in the Bure and Ant valleys.

Whereas the saw-sedge communities of the *Cladietum marisci* are confined to former peat workings, those of the *Peucedano-Phragmitetum Schoenetosum* typically occur in areas which have never been exploited as a source of fuel. Stands referable to this sub-association are frequently associated with communities of the *Peucedano-Phragmitetum Myricetosum*. Marsh Fern (*Thelypteris palustris*) is always common in this, together with a variety of shrubs including Birch (*Betula pubescens*), Creeping Willow (*Salix repens*), Common Sallow and, less frequently, Alder. Neither of these sub-associations is well developed in the Yare and Waveney fens, being generally confined to small, scattered patches near the valley margins.

In addition to the five Associations described above, Wheeler places three species-poor communities in the MAGNACARICION. These are dominated respectively by Reed, Saw-sedge or Reed-grass, and the first two are of great economic importance since they are still exploited as a source of thatching materials. In addition, though classed as 'species-poor', these reed and saw-sedge dominated communities often contain plants of considerable distinction. Most sedge-beds, for example, contain Milk Parsley, the food plant of the caterpillar of the Swallow-tail Butterfly (*Papilio machaon*), whilst Marsh Sow-Thistle, a species particularly characteristic of reed-covered ronds (see page 71), is frequent in the Yare valley fens, and on reedy flood-banks around the Thurne broads. Another national rarity which is mainly confined to reed-dominated communities, especially those which have not been cut for a few years, is the Marsh Pea (*Lathyrus palustris*). A survey by Miss P. Gammell during the mid-1970s showed that this species is frequent in many parts of the region, being locally abundant on the Strumpshaw, Upton and Woodbastwick reserves. It was thought to be absent from the fens around the Thurne broads, not having been recorded from here for many years (Lambley, pers. comm.). However, it was found beside Catfield Dyke (at the western end of Hickling Broad) in 1989 (Russell, *in litt.*).

Species-poor stands of *Glyceria maxima* are specially characteristic of the Yare valley fens, and in the past were regularly mown to produce a coarse fodder for cattle. In some circumstances (see page 178) the *Glyceria* is replaced by *Phragmites*, and it is frequently succeeded near the water's-edge by dense thickets of Sallow (usually *Salix purpurea* or *S. cinerea* or their hybrids).

Four other groups of herbaceous fen communities occur in Broadland's flood plain mires. The first of these is normally dominated by Purple Moor-grass, and forms a well-marked Association, the *Cirsio-Molinetum*. Several sub-divisions of this have been recognized by Wheeler elsewhere in England and Wales, but of the two which occur in Broadland, only one is of importance, the *Nardetosum*. This is confined to the margins of the Ant valley fens, and to the extreme western end of the Hickling reserve. Its characterizing species are Cross-leaved Heath (*Erica tetralix*), Mat-grass (*Nardus stricta*), Heather (*Calluna vulgaris*) and *Sphagnum plumulosum*, and it frequently grades on one side into stands of the *Potentillo-Caricetum rostratae*, and on the other, into patches of dry heathland on the upland margin.

The second group of herbaceous communities have been termed 'Fen meadows' by Wheeler, and consist of vegetation dominated by rushes or sedges (typically *Juncus subnodulosus*, *Carex acutiformis* and *C. disticha*), and containing a wide range of characterizing species, including the grasses, *Agrostis stolonifera*, *Holcus lanatus* and *Poa trivialis*. Such communities, which are included in an Alliance known as the CALTHION PALUSTRIS, normally occur on, or near, the valley margins, often on quite shallow peat, the best examples being at Burgh and Hemsby Commons. They are commonly mown for Marsh Hay or used as rough pasturage.

The last two groups of herbaceous communities in the flood plain mires are included within the FILIPENDULION Alliance. Both are species-poor, the first being characterized by Great Hairy Willow-herb, and/or Meadowsweet (*Filipendula ulmaria*), together with a limited range of other nutrient-demanding species, including Goosegrass (*Galium aparine*), Stinging Nettle, Wild Angelica and Woody Nightshade (*Solanum dulcemara*), while the other typically comprises a mixture of Reed and Stinging Nettle. This often develops when the water-table of a fen is lowered, whilst the *Epilobium-Filipendula* community is characteristic of long-neglected grazing and mowing marshes which are subject to enrichment. Good examples occur near the Whitlingham sewage treatment works, and between Bramerton and Surlingham Ferry.

Wheeler places the scrub and woodland communities of Broadland's flood plain mires into two Alliances, the SALICION CINEREAE and the ALNION GLUTINOSAE. The former comprises four communities, of which the first is an Association known as the *Myricetum gale* on account of the abundance of Bog Myrtle within it. It contains several of the species characteristic of the *Peucedano-Phragmitetum Myricetosum*, from which it probably frequently develops; its seral character is also suggested by the occurrence within it of saplings of Alder and Birch. Although it is a frequent component of the Ant and Bure valley fens, and occurs at Barnby, it has not been recorded from the Yare valley.

The second Association in the SALICION CINEREAE, the *Betulo-Dryopteridetum cristatae*, occurs in the fens beside Hickling Broad and Horsey Mere, and in the Bure and Ant valleys, but has not been recorded from anywhere else in Britain. In addition to the Crested Buckler-fern, the characterizing species of this Association include the Narrow Buckler-fern (*D. carthusiana*), young birch trees and several species of *Sphagnum*, the swards of the latter being especially vigorous where the birch canopy is relatively open. Associated shrubs include Bog Myrtle and Creeping Willow.

The *Betulo-Drytopteridetum cristatae* often takes the form of a narrow strip of vegetation separating 'islets' of closed-canopy birch scrub from herbaceous, species-rich communities. Giller and Wheeler (1988) have demonstrated that it is almost always developed over shallow peat cuts which were colonized initially by *Phragmites* and *Typha*, and that it is, in consequence, usually less than 150 years old. The comparatively recent formation of this acidiphilous community may therefore be contrasted with the situation at Woodwalton Fen, Cambridgeshire, where 'raised bog' vegetation developed on top of the fen peat from a very early date, but was subsequently removed from much of the site by peat cutting (Poore, 1956).

Floristically, the most outstanding feature of the *Betulo-Dryopteridetum cristatae* is the comparative abundance within it of the nationally rare Crested Buckler-fern. Although this species appears to be decreasing elsewhere, surveys carried out by Crompton (1977) and Wheeler (1978) have shown that it occurs at numerous sites in Broadland, sometimes in considerable quantity. For instance one of three colonies found at Hickling in 1977 contained over 1000 plants. Whether this fern is actually extending its range in the region, or whether its distribution is now better known as a result of the surveys carried out during the past few years, is not clear.

The *Betulo-Myricetum*, the third scrub-dominated Association found in Broadland, usually consists of thickets of Birch, in which there is much Bog Myrtle, Common Sallow, and less frequently, Alder Buckthorn (*Frangula alnus*) and Creeping Willow. Common herbaceous components include Yellow and Purple Loosestrife, and several species of ferns, while the Round-leaved Wintergreen (*Pyrola rotundifolia*) occurs at some sites, including the fens around Upton Broad. The moss flora is well developed in some stands, Bog-mosses (*Sphagnum* spp.) being present where the community has developed serally from the *Betulo-Dryopteridetum cristatae*.

The fourth and last scrub community is dominated by Common Sallow. It is a rather variable, and poorly defined community which is best developed on abandoned mowing fens. It commonly grades into the wet, alder-dominated woodland which now occupies much of Broadland's river valleys, and which is known to phytosociologists as the *Osmundo-Alnetum*; included within this Association are the communities referred to by Lambert (1951) as Swamp Carr, Semi-swamp Carr and Fen Carr. Most alder woodlands in Broadland contain an assemblage of species somewhat different from that found elsewhere in England and Wales, and for this reason have been placed by Wheeler in a separate sub-association, the *Osmundo-Alnetum lycopetosum*. The characterizing species of this include Marsh Fern, Milk Parsley, Yellow and Purple Loosestrife, Purple Small-reed and the sedges, *Carex elata* and *C. remota* as well as Gipsywort (*Lycopus europaeus*). Alder is almost always the dominant tree, and may attain a height of over 12 m, especially when growing on solid, unworked peat deposits, such as those west of Buckenham Broad. Other trees growing with the Alder include Birch and occasional Oak (*Quercus robur*). Suppressed Ash (*Fraxinus excelsior*) saplings are often abundant, and if an Alder is wind-thrown, or dies, one or more of these will quickly grow into the gap in the canopy thus created (see Plate XXV). Particularly good examples of this can be seen between stopping points 6 and 7 on the Hoveton Great Broad nature trail.

Alder was formerly much in demand for turnery and brush making, and most of the trees in Broadland's carrs display the multi-stemmed growth which results from past coppicing and subsequent neglect.

Stands of single-stemmed or 'maiden' alders are confined to areas which, because of their inaccessibility or their relatively recent formation have never been exploited by the woodman. They are frequent around the margins of broads where peat has formed over the lake sediments to a depth sufficient to support the weight of the trees, without developing into the 'pool and tussock' formation characteristic of Swamp Carr. Good examples of maiden alder woodland are to be seen to the south of Hoveton Great Broad (see Plate 18), and on the west side of Cockshoot Dyke.

Mature alder woodland overlying solid, unworked peat typically contains an understorey of Hawthorn (*Crataegus monogyna*), Alder Buckthorn, Purging Buckthorn (*Rhamnus cathartica*), Holly (*Ilex aquifolium*) and Guelder-rose (*Viburnum opulus*), and beneath this there is a range of lower-growing woody species, such as Black and Red Currant (*Ribes nigrum* and *R. rubrum*), Dog Rose (*Rosa canina*) and Wild Raspberry (*Rubus idaeus*). However, in carrs which have formed over lake sediments, these communities, being relatively immature, contain fewer species. In addition, the species composition of the carrs varies somewhat in the different valleys. For instance, Guelder Rose is commoner in the Yare fens than elsewhere, whereas Alder Buckthorn is much rarer.

The field and ground layers within Broadland's alder woodlands are usually very well

developed and floristically diverse. The sedges *Carex acutiformis, C. elata, C. pseudocyperus* and *C. remota* are often abundant, as too are Yellow Iris (though seldom flowering because of the dense shade), Stinging Nettle, the Bitter-cresses, *Cardamine amara* and *C. flexuosa*, Marsh Valerian (*Valeriana dioica*) and Marsh Fern. Reed is frequent in immature alder woodland, but is much less common, or even locally absent from older stands as a result of shade-suppression.

Royal Fern (*Osmunda regalis*) is frequent in many of the carrs of the Bure and Ant valleys, and may attain a height of almost 2 m. At one site near Sutton, the plants are so numerous that few other herbaceous species can survive. The Victorians had a passion for collecting this, and other ferns, and both they, and later generations, frequently transplanted it to places where it did not occur naturally; the plants at Whiteslea Lodge on the Hickling Broad reserve, and near Calthorpe Broad, are examples of such introductions.

(d) The vegetation of the valley mires

Broadland's two valley mires are very different from one another ecologically. Small-burgh Fen is fed with highly calcareous water, and according to Wheeler (1978) is largely clothed with an excellent example of the *Schoeno-Juncetum subnodulosi*, an Association of the Alliance CARICION DAVALLIANAE. Bog-rush, various sedges, Blunt-flowered Rush and Purple Moor-grass predominate, and moss carpets, made up largely of *Bryum pseudotriquetrum, Drepanocladus revolvens* and *Fissidens adianthoides* are well developed in places. Near the valley bottom, this community grades into unmanaged sallow scrub and alder-dominated woodland, and tussocks of the bog-moss, *Sphagnum palustre*, occur near the fen margin. Several uncommon plants occur on the site, including Grass-of-Parnassus, Bog Pimpernel and Dioecious Sedge (*Carex dioecia*), and it forms the only locality in Norfolk for the rare moss, *Brachythecium mildeanum*.

The other valley fen in Broadland is East Ruston Common. The communities here are very different from those at Smallburgh Fen since they receive water from deposits of nutrient-poor, decalcified Norwich Brickearth. The dominant sedge is *Carex rostrata*, with smaller quantities of *C. curta* and *C. nigra*, and the community is similar to the stands of the *Potentillo-Caricetum rostratae* which occur near the margins of the Ant valley, and at the western end of the Hickling Broad reserve. Unfortunately, the water-table of East Ruston Common has been lowered during the past few years as a result of groundwater abstraction at a nearby waterworks operated by the AWA (now Anglian Water Services PLC), and the sedge-dominated communities are drying out, and regressing towards alder woodland.

The management of the fens today

(a) Introduction

Small quantities of Litter and Sheath are still cut here and there, for instance at Ranworth Flood, and two blocks of alder coppice were cut at Woodbastwick in the mid-1970s, the materials being sold to the Briton Brush factory at Wymondham. Unfortunately, this closed down in 1985, and it will therefore be necessary to find an alternative market when the time comes to re-coppice these compartments, probably in the mid-1990s. Mature, formerly coppiced, alders are also being felled in the Bure valley fens, the timber subsequently being sawn into rectangular blocks for use in coal mines. But the importance of these crops pales into insignificance compared with Saw-sedge

Fen Carr to the south of Hoveton Great Broad – 1969. Plate XXV

Ash saplings, such as the one to the right of the figure, are often abundant in this community, and although normally suppressed, are capable of quickly filling gaps in the alder canopy caused by disease or windthrow. The photo was taken from the walkway laid out by the Nature Conservancy on this part of the Bure Marshes National Nature Reserve in 1968.

Photo: Peter Wakely/Nature Conservancy Council

and Reed, large quantities of which are still being harvested for use by thatchers. The reed-cutting industry therefore provides, directly or indirectly, a considerable amount of local employment. In addition, conservationists are keen that reed and sedge-cutting should continue, as they see this as a way of ensuring that fens remain in an 'open', and therefore ecologically interesting, condition. On the other hand, the objectives of reed-cutters and conservationists are not always fully compatible, an issue which is dealt with more fully in Chapter 13.

(b) Saw-sedge

Most, if not all the Saw-sedge cut in Broadland is referrable to the MAGNOCARICION, some communities containing a sufficient number of other species to warrant being placed in the *Peucedano-Phragmitetum Schoenetosum*, whilst others are virtual monocultures of *Cladium*. In either event, beds of Saw-sedge are normally harvested on a three to four-year rotation. Such a regime tends to suppress *Phragmites*. However, if cutting is left too late in the season, the saw-sedge plants may not have time to produce new shoots, and are then liable to be killed, either by severe frosts, or prolonged flooding. In these circumstances, the *Cladium* may be replaced by *Phragmites*. Conversely, if the sedge-bed is left uncut for a number of years, so much litter accumulates that other plants tend to be suppressed, and a species-poor stand of *Cladium* develops.

After the Saw-sedge has been dried and bundled, it is used as a capping for thatched roofs, about 40 'bunches' being required per 10 feet (*c.* 3 m) run. Although it is the most durable crop for this purpose, usually lasting some 20 to 25 years, thatchers find it hard on their hands, and in recent years have tended to use 'Sheath' instead. Despite this, the market for Saw-sedge remains firm and in 1989, bunches were being sold by growers for about 60p each. Between 11 and 14 thousand bunches are cut each year at the northern end of the Brayden Marshes on the Horsey Estate, the average yield being about 2000 bunches per hectare (Buxton, pers. comm.). About 6000 bunches are harvested each year from the Catfield fens, and 4000 from the Hickling Broad reserve, whilst smaller quantities are cut on the How Hill estate, from Woodbastwick Fen, and from around Martham South Broad. Saw-sedge is less easy than Reed to harvest mechanically, and hand sythes are still used to cut the crop at several sites (see Plate XXVI).

(c) Reed

Species-poor stands of *Phragmites* occur over both solid and worked deposits of peat, and range in size from small patches of reed-dominated fen to extensive, commercially managed reed-beds. They are best developed on fens subject to shallow flooding by water containing moderate concentrations of nutrients.

According to Haslam (1972a) *Phragmites* performs well in stagnant conditions, and has a competitive advantage over other species at such sites. However, in practice, most commercially cut reed-beds are located fairly close to a river or broad, or are traversed by well-flushed dykes. There is evidence (Wheeler & Giller, 1982a) that the peat underlying such sites is subject to freer drainage than that further away, and anecdotal confirmation of the importance of this is afforded by local marshmen who often assert that the best Reed grows in well-drained sites. In addition, the most robust stands of *Phragmites* in a reed-bed are almost invariably to be found beside its dyke system.

Partly because of the abandonment of many reed-beds and their consequent invasion by woody species, and partly because of the practical difficulties involved in harvesting Reed from around the margins of the broads, and from sites in the fens where, by definition, there is no control over the water regime, several areas of semi-derelict grazing marsh have been embanked so that they can be used for reed production under controlled conditions. The first such 'flood' was created by the late Col. H. J. Cator near Ranworth, following the deliberate flooding in the early 1920s of a marshy 'low' (probably created originally by peat digging) to form a new flight pond. Reed soon colonized the grazing marshland adjoining this, and the whole area (amounting to *c.* 35 ha) was subsequently embanked. Similar 'floods' were created at Horsey and Hickling in 1963 and 1968 respectively, and in each case, sluices were provided so that water could be gravitated onto and off the site as necessary.

Each area is flooded to a depth of about 6 inches (15 cm) as soon as possible after reed-cutting has ended in early April, so as to provide optimum conditions for growth. During the summer, water is allowed to flow into, and out of, the 'flood' to prevent it stagnating, but the inflow is cut off in August or early September to allow the site to drain off ready for the beginning of the new reed-cutting season in late December. By this time, the plants will have lost their leafage ('flag'). In addition, frosts will have hardened the stems, thus making them more durable when used for thatching. Both in the 'floods' and elsewhere, harvesting ends when the new season's shoots ('colts') start to emerge, usually in the first or second weeks of April.

During the past few years, it has proved increasingly difficult, particularly at Ranworth, to draw off sufficient water from the adjoining river to keep the 'floods' irrigated to the required depth during the summer months. No measurements have been made, but it is strongly suspected that their surface levels have been raised as a consequence of peat accrual to the extent that water will only gravitate onto them during high spring tides, or following heavy rainfall or a surge. Since a plentiful supply of water is essential during the growing season, arrangements were made to pump water onto Ranworth

Cutting and bundling Saw-sedge on the Broads Authority's How Hill estate – 1985.   Plate XXVI

The demand for this crop, which is used as a capping on thatched roofs, remains high, most of the 'sedge' produced in the region being cut in the Ant valley fens (as here), on the Hickling reserve, or on the Brayden Marshes, north-west of Horsey Mere. Hand scythes, rather than mechanical cutters, are still frequently used, the sedge beds being harvested in the summer months, on a three to four-year rotation.

Photo: Richard Denyer

Flood during the summer of 1989. A further problem at this site is that the quality of the Reed growing here has deteriorated to a marked extent during the past 10 years or so. This is probably attributable, at least in part, to the shortage of water, but the adverse effects of this may well have been exacerbated by the water quality problems alluded to later in this Chapter.

Because of their relatively recent origin, reed 'floods' will contain a less diverse invertebrate fauna than fens from which Reed has been harvested for many years. On the other hand, reed-cutters rarely cut the entire area available. Parts of each site are usually cropped in alternate years on a 'double-wale' basis, whilst bushed-up corners and small patches of sub-standard reed are left uncut, so forming nesting sites for birds, such as Reed, Sedge and Grasshopper Warblers and Bearded Tits. In addition, when flooded the reed 'stubbles' prove attractive to Snipe, Redshank and dabbling duck such as Teal, Shoveler and Mallard.

Some actively managed reed-beds consist of almost pure stands of *Phragmites*, but Milk Parsley, Great Hairy Willow-herb, Lesser Pond-sedge and Creeping Bent occur in many sites. The last two, which are known to reed-cutters as 'cheat' and 'water-grass' respectively, can be very troublesome in a commercially managed reed-bed, because once they gain a foothold, as happened at Ranworth Flood in the mid-1970s, they can rapidly form a thick mat of vegetation. At best, this adds greatly to the amount of litter which has to be combed out of the cut reed before it can be bundled up ready for sale, and at worst, it appears to be associated with a decline in the productivity of the reed plants. Fens beside Hickling Broad, which until the early 1960s were regularly producing good crops of Reed, but in which the *Phragmites* is now very depauperate, with most shoots a metre or less tall, have been particularly heavily invaded by Creeping Bent, and it has been suggested that this may be due to the increasing salinity of this site. However, Wheeler (pers. comm.) has pointed out that the same phenomenon is occurring at fens having comparatively low levels of sodium. He has also shown experimentally that if a mixed community of *Phragmites*, *Typha* and *Agrostis* is mown during the summer months, the latter becomes increasingly common, and that the removal of the *Agrostis* 'litter' has little effect on either of the other two species.

The interreactions between *Phragmites* and *Agrostis* were studied by Dr Sylvia Haslam during the course of a series of investigations between 1963 and 1975 into the effects of various external influences on the growth of Reed (her principal results, and references to her published work on this species, are summarized in Haslam, 1972b). Briefly, she claims that if litter is allowed to accumulate in a reed-bed as a result of lack of management, the density of the reed shoots decreases, whereas any *Agrostis* present is unaffected. She suggests that this species is normally kept in a suppressed condition by the shade cast by the *Phragmites*, but that if the latter's performance deteriorates, more light is available near the ground, and the productivity of the *Agrostis* increases. The thickening layer of litter which it produces under these circumstances delays the emergence of the *Phragmites* shoots in the spring, thus still further reducing their number; Haslam asserts that in extreme cases, the *Phragmites* shoot density can be reduced by 90 per cent.

Haslam also claims that the relationship between Reed and other species is affected by what she terms 'below ground control', and by variations in the water regime. She found, for example, that if a fen containing Reed and Creeping Bent is flooded to a depth of *c.* 10 cm throughout the year, the latter is largely eliminated, leaving a monodominant stand of Reed.

Haslam's findings have not been confirmed by other ecologists. Wheeler (pers. comm.), for example, has found no evidence that *Agrostis* suppresses Reed, and considers that it only starts to increase in reed-beds when the *Phragmites* is performing poorly. Such a malaise could result from a number of factors, including an inadequate supply of water during the reed growing season.

There is some anecdotal evidence that 'cheat' is frost-sensitive when cut, and that it can therefore be suppressed if the reed-bed is harvested early in the season. It has also been claimed that if litter is allowed to accumulate on the surface as a result of the use of mechanical, rather than hand scythes, this increases both the rate of peat accrual, and the likelihood that the reed-bed will be invaded by 'cheat' or 'water-grass'. When shown such a site, older marshmen will say that it has 'gone rotten' and that the remedy in the past was to 'turf it out'. According to Mr. H. Grapes, one time marsh foreman on the

Ranworth Estate, this involved digging away the top 18 inches or so (*c.* 45 cm) in *c.* 10 feet (3 m) wide strips. The peat thus obtained was allowed to dry out on the baulks left between the 'reed dykes', before being barrowed away for use as a fuel; later, the baulks themselves might be cut away. Once this herculean task had been completed, the Reed would, it is alleged, start to grow again with renewed vigour. The NCC is currently using this technique experimentally at Ranworth Flood to see whether a compartment which has been invaded by Lesser Pond-sedge to a point when the Reed is no longer worth cutting commercially, can be restored to good condition. But, needless to say, only small areas have been treated in this way. Moreover, the surface layers of peat were removed with an hydraulic excavator, rather than a becket!

More recently, the Teesside Development Corporation decided, as part of a major environmental improvement scheme, to create a new, *c.* 20 ha reed-fringed lake near Billingham. Following discussions with the Broads Authority and the NCC it was agreed that the Reed required would be taken from Ward Marsh (opposite St. Benet's Abbey), but no one knew how practicable this would be, and in particular whether the reed rhizomes would remain viable when transported in bulk. In the circumstances, a trial was carried out in April 1988, involving the stripping of surface peat from about a quarter of a hectare of Ward Marsh. The material, which weighed some 120 tonnes, was then transported by road to Teesside, where it was planted in a small, specially-excavated lagoon at Haverton Hole.

First indications are that this transplant was successful, and it is likely that some 10 ha of Ward Marsh will be stripped of its surface peat during the winter of 1991/92. If this project does, indeed, go ahead, it will serve to rejuvenate a typical Broadland reed-bed, and create a new, ecologically-interesting habitat in Teesside. It will also provide excellent opportunities for research at both the donor and the receptor sites.

Until the early 1950s, the entire reed crop in Broadland was cut by hand, the favoured tools being a maigue (or meek), which was a sickle with a long, curved blade, and a scythe; this was invariably fitted with a hoop or 'bile' (usually made of hazel) which pushed the cut material clear of the blade (see Plate XXVII).

Conscious that the escalating cost of labour, and the increasing difficulties being experienced by landowners in finding men willing to become reed-cutters, would soon lead to a serious drop in production, the Norfolk Rural Industries Bureau decided in 1953 to invite three firms to see whether the grass-cutting machinery then in use could be modified so that it could be be used to harvest Reed. At a demonstration arranged at Hickling in November that year, it was found that an 'Allen Scythe' gave very satisfactory results, provided it was fitted with a box to hold the cut reed in a perpendicular position, and during the 1960s most reed-beds in the region were cut with such machines. A Scandinavian 'Seiga', capable of harvesting up to 4000 bunches ('shoves') of reed per day was used at Ranworth Flood between 1957 and 1971, and a larger machine made by the same firm was employed at several sites on a contract basis in the mid-1970s. Meantime, 'Mayfields' were gradually replacing 'Allen Scythes', and in 1977, the Norfolk Naturalists' Trust was presented with an Italian-made 'Olympia' modified rice-harvester for use on the Hickling reserve (see Plate XXVIII). This, like a 'Seiga', has the great advantage of being able to tie the Reed into bunches after cutting it. This reduces labour costs, and enables the crop to be taken off the reed-bed quickly, thus reducing the chance of it being damaged by rain or floodwater. Although the bunches usually contain broken reed stems and other unwanted material, the job of combing this out and re-tying the bundles ready for sale, can be done when the conditions are too bad to work out-of-doors, or after the end of the reed-cutting season. Although several 'Olympias' are now in use in the region, some of the reed crop is still harvested with 'Mayfields', and a little is cut in the traditional way, with a scythe.

The very real advantages of using machines in connection with the reed harvest are offset by the fact that they tend to compress the surface peat. This does, as Haslam (1972a) has pointed out, have an adverse effect on the performance of the reed plants; indeed, the ruts made on the Hickling reed 'flood' are often marked by lines of depauperate Reed (Linsell, pers. comm.). A further problem is that machines often cut the Reed too high above the ground, usually because of minor irregularities of the fen surface, but sometimes because the operator is cutting too late in the season, and consequently finds it necessary to raise the cutter bar to avoid damaging the emerging 'colts'. Either way, this practice allows litter to accumulate. In addition, and more seriously, since lignification is greatest where the stem emerges from the rhizome, and quickly declines upwards, it is suspected, though not proved, that the butts of Reeds cut by machine will tend to be less resistant to weathering on a roof, than materials cut with a hand scythe as close as possible to the fen surface. Finally, there is anecdotal evidence that machines do not cut reed stems quite so cleanly as does a sharp scythe, and it has been suggested that the slightly frayed ends of such stems reduce their durability when used for thatching.

It has become something of a status symbol to live in a thatched house (Humphries, 1980), and owing to the shortage of combed wheat 'reed' and long straw, houses in many parts of Britain are being re-thatched with 'Norfolk Reed' as a substitute for these

Plate XXVII

Reed cutting in progress on the Broads Authority's How Hill estate.

One of the advantages of using a hand-scythe is that it is possible, as here, to cut the reed stems very close to the ground surface. Since the amount of fibre (sclenchyma) present in each shoot, and its thickness, is greatest near its base, this practice ensures that when the reed is used as thatching material, those parts of the stem nearest the surface of the roof, will contain the maximum possible amount of fibre. It is suspected, though not yet proved, that the greater the amount of fibre in thatching reed, the greater its durability.

Note that the scythe shown in the photograph is fitted with a hoop-like 'bile' to prevent the cut stems falling back onto the blade.

Photo: Courtesy of the Eastern Daily Press

materials. This, plus the need to re-thatch buildings already roofed with Reed, has generated such a strong demand, that reed-cutters have up to now encountered little difficulty in selling every bunch they produce.

The total annual crop varies according to the number of cutters at work, and the weather conditions, both during the growing season and the period when the Reed is being harvested. However, it has been estimated by the Norfolk Reed-growers Association that about 150 000 bunches are produced in Broadland in most years; this represents about a third of the total British crop.

The shoot height, density, stem thickness and flowering time of different stands of

An 'Olympia' reed-harvester in action on the How Hill Estate – 1986.　　　　Plate XXVIII

Several of these machines, which are modified rice-harvesters manufactured in Italy, are in use in the region. They have the great advantage over conventional motor-scythes in that they are able to tie up the reed into bundles, as well as cut it.

Although the bundles almost always contain a certain amount of 'litter' and other unwanted material, they can be taken apart, cleaned and re-tied after the reed-cutting season has ended, or during wet weather when the reed cannot be harvested.

Photo: R.N. Flowers

Phragmites vary considerably, plants growing beside an enriched river or dyke, tending to produce much coarser and taller shoots than those growing in a fen or 'flood'. These variations are reflected in the productivity of the species since Wheeler and Giller (1982a) found that the standing crop in September ranged from 404 to 1932 g/m^2, with the highest figure from eutrophic fens in the Yare valley. These figures are compatible with those of Mason and Bryant (1975a) who reported that the net productivity of the Reed growing in an unmanaged fen beside Alderfen Broad was 1080 g/m^2. Although dead *Phragmites* shoots only contain some 10 to 20 per cent of their summer mineral content (Haslam, 1972a), the productivity of a reed-bed, particularly one on a nutrient-poor site, can decline if it is subject to annual ('single wale') cutting for a prolonged period, and for this reason, many beds tend to be harvested on a 'double wale' basis.

Variations in the physical dimensions, and appearance, of the plants can frequently be seen in a single reed-bed, a fact which is often particularly noticeable at flowering time. Some of these variations are attributable to inherited (or genotypic) characters of the Reed, whilst others result from environmental factors, such as minor differences in the topography, water regime, soil or past management. Stands of Reed are also subject to localized attacks by the smut fungus, *Ustilago grandis*, or the stem-boring larvae of certain Wainscot moths, and these too, can produce variations in the appearance of a reed-bed in late summer. In addition, Dutch workers have recently demonstrated that the reaction of reed plants damaged by the attentions of the Twin-spotted Wainscot (*Archanara geminipuncta*) is to produce thinner shoots the following year (Mook & van der Toorn, 1985).

Since it is often difficult to decide what particular factors are responsible for the dissimilarities observable in most reed-beds, continental workers refer to different kinds of Reed as 'biotypes', and this terminology has been adopted by Haslam (1972a) in her summary report on the ecology and management of the species. One of the points on which she rightly lays particular stress concerns the need for continuity in the management of reed-beds. Sites left uncut for a few years quickly deteriorate, and much time and effort may have to be expended before a worthwhile crop can once again be obtained.

Productive reed-beds yield about 960 bunches per hectare if cut each year, and up to 1200 bunches if harvested on a 'double wale' basis, one man being able to deal with about 25 ha per year. The Norfolk Reedgrowers' Association has defined a standard bunch as one which has a circumference of 24 inches (61 cm) at a point 12 inches (30.5 cm) above the butt. Such a bunch will contain about 2000 reeds, and six of them will constitute a 'fathom', one hundred of these making up a 'load'. In 1989, reed-cutters were selling their produce at between £1 and £1.20 per bunch according to quality, a price only marginally greater than in 1985 owing to the competition provided by imports of Reed from the Continent. The Norfolk Reedgrowers' Association has calculated that the profit obtainable by a reed-cutter, after fixed and variable costs had been deducted, would have been just over £11 000 in 1986, had he sold his Reed for £1 per bunch (Burgess & Evans, 1989).

Most thatchers expect to use between 90 and 100 bunches per 'square' – i.e. 10 × 10 feet (*c*. 9.2 sq. m) – to cover a roof to the customary depth of between 12 and 15 inches (30 to 40 cm). Thus a small cottage with a roof of 12 'square' will require between 1080 and 1200 bunches, or the crop from a one-hectare reed-bed cut 'double wale' (Rural Industries Bureau, 1961).

The main disadvantages of a reed-thatched roof are, first, its relatively high cost – thatchers were charging between £400 and £600 per square in 1989, a figure well in excess of that for re-tiling – and second, the high fire risk. Because of this, insurance companies charge a premium at least twice as great as that on a brick-and-tiled property. In addition, the building regulations effectively prevent houses on small plots being thatched, as they require that there is a gap of at least 12 m between a roof of this material and the boundary of the property. For these reasons, few new thatched buildings have been built in Broadland since the Second World War, though four were constructed on Mr Francis Cator's estate at Ranworth between 1968 and 1973.

The advantages of thatch include the fact that it is self-insulating, and therefore warm in winter and cool in summer. According to Dunning (1981), the thermal transmittance (i.e. the 'U' value) of a roof with a pitch of 50° which has been thatched with 12 inches of reed is 0.40 watts per square metre per degree centigrade. Reed is also reckoned to be a more durable material than long straw or combed wheat reed, though the oft-repeated assertion that a roof thatched with Norfolk Reed has a useful life of 60 years was probably only attained in favourable circumstances, and when prime, hand-scythed material was employed.

Since the mid-1970s, the Council for Small Industries in Rural Areas (COSIRA), which acts as an umbrella body for both thatchers and reed-growers, has received increasing numbers of complaints that some of the Reed harvested in Broadland during the past 15 years or so has deteriorated very quickly on roofs, paticularly in the West Country, with its high rainfall. This is a matter of much anxiety to all concerned, given the possibility that the owners of roofs which show signs of premature degradation may sue those responsible for damages. Thatchers often buy their Reed through agents, rather than direct from the men who have cut it, and they therefore frequently do not know the exact source of the material they have used. Thus, although only certain fens are affected – indeed, good quality reed is still being produced in many parts of the region – there is a real risk that thatchers will decline to purchase any Reed from Broadland in order to avoid the possibility of proceedings being taken against them. The resultant collapse of the reed-growing industry would lead to a further diminution in the amount of open, unbushed fen in the region. It would also result in job losses locally, and an increase in the amount of continental reed being imported into the UK. According to COSIRA, this already accounts for about half the total used in this country, this despite anecdotal reports suggesting that its quality is just as variable as that currently being harvested in Broadland.

In the light of these factors, COSIRA invited Professor Oxley of Birmingham University, and later MAFF's Agricultural Development and Advisory Service at Cambridge, to investigate the causes of the limited durability of some of the thatching reed being harvested in the region. Their analyses (Yarham, 1981) indicated that 'poor' samples of Reed have higher nitrogen levels than 'good' samples, and an analogy was drawn between the nitrogen-enrichment to which many reed-beds in Broadland are subject today, and the increased susceptibility of cereal crops to 'lodging' as a result of the higher nitrogen levels being applied to them now than in the past. This finding may be related to the claim by Klotzli and Zust (1973) that the mechanical strength of reed stems is reduced when the plants are subject to flooding by nitrogen-rich water. Similarly, during the course of their investigations into the reasons why marginal reedswamp has regressed, or even disappeared from many broads (see Chapter 6), Boar, Crook and Moss (1984) demonstrated under laboratory conditions that the amount of sclerenchyma in the shoots of *Phragmites*, and their resistance to breakage, are affected by the nitrogen to potassium ratio. Under high nitrogen and low potassium conditions, the shoots contain less sclerenchyma, and are significantly weaker mechanically, than are those of plants grown under conditions where the N:K ratio is balanced at either a high or a moderate level.

A new and more detailed investigation of the reed-thatch durability problem was, on the initiative of the Norfolk Reedgrowers' Association, launched in January 1988. The project is being co-ordinated by Dr Brian Moss, and consists of three interlinked studies. The physical and chemical condition of the soil and water in twelve reed-beds (all but one of which are located in Broadland), and the manner in which the morphological characteristics of the plants therein respond to the way in which they are being managed, is being examined by Dr Ros Boar of the University of East Anglia, with a view to determining the environmental conditions which influence reed quality. Dr Boar has also been asked to make recommendations as to what additional research is required, and what action can be taken in the meantime to improve the durability of the material being harvested. This part of the project is being funded by the DoE and the Broads Authority, with a smaller contribution from the NCC. Closely linked with Dr Boar's work, is an investigation of the agents and processes of decay thought to be contributing to the premature deterioration of reed-thatched roofs. This is being carried out by Dr Alan Rayner and Dr Jo Kirby of the University of Bath, who had previously been engaged in similar studies on roofs thatched with wheat straw. This part of the project is being funded by MAFF, with additional support from the DoE. The third aspect of the project is an investigation by Dr Kerry Turner of the University of East Anglia of the social and economic consequences of changes in reed quality and, in particular, the implications to Broadland's reed-growing industry of a decline in the demand for its produce. This work is being funded by the Development Commission, on behalf of COSIRA.

Table 7e   The 'macrolepidoptera' recorded from Broadland over the past 30 years, and their status

	Bure fens & marshes	Ant fens & marshes	Thurne fens & marshes	Yare fens & marshes	Status
* Reed Leopard (*Phragmataecia castaneae*)	X	X	X	—	2
Goat Moth (*Cossus cossus*)	—	—	X	X	Nb
The Forester (*Adscita statices*)	—	—	X	—	Nb
White-barred Clearwing (*Synathedon spheciformis*)	X	—	—	—	Na
Barred Hook-tip (*Drepana cultraria*)	X	—	—	—	Nb
Blotched Emerald (*Comibaena bajularia*)	—	X	—	—	L
* Rosy Wave (*Scopula emutaria*)	—	—	X	—	Nb
Purple-bordered Gold (*Idaea muricata*)	—	X	—	X	Na
* Single-dotted Wave (*I. dimidiata*)	X	X	X	X	—
* Small Scallop (*I. emarginata*)	X	X	X	X	—
* Oblique Carpet (*Orthonoma vittata*)	X	X	X	X	L
Red-green Carpet (*Choroclysta siterata*)	X	X	—	—	L
Scarce Tissue (*Rheumaptera cervinalis*)	X	—	—	—	Nb
Brown Scallop (*Philereme vetulata*)	—	X	—	—	Nb
Dark Umber (*P. transversata britannica*)	X	X	X	X	L
* Marsh Carpet (*Perizoma sagittata*)	—	—	—	X	2
* Valerian Pug (*Eupithecia valerianata*)	—	—	X	X	Nb
* Dentated Pug (*Anticollix sparsata*)	X	X	X	X	Na
* Dingy Shell (*Euchoeca nebulata*)	X	X	—	—	L
* Small Seraphim (*Pterapherapteryx sexalata*)	X	X	X	X	L
* Bordered Beauty (*Epione repandaria*)	X	X	X	X	—
Dark Bordered Beauty (*E. paralellaria*)	—	—	X	—	3
Satin Beauty (*Deileptenia ribeata*)	X	—	—	—	Nb
* Common Wave (*Cabera exanthemata*)	—	X	X	X	—
Broad-bordered Bee Hawk-moth (*Hemaris fuciformis*)	—	—	X	—	Na
Alder Kitten (*Furcula bicupsis*)	X	X	X	X	Nb
Poplar Kitten (*F. bifida*)	X	X	—	X	L
Maple Prominent (*Ptilodontella cucullina*)	X	X	X	X	Nb
Small chocolate-tip (*Clostera pigra*)	—	X	X	—	Nb
Scarce Vapourer (*Orgyia recens*)	X	X	—	X	2
* Round-winged Muslin (*Thumatha senex*)	X	X	X	X	L
Muslin Footman (*Nudaria mundana*)	—	X	—	—	L
* Dotted Footman (*Pelosia muscerda*)	X	X	X	—	3
* Small Dotted Footman (*P. obtusa*)	—	X	X	—	1
Orange Footman (*Eilema sorocula*)	—	—	—	X	Nb
* Water Ermine (*Spilosoma urticae*)	X	X	X	—	Nb
Dotted Rustic (*Ryacia simulans*)	—	—	—	X	Nb
Lunar Yellow Underwing (*Noctua orbona*)	—	X	—	—	Nb
* Fen Square-spot (*Diarsia florida*)	—	X	X	—	L
Square-spotted Clay (*Xestia rhomboidea*)	X	—	—	—	Nb
Heath Rustic (*X. agathina agathina*)	—	X	—	X	L
Silvery Arches (*Polia hepatica*)	—	—	—	X	Nb
Bordered Gothic (*Heliophobus reticulata marginosa*)	X	X	—	—	Nb
Light Brocade (*Lacanobia w-latinum*)	—	X	X	—	L
Dog's Tooth (*L. suasa*)	X	—	X	X	L
Marbled Coronet (*Hadena confusa*)	—	—	—	X	L
* Striped Wainscot (*Mythimna pudorina*)	X	X	X	X	L
* Southern Wainscot (*M. straminea*)	X	X	X	X	L
* Obscure Wainscot (*M. obsoleta*)	X	—	X	X	Nb
* Flame Wainscot (*Senta flammea*)	X	X	X	X	3
Star-wort (*Cucullia asteris*)	—	—	X	—	Nb
The Suspected (*Parastichtis suspecta*)	X	X	X	—	L
* Pink-barred Sallow (*Xanthia togata*)	—	X	X	X	—
Dusky-lemon Sallow (*X. gilvago*)	X	—	—	X	L
* Reed Dagger (*Simyra albovenosa*)	X	X	X	X	Na
* Double Kidney (*Ipimorpha retusa*)	—	—	—	X	Nb
Angle-striped Sallow (*Enargia palacea*)	—	—	X	—	Nb
* Crescent Striped (*Apamea oblonga*)	—	—	X	—	Nb
* Small Clouded Brindle (*A. unanimis*)	X	X	X	X	—
* Double Lobed (*A. ophiogramma*)	X	X	X	X	L
* Middle-barred Minor (*Oligia fasciuncula*)	X	X	X	X	—
Lyme Grass (*Photedes elymi*)	—	X	X	—	Na
* Mere Wainscot (*Photedes fluxa*)	—	X	X	—	Na
* Small Wainscot (*P. pygmina*)	X	X	X	X	—
* Fenn's Wainscot (*P. brevilinea*)	X	X	X	X	3

* Species confined to fens, marshes or wet woodland.

The fauna of the fens

(a) Insects

A perusal of the annotated lists compiled by E.A. Ellis (1965a) shows that the insect fauna of Broadland in the 1940s and 1950s was just as rich and diverse as its flora. Unfortunately, most of the systematic recording carried out during the past 30 years has been focused on the more popular orders, notably the Lepidoptera, Coleoptera and Odonata. Nevertheless, judging by the results obtained, the insect life of the region, and in particular its fens, has survived largely unscathed. For instance, no less than 440 out of the 860 'macrolepidoptera' (larger moths) described by Skinner (1984) have been recorded since 1960 by entomologists such as C. G. Bruce, Tim Peet, Ken Saul, J. M. Chalmers-Hunt, the late H. E. Chipperfield, the late J. V. Gane and D. J. P. Miller. Although many of these species occur in wetlands, they are not confined to them, but are associated with a variety of other habitats in or near Broadland, such as grassy verges, heaths, scrub and waste ground. The number of woodland species recorded from the region is also particularly high because of the presence in the fens of the sallows, alders, birches, oaks and other trees which constitute their larval foodplants.

The macrolepidoptera recorded from Broadland during the past 30 years which are rare or local in Britain are listed in Table 7e, those insects confined to fens, marshes or wet woodland being asterisked. Two or three doubtful records have been excluded from the list

Table 7e   *(continued)*

	Bure fens & marshes	Ant fens & marshes	Thurne fens & marshes	Yare fens & marshes	Status
* Ear Moth (*Amphipoea oculea*)	X	X	X	—	—
* The Butterbur (*Hydraecia petasitis*)	X	X	—	X	Nb
* Haworth's Minor (*Celaena haworthii*)	—	X	X	X	L
* The Crescent (*C. leucostigma leucostigma*)	X	X	X	X	L
* Bulrush Wainscot (*Nonagria typhae*)	X	X	X	X	—
* Twin-spotted Wainscot (*Archanara geminipuncta*)	—	X	X	X	Nb
* Brown-veined Wainscot (*A. dissoluta*)	X	X	X	X	Nb
* Webb's Wainscot (*A. sparganii*)	—	X	X	X	Nb
* Rush Wainscot (*A. algae*)	—	—	X	X	3
* Large Wainscot (*Rhizedra lutosa*)	X	X	X	X	—
* Fen Wainscot (*Arenostola phragmitidis*)	X	X	X	X	L
* Small Rufous (*Coenobia rufa*)	X	X	X	—	—
* Silky Wainscot (*Chilodes maritimus*)	X	X	X	X	Nb
Marbled Clover (*Heliothis viriplaca*)	X	—	—	—	3
* Silver Hook (*Eustrotia uncula*)	X	X	X	X	Nb
* Silver Barred (*Deltote bankiana*)	—	—	X	—	2
* Cream-bordered Green Pea (*Earias clorana*)	X	X	X	X	Nb
* Gold Spot (*Plusia festucae*)	X	X	X	X	—
* Lempke's Gold Spot (*P. putnami gracilis*)	—	—	X	X	L
Scarce Silver Y (*Syngrapha interrogationis*)	X	—	—	—	Nb
* Straw Dot (*Rivula sericealis*)	X	X	X	X	—
* Pinion-streaked Snout (*Schrankia costaestrigalis*)	X	X	X	X	L
* Marsh Oblique-barred (*Hypenodes humidalis*)	—	X	—	—	Nb
* Dotted Fan-foot (*Macrochilo cribrumalis*)	X	X	X	X	Na

* Species confined to fens, marshes or wet woodland.

Key to Table 7e

The numbers in the 'status' column relate to the following:

1) Species categorized as 'Endangered' in the Red Data Book on Insects (Shirt, 1987), i.e. RDB 1 species;

2) Species categorized as 'Vulnerable' in the Red Data Book on Insects. i.e. RDB 2 species;

3) Species categorized as 'Rare' in the Red Data Book on Insects, i.e. RDB 3 species;

Na   Notable species which have a very restricted distribution nationally, being recorded from 30 or fewer 10 km squares;

Nb   Species which a restricted distribution nationally, being recorded from 100 or fewer 10 km squares.

Sources: NCC data compiled from papers and reports by, *inter alia*, T. N. D. Peet (1963 & 1974), J. V. Gane (1976b), C. G. Bruce (1962), K. Saul (1982, 1983 & 1988), R. G. Pointer (1986) and D. J. P. Miller (1987).

(e.g. the White-spotted Pinion (*Cosmia diffinis*) and the Least Minor (*Photedes captiuncula*)), as have several uncommon species known to occur on the sand-dunes of the Winterton-Horsey area, and which have occasionally been recorded on the Hickling reserve; examples of such vagrants include the Pigmy Footman (*Eilema pygmaeola*), Archer's Dart (*Agrotis vestigialis*) and the Shore Wainscot (*Mythimna litoralis*).

Most of the wetland species listed in the Table have become rarer in Britain during the past 20 to 30 years, and two of them are Broadland 'specials'. One of these, the Dotted Footman (*Pelosia muscerda*), formerly occurred in Kent, but is now confined to fens in the Bure, Ant and Thurne valleys, where it is associated with alder carrs, whilst the other, the Small Dotted Footman (*P. obtusa*), was first recorded near Barton Broad in 1961. It has subsequently been found twice on the Hickling reserve (Cadbury, 1964; Peet, 1979) where it frequents old undisturbed reed-beds. Two other species are worthy of special note. Fenn's Wainscot (*Photedes brevilinea*) is widely distributed in Broadland, but is elsewhere confined to a few sites on the East Suffolk coast; it is also rare on the Continent. Similarly, the Reed Leopard (*Phragmataecia castaneae*), though recorded fairly frequently from fens beside the rivers Bure, Ant and Thurne, only occurs in two other counties in Britain, Cambridgeshire and Dorset.

The diversity of the macrolepidopteran fauna of the region has been demonstrated by Peet (1974), who noted that over 70 species occur on the Hickling reserve but not at Wheatfen in the Yare valley, while over 40 different moths were observed at the latter site, but not at Hickling. He ascribed this to the larger amount of water and open fen at Hickling, and the presence at Wheatfen of more alder carr and oak-dominated woodland.

The 'microlepidoptera' have, as elsewhere, attracted far less attention than the 'macros', and the opportunities for further studies on this large and diverse group were demonstrated in 1976, when Tim Peet discovered at Hickling Broad a new species for the British list, *Coleophora hydrolapathella*. The larva of this insect, which has subsequently been recorded from two other sites in the region, feeds on Great Water Dock (Peet, 1978). At least 24 other 'micros' recorded from Broadland during the past 25 years have an extremely restricted distribution in Britain, and two wetland species, *Monochroa divisiella* (whose larvae feed on Yellow Iris) and *Opostega auritella* [thought to be associated with Kingcup (*Caltha palustris*)], are likely to be given an 'endangered' rating in a future edition of the Red Data Book.

The insect for which Broadland is chiefly renowned, the British race of the Swallow-tail Butterfly (see Plate 19), differs from its continental counterpart in its colour, the types of habitat occupied, and in its foodplant, which in the wild is almost invariably Milk Parsley.* It has its chief stronghold in the Saw-sedge beds and mowing fens which border the Thurne broads, but is also frequent in those parts of the Bure and Ant valley fens which have not been too heavily colonized by woody vegetation. The adult insect is on the wing from late May until mid-July, the males taking up territories which are usually centred on an isolated bush or tree. At Hickling, the spiralling display flight, first noted by the late Bob Sankey in 1969, but not yet recorded in the literature, has several times been seen to take place around the tops of the oak trees beside the observation tower. The eggs are almost always laid on the exposed upper parts of the *Peucedanum* plants; indeed, Dempster *et al.* (1976) found that of 180 deposited in their Hickling study area in 1973, only 11 were below the level of the surrounding fen vegetation.

The eggs hatch in about a fortnight, and the caterpillars feed in full view after their second moult. The early instars are subject to heavy predation pressure by arthropods, chiefly spiders, but birds are responsible for most of the mortalities which occur during the fourth and early fifth instars. Reed Buntings are the main culprits, but Dempster *et al.* note that the caterpillars are also taken by Sedge Warblers and Bearded Tits. The surviving larvae are usually ready to pupate by late July. Most pupae overwinter, but in some years, a few hatch in August to produce a second brood. In favourable years these can produce pupae which overwinter in the usual way, but if bad weather intervenes, there may be insufficient time for the larvae to feed up and metamorphose. During the exceptionally dry summer of 1976, a large number of second-brood insects appeared on the wing, and the subsequent failure of their progeny to reach the pupal stage is thought to have been the temporary undoing of the colony in the Strumpshaw, Rockland and

---

* But a larva observed by the author at Strumpshaw Fen for several days at the end of August 1988 fed exclusively on the flower heads of Wild Angelica.

Surlingham fens. The occasional Swallow-tails seen flying over these sites between 1977 and 1982 are thought to have been stragglers from the Bure valley, but numerous sightings were made in 1983, and the colony has now re-established itself.

P. machaon originally occurred in the Fens, and possibly beside the rivers Thames and Lea, as well as in Broadland (Bretherton, 1951), and a small colony persisted in the wild state at Wicken Fen, Cambridgeshire, until the early 1950s. Repeated attempts to re-introduce the insect to this site proved abortive, and Dempster *et al.* concluded that the main reason for this was that the Milk Parsley plants at Wicken were too small to be found by females wishing to lay their eggs. In contrast, many of the *Peucedanum* plants growing in Broadland's open fens are sufficiently tall to stand well clear of the surrounding vegetation, and can therefore be readily seen by prospecting females.

The larva of the Swallow-tail is liable to be parasitized by *Trogus lapidator*, a host-specific ichneumon which was most recently observed near Barton Broad in 1976. The absence of subsequent records is probably mainly attributable to the very small number of entomologists able to recognize it. Nevertheless, this parasite is thought to be rare, and probably deserves to be listed as 'vulnerable' in a future edition of the Red Data Book; this would bring it into line with the designation already conferred upon its host by Shirt (1987).

The beetles of Broadland are at least as numerous and varied as the moths. For instance, during the course of ten visits to the Hickling Broad NNR between August 1978 and August 1979, A. J. Drane recorded no less than 280, mainly terrestrial, species. Amongst these are four for which Broadland is a stronghold: the Carabids *Odocantha melanura* and *Dromius longiceps* (both of which occur in stands of Reed or Lesser Reedmace), the False Soldier Beetle (*Cerapheles terminatus*), and the Curculionid weevil *Tapinotus sellatus*, which is always associated with Yellow Loosestrife (Drane, 1979). One of the Carabids, *Dromius longiceps*, is listed as 'vulnerable' in the Red Data Book on Insects, while a number of other species recorded by Drane are generally uncommon away from Broadland. Numerous beetle species are associated with reed and saw-sedge beds, and many have localized distributions in Britain. *Bembidion fumigatum, Stenus lustrator, Sepedophilus pedicularis, Anthocomus rufus, Psammoecus bipunctatus, Atomaria guttata, A. mesomela* and *Corylopus cassidoides* are all examples found during Drane's study. This, plus the fact that large numbers of commoner beetles were recorded by Drane in such communities, serves as a reminder of how important it is that Reed, Saw-sedge and other crops should continue to be harvested from Broadland's fens. Confirmation of this was provided in 1979, when *Meotica lohsei*, a Staphylinid not previously recorded in Britain, was collected by Professor John Owen from saw-edge debris at Catfield Fen (Owen, 1982).

Broadland has been known to possess a rich water beetle fauna since the late F. Balfour-Browne studied the group while based at the Sutton Broad Laboratory at the beginning of this century (Balfour-Browne, 1905), and confirmation that much of it has survived was obtained in 1977, when Dr. G. Foster recorded 62 species from the Ant Valley. Subsequent work by Dr Foster, and by Professor J. Owen, Dr. R. Angus, P. Hodge and M. Sinclair has resulted in a further 22 species being added to the list which now covers more than a third of the water beetles occurring in Britain.

Dr Foster comments (*in litt.*) that fenland dykes which have been maintained in good condition, such as those at Woodbastwick, contain many of our larger species, including the Great Silver Water Beetle (*Hydrophilus piceus*), and five of our six great diving beetles (*Dytiscus* spp.). The Ant valley fauna is, according to Foster, more specialized and consists mainly of small beetles living in moss carpets. These include three species, *Hydroporus melanarius, H. obscurus* and *H. tristis* which, though common in Northern England and Scotland, are now rare elsewhere; and also *H. scalesianus* (named after a Mr. Scales who first found it in Norfolk), *H. neglectus, Bidessus unistriatus, Lacornis oblongus, Agabus striolatus, A. unguicularis, Ilybius guttiger, Hydraena palustris* and *Dryops anglicanus*. All nine of these species are now very local or rare nationally, doubtless because many of the mossy fens in which they once occurred have altered ecologically as a consequence of lack of management, nutrient enrichment, drainage or natural succession, and one of them, *Bidessus unistriatus*, is listed as 'endangered' in the Red Data Book on Insects. Two other Ant Valley 'specials', *Hydroporus scalesianus* and *Agabus striolatus*, are classed as 'vulnerable', though both have been found recently on the Hickling Broad NNR, while the latter species has also been recorded from the Bure

Marshes NNR, where it frequents small pools in *Myrica* and *Salix* carr (Foster, 1982). Overall, the Woodbastwick fens are not so rich faunistically as are those at Catfield; nevertheless, Foster (1983) lists 41 water beetle species which he and some other entomologists found here in May 1983. In addition, other groups of Coleoptera are well represented on the site. *Quedius balticus*, a Staphylinid given an 'endangered' listing in Shirt (1987), was found here by Malcolm Sinclair in 1988, and this species, plus another rarity, *Lathrobium rufipenne* – afforded a 'vulnerable' status by Shirt – was recorded by Professor John Owen during visits to Woodbastwick later the same year, and in April 1989 (Owen, *in litt.*).

A recent taxonomic study (Berge Henegouwen, 1988) has shown that some of the water beetles collected by Dr Balfour-Browne in the Ant Valley fens around the turn of the century, and named by him as *Hydrochus brevis*, are in fact a closely related, but hitherto undescribed species, *H. megaphallus*. Surveys by Dr Garth Foster and Dr. R. Angus have demonstrated that both species still occur in the Ant Valley, albeit very sparingly. Unfortunately, this is not the case with *Graphoderus bilineatus*, another species recorded by Balfour-Browne from the Catfield area; this has not been seen since 1906, and may well be extinct in Britain (Angus, 1976: Shirt, 1987).

Numerous rare and local Diptera have been recorded in the region, but most of these observations date from before, or just after the Second World War, and the group has received relatively little subsequent attention. Nevertheless, on the basis of the families which have been studied, it would seem that the fens still possess an extremely rich and diverse dipteran fauna. Alder Milkcarr, for instance, provides a habitat for several groups, particularly those whose larvae develop in rotten wood, fungi, damp soil or small pools. Such conditions are specially favoured by craneflies and fungus gnats, and these families are well represented in the region. For example, the cranefly *Prionocera subserricornis*, which is confined to Norfolk, has been found at a number of Broadland sites in recent years, while the fungus gnat, *Mycetophila confusa*, has been recorded from various localities in the Bure and Ant valleys. Both these species are listed in the Red Data Book and are given 'endangered' and 'vulnerable' ratings respectively.

Other dipteran groups are more often associated with open fen communities, the larvae of such insects frequently being aquatic, or associated with specific host plants. The Agromyzid, *Phytomyza thysselini*, which was recently discovered in this country by Irwin (1985), has larvae which mine the leaves of Milk Parsley. This fly is at present only known from Broadland. Other species favouring open fen conditions include certain hover flies (Syrphidae), soldier flies (Stratiomyidae) and snail-killing flies (Sciomyzidae). However, some of the rarest representatives of these groups (for example, the soldier fly *Odontomyia ornata*) have not been recorded in recent years, possibly because of the number of sites which, through lack of management, have been overgrown with bushes and trees.

Among other orders the bug, *Pachycoelus waltli* (Hemiptera, Discoridae), has its only East Anglian, and most northerly British site at Catfield. Similarly, the weevil, *Ceutorhynchus querceti*, known only from Broadland, and listed in the Red Data Book as 'vulnerable', still occurs on *Rorippa* in the Barton Broad area, and one other site not far distant. Partly because of this, and the large number of other 'specials' recorded from this part of the region, Dr. A. G. Irwin of the Norfolk Museums Service has stated (*in litt.*), "I doubt if there is any other ten square-mile area of wetland in Britain which could compare with the Ant valley in terms of invertebrate interest".

Heartening as this statement is, it has to be tempered with the knowledge that some species which once had their headquarters there have been lost, the best known example being the damselfly, *Coenagrion armatum*. This was discovered by the late F. Balfour-Browne near Sutton Broad in 1903, and although it was subsequently found at Hickling Broad, and at a site in the Bure valley, it has never been recorded outside Broadland. It was last seen in the Ant valley in 1956, and prolonged searches by John Buckley, Norman Moore, John Ismay, David Chelmick, Alan Stubbs and others during 1974 and 1975 not only failed to reveal it, but served to show that many of the reedy fens where it used to fly are overgrown with bushes, and that the pools in which its nymphs occurred are mud-filled and derelict. Another insect known to have been present in the Ant valley at the turn of the century, but not seen there since is the weevil, *Lixus paraplecticus*. Although this was recorded from various sites in Southern England in the 1940s and 1950s, it has not been found subsequently (Shirt, 1987), and, like *Coenagrion armatum* may, in fact, be extinct.

Apart from the Downy Emerald (*Cordulia aenea*), which has not been recorded since 1975 when it was seen at Ormesby, the other 20 species of Odonata mentioned by Ellis (1965a) as being permanently resident in the region, still occur. However, as in other parts of Britain, many of these wetland-dependent insects are less widely distributed than they were in the past. For instance, the Scarce Chaser (*Libellula fulva*), noted by Ellis as "a familiar sight . . . quartering the marshes drained by the rivers Bure, Ant and Thurne" seems to have disappeared from this part of Broadland, and is now confined to three or four sites in the Yare and Waveney valleys. Fortunately, the Norfolk Aeshna (*Aeshna isosceles*) is quite common, both in the fens and the Drained Marshland Area (see page 270); indeed, it seems, if anything to be currently extending its range, and it certainly does not deserve the 'endangered' status conferred upon it by Shirt (1987). Other noteworthy species are the Hairy Dragonfly (*Brachytron pratense*) and the Variable Damselfly (*Coenagrion pulchellum*), both of which are quite frequent in the fens and marshes of the Bure, Ant, Thurne and Yare valleys (but which occur in fewer than 100 ten-kilometre squares elsewhere in Britain), and the Red-eyed Damselfly (*Erythromma najas*) which is common in places where water-lilies still occur.

Pools and dykes in alder carr which are overhung by sedges and rushes are frequented by a number of rare insects, notably the Lesser Water-measurer, *Hydrometra gracilenta*, and a water cricket, *Microvelia umbricola*. Both were recorded during the 1930s from near Barton Broad, and at that time were new to Britain (Walton, 1938). They were subsequently found at several other sites in the region and elsewhere (Ellis, 1977), and *M. umbricola* was recorded from Catfield Fen as recently as 1981 (Allen, 1984). Although *H. gracilenta* has not been seen in Broadland, or its other previously known locality in Britain, the New Forest, since the 1950s, it was recorded from the Pevensey Levels, Sussex, by Peter Kirby of the NCC in 1988 (Kirby, *in litt.*).

(b) Other invertebrates

Our knowledge of the present distribution and status of other invertebrate groups in the fens is woefully deficient; indeed, so little systematic recording has been carried out during the past 25 years that it would be impossible, even if space permitted, to update the descriptive accounts of the molluscs, spiders and other groups produced by A.E. Ellis, E. A. G. Duffey and E. A. Ellis in 1965. Nevertheless, what information does exist suggests that despite the ecological changes which have occurred, these groups are still well represented in the fens. For instance, at least three very local arachnids occur on the Hickling reserve, the Pond Spider (*Argyroneta aquatica*) (Britain's only truly aquatic species), and two linyphids, *Floronia bucculenta* and *Trichopterna thorelli*, while two species, *Clubiona juvenis*, recorded in the early 1970s beside Meadow Dyke and from the Ant valley fens, and *Carorita paludosa*, observed in the latter area at about the same time, are likely to be given a 'vulnerable' rating in the Red Data Book on Spiders, now in course of preparation. *Clubiona juvenis* normally occurs in reed or saw-sedge dominated swamps, while *Carorita paludosa* is usually found in cut litter.

Ellis (*in litt.*) has pointed out that the tall upstanding tussocks of *Carex paniculata* which occur here and there in the *Angelico-Phragmitetum* and other communities, and which once formed the principal feature of the *Caricetum paniculatae*, form the preferred habitat of *Ligidium hypnorum*, a woodlouse with a restricted distribution in Britain. They are also used during the winter months by a host of hibernating invertebrates, including heteropteran bugs, ichneumons, beetles, immature spiders and molluscs such as *Cepaea nemoralis* and *Arianta arbustorum*. Although some of these creatures, notably the snails, are adapted to resist periodic immersion, their chances of surviving prolonged floods are probably enhanced if they have been able to seek refuge in a sedge tussock.

(c) Birds

The avifauna of the fens shows considerable variation as a result of the range of plant communities present. The alder carrs, for example, are frequented by species such as Marsh, Willow and Long-tailed Tits, Great and Lesser Spotted Woodpeckers, Wren, Blackcap, Chiffchaff and Redpoll. Sparrowhawks are also characteristic of such terrain, but were severely reduced in number in most parts of Britain during the 1960s as a result of deaths and reduced fertility following the ingestion and accumulation of organochlorine pesticide residues in their bodies (Cramp, 1963; Newton, 1974). However, the species continued to breed here and there in Broadland during this period, and is now once again quite common.

Sallow thickets, particularly those near water, form the haunt of one of our most recent avian colonizers, Cetti's Warbler. This species first bred at Stodmarsh National Nature Reserve, Kent, in 1972 (Hollyer, 1975), but the first intimation that it might be about to spread into Broadland came the following year, when a bird ringed in Belgium was picked up dead in Norwich. In 1974, there were 4 singing males in the Yare valley fens, at least one of which paired up and bred, while 12 and 22 males were heard in this area in 1975 and 1976 respectively. Owing to their skulking behaviour, proof of breeding is always difficult to obtain, but at least two pairs are known to have reared young in 1976. Initial fears that this Southern European species would not survive prolonged spells of hard weather have proved groundless, and it has now spread to other parts of the region, some 60 singing males being located in 1984, of which about half were in the Yare valley, the principal stronghold of this species (Seago, 1954–1988).

The open fens form the preferred habitat for a different group of birds, the commonest being Reed, Sedge and Grasshopper Warblers, and Reed Bunting. M. Blackburn (pers. comm.) found that the territories for each of the two latter species at Strumpshaw Fen covered about 1500 sq m in 1979, whereas the corresponding figure for Sedge Warblers was about 600 sq m. Reed Warblers are much more difficult to count accurately since they cease singing as soon as they have paired up. They are also much more selective in their habitat preference, being confined to more or less pure stands of *Phragmites*. Blackburn found that tall (*c.* 2 m) Reed which had not been cut for the previous two years, and which was growing in shallow water, was particularly favoured, and during the course of 10 early morning visits to such terrain obtained one visual or audible 'registration' per 50.5 sq m. This figure altered to one registration per 56.5 sq m in Reed which was growing less vigorously, and which had not been cut during the past two or three years, and to one registration per 96 sq m in reed-beds which had been harvested the previous year. Reed Warblers, and to a lesser extent the other three species are frequently brood-parasitized by Cuckoos, the males of which each year establish between 3 and 5 territories on *c.* 120 ha of fen at Strumpshaw (Blackburn, pers. comm.).

Savi's Warbler is another species characteristic of open, or lightly bushed fen (Bibby & Lunn, 1982). It became extinct in Broadland in the mid-nineteenth century (Seago, 1967), but started to breed again at Stodmarsh NNR in Kent in 1960 (Pitt, 1967). A singing male was noted at Strumpshaw for a few days in May 1973, and since then the species has been recorded every year, mainly from around the Thurne broads. Peak numbers were attained in 1980, when 15 singing males were located, 8 of which were on the Hickling reserve, but the *Norfolk Bird Reports* show that the species has only been present in ones and twos since 1983.

Interesting as these species are, most bird-lovers will associate Broadland's fens with three 'specials', the Bittern, Bearded Tit and Marsh Harrier. The former (see Plate 20) was much persecuted by specimen hunters and egg collectors during the nineteenth century, and it eventually succumbed as a breeding species. A young female with down still attached to its feathers was found at Ludham in 1886 (Gurney & Southwell, 1887) but Bitterns probably did not breed again until 1911, when a nest was found at Sutton Broad (Turner 1912). According to Underhill-Day and Wilson (1978), the breeding population had increased to 9 pairs by 1918, probably as a result of the legislative protection which had by then been afforded this (and other) species (see Chapter 13). In 1919, a pair nested for the first time for many years in the Bure valley, near Hoveton, and by 1924, there were believed to be 16 to 17 pairs breeding, eleven of which were in the Hickling-Horsey area. The Yare valley fens were re-colonized in 1928, and by then it was estimated that there were between 23 and 25 breeding pairs in the region.

A census in 1954 revealed that there were 55 'boomers' (calling males) in Broadland, the main strongholds still being the Barton, Hickling and Horsey areas (Seago, 1967).* Soon afterwards, a decline set in, and by 1970, only 27 pairs were thought to be

---

* Recent, and as yet unpublished, research by Glen Tyler of the RSPB, involving an audio-analysis of the taped calls of individual 'boomers', has shown that it is easy to over-estimate the number of bitterns in a given reed-bed. Many sites in Broadland would have formerly been subject to multiple occupancy by this species, and the figures given in this section should therefore be treated with circumspection.

breeding. Six years later, the population had decreased to 9 pairs, and for the first time since 1917, no males were heard at Hickling (Underhill-Day & Wilson, 1978). According to the *Norfolk Bird Reports*, the number of boomers in Broadland between 1977 and 1984 varied between 9 and 5, while in 1985, there were only 3 in May, though 4 others, possibly unattached males, were heard the following month. The numbers of regular boomers in 1986, 1987 and 1988 were respectively 4, 3 and 5, while in 1989, there were 3, all in the fens associated with the upper Thurne and its broads (Seago, pers. comm.).

Underhill-Day and Wilson noted that the decrease in Broadland's population had been paralleled in most other parts of Britain, including Wales, Lincolnshire and Kent, but not at that time in East Suffolk or Lancashire, and after discussing several possible causes for these changes, including hard weather, reed-bed management, the presence of Coypu, loss and deterioration of habitat and human disturbance, they concluded that the pollution of the waterways, allied with the two latter factors, was probably the main reason why the species had declined in Broadland.

The causes and symptoms of the ecological malaise which has affected the region during the past 35 years are better understood now than when Underhill-Day and Wilson's paper was published, and their 'pollution and habitat deterioration' hypothesis, which is further developed by Day (1983), provides the most plausible explanation so far advanced for the decrease. Bitterns prefer to feed in shallow pools and dykes in the fens, since their reed-fringed margins afford these secretive birds the cover they need. However, in Broadland, as in some other parts of the country, most of these water bodies have become ecologically degraded during the past 30 or 40 years as a result of the combined effects of enrichment, a high rate of sedimentation, and lack of management. Bitterns have therefore found it increasingly difficult to obtain the small fish, amphibians and crustaceans on which they feed.

If this hypothesis was correct, one would expect to find that Herons had maintained their status in the region, since these birds, being much less secretive than Bitterns, are not confined to the fens, but are prepared to feed in full view in the rivers and in the dykes of the Drained Marshland Area, many of which still contain small fish and invertebrates (see Chapter 8). In fact, the number of Herons in Broadland has declined almost as sharply during the past 15 years, as has the number of Bitterns. There were only 60 occupied Heron nests in the region in 1983, whereas the mean number between 1954 and 1969 was 156, with peaks of 202 in 1961 and 1962 (Jones, 1984). This downward trend is reflected in the fact that in 1973 there were two heronries on the Hickling reserve, with a total of 28 occupied nests, whereas in 1985, there was only a single heronry with 11 nests. Similarly, only 2 pairs bred at Ranworth Fen in 1985, compared with 20 in 1977 (Phillips, 1987).

The 'pollution and habitat deterioration' hypothesis advanced by Underhill-Day and Wilson also fails to explain why the number of Bitterns has tended to decline elsewhere in Britain during the 1980s, for instance on the RSPB's Minsmere nature reserve, this despite the measures taken there to provide the right habitat conditions for these birds.

Although the Bearded Tit, like the Bittern, was heavily persecuted during the Victorian era, it continued to breed in small numbers. However, its population has always tended to fluctuate, since the species is subject to heavy mortality during hard weather. Seago (1967) has pointed out that its numbers increase during a succession of mild winters, only to crash during periods of heavy snowfall and freezing fog, such as were experienced during the winters of 1947 (following which only one male was seen in Norfolk) and 1962/3.

The fens beside the Thurne broads have long been the stronghold of this species and over a hundred breeding pairs were recorded here in 1964, 1965, 1976, and each year between 1980 and 1984. However, only 12 pairs nested on the Hickling Broad reserve in 1978 following the hard spell which occurred the preceding winter, and although the numbers subsequently recovered, they fell to 16 pairs in 1987 as a result of an exceptionally severe frost in February that year.

Since 1959, Bearded Tits have tended to disperse or 'erupt' from their favoured haunts after a successful breeding season, particularly during a period of hard weather. For instance, there was a mass emigration of about 300 birds from the Strumpshaw nature reserve in February 1978, and only two pairs bred on this site that summer (Seago, 1954–1988).

Bearded Tits are reluctant to show themselves on windy days, preferring to seek shelter low down amongst the reeds, but they are fairly confiding birds, and their 'pinging' call notes are a familiar sound wherever there are large stands of *Phragmites*. They are unaffected by reed cutting; indeed, when this is in progress, they can frequently be seen or heard nearby, hunting for insects and spiders which have been accidentally dislodged.

Underhill-Day (1984) has pointed out that the Marsh Harrier was formerly a widespread breeding species in Britain, and although it had begun to decline almost everywhere by 1850, Lubbock (1845) could still report that "in the Broads almost every pool of any extent had its pair of these birds". The numbers rapidly decreased during the ensuing 50 years, and by the end of the century Marsh Harriers were no longer breeding in Britain; the last pair in Broadland were trapped at the nest in 1899. Part of this decline can be attributed to improved drainage, but the activities of gamekeepers and collectors undoubtedly played a major role.

According to Underhill-Day (pers. comm.), a pair of Marsh Harriers attempted to nest at Horsey in 1911, but the eggs were taken, and the species did not breed again until 1915, when two young were fledged. Sporadic attempts to nest were made during the ensuing years, but Marsh Harriers did not start to breed regularly in the region until 1928, when 3 pairs nested at Hickling and Horsey, rearing 8 young. This was the start of an almost unbroken run of breeding records lasting until 1960; in only three years, 1937, 1940 and 1960, were no young produced in the region. During these 33 years, some 230 young were fledged with a maximum of 6 breeding pairs in 1948, and a maximum of 20 young produced in 1956. In all, an average of 7 young were successfully fledged by an average of 3.3 pairs each year. This success was largely due to the care and protection given to the birds by the owners of the Hickling and Horsey estates and their staff, and it is a measure of this that clutches are known to have been taken by egg collectors only twice (in 1938 and 1946), though desertions caused by photographers, or the activities of reed-cutters, fishermen and holiday makers occurred from time to time.

A pair of Marsh Harriers summered, but failed to breed in 1961, and although there was an abortive breeding attempt in Broadland in 1965, there were no further records until 1972, when one pair raised 4 young. This failure to breed was probably due to the ingestion of toxic chemical residues, but little research was carried out on this species, compared with that on Peregrines, Sparrowhawks and other raptors. During the 1970s, the numbers of Marsh Harriers breeding in the region gradually increased, and an average of 16.6 young were reared in each year between 1975 and 1985, the maximum number of nests being 10 in 1985 (Underhill-Day, pers. comm.).

(d) Mammals

Ellis (1965b) has provided an annotated list of the mammals found in the region, and the reports published annually by the Norfolk and Norwich Naturalists' Society frequently contain statements, usually of an anecdotal nature, about their status. In general, little new information has been obtained during the past 25 years about the ecology of the species especially characteristic of Broadland. However, during the course of an investigation into the social behaviour and population dynamics of the Water Vole (*Arvicola amphibius*), Leutze (1976) found that tussocks of *Carex paniculata* are of considerable importance to this species, since the females prefer to build their nests on these, rather than in the litter lying on the fen surface. She also found that these animals store large quantities of food in the tussocks in the autumn, and it is likely that they seek shelter on them when the fens are flooded (Leutze, *in litt.*).

Two carnivores are worthy of special mention. Foxes (*Vulpes vulpes*) were rare in Broadland until the mid-1950s, when their numbers began to increase, and they are now very common. One possible explanation is that the post-1954 myxomatosis-induced collapse in the rabbit population, and a simultaneous increase in the number of Coypu (see page 231) attracted foxes to a region which they had previously shunned. But whatever the reasons, foxes have frequently been observed quartering the fens during the bird breeding season, and they undoubtedly exact a heavy toll on ground-nesting species. At Hickling, for example, the regular predation by foxes of the nests of Redshank, Little Tern, Ringed Plover, Oystercatcher and in one year, Avocet, made it necessary to institute vigorous control measures, and 6 foxes were shot on this site in 1986 alone. But on most other reserves, little, if any, attempt is made to control this species, and despite the measures taken against it on keepered estates in the region, it is suspected that predation by foxes has contributed significantly to the observed decline of ground-nesting species such as Water Rail and Bittern.

The other carnivore deserving special comment is the Otter (*Lutra lutra*). These animals were originally so numerous in the region that the regulations governing the fisheries on the R. Yare between Norwich and Hardley Cross in 1556 contained an edict that "every man (? fisherman) shall be bound to keep a dog to hunt the otter twice or thrice in the year or more at time or times convenient upon pain to forfeit ten shillings" (Southwell, 1888). Norgate (1884) states that "otters are common in most of our broads", and there is no reason to believe that their status altered appreciably during the first half of the present century; indeed, Stephens (1957) was informed that they were still very plentiful in the region in the early 1950s. But Chanin and Jefferies (1978) who analysed the records of the Eastern Counties Otter Hounds believe that their numbers started to decline in this, and most other hunt areas, in the mid-1950s. Ellis considered that the population in Broadland in the early 1960s was not very large, though widely distributed, and a perusal of the mammal reports for subsequent years published in the *Transactions of the Norfolk and Norwich Naturalists' Society* suggests that the decline continued thereafter, the last definite breeding records being in 1970. Sightings were still occasionally made, either of the animal itself, as at Bridge Broad (west) in 1979, or its spraints or tracks (e.g. beside Cockshoot Dyke in 1982), but it would seem that by the early 1980s, the species was on the verge of extinction in Broadland, as in other parts of East Anglia.

Habitat destruction is unlikely to have been the principal cause of this decline in Broadland, given the huge expanses of unreclaimed fen which still border the rivers, and although many writers have speculated that otters have disappeared from the region as a result of the increasing disturbance caused by anglers and heavy boat traffic, the evidence for this is, at best, anecdotal; indeed, recent studies by Jefferies (1987) suggest that otters are fairly tolerant of such activities, except when breeding. Mason and Macdonald (1986) consider that although habitat destruction and increased disturbance are partly responsible for the decline in the numbers of otters in much of Britain and Western Europe during the past 30 years, this is mainly attributable to the effects of bio-accumulating pollutants, especially organochlorines such as polychlorinated biphenyls (PCBs). In the circumstances, it is disturbing that a male weighing 7.4 kg which was found drowned in a fyke net set in Breydon Water in October 1984 contained 0.79 ppm of dieldrin, plus other organochlorine residues and PCBs in its liver (Jefferies, 1985).

Despite this finding, and mounting evidence that the sediment in some of the rivers and broads contains mercury, lead and other bioaccumulating contaminants (see page 156), the Otter Trust decided, on the basis of the successful release technique it had developed (Jefferies *et al.*, 1986), and the fact that at least 19 litters of cubs are thought to have been reared in the wild by the 13 animals liberated at various sites in East Anglia between 1983 and 1988 (Otter Trust, 1988), to try and re-introduce otters into Broadland. Accordingly, a male and two females were released at a fen beside one of the northern rivers in September 1988. Sadly, one of the females, by then pregnant, was found drowned in the river the following summer. It is not altogether clear how it met its fate, but suspicions have been voiced that, like the Breydon casualty, it became trapped in an unguarded fyke net.

One species about which more is known now than when Ellis compiled his list is the Chinese Water Deer (*Hydropotes inermis*). Small deer were seen on several occasions in Broadland during the 1960s, but these were always assumed to be Muntjac (*Muntiacus reevesi*). However a deer killed on the Stalham bypass in 1968 was identified as *Hydropotes* (Goldsmith & Banham, 1970), and it became apparent that most, if not all the sightings, particularly those made in the vicinity of Hickling Broad between 1967 and 1969, were mis-identifications of this species. Chinese Water Deer, sometimes with fawns at heel, have since been seen on numerous occasions in the fens bordering the R. Bure and its tributaries, the first record from the Yare valley being made in 1977, when a female was found drowned in Surlingham Broad. It is believed that there are now at least 100 of these animals in the region.

The origin of these deer is something of a mystery (Goldsmith, *in litt.*). Two animals escaped from a private collection at Stalham in 1967, but these were both males. The nearest known wild group is centred on Woodwalton Fen, Cambridgeshire, some 120 km from Wroxham, and it seems unlikely that the animals originated from there because much of the intervening countryside is intensively farmed, and therefore relatively inhospitable to them. It is suspected, but not recorded, that deer of this species were kept in captivity in the Horning area during the 1950s and early 1960s, and that some, or all, of these escaped into the nearby fens.

Chinese Water Deer spend most of their time in thick cover in the fens, but they

Plate XXIX

Research on Coypu at Calthorpe Broad – 1986.

In 1965, the NCC gave the Ministry of Agriculture, Fisheries and Food permission to erect an 18 ha coypu enclosure on its Calthorpe Broad reserve, in order to facilitate the latter's research on the biology of this introduced mammal. This continued in use until shortly before the 'wild' population was finally exterminated in 1986.

When the research was in progress, the captive animals were periodically cage-trapped, as in the photograph, and then re-released after they had been weighed and measured.

Photo: R.N. Flowers

sometimes venture onto arable land to graze on young cereal crops; on one occasion an animal was seen feeding on the weeds between the rows in a sugar beet field. There is some evidence that mortalities occur after heavy snowfall; corpses have also been found drowned in steep-sided drainage dykes. Road traffic and fox snares account for some, and a few are shot.

According to Goldsmith and Banham, Chinese Water Deer thrive on grasses and low herbs, and rarely, if ever, damage trees and bushes; the species is therefore most unlikely to have had any significant effect on the ecology of Broadland. But the same cannot be said for another fairly recent addition to the list of mammals resident in the region, the Coypu, an aquatic, web-footed rodent native of South America. In Britain, the full grown male averages 6.7 kg in weight, and 99.5 cm in total length, the females being slightly smaller (see Plate XXIX). Sexual maturity is reached at between 3 and 7 months, according to season and gender, and breeding can continue throughout the year, with a gestation period of 19 weeks, and an average litter size of 5.3 (Newson, 1966). Coypu are normally herbivorous, but they will take *Anodonta* and other freshwater bivalves if these are available.

The animals possess a dense underfur, and from about 1929 onwards, stock was introduced to an increasing number of fur farms, the pelts being marketed as 'nutria', the Spanish word for an otter. Despite the measures taken to prevent escapes [which are described by Carill-Worsley, (1932)], these occurred during the 1930s in places as far apart as Sussex and Elginshire (Warwick, 1935). Numerous animals were also set free at the outbreak of the Second World War, when the 50 coypu farms which had by then been established had to close down. Two wild populations, one centred on the Yare valley, and the other in Buckinghamshire, became established during the early 1940s, but the latter had died out by about 1954 (Norris, 1967). Some trapping was organized by the Norfolk War Agricultural Executive Committee between 1943 and 1945 [when according to Laurie (1946) 193 animals were accounted for] and many coypus died during the hard winter of 1946/7. But despite these setbacks, the animals gradually increased in number, and as additional areas were colonized, it became apparent that they were causing considerable damage to sugar beet and other farm crops (Davis, 1956). They also displayed a propensity to burrow in tidal embankments, thus increasing the risk of drained marshland being flooded (Cotton, 1963). The population rapidly expanded during the late 1950s, and by the early 1960s, they were having a profound effect on the region's ecology. Ellis (1963 & 1965b) recorded that the animals were destroying the reedswamp bordering the broads, thus causing an apparent increase in the amount of open water. He also noted that saw-sedge beds were being damaged, and that . . "large patches of fen have been converted into expanses of black mud and shallow water". Many of these areas were subsequently re-colonized by plants but some have persisted, for example in the fens bordering Hickling Broad.

Coypus feed selectively, particularly in the summer (Gosling, 1974), and in 1961 and 1962, when their numbers were at a peak, some plant species were almost eliminated, while others became abnormally abundant. Purple Loosestrife, for example, is avoided by coypus, and therefore proliferated everywhere, whereas Cowbane and Great Water Dock almost disappeared (Ellis, 1963). The animal's partiality to the former is interesting toxicologically, since even small quantities of this plant are lethal to cattle.

In 1960, following widespread representations from farming and drainage interests, it was arranged that Rabbit Clearance Societies should be enabled to recoup from MAFF half the cost of operations against coypus. However, although 70 000 were killed during the year ending April 1962 by these organizations, and by the 15 trappers who had been taken on by the East Suffolk and Norfolk River Board, it became clear that additional, and more drastic measures would be required if the burgeoning population was to be brought under control. In 1962, therefore, a three-year campaign was launched by the Ministry to prevent the animals spreading further afield, eliminate them outside their main stronghold in Broadland, and reduce their numbers in the latter area to the maximum possible extent (Norris, 1967). The scheme allowed for the appointment of eight trappers and three supervisors, but in practice, a much larger number of individuals were trapping the animals at any one time. Simultaneously, a Coypu Control Co-ordinating and Advisory Committee was set up to act as a link between the different organizations having an interest in coypu control, and provide the MAFF with advice and assistance.

The launching of the new control campaign coincided with the exceptionally severe winter of 1962/3. This is thought to have killed 80 to 90 per cent of the animals, through the combined effects of cold, starvation and disease. But no-one knows for sure just how many coypus there were in Broadland prior to the population crash, and the widely quoted figure of 200 000 (Norris, 1967) is now thought to have been a substantial over-estimate (MAFF, 1978).

By the time the campaign ended in 1965, coypu numbers were at a very low ebb, and in most places it was left to occupiers to make their own arrangements for continued trapping. However, in Broadland it was arranged that the main burden of control should be assumed by the Acle and District Rabbit Clearance Society. When the 50 per cent MAFF grants for which such organizations were eligible were ended in 1971, an exception was made for this Society on account of its responsibility for coypus, and it changed its name to Coypu Control.

In order to obtain information about the breeding biology and ecology of Coypu, the MAFF established a research laboratory in Norwich in 1962, and three years later, the Nature Conservancy agreed that a 18 ha fenced enclosure for field experiments by staff based at this could be established at Calthorpe Broad. Studies on populations of coypus kept in this enclosure provided information about their selective breeding habits (Gosling, 1972),and supplemented the data obtained from an extensive programme of research carried out by MAFF on the population dynamics and breeding biology of the species, both in the wild, and in captivity (Newson, 1966; Gosling, 1974, 1981a & b, 1985).

One of the principal functions of the research carried out at the laboratory from 1970 onwards was to produce short-term predictions about coypu numbers, and the response of the population to different intensities of trapping. In practice, the predictions were primarily concerned with the number of trappers required to bring about a decline in coypu numbers. As more and more information was collected, the simulation model used to make these forecasts became increasingly reliable, and by the 1980s good correspondence was being obtained between the predictions and the numbers of animals in the wild, as assessed from subsequent trapping returns (Gosling, Watt & Baker, 1981; Gosling, Baker & Skinner, 1983; Gosling & Baker, 1987).

MAFF's records show that the total number of Coypu trapped in Norfolk (including sites on the coast as well as in Broadland), declined from 1521 in 1966 to 699 in 1969, suggesting that the population was decreasing in size during this period. Thereafter, it started to expand as a result of improved breeding success following a succession of mild winters (see Fig. 7A), and the numbers trapped in the county rose from 1001 in 1970 to 4783 in 1973. The trapper force was increased from 6 to 15 in 1973, but despite this, the population continued to expand, the numbers of animals killed in the 13 ten-kilometre squares which encompass Broadland rising from c. 4300 in 1973, to c. 6900 the following year. Just over 90 per cent of these animals were killed by Coypu Control trappers, the remainder being accounted for by MAFF personnel, gamekeepers and road deaths.

Concerned at the mounting cost of holding the population in check, the MAFF appointed a Coypu Strategy Group in August 1977, to assess the prospects of eradicating the species, and make recommendations as to how best this could be achieved. After taking evidence from a wide variety of different organizations, including the NCC, the RSPB and the Norfolk and Norwich Naturalists' Society, the Group concluded that the . . . "abandonment of centralized control would lead to a dramatic population expansion which only the most severe winter would check. Pre-1962 levels would be achieved within 3 years, and the extension of the population throughout lowland Britain would be inevitable" (MAFF (1978). The Group decided that it would be unthinkable to adopt such a *laissez-faire* policy, and it therefore turned its attention to ways of either drastically curtailing the population, or eliminating it altogether.

Aware that many sceptics took the view that because of the fecundity of coypus, and the difficulties inherent in trapping them in their fenland redoubts, it would be impossible to eradicate them altogether, the Group was particularly influenced by evidence presented by staff of the research laboratory concerning a field trial which they had started in 1975 on a 30-km stretch of the Yare valley between Norwich and Reedham. This had been set up partly to test new forms of trapping technique, including baited rafts, but more especially to determine how readily a population of Coypu could be eradicated from a defined area. Although the experiments were still in progress, it had

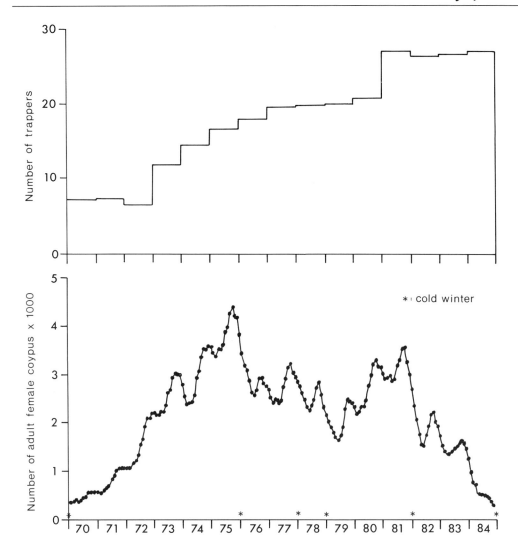

Fig. 7A

Monthly changes in the numbers of adult female Coypus, and in trapping effort, between 1970 and 1984.
NB. These figures relate to the whole of the area colonized by Coypus, and not just to Broadland.

Source: Gosling (1985)

already become clear that by using a fairly large number of trappers, the animals resident in the area could in fact be exterminated. Indeed, the main problem encountered had been that coypus tended to move into the study area from adjoining marshland which at that time was not being trapped so effectively (Gosling, Baker & Clarke, 1988).

After considering the costs of the different options available to them, the Group recommended that the team of trappers operating in the areas colonized by Coypu should be increased to 24. This would probably "not eliminate the population within the next decade, but would effect a gradual decline even under mild winter conditions". The Group also urged that the progress of the control campaign be closely monitored, and that methods of detecting and trapping coypus at near-extinction levels should be investigated. These recommendations were accepted by the Government in January 1980, and it was arranged that the total cost (estimated at £215 000 in the first year, and £180 000 in subsequent years at 1980 prices) would be shared in the ratio of the Treasury 50 per cent, the AWA 40 per cent and the Internal Drainage Boards 10 per cent.

The enhanced campaign got under way in April 1981, and the trapper force employed by Coypu Control was increased to 24, plus 3 foremen. Partly because of this, and partly due to the use of improved equipment, the number of 'trap-nights' rose from 96 543 in 1979/80 to 194 884 in 1981/2, and in subsequent years was over 200 000. The operation was also made more effective by the increasing use of pre-baited rafts. These had been shown by experiment to be 50 per cent more likely to catch coypus than traps set in 'runs' at the water's-edge, an advantage only partly offset by the difficulties involved in man-handling the rafts to the required location. Rafts were also of benefit to conservation since their use reduced the number of ducks, moorhens and other non-target species caught, and sometimes killed in the traps.

It will be seen from Fig. 7A that the number of adult females was increasing when the campaign was revitalized in 1981. However, after reaching a peak of about 3500 in the autumn of that year, the number declined very considerably, particularly during the ensuing hard winter (when many juveniles perished, and very few, if any, females bred successfully), and it has been estimated that only about 400 adult females were left by the autumn of 1984 (Gosling, 1985). If adult males, as well as females are included, the population is thought to have been reduced from over 5200 in 1981, to less than 20 by the end of 1986, a total of over 35000 animals having been caught during this period (Morris, 1988). These figures relate to the whole of the area colonized by coypus, but the trapping returns from Broadland, which remained the stronghold of the species, reflect the fluctuations in the population of adult females, as the numbers killed range from peaks of *c.* 6600 in 1975 and *c.* 6700 in 1981, to *c.* 2300 in 1979, and *c.* 960 in 1984 (Gosling, *in litt.*).

Not the least of the uncertainties regarding the feasibility of eradicating coypus was centred on the fact that those responsible would be 'trapping themselves out of a job' in the event that they were successful. To overcome this difficulty, a bonus scheme was devised, whereby each trapper would receive a lump sum equivalent to three annual salaries in the event that the animals were eliminated before March 1987. The bonuses payable would be reduced thereafter, but each man would still receive a full year's salary provided coypus were exterminated by 1991.

The job of checking whether eradication had been achieved was carried out independently of Coypu Control by field staff based at MAFF's research laboratory in Norwich, the techniques used including automatic photography at baited rafts. It was arranged that the campaign would be continued for at least 21 months after the last definite evidence had been obtained by the validation team that coypus were still present. Only then would a decision be taken as to whether the control organization should be disbanded.

In the event, only 12 coypus were trapped in 1987 (compared with 788 in 1985 and 174 in 1986), and none has been found in Broadland since March 1986, when a decision was taken to trap out a small population of marked animals at Cantley. In the absence of any further records, despite a continuation of a vigorous trapping programme, the Minister of Agriculture announced in January 1989 that the campaign would be terminated, and that each of the 24 trappers would receive a bonus of *c.* £20000.

Reports of sightings continue to be received from the public, and each of these has to be checked out by MAFF staff. In most cases, such records prove to be misidentifications, but single animals have been trapped or found dead at Barton Bendish in July 1988, Peterborough in September 1988, and by the Little Ouse near Feltwell in December 1989.

Chapter 8
The Drained Marshland Area

Early history

The progressive embanking of the rivers to enable the alluvial land bordering them to be drained for agricultural use would have profoundly altered the appearance and ecology of the region. Most of the land beside Breydon Water and the lowermost reaches of the rivers consisted of saltings in the thirteenth century, and even today, the meandering drainage channels characteristic of such terrain can still be made out, either in fossil form, or as a part of the present-day drainage system. Nearer the margins of the valleys, the saltmarshes gave way to brackish and freshwater fen communities fed by run-off from the adjoining uplands, and further upriver, where tidal influences and salinities were less, similar communities extended right across the valley floor.

Far less is known about the land-use history of what is now the Drained Marshland Area than about that of other alluvial regions, like the Fens and Romney Marsh. However, there were numerous sheep in the region at the time of Domesday (Darby, 1971), and the saltmarshes were probably used as communal sheep walks during the summer months, the animals being 'drifted' over the saltings and taken off when the latter were about to be flooded by a series of high spring tides, as was the practice in North Norfolk up to the outbreak of the Second World War.

The lack of winter feed for livestock, and the consequent need for a heavy annual slaughter, led to a strong demand for salt for preserving the meat, and this is reflected in the numerous saltpans listed for East Norfolk in the Domesday survey. Most of the vills (settlements) in Flegg had several pans, whilst Caister is credited with forty-five. Cantley, North Burlingham, Sutton and South Walsham were also taxed on the revenue from salt pans, but these would have been located on land bordering the seaward end of the estuary, detached from the main part of the vill concerned.

In 1948, a mound at Ashtree Farm beside the Acle New road was partially excavated, and found to have an eleventh to thirteenth century occupation surface at a level one metre below OD; this was covered by a layer of slag. The suggestion by archaeologists that this site may have been a salt pan is little more than a guess (Green & Hutchinson, 1960), but its stratigraphy tends to confirm that the water-table in the valleys during this period was at least a metre below its present level.

Sheep probably continued to predominate on the marshes during the thirteenth and fourteenth centuries, and Campbell (1983) presents evidence that some of the flocks were quite large. The Earl of Norfolk, for example, had 1800 head on his three manors in 1278, while the Abbot of St. Benet at Holm had over 1500 in 1343. Campbell points out that the sheep being grazed on the more accessible marshes were probably removed each evening, and 'folded' on the higher ground nearby, thereby enhancing its productivity.

It is not known when a start was made on embanking the rivers but Cornford (1982), who has examined the surviving medieval Account Rolls for various manors in Flegg, points out that ditching and embankment works ('fossatum') were being carried out in this part of Broadland during the late thirteenth and fourteenth centuries, and that some of these references clearly apply to low-lying marshy ground near streams, rivers and broads, rather than to the higher ground nearby. But although she argues that the amount of time and effort devoted to 'fossatum' during this period may have been necessitated by a progressive rise in water levels in the valleys, the carrying out of these works is, in the author's view, more likely to have been motivated by a desire to bring hitherto undrained land into permanent agricultural use, and improve its productivity. Some confirmation of this, albeit of an anecdotal nature, is provided by Patterson (*c.* 1930), who mentions that King Henry VII encouraged the Flemings . . . "to begin a system of bank raising and drainage of the swamps", following his visit to St. Benet's Abbey in 1486.

The work of embanking the rivers undoubtedly extended over several centuries. In 1555, for example, some "russhy" (sic) ground at East Somerton was dyked by Sir John Clere after . . . "it had long yielded him little profit by cause it lay opyn and onclosid" (Allison, 1955). The wording of this sentence suggests that the word dyked was being used to denote 'embanked', rather than 'ditched'. Moreover, given the continuing rise in sea and therefore river levels relative to the land, little purpose would have been served by ditching these, or indeed any other marshes unless they had first been afforded a reasonable measure of protection against flooding.

Manship (1619) notes that the dredging and re-alignment of the entrance to Yarmouth Haven in 1560 (see page 342) by the Dutch engineer, Joas Johnson, was followed by the reclamation of thousands of acres of marshland previously subject to flooding, so rendering these areas "useful and valuable" for grazing livestock. Evidence that the Dutch probably also assisted with the task of embanking the rivers and draining the marshes is provided by a floorstone in Haddiscoe Church which commemorates the daughter of Jan Piers Piers, who in his native country was acknowledged as an expert in reclaiming marsh and fen (Teasdel, 1935). The inscription on the stone is in medieval English and difficult to decipher, but Teasdel has provided the following translation:

> Here lies buried Mistress Bele, daughter of John, wife to Peter, son of Peter, the Dike reeve, who died 2nd December 1525.

Some of the newly embanked and drained marshes were certainly utilized as parts of fold courses in the Middle Ages. For example, in 1564 the Manor of Earls in East and West Somerton possessed a fold course consisting of 40 acres of "feeding marsh", 50 acres of heath, 40 acres of pasture and 20 acres of "land in the fields" (Allison, 1955). But the Norwich Bishops' chapel inventories for Thrigby (1595), Hoveton St. Peter (1595), Hardley (1596), Caistor (1617) and Tunstall (1647), show that cattle as well as sheep were being kept on the drained marshes by the end of the sixteenth century. By analogy with the farming scene today, this may have reflected a change in farm economics, and in particular an increase in the relative profitability of raising cattle rather than sheep. But it needs to be borne in mind that the marshes would have remained prone to flooding, despite being embanked, and that this problem would have tended to worsen as a consequence of the continuing rise in the level of the sea, relative to that of the land. Cattle would have fared better on the marshes than sheep under these circumstances, not least because the latter would have been susceptible to attacks by liver fluke, whose most usual intermediate host, the Dwarf Marsh Snail, *Limnaea truncatula*, still occurs in the vicinity of Breydon Water (Ellis, 1965).

The passing of the *Statute of Sewers* in 1531 was a landmark in the history of local government, as well as drainage and flood control, as it established the general principle that property could be taxed to pay for services provided by local agencies. But although it paved the way for a Commission of Sewers to be set up in Broadland in 1564 (Cornford, 1979), this is thought to have been responsible solely for maintaining and strengthening the sea defences between Happisburgh and Winterton, and there is no evidence that it carried out any river embankment works. Indeed, such bodies were specifically precluded from undertaking such capital projects, which were therefore left to the initiative of local landowners, sometimes working on a cooperative basis.

Confirmation that marshland in the middle Bure valley had been embanked and drained by the late seventeenth century is provided by the fact that in 1690 the Oby Hall estate consisted of 235 acres of good arable and pasture land, and 345 acres of "rich feeding marsh and meadows" (Allison, 1955). But there are many uncertainties, not least about land tenure in the Drained Marshland Area at this time. An indication that many of the marshes were still subject to communal grazing rights comes from the boundaries of Broadland's parishes. These were amended in 1935 by the Norfolk Review Order (made under the *Local Government Act*, 1929), but prior to that date, many parishes contained blocks of marshland located some distance away from the settlements concerned. Marshes in the Halvergate triangle, for example, were allocated to the parishes of Cantley, Postwick, South Walsham, Freethorpe, Burlingham St. Andrew, Beighton, Moulton and Freethorpe, as well as to the nine other parishes which, until the boundary revision order was made, actually bordered this area. Some parishes had several such 'detached' blocks of marsh prior to 1935; on Haddiscoe Island, for instance, Raveningham and Chedgrave had two each, while Stockton had five.

It is not known whether the rivers were first embanked in their lower reaches, or further up-valley, where tidal action was less, and where the relative narrowness of the flood plains would have made it possible to build crosswalls to isolate the land being reclaimed from the adjoining fens, and thus create a system of separately drained marsh 'levels'. Further down-valley, the greater tidal range, and the wave action generated on the open waters of the estuary would have made it much more difficult to construct embankments, even though these were set well back from the water's edge. It is significant that the remnants of several former flood banks can be discerned behind the Breydon North Wall, indicating that the saltings in this area were reclaimed in several stages (see page 38). The sub-parallel rivulets which occur in fossil form in several parts of the central Halvergate marsh complex and which can best be made out on aerial photographs (Coles & Funnell, 1981), suggest that intertidal mudflats as well as saltings were cut off from tidal influence when the estuary was first embanked.

Although it would have proved technically difficult to embank the lowermost reaches of the rivers, the saltmarsh creeks would have formed a ready-made system of drainage ditches, and it would only have been necessary to install culverts under the flood walls, and provide these with flap sluices, in order to achieve a rudimentary gravitational drainage system. To improve on this, the early reclaimers arranged that the land bordering Halvergate Fleet, which was originally the largest of the saltmarsh creeks draining into the estuary, should be used as a 'washland' for the temporary storage of flood water. Six wind-powered drainage mills spaced out along the length of the Fleet, lifted water into it from the adjoining marsh dykes, and this was then allowed to gravitate into Breydon Water via a flap sluice. When this was tide-locked, the water in the Fleet was initially prevented from spilling over onto the adjoining washes by low banks, known as the 'summer walls'. However, in wet weather, these were overtopped, and the water then flooded the main washland areas, being confined within the latter by the higher 'winter walls' (Harrison, 1974). This system was certainly in use by the end of the eighteenth century, since Marshall (1795) refers to the . . . "natural drainage channels or reed ronds, which form the main drains, and which are detached from the main grassy areas by banks of spoil". He also records that thatching materials and marsh hay were being harvested from the washlands, and judging by the symbols used on OS maps, parts of them continued to be used in this way until at least 1928.

Further up-valley, where the rivers were bordered by fen vegetation, rather than salt or brackish marshes, it would have been necessary, not only to construct embankments, but to create an extensive system of hand-dug ditches to drain the land and convey the water by gravity to sluices in the flood banks. Just how much time and effort must have been expended on this task can be gauged from the fact that on Haddiscoe Island at the time of the 1907 OS survey, there were 63 m of ditch per hectare, giving an average marsh size of 5.7 ha, whilst the marshes on the Strumpshaw Level averaged only 2.1 ha, with over 152 m of dyke per hectare (RSPB, *in litt.*). These figures do not include the numerous 'foot-drains' which were dug to convey surface water from near the centre of each marsh to the dykes around its margins.

Whenever possible, the drainage dykes were aligned so that they intercepted the principal springs in the flood plain, but a few areas defied all attempts to drain them, and remain to this day as small, spring-fed fens; Poplar Farm Meadow at Langley forms a good example. Numerous small hollows, often clothed with Reed-grass or sedges (*Carex* spp.) and fed by small springs also occur, particularly near the valley margins. Such areas are sometimes used as a source of water, a perforated pipe being driven into them to form a simple artesian wall. This was done at several places during the drought years of 1976 and 1991, when salt concentrations lethal to livestock developed in parts of the dyke system.

Tributary streams carrying water from the uplands to the river were embanked where they crossed land which was being reclaimed. However, it was usual for the banks to be set back a little from the channel, so that when the flap sluice at its outfall was tide-set back a little from the channel, so that when the flap sluice at its outfall was tide-locked, water could be temporarily stored, thus reducing the risk of the banks of the tributary being breached following periods of heavy run-off, with consequent flooding of the adjoining marshes. Carleton Beck, which discharges to the R. Yare near the Beauchamp Arms public house, is an example of an embanked, high-level watercourse, which has survived in its original state. But many others were integrated into the main drainage system when modern diesel and electric pumps came into use; examples include Heckingham Beck and Pickerill Holme, which formerly discharged to the rivers Chet and Bure respectively.

In order to intercept water draining from the adjoining uplands, and so reduce the risk of flooding, a 'landspring' dyke was normally dug around the landward margin of each marsh level. However, in spite of this, some spring-fed sites near the valley edge proved too wet to drain and convert to grazing marsh. Such areas would have been used for the production of reed, sedge and other crops, or allowed to develop into alder-dominated woodland so that they would serve as a source of timber and firewood. Many of these sites are so wet that they remain undrained to this day. They are of considerable interest to the geographer, since like other areas of unreclaimed fen they have evolved directly from the vegetation which existed near the valley margins at the time of the Second Marine Transgression.

Contemporary accounts indicate that by the early eighteenth century, the Drained Marshland Area was being managed in much the same way as it is today. Livestock, consisting mainly of cattle to be fattened, but with smaller numbers of dairy cows, sheep and horses, would have been put out in the spring, the freeboard in the dykes being reduced to about 0.5 m so as to provide the animals with a source of drinking water, and at the same time prevent them straying from one marsh to another. At the end of the grazing season, usually in early November, the dyke water levels would have been lowered to a metre or more below the marsh surface in order to provide as much storage capacity in the system as possible and thus minimize the amount of flooding which took place in the winter and early spring.

Daniel Defoe (1722) greatly admired what he called the largest tract of meadowland in England, and following a visit noted:

> The gross of all the Scots cattle which came yearly to England are brought thither [to Broadland], being brought to . . . Horsham St. Faiths where the Norfolk graziers go and buy them. These Scots 'runts' as they call them, coming out of the cold and barren mountains of the Highlands of Scotland, feed so eagerly on the rich pasture of its marshes that they thus in an unusual manner grow monstrously fat, and the beef is so delicious for taste that the inhabitants prefer them to the English cattle which are much larger and fairer to look at . . .

Defoe was told that most of the 40 000 Scottish cattle arriving in Norfolk 'on the hoof' each year were fattened on the Broadland marshes. Allowing for the presence of some home-bred beasts, this suggests that the stocking rate was not dissimilar to that customary today, if it is assumed that the process of reclamation had been largely, if not wholly completed by the beginning of the eighteenth century.

Marshall (1787) observed that the cattle brought south to the markets at St. Faiths and elsewhere by drovers consisted of 'Highlanders' and 'Isle of Skyes', most of which were males, and Galloways and 'Lowland Scots', which were usually spayed heifers; only small numbers of animals were derived from Ireland during this period. The 'Highlanders' and 'Isle of Skyes' were almost certainly West Highland 'kyloes' since these, and Galloways, were the two main breeds taken south during the seventeenth and early eighteenth centuries (Bonser, 1970), whilst Marshall's 'Lowland Scots' probably consisted of a mixture of the other two breeds concerned in the trade, namely Ayrshires and polled Angus cattle.

Four years was adjudged to be the most favourable age for fattening up the Scottish cattle, but home-bred animals were usually a year younger. Stock which was to be over-wintered was fed on turnips, and this could be done in the farmstead, or on the arable land bordering the valleys, thus helping to improve the fertility of the soil. Bonser states that after being fattened, the cattle not required for local consumption were taken southwards by drovers, and sold at Smithfield, or at one of the various markets *en route*, the average progress made being about 15 miles per day.

It is clear from Marshall's report that large numbers of individuals owned and oc-cupied land in the Drained Marshland Area at the end of the eighteenth century, even if his claim that . . . "every farmer within 15 to 20 miles has a marsh" was a slight exaggeration. He mentions that the higher, and therefore less frequently flooded, areas were clothed with very luxurious herbage containing the "choicest meadow grasses" and that 'slat', a long wiry kind of 'grass'* much favoured by cattle, grew in the wetter areas. Later, and not altogether consistently, he remarks that many of the marshes were very neglected, heavily poached and 'tussocky'. He probably used this word to denote land which had been invaded, either by Tufted Hair-grass (*Deschampsia cespitosa*) or rushes† (*Juncus* spp.). The latter were certainly abundant in the Hickling-Horsey-Somerton area in Victorian times, because statements obtained in 1853 by Thomas Brightwell for Sir Joseph Hooker (copies of which are at Kew and the Castle Museum, Norwich), show that large quantities of *J. effusus* and *J. conglomeratus* were formerly harvested from here in late June for making into rush lights. After the epidermis had been partially stripped, the stems were soaked in running water to remove the sap, and after drying, were packed into 'whips' containing 12 rushes each; a gross of whips would therefore have been sufficient to make 1728 candles. During the mid-nineteenth cen-tury, most of the material was sold at annual rush fairs held at the beginning of August in the yard of the Artichoke Inn, near Magdalen Gate, Norwich. Hooker was informed that 504 gross of whips were sold here in 1853 at prices ranging from two shillings and sixpence to eight shillings per gross, at an average of four shillings and sixpence‡.

Rising water levels in the rivers would have made the gravity sluice on its own an increasingly inefficient method of ridding the dyke system of surplus water after a flood or heavy rainfall, and the introduction of windpumps in the mid-eighteenth century (and possibly earlier in some places) would have brought about a great improvement in drainage standards. Marshall confirms this by noting that the land near Halvergate was . . . "until about 20 years ago, principally under water except in a dry summer. But since then a number of windmills have been erected, which throw the water into main drains for this purpose. By this means, the principal part of the marshes are freed from surface water, so that cattle can be turned out on them by the beginning of May, and kept there until Christmas".

'Horse-mills' (scoop-wheels driven by a whim made to revolve by horses) were em-ployed instead of windpumps in some places. But Bacon (1844) notes that such a machine at Surlingham had proved so "troublesome and expensive", that a hollow-post mill had been erected to drain the marshes, the horse-powered scoop being kept as a stand-by for times of flood.

Much of the Drained Marshland Area remained subject to common rights until the end of the eighteenth century, but all too often such land was ill-managed compared with that in private ownership. When Marshall rode out from Halvergate to inspect the nearby marshes in 1782, his horse was knee-deep in water for the first mile, despite the fact that it was high summer, and he revealingly commented that the land he crossed

---

* The identity of 'slat' is not known. But it is more likely to have been a sedge than a grass.

† Alan Davison has kindly drawn the author's attention to an Indenture in the Norfolk Record Office (NRS 15328 30 F.11), dated 1648, which refers to the presence of several 'junckeryes' in the parish of Heckingham. From another source, it is known that some, if not all these parcels of land were located in the Chet valley. 'Junckerye' is almost certainly an anglicized form of the latin *juncaria*, a word used several times in a fifteenth century Terrier for the parish of Hardley (NRO BEA 407 493 x 3) (Davison, *in litt.*). According to Dr John Harvey (*in litt.*), the suffix *-aria* implies that the land was specifically set aside for the growing of rushes (*junci*). The French words *jonc* (a rush) and *jonchaie* (a rush-bed) are clearly derived from the same source.

‡ See footnote on page 88 for information about the old currency.

was . . . "common to the village, and therefore no persons responsibility to drain it" (Marshall, 1787). Landowners naturally regarded Enclosure as an excellent opportunity to get such land properly embanked and drained, and the Acts for many parishes required the General Commissioners to construct flood banks, dykes and drainage mills, and then allot the land which had been improved as a result of their endeavours. The 1808 Award for Hickling, for example, shows that the Commissioners had constructed Eastfield and Stubb Mills, and had arranged that water from the latter could be discharged into Meadow Dyke via the adjoining boat dyke. Other new drains (one of which is still known as the Commissioner's Drain) collected water from the marshland in the parish, and conveyed it to the pumps. These works had made it possible to eliminate three open water sites, Wigg's Broad to the north-east of Hickling Priory, and Gage's and Hare Park Broads between Eastfield Road and Stubb Road. Chapman's Broad, too, had been embanked off from Hickling Broad and, all told, some 1500 acres (607 ha) were drained under this Award (Barringer, 1971).

Similar changes had taken place a few years previously as a result of the 1801 Award for Potter Heigham. This had provided for the construction of a 'New Bank' on the alignment of the present flood wall on the south side of Hickling Broad, thus facilitating the drainage, reclamation and allotment of an area shown on Faden's map as part of the latter.

A considerable amount of land improvement also took place in the Horsey area about this time, but this can be attributed to the actions of an entrepreneurial owner, rather than to the Enclosure Commissioners. Faden's map shows that there were four sizeable, albeit unnamed, pools between the villages of Somerton and Horsey at the end of the nineteenth century, and given its near-level topography, the whole area must have been a quagmire for much of the time; indeed, the only road between Somerton and Sea Palling lay immediately to the rear of the coastal dunes. However, in the early 1800s, the Horsey Estate was acquired by the Rising family, who laid out a new track on the alignment of the present coast road (B 1159) and drained the marshland, so as to render it . . . "one of the most fertile estates in the county" (White, 1845).

One of the beneficial effects of Enclosure was that it enabled separate holdings to be amalgamated. Young (1804) notes that common marshes at Upton which were formerly under water and worth only 5/– (five shillings) an acre, were let at 18/– to 20/– per acre after being drained and "made contiguous" as a consequence of Enclosure. At Acle, too, Enclosure resulted in holdings being amalgamated, but here the marshes were afterwards treated with chalk at the rate of 8 to 9 cartloads an acre (probably *c.* 40 to 45 tonnes per hectare). Young remarks that prior to this, they . . . "have for centuries yielded much stuff, as rushes for making dung, and this contributed to the great fertility of the country". Bacon (1844) too, remarks on the keen demand for "reeds and rushes" for use as a manure and for fodder, and points out that a waggonload of this type of produce sold for between £2 and £2.10s.0d.

The quality of the marshes in different parts of the region has always tended to vary, not only according to the soil type, and the amount of money spent on improving the sward by ploughing and re-seeding, controlling weeds and applying fertilizers, but with the efficiency with which it is being drained. Young noted in 1804 that the meadows at Thorpe were . . . "very good and let at 50/– an acre", whereas those at Whitlingham were neglected and therefore only worth 20/–. At Buckenham Ferry, Rockland and Cantley . . . "they were in a bad state, wanting much improvement, by draining and embanking, and clearing from rubbish; these are not (worth) more than 8/– an acre". Young reports that Enclosure had resulted in the construction of five miles of river bank at Langley, the marshes behind being . . . "part drained by mills, and part by sluices". He also notes that the marshes between Langley and Yarmouth were being let at between 20/– and 30/– an acre, whilst Bacon (1844) records that the freehold of a 300 acre (121 ha) block of good quality grazing marsh in the same general area had recently changed hands for £50 per acre.

In his report on the Land Utilization Survey he carried out in the early 1930s, Mosby (1938) provides confirmation of the varied quality of the marshes, those nearer the rivers being superior to the peaty areas beside the valley margin which, he noted, tended to be fly-ridden, and more difficult to reclaim. Mosby notes that the best marshes near Acle were being let for about £4 per acre per annum (*c.* £61 at 1980 prices), whilst poorer land was only fetching about £1.10s.0d. (*c.* £23 at 1980 prices). It is interesting

Table 8a Early Drainage Authorities in Broadland*

1. Drainage commissions set up as a consequence of Enclosure Awards

Date of Award	Name of Commission	Acreage
1801	Burgh and Billockby	321
1803	Cantley and Hassingham	479
1808	Catfield and Sutton	?
1812	Hempstead, Happisburgh, Eccles, Palling next the Sea, Lessingham and Ingham	?
1801	Hickling	1527
1812	Horsey	?
1802	Ludham	572
?	Martham	?
1817	Norton Subcourse and Heckingham	572
1806	Potter Heigham	1054
1809	Repps (with parts of Eccles)	?
1802	Runham	302
1807	South Walsham	426
1814	Thurlton, Haddiscoe and Thorpe next Haddiscoe	?
1820	Thurne	234
1802	Upton and Fishley	734
1805	Winterton, E. Somerton and W. Somerton	?

2. Commissions of Sewers set up prior to the 1861 Land Drainage Act

Date Estd.	Name	Acreage
1802	Commission of Sewers for the Eastern Hundreds of Norfolk (The Sea Breach Commission)** New Commissions were established in 1812, 1822, 1844, and 1855)	56 000

3. Commissions of Sewers set up under Pt. 1 of the 1861 Act

1863	Martham and Repps cum Bastwick †	594
1864	Winterton and Somerton ††	1055
1869	Muckfleet Improvement Drainage Committee	1373

4. Drainage Authorities created under Pt. 11 of the 1861 Act.

1868	Haddiscoe, Thorpe and Aldeby	1628
1883	Burgh St. Peter	840
1884	Burgh Castle	1615
1896	Langley, Chedgrave and Toft Monks	1930
?	Thurlton and Haddiscoe	586
1907	Oulton, Carlton Colville and Barnby	1362
1915	Raveningham, Norton Subcourse etc.	648
1926	Limpenhoe and Reedham	416

5. Other pre-1930 Drainage Authorities which may have been set up under the 1861 Act

	Acle Marshes	980
	Claxton and Rockland	578
	Chet Valley	842
	Repps with Bastwick † † †	254
	Martham † † †	?

Notes:

*   –   It is doubtful whether any of these lists is complete.

**   –   A Sea Breach Commission was first set up in 1609, following a major sea flood (see Chapter 10). According to Cornford (1979), this was required to 'maintain the drainage system of the marshes', but it is unclear whether this related to the whole of the Drained Marshland Area, or just those parts of it nearest the dunes between Happisburgh and Winterton.

†   –   This body seems to have been subsequently reorganized as two separate Drainage Authorities.

††   –   This probably represented a reorganization of the Drainage Commission set up in 1805.

††† –   In 1942, the functions of these organizations, and those of the Thurne Drainage Commission, were assumed by the Repps, Martham and Thurne Internal Drainage Board.

Source: The information in this Table is mainly derived from the Report of the Royal Commission on Coast Erosion (1907).

that similar prices prevailed in 1980, the feed on high quality marshes with good access being let for between £50 and £70 per acre, whereas that on unimproved land with poor access only realizing between £15 and £20 per acre.

It was obviously desirable that the works carried out at the time of Enclosure to improve the drainage of the marshes, and in particular the main (arterial) drains, sluices and pumps, should be maintained in good condition, and some Acts specified that special Commissions should be established to fulfil this function (see Table 8a). The members of these normally consisted of the Lord of the Manor, the parson, and those who owned at least 20 acres (and in the case of Winterton and Horsey, 30 or 40 acres respectively) of the marshland which had been drained as a result of the Act. In other parishes, responsibility for maintaining the new drainage works was placed by the Enclosure Commissioners on the landowners who benefited most from them. In this event, subsequent changes in title, and the boundaries of the holdings concerned, often made it difficult to determine who was responsible for initiating the necessary action, and how the resulting costs should be shared out. The problems were exacerbated by the fragmented ownership of the marshes. Thus when the drainage of 350 acres at Limpenhoe and Southwood was improved in 1831, the capital outlay and expenses of upkeep had to be apportioned between eleven individuals (Mosby 1938). In this case, the cost of draining the land, and constructing the necessary sluices, mill and marsh-man's cottage amounted to £744. However, this may have been an unusually inexpensive scheme since Caird (1852) notes that . . . "the whole cost of embanking, ditching, and erecting a steam-engine, is said not to exceed £10 an acre in situations at all favourable for the operation."

Throughout the sixteenth, seventeenth and eighteenth centuries, the Commissions of Sewers continued to be precluded from carrying out capital projects, even when a majority of the landowners concerned agreed on the need for them. However, this anomaly was rectified by an Act of 1833, which also empowered such Commissions to divide their areas of responsibility into separately-rated districts. In addition, the qualifications set for membership of the Commissions were standardized, only those owning at least 10 acres of land in the area, occupying 20 acres or more, or acting as the agent for a person so qualified, being eligible – an arrangement which in slightly modified form pertains to this day.

Further important improvements in the way land drainage and flood control were organized in Victorian times were made following the passing of the *Land Drainage Act* 1861. This clarified the powers and responsibilities of the Commissions of Sewers, and the way these could be established, and also provided for the establishment of Elective Drainage Boards. These had the same powers as the Commissions, but their members were elected by the drainage ratepayers, instead of being appointed by the Crown. An early example was the Langley, Chedgrave and Toft Monks Drainage Board, which was founded in 1896 to look after Haddiscoe Island, and which has continued to do so to this day. Other drainage authorities known to have been established under the 1861 Act are listed in Table 8a. However, even after the passing of this legislation, certain blocks of marshland continued to be drained by private landowners, as at Ranworth, Oby and Strumpshaw, whilst at Horsey, the functions of the Drainage Commission established at the time of Enclosure have been exercised by the local Estate for at least 75 years, and probably much longer (Buxton, pers. comm.).

The natural history of the marshes in the past

The Drained Marshland Area must have literally teemed with birds up to the time of Enclosure. Huge numbers of the commoner waders and wildfowl, such as Redshank, Snipe, Lapwing, Curlew, Shoveler, Pintail and Wigeon would have frequented the lush, winter-flooded meadows and fleets, and we know from the writings of Sir Thomas Browne (*c.* 1660) and others that a host of species, now rare or even extinct, were quite frequent in the seventeenth, eighteenth and early nineteenth centuries. Spoonbills, for example, were breeding at Claxton and one or two other localities in the mid-seventeenth century, whilst according to the Paget brothers (1834) Black-tailed Godwits were still common in the Breydon area as late as 1834. Similarly, Lubbock (1878) notes that Ruff, another species characteristic of wet pastures, were quite numerous in parts of Broadland prior to 1820, but that by 1827 they were becoming increasingly scarce, and had been virtually eliminated six years later. The status of such species would undoubtedly have been jeopardized by the drainage of the marshes, and the consequent loss of their preferred habitat. However, their demise was certainly hastened by the Victorians' obsession for collecting (see page 450) and by the failure of local people to adjust the level at which they were exploiting the populations of such species to take account of the changed circumstances. For instance, the Yarmouth dealer who in the Pagets' time was in the habit of collecting from the Oby, Thurne and Acle area between six and seven hundred Lapwing eggs a week during the breeding season for dispatch to the London markets would soon have exceeded the sustainable yield of this species once the drainage of these marshes had been improved.

In an introduction to their list of plants, the Pagets complain bitterly about the improved drainage to which the marshes were subject . . . "which has not only exterminated many species known to have existed some years ago, but has confined those which are left to particular spots, for the most part small, and still continuing to grow less". One of the species made extinct was Marsh Fleabane (*Senecio congestus*, formerly *S. palustris*), a plant once common enough to be given its own vernacular name, Trumpets. The Pagets note that . . . "this used several years ago to grow in the greatest abundance in a marsh at Caistor (*sic*)* and elsewhere. It is now very rarely and uncertainly seen at Belton, or by Ludham and Heigham bridges". According to Petch and Swann (1968), this species undoubtedly succumbed as a consequence of improved drainage, the last authenticated record being at Fleggburgh in 1898, but Ellis (1972) has pointed out that its final demise was hastened by over-collecting. The Grass-of-Parnassus, with its beautiful chalice-like flowers, was common in the Pagets' time, but is now only rarely found in the Drained Marshland Area, whilst another plant now confined to only one or two sites (e.g. Strumpshaw) is Adder's-tongue (*Ophioglossum vulgatum*).

Saltmarsh plants, too, were lost as a result of the embankment works carried out around Breydon Water. Sea Lavender, for example, . . . "had disappeared fifty years ago" according to the Pagets, while Sea Clover (*Trifolium squamosum*) was "long lost". The Pedunculate Sea Purselane on the other hand, was still plentiful at Cobholm and Runham in the early eighteenth century, though very rare if not extinct, by 1914, when Nicholson compiled his *Flora of Norfolk*.

Drainage and flood control from the nineteenth century onwards

Although most, if not all, the embankments beside the rivers were created in the first place by the owners of the marshes which were thereby protected against flooding, responsibility for their management was normally assumed by local drainage commissions, once these had been established. Thus in 1915, the Clerk to the Ludham Drainage Board arranged that when the Bure Commissioners were next dredging the river, the material would be placed on a section of tidal embankment for which his Board was responsible, and which needed to be raised. Similarly, in 1921, the Runham Drainage Commission decided to seek a grant of £200 from the Ministry of Agriculture towards the cost of making a new soke-dyke, so that the tidal embankment could be strengthened (Runham DC minutes). In some cases, drainage authorities were established primarily to secure the flood defences, rather than effect an improvement in the way the land within their districts was drained. For instance, the 1883 petition to the Enclosure Commissioners which led to the establishment of the Burgh Castle Drainage Board refers to . . . "the marsh land which would be greatly improved by better drainage – but more important still is that the wall next the Breydon Tidal Water should be strengthened and raised to resist high tides such as the one in February last". Similarly, the minutes of the Langley, Chedgrave and Toft Monks Board show that until the early 1940s, its responsibility was limited solely to repairing the embankments of Haddiscoe Island. The cost of this work was defrayed by levying a rate of sixpence per acre (*c.* 1p/ha) on the marsh owners, the occupiers not being required to make a contribution until 1925 (Gaze, undated).

The large number of separate drainage authorities created from the early nineteenth

---

* This is undoubtedly a misspelling of Caister.

century onwards, and the fact that some of them were either moribund or more or less permanently insolvent meant that the standards of drainage and protection against flooding were very uneven in different parts of the region, the problems being compounded by the fact that many blocks of marshland were looked after by individual landowners, rather than by drainage commissions. The topography of the area is such that if one section of river bank was breached or over-topped as a consequence of inadequate maintenance, neighbouring land managed by other landowners or by a different commission was likely to be flooded, a certain recipe for disputes between those concerned. Further difficulties arose as a result of the fragmented ownership of the marshes. Bacon (1844) for example, notes that although there was a drainage commission for the Hickling-Horsey area, some of the . . . "vast number of small proprietors, over which there is no control, . . . erect their own skeleton mills, and while they drain their own marsh, deluge their neighbours without remorse".

In a bid to resolve what had become a thoroughly unsatisfactory situation, a consortium of local landowners and drainage interests prepared a 'memorial' in 1922 inviting the Minister of Agriculture to establish an East Norfolk Drainage Board which would, *inter alia*, assume responsibility for all the tidal embankments in the region. At a subsequent conference held in Norwich, the Great Yarmouth Port and Haven Commissioners indicated that whilst they did not wish to oppose the formation of such a Board (at least publicly!) they feared that it might interfere with their responsibilities as a navigation authority, and in particular their desire to deepen the R. Yare so that it could accommodate the larger vessels which were by then coming into use, and which needed to be able to reach Norwich. Reservations were also expressed by the Town Clerk of Norwich, who pointed out that as drafted, the Order would result in part of the city being rated twice in respect of river drainage (EDP, 1922).

No further action seems to have been taken to promote the Order, but in 1927, a committee of drainage authorities and marsh owners in Norfolk, submitted evidence to the Royal Commission on Land Drainage in England and Wales. Most of the recommendations made in the Commission's Report (Cmd. 2993) were subsequently incorporated in the *Land Drainage Act* of 1930, which provided for the establishment of Catchment Boards, having 'main river' and sea defence responsibilities, and empowered to abolish, re-create or alter the boundaries of the drainage authorities in an area, and create new ones.

On its establishment in 1931, the East Norfolk Rivers Catchment Board became responsible for ensuring that the embankments of the waterways which had been designated under the Act as 'main rivers' (i.e. the Bure, Ant, Thurne, Yare, Wensum and Waveney, plus their tributaries, boat dykes and associated navigable waters) were maintained in good condition. It also set about the task of reorganizing the drainage authorities in the region into a series of Internal Drainage Boards (IDBs). Most of the larger boards were formed during the 1930s – the Smallburgh IDB for example was set up in 1936 to take the place of four commissions, and is responsible for *c.* 5465 ha – but some of the smaller boards, for instance, the Repps, Martham and Thurne IDB (*c.* 650 ha), and the Lower Yare Fourth IDB (*c.* 375 ha) were not formed until five or six years later. In addition, three of the IDBs created initially by the Catchment Board proved too small to be effective, and were amalgamated in 1935 to form the Lower Bure, Halvergate Fleet and Acle Marshes IDB.

By the time the East Suffolk and Norfolk River Board took over the Catchment Board's responsibilities in 1952, Broadland had been divided up into 18 internal drainage districts (see Table 8b). The boundaries of some of these have been slightly altered subsequently, but the constitution and functions of the boards responsible for them have remained basically unchanged. Each operates by levying a drainage rate on both the owners and the occupiers of the land within its district. The revenue derived from the former is intended to cover the cost of new works and improvements to existing ones, as well as annual payments to the National Rivers Authority* (because this has inherited the responsibility for looking after the main rivers and their banks, thus protecting each drainage district against flooding), whilst the occupiers' rate is

---

* The National Rivers Authority's estimates for 1991/2 indicate that the contributions from the 18 IDBs listed in Table 8b are expected to amount to £294 635.

intended to be spent on administration and maintaining the arterial drains and pumps for which the Board is responsible. The IDBs have powers to divide their districts into sub-districts, and to levy different drainage rates in each if this can be justified on grounds of differential benefit. Members of the boards are elected by those who pay drainage rates, under a system which, within certain limits, relates franchise to the extent of liability for rating. This means, in effect, that those with large holdings in a drainage district get more votes than those owning or occupying smaller parts of it. To qualify for election as a member, a person must within the drainage district own more than one hectare or occupy more than 8 ha, represent a person so qualified, or occupy land which had a rateable value of more than £35 in 1935. In practice, elections are often not contested, so this out-dated voting system is seldom used (MAFF, 1985).

Like the organizations previously responsible for flood defence, pollution control and fishery management – namely the AWA, the East Suffolk and Norfolk River Authority and the East Suffolk and Norfolk River Board – the National Rivers Authority exercises a general supervision over land drainage. However, as autonomous bodies, the IDBs

Table 8b   Present-day Drainage Districts in Broadland

Name	Size (ha)
Middle Bure	2023
Lower Bure, Halvergate Fleet and Acle Marshes	4074
Smallburgh	5463
Happisburgh to Winterton	3237
Repps, Martham and Thurne	664
Muckfleet and South Flegg	2734
Lower Yare First	1607*
Lower Yare Second	1219
Lower Yare Third	855
Lower Yare Fourth	375
Limpenhoe and Reedham	357
Langley, Chedgrave and Toft Monks	803
Burgh Castle and District	809
Lower Waveney	1905
Lower Waveney Second	1431
Lower Waveney Third	591
Blundeston, Flixton and Oulton	247
Oulton, Carlton Colville and Barnaby	444
Total:	28838

* An area of 692 ha within this District is not drainage-rated as it forms a washland for the R. Yare.

decide for themselves when and where to carry out maintenance work and improvement schemes; indeed, the Rivers Authority may not officially learn about the latter unless a board's proposals are likely to affect a designated 'main' river, or its embankments, when consultations between the two organizations are, of course, obligatory. Each board employs a clerk (who will usually be a solicitor or an engineer) to administer its affairs, but in Broadland it is customary for one individual to service three or four IDBs. Some boards arrange for contractors to maintain their arterial drains, but many now own hydraulic excavators so that they can undertake this task themselves, and also carry out work for their drainage ratepayers on a repayment basis.

The greater degree of security against tidal flooding which was progressively afforded the region by the Catchment Board's activities, together with the steps taken by the newly formed IDBs to improve the drainage of the marshes, soon began to reduce the amount of birdlife in the latter. In 1934, for example, a diesel-driven pump with an output of 35 tons of water a minute was installed at Breydon Sluice to reduce the depth and duration of flooding of the Halvergate Fleet washlands, and in 1946 this was, in turn, replaced with electric pumps having a combined capacity of 80 tons of water a minute. These obviated the need to use the washes for the temporary storage of flood

Plate XXX

Boardman's Mill, How Hill – 1987.

Numerous trestle (or 'skeleton') mills like this were working in Broadland in the nineteenth century, but since they were built largely of wood, few have survived. This example is located on the left bank of the R. Ant, and was restored by its owners, the Norfolk Windmills Trust, in 1980. The piles protecting the mill's outfall sluice (visible in the centre of the photo) now project well out into the open water, an indication that bank erosion has significantly widened the river since the mill was built.

The attractive thatched boathouse in the middle distance was constructed for the Broads Authority in the mid-1980s as a replacement for an older, derelict building. How Hill staithe lies immediately downstream of it.

Photo: R.N. Flowers

water, thus eliminating one of the principal resorts for wildfowl in the region. According to Harrison (1972), Wigeon numbers declined very rapidly after 1947, and although Pink-footed and White-fronted Geese continued to frequent the area in declining numbers for the next ten years or so, the Fleet washes had been largely forsaken by these birds by 1972. Apart from a relict reed-bed about a kilometre south of the Manor House, most of the Fleet washes are now cattle-grazed, and therefore floristically indistinguishable from the adjoining grass marshes. Moreover, the washes nearest Breydon Sluice were put under the plough in the early 1970s, and the Fleet itself was converted into a low-level arterial drain in 1982 (see Chapter 9).

During the 1940s, IDBs came under pressure from the War Agricultural Executive

Committee to carry out works which would enable farmers to enhance the productivity of their marshes. In 1944, for instance, the Langley, Chedgrave and Toft Monks Board built a new road and dwarf wall beside the New Cut, so as to improve access and at the same time alleviate the flooding problem to which Haddiscoe Island had long been subject as a consequence of the inadequate height of the Cut's southern embankment. But the minutes of the Board show that until about 1948, when it installed new electric pumps, the Island's drainage system was dependent on an ancient 10 hp steam engine and four windpumps (one of which was powered by a tractor from 1941 onwards), all privately owned and in a very poor state of repair.

The Brograve Level is another area which was very badly drained in the past; indeed, despite the late eighteenth century efforts of Sir G. B. Brograve (which involved the building of Brograve Mill in 1771), this is one of the very few areas shown on the 1907 OS 6-inch map as being "liable to flood". This wording is absent from the 1950 version of the map, probably because a diesel pump had by then been installed to drain the Level, following the destruction of the Mill in the great storm which caused the 1938 sea-flood (see Chapter 10). Parts of the Level were again inundated in 1953, but by then the Happisburgh to Winterton IDB had set about the task of reorganizing the drainage system of the area. This involved creating a new main drain running past Calthorpe Broad and Long Gore, and thence down the centre of the Brograve Level, and linking this with a new, electrically-powered pumping station beside the remains of Brograve Mill. The section of Waxham Cut upstream of Bridge Farm (into which drainage water from the northern end of the Brograve Level had originally been discharged by Lambridge Mill) was stopped off, the net effect being greatly to improve the efficiency of the drainage system of the whole Level, and enable the IDB to respond to requests by persons owning land within it to lower the water-table so that they could put their marshes under the plough.

Most IDBs (though not the Langley Board) assumed responsibility for the pumps and arterial drains within their districts very soon after they were formed. But the onus for looking after the great majority of the dykes in a drainage district remained vested in the owners of the marshes, and it was soon found that some individuals tended to skimp their maintenance programmes, thus disadvantaging their neighbours. To overcome this difficulty some Boards have assumed responsibility for an increasing proportion of the dykes within their districts; indeed at least one Board (the Lower Waveney Second) now manages all the dykes within its district.

The earliest drainage mills would have been timber-built, and probably had sails mounted on a fixed cap in such a way that they could not be swivelled round to face into the wind; an illustration of a mid-seventeenth century machine of this type appears in Freese (1957). Smock mills with movable caps, similar to the restored example at Herringfleet (see Plate 3), probably came into use soon afterwards, but brick-towered mills are unlikely to have been built until the following century. The earliest known example in Broadland is at Oby, and is dated 1753 (Smith, 1978). Smaller blocks of marshland tended to be drained by Trestle ('Skeleton') or Hollow-post Mills (see Plates XXX & 21); it is not known when these first started to be used in the region, but Bacon, writing in 1844, implies that the inventor of hollow-post mills was at that time still alive.

The early tower mills were low in stature so that the canvas cloths of their 'common' sails could be set and, when necessary, reefed, from the ground. Sails fitted with vanes which opened and shut automatically according to the wind strength were introduced into Broadland soon after their invention in 1807, and these made it possible to use taller towers, and therefore larger sails, and more powerful machinery. Some of the older buildings, such as Thurne Dyke Mill, were heightened, or to use the Norfolk word 'hained', to take larger, vaned sails. The caps of the tower mills were traditionally boat-shaped, and were at first turned manually to face the wind by means of a tail-pole: fan-tails, which luffed (or 'winded') the caps automatically were invented in 1745, but were probably not used in Broadland until much later.

Scoop wheels were employed at first and continued to be fitted to some mills, even though vane-type pumps known locally, if somewhat inaccurately, as 'turbines' were introduced soon after they were invented by Appold in 1851. These were supposed to lift half as much water again as a scoop wheel, especially in a steady wind. Scoops were said by marshmen to have a lift of about three-eighths of their diameter, and the 15 foot by 7 inch wheel at Ashtree Farm Mill was alleged to lift 8 tons of water per minute when turning at 15 revolutions per minute (Wailes, 1956). The same worker points out that the efficiency of different types of mill was reflected in the size of the areas they drained. For example, High's Mill beside Halvergate Fleet, whose 'common' sails drove a 12-foot diameter scoop, drained 200 acres; Fleggburgh Mill, with vaned sails, turned a scoop with a diameter of 17 feet 6 inches, and drained 394 acres, whilst High's Mill, Potter Heigham, drove a 'turbine' and drained over 1000 acres, assisted when necessary by a steam engine.

According to Anthony Ward (*in litt.*), there were once about 200 wind-powered mills in Broadland, of which some 20 were still in use in the 1930s. But most of these succumbed during the next ten to fifteen years as electrically-powered machinery came

Plate XXXI

Berney Arms Mill.

This mill, which is owned by English Heritage, was built in about 1865. It originally drove a cement clinker grinder, as well as a large (diameter 7.3 m), detached scoop wheel. Although the sails have no shutters, they turn in a strong breeze. The building is open to the public, and superb views can be obtained from its upper storey.

The small brick building on the left houses an electric pump which is operated by the Lower Bure, Halvergate Fleet and Acle Marshes Internal Drainage Board; its future was subject to much discussion during the Halvergate controversy. In 1985, when the furore over the latter was beginning to subside, the RSPB established a new marshland nature reserve in the Berney Arms area; the launch used in connection with this can be seen on the right.

Photo: R.N. Flowers

increasingly into use. Some caught fire (usually because of an overheated brake), others were tail-winded, as was Brograve Mill in the great storm of February 1938, but most were simply not repaired when they became unserviceable. The last in use, Ashtree Farm Mill, was set to work to help clear the 1953 floods, but a sudden change in wind direction put it out of action.

Drainage mills in varying states of repair can be seen at 71 sites, and both individually and collectively, they form one of Broadland's most characteristic landscape features. Although other areas, notably the Fens, were originally drained in the same way, soil shrinkage there was so great, particularly in the peatland areas during the Victorian era, that virtually all the wind-powered mills had to be replaced with steam-driven machinery as a consequence of their inability to raise water through a vertical distance of more than a metre or so. As a result most have long since been demolished. In contrast, the water-table of almost all Broadland's marshes was, until the mid-1960s, maintained at a much higher level than in the Fens, soil shrinkage has been correspondingly less, and wind-power could be employed until much more recently. In addition, the relatively small economic rate of return obtainable from Broadland's unimproved pastures, meant that drainage rates were generally lower than in the Fens, where much of the land had been intensively cropped for a century or more. As a result, the rate of investment in replacement pumping machinery tended to be slower in Broadland than in the Fens (Wailes, 1956).

Of the 71 buildings which survive, 2 are hollow-post mills, 3 are smock mills (one of which has been converted to a residence), 3 are trestle mills and 63 are brick-towered structures. Amongst the latter are the mills near Wayford Bridge and at Swim Coots, Hickling, both of which were used for grinding corn, as well as draining the land. The mill at Berney Arms (see Plate XXXI) was another dual function building, since it formerly powered not only a large scoop wheel, still to be seen today, but a grinder for the clinker produced by the cement works at Berney Arms (the ruins of which can be seen beside the Mill), and at Burgh Castle, on the other side of the river. The windmill in the ruined gatehouse of St.Benet's Abbey, which is believed to have been in existence in 1740 (Martin, 1970), and which forms one of the region's best known landmarks, is excluded from the list as it seems to have been used mainly, if not exclusively, for grinding cole-seed (better known today as oil-seed rape) to make lamp-oil. Experts disagree as to whether it was later used for drainage purposes. Structurally, there is no evidence for this (Smith, 1978); on the other hand, Apling (1984) points out that several contemporary reports refer to the presence of a drainage mill at St. Benet's.

Increasingly aware of the landscape and historical importance of Broadland's drainage mills, the Norfolk and East Suffolk County Councils started to preserve selected examples soon after the Second World War. The Norfolk Windmills Trust, founded in 1963, gave increased impetus to this task and over the past 25 years has spent many tens of thousands of pounds on repairing and maintaining the buildings for which it is responsible (see Table 8c). It has also actively encouraged other bodies and private individuals to restore their mills, by providing them with grants and technical advice.

In 1980, following a comprehensive survey, the Trust identified a number of buildings which possess special features of interest and which were still capable of restoration, and work was put in hand on several of these in 1981 (see Plate XXXII). Strong support for this programme of work was forthcoming from members of the Broads Authority; indeed, much of the latter's expenditure on drainage mills (summarized below) was devoted to projects devised and carried out by the Trust, following discussions with the Authority.

Broads Authority expenditure on drainage mills – 1980/1 – 1988/9

1980/1	—	£9625
1981/2	—	£5452
1982/3	—	£12484
1983/4	—	£10525
1984/5	—	£27266
1985/6	—	£9395
1986/7	—	£19997
1987/8	—	£33094
1988/9	—	£25105

Details of the 16 drainage mills which have been, or are being, restored are summarized in Table 8c; a further towered building, Ashtree Farm Mill (TG 507695), built in 1912, and containing much machinery fabricated out of cast iron, is likely to be renovated shortly. The 11 mills listed in Table 8d have been protected against the wind and weather so that they can be restored later, in most cases by the Trust. Of the remainder, a smock mill and 16 towered buildings have been converted to residential accommodation; 5 of the latter still retain much of their machinery, but the rest have been drastically altered during conversion. 16 towers, of which 6 are roofed, remain in passable condition, and although they have probably deteriorated too much to warrant restoration, many of them contain machinery which the Trust considers worthy of preservation. The remaining 9 towers, plus a smock mill beside Tunstall Dyke, are in a derelict condition.

Sites where tower mills once stood can still be discerned at several places, an example being Eastfield Mill (TG 438234) which was blown up by its owner in the 1950s. The other types of mill, being built largely of timber, are less durable than brick structures.

Table 8c   Restored drainage mills

	NWT	Smith	Name of Mill	NGR	Owner	Type	Pump	Special Features
1.	7	64	Stracey Arms	TG442090	NCC/NWT	Tower	Turbine	—
2.	22	69	Palmers Hollow Post Mill	Moved from TG404103 to TG403129	R.M. Seago	Hollow Post	Plunger Pump	Only Hollow Post Mill with plunger pump. Springsails and twin winding tails
3.	23	56	St. Benets Level	TG399156	Norwich Union Insurance Co.	Tower	Turbine	—
4.	24	65	Thurne Dyke	TG401159	R.M.Morse Leased to NCC/NWT	Tower	Turbine	Good example of heightened tower
5.	33	32	Horsey	TG457222	National Trust NWT Cap	Tower	Turbine	Widest tower
6.	41	6	Turf Fen	TG369188	NCC/NWT	Tower	Scoop wheel	Double scoopwheel with choice of high and low gears
7.	42	37	Boardman's Mill	TG369192	NCC/NWT	Trestle	Turbine	Only trestle mill with turbine
8.	43	61	Hunsett	TG364240	Private	Tower	Scoop wheels missing	—
9.	46	9	Berney Arms	TG465049	English Heritage	Tower	Scoop wheel	Tallest tower. Also used for grinding cement clinker. Detached scoopwheel
10.	68	21	St. Olaves	TM457997	Lord Somerleyton (leased to NCC/NWT)	Boarded Trestle	Scoop wheel	—
11.	69A	70	Clayrack Mill	moved from TG367148 to TG369194	NCC/NWT	Hollow Post	Scoop wheel	Only Hollow Post Mill with Scoopwheel
12.	70	74	Herringfleet	TM466976	Lord Somerleyton (leased to Suffolk County Council)	Smock	Scoop wheel	Only Smock Mill remaining in good condition. 'Common' sails winded by tail pole

Mills under restoration

	NWT	Smith	Name of Mill	NGR	Owner	Type	Pump	Special Features
1.	5	54	Runham Swim	TG470100	W.R.Watts	Tower	Internal scoop wheel missing	—
2.	15	30	Hobbs' Mill	TG347163	East Anglian Water Company Leased to NCC/NWT	Trestle	Scoop	Only trestle mill with scoopwheel
3.	58	27	South Walsham	TG462073	R.M.Seago	Tower	Scoop	Cast iron sheer extensions
4.	60	25	Muttons Mill	TG442063	P.Reynolds & D.High	Tower	Scoop	Only tower with complete internal scoopwheel

Key:
The numbers in columns 2 & 3 refer to the listings of the Norfolk Windmills Trust (NWT), and Smith (1978 & 1990) respectively. 'NCC' in this Table refers to the Norfolk County Council.
Source: Stephen Earl (pers. comm.).

Turf Fen Mill (How Hill), under restoration – 1987.

Plate XXXII

This is one of the 12 drainage mills in the region which have been restored, the majority by the Norfolk Windmills Trust. 15 others are currently (1990) being restored, or have been 'protected', so that they can be restored later, when funds permit. Turf Fen Mill is of special interest on account of its double scoop wheels (one of which is visible in the photograph, albeit in a ruinous condition), and the fact that the mill-man was able to choose between high and low gears, depending on the wind strength.

The stocks for the sails are very heavy, and their replacement is always a tricky operation, particularly, as here, when there is no hard standing nearby, and the job has to be done with a block and tackle, rather than a crane.

Photo: R.N. Flowers

But despite this, the fragmentary remains of trestle mills can be seen north of Barton Broad (TG 359231), east of Sutton Broad (TG 380232), south of Ludham Bridge (TG 374169), and south of Horsey Mere (TG 450219).

Short descriptions of all but two of Broadland's 71 remaining drainage mills are given by Smith (1978), the ones he overlooked being a derelict tower mill in Catfield Fen (TG 372211), and a hollow-post mill at Ranworth*. The latter has recently been restored to working order and re-erected at How Hill by the Norfolk Windmills Trust, and is unique in that it can be used to drain the adjacent marshland (see Plate 21).

In the past, each drainage mill was tended by a marshman who, in addition, was expected to slub out the main drains, adjust the sluices, and look after the cattle on his level. Occasionally, as at Stubb Mill, Hickling, he and his family lived in the windmill itself. More usually, however, the marshman was given a 'tied' cottge nearby. Such buildings were often damp, and located miles from the nearest village. But despite this,

Table 8d   Protected drainage mills

	NWT	Smith	Name of Mill	NGR	Owner/Condition	Type	Pump	Special Features
1.	3	52	Five Mile House	TG478099	Private NWT Cap	Tower	Scoop	—
2.	4	53	Perry's Mill, Runham	TG472099	Private NWT Cap	Tower	Turbine	—
3.	13	3	Oby (Wiseman's Mill)	TG409138	Private NWT Structural Repairs to Cap Frame	Tower	Turbine	Oldest dated tower (1753)
4.	19	22	Kerrison's level	TG461098	Private NWT Cap leased to NCC/NWT	Tower	Scoop	Reused cap frame from earlier Smock Mill
5.	42	46	Heigham Holmes	TG449203	Private NWT Cap	Tower	Turbine	—
6.	40	5	Neaves	TG362182	Private leased to NCC/NWT NWT Cap	Tower	Scoop	Cast iron sheer extensions
7.	49	48	Cadges	TG446036	NWT flat roof. NCC/NWT Ownership	Tower	Scoop	—
8.	51	49	Polkey's	TG444035	NWT Cap. NCC/NWT Ownership	Tower	Scoop	—
9.	57	10	Lockgate	TG480072	Private NWT Cap	Tower	Scoop	—
10.	59	26	Highs Mill	TG457072	Private NWT Cap	Tower	Scoop	Rare 18th C. machinery including trundle wheel
11.	64	19	Caldecott	TG465021	Private NWT Cap	Tower	Scoop	—

Key:
The numbers on columns 2 & 3 refer to the listings of the Norfolk Windmills Trust (NWT), and Smith (1978 & 1990) respectively. 'NCC' in this Table refers to the Norfolk County Council.
Source: Stephen Earl (pers. comm.)

and the arduous nature of his work, a marshman's wages were very low, and he usually had to supplement them by wildfowling and fishing.

Ward (*c.* 1964) who has described and illustrated many of Broadland's wind and steam-powered pumps, believes that the latter were first introduced in about 1840. Beam engines were sometimes used, as at Hardley and Langley, but conventional horizontal or vertical machinery was much more often employed. Some crank-overhead engines were also installed, for instance at Beccles (1857), Haddiscoe (*c.* 1870) and West Somerton (1886). Robert Morse, who has preserved and rebuilt the two latter engines, believes that the one at Haddiscoe was capable of lifting about 150 tons of water a minute; it was last steamed in 1953, following the surge-tide floods.

Ward describes 46 steam pumping stations, about 30 of which were still in use in 1938. Unfortunately, no steam-powered mills have survived intact, and even their chimney stacks, once a commonplace feature of the landscape are now rarities. Only two complete examples survive, these being at Strumpshaw Mill (see Plate 22), and

---

* The latter is described by Smith in an expanded and updated account of the wind-powered drainage mills in Norfolk (Smith, 1990).

Black Mill (opposite Somerleyton on the R. Waveney), but a third chimney, beside the R. Yare at Seven Mile House, has been partially reconstructed.

In many cases, the mill which drained a level was abandoned once a steam-driven pump had been installed nearby. However, at Buckenham, Horsey and elsewhere, the windpump was adapted so that its machinery could be turned by a steam engine in time of need. Auxiliary paraffin and diesel engines were also used at some sites. For instance, a 16 hp paraffin engine installed in Runham Mill in 1916 could drive the scoop wheel through a clutch when there was insufficient wind to turn the sails (Runham DC minutes). The first mill to be fitted with an auxiliary electric drive was that at Repps, where a 25 hp motor was used from 1932 (Wailes, 1956). At some sites, for example Pettingell's Mill on Haddiscoe Island, a tractor was employed to drive the pump, and thus save the expense of installing new machinery (Gaze, undated).

The first pumping station to be wholly dependent on an internal combustion engine was that at Limpenhoe, where a diesel-powered pump was used from 1913 onwards. Hot-bulb paraffin engines were employed here and there, for instance at Mautby in 1919, and even petrol engines were used occasionally, as at Tunstall in 1939. Motor-driven pumps such as these were doubtless more efficient than windpumps, but the drainage rates almost always had to be increased to meet the cost of installing them, and keeping them fuelled and in good repair. For instance, the charges levied by the Runham Drainage Commission between 1890 and 1916 varied between 4 and 8 shillings per acre per year, but had to be raised to 14 shillings per acre (*c.* £44 /ha at 1990 prices) between 1917 and 1920 to pay for the auxiliary engine installed in 1916 (Runham DC minutes).

Internal combustion engines were supplanted by electric motors from the late 1930s onwards; for example, all seven of the pumping stations constructed by the Lower Bure, Halvergate Fleet and Acle Marshes IDB during the 1940s were electrically powered (see Table 9a). Axial-flow pumps were commonly employed, but at several sites, including Strumpshaw, Limpenhoe and Horsey, it was arranged that the existing centrifugal pumps would be left in place, and be belt-driven by electric motors, instead of by steam or diesel engines as in the past.

The use of electrically-powered machinery produced an immediate saving in fuel delivery costs, particularly in the case of the more remote pumping stations which had previously had to be supplied by boat. But it was still necessary for an attendant to be on hand to start up the motor, 'take it through the phases' and shut it down when the water level in the dyke system had been lowered sufficiently, and it was not until the introduction in the late 1950s of automatic starting equipment and switch gear controlled by water levels in the adjoining main drain, that pumps could be left untended for days at a time. Even now, periodic visits have to be made by an attendant to check over and grease the machinery, and clear the screens which prevent the pump-intakes becoming choked by floating weed and other debris.

Increased tidal action, and the progressive rise in the mean water level in the rivers have made it necessary to install pumps in many of the marsh levels which previously relied on gravitation; however, gravity systems survive in a few upriver sites, such as Geldeston and Whitlingham. The Seven Mile Level continued to be drained by diesel-powered pumps until the spring of 1985, and similar machinery was used near Barnby during the winter of 1985/6 following a breakdown of the electric pumps. But although diesel engines have now been supplanted virtually everywhere, it is still possible at some sites to see relics of the different types of machinery formerly used to drain a marsh level. At Upton, for example, there is a tower mill, dated 1800, which has been converted to a residence, the remains of a boiler used in connection with a steam engine, and a large single-cylinder diesel engine, dating from *c.* 1935, which is currently awaiting restoration. The 'turbine' driven by this engine is still in place, but the Level is now drained by twin submersible pumps installed by the Middle Bure IDB in *c.* 1973.

Land ownership and tenure

As in William Marshall's time, the ownership of much of the Drained Marshland Area is very fragmented. This is especially true of the Halvergate triangle where many of the holdings consist of small blocks of marsh owned by trustees of poor's land, executors of owners now deceased, or corporate bodies. Some of the land is glebe, whilst much of the remainder is owned by persons living 20 miles or more away. In contrast, the majority of the land further up-valley is in the form of quite large holdings, and is often owned or managed by dairy farmers, or by individuals who own substantial blocks of arable land on the higher ground bordering the valleys.

A survey by Rendel, Palmer and Tritton (RPT) showed that in 1976 there were 389 rateable farmholdings of more than 10 ha in a study area of 18 367 ha. The total number of ownerships of less than 10 ha was not determined, but was thought to have been in excess of 300; RPT estimated that they together accounted for 14 per cent of the marshland. The number of farm holdings of more than 10 ha in the study area, and the proportion of the total hectarage they represented (see Table 8e) varied greatly in

Table 8e   The numbers and size of marsh holdings in the Drained Marshland Area

10–20 ha		21–40 ha		41–120 ha		121 ha & over		Total ha	Total no. of farm holdings
Area	*No. of farm holdings*	*Area*	*No. of farm holdings*	*Area*	*No. of farm holdings*	*Area*	*No. of farm holdings*		
2110	152	3037	103	7487	108	5733	26	18 367	389
11%	39%	17%	26%	41%	28%	31%	7%	100%	100%

Notes: 1.   The 18 367 ha study area to which these figures relate does not include the whole of the Drained Marshland Area.

2.   The number of holdings will have declined since 1976 owing to amalgamations prompted by the desire to convert marshland to arable.

3.   The number of operational units (371) in the study area was slightly less than the number of rateable farm holdings (389) since an operational unit can fall into two internal drainage districts and thus be rated by each.

Source: Rendel, Palmer & Tritton (1977).

different drainage districts. The Lower Yare Fourth, for example, only had four, whereas there were 75 in the Lower Bure, Halvergate Fleet and Acle Marshes drainage district. There were a further 103 holdings of less than 10 ha within the latter, but together these accounted for only 7 per cent of the district's total area.

Registrations in the Broads Grazing Marshes Conservation Scheme (see page 482) provide a further insight into the pattern of land ownership and tenure in the Drained Marshland Area (see Table 8f), although it needs to be borne in mind that the statistics given are incomplete, as subsidy was not paid on some of the marshland covered by this experimental project.

The large number of marsh holdings can be attributed partly to the way the land was parcelled out when it ceased to be subject to communal grazing rights, and partly to the custom of dividing up an estate amongst the relatives of its deceased owner; any marshland was traditionally handed on to the daughters, in order to provide them with an income, whilst the sons inherited any arable land. But the pattern of ownership in the region has significantly altered since the mid-1960s as an indirect consequence of the MAFF-sponsored drive to improve the productivity of farm land and, more recently, Britain's entry into the Common Market. Both factors have made it more profitable to put marshland down to arable than continue to graze stock on it, and the owners of many small blocks of grass pasture have sold out to those wishing to enlarge their own holdings and put them under the plough. This trend has been specially apparent in areas subject to comprehensive drainage improvement schemes (see Chapter 9).

The livestock used on the marshes

Although drovers continued to bring in cattle from Scotland throughout the eighteenth and early nineteenth centuries, local graziers became increasingly disenchanted with the high prices they were expected to pay, and started to use more home-bred stock; the trade with Scotland was also affected by several serious outbreaks of rinderpest. But it was the arrival of the railways which sealed the fate of long-distance droving (Bonser, 1970). Rail-side markets were soon established at NorthWalsham, Stalham, Acle, Beccles and Yarmouth, and increasing numbers of beasts started to arrive and leave the region in cattle-trucks, instead of on the hoof. Cattle from Ireland also became more popular. Mosby (1938) notes that Irish Shorthorns and polled Scotch Angus fared particularly well on the marshes, and that although some beasts were imported from Devon, Cumberland and Wales, these performed relatively poorly. Supplementary food in the form of 'cake' was almost always provided, and those beasts which were not sold

Table 8f   Types of ownership and tenure in the Broads Grazing Marshes Conservation Scheme

	Halvergate/Haddiscoe/ Belton/Fritton/ Limpenhoe*		South Walsham/Upton/ St. Benets Levels* (1986)		Waveney Valley* (1986)	
Areas of grass marsh receiving subsidy	*No. of holdings*	*Ha*	*No. of holdings*	*Ha*	*No. of holdings*	*Ha*
a. New Institutions (e.g. Pension Funds, Insurance Companies etc)	3	230	2	24	—	—
b. Private Trustees	3	453	—	—	—	—
c. Public companies	1	47	—	—	—	—
d. Private limited farming companies	15	500	6	84	5	88
e. Private individuals (i.e. family farms, private landlords etc.)	80	2157	22	428	16	267
Total:	102	3387	30	536	21	355
Other areas of grass marsh eligible for subsidy	n/a	401	n/a	27	n/a	31
Areas of arable and improved grass ineligible for subsidy	n/a	1066	n/a	303	n/a	132
Grand Total:	—	4854	—	866	—	518
Tenure of marshland receiving subsidy						
Owner occupied		1030		164		255
Subject to full agricultural tenancy		166		276		53
Subject to annual grazing lets		2191		96		47
Total		3387		536		355

* The boundaries of these areas are shown on Map 13.1.

Source: Turner & Pritchard (1988).

in the autumn were taken off the marshes and over-wintered in stockyards where they were fed on mangolds and swedes. Shorthorn bullocks imported from Ireland continued to predominate in the 1940s and 1950s, and because of their heavy build 'finished' very well on Broadland's marshes. Their numbers declined during the 1960s, and few arrived after the mid-1970s, the demise of the trade hastened by British Rail's disinterest in continuing to convey cattle to and from the region.

Store cattle of local origin, and therefore consisting mainly of Friesians, have been used by some graziers in place of imported beasts, but these rarely fare so well on the marshes; indeed, Friesian bullocks now tend to perform even more poorly than in the past, owing to the introduction of Holstein genes into the breed by dairy interests (Edrich, pers. comm.).

The declining profits to be made out of raising beef animals [which according to the *Farmers Weekly* (1987) fell by 16 per cent in real terms between 1983 and 1986], was responsible for a 16 per cent reduction in the size of the UK beef herd between 1975 and 1979, and a further fall of 13 per cent between 1980 and 1986. This trend was apparent in Broadland from the 1950s onwards, and resulted in the closure of most of the smaller cattle markets in the region by the early 1960s. Acle, being larger, lasted longer, and 12 700 fat cattle were sold here in 1967. However, the numbers had decreased to *c.* 2400 by 1980, and the last sale was held in April 1982, when 30 head of cattle changed hands (Edrich, pers. comm.) Most beasts are now taken to Norwich market, but even here the numbers involved have fallen very considerably since the late 1970s.

Although Broadland's marshes have traditionally been used for fattening cattle, numerous dairy holdings were established in the region during the agricultural slump of the 1920s and 1930s. Many of these were started by Scottish families since the Caledonian Bank was one of the very few institutions prepared to offer farmers loans for land purchase during this period. These, and other dairy holdings created during the Second

Plate XXXIII   **Marshland in the Halvergate 'triangle' – 1988.**

This photograph, taken near Wickhampton, illustrates many of the scenic features most characteristic of the Drained Marshland Area. These include the distant trees, the livestock, the drainage mill (in the left background), the dyke and its 'ligger' (plank bridge) and, above all, the wide expanse of sky. The marsh on the left will have been cut for hay later, whereas that on the right has been closely grazed by the dairy cattle (whose presence is a clear indication that the photo was taken fairly near the landward margin of the Halvergate marsh complex).

Cowbane – an umbellifer characteristic of dyke margins – can be seen in flower on the left, whilst the mass of algae (probably a species of *Enteromorpha*) in the dyke itself indicates that it is either slightly brackish or, as is more likely in this case, that it has been enriched by nutrients.

Photo: Richard Denyer

World War, tend to be located near the valley margins, as the proximity of the farmstead makes it relatively easy to take the cows to and fro for milking. Several suckler herds were established after the War, and the consequent increase in the number of young female animals, as well as cows being grazed on the marshes, helped to offset the declining numbers of store cattle. On Haddiscoe Island, for instance, bullocks comprised 100 per cent of the stock in pre-war days, 40 per cent in the mid-1950s and only between 5 and 10 per cent in 1982 (Mace, pers. comm.). Unlike bullocks, which are usually fattened in a single season, dairy youngstock are normally put out on the marshes for two summers.

The MAFF's parish statistics do not distinguish between the livestock kept on the marshes, and that on the adjoining higher ground, and they do not therefore provide an altogether reliable indication of the trends in the pattern of livestock production which have occurred in Broadland over the years. However, anecdotal reports suggest that more sheep are now being kept on the marshes than in the 1970s, doubtless because it is proving, at least temporarily, more profitable to raise these animals than cattle. The numbers of ponies, on the other hand, seem to have remained fairly static, the majority being grazed on land near towns and villages.

The management of the grazing marshes

Although parts of the Drained Marshland Area are under arable, about 11 750 ha, or *c.* 63 per cent of the total area, are currently (1989) in grass. Most of this is 'unimproved' in the sense that the land is only ploughed and re-seeded when the sward has become heavily infested with couch grass and other non-nutritive species. In addition, such marshes receive little nitrogen – annual rates of 70 units/acre (87.5 kg/ha) or less being the norm. However, some of the larger, owner-occupied and tenanted dairy holdings have been subject to increasingly intensive forms of management during the past 20 years or so. Herbicides, for example, are now regularly used, and relatively large quantities of nitrogen [200 to 300 units/acre (250 to 375 kg/ha)] are applied to the marshes, so that they can be cut two or three times a year for silage, rather than once for hay, as in the 'unimproved' areas. The stocking density on land which has been 'improved' in this way is usually rather higher than on the latter, and the cattle (and on some holdings, sheep) which are put out to graze are cared for by the farmer's own employees, rather than by marshmen.

Dairy herd owners in Broadland, as elsewhere, suffered a major set-back in 1984 with the introduction of a milk quota system. Although none of them has, as far as is known, been obliged to sell up, or put the whole of their holdings down to arable, the majority have had to reduce the size of their herds, and this in turn has reduced the number of young female animals to be put out to graze on the unimproved as well as the improved marshes.

Most of the 'unimproved' grassland in the region is in the form of medium and small-sized holdings, and is typically grazed at a stocking density of between 0.5 and 1.5 Livestock Units* per acre (see Plate XXXIII). Some of the marshes may be cut for hay, and afterwards grazed, and this form of husbandry has tended to increase since the late 1970s as a consequence of the decline in the amount of livestock in the region, and in particular the reduced number of beef animals. Some marsh owners elect to run their own beasts on their land, while others hire out the grazing rights each year. But the feed on other blocks of marsh is auctioned off each year at 'grass lettings'. These are held each spring, the marsh owner specifying how many and what types of stock may be grazed on his land during the season (1 April to 31 October). Provided he adheres to these conditions, the purchaser of the grass feed may use it in the way he wants. Thus some individuals may run their livestock on the marsh more or less continuously throughout the season, others take a crop of hay off it before grazing the aftermath, whilst the grass feed on other areas ('accommodation marshes') is acquired by dealers

---

* Livestock Units (LU) are commonly used to define grassland stocking rates. In the Broads Environmentally Sensitive Area a dairy cow is equivalent to one LU, whilst other farm animals are given the following rating:

A bull or other bovine animal over two years old . . . . .0.7 LU
A bovine animal from one to two years old . . . . .0.6 LU
A bovine animal less than a year old . . . . .0.4 LU
A ewe including lambs. . . . . .0.15 LU

for cattle which are awaiting re-sale or consignment to the slaughterhouse.

Prior to, and just after the Second World War, the annual grass sales covered a much more extensive area than they do today; nevertheless between 856 and 984 ha were auctioned in this way each year between 1980 and 1985. The mean rentals for grass keep in the Halvergate triangle increased from £126/ha in 1981 to £198/ha in 1984, probably because of the amount of arable conversion taking place in the region, and a consequent increase in the demand for good quality grazing marsh. But prices since then have slumped as a result of the introduction of dairy quotas, and a decline in the profits to be made out of store cattle. Average prices attained at Howlett and Edrich's grass sales at Acle fell from £198/ha in 1984, to £148/ha in 1985, and £100/ha in 1986 and 1988, and declined to £75/ha (range – £47 to £128/ha) for the 647 ha auctioned in 1989 (Edrich, pers. comm.). The average figure attained that year for the 27 lots of 5 ha or less was £28.30/ha, while the 31 lots covering between 5 and 10 ha of marsh fetched, on average, £30.90/ha; lots larger than this averaged £33.73/ha.

The marshland swards on Haddiscoe Island are of better quality than those on most other sites, and this is reflected in the higher prices attained at the annual grass sales. In addition, the owners of this area decided in 1985 to pass onto the graziers 40 per cent of the subsidy they received from the Broads Grazing Marshes Conservation Scheme (see page 482), thus reducing the prices paid by the latter for grass feed that year from about £200/ha to £150/ha. The owners continued this arrangement following Broadland's designation as an Environmentally Sensitive Area.

One of the lessons learned from the Broads Grazing Marshes Conservation Scheme was that the management systems in use in the region are extremely varied; indeed, at least 18 different types of stock-grazing regimes are currently employed (Turner & Pritchard, 1985). The position is further complicated by variations in the way beasts 'do'; beef cattle, for example perform better on firm, clay-based marshes, whereas peaty areas are better suited to heifers. But whatever the type of tenure and management system in use, it is in the owner's interest to maintain his land in good heart, and he will therefore apply lime or phosphate to it as needed, and have the dykes cleaned out periodically. If he intends to run his own animals on the land, he will also carry out any other necessary management works, such as applying nitrogen, and herbicides. However, if the land is to be grazed by another farmer's stock, either under the terms of an annual licence, or because the grass feed has been sold off at auction, it is up to this individual to carry out these tasks. But since he has no security of tenure, he will often do no more than apply a little nitrogen in the spring, in order to obtain an early bite for his cattle, and later in the season, spray the thistles and nettles with MCPA. As a result, such marshes are often in rather poor condition compared with owner-occupied land.

Given the large numbers of animals being grazed on some of the more extensive blocks of marshland (e.g. Halvergate and Haddiscoe Island), and the complex land tenure, it is impracticable for each person owning livestock to manage his beasts himself, and for centuries it has been customary in these areas for this task to be entrusted to marshmen. Each of these individuals is responsible for up to 1000 animals, and receives acreage, or less usually 'headage' payments from the stock-owners for whom he acts. In addition to checking regularly the beasts in his charge, and giving them simple veterinary attention when required, the marshman has to maintain the water in the dyke system of his area of responsibility at the required level. In some places, as on Haddiscoe Island, Oby and, until the commissioning of a new drainage pump at Tunstall, Stracey Arms, this may necessitate opening sluices in the tidal embankments during dry weather in order to top up the dykes. However, care has to be taken to ensure that this is only done when the river water is of negligible salinity, since, if brackish water is used, subsequent evaporation may render the dykes so saline that cattle drinking from them may suffer from salt poisoning. A similar problem can occur in dry years as a result of leakage through the embankments fronting the lower reaches of the rivers. In 1976 and 1991 salinities in dykes in parts of the Halvergate/Haddiscoe area became so high that many graziers were obliged to supply their beasts with drinking water by bowser, or take them off the marsh altogether.

It is essential to maintain an adequate depth of water in the dykes, not only to prevent the beasts straying from one marsh to another, but to ensure that if one of them falls in, it can either get out itself, or be extricated fairly easily. If the freeboard is more than about half a metre, or if the battered margins of the dyke are too steep (an angle of about 1 in 3 is the norm), the animal is more likely to become exhausted and die of exposure.

Most marshmen supplement their incomes by carrying out routine management tasks, such as applying nitrogen or herbicides to the marshes. They may also receive a fee from the IDB for looking after its pumps and sluices. In addition, each man usually owns, or has the use of, two or three marshes on which he can graze his own beasts.

During the winter months, when the cattle and other livestock have been taken off the marshes, some of the marshmen earn a living by reed-cutting. But in most cases, they undertake the maintenance of the marsh owner's dykes. In the past, this involved raking out the mud and decaying waterweeds with a 'crome', and trimming back the marginal vegetation with a scythe or sidecutter. But every few years, the dykes had to be 'bottom-fied'. This involved damming off a short section, baling out the water, and digging out the accumulated sediment to a depth of a metre or more, before removing the dams and re-flooding. The marshmen were also responsible for digging out the foot-drains. These convey surface water from the centre of a marsh to the dykes around its margins, and they are rendered necessary by the fact that each marsh gradually becomes slightly saucer-shaped owing to the repeated deposition on its edges of sediment removed from the dykes around its periphery. The length of foot-drains was measured by the 'marsh score', equivalent to 140 yards (128 m), and a man armed with a turf-cutter (a half-moon shaped knife, mounted on a long handle), and a wooden spade (usually known as a 'hodder') was expected to dig out about two score a day under favourable conditions (Lacey, pers. comm.).

Nowadays, the marshmen use tractor-mounted flails or cutter-bars to trim the dyke-side vegetation whilst the dykes themselves are slubbed out with a 'back-fab', or more usually by contractors using hydraulic excavators.

The natural history of the grazing marshes today

Jackson and Charter (1978), who carried out a botanical survey of some 10 000 ha in the southern part of the Drained Marshland Area, identified five categories of grass and fen vegetation. Of these, "grazing pasture" was by far the most widely distributed, occupying some 60 per cent of their study area. The commonest grasses found in this community are Common Bent-grass (*Agrostis capillaris*), Marsh and Meadow Foxtail (*Alopecurus geniculatus* and *A. pratensis*), Lop-grass (*Bromus hordaceus*), Crested Dog's-tail (*Cynosurus cristatus*), Cock's-foot (*Dactylis glomerata*), Yorkshire Fog, Meadow Barley (*Hordeum seculinum*), Rye-grass (*Lolium perenne*) and Annual Meadow-grass (*Poa annua*), while the commoner dicotyledonous species include Daisy (*Bellis perennis*), Common Mouse-ear Chickweed (*Cerastium fontanum*), Creeping and Spear Thistles (*Cirsium arvense* and *C. vulgare*), Musk Thistle (*Carduus nutans*), Cat's Ear (*Hypochoeris radicata*), Ribwort Plantain (*Plantago lanceolata*), the Meadow, Bulbous and Creeping Buttercups (*Ranunculus acris*, *R. bulbosus* and *R. repens*), Curled Dock (*Rumex crispus*), Ragwort (*Senecio jacobaea*), Hop Trefoil (*Trifolium campestre*), Red and White Clover (*Trifolium pratense* and *T. repens*) and Stinging Nettle.

The second category identified by Jackson and Charter can probably be regarded as a variant of the first community, since it comprises marshes which are cut for hay prior to being grazed. The most typical grasses are Soft Brome, Meadow Barley, Rye Grass and Annual Meadow Grass, whilst Yorkshire Fog is particularly plentiful, and gives the marshes a beautiful purplish sheen when in flower.

Rush-dominated areas were categorized as "*Juncus* marshland". They are usually poorly drained, and may have standing water on them after heavy rain. In addition to grasses, the sward typically includes Lesser Tussock Sedge, False Fox-sedge (*C. otrubae*), Marsh Thistle (*Cirsium palustre*), Meadowsweet, Jointed Rush (*Juncus articulatus*), Sharp-flowered Rush (*J. acutiflorus*), Soft Rush, Hard Rush (*J. inflexus*), Blunt-flowered Rush, Greater Birdsfoot-trefoil (*Lotus uliginosus*), Ragged Robin (*Lychnis flos-cuculi*), Purple Loosestrife, the terrestrial form of Amphibious Bistort, Fleabane (*Pulicaria dysenterica*) and Tufted Vetch (*Vicia cracca*).

Jackson and Charter called their fourth category "species-rich grassland", since it contains a wealth of different grasses, sedges, rushes and herbs. Like the *Juncus* marsh-land, this community was probably of widespread occurrence in the days when the land was drained by windpumps, but it is now represented by small, scattered fragments, usually located on spring-fed peatland near the valley margins (see Plate 23). Although somewhat variable floristically, the sward characteristically consists of a mosaic of different plant associations, usually with patches of short and tall vegetation. The following plants typically occur in this biologically most interesting community: Bog Pimpernel, Quaking Grass (*Briza media*), Sweet Vernal-grass (*Anthoxanthum odoratum*), Carnation-grass, Marsh Thistle, Common Spotted Orchid (*Dactylorhiza fuchsii*), Common Marsh Orchid (*D. praetermissa*), Tufted Hair-grass, Meadow-sweet, Fen Bedstraw (*Galium uliginosum*), Soft rush, Hard Rush, Blunt-flowered Rush, Field Woodrush (*Luzula campestris*), Ragged Robin, Self-heal (*Prunella vulgaris*), Yellow-rattle (*Rhinanthus minor*) and Marsh Ragwort (*Senecio aquaticus*).

Where the ground is permanently wet, Kingcup (*Caltha palustris*), Marsh Pea, Bog-bean, Red-rattle and Lesser Spearwort (*Ranunculus flammula*) occur, whilst the following plants are found occasionally: Meadow Plume Thistle (*Cirsium dissectum*), Saw Sedge, Marsh Helleborine (*Epipactis palustris*), Twayblade (*Listera ovata*), Bog Myrtle, Grass-of-Parnassus, Common Butterwort (*Pinguicula vulgaris*), Primrose (*Primula vulgaris*), Bog-rush, Marsh Valerian, Marsh Fern and the easily overlooked Adder's-tongue.

Jackson and Charter categorized the last of their communities as "fen", and pointed out that it usually occurs in peaty, spring-fed sites where there is standing water. Reed is dominant, and other common species include Marsh Thistle, Great Hairy Willow-herb, Hemp Agrimony, Meadowsweet, Reed-grass, Hop (*Humulus lupulus*), Yellow Iris, Yellow Loosestrife, Reed Canary-grass, Water Betony (*Scrophularia auriculata*), Meadow Rue (*Thalictrum flavum*), Stinging Nettle and Common Valerian (*Valeriana officinalis*).

These areas of 'fen' vegetation are small in size, but appear to have affinities with the *Angelico-Phragmitetum* Association described by Wheeler (1980a). They are now rarely grazed or mown, and most of them therefore show signs of invasion by sallows and young alders.

The grasslands which occur in the northern and eastern parts of the drained marsh-land area have not been looked at in such detail as those in the south. However, the marshes in the Thurne catchment tend to be rather more acidic than in other parts of the region, and the species composition of the sward reflects this; Tormentil (*Potentilla erecta*) for instance, is frequent in the *Juncus* marshland which predominates in the Horsey Level. Species-rich acidiphilous communities, containing plants such as the Heath Spotted Orchid (*Dactylorhiza maculata* ssp. *ericetorum*), and Heath Grass (*Danthonia decumbens*) occur on the peaty soils south of Calthorpe Broad, whilst the high acidity of the marshes south-west of Potter Heigham is demonstrated by the presence of Cross-leaved Heath, Lousewort (*Pedicularis sylvatica*), Round-leaved Sun-dew (*Drosera rotundifolia*), Cotton-grass, and several species of bog-moss (*Sphagnum* spp.).

The exact relationship between soil type and the communities identified by Jackson and Charter has not been investigated, but in general, their 'fens' and 'species-rich grasslands' are associated with peaty soils, whilst the other communities they describe are less diverse floristically, and typically occur on silt, or clay-based soils. Although these are ploughed and re-seeded from time to time, the sward is, according to marsh-men, taken over by what they call 'natural grasses' within ten years or so. But no objective data is available about this process, nor about the way the marsh flora responds to the other forms of management practised in the area, such as periodic applications of lime and herbicide, different stocking densities and dyke water levels, and haying the marshes and grazing the aftermath, rather than running livestock on them throughout the season.

It would seem that the majority of the communities referred to by Jackson and Charter as 'grazing pasture' and 'hay meadows' fall into the *Lolio-Cynosuretum*, as defined in the National Vegetation Classification (Rodwell, 1982). But if these communities have been re-seeded during the past few years, they may still be referrable to one of the different types of *Lolium perenne* leys, as defined in the Classification. Many of the poorly drained communities categorized by Jackson and Charter as '*Juncus* marshland' fall within the *Holco-Juncetum effusi*, but there is much inter-grading between these swards, and those of the *Lolio-Cynosuretum* The latter may develop into the *Holco-Juncetum effusi* if the marsh is regularly over-grazed and poached, or if the drainage system is neglected; conversely, if the drainage is improved, and the land fertilized, this community may revert to the *Lolio-Cynosuretum*. Marshes which are left ungrazed for several years, and which are also subject to nutrient enrichment, usually as a consequence of being periodically flooded by river water, are typically colonized by various coarse species, including Great Hairy Willow-herb, Bellbine (*Calystegia sepium*) and Stinging Nettle; such communities are referrable to the FILIPENDULION, as defined by Wheeler (1980c).

Arable conversion and its effects on the bird life of the marshes

Although most of the Drained Marshland Area has traditionally been used for fattening livestock, some of the more accessible areas have undoubtedly been under the plough in the past. Lubbock (1878) noted in 1847 that oats were being grown on marshes at Buckenham where . . . "seven or eight years back one hundred and twenty-three snipes (*sic*) were killed in one day by the same gun", whilst older residents at Upton can remember the nearby marshes being under arable prior to the First World War. Tile drains have been unearthed from a depth of nearly a metre near Oby, and to the east of the Manor House, Halvergate, and 'ridge and furrow' can sometimes be discerned in the latter area, particularly when snow covers the ground (Lacey, pers. comm.). Mosby (1938) points out that only a few areas near Yarmouth and Horsey were under the plough in the early 1930s, but that . . . "up to about 50 years ago, quite a number of marshes grew mangles [mangolds], wheat and oats".

The relative amounts of marsh under grass and arable at any one time (or in farming parlance, the balance between 'horn and corn'), would, as today, have been governed by economics. If a farmer found that the profits to be made out of raising livestock were declining in relation to those obtainable from growing cereals or root crops, he would have been tempted to put his marshes under the plough, particularly if these were reasonably accessible. Moreover, whilst it has been generally assumed that the standard of drainage in the eighteenth and nineteenth centuries was poor compared with that of today, and that this would have made it too risky for farmers to plough up their marshes, this is not altogether true. Gravity sluices used in conjunction with windpumps would have been quite an effective way of draining the land when the mean water level in the rivers relative to that of the land was significantly lower than it is today. Anecdotal reports suggest that steam-powered pumps, too, were surprisingly efficient. For instance, Bacon (1844) notes that a friend who had been invited to inspect one working near Acle found on arrival that it had stopped, the reason being that . . . "in the course of a few hours it had so entirely drained the tract (of *c*.40 ha) that the ditches were empty". Furthermore, although the embankments were doubtless overtopped now and then during the winter following heavy rainfall and surges, they would have been fairly resistant to damage as they were regularly grazed by cattle, and therefore clothed with a compact, flood-resistant sward. Consequently, breaching of the embankments would only have taken place occasionally, and most floods would have been of limited duration. In addition, the ronds had not yet become subject to serious erosion, and were therefore wider than they are today. Consequently, leakage through and under the embankments at high tide would have been much less than it is today.

In some parts of the region, farmers wishing to convert their marshes to arable would have been able to maintain a freeboard of about 1.25 m in the dykes throughout the year, and in these circumstances, it would have been worthwhile under-draining the land to be cropped. More usually, however, the water-table had to be kept about half a metre below the marsh surface during the summer months in order to avoid interfering with the interests of neighbouring graziers, who, as we have seen earlier, require plenty of water in their ditches to serve as a source of drinking water for their beasts, and prevent the latter straying from one marsh to another. Yields under these conditions were slightly lower than from marshes whose water-table could be permanently lowered, and there was also a risk of surface flooding in the spring, with consequent crop loss. Nevertheless, this was the predominant type of arable marsh in the region until the late 1960s, the pattern of cropped land and grass tending to vary from year to year owing to the fact that many marshes were only cultivated for a few years before being put back to grass.

During the 1950s, a number of farmers, including Mr. R. C. Loades and Mr. P. R.

Riches of Langley, Mr. E. Burroughes at Wheatacre and Mr Charles Wharton (senior) of Filby, demonstrated that excellent crops, particularly of winter wheat, could be grown on silt and clay-based marshes beside the middle and lower reaches of the rivers, provided the water-table could be lowered to about 1.25 m below the surface. This objective was often not easy to achieve in practice, owing to the need to ensure that neighbouring graziers could retain sufficient water in their dykes during the summer months; indeed, it was frequently necessary to buy out these individuals, in order to assemble a holding large enough to make arable conversion worthwhile. Despite these difficulties, more and more land was put under the plough from the late 1960s onwards in response to changing farm economics, and in particular the much larger profits to be made out of growing cereals on the marshes, than fattening livestock on them. Conversion proved especially popular amongst those who had largish arable holdings on the uplands and who therefore already possessed the necessary equipment and expertise.

From the mid-1970s onwards, several factors, including the continuing availability of MAFF grants to improve the productivity of farm land, a further decline in the profitability of raising livestock on the marshes, and the fact that many of the pumps in the Drained Marshland Area were increasingly in need of replacement, combined to prompt many of the larger landowners in the latter to bring pressure to bear on their IDBs to carry out comprehensive drainage improvement schemes (see Chapter 9). These were designed to enable farmers permanently to lower the water-table of their holdings, level, under-drain and plough them, and grow 'improved' grass, wheat or other crops on them. Experience has shown that many of the graziers in areas subject to such improvement schemes are unable to pay the higher drainage rates which result and still make a reasonable living, and they consequently tend to sell their holdings to neighbouring owners who intend to put their land under the plough, and who are anxious to increase their turnover still further. Because of this, the carrying out of a drainage improvement scheme normally leads to a decline in the number of marsh holdings within the area concerned, as well as a reduction in the amount of unimproved grassland.

By the late 1970s, environmentalists were becoming increasingly concerned by the amount of marshland being put under the plough, their apprehensions reinforced by the knowledge that the Yare Basin Flood Control Scheme (see Chapter 10) was at that time being promoted on the basis that it would speed up the process still further. Particular anxiety was felt about the scenic effects of conversion, because to obtain the maximum benefits, it is usually necessary not only to level the land by filling in any relict saltmarsh creeks, hollows and foot-drains, but flatten the slightly raised margins which each marsh possesses as a consequence of the long-continued deposition on it of spoil dredged from the dykes around its periphery. These levelling operations destroy the characteristic uneven, rough-textured and sometimes almost undulatory appearance of the marshland. Moreover, even if it is later put back to grass, it looks flat and featureless compared with unimproved land.

Ornithologists, too, were concerned about the changes taking place in the Drained Marshland Area. Some formerly common breeding species, such as Black-tailed Godwit and Ruff, were known to have been virtually eliminated after the Second World War as a result of improved drainage, but little information was available about the distribution and status of other species in the area, and the extent to which they were being affected by arable conversion. Accordingly, it was arranged that Phil Round of the RSPB would carry out a census of the birds breeding in the middle and lower sections of the Broadland river valleys. His Study Area consisted of 10 225 ha, of which about 1720 ha were under the plough, and his principal objective was to determine the distribution of selected species of waterbirds, to relate these to land-use management, to identify the areas of particular ornithological importance, and assess the effects which the Flood Control Scheme would have on the birdlife of the study area (Round & Campbell, 1979).

The numbers, and overall distribution of the eleven species selected for sampling are listed on the opposite page.

Round demonstrated that Oystercatchers, Lapwing and Redshank displayed in that order an increasing dependence on wet fields, and that Snipe only bred in such situations. Oystercatchers, however, also preferred to nest near rivers, while Redshank, which were mainly concentrated around Breydon Water, the Lower Bure and Haddiscoe Island, showed a marked preference for the river ronds. 3 species, Lapwing,

Species	Numbers	Density per sq km
Mute Swan	49 breeding pairs (BP)	0.6 pairs
Mallard	433 males	4.2 males
Gadwall	11 BP	0.1 pairs
Garganey	3 pairs, plus two singles	–
Shoveler	34 males	0.3 males
Pochard	4 females with broods	–
Oystercatcher	68 BP	0.7 pairs
Lapwing	481 BP	4.7 pairs
Snipe	15 drumming males	0.1 pairs
Redshank	233 BP	2.1 pairs
Yellow Wagtail	457 BP	4.7 pairs

Oystercatcher and Yellow Wagtail, listed in increasing order of preference, selected arable rather than grass marshes. However, Yellow Wagtails, whilst obviously favouring cereal fields to breed in, flew out to feed on adjoining grassland.

The slight preference shown by Lapwings for arable is attributed by Round to their liking for areas of short vegetation or bare ground, both for nesting and feeding. Although Oystercatchers, too, prefer to breed on arable land, their young seem to need to feed on grassland, as do young Lapwing.

After comparing the breeding populations of Lapwing, Snipe, Redshank and Yellow Wagtail found in the Study Area, with those occurring on the Ouse Washes, Nene Washes, Somerset Levels and Pevensey Level, Round predicted that Redshank, and probably Oystercatchers, would decline in numbers if further marshland was ploughed up. Yellow Wagtails, on the other hand, would probably not be unduly affected, provided sufficient areas of grass marshland were left uncultivated.

In 1982 the numbers of breeding pairs of Lapwing, Snipe, Redshank and Oystercatchers in Round's study area were counted again by Murfitt and Weaver (1982). The Oystercatcher population had undergone a marked increase, with several new areas colonized, thus reflecting the national trend towards inland breeding for this species, while the numbers of breeding Lapwing and Snipe had also increased, albeit not significantly. The size of the Redshank population had, in contrast, declined considerably. Murfitt and Weaver point out that although this may have been due in part to the ploughing up of marshland, the 1982 season was exceptionally dry, and therefore an unfavourable one for this species. Overall densities (in pairs per square kilometre) for the 4 species were: Oystercatcher 1.1, Lapwing 5.0, Snipe 0.2, and Redshank 2.0.

A report on the wintering birdlife of the drained marshland area was produced for the RSPB by Dr. L. H. Campbell in 1980. This embodies the results of a survey carried out by J. B. Halliday during January and February that year, an account by John O'Sullivan of the flock of Bean Geese which has for at least 60 years, and probably much longer, overwintered in the Yare valley, and a collation of data from other sources, including the Birds of Estuaries Enquiry, the Norfolk Bird Reports, and local ornithologists, notably P. R. Allard.

It is clear from Campbell's review, and the work of Harrison (1972) and others, that the drained marshes do not attract anything like as many migratory wildfowl as they did in the past. The numbers of Pink-footed and White-fronted Geese, for example, were at a maximum during the Second World War, and in 1946 over 3000 of the former and 2000 of the latter wintered in the area, the Halvergate marsh complex being specially popular. But by 1955/6 only 100 Pink-feet and 500 White-fronts were resident, and today the former is often only present in single figures, while there are seldom more than 150 White-fronts in the entire region.

Geese are notoriously prone to desert one district for another, but Harrison believed that the main reason why Pink-foot and White-front numbers declined so dramatically was improved drainage, and the absence of 'floods' on the marshes. Some confirmation of this is afforded by the large number of wildfowl which are attracted to blocks of marshland which become temporarily flooded, usually because of a pump breakdown. For instance, in 1979 about 4500 Wigeon were attracted to marshes near Berney Arms which had become flooded in this way.

Campbell's survey revealed that two areas of marshland are of particular ornithological importance during the winter months – the Buckenham and Cantley Levels, and the

St. Benet's Level. The former is the area chiefly favoured by Bean Geese, and is also regularly frequented by large numbers of Wigeon, the population of the latter having increased from a running mean of 40 in the early 1960s, to over 5000 since 1983 (Allport, in litt.). In addition, a small flock of White-fronts (peak count – 310 in January 1989) overwinters on the Cantley Level. Campbell found that St. Benet's Level is a major site for Golden Plover (with peak counts of 750 in 1980, and 3100 recorded here and on the Upton Level in October 1976), as well as being a secondary resort of Wigeon and Lapwing (600 and 1000 in 1980 respectively).

In his contribution to Campbell's report, O'Sullivan points out that little is known about the status of Bean Geese in Broadland prior to the 1920s. However, between 200 and 300 frequented the Claxton and Langley Levels during the winters of 1924, 1925 and 1926, and the following year, the quite exceptional total of 5000 was estimated. The species is thought to have over-wintered on the north side of the valley for the first time in 1930, and at least 200 birds were present here in each of the following 10 years, with over 1000 (plus 2000 to 3000 White-fronts) present in 1936/7 (Seago, 1981). The Buckenham area was forsaken by Bean geese in 1940, when some of the marshes were ploughed and re-seeded, and for the next few seasons, they once again frequented the

Table 8g   Maximum numbers of Bean Geese in the Yare Valley – 1963/4 to 1988/9

1963/4	38	1976/7	122
1964/5	25	1977/8	103
1965/6	36	1978/9	141*
1966/7	46	1979/80	155
1967/8	48	1980/1	165
1968/9	40	1981/2	329
1969/70	66	1982/3	197 (175)
1970/1	73	1983/4	238 (198)
1971/2	67	1984/5	372 (297)
1972/3	77	1985/6	340 (274)
1973/4	109	1986/7	310 (284)
1974/5	102	1987/8	420
1975/6	102	1988/9	370

* Excluding a separate flock of *c.* 100 birds which overwintered in the Winterton – Horsey area in 1978/9.

( ) These figures relate to the mean numbers of birds in the flock during December, January and early February (RSPB records).

Sources: 1963/4 to 1974/5 – Campbell, L.H. (ed.), 1980.
1975/6 to 1988/9 – Salmon *et al.* 1975–1990.

Claxton and Langley Levels. Although they returned to the north side of the valley in 1946, O'Sullivan notes that their numbers dropped to the 100 mark during the 1950s. The decline continued in the early 1960s reaching a nadir of 25 in the winter of 1964/5, but the numbers have subsequently gradually increased (see Table 8g), reaching 420 in 1987/8, and a peak of 485 in 1990/91 (Blackburn, pers. comm.).

Between the mid-1940s and the mid-1970s, the geese spent most of each winter on the Buckenham marshes, but since then, they have tended to favour the Cantley area. This can be attributed to a change in farm economics which prompted the owners of the Buckenham Marshes (the East Anglian Real Property Company) to allow sheep to be grazed on them, rather than cattle as in the past. The sheep produce a closely grazed sward unattractive to the geese, and this problem has been exacerbated during the past few years by a spectacular build-up in the number of Wigeon on the Buckenham marshes – a maximum of 10 500 birds being recorded there in the winter of 1985/6, compared with previous peak counts of 4500 in 1976 and 3700 in 1980.

The Yare valley Bean Geese, which belong to the race *fabilis*, are by far the largest concentration of this species in the British Isles, and the only flock regularly overwintering in England. They normally arrive in November, and spend each day feeding on grass marshland, before flighting off in the evening (often after dark) to roost on a nearby broad. They tend to become more restless in February, and often move further down valley to spend part of the time in the Haddiscoe area, prior to departing for their breeding grounds at the end of that month, or early March.

The Buckenham – Cantley area is probably favoured by the Bean Geese on account of the presence, not far distant, of several broads. But more importantly, it is never (Buckenham) or only very occasionally (Cantley) shot. Most marshes elsewhere in Broadland are visited fairly frequently by wildfowlers, and although the bags they obtain are usually quite small (at least one club – the Great Yarmouth and District Wildfowlers Association – have a rule which prohibits its members selling what they shoot), the birds quickly learn where the 'no shooting' areas are. Birds elsewhere also tend to be disturbed by dogs, the use of machines on the marshes and, most of all, by low-flying jets and helicopters.

Recent research by Gary Allport, a PhD student at the University of East Anglia, has thrown further light on the ecological requirements of over-wintering Bean Geese. He has, for example, demonstrated that the birds prefer a relatively tall sward, and that they avoid marshes re-seeded with Rye-grass, because of their inability to digest this species (Allport, 1989). This information is being used by the RSPB to devise, in conjunction with the East Anglian Real Property Company, a strategy whereby the long-term future of Bean Geese in this part of Broadland is safeguarded.

Although the general pattern which emerges from Campbell's work is one of decline, wild swans, as well as Bean geese, show an opposite trend. Bewicks were formerly irregular visitors to the region, but in 1962 a group of 13 spent part of the winter on marshes between Reedham and Haddiscoe (Allard 1973). Since then, their numbers, and the duration of their visits, have increased, and in 1981/2 it was estimated that at least 150 were present in the region, plus birds passing through on the way to and from the Ouse Washes and Slimbridge. The preferred areas are the Halvergate marsh complex (where 118 were seen in March, 1976) Somerton Holmes, Tunstall, Haddiscoe, the St. Benet's Level, the Muckfleet area and the lower Bure marshes (where 268 were recorded in 1977). Whooper swans, too, have been recorded in increasing numbers during the past few years, and in 1981/2 there were at least 55, mainly in the Hickling – Heigham Holmes area.

The natural history of the dyke system

(a) Introduction

Casual observations during the late 1960s showed that many of the aquatic plants and animals which were fast disappearing from the broads and rivers were still present in the dykes of the Drained Marshland Area, and in the early 1970s, the NCC decided to commission an ecological survey of these water bodies, and the ways in which they were affected by varying forms of management. Between 1972 and 1975 the northern part of the area was examined by R. J. Driscoll, (assisted during 1972 by A. J. Lees and in 1973 by A. J. Lees and D. J. Harcombe) whilst the marsh dykes south of the R. Yare and in the Waveney valley were studied by M. J. Jackson and Miss E. Charter during 1978. The latter workers only had a single season in which to cover their 10 000 ha Study Area but despite this, they surveyed about two thirds of the dykes within it. No attempt was made to record the distribution of the rarer water plants or the invertebrates, but they concentrated on giving each dyke visited a conservation rating on a three-point scale – rich, reasonable or poor – according to the diversity of the commoner submerged, floating and emergent plants growing in it (Jackson & Charter, 1978).

The dykes of the northern part of the Drained Marshland Area have been examined in much greater detail than those of the south. From the data collected between 1972 and 1974, Driscoll prepared distribution maps for over 350 species of aquatic plants and animals, based on 11 413 plant records and 10 135 animal records collected during visits to 892 sites (Driscoll, 1976). During the ensuing years Driscoll continued and greatly extended the scope of his surveys. Many sites were visited on several occasions so that the effects of cattle grazing, haying, conversion to arable, slubbing out and other forms of management on the ecology of marsh dykes could be assessed (Driscoll, 1981a & 1983a). Whenever possible, Driscoll has presented his data in the form of maps, showing, for example, the number of species per dyke, the quality of the aquatic flora and fauna in different areas, and the amount of dyke-infilling which took place when a block of marshland was converted to arable (Driscoll, 1981b, 1981c, 1981d & 1982). In addition, much subsidiary information was obtained, for instance about the physical dimensions of the dykes examined, and their turbidity, pH and water chemistry (e.g. Driscoll, 1984a). Driscoll has also produced evidence that the dyke flora found in the vicinity of Oby and Thurne in the 1970s was very similar to that recorded 80 years previously, and has concluded from this that the management of the dykes of this area, and probably much of the remainder of the region, hardly altered during this period (Driscoll, 1984b).

Driscoll demonstrated that the variations which occur in the diversity and species composition of dykes are primarily due to differences in the way they, and the adjoining marshes, are managed. In particular, ditches bordered by unimproved pasture normally contain a much greater wealth of plant and animal life than those associated with marshes which have been converted to arable, with a permanently lowered water-table. The mean number of waterweeds in 352 grazing marsh dykes sampled in 1974 was 14.3 (range 1 to 32), whereas the comparable figure for 77 arable marsh dykes examined between 1972 and 1974 was 8.4 (range 1 to 25) (Driscoll, 1985b). But Driscoll found that water quality is also an important factor. For instance, dykes which are slightly brackish as a result of leakage through the embankments or, as in the Hickling/Horsey/Somerton area because of the proximity of the North Sea, contain very different communities from those fed by fresh water. Another important point to emerge from Driscoll's work was that the rarer species of plants and invertebrates are invariably found in dykes having a diverse aquatic flora. Although much of the data on which these conclusions are based is unpublished, Driscoll (1983b) has produced a useful account of where this, and other land-use surveys carried out in the region during the past 50 years, can be inspected by those interested.

In the face of the continuing drive to improve the agricultural productivity of the marshes, and following discussions with the NFU and local IDBs, the Broads Authority decided in 1980 to commission further research on the flora and water chemistry of the dykes in its Executive Area. The study, which was part-funded by the NFU, was carried out by C. Doarks at the Centre for East Anglian Studies of the UEA, and in its early stages involved sending out questionnaires to a large number of marsh owners and occupiers asking whether they would agree to their dykes being examined by an ecologist. Following a preliminary investigation (Doarks, 1980), 280 sample dykes wre randomly selected for more detailed study, the principal objectives being, first, to examine the extent to which the dyke flora is affected by the chemistry of the water and by different management practices, and second, to determine what measures can be taken to enhance the ecological condition of a dyke so that it provides a habitat suitable for diverse aquatic communities (Doarks, 1984).

(b) The dykes of grazed marshland

Despite the introduction of mechanical methods of dyke management in place of the manual techniques used in the past (George, 1977), the dyke system of those parts of the Drained Marshland Area still under grass is remarkably diverse ecologically (see Plate 24). Driscoll (1983c), who used a TWINSPAN (TWo-way INdicator SPecies ANalysis) computer programme to analyse the data he collected from 426 dykes in the Bure and Yare valleys in 1974, recognizes eight vegetation classes:

Group A Occurs in moderately species-rich, freshwater dykes. Water-Plantain (*Alisma plantago-aquatica*), Broad-leaved Pondweed and Branched Bur-reed (*Sparganium erectum*) are particularly common, whilst a few species, notably Floating Scirpus (*Eleogiton fluitans*), and to a lesser extent Water Violet and Greater Bladderwort, are virtually restricted to dykes of this group.

Group B This is rather more species rich than Group A. It contains most of the same species, with the addition of Frogbit, Arrow-head, Water Soldier, Flowering Rush, Flat-stalked Pondweed, Tubular Water-Dropwort (*Oenanthe fistulosa*) and the duckweeds, *Lemna minor* and *L. trisulca*.

Group C This is moderately species rich, but many of the species typical of Groups A and B, e.g. Bur-reed, Water Soldier, and Water Plantain are absent. Hornwort and Reed-grass are more frequent in this group than any other.

Group D Although floristically similar to Group C, many of the species are less frequent. Filamentous algae and *Enteromorpha* sp. are commoner in this group than any other. The community often occurs in dykes fed with river water seeping through the tidal embankments.

Group E Commonly occurs in brackish dykes but is floristically impoverished and lacks
the typical brackish water species which occur in Groups F & G.

Group F This typically occurs in brackish dykes and usually consists of between 6 and
10 species. Fennel-leaved Pondweed, Spiked Water-milfoil, Sea Club-rush,
Lemna trisulca and *Enteromorpha* sp. are the commonest components.

Group G This community, which occurs in brackish dykes, is similar to Group F but
contains fewer species.

Group H This occurrs in a single, very saline dyke beside Breydon Water. *Ruppia* sp.
predominates, with smaller amounts of Sea Aster and Annual Seablite.

The status of the different groups was as follows:

	A	B	C	D	E	F	G	H
No. of spp.	80	100	88	75	41	24	22	3
No. of dykes	32	149	89	74	32	17	30	1
Mean no. of spp. per dyke.	13.2	18.7	15.2	12.3	6.1	8.4	4.7	3
Range	2–24	7–33	3–32	2–23	1–14	4–11	2–8	–

In many cases, the communities identified by Driscoll reflect the ecological requirements of their component species. For instance, plants such as Water Soldier, Bur-reed
and the horse tails, *Equisetum fluviatile* and *E. palustre* are intolerant of salt, and are
therefore absent from dykes which are slightly brackish as a consequence of leakage
through the tidal embankments, or because of the presence in them of saline springs.
Fennel-leaved Pondweed is often abundant in such dykes, but where the conditions are
more extreme, *Enteromorpha* sp. and filamentous algae tend to predominate. Driscoll
considered that this is probably due, not so much to the high salinity which can develop
as a result of evaporation during dry sunny weather, but to the fluctuations in salinity to
which such dykes are subject at different times of the year.

Driscoll's principal findings were confirmed by Doarks (1984), who used statistical
techniques to demonstrate that the floristic diversity of dykes was greatest where the
chloride ion concentration of the water was less than 1000 milligrams per litre (mg l^{-1}),
and that the flora was markedly less diverse in dykes containing between 1000 and 3200
mg Cl^{-1} l^{-1}. Above this figure, the flora was very impoverished, and consisted of brackish
water species only. Other factors shown by Doarks to be conducive to the development
of a diverse aquatic flora were an alkalinity value of less than 4 milliequivalents per litre,
and a pH value in the range of 6.5 to 8.5 throughout the year. Both Driscoll and Doarks
noted that dykes subject to nutrient enrichment as a consequence of the discharge into
them of treated sewage effluent, septic tank overflows or slurry from livestock units (see
Plate 25), were ecologically impoverished, and Doarks found that diverse plant communities would only develop if the soluble reactive phosphorus concentration was low, and
if the water contained nitrate nitrogen and ammonium ion levels of less than 7 mg l^{-1}
and 1.5 mg l^{-1} respectively.

Some of the dykes of the Drained Marshland Area are not only ecologically diverse,
but very rich floristically and faunistically. Of the 187 different species of water-loving
plants recorded by Driscoll, Doarks and others since the early 1970s, 108 can be
classified as submerged, floating-leaved or emergent; together these represent 57 per
cent of the British species included in these categories.

Eleven of the 108 species occur in fewer than 100 of the 3500 ten by ten kilometre
squares of the national grid, and thus satisfy the criteria laid down to denote nationally
rare and uncommon species (see Table 8h).

In common with many other wetland plants (Palmer & Newbold, 1983), the Sharp-
leaved and Hair-like Pondweeds (*Potamogeton acutifolius* and *P. trichoides*) have become
much rarer nationally during the past 30 to 40 years. The former was recorded from 28
ten-kilometre squares during the compilation of the *Atlas of the British Flora* (Perring &
Walters, 1982), but according to the Biological Records Centre had been reduced to
eight squares by 1982. As a result it will have to be listed in a future edition of the Red
Data Book on vascular plants. *P. trichoides* has undergone a similar decline: from 70
squares in 1962, to 20 in 1982.

Two of the other species listed in the Table are of importance in a national context.

Table 8h   Nationally rare and uncommon waterweeds found in Broadland's Drained Marshland Area

Species	No. of 10 km squares	Present distribution in Broadland
Spineless Hornwort (*Caratophyllum submersum*)	38	A mesotrophic species restricted to dykes on peaty soils
Whorled Water-milfoil (*Myriophyllum verticillatum*)	93	Widely distributed
Water Parsnip (*Sium latifolium*)	97	Mainly restricted to base-rich dykes in the middle Bure valley, but also occurs east of Wickhampton
Fine-leaved Water-Dropwort (*Oenanthe fluviatilis*)	79	Common in dykes in the Upton Level; occasional elsewhere
Floating Water-Plantain (*Luronium natans*)	27	Restricted to base-poor dykes near Potter Heigham
Water Soldier (*Stratiotes aloides*)	21	Widespread in dykes with good quality water
Fen Pondweed (*Potamogeton coloratus*)	44	Mainly restricted to base-rich dykes near Upton, but found near Horsey in 1982
Flat-stalked Pondweed (*P. friesii*)	89	Widely distributed, particularly in dykes on peat
Hair-like Pondweed (*P. trichoides*)	20	Very local; in mesotrophic dykes on peat
Grass-wrack Pondweed (*P. compressus*)	45	Restricted to base-rich dykes on the Upton and South Walsham Levels
Sharp-leaved Pondweed (*P. acutifolius*)	8	Local; mainly in the Yare valley. Formerly quite common in the Limpenhoe Level; successfully introduced into dykes on the Strumpshaw reserve in 1982.

Sources: Perring & Walters (1962); Perring & Farrell (1983); Driscoll (pers. comm.).

The Floating Water-Plantain (*Luronium natans*) is characteristic of nutrient-poor waters in the north and west of the country, and has at Potter Heigham its most easterly locality in Britain, whilst the other specially noteworthy plant is Water Soldier. Broadland has long formed the principal stronghold of this species in Britain, and although it is now confined to one broad (Calthorpe), and to fen dykes which have been carefully managed, it is still abundant in parts of the Drained Marshland Area. It is a species of exceptional natural history interest, not least because only female plants occur in this country; it can thus only propagate itself vegetatively. In addition, it has the ability to sink to the bottom of a dyke (or broad) during the winter months (a facility which may help prevent its foliage being damaged by hard frosts) and then rise to the surface in the spring so that the tips of its leaves are thrust clear of the water. The means by which it achieves these vertical movements are not wholly understood, but at least two hypotheses have been advanced:

(a) the oxygen produced by vigorous photosynthesis in the spring is stored in the aerenchymatous tissue of the leaves and stem, thus increasing the buoyancy of the plant. Photosynthetic activity decreases in the autumn, and the reduced amounts of oxygen stored in the plant's tissues allows it to sink to the bottom. A variant of this hypothesis is that starch, as well as oxygen, is stored within the leaves, and that this alters the specific gravity of the plant.

(b) that marl is deposited on the outermost leaves of the plant during the summer months as a result of its vigorous photosynthetic activity in the calcium-rich water commonly found in Broadland. This ultimately causes the plant to sink, but in the spring, the outer leaves are shed, so reducing the specific gravity of the plant and allowing it to float to the surface.

The offsets of *Stratiotes* are thought to be short-lived, and this, together with the plant's inability to reproduce by seed in this country, renders it vulnerable to intensive forms of dyke management, and changes in water quality, even if only of a temporary nature. Nevertheless, experimental re-introductions at Woodbastwick, Cockshoot Dyke and elsewhere have shown that it is capable of proliferating very rapidly if the habitat conditions are right.

The flora of 'good' grazing marsh dykes is probably at least as diverse as that of the broads when they were still in their heyday; indeed, three submerged species found in dykes, Alternate-flowered Water-milfoil (*Myriophyllum alterniflorum*), Sharp-leaved Pondweed ((*Potamogeton acutifolius*) and Opposite-leaved Pondweed (*Groenlandia densa*), have never been recorded from a broad. Of more importance from the conservation point of view is the fact that several floating and submerged species which have not been recorded from the broads for 15 years or more still occur in grazing marsh dykes, thus confirming their value as a 'refuge' for species temporarily lost from the main water bodies in the region (see Table 8j).

The emergent vegetation of grazing marsh dykes is also much more diverse than that of the broads, including as it does uncommon species such as Water Parsnip, the Water-Dropworts *Oenanthe lachenalii* and *O. fluviatilis*, and Lesser Water-Plantain which have never been reported from the broads. Against this must be set the fact that 6 waterweeds, namely the Pondweeds *Potamogeton praelongus* and *P. alpinus*, Holly-Leaved Naiad, White Water-lily, Pillwort (*Pilularia globulifera*) and Shore-weed (*Littorella uniflora*) occur, or formerly occurred, in the broads, but have never been recorded from the Drained Marshland Area.

It has long been realized that the invertebrate fauna of the grazing marsh dyke system is of outstanding interest, and ample confirmation of this has been provided by Driscoll, who found up to 40 different invertebrates in some of the dykes he examined. All told, he has recorded over 200 different species of invertebrates since 1972, including 9 flatworms, 30 molluscs, 9 leeches, 28 water bugs and 10 crustaceans (excluding cladocerans and copepods). Much of this data is, as yet, unpublished, but he has produced a report on the distribution of the 65 different species of water beetle he has found in the area; these include the Great Silver Water Beetle (*Hydrophilus piceus*) (Driscoll, 1978).

The dykes form a refuge for many rarities. For instance, the Shiny Ramshorn (*Segmentina nitida*) occurred in 77 ten-kilometre squares in Britain prior to 1950, but since then it has only been recorded from 11, all but 4 of which are in Broadland (Kerney, 1976). Similarly, in 1979 Dr. A. G. Irwin recorded *Hydrellia stratiotae*, a leaf-mining ephydrid fly new to Britain, on Water Soldier plants growing in a dyke at Share Marsh,

Table 8j **Floating and submerged waterweeds still found in grazing marsh dykes, but not recorded from any broad for 15 years or more**

Species	Broad where last seen	Period
Water Fern (*Azolla filiculoides*)	Ranworth Inner	1965–1969
Water Crowfoot (*Ranunculus aquatilis*)	Martham South	1970–1974
Spineless Hornwort (*Ceratophyllum submersum*)	Wheatfen	1940–1944
Frogbit (*Hydrocharis morsus-ranae*)	Upton & Martham South	1970–1974
Water Soldier (*Stratiotes aloides*)	Ormesby & Calthorpe	1970–1974
Broad-leaved Pondweed (*Potamogeton natans*)	Upton & Calthorpe	1970–1974
Bog Pondweed (*P. polygonifolius*)	Upton	1970–1974
Fen Pondweed (*P. coloratus*)	Hickling	1900–1904
Perfoliate Pondweed (*P. perfoliatus*)	Hickling & Horsey Mere	1945–1949
Flat-stalked Pondweed (*P. friesii*)	Upton & Calthorpe	1970–1974
Grassy Pondweed (*P. obtusifolius*)	Calthorpe	1970–1974
Hair-like Pondweed (*P. trichoides*)	Sutton	1945–1949
Grass-wrack Pondweed (*P. compressus*)	Sutton	1945–1949
Gibbous Duckweed (*Lemna gibba*)	Wheatfen	1930–1934

Source: Jackson (1981)

west of Oulton, whilst *H. grisea*, another species not previously found in Britain, has been recorded by Irwin from the Upton Level.

More striking in appearance is the Norfolk Aeshna (*Aeshna isosceles*), a hawker dragonfly which does not occur anywhere else in Britain, and which, as a Red Data Book 'endangered' species, is afforded special protection under the *Wildlife and Countryside Act*. In 1974 and 1975, a team of entomologists recorded this insect from 6 localities, four of them in the Drained Marshland Area (Ismay & Wright, 1975), and in 1983, it was seen on the wing at a further 3 sites within the latter (Driscoll, 1984c). Since then it has been observed on both the Woodbastwick and the Strumpshaw reserves. In contrast, larvae have so far only been recorded from two localities, despite a very thorough search (Merritt, 1985). The insect usually takes to the wing in mid-June, a little earlier than *A. grandis* the only species with which it could possibly be confused, but it seldom strays far from the dykes in which the females lay their eggs, and where the larvae grow and metamorphose*.

As a result of his studies between 1972 and 1984, Driscoll has shown that the greater the number of different plants present in a dyke, the more diverse is its aquatic fauna. This positive correlation was also observed at Strumpshaw by Willis (1980), who noted that the loss of floristic diversity which occurs when dykes are left untended for a prolonged period is accompanied by a decrease both in the number of invertebrate species present, and their population sizes. The diversity of the fauna also declines owing to a reduction in the abundance of the rarer and more sensitive species, and a corresponding increase in the population size of a few relatively tolerant species. Conversely, the wider range of different water plants present in a fairly recently dredged dyke, and the greater depth of water therein, makes it capable of supporting a larger, and more varied, population of invertebrates.

These results are of considerable importance to conservationists, since they suggest that management prescriptions conducive to the establishment of a varied growth of waterweeds in a grazing marsh dyke, will be equally beneficial to its invertebrate fauna.

Driscoll demonstrated that when dykes containing good quality water are slubbed out, they are quickly re-colonized by plants which have fortuitously survived the treatment, or which have regenerated from seeds, turions or other vegetative propagules in the residual sediment. But if the cleaning-out process has been more than usually thorough, or if a new drain has been created, colonization will have to take place from the adjoining dykes, and will thus take longer. A recently slubbed-out dyke usually possesses only a limited range of plants. Moreover, different groups of plants tend to appear in adjoining sections of the same dyke owing to the haphazard manner in which propagules are left behind during the slubbing out process. Although the flora becomes increasingly diverse in succeeding years, the chance circumstances which led to the initial re-colonization of the dyke continue to be reflected in the wide range of different associations found within a short distance of one another. Maximum floristic diversity is attained after about four years, and at this stage, the dyke will possess a wide variety of submerged and floating-leaved species. Numerous emergent species, resistant to periodic grazing by cattle, will have invaded the shallow water at the edges of the dyke, whilst the gently sloping margins of the latter, often trampled by the animals into a stepped formation, will have been invaded by a host of moisture-loving plants. Species specially characteristic of the poached margins of grazing marsh ditches include the Water Forget-me-nots *Myosotis scorpioides* and *S. laxa* spp. *caespitosa* and Celery-leaved Crowfoot (*Ranunculus scleratus*).

The dyke is normally slubbed out after about five years, and although this has a catastrophic effect on the aquatic fauna and flora at the time, this form of management is ultimately beneficial ecologically, since dykes which are neglected become biologically impoverished as a result of the increasing abundance of the more aggressive submerged and emergent species. As time goes on, the dyke also becomes shallower as a consequence of the accumulation in it of organic debris from the breakdown of the plants, and silt from its cattle-grazed margins, and this too reduces its natural history interest.

---

* There is some evidence that this species is not only extending its range in Broadland, but is becoming more numerous in its known localities. No fewer than 76 specimens were observed on the wing by Stewart Linsell during a 2 day survey of a 73 ha block of grazing marsh in the Thurne valley in July 1991.

Plate 17

Plate 18

Fen Orchids in flower in the Ant valley – 1975.

The fenland form of this species (as distinct from var. *ovata*, which is found in dune slacks in South Wales) used to occur in several parts of East Anglia, notably in the valley fens of the Norfolk–Suffolk border. However, it is now confined to Broadland, its other localities having been rendered unsuitable for it, usually as a consequence of a lowering of the water-table, and the subsequent overgrowth of the site by trees and bushes. Even in its two remaining strongholds in Broadland, both of which are located in the Ant valley, the species is considered to be under threat, and it certainly deserves the special protection afforded it under the *Wildlife and Countryside Act* 1981. Its precarious status was recognized internationally in 1991 when, with 8 other flowering plants which are rare in Britain, it was added to Annexe 1 of the Berne Convention. Under this, the government of each Council of Europe member state is committed to safeguarding, not only the species listed, but the sites where they occur.

The Fen Orchid is a very inconspicuous plant, and in some years, few flowering spikes are produced. It usually occurs in moss-rich communities, such as those shown in the photograph, but is sometimes found growing on the small tussocks produced by the sedge, *Carex appropinquata*.

Photo: D.M. Turner Ettlinger

Alder woodland south of Hoveton Great Broad – 1973.

When cut down, an alder produces numerous shoots from the stump, and trees which have been felled on one or more occasions, usually as a source of coppice material for turnery, or for firewood, are therefore multiple stemmed. In contrast, it is occasionally possible to find examples of alder woodland which have never been felled, usually because of the difficulties inherent in extracting the felled timber. In this event, the trees are single stemmed or 'maidens'.

This example of maiden alder woodland – one of the best in the region – was photographed from the walkway laid out by the Nature Conservancy through the fens bordering Hoveton Great Broad in 1968. Most of the trees are only about 10 m tall, and the canopy is fairly open. As a result, the ground flora is very well developed.

Photo: Martin George

Plate 19

Swallowtail butterfly – 1989.

This superb insect is now confined to Broadland, repeated attempts to re-introduce it to Wicken Fen (Cambridgeshire) – its *locus classicus* – having failed. The fens around the upper Thurne broads form its principal stronghold but, contrary to what is sometimes stated, it is widely distributed in the region. Although the species is not under any great threat, it is afforded special protection under the *Wildlife and Countryside Act* 1981, and cannot therefore be collected, except under licence.

The flowers of Ragged Robin, on which this particular insect was photographed, form an important source of nectar for the adult butterfly. Its larval food plant is Milk Parsley, itself a species which is far commoner in Broadland than anywhere else in Britain.

Photo: John Buxton

Plate 20

A Bittern in snow – 1987.

For reasons not fully understood, the number of Bitterns breeding in Broadland has declined greatly since the 1950s, and there are now often only 4 or 5 'boomers' in the whole region. Habitat degradation, increased predation by foxes (a species which has become much more numerous in Broadland during the past 20 to 30 years) and a succession of hard winters have all been advanced as possible explanations, and each is likely to have played a part.

Bitterns, like Water Rails and Kingfishers, are much affected by hard weather, and are more likely to be seen hunting for food under such conditions, than at other times of the year. If the hard spell is prolonged, they tend to leave the region in a bid to find more congenial surroundings.

Photo: John Buxton

Clayrack Mill, How Hill – 1990.   Plate 21

This mill was discovered in a derelict condition at Ranworth in the late 1970s, and was reconstructed by the Norfolk Windmills Trust on a site at How Hill in 1987/8. It is unique in the region in that it can actually be used to drain the land – in this case, the grazing marshes within the Broads Authority's How Hill estate.

The only other hollow-post mill in Broadland is located near Upton Dyke, having been moved there from its original site near Acle, prior to restoration. It differs from Clayrack Mill in that it is fitted with a plunger pump, instead of a scoop wheel.

Photo: Simon George

Plate 22

Strumpshaw Mill – 1962.

Apart from Black Mill, beside the R. Waveney opposite the Somerleyton Marshes, this is the only former steam-powered mill in the region with a complete chimney stack. There was a steam engine and boiler here until the end of the Second World War but, sadly, these were then removed. The original centrifugal pump is still in regular use, though this is now driven by an electric motor.

Black Mill still houses a rusting boiler, and other steam age relics can be seen here and there, for instance at Upton. But unlike the Fens, no steam engine has been preserved *in situ*, and in order to see the sort of machinery formerly used to drain Broadland's marshes, it is necessary to visit the museums at Strumpshaw and Flegg; these are run respectively by Wesley Key and Bob Morse.

Photo: Martin George

Plate 23

Species-rich grazing marshland at Strumpshaw – 1990.

The vast majority of Broadland's grazing marshes have been improved agriculturally over the past 40 to 50 years, and even the region's peat-based marshland, which always tends to possess a more diverse flora than marshland underlain by mineral soils, has been impoverished floristically. Fortunately, there are a few exceptions to this, and of these, the marshes within the RSPB's reserve at Strumpshaw, are of particular importance on account of the wide range of plants still found here, and the comparatively large size of the area concerned.

Each year, the Society's staff mow a path across the site (seen here in the foreground), so that visitors can appreciate just how rich and varied the plant life of such peat-based marshland can be.

Photo: Martin George

Plate 24
Plate 25

A grazing marsh dyke on the Ludham Marshes National Nature Reserve – 1990.

The dykes of grazing marshland are of immense nature conservation importance, as they harbour many of the aquatic plants and animals which used to occur in the rivers and broads, but which have been lost as a consequence of nutrient enrichment and other problems. Note that the dyke water level is only about 50 cm below that of the marsh surface, and that the margins of the dyke have a very gently sloping 'batter'. This has allowed cattle to trample and close-graze the dyke edges, thus preventing them being colonized by Reed and other tall, shade-casting species. This in turn ensures that Water Soldier (seen here in the foreground) and other waterweeds can continue to thrive in the dyke.

Photo: Martin George

Slurry from a livestock unit in a dyke near Runham – 1980.

Even quite small quantities of cattle or pig slurry have a disastrous effect on the aquatic plant and animal life of a dyke or river, and, sadly, this is a very widespread problem in Broadland and, indeed, in other parts of the country. Remedial action is, from the farmer's point of view, often difficult, as well as very expensive, since the amounts of liquid and solid wastes produced by even quite a small livestock unit, are very large indeed. Fortunately, the rate of grant available from the Ministry of Agriculture for slurry disposal facilities was increased in 1989, and alleviative measures have now been taken at some of the most glaring trouble spots in the region, including the one illustrated. Nervertheless, the National Rivers Authority will have to exercise continued vigilance throughout the region if the improvements brought about during the past few years are to be maintained and extended.

Photo: Martin George

Plate 26

Grass marshland in the Halvergate 'triangle', just west of Great Yarmouth – 1977.

Ponies kept on the marsh on the left have kept the dyke margin on this side closely grazed, whereas the marsh on the right has been kept for hay. As a result, the right-hand dyke margin has been left ungrazed, thus allowing a luxuriant stand of Reed to develop. Although this would probably have been checked, had livestock been put out on this marsh to graze the aftermath, the right-hand side of the dyke would have been fairly heavily shaded until early August, when the photograph was taken. If a tall stand of Reed had been able to develop on both sides of the dyke, the water therein would have been much more shaded, and the adverse effects on the aquatic plant and animal life would have been correspondingly greater.

Photo: Robert Driscoll

Plate 27   **A dyke in arable marshland in the Upton Level – 1980.**

Note the dyke's steep 'batter', and the fact that it has a freeboard of about one and a half metres, instead of the *c.* 50 cm typical of a grazing marsh ditch. The water in the dyke is also far shallower, being only a few centimetres deep for much of the year. The small protruding pipes are the ends of field drains. Were it not for the fact that the dyke edges in this Level are regularly 'swiped', they would, in the absence of grazing, quickly become overgrown with Reed and other rank vegetation.

The dykes in the arable parts of the Upton Level contain quite a good range of waterweeds, on account of the large flow of good quality water through the system. But most arable marsh dykes are floristically impoverished, because of the deep shade cast by the vegetation growing on their margins and the limited depth of the water therein. It is also suspected, though not yet proved, that many arable marsh dykes are contaminated by farm chemicals washed out of the adjoining land.

Photo: Robert Driscoll

Plate 28

(A)

(B)

Dyke infilling in the Halvergate 'triangle' at Scaregap, just west of Great Yarmouth – 1979-1982.

Dyke infilling was commonplace when arable marsh conversion was at its height in the late 1970s and early 1980s. But although conservationists could appreciate that farmers found it very difficult to use combine harvesters and other large machines on the pocket handkerchief-sized marshes typical of the Drained Marshland Area, they nonetheless deplored the trend, on account of the gross losses of wildlife habitat which resulted.

Photograph (A) was taken in October 1979, (B) in September 1980, (C) in September 1981 and (D) in August 1982. Note how quickly Reed colonized the margins of the dyke as soon as grazing ceased.

Photos: Robert Driscoll

(C)

(D)

Plate 29

The new pumping station at Stokesby under construction – 1980.

The twin Archimedes screw pumps installed in this pump-house by the Muckfleet and South Flegg Internal Drainage Board are capable of raising *c.* 80 tonnes of water per minute through a vertical height of 5 m. They drain some 773 ha of marshland and, when commissioned in 1980, replaced four obsolete drainage pumps. The new station is normally operated at 'off-peak' times, in order to save on electricity costs.

When, after heavy rain, both screws are turning, a substantial current is generated in the main drain leading to the pump-house, and extra piling had to be installed to prevent the banks slumping into the channel.

Photo: Martin George

Plate 30 **Deposits of ochre in a dyke near East Somerton – 1983.**

The bright orange deposits of ochre which are produced when calcium-deficient acid sulphate soils are deep-drained are extremely unsightly. In addition, when such water is discharged into the main rivers, these in turn become discoloured. Horsey Mere, a site owned by the National Trust, is particularly badly affected, as a result of the large quantities of ochre finding their way into it via Waxham Cut.

The dyke in the photograph cuts through blown sands associated with the nearby Horsey–Winterton dune system. Its margins are, in consequence, very unstable, particularly when a freeboard of a metre or more has to be maintained in it to enable cereals to be grown on the marsh on the right.

Photo: Robert Driscoll

The margins of dykes beside marshes regularly mown for hay are not grazed until mid-summer at the earliest, and therefore tend to be colonized by coarse, emergent species such as Reed and the Greater and Lesser Pond-sedges, *Carex riparia* and *C. acutiformis* (see Plate 26). These suppress the more delicate plants found on dyke edges which are cattle-grazed throughout much of the season. Moreover, many of the submerged and floating-leaved species in the ditch tend to perform poorly in the shade cast by the rank growth of marginal vegetation, and may succumb altogether if the dyke is bordered on both sides by such communities.

Until about 25 years ago, most dykes were slubbed out in an irregular sequence, and this meant that examples could be found at any one time of all stages of the succession within a given marsh level. This made it unlikely that any particular plant or animal would be totally eliminated, save perhaps for those few species, such as *Luronium natans*, which are confined to only one or two isolated dykes. Unfortunately, the widespread tendency to use hydraulic excavators, instead of the relatively inefficient dydles or tractor-drawn scoops employed previously, means that newly slubbed out dykes contain fewer residual organisms than in the past; in consequence, re-colonization is slower. Moreover, farmers and IDBs now often find it cheaper to have a large number of dykes cleaned out by a contractor in a single operation, rather than have the work carried out on a piecemeal basis, as a marshman would have done in the past. This is more likely to result in rarities being lost; it also tends to produce a less biologically diverse dyke system than existed in the past.

Important as the management regime is in regard to the natural history of dykes in the Drained Marshland Area, observations by Clive Doarks, NCC staff and others have shown that the flora of grazing marsh ditches has been subject to changes over the past 15 years or so which cannot readily be ascribed to this factor. In view of this, and Broadland's importance in a national context, Clive was employed by the NCC to carry out a further dyke survey in 1988 and 1989. It was decided at the outset to confine this study to grazing marsh dykes (unlike Rob Driscoll's surveys, which had encompassed ditches adjoined by arable as well as grass marshland), and in the event, the aquatic flora of 2834 dykes was sampled.

The results obtained during the first year of the project (1988) were used by Clive's colleagues in the NCC's Chief Scientist's Division to develop three TWINSPAN classifications. The first of these embodied the data collected on the status of the emergent vegetation, as well as the aquatic species, while the other two classifications dealt with these groups of plants separately. The results were written up in time for use during the 1989 field season (Reid, Newlands & Leach, 1989), and the information collected that year was then used to refine the classifications. These were subsequently published (Doarks & Leach, 1990), and supersede the preliminary TWINSPAN scheme developed by Driscoll (1983c). The remaining data collected during the course of the survey [Doarks & Storer, (1990) and Doarks *et al* (1990)] do, as far as possible, relate the communities present in the region's grazing marsh dyke system to those recognized in the National Vegetation Classification currently being developed on behalf of the NCC by Dr John Rodwell of the University of Lancaster.

The most important aspect of the 1989/90 survey for the conservationist was that 321 of the dykes examined by Doarks had been sampled by Driscoll between 1972 and 1974, thus enabling direct, 'then and now' comparisons to be drawn. The results of this exercise are fully described by Doarks (1990) and it will suffice here to indicate that there have been major declines in the status of the mesotrophic*, species-rich communities which form such a special feature of the dyke system of Broadland's Drained Marshland Area. These are characterized by the presence of species such as Broad-leaved Pondweed, Water Soldier, Water Violet, Whorled Water-milfoil and Hornwort. In contrast, eutrophic and brackish-water communities, many of which contain a preponderance of filamentous algae and *Enteromorpha*, rather than flowering plants, have become more widespread. In addition, there has been an increase in the number of dykes in which a mixture of Floating Club-rush and Broad-leaved Pondweed occurs; Doarks thinks that this may be related to the more widespread occurrence of acid sulphate soils.

---

* A rather unsatisfactory term which can be broadly defined as a type of community containing a moderate quantity of nutritive salts.

The decline in the status of Broadland's mesotrophic dyke communities (which roughly coincide with Groups A and B in the TWINSPAN classification developed by Driscoll) is highly regrettable, since they contain many rare plant species. In addition, they do, as already indicated, support a much more diverse invertebrate fauna than other dyke communities.

In the 'Discussion' section of his report, Doarks accepts that some dykes have probably been impoverished as a consequence of the unsympathetic way they have been managed over the past 15 to 20 years. But he produces evidence that this is certainly not the sole reason for the observed changes. For instance, he was able to demonstrate that the dykes within the Ludham Marshes National Nature Reserve are not so rich floristically as they were in the 1970s, this despite the strenuous efforts made by the NCC since it purchased the site in 1983 to manage them in a way best suited to the maintenance and enhancement of their ecological interest. In the circumstances, Doarks puts forward a number of alternative explanations. One of these concerns the fact, substantiated by chemical evidence, that there has been an increase in the amount of brackish water leaking through the tidal embankments at high tide. Doarks was able to show that this has certainly affected some dykes. But ditch communities in a degraded condition are not always close to river banks; indeed, in some cases they are situated near the upland margins of a marsh.

Another possible explanation discussed by Doarks concerns the pollution of the dykes by nitrogenous fertilizers, and perhaps other chemicals. These could either have been washed off the adjoining marshlands, some of which could be under arable, or be finding their way into the dykes in the form of upland run-off. In the absence of firm evidence, no definite conclusion can be drawn, but Doarks makes the cogent point that if the present decline continues, the dyke vegetation in the region will gradually degrade into a monotonous collection of species-poor and brackish-water communities. Further research is obviously called for, and this needs to be linked with a carefully thought out dyke-monitoring programme.

(c) The effects of arable conversion on the fauna and flora of dykes

Although modern methods of dyke management have undoubtedly impoverished the aquatic plant and animal life of Broadland's grass marshland, arable conversion poses a much greater threat. Many marshes are too small or awkwardly-shaped to be worked conveniently by modern farm machinery, and in these circumstances, some of the dykes have to be filled in. Most farmers are content with a field size of between 5 and 15 ha, but amalgamations larger than this are not unusual. For example, during the course of an improvement scheme on the Somerton Level, marshes of 23 and 26 ha were formed by filling in 18 and 17 ditches respectively – the total length of dyke in this 746 ha Level declining from 51.22 km in 1973 to 34.06 km in 1981 (Driscoll, 1983d) (Fig. 8A).

The owner of Peto's Marsh (which comprises some 68.5 ha to the west of Oulton Dyke) took 'improvement' in the 1970s to even more extreme lengths, by infilling the entire internal ditch system (which extended to *c.* 6.8 km), and replacing this with *c.* 1.2 km of new drains.

Where, as at most sites, some at least of the dykes are retained, these are usually widened and deepened to provide additional storage capacity, thus reducing the risk of water backing up the underdrains, or, worse still, flooding the marsh surface. A freeboard of between 1.75 and 1.5 is maintained in most arable dykes throughout the year, and they will seldom have more than about 20 cm of water in them, whereas that in a typical grazing marsh dyke will be twice or even three times as deep as this during the summer months. To minimize land 'take', arable dykes are normally given a batter of 1 in 1.5 or even 1 in 1 and are therefore much steeper-sided than the ditches in grazing pasture.

The infilling of dykes obviously reduces the amount of aquatic and water's-edge habitat available in the region for plants and animals. In addition, the steeply battered sides of the ditches which are retained are, in the absence of grazing, quickly colonized by Reed, Great Hairy Willow-herb, False Oat-grass, Stinging Nettle and other coarse species. These suppress the less robust species which typically occur beside grazing marsh dykes. They also cast such a dense shade that waterweeds, already under pressure as a result of having to grow in water which for much of the year is very shallow, succumb. This in turn impoverishes the invertebrate fauna of the dykes.

Although the main drains associated with ploughed-up marshland are, like the smaller dykes, colonized along their edges by Reed and other tall-growing plants, they are so wide that the water in them is not affected by shade to the same extent. However, unless they are regularly flushed by good quality water from the adjoining uplands, they do not support anything like such a rich and varied plant and animal life as do grazing-marsh dykes. Instead, they often contain a large standing crop of phytoplankton, or dense masses of *Enteromorpha*, *Cladophora* and other green algae.

The authors of the Environmental Impact Analysis published by the Broads Authority in 1980 point out that such changes can probably be attributed, at least in part, to the effects of nutrient enrichment, since experience elsewhere has shown that the losses of nitrate nitrogen from arable land are often up to five times as great as from land under grass even when both are receiving similar applications of fertilizer (Cooke, 1976). In support of this claim, they note that nitrogen levels are consistently higher in the water discharged by the Brograve pumps, the catchment of which is largely under the plough, than in the water from the Horsey pump, which drains a level in which unimproved grass marshland still predominates (see Table 8k). At both sites, maximum phosphorus levels occur in the summer when water flows are at their lowest, suggesting that phosphorus is released from the sediment in the dykes during the summer months.

Further evidence that the dykes, and therefore the rivers and broads, receive larger quantities of nutrients when the marshland adjoining them is put under the plough is

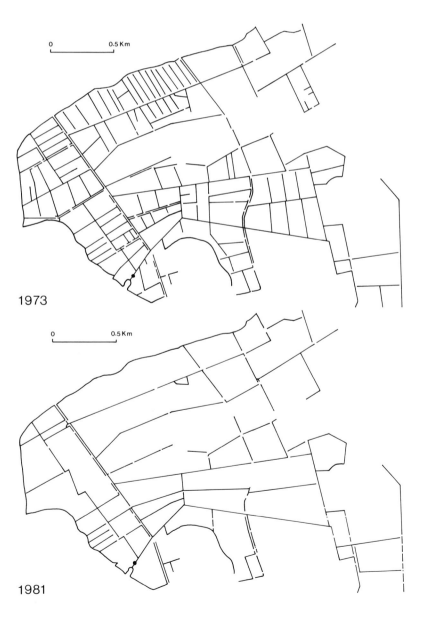

0   0.5 Km

1973

0   0.5 Km

1981

Fig. 8A

The dyke system of sub-area 1 of the Happisburgh to Winterton Internal Drainage District in 1973 and 1981.

Source: Driscoll (1983d)

273

Table 8k Comparison between the nitrogen and phosphorus contents of water pumped from two Broadland catchments. Nov 1974 – Oct 1976

mg l⁻¹	Brograve Mill (pump draining 75% arable and 25% grass) range	Horsey Mill (pump draining 25% arable and 75% grass) range
NO_3–N	0.2 – 9.86	0 – 3.64
NH_4–N	0.89 – 8.95	0 – 0.933
Total P	0.015 – 0.173	0.038 – 0.224
Mean N	5.67	1.82
Mean P	0.05	0.06

Source: Data supplied by R. Watson of the Norwich Division of AWA, and included within the Environmental Impact Assessment (ERM Ltd. & TE Ltd., 1980).

provided by Schudel and Moss (in prep.) who demonstrated that between March and August 1982, the groundwater of marshes under wheat in the Claxton Level of the Yare valley, contained much more nitrate nitrogen and soluble reactive phosphorus, than that of adjoining land still under grass (Figs. 8B & C). By comparing the nitrogen and phosphorus concentrations in the ground water, the rooting zone and the dykes surrounding the marshes, they calculated that the mean rates of loss of nitrate nitrogen from grass and arable marshes during this period were 2.35 and 3.53 kg N ha⁻¹ respectively, and that the corresponding figures for soluble reactive phosphorus were 0.02 and 0.1 kg P ha⁻¹.

Instead of using flails and other machines to control the growth of dyke-edge vegetation, some arable marsh farmers employ Round-up and other total weedkillers, and Doarks (1984) presents evidence that dykes managed in this way tend to have a very

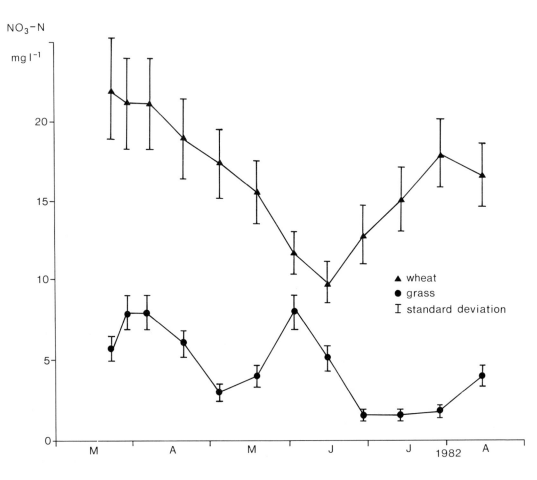

Fig. 8B

Mean nitrate nitrogen concentrations in the groundwater of marshes under wheat and grass in the Yare Valley at Claxton.

Source: Schudel and Moss (in prep.)

impoverished aquatic flora. Herbicides and pesticides are also applied freely to marshes under arable cultivation, and although Doarks was unable to draw any firm conclusions, anecdotal reports suggest that dykes adjoining such land may be affected as a result of accidental drift during spraying operations, and possibly also as a consequence of receiving leached residues from the under-drainage system.

The effects of arable conversion on the dyke flora and fauna are complicated in acid sulphate soil areas (see page 20) owing to the presence of ochre in the water. In addition, dykes near the coast are liable to become increasingly saline when the water-table is lowered. Driscoll (1985b) notes that in 1974 the mean chloride ion concentration of dykes in the Somerton Level was 1380 mg l^{-1} (range 120 to 2050), but had risen

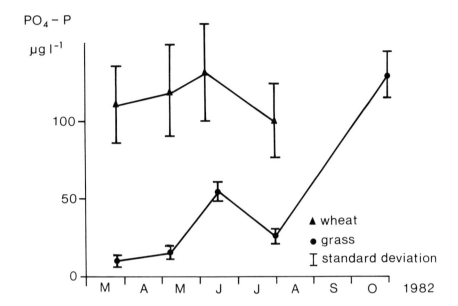

Fig. 8c

Mean soluble reactive phosphorus concentrations in the groundwater of marshes under wheat and grass in the Yare Valley at Claxton.

Source: Schudel and Moss (in prep.)

to 1830 mg l^{-1} in 1983 following the conversion by the Burnley Hall Estate of most of this Level to arable between 1979 and 1981. He attributes this to the lowering of the water level in the dykes, and a consequent increase in the amount of infiltration from the saline water-table which underlies this part of Broadland (Goldsworthy, 1972).

The floristic changes which can occur on such occasions have been described by Driscoll (1983a & 1985b), who in 1973 surveyed the dykes of the Horsey (646 ha) and Somerton (746 ha) Levels, both of which at that time consisted of poorly drained land used mainly for grazing and the production of hay. 25 species of waterweeds and bryophytes were recorded from 70 sample sites on the Horsey Level, and 46 species from the Somerton area (64 sample sites), the mean number of species recorded from each dyke being 4 at Horsey (range 1 to 11), and 8 at Somerton (range 2 to 20).

When the two Levels were re-surveyed in 1981, Driscoll found that the management of the marshes at Horsey had not been significantly altered, 33 species of water weeds and bryophytes being recorded from 26 sample sites; moreover, the mean number of species per dyke in this Level had risen to 8 (range 1 to 15). In contrast, many of the dykes in the Somerton Level in 1973 had been widened and deepened in connection with the drainage improvement scheme mentioned above. Although 41 species were found in the 33 dykes sampled, most of the plants were much less abundant than in 1973; indeed, only 5 species were recorded in more than 10 dykes, and the mean number of species per dyke had dropped to 6 (range 1 to 20). Many of the plants recorded in 1973, for example the Water Milfoils, *Myriophyllum spicatum* and *M. verticillatum*, Canadian Pondweed and Water Star-wort (*Callitriche* sp.) were much less common than they had been; conversely, some species, notably the Pondweeds *Potamogeton pusillus*, *P. crispus* and *Zannichellia palustris*, had become much more abundant.

The changes in the aquatic fauna which followed the conversion of most of the

Somerton Level to arable have been catalogued by Driscoll (1986). The dykes here were already fairly impoverished faunistically owing to their brackish character. But although some invertebrate groups, notably the water bugs and beetles were hardly affected by arable conversion, all the flatworms (5 species) and leeches (2 species), and some of the molluscs recorded in 1973 disappeared. Quantitative changes also occurred. The mean number of species recorded per dyke in 1973 was 9.1 (range 3 to 22, n = 33) and this fell to 4.9 (range 0 to 18, n = 33) in 1981; the following year the mean number of species per dyke increased to 6.9 (range 0 to 17, n = 33). Driscoll attributes these changes partly to the sensitivity of some invertebrates to variations in salinity, and partly to the changes in the dyke flora which occurred as a consequence of arable conversion.

(d) Conservation implications

The studies embarked upon in the early 1970s quickly showed that dykes adjoining marshes under the plough are ecologically impoverished compared with grazing marsh ditches. However, subsequent work by Driscoll, Doarks and others demonstrated that, as with other generalizations, the situation is much more complex than was first apparent. Many grazing-marsh dykes are slightly brackish and consequently contain relatively few species, whilst conversely, arable marsh dykes which are regularly flushed with good quality water sometimes support a rich assemblage of waterweeds. Doarks (1980) pointed out that such dykes are most often to be met with near the valley margins, the very place where the soils are likely to be peaty and therefore unsuitable for conversion to arable, and this is important, since it demonstrates that it is in the best interests of both farming and conservation that valley-edge marshes, and certainly those on peat, should be kept under grass with a high water-table during the summer months. But although this finding was publicized in a Technical Note compiled by MAFF in April 1981, this did not, as conservationists would have wished, go as far as to urge farmers to leave such marshes unimproved, but merely drew attention to the problems they might encounter if they did convert them.

Doarks also found that although dykes near the valley margins tend to receive good quality water from the adjoining higher ground, the ecological benefits which would normally accrue from this are all too often marked by the discharge into them of phosphorus - rich slurry from nearby livestock units. He concluded that . . ."In ecologically promising dykes, the removal of such nutrient sources would allow the resuscitation of the original floral variety in a relatively short time".

In his second (1984) Report, Doarks made a number of other recommendations as to how the adverse effects of arable conversion could be mitigated. Before work commences, each dyke should be dredged to remove emergent species, and thus facilitate its colonization by aquatic plants. Even more importantly, the water in the dykes should be at least 40 cm deep throughout the summer. The batter of the dyke edges should not be greater than 45° in order to prevent the aquatic flora and fauna being heavily shaded by emergent species, and Doarks also suggested that once the latter had become established, their growth should be controlled during the summer months by a weed-wiper, rather than by cutting or the use of herbicides. However, it is doubtful whether this last recommendation is altogether practicable, since few farmers will wish to carry out any dyke maintenance until after they have harvested the crop on the adjoining marshland, by which time, Reed and other emergent species will have grown up sufficiently to be casting a dense shade over the dyke bottom. This reservation aside, few farmers who have put their marshland under the plough appear to have implemented any of Doarks' other suggestions. Given the importance of the Drained Marshland Area as a refuge for wildlife, and in particular for those aquatic plants and animals which have been lost from the broads and rivers, it is fortunate indeed from the conservation point of view that for the reasons set out in Chapters 9 and 13 the rate of conversion slowed down during 1984 and 1985, and has now ceased.

Chapter 9
Drainage Improvement Schemes

Introduction

The long-running controversy concerning the future of the Drained Marshland Area, which made 'Halvergate' a household name in the early 1980s, was symptomatic of fundamental differences in the outlook of farmers and conservationists. The latter could point to the fact that most comparable areas elsewhere in Britain had already been put under the plough, that grass marsh is one of the most characteristic features of the Broadland landscape (see page 1) and that, as explained in the previous Chapter, the dyke system of much of the area is of exceptional importance since it forms a refuge for most of the aquatic plants and invertebrates which formerly occurred in the broads and rivers. In contrast, farmers claimed, not unreasonably, that they were finding it increasingly difficult to make a living out of running cattle on the marshes, that the latter had been shown to be capable of producing very good crops when put under the plough, and that it was in the national interest that this potential should be more fully exploited.

To a large extent, this latter attitude reflected the economic milieu in which farmers had had to operate, which in turn was influenced by the vigorous, and highly successful measures taken by the MAFF since the Second World War to improve the productivity of farm land. The provision of government grants to achieve this (a development foreshadowed in the *Marketing Acts* of 1931 and 1933) was specifically allowed for in the *Agriculture Act* 1947. This was based on the premise of self-sufficiency in temperate foodstuffs, a requirement reiterated in several subsequent policy statements, notably in 'Food from our own Resources' (MAFF, 1975), and 'Farming and the Nation' (MAFF, 1979). Improved farm management techniques, including the employment of herbicides and pesticides, and greater fertilizer usage (according to the Fertilizer Manufacturers' Association the consumption of nitrogen rose from *c.* 210 000 tonnes in 1949/50 to *c.* 1.58 million tonnes in 1985 — DoE, 1986) led to increased productivity, whilst the yields of cereals were dramatically enhanced as a result of the introduction of new strains developed by plant breeders. The average yield of wheat is about 3.4 tonnes per hectare greater now than it was in 1948 (Murphy, 1984), and it rose from 3.9 tonnes per hectare in 1963, to 6.4 tonnes per hectare in 1983 (Government Statistical Service, 1985). These increases in productivity were also stimulated by Britain's entry into the Common Market in 1974, since its interventionalist policies gave farmers a guaranteed market for their produce (Bowers & Cheshire, 1983). Cereal production in the United Kingdom rose from about 15 million tonnes per year in 1972/3 and 1973/4 to *c.* 21 million tonnes per year in 1982/3 and 1983/4, whilst the production of wheat doubled from *c.* 5 million to *c.* 10 million tonnes per year during this period (Thompson, 1986).

Another effect of the Common Agricultural Policy was to widen the difference between the profits to be made out of growing cereals, and raising beef cattle. As a result, the number of such animals in England fell from *c.* 800 000 in 1975 to *c.* 507 500 in 1986, a trend reflected in what Murphy (1984) has termed a "remorseless decline" in the number of bullocks in the eastern counties; indeed the total number of cattle in this area fell by 12 per cent between 1979 and 1982. This decline was accelerated by the introduction in April 1984 of a quota system for dairying, since this forced many farmers in Broadland (as elsewhere) to reduce the size of their herds, so decreasing the number of young female animals to be put out on the marshes. As a consequence of these various factors, the owners of grassland in the region were increasingly tempted, and in some cases forced out of economic necessity, to put it under the plough during the 1970s and early 1980s, or sell it to neighbours who had already converted their marshes to arable, and who were anxious to increase the size of their holdings.

Good field drainage is essential if arable crops are to be grown successfully on marshland, and the farm improvement grants available from the MAFF provided farmers with a further incentive to plough up their holdings. Replacing a series of measures dating back to 1940 (Bingham, 1983), the Farm Capital Grant Scheme (FCGS) came into effect in 1971, and was followed three years later by the Farm and Horticulture Development Scheme (FHDS), which was drawn up in response to an EEC Directive (72/1599) on farm modernization. Following a Rayner review of the Agricultural Development and Advisory Service of MAFF, the two schemes were replaced in 1980 by the Agriculture and Horticulture Grant and Development Schemes respectively (AHGS and AHDS), and at the same time the eligibility condition that farmers had to obtain the Ministry's prior approval for planned expenditure was abolished, save for Sites of Special Scientific Interest (SSSIs) and National Parks. The AGHS and AHDS gave way to the Agriculture Improvement Scheme (AIS) in October 1985, but instead of running to 1994, as originally planned, this was closed in November 1988, and the Government announced that from February 1989, it would be replaced by a new Farm and Conservation Grants Scheme. Under this, finance for drainage is available for replacement works only. Moreover, it places increased emphasis on a number of 'green' measures likely to have beneficial effects in Broadland, notably the availability of grants of up to 50 per cent for projects designed to prevent dykes and rivers being polluted by farm wastes, such as silage liquor and slurry from intensive livestock units. This is a very welcome development, given the substantial damage which pollutants of the latter type can cause to the aquatic fauna and flora of grazing marsh dykes (see Plate 25)

Rates of grant for field drainage – 1970 to 1988

FCGS (1971 – 1980)	AHGS (1980 – 1985)	FHDS (1974 – 1980)	AHDS (1980 – 1985)	AIS (1985 – 1988)
50%	37.5% 1980 – 1983 30% 1983 15% 1984 – 1985	60%	50% 1980 – 1984 32.5% 1984 – 1985	15%

The high rates of drainage grant available during the 1970s undoubtedly served as a stimulus for marsh conversion, and although they were progressively reduced from 1980 onwards, the profits to be made out of growing cereals, relative to those obtainable from using the marshes for grazing, continued to increase for a time; indeed, by 1983, the differential was so large that some farmers would have been tempted to plough up their marshland even if no drainage grants were available. However, this situation did not last for long, and by 1986 a combination of lowered profits from cereal growing, a very significant reduction in the rate of grant available for field drainage, and the introduction of subsidies for remaining in grass (see page 482) had brought arable conversion to a halt in the region.

In addition to being able to take direct advantage of the system of grants and subsidies operated by MAFF and the EEC, farmers wishing to improve the productivity of their marsh holdings during the 1970s and early 1980s benefited indirectly from the financial support available to IDBs. These bodies were able to apply for the grants available from the EEC's Agricultural Fund (FEOGA) during this period for installing new pumps, reorganizing their arterial drainage systems, and carrying out other improvements. Under the *Land Drainage Act* 1976, such works are also grant-aidable by MAFF, provided the latter is satisfied that the IDB's proposals are sound economically and technically. But a board has to borrow the remaining funds it needs from the Public Works Loan Board, as it is not allowed, under the Land Drainage Acts, to put aside moneys towards the cost of replacement pumps and other equipment. Consequently an IDB which carries out a major improvement scheme invariably has to increase its drainage charges, sometimes by as much as 300 per cent or more. Experience in Broadland during the 1970s showed that it was difficult, if not impossible, for the owners of small marsh holdings (many of whom let out their grass feed at auction each year) to pay charges as high as this, and still make a profit, and thus the system under which IDBs have to operate increased the likelihood that grass marshland would be sold and put under the plough during this period. Fortunately from the environmental point of view, the rate of grant available to IDBs was reduced in March 1984 from 50 per cent to 45 per cent, and to 32 per cent the following year, and from April 1986 onwards has been 26 per cent. As a result, very few major arterial drainage improvement schemes have been embarked upon in the region since 1984.

A typical IDB improvement scheme during the 1970s and early 1980s involved the replacement of one or more obsolescent pumps, the construction of a new pumping station, the laying out of a concrete access road and power supply to the latter, the rationalization of the arterial drainage system (which often necessitated the amalgamation of adjoining marsh levels), and the deepening of the main drains so as to provide a freeboard of at least 1.25 m throughout the area covered by the scheme. This allowed the water in the dyke system to be maintained at a level below that of the outfalls of the under-drains which farmers normally install before putting their marshland under the plough, thus ensuring that these are not blocked by sediment backed up from the dyke into which they discharge. The main drains were also widened so that large volumes of run-off could be stored temporarily in them. This reduces the risk of flooding after prolonged periods of heavy rain, or as a result of over-topping of the tidal embankments during a surge, and also enables the IDB to operate its pumps at times when cheap-rate electricity is available. The pumps themselves are capable of running for long periods between maintenance overhauls. They are typically able to raise water through a greater vertical distance than the ones they replaced, and have a larger output. This was a necessary precaution, given the poor condition of the embankments, and the fact that the thinner these become as a consequence of boat wash and other forms of erosion, the more water leaks through and under them during high tides and surges. Archimedes screw pumps were installed at two sites in the 1970s, but submersible pumps, such as those manufactured by Flygt Ltd., were the preferred choice in later schemes, because of their greater efficiency.

In most drainage districts, the existing pumps were 30 years or more old, and therefore unreliable, and expensive to maintain. This, plus the inadequate size of the arterial drains, provided those members of an IDB who wished to put their marshland under the plough with a strong incentive to persuade the remainder of the Board to agree to a comprehensive improvement scheme being carried out. Such individuals, who often owned an arable holding on the adjacent upland, and who could therefore convert their marshes without the need to invest in a lot of new machinery and equipment, were usually in a good position to bring the necessary pressure to bear, given the fact that many of the owners of small marsh holdings were disinclined to seek election as members of IDBs; indeed, in some cases, they owned so little land that they were not eligible for membership. A decision to proceed with an improvement scheme could be taken on a majority vote, but in fairness, an IDB would always try to ensure that those of its ratepayers who, despite the poor returns obtainable, wished to continue to raise livestock on their marshes, could do so. Experience showed that this objective could often be achieved by establishing a 'split-level' system. This involves the provision of dams and overspill sluices to enable the water in the dykes of the areas to be left under grass to be maintained at a high level during the summer months, whilst the water-table of the land to be put under the plough is kept a metre or so lower (see Plate 27). At some places, for example in the Upton and Oby Levels, high-level water has to be piped across low-level drains in order to top up the grazing marsh dykes on the far side. In most places, it was the clay and silty marshland nearest the river which was ploughed up during the 1970s and early 1980s, and the areas nearest the valley margins, which are often peaty, or liable to acidify when drained, which were left under grass.

A particularly good example of a split-level system was designed and put into effect on the Upton marshes by Mr Nicholas Crane in 1977. This made it possible for his firm to under-drain, and thus improve the productivity of just over 100 ha without interfering with the management of the remainder of the Level, which has been retained by its owners and occupiers as unimproved grassland. The water required to top up the dykes of the latter during the summer months emanates from the fens around Upton Broad, which in turn are spring fed from the adjoining uplands. However, elsewhere, for example in the Oby Level, and the Halvergate Marsh complex, the necessary water is drawn from the river. In such cases, care has to be taken to ensure that the sluices are not opened when the river water has been rendered brackish as a consequence of a surge.

In the past, the poor accessibility of much of the Drained Marshland Area formed a major deterrent to those wishing to improve its productivity. The track leading from Wickhampton to Berney Arms, for example, is impassable even to a Land Rover for much of the winter. An all-weather access road is essential if an arable holding is to be worked successfully, but the fragmented ownership of the land, and the fact that stock are taken off the marshes during the winter months (thus obviating the need for the grazier to have access to them), often makes it difficult to obtain contributions towards the cost of such a road, even if the necessary permissions are forthcoming. Despite these problems, the accessibility of the area was gradually improved from 1970 onwards. In some cases, this resulted from private initiatives; for example, the track across the Upton Level was concreted by one of the principal landowners in the area in 1980. But in levels whose arterial drainage system was being modernized by the IDB with the help of a grant from the MAFF, a farmer was often able to enhance the accessibility of his holding by adding a spur to the all-weather road which the Board was, at the Department's insistence, obliged to provide for the new pumping station. The access and water level control problems which had to be surmounted by a farmer before he could convert his grass marshes to arable were offset by the relative ease with which he could level them, fill in unwanted ditches and install an under-drainage system (see Plate 28). Hydraulic excavators, in particular, though now taken for granted, can perform tasks which even thirty years ago would have been deemed prohibitively time-consuming and costly. Under-drainage, too, is now usually done with machines capable of laying corrugated PVC piping in at least 6 ha of marsh per day, a laser being used to ensure that this is installed at the requisite gradient (usually between 1 and 6 mm per metre run). Zijlstra and Van Someren (1980) note that three men are able to lay 2000 m of piping per day with such a machine, whereas in the past between 46 and 60 man days would have been required to hand-lay the same length of 'tiles' (clay pipes).

The Muckfleet and South Flegg Internal Drainage District

Two of the earliest, and most striking examples of comprehensive improvement schemes in Broadland were carried out by the Muckfleet and South Flegg IDB during the late 1970s (Stern, 1980). The first necessitated the amalgamation of the Mautby and Caister Levels, and the installation of a pair of Archimedes screw-type pumps at Mautby (see Map 9.1). Unlike the axial-flow pumps commonly used in the region in the 1940s and 1950s, these auger-like machines work just as efficiently when water levels in the river are high, for example, during a surge, as when they are low. The ones at Mautby are together capable of lifting some 80 tonnes of water a minute through a vertical height of 5 m and they replaced the three separate pumps which formerly drained these levels. About 9000 m of arterial drains had to be deepened, the aim being to maintain a freeboard of 1.52 m in the lowest and wettest areas. About 993 ha of marsh benefited from the scheme, whose total cost was, according to Daniels (1982), about £206 000, of which £103 000 came from the MAFF, and a further £32 053 from a FEOGA grant.

The other scheme carried out by the Muckfleet Board involved the amalgamation of the Stokesby, Great Winkle, Clippesby and Muckfleet Levels, and the construction of a new pump-house west of Stokesby (see Plate 29). The twin Archimedes screws installed within this replaced four obsolete pumps, one of which dated from 1918. 8570 m of arterial drain were improved so as to enable the water-table of some 773 ha of marsh to be lowered sufficiently to permit its conversion to arable. The new pumps were commissioned in 1980, and according to Daniels, the total gross cost was about £287000, £48232 of which came from FEOGA funds, and £143500 from MAFF.

Parts of the levels affected by these improvement schemes were already under the

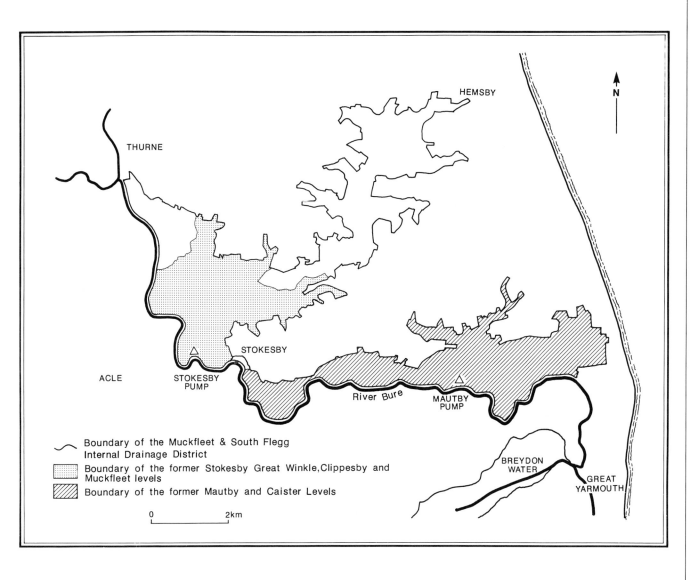

The boundary of the Muckfleet and South Flegg Internal Drainage District, showing the areas affected by the improvement scheme implemented during the late 1970s. The Stokesby pump receives water from the Trinity Broads and their *c.* 40.5 square-kilometre catchment, as well as from the stippled area.

Source: IDB map

Map 9.1

plough before work started on them, but the productivity of the land in question was low owing to the impossibility of obtaining sufficient freeboard, the absence of under-drainage, and the consequent risk of surface flooding following heavy rainfall. By enabling farmers to overcome these problems, the schemes led to an overall improvement in productivity. About three-quarters of the land affected is now under wheat, sugar beet and other crops, whilst a further large block of marsh near Billockby has been ploughed and re-seeded with high-yielding grass mixtures for use in connection with a dairy enterprise. Another, smaller area at Oby remains under grass, and arrangements have been made to ensure that its dyke system can, when necessary, be topped up with water drawn from the river. Similarly, at Mautby, a split-level system has been devised to ensure that one or two individuals who wished to continue to cattle-graze their marshes, could retain sufficient water in their dykes. But both here, and elsewhere in the drainage district, what little unimproved grass remains is in the form of fairly small marshes, mostly located near the valley margin where the peaty soils are not well suited to arable conversion.

The Halvergate Marshes

(a) Technical details of the Phase I, II and III proposals

Conservationists were horrified by the effects the Muckfleet Board's schemes had had on the landscape and ecology of the Bure valley, and their apprehensions lest other areas of high amenity interest should suffer a similar fate were confirmed when it became known that the Lower Bure, Halvergate Fleet and Acle Marshes IDB was planning to improve the arterial drainage of the great triangular block of marshland lying between the R. Bure in the north, and the R. Yare and Breydon Water in the south and south-west. Although popularly known as the 'Halvergate Marshes', this area, which extends to some 3625 ha does, in fact, comprise land in six other parishes besides Halvergate – Acle, Freethorpe, Reedham, Yarmouth, Mautby and Stokesby with Herringfleet. According to a map compiled by the Broadland Friends of the Earth, there were some 167 separate holdings in 188 different ownerships in the area in 1984.

In 1980, the Landscape Working Group of the Broads Authority had endorsed a report which argued . . . "that of all the Broads landscape types, this (Halvergate) is

Table 9a Pumping Stations being operated by the Lower Bure, Halvergate Fleet and Acle Marshes IDB in 1982

Name	NGR	Capacity (tons/min.)	Date installed	Diesel or Electric
Seven Mile House	TG 447036	55	1937	D
Berney Arms	TG 465049	40	1946	E
Breydon	TG 478070	80	1946	E
Ashtree Farm	TG 503093	30	1949	E
Five Mile House	TG 478098	40	1944	E
Stracey Arms	TG 442090	28	1942	E
Tunstall	TG 423092	25	1941	E
Acle	TG 409107	40	1949	E

Source: Fielding (pers. comm.)

probably the most important nationally, and also the most sensitive to change". Moreover, in the Landscape Character Classification which had been formally adopted by the Authority in December 1980, and which was subsequently incorporated in the Landscape Working Group's Report (Broads Authority, 1982b), and in its draft Strategy and Management Plan (Broads Authority, 1982e), most of the Halvergate Marshes had been categorized as a Grade I (exceptionally good) example of 'extensive open' landscape. Even the northernmost part of the area, much of which was under the plough by 1980, was considered to be of Grade 2 importance (see Map 9.2). These assessments caused much controversy, but it was invariably found that those who disputed them most vociferously, had failed to realize that they were judgements of the 'typicalness' of the landscape, rather than its intrinsic beauty. The latter does, of course, vary not only according to 'the eye of the beholder', but seasonally, a point well made by MAFF (1984).

> On a summer's day it [Halvergate] can be an idyllic pastoral scene with cattle, sheep and horses grazing, wide horizons and a quietness only interrupted by the sounds of the cattle and birds. But when the mist rolls in from the North Sea and the northeast wind blows straight from the Arctic it becomes a bleak and dreary place.

What was not appreciated by environmentalists, was that the Lower Bure Board had

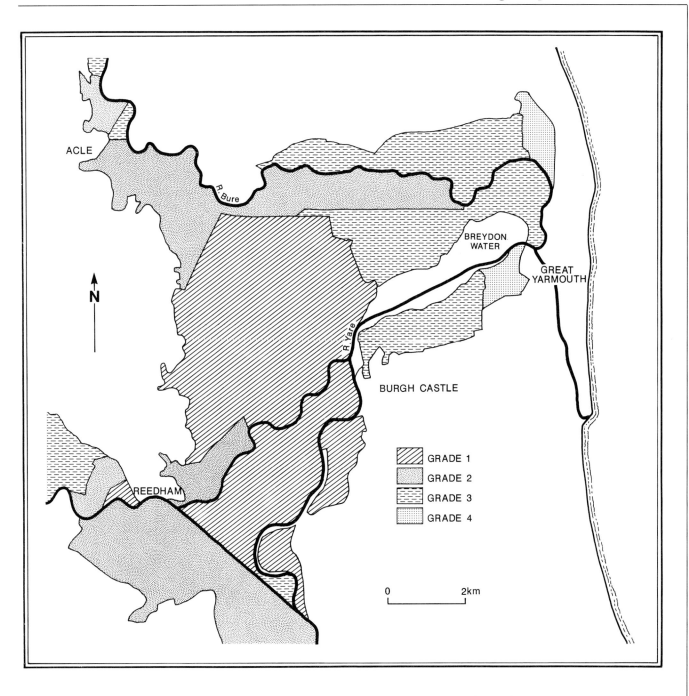

Map 9.2

Landscape quality in the Halvergate 'triangle', and the surrounding area.

Source: Broads Authority data

long been concerned about the inefficient drainage of its district which was dependent on eight pumping stations, all of which contained machinery of pre-1950 vintage (see Table 9a). Ways in which the system could be rationalized had been investigated in the mid-1970s, and in 1977, a scheme was devised by the AWA (which at that time was providing a consultancy service for IDBs) which would have involved the replacement of the obsolete, diesel-driven pumps at Seven Mile House, and improvements to the arterial drainage of 840 ha of marsh in their catchment. In the event, this project was delayed as a consequence of an unsuccessful application by the Board for an FEOGA grant, but in 1980, following pressure from drainage ratepayers wishing to improve the productivity of their land in the Tunstall, Calthorpe, Acle and Stracey Levels, it was agreed that a new scheme to embrace some 2333 ha, or two-thirds of the Halvergate triangle should be devised (see Map 9.3). This task was entrusted to John Dossor & Partners, as the AWA had by then decided that it could no longer provide a drainage consultancy service.

The Board decided that for the sake of economy, it would be essential to carry out the project in three phases, and that despite the pressures being exerted by its ratepayers in the Tunstall/Acle area, priority would have to be given to replacing the pumps at Seven Mile House. However, on Dossors' recommendation, it was agreed that the arterial

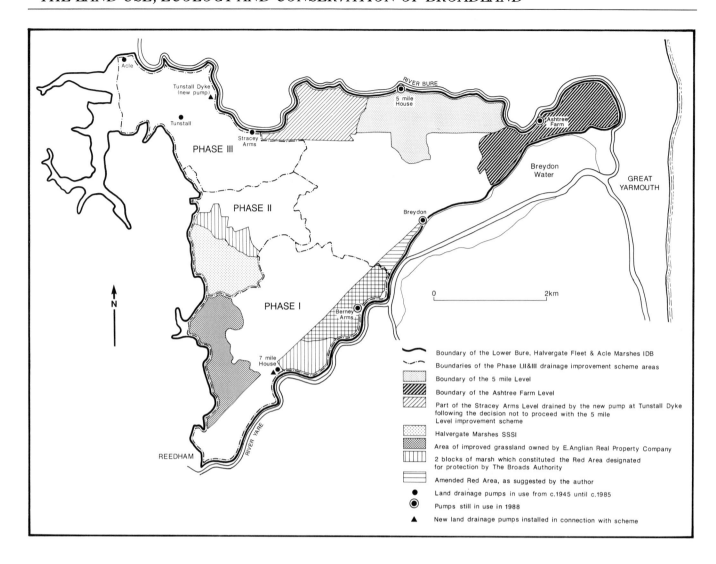

Map 9.3

The areas affected by proposed drainage improvement schemes in the Halvergate 'triangle', and their location in relationship to the NCC's Site of Special Scientific Interest, and the 'Red Area' designated by the Broads Authority.

Source: Broads Authority data

drainage system of the Berney Level should be rationalized and improved at the same time as that of Seven Mile House, the two together forming Phase I of the overall scheme.

Dossors proposed that 11787 m of arterial dykes should be improved in the catchment of the Seven Mile House pumping station and a further 7219 m in the Berney Level. The drains nearest the pumps would have a maximum bed-width of 2.5 m and a top-width of 14 m, reducing to 1 m and 4.5 m respectively in the headwater dykes. Three culverts under the railway would have to be lowered, and over thirty other small bridges rebuilt to allow continued access to the marshes. A concrete access road 4.3 km long would link Berney Arms with Wickhampton village, the Seven Mile House pumping station being connected to this by a 1.1 km-long spur road.

In order to accommodate the flows which would result in the event that 9.5 mm of rain fell in 24 hours on the marshes, and 12.7 mm on the upland nearby, Dossors recommended that twin Archimedes screw pumps of diameter 1800 mm, and having a combined capacity of 94 tonnes/minute should be installed at Seven Mile House, and that a single screw, capable of evacuating 27.6 tonnes/minute should replace the existing axial flow pump at Berney Arms. The two pumping stations would be linked by an arterial drain, partly to minimize the risk of flooding in the event of a mechanical breakdown or prolonged power failure, and partly to ensure that for the sake of economy, the entire area could be drained by a single pump during times of low rainfall.

The Phase II proposals involved the provision of a pump at Manor House, similar to that at Berney Arms, which would lift water from the adjoining Level into the Fleet. This would serve as a high level watercourse, from which water could, when necessary, be gravity-fed to the dyke system of the marshes to the south. However, for most of the time, water would flow down the Fleet to the existing pumps at Breydon Sluice, which would discharge it into Breydon Water.

For the Phase III area, Dossors proposed that the pumps at Acle, Tunstall and Stracey Arms should be replaced by twin Archimedes screws, together capable of raising 65 tonnes of water a minute against a static head of 4.45 m, and installed in a new pump-house located at the northern end of Tunstall Dyke. 8563 m of arterial drain would have to be widened and deepened, but only a short length of new road would be needed to link the new pumping station with the nearby Acle New Road (A47).

Past experience, for instance during 1976, had shown how essential it is in times of drought to be able to withdraw water from the R. Bure at Stracey Arms to replenish the dykes of the adjoining grazing marshes, and Dossors recommended that the existing arrangements should continue, and that the arterial drainage system of the Acle–Tunstall area should be linked with that of the Manor House Level. This would ensure that water from the R. Bure could, when necessary, be conveyed to the Manor House pump, and thence via the Fleet to the dyke system of the Berney and Seven Mile House Levels, thus making it possible for graziers in these areas to continue to keep stock on their marshes throughout the summer, even though the water-table of adjoining land had been lowered.

Table 9b   The costs (1980 prices) of Dossors' proposals for the Phase I, II and III schemes

Scheme	Arterial Drainage costs	Assoc. farm improvement costs
Phase I – Berney/Seven Mile (1178 ha)*	£719 000	£550 000†
Phase II – Manor House (440 ha)	£183 000	£155 650
Phase III – Acle/Tunstall (715 ha)**	£365 000	£359 000
Total scheme – (2333 ha)	£1 267 000	£1 064 650
Likely amount of MAFF grant	£633 500	c.£425 000††

*   plus 460 ha of upland catchment

**   plus 170 ha of upland catchment

†   This figure is based on the following estimates:

    Extension of 5km farm access roads £150 000

    Underdraining, ditching, levelling and reshaping 400 ha of arable land @ £600/ha £240 000

    Grassland improvement: reseeding, fencing etc. 600 ha @ £100/ha £60 000

    Additional buildings and machinery £100 000

††   This figure would have varied according to whether landowners opted for assistance under the AHDS or AHGS.

Source: John Dossor & Partners (1980 & 1981)

At the IDB's request, discussions took place during the autumn of 1980 between Dossors and the NCC concerning Wigg's Carr (which had been scheduled as an SSSI in 1971), and a 162 ha block of grazing marsh near the villages of Wickhampton and Halvergate which the NCC was proposing to schedule on account of its very considerable natural history interest. These consultations showed that Wigg's Carr would not be affected by the drainage proposals, and that if a minor modification was made to the Phase II scheme, involving leaving a short section of arterial drain unimproved, the water regime of the proposed Halvergate SSSI would not be affected. The IDB subsequently agreed to the scheme being modified in this way.

Dossors also sent details of their proposals to the Broads Authority, and it quickly became apparent that it would object, on the grounds that most of the marshland affected had been categorized as being of Grade I landscape quality, and that the drainage schemes would, by facilitating the conversion of grassland to arable, entirely alter the character of the area. This line of argument proved difficult for members of the IDB to accept, for although they were prepared to agree that some of the marsh dykes in their drainage district were of special ecological importance, there was, they claimed, "nothing special" about the Halvergate landscape; indeed, few people could tell the difference between unimproved grass and young wheat!

None of those who took part in these early discussions could have foreseen just how complex, contentious and time-consuming the subsequent negotiations would prove to be. Some at least of the difficulties stemmed from the fact that both the IDB and the Broads Authority were treading new ground. No mention is made in the *Land Drainage Act* 1976, of the need to reconcile nature conservation and amenity interests with those of agriculture, and although all IDBs were supposed as public bodies to "take these into account" under Section 11 of the *Countryside Act* 1968, it had been customary for them to ignore this provision. In the circumstances, the Authority's objections to Dossors' proposals presented the members of the Lower Bure Board with an unwelcome and quite unexpected constraint on their freedom of action. Their concern was accentuated when they learned that MAFF had given undertakings in September 1980 that it would not approve an arterial drainage grant application until any objections by the Countryside Commission, NCC or Broads Authority had been resolved. If this could not be achieved locally, the application would have to be referred to Ministers for decision.

Members of the Board repeatedly pointed out during the course of the discussions, that each month that went by saw an increase, both in the cost of the schemes, and the likelihood that marshland would be flooded as a consequence of a pump breakdown. The IDB also argued that its primary task was to enable its ratepayers to improve the productivity of their holdings, and that it could not subsidize conservation interests, either directly or indirectly. Moreover, it had no control over the way the marshes in its district were managed, and could not therefore guarantee that any area identified by the Broads Authority as being of special environmental importance would be retained as unimproved grass.

In contrast, the Halvergate affair represented for the Broads Authority the first real test of its strength of purpose. Its members, being representative of a wide range of different interests, were torn between their desire to preserve some semblance of unity amongst themselves, their wish to adopt policies consistent with those of their principal funding body, the Countryside Commission, and their anxiety to be seen to be taking a firm, yet conciliatory line. Their difficulties were compounded by the very strong pressure exerted on them, both by agricultural and amenity interests. Numerous letters appeared in the correspondence columns of the national and the local press, many questions were raised in Parliament, and a long series of articles and reports were published, often highly critical either of the drainage proposals, e.g. Buxton (1981a), Grove-White (1981) and Lees (1982), or the delays occasioned by the Authority's intervention, e.g. Hooson (1981) and Shearman (1982).

The problems were exacerbated by differences in the negotiating style of the organizations principally concerned – the IDB being less encumbered with administrative procedures than the Authority or the Commission and therefore able to respond much more quickly to proposals and counter-proposals. To make matters worse, the Strategy Committee's recommendations were not always accepted by the full Authority, whose policies were, in turn, at variance with those of the Commission on at least two occasions. Moreover, both the Authority and its Strategy Committee frequently had to discuss the Halvergate issue, and in particular its financial implications, in private. It was perhaps inevitable in these circumstances that suspicions were sometimes voiced by farming interests that their views were not being fairly presented to the Authority. Although most would now agree that these accusations were groundless, they caused considerable bitterness at the time.

Several other factors contributed to the complexity of the negotiations. First, they were commenced at a time when the Wildlife and Countryside Bill, with its more legalistic attitude towards the safeguarding of sites, was making its tortuous and highly controversial passage through Parliament. The Bill's provisions for compensating farmers on a 'profits forgone' basis caused particular unease, both inside and outside Westminster (Buxton, 1981b). In addition, local interests concerned with the Halvergate affair were conscious that their decisions were likely to be construed elsewhere as setting precedents, and conversely, that their policics must reflect the attitudes being adopted by their respective lobbies during the debates on the Bill.

Second, the negotiations were initiated at a time when conservationists were becoming increasingly concerned about the amount of habitat destruction which was occurring throughout Britain as a result of the relentless drive to improve the productivity of farm land. Evidence for this had emerged from a survey of the losses and damage sustained by

SSSIs during 1980 (NCC, 1982), and it was inevitable that in these circumstances the Halvergate issue – involving as it did a scheduled wetland site – should be seen as something of a test case. But the NCC had to make it clear that it was not in a position to enter into management agreements over the Halvergate Marshes SSSI, and thus safeguard it against adverse changes of land use, until the new legislation came into force. A further complication was that the IDB was not legally obliged to 'further the cause of conservation' (insofar as this was compatible with its duties under the *Land Drainage Act* 1976) until the Wildlife and Countryside Act had received the Royal Assent.

Third, the negotiations were handicapped, at least initially, by the absence of legislation enabling sites of special landscape significance (as distinct from SSSIs) to be safeguarded in the face of changes in land management practice*. Even when the new Act came into force, there was strong resistance from local authorities (including the Broads Authority) to use its provisions (and in particular Clause 39) to pay farmers compensation for maintaining the *status quo*.

Last, but not least, it was becoming increasingly apparent during the late 1970s and early 1980s that the conversion of more and more marshland to arable was resulting in the production of a commodity, wheat, which was already heavily in surplus in the Common Market countries. The concern and frustration felt by environmental economists on this score were heightened by suspicions that the cost-benefit methodology used by MAFF to decide whether a drainage scheme was eligible for grant was faulty (Bowers, 1983; Turner, 1983; Turner, Dent & Hey, 1983). In addition, many conservationists were aggrieved by MAFF's steadfast refusal to agree that the pros and cons of a drainage improvement scheme as large and as controversial as that at Halvergate should be scrutinized at a public inquiry as allowed for under Section 96 of the *Land Drainage Act* 1976 (RSPB, 1983). MAFF was also criticized in some quarters for being unwilling to assist conservation agencies offset the effects of a drainage improvement scheme on amenity and wildlife by, for example, helping them pay farmers compensation for not ploughing up their marshes. The Department's response to this was that it would be acting *ultra vires* if it did this, but that it could grant-aid a scheme which reconciled the interests of conservation and agriculture, provided an overall improvement in the productivity of farm land resulted.

Scepticism about the need for a drainage scheme at Halvergate, and unease about the economic arguments advanced in support of it, were implicit in several of the queries put by the Broads Authority to the IDB in December 1980. These were referred to Dossors, whose response was concerned with five main issues:

(1) The implications of doing nothing: it was concluded that the marshes would become flooded for long periods, and that they would consequently regress to reed-beds and saltings.

(2) The cost of retaining the land under grass with a high water-table: Dossors claimed, not altogether convincingly, that to do this, it would be necessary to replace all eight existing pumps at a gross cost of £650 000. This expenditure was thought unlikely to qualify for MAFF grant [although the Secretary of State for Agriculture subsequently announced (Hansard, HL Cols. 634-635, June 1981) that in view of the age of the existing pumps, grants would be available for replacements, even if these were of equal, rather than greater capacity], and it was considered that although the pump maintenance costs would fall (so allowing the occupier's rate to be reduced from £8.90/ha to £8/ha), the loan charges incurred by the Board would oblige it to increase the total drainage rate from £13.50 to about £41.60 per hectare. This would reduce the revenue obtainable from the marshes to about £25.40/ha [see Table 9c (i)], thus making it most unlikely that they would remain as unimproved grass. In contrast, if a grant-aided scheme was carried out, and the land was managed as improved rather than unimproved grass, a margin of *c.* £63.40/ha would be obtainable [see Table 9c (ii)].

(3) The environmental implications of the scheme: Dossors somewhat blandly concluded that . . ."the drainage proposals and the consequential change to a mixed pattern of farming will not reduce the amenity value of the area as a whole".

---

* The difficulties inherent in protecting areas of high quality landscape led to several new initiatives being taken by the Government in the mid-1980s. These are described in Chapter 12.

(4)   The amount of compensation which would be needed to ensure that owners kept their land in an unimproved state: Dossors estimated that once the pumps had been replaced, a profit of £149.90/ha would be obtainable from marshes put down to wheat [see Table 9c (iii)], and they therefore concluded that a premium of at least £124.50/ha (representing the difference between this figure and the £25.40/ha likely to be obtained if the same land was left as unimproved grass) would be needed.

Table 9c   Dossors' estimates of the profitability of different types of usage after pump replacement (1980 prices)

(i) Unimproved pasture – summer grazing

Stocking rate . . . . 2.25 head/ha . . . . cost – £846	
Sale rate @ £455 – £1023 – Profit/ha	£177
Deduct variables	(£25)
Gross margin/ha	£152
Special charges – Marshman and Transport	(£25)
Servicing capital – £846 @ 14% for 6 months	£60
Net Working Margin/ha	£67
Less Owner's drainage rate ha £4.60	
Occupier's drainage rate ha (covering maintenance and running costs) £8.00	
Annual cost of servicing and paying off sum borrowed by IDB for replacing pumps (assuming no MAFF grant and no improvements to dykes, drains or roads) £29.00	
Total costs/ha . . . . (£41.60)	
Available for rent and profit	£25.40/ha

(ii) Improved grass – summer grazing

Stocking rate . . . . 2.5 head/ha cost – £940	
Sale rate @ £475 – £1188 – Profit/ha	£248
Deduct variables	(£25)
Gross margin/ha	£223
Special charges – Marshman and Transport	(£22)
Servicing capital – £940 @ 14% for 6 months	(£66)
Net Working Margin/ha	£135
Less Owner's drainage rate ha £4.60	
Occupier's drainage rate ha £9.50	
Annual cost of servicing and paying off sum borrowed by IDB for improvement scheme after 50% grant £44.00	
Access roads maintenance in present condition £2.00	
Grass improvement – Net cost £60/ha for 10 yrs @ 14% £11.50	
Total costs/ha . . . . (£71.60)	
Available for rent and profit	£63.40/ha

(iii) Cereals

Yield . . . . 6.2 tonnes/ha @ £100	£620
Deduct variables	(£160)
Gross margin/ha	£460
Deduct cultivation, drilling & harvesting costs	(£120)
Servicing cash flow – £300 for 12 months @ 14%	(£42)
Net Working Margin/ha	£298
Less Owner's drainage rate/ha £4.60	
Occupier's drainage rate/ha £9.50	
Annual cost of servicing and paying off sum borrowed by IDB for improvement scheme after 50% MAFF grant (includes new pumps & drains) £44.00	
Access roads – Net cost £125/ha for 15 yrs @ 14% £18.00	
Field drainage – £374/ha net, capitalized over 10 yrs @ 14% £72.00	
Total costs/ha £148.10	
Available for rent and profit	£149.90/ha

Source: John Dossor & Partners (1980 & 1981)

(b) The Economics of marsh conversion

The fifth issue raised by the Broads Authority concerned the economic justification for the schemes, and by way of a reply, Dossors produced copies of the cost-benefit analyses which they had prepared for the IDB. On the assumption that the existing gross margins for marshes under unimproved grass, improved grass and arable (winter wheat yielding only 5 tonnes/ha because of the high water-table) were £100/ha, £170/ha and £340/ha respectively, they estimated that prior to the carrying out of the Berney/Seven Mile improvement scheme, the agricultural value of the area concerned was:

```
1048 ha of unimproved grass ..........................................£104 800
100 ha of improved grass .............................................. £17 000
30 ha of arable ...................................................... £10 200
TOTAL ................................................................ £132 000*
```

* This was, in fact, an under-estimate, since *c.* 170 ha was under improved grass at the time rather than 100 ha.

Dossors then used this figure to predict the increase in gross margins likely to be obtained five, ten, twenty and thirty years after the scheme had been completed (see Table 9d). In doing so, they assumed that the average yield of winter wheat would increase to 6.2 tonnes/ha, and that the gross margins from this crop, and from dairy farming would be £460/ha and £475/ha respectively.

Table 9d   Dossors' forecast of developments following completion of the Phase I drainage scheme

	5 years		10 years		20 years		30 years	
	ha	£	ha	£	ha	£	ha	£
Unimproved Grass £100 ha	703	70 300	458	45 800	298	29 800	178	17 800
Improved Grass £170 ha	125	21 250*	200	34 000	300	51 000	400	68 000
Dairy Farming £475 ha	150	71 250	200	95 000	200	95 000	200	95 000
Arable Winter Wheat £460 ha	200	92 000	320	147 200	380	174 000	400	184 000
Total GM		254 800		322 000		350 600		364 800
Deduct Existing GM		132 000		132 000		132 000		132 000
Increase in Gross Margin		122 800		190 000		218 600		232 800

* This was an under-estimate, since *c.*170 ha was already under improved grass in 1980 when Dossors produced these figures.

Source: John Dossor & Partners (1980)

Dossors then amortized the total estimated capital cost of the scheme, £1 267 000 (see Table 9b), and compared the resulting annuity with the annual gain in gross margins undiscounted, 20 and 30 years after it had been completed. This led them to conclude that at the 5 per cent discount rate, the capital expenditure would be amply covered, whichever period was chosen.

	Discount Rate		
	5%	10%	16%
Capital cost amortized over 30 yrs (benefit – £232 800)	£82 553	£134 613	£205 439
Capital cost amortized over 20 yrs (benefit – £218 600)	£101 829	£149 048	£214 032

Dossors' cost-benefit analysis was strongly critized by Dr John Bowers, an economist at the University of Leeds, on the grounds that the capital cost of the scheme had been estimated gross of (i.e. before) subsidy, whilst the benefits "mysteriously" included subsidy. In other words, they were returns to the farmer, and not to the nation. Bowers estimated that if the subsidy element was omitted from the calculations, the gross margins obtainable from the land would be: winter wheat, £263/ha (rather than £460/ha); dairying, £243/ha; beef on improved and unimproved grass, £117/ha and £69/ha respectively. Using these figures and Dossors' predictions regarding the rate of marsh conversion (see Table 9d), he calculated that the increase in gross margins would be £113 000 after 20 years, rising to £121 800 after a further ten years, or only about half the values claimed by Dossors. Bowers also pointed out that once the benefits of a scheme have been calculated, the correct procedure is to discount them and compare with the capital cost, rather than adopt the technique employed by Dossors. On the basis of these adjustments, Bowers concluded that the Phase I scheme would have a rate of return of between 4 and 5 per cent.

Scepticism concerning Dossors' claims increased following the publication by the Broads Authority of a report in which independent consultants examined the economic arguments put forward by those advocating the conversion of grass marsh to arable (Environmental Resource Ltd. & Trans Econ Ltd., 1981). In this study, the consultants examined the pros and cons as seen by a farmer, and did not carry out a full-scale cost-benefit analysis which, they argued, ought to take account of the expenditure incurred by the AWA in protecting the land against flooding, the real crop value (i.e. exclusive of subsidy and EEC intervention), and environmental costs (insofar as these can be quantified in financial terms). Instead, the consultants presented six worked case studies, each representing a different combination of crop and soil type, and based as far as possible on data obtained from practical experience in Broadland, rather than on national averages. Assuming that the crop would not be damaged by flooding, and that the farmer was intending to convert a largish holding – potentially a much more lucrative proposition than a small block of marsh would be – the consultants concluded that it would be profitable to grow wheat, with break crops of barley and oil-seed rape, on clay soils such as those found in much of the Halvergate area, provided that any acid sulphate layer (see page 20) was more than 60 cm below the surface. An internal rate of return of 79 per cent could be expected if wheat grown on calcareous clays yielded 6.4 tonnes/ha (the best figure recorded in Broadland in 1980), but this declined to zero if the yield was only 5 tonnes/ha (a more realistic figure for most marshes). On the assumption that productivity would be reduced by 20 per cent on clay soils with an acid layer at 60 cm or less – a very conservative estimate – the internal rate of return obtainable from wheat would be negligible, even if lime was applied.

The consultants took the view that it would not be worthwhile growing cereals on acid peats or interlayered clays and peats as are found along the eastern margin of the Halvergate marshes, though potatoes or some other high-yielding crop would give a reasonable rate of return provided the acid layer was more than 60 cm deep. If it was less than this, liming would be required, and a very high yield would have to be obtained to achieve profitability.

(c) The controversy unfolds

Following a site visit and a lengthy discussion, the Broads Authority's Strategy Committee decided in January 1981, to reject a set of recommendations drafted by its officers, which indicated *inter alia*, that the landscape changes which would result if the Phase I scheme was carried out, would be "unacceptable" and that the Authority should press for a public inquiry. Instead, the Committee passed the following resolution:

(1)　It is recommended that the Broads Authority advise the MAFF that the change in the distinctive character of the Broadland landscape which would result from the Seven Mile/Berney rationalization proposal should be minimized;

(2)　Should the MAFF in seeking a balance between conservation and agricultural interests decide to support the implementation of the scheme, that in the light of negotiations and discussions which have been held with the Drainage Board, the Authority endeavour to examine with the Board and its consultants whether an appropriate proposal may be agreed which retains to the maximum extent practicable the distinctive character of the area.

These very conciliatory recommendations generated a storm of criticism, particular exception being taken to the view expressed by one of the Committee's members that . . ."it would put a lot of people's backs up" if the drainage proposals were condemned completely. Many believed that it was naïve to think that the Authority could fulfil its objectives without coming into conflict with some of the disparate interests operating in the region, a point hammered home in a forthright leader in the *Eastern Daily Press*:

> The history of the Broads over the past 60 or more years is one of conflict; conflict between exploitation and conservation, conflict between urban and rural values, between various leisure interest groups, but perhaps above all a conflict between those who want water, and those who want to get rid of it. The lowering of the water table regardless of the ecological changes resulting, continues almost inexorably, even it seems under its latest guardians. *Plus ça change . . ?* (EDP, 1981)

The anomaly inherent in public funds having to be paid out to counteract the effects of a project grant-aided by a government department – the 'double payment issue' – was aired in the correspondence columns of the same paper, the point being made that . . . "the MAFF grants will, as usual, benefit a very small, but vocal group of people, who will then proceed to add to the grain mountain at present standing at 617 000 tonnes. Once again, public money for private profit" (Edwards, 1981).

The Committee's recommendations were also criticized by Mr (now Lord) David Ennals, the then MP for Norwich North, who claimed that its members . . ."had slipped at one of their first hurdles", whilst others castigated the Committee for being parochial in its outlook, and for failing to press home the point that a nationally important landscape was being jeopardized as a consequence of the policies being pursued by central government, and that the latter should therefore be prepared to help meet the cost of the conservation measures made necessary as a result.

Pressures were also brought to bear on the Authority from outside the region. The Council for the Protection of Rural England (CPRE), for instance, issued a Press Release urging the Authority to "stand firm" on the Halvergate issue, and claiming that . . ."the conversion of pastures to arable land is reaching unprecedented proportions at the national level", and that . . ."the increasing sums of public money supporting land drainage operations are not being reflected in improved accountability arrangements". Similarly, the Countryside Commission resolved that whilst its officers should continue their endeavours to find . . ."ways in which extensive grazing might be retained on the Broadland marshes, and a balance achieved between conservation and farming profitability," it would . . ."register an objection to the Phase I scheme on the grounds that it would have an unacceptable impact on this stretch of nationally important Broadland landscape". The Commission also resolved that . . ."should the Minister of Agriculture . . . be minded to approve the scheme, the Commission would expect a public inquiry to be held . . . in view of the serious damage which the proposals would do to the nationally important landscape of Broadland".

Any lingering doubts which members of the Broads Authority may have had about the concern with which the Halvergate affair was viewed by conservationists, must have been dispelled when they arrived for their meeting on 27 February. Not only did they have to make their way past a group of vociferous, placard-carrying pickets from the Friends of the Earth, but the council chamber was filled to capacity by those wishing to listen to the debate. In the event, after a discussion lasting one and a half hours, they resolved by a 13 to 7 majority:

(1)   That the Broads Authority advise the MAFF that the change in the distinctive character of the Broadland landscape which would result from the Seven Mile/Berney Drainage Rationalization Proposal is unacceptable.

(2)   Should the MAFF decide to support the implementation of the Scheme, that the Broads Authority would seek an opportunity to express its views at a public inquiry.

(3)   That the Broads Authority instructs its officers to continue their discussions with officers of the Countryside Commission, Nature Conservancy Council, Anglian Water Authority, local landowners and their representatives with the aim of finding ways in which extensive grazing might be retained on the Broadland Marshes and a balance achieved between conservation and farming profitability.

In April, during the course of the first of a long series of meetings between representatives of the MAFF, IDB, Broads Authority, Countryside Commission, NCC, Country Landowners Association (CLA) and National Farmers Union (NFU), Aitken Clark (the Broads Officer) outlined his proposals for a compromise. On the basis that the NCC would be statutorily obliged to try and safeguard the Halvergate Marshes SSSI, which embraced 162 ha of valley-edge marshland between Wickhampton and Halvergate villages, and that a further *c.* 190 ha of skirt land between Halvergate and Reedham was unlikely to be put under the plough because its owners (the East Anglian Real Property Company) were using it in connection with a newly established dairy enterprise, Clark proposed that some 223 ha in the Seven Mile and Berney Levels, to the south and east of the Reedham to Yarmouth railway should be maintained as unimproved grassland (see Map 9.3). There were several reasons why this 'Red Area' was chosen, one of the most important being that visually it is fairly self-contained, being more or less isolated from the main part of the Halvergate triangle by the low embankment on which the railway is built. In addition it was considered that although the majority of the marshes owned by the East Anglian Real Property Company had been improved, they would link the Red Area visually with the Halvergate Marshes SSSI, the three blocks of marsh together forming a crescent-shaped area, situated in close juxtaposition to Haddiscoe Island, the only other example of 'extensive open' landscape in the region. It was also argued that unlike most parts of the Halvergate triangle, the Red Area could be seen by large numbers of people. Not only is it located beside a railway line, but it is bounded to the south by the left bank of the R. Yare along which there is a public footpath. More important, it lies adjacent to the Berney Arms drainage mill which, with the nearby public house, is visited by numerous holidaymakers during the summer months.

Discussions also took place about how the marshes in the areas affected by the IDB's proposals could best be safeguarded. The Countryside Commission's representative on the working party suggested that land owners in the Red Area should be invited to conclude agreements whereby they undertook not to plough, level or otherwise alter the management of their marshes for a period of 20 years. For its part, the IDB would apply for a Differential Rating Order, so that drainage charges in the Red Area could be pegged at their existing levels, thus ensuring that graziers could continue to make a reasonable living out of the land. Conceptually, this was an attractive idea, since it would mean that those who improved their land, and who thus benefited most from the drainage scheme, and the public funds invested in it, would have to pay higher drainage charges than those who derived little, if any, advantage from it.

It was also proposed that those who owned land elsewhere in the Phase I, II and III areas be invited to conclude less onerous 'White Area' agreements, under which they agreed to manage their dykes in the way suggested by the Authority, and would notify it if they intended to improve or plough up their marshes, or construct new roads or buildings on them. If the Authority registered an objection, there would be a standstill for, say, 3 months, during which time negotiations would take place between the parties concerned. It was also proposed that the design of the pump-houses, and the routing of the roads and power lines leading to them, should be subject to prior approval by the Authority and the Commission, and that if modifications were required, the relatively small extra costs involved would be met by the IDB, which would be eligible for MAFF grants. Finally, it was suggested that a Marsh Liaison Panel should be established to provide a forum for discussions between farming and conservation interests, not only about Halvergate, but about similar drainage improvement schemes elsewhere in the region.

During the ensuing discussions, it became apparent that the IDB would be unwilling to contribute anything towards the cost of modifying the design of the pumping stations, or altering the route of the power lines and roads leading to them. The Board's representatives also took strong exception to the idea of a differential rating order, on the grounds that even if the scheme went ahead immediately, the drainage rates payable by an owner-occupier would have to be substantially increased, and that if the Red Area was exempted, the rates levied on the White Area would have to rise even more. It was claimed that this would be unacceptable to owners and occupiers as they would, in effect, be subsidizing conservation interests. Moreover, such an arrangement would make it even less likely that marshes in the White Area would remain unimproved.

During the next 18 months, strenuous efforts were made by the parties concerned to arrive at a mutually acceptable solution, the Board being motivated by the escalating cost of the scheme (estimated to be increasing by £5000 per week), and by the inadequacy of the existing drainage system (heavy rainfall in April 1981, made it necessary to take the cattle off the marshes for a time, even though the Board's electric pumps were run non-stop for five days), while the Broads Authority and the Commission were determined to find a way of ensuring that the majority of the Halvergate triangle remained in its existing, unimproved state, without having to pay the owners and occupiers of the area huge sums in compensation.

The main stages in the negotiations between May 1981 and October 1982 can be summarized as follows:

(1)   The IDB offered to urge owners to conclude 'interim agreements' with the Authority, and in the meantime not to alter the existing water levels in the Red Area. This suggestion was rejected by the Authority on the grounds that such agreements would not legally commit owners to maintain their marshland in its existing, unimproved state. In addition, a very expensive and dangerous precedent would be set if the Authority accepted sole responsibility for safeguarding the marshes.

(2)   In June 1981, the scope of the discussions between the parties was extended to include the Phase II and III areas. Much of the latter had already been put under the plough, and the Authority therefore decided to seek only White Area agreements over it. In contrast, the 440 ha covered by the Manor House scheme were of Grade I landscape importance. However, rather than try and safeguard the whole of this area, the Authority agreed to compromise by extending the Red Area to include *c.* 57 ha immediately to the north of the Halvergate Marshes SSSI.

(3)   Following lengthy discussions about the scope of the Red Area agreements, it was decided that no herbicides were to be used on the dykes, that there should be no levelling or re-seeding of the marshes, and that no new fences should be erected without the Authority's prior approval. The amount of fertilizer to be applied to the land would also have to be agreed beforehand, whilst water levels in the arterial drains would be adjusted to take account of the Authority's requirements. It was proposed that these provisions should be embodied in a legally binding, 10-year agreement between the Authority and the IDB, and that the latter would ensure that its ratepayers complied with the undertakings by means of by-laws. Up to £25000 per year would be made available by the Authority for compensating farmers for loss of profits, and these payments would be index-linked on the basis of a formula to be agreed later.

(4)   The Countryside Commission subsequently decided that these proposals . . ."would not satisfactorily protect the natural beauty and amenity of the Broadland landscape, which they recognize as of a quality equivalent to that of a national park". Moreover, the Halvergate case raises . . ."issues of such national importance to both the agricultural community and conservation interests that the Commission believe that a scheme acceptable to the farmers, while affording adequate protection to the natural beauty and amenity of the area, is most likely to be found by allowing all parties to present their case at a public inquiry".

(5)   Despite its anxiety to adopt a policy consistent with that of the Commission, the Authority did not share the latter's enthusiasm for an inquiry. Instead, it decided to support the arrangements tentatively agreed between the parties, provided the Commission agreed to find half the cost of the compensation payable in respect of the Red Area. It also resolved that a joint approach should be made to Government . . ."to emphasize and establish and qualify the national dilemmas facing the local bodies concerned".

(6)   The conciliatory attitude adopted by the Authority generated renewed controversy, both locally and nationally, and in a vigorous riposte to the militant attitude being adopted in some quarters, J. E. Hooson of the NFU claimed that:

> There is no lack of goodwill on the part of the farming community, but the onus is now clearly on the conservation agencies and bodies such as the CPRE to put

a value on the existing landscape and to make positive and practical proposals to farmers in the areas they wish to conserve. (*The Times*, 10 June 1981)

(7) The policy differences which had temporarily developed between the Authority and the Commission were resolved at a meeting in late June, when it was agreed that the Red Area agreements would have to run for twenty years rather than ten, and that farmers would be offered a choice of compensation formulae similar to that used in the Exmoor National Park. Equally important, it was decided that the Red Area would have to be safeguarded by agreements negotiated between the Authority and the marsh owners rather than by means of IDB by-laws. This was because it was doubtful whether an IDB could employ the latter to restrict the way its ratepayers managed their land. In addition, the only sanction against those in breach of such regulations would be a fine, and no-one was convinced that this would be a sufficient deterrent, given the substantial financial advantages accruing at that time from converting unimproved grassland to arable.

(8) The role of central Government in the controversy was discussed in London the following month. It was stated that MAFF could not legally offer any financial assistance towards the cost of compensating farmers who agreed not to plough their land (a point subsequently confirmed by Lord Avon during a debate in the House of Lords on the Wildlife and Countryside Bill), whilst any funds from the DoE would have to be channelled through the Countryside Commission or the NCC. The latter's interest in the affair was centred on the need to safeguard the Halvergate Marshes SSSI, but a shortage of resources would preclude it from reaching management agreements over the site unless its ecological interest was directly threatened. This criterion was not met since the Board had assured the NCC that the arterial drainage system of the site would not be altered.

(9) Subsequent talks in Whitehall led to the Authority being informed that 75 per cent of the cost of any agreements it negotiated in the Red Area would be funded by the DoE through the Commission. Originally a figure of up to £57 000 was mentioned, but following a bout of what O'Riordan (1986) has termed "horse-trading", this figure was raised to £65 000. The same worker claims, probably correctly, that no responsible agricultural economist could have justified such a sum, and it was certainly not based, as it should have been, on a detailed study of the needs and expectations of landowners in the Red Area.

(10) Despite strong reservations, the Commission subsequently endorsed the arrangements worked out in Whitehall. However, it reiterated its belief that a clause should be inserted in the Wildlife and Countryside Bill (then at a critical stage in its passage through Parliament) empowering MAFF to contribute towards the cost of conservation agreements rendered necessary by its continued drive to improve the productivity of farm land.

(11) Although the DoE's offer was also accepted by the Authority, it re-affirmed its decision not to withdraw its objections to the Phase I and II schemes until Red Area agreements had been negotiated. However, noting that the existing pump at Tunstall was in urgent need of repair, and that the IDB was understandably reluctant to spend money on it when it was soon to be replaced, the Authority also resolved:

> That subject to appropriate letters of intent from appropriate bodies (i.e. the NFU, CLA and IDB) concerning their intention expeditiously to pursue the securing of agreements with landowners, the Broads Authority withdraws its objection to the Tunstall pump replacement. This is without prejudice to the remaining objection covering other areas, and is intended as a declaration of confidence in achieving an overall satisfactory series of agreements.

(12) On learning this, the Director of the CPRE wrote begging the Authority not to make such a concession, and stressing again the need for a public inquiry. The Earl of Onslow and Lord Buxton, both of whom were actively involved in the discussions in Parliament concerning the Wildlife and Countryside Bill, also wrote suggesting that . . ."it would be wrong of the Broads Authority to go

against its stated policy of objection until all management agreements are signed, sealed and delivered", and asking that no further action be taken until after the issue had been debated in Parliament.

(13) These interventions led members of the Strategy Committee to have second thoughts. But they were also advised that letters of intent would not legally commit landowners in the Phase III area to conclude 'White Area' agreements with the Authority. In addition, it was doubtful whether the owners fully appreciated the restrictions to which they would become subject if they signed such undertakings. But most telling of all, the Committee was informed that the Tunstall pump had been repaired, thus apparently removing the need for the Authority to make a quick decision on the Phase III proposals. The Committee's recommendation that the Authority should, after all, sustain its objection to the Tunstall scheme until the terms of the White Area agreements, and the statements of intent, had been reviewed, was duly accepted, though misgivings were expressed lest the Authority be accused of reneging on its previous undertakings.

(14) Meantime, discussions had been taking place about the methods to be used in calculating the compensation payable to the signatories of Red Area agreements. It had originally been intended to keep the size of the sum available confidential but the figure quickly became known locally; indeed, it was published in *The Times* just four days after it had been discussed 'in confidence' at a meeting of the Strategy Committee from which the Press and public had been excluded. Worse still, it was widely assumed by farming interests that it would be shared out on a pro-rata, acreage basis. In mid-August for example, the *Farmers Weekly* carried an article stating that . . . "the Government is expected to agree to compensation payments of £65000 a year, or an average of £58 per acre to farmers to conserve 453 hectares (1119 acres) in the Norfolk Broads".

(15) Grave doubts about the financial propriety of such a 'share-out' had been expressed on previous occasions by the Authority's advisers, and in October the Strategy Committee agreed that the compensation payments would have to be assessed on the basis of 'profits forgone' – in other words, the net loss of revenue which those signing the agreements would incur by maintaining their land in its existing condition, rather than improving its productivity. Those claiming compensation would also have to demonstrate their intention to plough and their ability to do so.

(16) The Committee also decided to resist the demands being made by the NFU and CLA that the compensation payable should be linked to the Retail Price Index. This was partly because of the size of the sums involved – it was calculated that if the RPI remained at 12 per cent, the Authority would be paying out £437000 per annum in respect of the Red Area when the agreements expired in 20 years time – and partly because the allocations made to the Authority by its constituent partners were unlikely to rise in concert with the RPI, thus giving rise to the possibility of a growing discrepancy between the cost of the indexed agreements, and the Authority's ability to afford them.

(17) The next round of negotiations centred on a proposal by MAFF that the Authority pay owners a sign-on fee of between £12.50 and £75 per hectare for 20 years at 12 per cent, plus compensation calculated annually on a profits-forgone basis. At 1982 prices, the latter would amount to about £300/ha, the difference between the gross margins for wheat (£450/ha) and beef cattle (£150/ha). However, the MAFF figures were not acceptable either to farming interests, who considered them too low, or the Broads Authority, which decided they breached its 'no indexation' condition.

(18) Increasingly desperate to reach a settlement, the IDB proposed that owners should receive sign-on fees together making up a third of the total sum available for safeguarding the Red Area during the first two years. From the third year onwards, farmers would be able to claim compensation on the basis of profits forgone. The monies not spent by the Authority on sign-on fees or compensation would be paid into a special fund, which would be used to top up the sums available for safeguarding the Red Area in later years when, as a consequence of inflation, the compensation payable annually would have risen

above the sum available. Although this proposal was acceptable to the Countryside Commission, the Strategy Committee had considerable reservations, not least because the cost of compensation could escalate in later years as a result of the interventionist policies operated by the EEC. It therefore decided to reiterate its previous recommendation that indexation could not be guaranteed, at least for the first three years of any agreements, and that the Authority should sustain its objection to the Phase III drainage scheme until a satisfactory compromise had been worked out between the parties.

(19)   In January 1982, a new set of proposals, this time devised by the Strategy Committee and its advisers, was considered at a meeting in London, attended by the three Ministers principally concerned, Earl Ferrers, Mr Tom King and Mr Neil MacFarlane, as well as by representatives of the parties directly involved. Marshes within the Red Area whose owners wished to sell would be bought up by the Authority, either by using part of its capital reserves, or by capitalizing part of the £65000 which it had previously agreed should be set aside for annual payments to secure, and subsequently pay back, a loan. Once purchased, the land would either be leased back to the original owner, or sold subject to restrictive covenants – a method favoured by the Ministers. The remaining parts of the Red Area would be subject to management agreements negotiated on a profits-forgone basis. The Authority would offer 3-yearly reviews of the compensation payments, and these would be indexed to a formula reflecting variations in agricultural productivity, to be worked out by the Department of Land Economy of Cambridge University. In return for this package, the Authority would expect the IDB to apply a differential rate so that owners and occupiers in the Red Area would not have to pay higher drainage charges once the scheme had been carried out. Despite a strong objection from the IDB's representative, these proposals were accepted by the others present as a basis for further discussion.

(20)   For members of the IDB, the resurrection of the idea of a differential rate – a proposal which they were determined to resist at all costs – allied with their belief that the Authority was acting unreasonably in sustaining its objection to the Phase III scheme, was the last straw, and at a special meeting in February, they decided to withdraw their grant application in respect of the Manor House Level (Phase II). Instead, they would carry out a modified scheme, involving the conversion of Halvergate Fleet into a low-level drain which would convey water from the adjoining marsh dykes to the existing pump at Breydon Sluice.

(21)   This change of policy had two important implications for conservation. First, it would be impossible to use the Fleet to supply freshwater drawn from the R. Bure to maintain dyke water levels in the Seven Mile and Berney Levels during times of drought as originally planned. This would increase the likelihood that owners would put their marshes under the plough. Second, it ruled out any chance of holding water on the land bordering the Fleet during the winter and early spring, thus re-creating the washland conditions which existed here prior to the 1930s (see page 237). Dossors had studied the feasibility of this proposal for the NCC during the winter of 1981/2, and had concluded that it was not only practicable, but would make it easier to supply freshwater to the central and southern parts of the Halvergate triangle (John Dossor & Partners, 1982). It was symptomatic of the general hardening of attitudes which occurred during the protracted negotiations that the IDB rejected the proposals devised by Dossors for the NCC without first giving the latter an opportunity to present its case. This prompted the author, as the NCC's Regional Officer, to remind the Board that Section 48 of the *Wildlife and Countryside Act*, requiring it to further the cause of conservation, had just come into force, and that its peremptory rejection of the proposals . . ."will be a great disappointment to those of us who saw the new Act as a chance to improve the working relationships between conservationists and land drainage interests".

(22)   The NCC came under further pressure in February, when it became known that Mr. R. Dunthorne, who had acquired Church Farm, Wickhampton, the previous autumn, had ploughed up 12.5 ha of marshland, 9 ha of which were

included within the Halvergate Marshes SSSI. Legally, he was within his rights to do this, since the site had not been re-notified under Section 28 of the *Wildlife and Countryside Act* and under the old (1949) legislation relating to SSSIs, he was not obliged to consult the NCC before altering the way the land was managed, even though he had been advised that it was of special interest. For their part, staff of the NCC had not felt it necessary to give the site priority attention because they had been reliably informed that the new owner intended to maintain his marshes in their existing, unimproved state. The site was, however, re-notified in March 1982, and following receipt of a formal notice from Mr Dunthorne, indicating that he wished to put the remainder of his marshes under the plough, a management agreement was negotiated under Section 15 of the *Countryside Act* 1968, whereby the whole of his 42 ha holding would be maintained as unimproved grass, the NCC paying Mr Dunthorne compensation calculated annually on a profits-forgone basis.

(23) In the meantime, discussions concerning the safeguarding of the Red and White Areas continued, a significant advance being made when the parties concerned agreed to adopt a methodology put forward by Messrs. I. M. Sturgess and M. C. Murphy of the Department of Land Economy of Cambridge University for calculating compensation payments on a profits-forgone basis, and assessing the extent to which these should be index-linked. However, the NFU and CLA remained adamant that each signatory of a Red Area agreement should receive an annual management fee until such time as he exercised his right to claim compensation, the main reasoning behind this being that the capital value of his land would be diminished when it became subject to such an agreement. The validity of this argument was not accepted by the DoE or the Countryside Commission, on the grounds that since compensation would be payable annually for a net loss of revenue, there should not, at least in theory, be any reduction in the capital value of the land. On this basis, it was considered that if the Authority offered to pay an annual management fee as well as compensation for profits forgone, it would be making a 'double payment', so breaching a fundamental principle of public accountability.

(24) By June 1982, several members of the Authority were becoming impatient at its continuing failure to reach an agreement with the farming interests, but their resolution calling for the abandonment of the negotiations and a public inquiry was defeated by 16 votes to 5. Instead, the Authority accepted the recommendations made by the Cambridge team, regarding indexation and compensation, and confirmed that to qualify for the latter, a farmer would have to satisfy them that he was financially and technically capable of carrying out the proposed works, MAFF's advice being enlisted on these points. A once-and-for-all sign-on fee of £12.50 per hectare would be offered to each signatory of a Red Area agreement, but this sum would have to be deducted from any compensation award made subsequently.

(25) Anticipating (correctly) that few, if any, landowners would be prepared to conclude agreements on this basis, Lord Middleton, the then President of the CLA, wrote to the Ministers concerned complaining that the terms being offered by the Authority ran contrary to the voluntary principles enshrined in the newly passed *Wildlife and Countryside Act*, and suggesting instead that the Authority should conclude notification agreements, under which owners would be obliged to give it advance warning if they intended altering the management of their land. Such a consultative arrangement would not, of itself, enable the Authority to prevent marshes being put under the plough, and was not therefore compatible with its declared aim of taking positive measures to safeguard the Red Area.

(26) In an attempt to prevent the negotiations breaking down completely, Derek Barber, the Chairman of the Countryside Commission, visited Broadland in mid-July, and addressed a meeting of Halvergate marsh owners. During the ensuing discussions, it became apparent that many of those present were not conversant either with the issues involved, or the options open to them, and it was therefore decided that each of the 18 individuals owning land in the Red Area would be invited to complete a questionnaire, indicating whether he

would be prepared to:

    a) sell his marshes to the Authority; or

    b) enter into an agreement imposing permanent restrictions on changes of management in return for compensation in the form of a once-and-for-all lump-sum payment; or

    c) enter into a 20-year agreement in return for (i) initial compensation for loss of capital value, and (ii) compensation for proven loss when the Authority intervened to prevent the management regime being altered.

(27)   The response to these questionnaires indicated that the majority of those who had holdings in that part of the Red Area to the north of the Halvergate SSSI were not prepared to cooperate with the Authority in any way. This was not altogether surprising given the fact that following the withdrawal of the Phase II proposals and the lowering of the water level in the Fleet, landowners in this area were much better able to drain and put their marshes under the plough, than they had been in the past; indeed, the only remaining deterrent to this was the poor access to much of the area. In contrast, most owners in the Seven Mile/Berney part of the Red Area were willing to consider selling their holdings to the Authority. However, critics doubted whether the latter would be wise to take up these offers in view of the difficulties involved in ensuring that the dykes in this area were supplied with an adequate amount of freshwater. It was also pointed out that even if the *c.* 223 ha involved were purchased at, say £3000 per hectare, and then sold off at half price with restrictive covenants applied, the net cost to the Authority would be in excess of £330 000.

(28)   In a last ditch attempt to find an acceptable compromise, and avoid the conflict and polarization of attitudes which seemed inevitable if the negotiations finally broke down, a revised 'package' was put forward by the author. In essence, this contained the following provisions:

    (a) The boundary of the Red Area would be adjusted to exclude the marshes north of the Halvergate SSSI, and nearest the Seven Mile pumping station, and include the land between Berney Arms and Breydon Sluice (see Map 9.3).

    (b) The Broads Authority would purchase the 178 ha of marsh in the 'new' Red Area, and then re-sell most of it to individuals willing to agree to the restrictive covenants which the Authority would apply to it (e.g. no herbicides or ploughing etc.).

    (c) The existing pump at Berney Arms would be left as a 'stand-by' and would not, as originally intended, be replaced by a new pump of greater capacity. This would obviate the need to build a new road to Berney Arms. Some of the water draining to the Berney pump would be diverted to the Breydon Sluice pumping station and the remainder to the new pump at Seven Mile House.

    (d) An auxiliary pump would be provided by the IDB at Breydon Sluice to supply freshwater from the Fleet to the 'new' Red Area.

    (e) The Authority would seek to conclude notification agreements with the owners of marshes in the Phase II and III areas, and those parts of the Seven Mile and Berney Levels which were not included within the new Red Area.

    (f) The Authority would, in return, lift its objections to the Phase I and III drainage proposals.

(29)   The George package had several advantages. Ornithologically, the new Red Area was an improvement over the old, since the marshes beside Breydon Water could have been subject to shallow flooding during the winter and early spring*; this would have greatly increased their attractiveness to wildfowl and waders and enhanced the value of the adjoining Local Nature Reserve. There would also have been a saving of some £140 000 as a consequence of the abandonment of the plan to provide a new pump at Berney Arms, and a road

---

* This, in fact, is what the RSPB has done, following its establishment of a nature reserve near Berney Arms in 1985.

Breydon Sluice and installing slightly larger pumps at Seven Mile House, but half the remainder, representing the saving in grant aid, could have been used to reduce the cost of the package to the Exchequer. The one apparent disadvantage of the scheme – that the new Red Area contained only *c*. 178 ha of marsh, rather than *c*. 280 ha (not 450 ha as stated by O'Riordan, 1986) – would have been more than offset by the fact that the auxiliary pump would have ensured that a plentiful supply of freshwater was available for the dykes, not only of the Red Area itself, but of the surrounding marshes, thus increasing the likelihood that they would continue to be cattle-grazed, rather than put under the plough. Thus the area retained as unimproved grassland could well have been considerably larger than the original Red Area, at less cost to the Broads Authority and the taxpayer.

(30)   The George proposals were welcomed by the NFU and CLA, and agreed in principle by the IDB. They were also accepted by the Strategy Committee on a majority vote, although it was implicit in this decision that the Authority would not have to find more than 25 per cent of the net cost of purchasing the land and subsequently re-selling it, and that the remaining funds required, estimated at just over £200 000, would be made available by Government. But despite the support being expressed both locally and nationally for the package, the Countryside Commission decided in October that it . . ."falls a long way short of its original indication of protecting the marshland landscape" . . . and that "it would be failing in its responsibilities by doing other than requesting a public inquiry".

In retrospect, the Commission's attitude probably reflected not only its dissatisfaction with the proposals put forward, but its disillusionment with the protracted negotiations; indeed, it is possible that the package would have proved acceptable had it been put forward earlier. Be that as it may, there was obviously no chance of the Government agreeing to fund the proposals when one of its environmental agencies was opposed to them, and in view of this, and the fact that no solution acceptable to all the interested parties had been found, despite nearly two years of negotiations, the Broads Authority decided to endorse the call for a public inquiry. The response from the NFU was both predictable and immediate; it flatly rejected the idea of an inquiry, and urged the Minister of Agriculture to make decisions on the IDB's grant applications without further delay.

(d) The Ministers' decision

Earl Ferrers responded to this request at a meeting in London in November 1982 chaired by Mr Tom King, and attended by the Presidents of the NFU and CLA, the Chairmen of the Broads Authority, Countryside Commission and NCC, and representatives of the IDB. The Ministers firmly rejected the call for a public inquiry, on the grounds that the issues had been subject to very full public debate during the past two years. They also resisted a proposal from the Countryside Commission that the Government should, as part of its decision on the IDB's grant applications, accede to the request made by the Broads Authority in March 1982, that its Executive Area should be designated as 'Special Area' under Section 41 of the *Wildlife and Countryside Act*, thus giving it a status comparable to that of a national park. Having heard the views of the organizations represented, Earl Ferrers announced that the MAFF would grant-aid the Phase III proposals, but that the application made in respect of the Berney/Seven Mile Levels was unacceptable. He would, however, approve a modified project, involving the replacement of the pumps at Seven Mile House with ones of similar capacity, together with the provision of the necessary power supply and access road, the object being merely to protect the area against flooding, and maintain the *status quo*. Grant would not be given for improvements to the arterial drainage of the Seven Mile Level, nor for the replacement of the pump at Berney Arms, which would therefore continue to operate as at present.

The Minister's decisions were generally welcomed by environmental agencies, who regarded them as an example of the way his Department was prepared to 'further' the cause of conservation when determining grant applications, in recognition of its new responsibilities under Section 48 of the *Wildlife and Countryside Act*. The NCC, for example, indicated in a Press Release that whilst the Halvergate controversy was primarily concerned with landscape preservation, rather than nature conservation, the Minister's attitude augured well for the future.

Privately, local conservationists were very dubious whether it would be possible to maintain the *status quo* in the Berney/Seven Mile Levels. A like-for-like pump replacement would not, of itself, do so, since the new pumps would, like the old, be capable of lowering the water-table sufficiently to allow the owners of marshes having an above-average freeboard to convert them to arable. In any event, no record existed of how water levels in the main drains had varied in the past, so how could the IDB arrange for them to remain unaltered once the new pumps had been installed? It was also pointed out that the Board's new road to the pumping station at Seven Mile House would encourage those farming adjoining land to put it under the plough, and that the owners of other holdings nearby would be tempted to add spurs to the new road in order to improve the access to their land. But most important of all, the Minister's decision did nothing to alleviate the underlying problem – the substantial financial benefits to be gained from growing arable crops on the marshes, instead of continuing to run livestock on them.

(e) The aftermath

A revised set of proposals for the Seven Mile Level was submitted to the Broads Authority for comment in February 1983, and negotiations took place during the ensuing months on points of detail relating to this, and the Phase III scheme. It was decided that submersible pumps would be much less visually obtrusive, and at the same time more efficient, than Archimedes screw machines, and that the control gear for the Seven Mile pumping station would be installed in a former drainage mill nearby. The alignment of the new road and power supply to this site proved much more contentious, whilst the IDB's suggestion that Tunstall Dyke (a formerly navigable channel) should be infilled as it would no longer have to serve as a high level watercourse, was wholly unacceptable to conservationists. Eventually, however, agreement was reached on these, and various other points, and in June 1983, two years nine months after the first exchanges between the parties, the Broads Authority and the Countryside Commission formally withdrew their objections to the Phase I and III drainage proposals.

Meanwhile, the Authority and its staff had become increasingly concerned about the amount of marshland in the region which was being converted to arable without their prior knowledge. The gravity of the situation was revealed during the winter of 1982/3, when surveys showed that at least 1340 ha had been put under the plough since 1980, in most cases without any advance warning having been given to the Authority*. The problem was exacerbated by the Minister's decision to defer making a Designation Order under Section 41 of the *Wildlife and Countryside Act*, since this meant, in effect, that farmers could continue to claim drainage grants from MAFF without first telling the Authority. Moreover, the abolition of prior approval in 1980, meant that unless the land had been scheduled as an SSSI, the Department would not necessarily learn that it was to be drained and put under the plough until after this had occurred; it was not therefore in a position to give the Authority advance warning, even if the individual concerned was prepared to waive his right that this information be kept confidential.

Several owners in the Carlton Colville area had already agreed to notify the Authority if they intended to change the way they were managing their land, and in January 1983, a formal notification agreement was drafted for use in the Halvergate area. After some initial disagreement, the terms of this were endorsed by the NFU and CLA, but it was soon found that by focusing attention on the possibility of claiming compensation, it actually triggered such applications; indeed, one or two landowners, when invited to sign, reacted by indicating their intention to plough up their marshes forthwith! In view of this, it was decided to rely on personal contacts as a way of ensuring that the Authority was kept informed of owners' intentions, rather than written agreements.

---

* The Broadland Friends of the Earth (1984) claimed (probably correctly) that a further 409 ha of grass marsh was converted to arable in 1983 and 1984. However, their assertion that prior notice was only given in respect of 55 ha of this total fails to recognize that the Authority's informal notification scheme was concerned primarily with the Halvergate area.

Those who had forecast that the Minister's decision would not be sufficient to preserve the *status quo* in the Berney/Seven Mile Levels were soon proved correct, and by September 1983, the Authority had been informed by three owners in this area that unless it agreed either to purchase their marshes, which together totalled *c.* 240 ha, or conclude profits-forgone management agreements over them in accordance with Section 39 of the *Wildlife and Countryside Act*, they would be obliged to put them under the plough. Those concerned planned to overcome the access problem by using a track owned by a neighbouring farmer to reach a point beside the river, from whence their crops would be shipped to Yarmouth by barge.

The Authority had by this time authorized the completion of a Section 39 agreement over a *c.* 91 ha block of marshland at Oby, but the farmer concerned (Mr Ray Cooke) had been prepared to accept an annual rate of compensation substantially less than the profits-forgone figure to which he would have been entitled. Even so, members of the Authority had been unhappy about the principle enshrined in this clause of the Act, which they regarded (somewhat unfairly) as a payment to farmers for 'doing nothing'. They had also been appalled to learn that under its proven-loss management agreement with Mr Dunthorne (part-owner of the Halvergate Marshes SSSI), the NCC was paying compensation in excess of £500 per hectare per annum. Although the sums payable per hectare would be less on the Seven Mile/Berney Levels (largely because of the very poor access to much of the area and the fact that, unlike Mr Dunthorne, none of the three farmers concerned would be able to integrate the management of his ploughed-up marshland with an arable holding on the adjoining uplands), members were advised that the annual compensation for the *c.* 240 ha would amount to at least £50 000 per annum. The Authority would have to find at least a quarter of this sum, and possibly a half, if the Treasury refused to accede to a request by the Countryside Commission that it be allowed to grant-aid 75 per cent of the cost of agreements negotiated by the Authority over land in the Seven Mile/Berney Red Area. Members were also very conscious that whilst the NCC had received a firm assurance that the funds it required to safeguard SSSIs by proven-loss agreements and other means would be made available by Government, local authorities had been given no such undertaking. Indeed, unless the rate of marsh conversion slackened, one third of the Authority's budget could, by 1990, be committed to paying farmers not to grow a crop which was already heavily in surplus! The Authority's reservations about concluding agreements of this nature were reinforced when it was informed that the Suffolk County Council – one of its constituent partners – had decided that it would be so costly to use Section 39 agreements to prevent the remaining areas of grassland in that county being put under the plough, that it would not authorize any negotiations with landowners on this basis.

The apprehensions of the Authority's members were increased still further when they were informed that in the autumn of 1983 the IDB had commissioned its consultants, John Dossor & Partners, to plan the modernization of the arterial drainage systems of two further blocks of marshland in the Halvergate triangle. One of these consisted of 188 ha in the Ashtree Level, whilst the other, totalling 538 ha, comprised the main part of the Five Mile Level, and the eastern end of the Stracey Level (see Map 9.3). Members were told that Dossors had advised their clients to replace the pumps draining the two former levels, both of which dated from the 1940s, with more powerful machinery, and to re-align and enlarge some 8800 m of arterial drain, at a total estimated cost of £569 000. It was also noted with some foreboding that Dossors were recommending that the marshland within these levels which was located south of the Acle to Yarmouth railway line should in future drain to the Breydon Sluice pumps, as . . ."the IDB was intending to replace these later".

In the event, consultants employed by the Broads Authority expressed doubts about the economic viability of both schemes, and a formal objection was lodged against the Five Mile proposals, on the grounds that the agricultural changes which would result would be detrimental to the landscape and wildlife of the area. In the light of this, and uncertainties as to whether MAFF would be willing to grant-aid the two schemes, the IDB decided in 1984 to defer further consideration of them for the time being.

Meantime, the Strategy Committee had considered a paper at its meeting in November 1983, in which it was suggested that it might be possible to safeguard grass marshland in the Seven Mile and Berney Levels (and elsewhere in the region), not only by outright purchase and proven-loss agreements, but by introducing a system of 'partnership payments' by the Broads Authority and MAFF. These would enable the latter to subsidize graziers on an hectarage basis, as well as providing grants for works directly beneficial to them, whilst the Authority would make bonus payments for environmentally desirable projects. It was thought that MAFF's contributions to this package would be in accord with the EEC's Farm Structures Regulations, the preamble to which states, *inter alia*:

> . . . In protected areas such as nature or national parks, measures should be taken in order to support farmers following agricultural practices which meet the needs of protection and improvement of the environment.

An alternative method of ensuring that marshland continued to be cattle-grazed would be for MAFF to offer 'headage payments' and enhanced rates of grant for those carrying out works aimed at improving the returns obtainable from green pasturage, as is done in Less Favoured Areas (LFA). Much would depend on how MAFF interpreted the EEC's LFA Directive (EC 75/268). However, the Authority's staff thought that Article 3(5) – under which the Scilly Isles are designated – was apposite to Broadland.

> . . . small areas affected by specific handicaps and in which farming must be continued in order to conserve the countryside and to preserve its tourist potential or to protect the coastline.

These proposals, and the Authority's unwillingness to conclude proven-loss agreements unless the Government undertook to find 90 per cent of the cost (as it had previously undertaken to do in respect of management agreements negotiated by the Exmoor National Park Authority), were discussed with senior officials of the Countryside Commission, MAFF and DoE in December. No agreement was reached and in February the Director of the Commission wrote to the DoE pointing out that the credibility of the *Wildlife and Countryside Act* would be irreparably damaged unless a solution to the Halvergate problem could be found. This point was accepted by Mr William Waldegrave, then Parliamentary Under Secretary of State for the Environment, who indicated that in future, the Commission would be allowed to find 75 per cent of the cost of agreements negotiated in the Halvergate area. But this concession did not satisfy the Authority, and in March, its representatives discussed the matter with Lord Belstead, Minister of State for Agriculture, and Mr Waldegrave. The latter again refused to agree that 90 per cent grants should be made available by the Commission for management agreements concluded by the Authority. But both Ministers acknowledged that the latter was in a difficult position, and indicated that an inter-departmental working group would be set up to examine ways in which further losses of grazing marshland could be prevented. The Authority was also advised that the MAFF now accepted in principle that the Executive Area should be designated under Section 41 of the *Wildlife and Countryside Act.* Such a designation would represent an important advance, since it would oblige owners and occupiers to obtain the consent of the Authority before undertaking operations for which they hoped to obtain a MAFF grant. But it would also mean that if grant was withheld as a consequence of an objection by the Authority, the latter would be required under the Act to offer the individual affected a 'proven-loss' management agreement.

Several meetings of the Working Group took place during the next two months, and although MAFF indicated that it would not be able to contribute to the partnership scheme favoured by the Authority, it was more sympathetic to the suggestion that Broadland be designated as a Less Favoured Area, this despite the fact that the United Kingdom already had a larger proportion of the land surface designated in this way than any other country in the EEC. The Group confirmed that a Section 41 designation would be helpful, and also supported a proposal from the Countryside Commission that it should be given funds to set up a 3-year Experimental Scheme under Section 40 of the *Wildlife and Countryside Act* . . . "to encourage farmers and landowners to continue livestock enterprises . . . so as to conserve the essential character of the Broadland landscape". This would be achieved by offering them a subsidy of £40* per acre (*c.* £100 / ha) and making available 75 per cent grants for capital works designed to improve the returns obtainable from grass pasturage. Dairy youngstock would be eligible, but it was thought that cows would have to be excluded, as it would be anomalous

---

* This sum was subsequently increased to £50 per acre.

to subsidize them, at the same time as operating a quota system on milk production.

The livestock support scheme would be applied to a 'Critical Amenity Area' to be agreed between the Countryside Commission and the Broads Authority, and probably covering all the Grade I and II landscape in the region, i.e. 8284 ha, plus certain other areas of lesser quality. 100 per cent take-up by farmers was considered most unlikely, and it was estimated that some 5320 ha would be covered at the end of the 3-year trial. It was envisaged that if the experiment was successful, it would be taken over by MAFF and administered under the LFA directive. The principal merit of the scheme was that it would greatly reduce the number of proven-loss agreements which the Broads Authority would be expected to negotiate, thus saving money, and allowing it to deploy its resources on other environmentally desirable projects.

The Group's report was submitted to Ministers at the beginning of June, and on 23 July during an Adjournment Debate in the Commons, Mr Waldegrave announced that the Countryside Commission would in future be allowed to find 75 per cent of the cost of any management agreements negotiated by the Authority, rather than those in the Halvergate area only. The Government had also decided to apply Section 41 of the *Wildlife and Countryside Act* to the Executive Area of the Broads Authority, subject to the satisfactory outcome of public consultation. However a decision on the Commission's Experimental Livestock Support Scheme would be deferred while the Minister of Agriculture, Mr Michael Jopling, tried to ensure that the EEC's Agricultural Structures Regulations were given a stronger environmental bias. As Lord Belstead explained in the House of Lords the same day:

> . . . the time has come for us to take a major new initiative . . . [and seek] a completely new title in the regulation-covering powers which would enable us in environmentally sensitive areas to encourage farming practices which are consonant with conservation . . . which would herald a totally new policy for balancing agricultural and conservation objectives . . . (Hansard; HL Col. 90)

In the event, the negotiations in Brussels proved much more difficult than expected, and at the end of September 1984, Mr Patrick Jenkin, Secretary of State for the Environment, wrote to warn the Chairman of the Authority that a decision on the livestock support scheme would be delayed, and to express the hope that the Authority would do its best to maintain the *status quo* in the meantime.

Although this request was sympathetically received, members were alarmed by the view being expressed by some of the constituent partners that the Authority was spending too much time and effort trying to safeguard grass pasture in the face of the inexorable commercial pressures to which farmers were subject. The Chairman of the Authority gave vent to these 'political' fears at a meeting of the Strategy Committee in October, when he claimed that they were seeking to protect too large an area, and that unless they worked towards a more realistic goal, they would prejudice their chances of retaining the support of the Norfolk County Council for the Parliamentary Bill setting up the new Broads Agency. Special concern was also expressed about the five, one-year agreements which had, as Mr Waldegrave had asked, been negotiated with farmers within the Berney/Seven Mile area. These covered some 307 ha, and although three of them were only costing *c.* £50 per hectare the fourth was significantly more expensive, whilst the fifth was a full proven-loss agreement, since the owner involved, Mr Michael Wright, had been just about to plough up his 36-ha holding when asked to desist. Four of the agreements were due to expire at the end of March 1985, and the Authority had promised to inform the farmers concerned by the end of December what future arrangements were to be made so they could plan accordingly. Unless this deadline was set, there was a real danger that they would despair of concluding a satisfactory deal with the Authority, and put their land under the plough. Some 36 ha of marsh between the Fleet and Berney Arms had already been converted following the rejection by its owner, Mr David Wright, of an offer of a one-year holding agreement of £50 per hectare, and the Strategy Committee's refusal, on a majority vote, to recommend that he be offered full proven-loss compensation. This decision was taken partly because the land in question was bordered on two sides by marshes already under the plough, and on another by the railway, and partly because it lay just outside the Red Area. But any losses of grass marsh within the latter would gravely weaken the Authority's credibility, and mean that the funds which it had spent on the holding agreements (which together totalled nearly £8000) would only have given the land concerned a temporary reprieve.

A clear indication of the Government's anxiety to find a solution was provided in mid-November, when Mr Jenkin toured the Halvergate Marshes, and afterwards indicated that they were . . ."a marvellous example of unspoilt countryside . . . [and] their value as an absolutely unique piece of wetland is immeasurable". Encouraged by this, and despite the reservations of some of its members, the Authority decided later that month to ask those farmers who already had holding agreements to allow them to run for a further year. Similar agreements would also be offered to the owners of *c.* 242 ha who, during the previous two months, had advised the Authority of their intention to put their land under the plough.

In mid-January, Mrs Peggy Fenner, Under Secretary of State for Agriculture, was obliged to inform Parliament that the Government proposal to amend the EEC's Structures Regulations had received virtually no support in Brussels (Hansard, HC 17 January, Col. 197), and following high-level discussions in Whitehall (allegedly involving the Cabinet), Mr Jenkin announced on 30 January that the Countryside Commission had been given the go-ahead to introduce its experimental livestock support scheme in time for the 1985 grazing season. Half the funds required, estimated at £1.7 million over the 3-year period would be found from the Commission's Grant-in-Aid (which had been increased by £2 million for 1985/6) while the other half would be made available by MAFF.

The new project soon became known as the Broads Grazing Marshes Conservation Scheme (see Chapter 13), and at its formal launching in Norwich in March 1985, Lord Belstead indicated that the Government had decided, in the light of the widespread support expressed during the consultative exercise, to designate forthwith the Executive Area under Section 41 of the *Wildlife and Countryside Act**. He also announced that the Council of European Ministers had, after all, agreed to the amendments to the Farm Structures Regulations which had been proposed by the UK Government, and that the necessary follow-up legislation, enabling the MAFF to fund conservation projects in Environmentally Sensitive Areas (ESAs) like Broadland, would be introduced into Parliament as soon as possible†. Though not acknowledged publicly, much of the credit for this change of heart by the EEC can be attributed to vigorous lobbying in Brussels by the RSPB, Council for the Protection of Rural England and other conservation agencies.

In May 1985 it was agreed that owners who informed the Authority under the S.41 procedure of their intention to put their marshes under the plough should be offered one-year holding agreements of £50 per acre if their land was of scenic or scientific importance, but outside the areas covered by the Broads Grazing Marshes Conservation Scheme. However, fearing an influx of such notifications, the Authority decided that the total area covered by such agreements should not exceed 1500 acres (607 ha). In the event, the Authority only found it necessary to conclude five additional holding agreements, together encompassing 130 ha. Moreover, eight of the nine owners who had previously had Section 39 agreements with the Authority decided in 1985 or 1986 not to renew them, but to include all their marshland (or in the case of one individual, part of it) in the Experimental Scheme. A tenth owner, Mr Michael Wright, sold his holding to the RSPB in 1985. Thus by March 1987, the Authority was left with two ten-year agreements, together covering 105 ha, plus six short-term holding agreements covering a total of 235 ha. The annual cost of these agreements amounted that year to £35 146, but 75 per cent of this was refunded by the Countryside Commission. Moreover, the majority of the owners concerned had by then indicated that they would apply for the subsidies payable under the Environmentally Sensitive Area scheme (see page 485), rather than continue with their agreements with the Authority.

The Limpenhoe Level

The Government's anxiety to help the Broads Authority safeguard parts of the Drained Marshland Area until ways could be found of improving the financial returns obtainable by graziers, and yet avoid creating a precedent costly in terms of public expenditure, was

---

* This designation (which was made on April 17 1985) was subsequently replaced by the provisions of Section 31(3) of Schedule 3 of the *Norfolk and Suffolk Broads Act* 1988.

† The powers to designate ESAs were subsequently enshrined in Section 18(1) of the *Agriculture Act* 1986.

particularly well illustrated at Limpenhoe during the summer of 1984. Mr David Archer, owner of *c.* 48 ha of this Level, had encountered increasing difficulty in finding graziers willing to hire his land, and in 1983 his net income had been so small that he decided to go into partnership with another farmer and put his marshes under the plough. Although only rated as being of Grade 2 landscape importance, Mr Archer's holding forms the most visible part of the Limpenhoe Level, being bordered to the south by a public footpath, and to the east by the road to Reedham Ferry. The area is also of natural history interest, since some of its dykes possess a very good aquatic fauna and flora. In the light of these circumstances, the Broads Authority decided that it should indicate its willingness to enter into a short-term management agreement over the land. But despite several meetings, this offer was rejected by Mr Archer, and as a last resort, it was proposed that an Article 4 Direction should be applied to the land under the terms of the *Town and Country Planning Act* 1971. Although this would not stop Mr Archer ploughing his marshes and cleaning out the existing ditches (since such works are not classed as 'development' in the planning legislation, and would not therefore be covered by an Article 4 Direction), he would have to obtain planning permission before he could carry out any engineering or building operations, as defined in Class 6 of Schedule 1 to the *General Development Order* 1977. These would include installing an underdrainage system, deepening, widening or infilling the dykes, or cutting new drains, all of which would be necessary if the land was to be cropped successfully. The original intention was that the Broads Authority should apply the Direction, but in June 1984 the Secretary of State for the Environment decided to do this himself . . ."in the exceptional circumstances of this case, and in order to allow time for further discussions about a management agreement". In the event, Mr Archer accepted a renewed offer from the Authority of a one-year holding agreement, involving a lump sum payment of £10 000 plus costs, and in 1985, he agreed, after further negotiations, to participate in the Broads Grazing Marshes Conservation Scheme.

Having fulfilled its purpose, the Direction was lifted by the Minister in September 1984. However, its use generated considerable interest in planning circles, as it was thought this was the first time that an Article 4 Direction had been employed to control the drainage of agricultural land (although one had been issued in 1974 in respect of the management of the R. Stour between Stratford St. Mary and Cattawade because it was considered that works on this river could allow farmers to lower the water-table of the adjoining land sufficiently to put it under the plough). It was also noted that by exercising his powers over a specific site, the Minister had conformed to the principle that Article 4 Directions should not be used to give 'blanket' protection to large areas. It was therefore most unlikely that he would have agreed that a Direction should be applied to the whole of the Authority's Executive Area, a possibility which the Broadland Friends of the Earth had actively canvassed during the summer of 1984.

The Ludham Marshes

In July 1984 the Authority's officers became aware that Mr R. J. Rogerson, owner of some 4 ha of marsh just south of Womack Water, was intending to under-drain it, prior to putting it under the plough. Although the land in question formed part of the Ludham Marshes SSSI, scheduled under Section 23 of the *National Parks and Access to the Countryside Act* 1949, the NCC had decided that this particular area did not merit re-notifying under the 1981 Act. The site was, however, located within an area classified as being of Grade 1 landscape importance, and in the light of this the Authority was recommended at its meeting on 27 July to negotiate a one-year management agreement with Mr Rogerson, involving the payment of compensation for profits forgone.

Differing views about this proposition were expressed at the meeting, several members, including the Chairman, taking the view that negotiating an agreement over this particular site would create a precedent which would "open the floodgates" to the extent that the Authority would not have sufficient funds to protect other, more important areas of marsh, or fulfil its other objectives. After considerable debate, the Authority decided by 9 votes to 6 not to enter into negotiations with Mr Rogerson, and the site was duly put under the plough.

Members of the Broadland Friends of the Earth, who were the first to forewarn the

Authority of the threat to the site, and who had camped out on it to prevent it being drained prior to the Authority's meeting,* were deeply aggrieved by this decision, particularly when taken in context with the Authority's near-simultaneous resolution to offer Mr David Archer a management agreement, this despite the fact that his land at Limpenhoe was only of Grade 2 landscape importance. The Chairman of the Broadland Friends, Andrew Lees, therefore lodged a formal complaint with the Commission for Local Administration in England (the 'Local Ombudsman') on the grounds that the Authority's attitude over the Ludham Marsh case had caused injustice to him and his members by breaching the Authority's overriding objective to conserve and enhance the natural beauty and amenity of Broadland, and by being inconsinent with its policy in respect of the Limpenhoe Level. In the event, the Local Ombudsman decided, after hearing the views of the two parties, to reject the complaint of maladministration, one of the key points being that the Authority's decision over the Limpenhoe case had been prompted by the larger size of the site, and its greater importance than the 4 ha at risk at Ludham.

Marsh acidity problems in the Thurne catchment

Apart from a narrow strip of marshland between Tunstall and Reedham, the soils of the Halvergate triangle contain sufficient calcium carbonate to ensure that the sulphate ions deposited therein when the area formed an open expanse of tidal mudflats and saltings, are retained as gypsum when the water-table is lowered. However, as we have seen in Chapter 2, the soils in many other parts of the Drained Marshland Area are deficient in lime, and consequently acidify and release ochre when the drainage is improved. These problems are particularly severe in the catchment of the Upper Thurne owing to the repeated saltwater flooding to which this part of Broadland has been subject over the centuries, and it is ironic that the first area to be subject to a comprehensive drainage improvement scheme after the Second World War was the Brograve Level, a principal component of this particular catchment.

In his description of the changes in land use management which occurred in the Upper Thurne catchment between 1931 and 1973, Driscoll (1984d) points out that most of the Brograve Level was converted to arable during the 1960s. As a result, increasing quantities of ochre were discharged by the Happisburgh to Winterton IDB's Brograve pumping station into Waxham Cut, which soon became so heavily silted as to become almost impassable to larger holiday craft. In 1971, the Rivers Commissioners were obliged to dredge the Cut downstream of the Brograve pumphouse in order to maintain it in a navigable condition, and further accumulations of particulate ochre had to be removed from near the outfall of the Cut into Horsey Mere in 1975 (2000 tons), 1978 (1440 tons) (Groves, pers. comm.) and 1987 (Buxton, pers comm.).

The Brograve Level also provides a dramatic illustration of the aesthetic consequences of deep-draining acid sulphate soils. At certain times of the year, notably in the early summer, so much ochre is discharged by the Brograve pumps that the water in Waxham Cut assumes the appearance of orangeade. Moreover, the band of discoloured water can be traced right across Horsey Mere, down Meadow Dyke and into Heigham Sound. Against this must be set the likelihood that the ochre causes some of the soluble reactive phosphorus in the water to precipitate out as ferric phosphate. In this state the phosphorus is unavailable to algae, and the presence of ochre in Horsey Mere and Heigham Sound (and in diluted form in Hickling Broad through tidal back-up) is therefore probably conducive to the development of a Phase II flora, in place of the Phase III communities currently found in these waters.

Preliminary studies suggest that few invertebrates can survive in waterways subject to heavy ochre deposition. Some waterweeds, on the other hand, seem to be surprisingly tolerant, even when their leaves are covered by a thick layer of orange sediment; examples include the pondweeds *Potamogeton pectinatus* and *P. pusillus*, both of which tend

---

* This was not the only occasion that this branch of the Friends of the Earth took direct action against a farmer engaged in improving the drainage of his marshland, prior to putting it down to arable. Similar measures were taken in August 1984 against Mr David Ritchie, a tenant of the Norwich Union Insurance Company who, because of the imposition of dairy quotas, was planning to plough up some 14 ha of grass marshland on the St. Benet's Level.

to increase at the expense of other plants when growing in marsh dykes containing ochre-rich water (see Plate 30).

According to the AWA, the water discharged from the Brograve pumping station contains significant quantities of salt as well as ochre (mean – 3531 mg Cl⁻ l⁻¹, range 1030 to 4440 mg l⁻¹). This is thought to be finding its way into the dyke system of the Level through the Middle and Upper Peat, both of which outcrop in the North Sea only a few kilometres to the east (Goldsworthy, 1972). In addition, the marshland itself is undergoing rapid shrinkage. This is only to be expected, given the fact that much of the Level is on peat, and is therefore subject to the same processes of wastage as are the drained peatland soils of the Fens. But despite this, farmers have continued to deep-drain and cultivate the Brograve marshes, regardless of the long-term consequences. By 1980, shrinkage in some places had become so severe that one owner, unable to obtain as much freeboard as he wanted, asked the IDB to lower the water-table of the Level still further. This request was turned down, but not because, as a conservationist would have argued, it would cause the soil to shrink even more, and increase the rate at which saltwater was infiltrating into the dyke system, but for the more mundane reason that it would be uneconomic to arrange for the pumps to raise water through a greater height than they are already.

Similar environmental problems have been encountered in respect of the Eastfield Level, which lies to the north-west of Horsey Mere. In response to pressure from a group of its ratepayers, the body responsible for the arterial drainage system of this area, the Smallburgh IDB, agreed in the 1960s to lower the water-table by about a metre so that marsh owners in the Level could put their land under the plough. Hardly had this been done, than substantial quantities of ochre began to be discharged by Eastfield Pump. As a result the narrow dyke, known as Gibb's Outlet, which conveys water from this pump across the Brayden Marshes to Waxham Cut, and thence into Horsey Mere, began to undergo rapid siltation, so causing ochre-rich water to back up, and damage the adjoining saw-sedge beds (see Map 9.4a). But despite several requests by the National Trust, as owners of the Horsey Estate (of which the Brayden Marshes form a part), and their tenant, John Buxton, the IDB resolutely refused to contribute towards the cost of dredging Gibb's Outlet on the grounds that ochre deposition was a 'natural phenomenon'.

In view of the strong views being expressed by conservationists about the environmental damage being caused by the Brograve and Eastfield pumps, the Broads Authority invited a consultant engineer, Arthur Alsop, to advise what remedial measures could be taken. In his report (Alsop, 1981), he identified four possible solutions:

(a) Re-directing the discharge from the Brograve pumping station to the sea;
(b) Re-organizing the drainage system so that both the Brograve and the Eastfield pumps discharged into either Meadow Dyke or Hickling Broad;
(c) Forming sedimentation lagoons adjacent to the pumps; and
(d) Raising the water-table of the two drainage Levels.

Alsop ruled out option (a) on the basis tht it would be enormously expensive to pipe to the sea the huge volumes of water produced by the Brograve pumping station. Conservationists would support him in this on the grounds that if the flow of water from the Hickling-Horsey catchment was reduced, increased volumes of nutrient-rich water from the Bure would find its way up the Thurne as a result of tidal back-up, thus reducing the chances of restoring Hickling Broad and Horsey Mere to a Phase II condition.

It was considered impracticable to reorganize the drainage system so as to obviate the need to discharge ochre-contaminated water into Waxham Cut, given the fact that it would be necessary to double the width of the receiving watercourses. Nor was it thought practicable to provide settlement lagoons for the pumps on account of their very large outputs. Alsop calculated that some 20 acres (*c.* 8 ha) would have to be set aside to store one day's pumping from the Brograve Level. Moreover, there was no guarantee that all the ochre would settle out in such a short period.

The fourth possibility – restoring water levels to the state they were in the 1940s and 1950s – would as Alsop put it . . . "mean a complete standstill on drainage improvements in the areas, and in fact a requirement to negate those carried out in the last few years". Given the climate of opinion at the time he produced his report, he decided that such a proposal would be completely unacceptable, particularly to the two IDBs concerned. However, times have changed since then, and this solution, though not yet put into effect, is no longer quite so unrealistic as it once appeared, given the fact that both the Brograve and the Eastfield Levels have been included within the Broads Environmentally Sensitive Area (see Map 13.2). This would, in theory, allow a farmer wishing to raise his water levels and convert his arable back to grass, to receive compensation at the Tier 1, or even Tier 2 rate, for doing so. However, as George (1990) has pointed out, neither ESA payments, nor management agreements negotiated under the provisions of the *Wildlife and Countryside Act* are likely to offer farmers a sufficient incentive to do this, and some way will therefore have to be found of augmenting the funds available. George has identified and discussed two ways in which this might be achieved. The first would, in effect, involve paying farmers to take their land out of production, and would necessitate taking advantage of the MAFF's 'Set Aside' scheme. The second and, in the

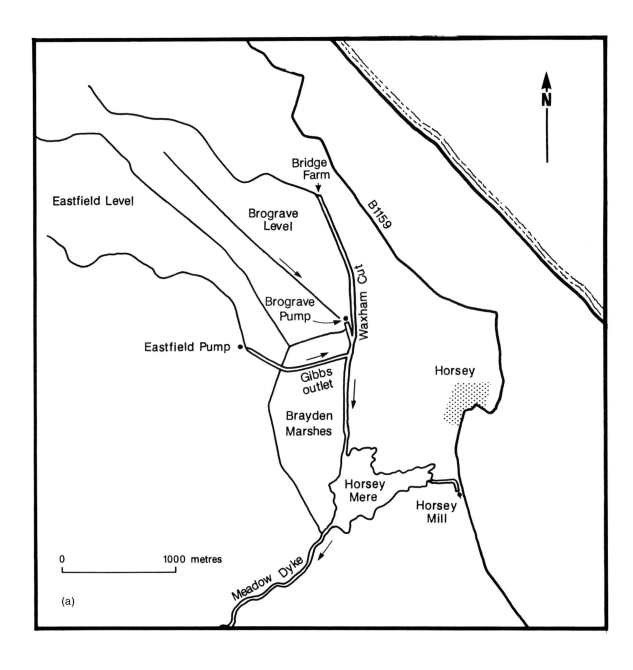

Map 9.4   The Eastfield Level pump, and the alignment of its original (a), and new (b) outfall channels. (© Crown Copyright).

author's view, more promising method of proceeding, would be for conservation agencies to acquire, either by freehold purchases, lease or nature reserve management agreement, a direct legal basis that the Brograve and Eastfield Levels form a principal component of the upper Thurne catchment, and thus constitute an integral part of one of the most important wetland systems in the region.

Aware of the continuing damage being caused to the Brayden Marshes by the operation of the Eastfield pump, the AWA decided as part of its programme of works for European Year of the Environment (1987) to alleviate the problem by creating a new outfall channel for it. This carries the water discharged by the pump around the northern edge of the Brayden Marshes, and thence into Waxham Cut at a point just downstream of Brograve Mill. AWA also built a dam to prevent water from the pump flowing down Gibb's Outlet as in the past, and provided an overspill sluice near the mouth of the new channel to reduce the amount of particulate ochre being carried into Waxham Cut, and thence into Horsey Mere (see Map 9.4b).

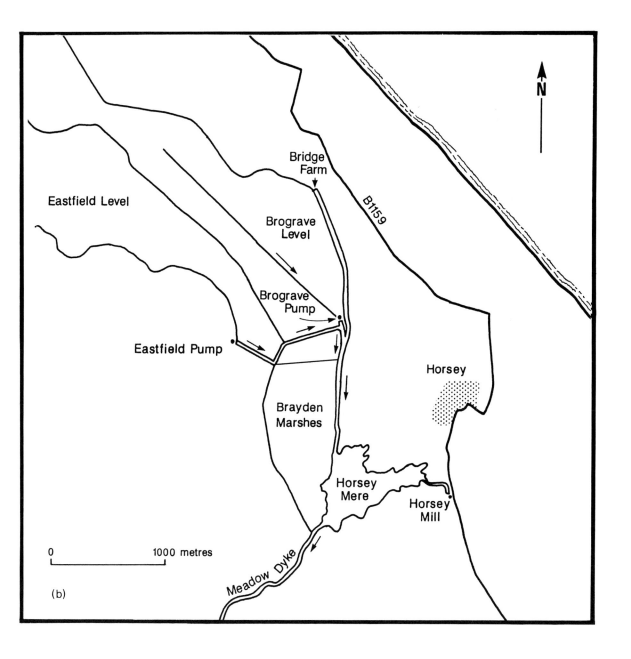

The Somerton Level (*c.* 325 ha) has for centuries been periodically flooded by sea water following breaches in the adjoining dunes (see page 314), and because of the consequent susceptibility of the soils to acidification, successive owners of the Burnley Hall Estate, which includes the majority of the Level, have considered it prudent to maintain a high water-table, and manage most of the marshland as unimproved pasture. In 1978, the Estate changed hands, and it subsequently became known that the Happisburgh to Winterton IDB had acceded to a request by the new owners that the water-table in the Level be lowered, thus enabling them to under-drain their marshes, and put them under the plough. Shortly afterwards, substantial quantities of ochre began to be released from the newly-drained marshes. This was a matter of the utmost concern to conservationists, since the pumping station at West Somerton which drains the Level discharges into Somerton Dyke at a point only about 600 m upstream of Martham North and South Broads. These sites are still in a near-pristine condition (see page 106), and it was feared that not only would the ochre alter their waterweed flora, and impoverish their invertebrate fauna (as had happened in Waxham Cut and Gibbs Outlet) but that their ecology would also be adversely affected by the greater quantities of salt, nitrogen and other chemicals which would be contained in the run-off from the newly cultivated land. That these fears were not groundless is indicated by the fact that AWA surveys have shown that the mean chloride level in the channel between the two broads rose from 1000 mg Cl⁻ l⁻¹ in 1976, to *c.* 1600 mg Cl⁻ l⁻¹ in the period June 1980 to June 1982.

Fortunately from the conservation point of view, the existing pumps – which are housed in a pontoon floating in the main collecting drain in the Level – did not have sufficient capacity to maintain the required freeboard following periods of heavy rainfall, and in 1980, the IDB asked MAFF for a grant towards the cost of providing a second pumping station to be located beside the existing one. The NCC lodged a formal objection to this, on the grounds that the water which it discharged would pollute Martham North and South Broads, and thus endanger part of a wetland site (Hickling Broad/Horsey Mere) which had been recognized as being of international importance under the Ramsar Convention, and which the Government was therefore committed to safeguarding.

During the course of subsequent discussions between the various interested parties, the author suggested that the second pumping station should be located so that the ochre, salt and nitrogen-laden water from it was discharged downriver of the two Martham Broads, rather than upstream of them as originally intended (Map 9.5). It was also proposed that dams be installed so as to ensure that the main block of marshland which had been put under the plough would drain to this pump, rather than to the existing pumping station near the head of Somerton Dyke.

With minor amendments, these suggestions were accepted by the IDB, and it was arranged that the additional capital costs involved (which amounted to about £17 000) would be shared equally by the NCC and the MAFF, thus fulfilling the Government's commitment under the Ramsar Convention to safeguard the two Martham Broads.

The Board was unwilling to accept responsibility for maintaining the lower reaches of the Hundred Stream into which the new pump was to discharge, and it was eventually agreed that the best way of overcoming this problem would be for the NCC and the MAFF to share the cost of dredging and widening this, and installing a weir to prevent ochre being carried downstream and deposited in the R. Thurne. In the meantime, the AWA would formally adopt this section of the Hundred Stream as a 'main river', thus making itself responsible for periodically removing the ochre and other sediments which had accumulated in it.

While these negotiations were taking place, the Broads Authority decided that the power supply to the new pumping station would be very obtrusive in the open landscape of the Somerton Level, and would also pose a threat to birds flying over the marshes. Accordingly, the Authority and MAFF agreed to share the additional cost (amounting to *c.* £9000) of putting underground the 400 m-long section of cable nearest the pump.

The original pumping station near the head of Somerton Dyke was later re-conditioned by the IDB, and continues to operate. Although the run-off from its catchment contains some ochre, this is diluted by a supply of good quality water from the higher ground to the south-west. In addition, the Board has, at the NCC's request, installed a weir between the pump's outfall and Somerton Dyke, with the object of

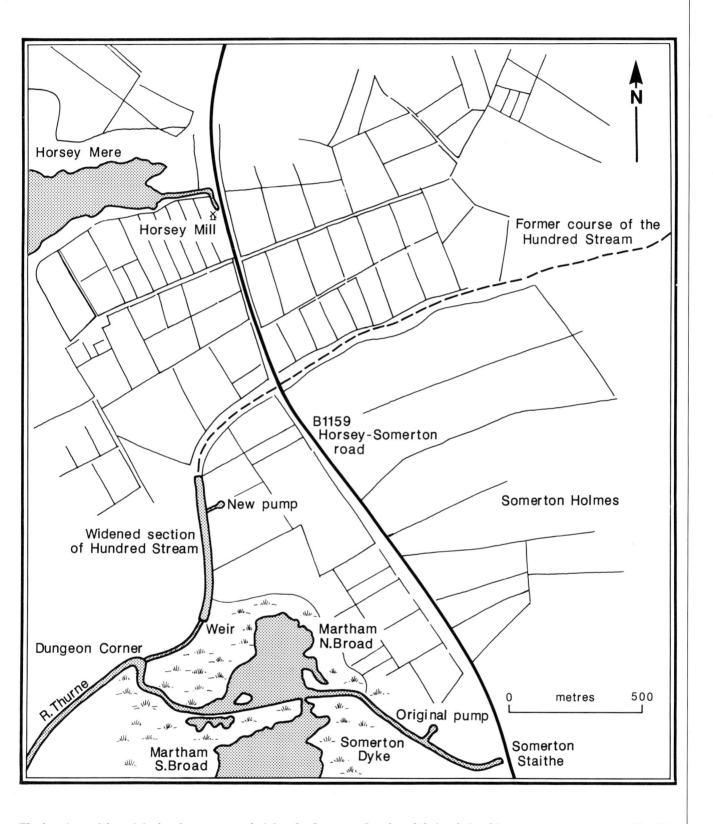

The locations of the original and new pumps draining the Somerton Level, and their relationship to Martham North and South Broads.

Map 9.5

Source: NCC data

giving the discharge time to sediment out before it flows away down the Dyke towards the two Martham Broads.

These arrangements have worked well, and Somerton Dyke is much less discoloured than it was immediately following the conversion of the adjoining marshland to arable. More importantly, both Martham North and South Broads remain in good ecological condition; indeed, there is some evidence (see Chapter 5) that the traces of iron ochre contained in the effluent discharged by the pump are helping to reduce phosphorus concentrations in the water, thus ensuring that these sites remain in a Phase I/II state.

Chapter 10
The Flooding Problem

Introduction

Much of Broadland lies at, or slightly below, high tide level, and the land use history and ecology of the region have been profoundly influenced by the periodic sea and riverine floods to which it has consequently been prone. The principal reason for the abandonment of most, if not all, the deeper peat workings was the increasing difficulty of keeping them free of water during the thirteenth and early fourteenth centuries (see Chapter 4), and further indications of the effects of floods on the lives of local people are provided by Blomefield (1805–1810) and other historians.

The Drained Marshland Area has been subject to periodic flooding ever since it was embanked. The flap-sluices on which its drainage originally depended would have been liable to tide-locking, and it is doubtful whether, following heavy rainfall, they would have been capable of evacuating water sufficiently quickly to prevent the adjoining marshes being temporarily flooded. The wind-powered drainage mills which progressively replaced the gravity systems (probably from the seventeenth century onwards) were liable to be damaged by storms, and thus put out of action. Even when they were in good order, the marshes were likely to be water-covered in late spring if a period of heavy rainfall was followed by a prolonged calm spell in March or early April. This would have delayed the start of the cattle grazing season, though this disadvantage would have been partly offset by the improved productivity which resulted from the deposition of silt on the marshes.

The incidence of surface flooding was progressively reduced as steam, and later oil-engined and electric pumps came into use, and thanks to the reliability of modern machinery, marshland is now seldom flooded as a result of mechanical breakdowns. On the other hand, the benefits which accrued as gravity systems of drainage and wind-pumps were phased out, have been offset by the increased tidal influence to which the rivers have been subject since the mid-nineteenth century (see page 61). This, together with the continuing rise in the level of the sea, and therefore the rivers, relative to the land, has increased the leakage through the tidal embankments, and made it more likely that they will be overtopped or breached during extra high tides, or following surges.

The likelihood of flooding has also been greatly increased by the erosion of which the river banks are now subject as a consequence of the large number of motor craft in use on the waterways (see Chapter 11). Last but not least, many sections of river are now bordered by marshes which have been converted to arable. As a result, the close-grazed, cattle-trampled grassy sward which previously clothed the embankments, and which helped to maintain them in a flood-resistant condition, has been replaced by thistles, nettles and other coarse species. Such communities provide the embankment with less protection against a wash-out if it is overtopped; it is also more difficult to prevent it being damaged by burrowing moles and rabbits. Even where a section of river is still bordered by grass marshland, farmers are reluctant to allow their cattle and sheep access to the ronds and embankments for fear that they be injured by the broken glass, plastic bags and other litter left behind by anglers and boat-borne holidaymakers.

Sea floods

Serious as the consequences of a breached embankment are, especially if the adjoining marshland is under the plough, the damage thus produced pales into insignificance compared with the havoc wrought in the past when, as a result of a major surge, the sea broke through the dunes between Happisburgh and Winterton, and flooded large parts of the region, often for months at a time. Events of this kind occurred in 1250, and again in 1287, when John of Oxenedes, a monk of St. Benet's Abbey, recorded in his chronicle how the sea . . . "broke through its accustomed limits, and flooded areas which had never previously been covered by salt water". Cattle and freshwater fish were killed, whilst at Hickling, 108 men, women and children lost their lives (Ellis, 1859). It was probably in response to events such as these, allied to the progressive rise in the sea and river levels relative to the land, that the floor surface of the Norman building on the site of the new Courthouse near Whitefriars Bridge was periodically raised during the thirteenth century (Ayers, *in litt.*).

There were further sea floods during the Middle Ages, but the next event of major significance occurred in 1608. On this occasion, the Broadland valleys were flooded as far upstream as Buxton Lamas and Trowse on the Bure and Yare respectively, and 2000 people had to be mustered to help repair the defences.

The following year an Act was passed . . . "for the speedye recoverye of manye thousand Acres of Marshe Groundes and other Grounde wthin the counties of Norffolke and Suffolke, lateleye surrounded by the Rage of the Sea in divers parte of the said Counties; and for the pvencion of the danger of like surroundinge hereafter" (7 Jac.1 1609–1610). The preamble to this Act* provides an insight into the scale of the disaster which had befallen the region, and the effects which it had had on the inhabitants:

> And now of late such have beene the extordinaire force and rage of the Sea upon that parte of the said Coast of Norff, that noe usuall Diligence or Meanes have been sufficient to withstand the violence thereof, but within six monthes now last past it hath broken downe and washed away the Cliffes and higher Grounde there, such as they were, and laid them flatt and levell with the said Inlande, and made Breaches so wide that the Sea hath broken in at evy Tide and with every Seawynde into the very Harte and Body as well of the said Countie of Norff as into some parte of the said Countie of Suff adjoyning wcth lye subject to the said Overflowes, and hath decayed surrounded and drowned up much hard Grounde, beside the greatest parte of the marshes and Lower Groundes wthin the Townes and Parishes hereafter mencioned (the same conteyning many Thousand Acres) upon whch a great part of the Wealth of the said Counties doth depend, being grounde of themselves very ritch, and without wch the Uplande, specially of the Countie of Norff, being of themselves for the most Parte vy dry and barren, cannot be so well husbanded or ymployed; And by meanes also of the said Overflowes of the saltwater, the fishinge of the Rivers, Creeke and other places there adjoyning (whereof there was great Plentie and whereby many poore Men were maynteyned, and the Markett sved with Fishe) are greatlie decayed wch said Breaches, as they happened very suddenly, and will require a psent and great Charge to repair and render them fensable against the Sea: so it is to be feared that in tyme to come further Mischief may followe by other Breaches . . . if mature remedie be not pvided . . . greatly anoyed and generally endangered or like to be endangered.

The main purpose of the Act was to set up a Sea Breach Commission. This was required to survey the breaches in the sea defences, levy a rate on those whose land had

---

* This preamble is of much interest in that it corroborates the evidence presented in Chapter 8 that extensive sections of the flood plains had been embanked and drained by the beginning of the seventeenth century. It also contains a clear indication that a much greater agricultural value was placed upon this reclaimed area, than on the 'dry and barren' land found elsewhere in Norfolk. The reference to the relationship between the uplands and the flood plain land is also of interest, since it implies that livestock were customarily transferred from one to the other. It is probable that 'fold courses' were still in widespread use at this time (see Chapter 8). In addition, 'green manure' harvested from the drained marshes was probably being used to maintain the fertility of the upland areas.

been flooded (and who would therefore benefit if the damage was repaired), and carry out the necessary remedial works (Cornford, 1979). The Commission consisted of eleven Justices of the Peace from Norfolk, and six from Suffolk, and sat under the chairmanship of the Bishop of Norwich.

Although the dunes were repaired, they were again breached in 1617, and in 1622 so much damage was caused that serious consideration was given to the idea of raising the causeway leading to Potter Heigham bridge, and allowing all the marshland to the east to become permanently flooded by the sea. This proposal was rejected in 1625 on the advice of Mr. Briggs, a Reader of Mathematics at Oxford University, but his counter-proposal to stop up the bridge, and pump water from the marshes to the east into the R. Thurne by "wyndmills or horsemills" was not acted upon. This, incidentally, is the earliest known reference to the use of wind power in Broadland for land drainage.

New Sea Breach Commissions were formed from time to time as the need arose, and attempts were made to repair the damage caused by further sea floods in 1717, 1718 and 1720. But each Commission experienced great difficulty in collecting the rates it levied on those who benefited from its activities and, in 1743, the one then in existence seems to have been disbanded in the face of a threat of legal action by a group of objectors (Cornford, 1979). No further Commissions were appointed that century, and the sea defences consequently got into a parlous state. A surge in 1791 damaged houses at Hickling and other places whilst the salt contaminated the cattle drinking water on the marshes and killed all the fish in Hickling Broad. By coincidence, the survey for Faden's map was carried out the following year, and this shows that nine separate breaches, together extending to a width of 444 m, were torn in the dunes between Horsey and Waxham on this occasion.

The projected enclosure and drainage of marshland in Winterton, Horsey, Hickling and other parishes near the coast made it imperative to repair and strengthen the dune defences and in 1802, following a petition, a Commission of Sewers for the Eastern Hundreds of Norfolk was formed. This was generally known as the 'Sea Breach Commission' as it was concerned solely with the sea defences between Happisburgh and Winterton, and was not responsible for other flood control measures in the region, or land drainage. In the first half of the nineteenth century, Commissions of Sewers were only appointed for ten years, and new Sea Breach Commissions therefore had to be created in 1822, 1832, 1844 and 1855. However, this costly, and seemingly unnecessary procedure was brought to an end by the *Land Drainage Act* of 1861, which laid down that all Commissions then in existence should be deemed to continue until superseded by the Crown.

To raise the funds it needed, each Sea Breach Commission was empowered to levy a rate on land liable to sea flooding, and this was later taken to include the *c.* 56 000 acres (*c.* 22 700 ha) of marshland in the valleys of the Yare, Bure and Waveney which lie 10 feet (3 m) or less above OD. The rate was levied as the need arose, rather than annually, and varied according to the distance of the land from the dune defences for which the Commission was responsible, owners nearby having to pay far more than those further inland. In his evidence to the Royal Commission on Coast Erosion (1907) the Surveyor to the Sea Breach Commissioners indicated that the rate that year varied from 8 shillings to 3 pence in the pound, the total product obtainable being about £8400 on a rateable value of £72 000. He also reported that his Commissioners spent about £400 a year, mainly on faggoting the seaward faces of the dunes. But in claiming that there had been no serious incursion of the sea during the past 100 years, he glossed over the fact that in 1897, the dunes at the former outfall of the Hundred Stream had once again been breached, this time by a surge of 10 feet above OD. However, in response to questioning, he admitted that only a few months previously (i.e. in 1907), the repairs carried out had been washed away, and that there had in consequence been a flood.

The functions of the Sea Breach Commission were taken over by the East Norfolk Rivers Catchment Board on its formation in 1931. But in December 1936, a storm once again damaged the defences near the former outfall of the Hundred Stream, and although the dunes were reinstated, nothing was (or perhaps could be) done about the severely scoured beach fronting them. According to Sainty *et al.* (1939), this contributed to the disaster of 12 February 1938, when a surge similar in height to that of 1897 tore a 642 m wide gap in the dunes. Sea water poured inland, overtopping the flood walls beside Somerton Dyke, Martham Broad and Horsey Mere, and raising the level of

Heigham Sound and Hickling Broad to such an extent that had not their embankments been hurriedly raised by volunteers, Potter Heigham and Hickling would have been flooded. Measurements made by the Norfolk Fishery Board and quoted by Sainty *et al.* show that the salinity of Horsey Mere equalled that of sea water for at least 8 days after the breakthrough, and was still about 8 per cent (or in present-day parlance 4860 mg Cl$^-$ l^{-1}) eleven months afterwards, mainly because saline water from the adjoining marshes was still being discharged into the Mere by Brograve, Horsey and other land-drainage pumps. "Many more months" elapsed before its salinity returned to its former level, quoted as between 1.5 and 2.0 per cent (911 to 1215 mg Cl$^-$ l^{-1}). In contrast, salinities at the northern end of Hickling Broad did not attain their maximum of about 23.5 per cent (i.e. *c.* 14276 mg Cl$^-$ l^{-1}) until May owing to the greater dilution afforded to the incoming sea water. However, as at Horsey Mere, this was more than sufficient to kill off the great majority of the aquatic plants, fish and invertebrates which occurred here prior to the flood.

Grave difficulties were experienced in filling the breach in the dunes as the inrush of sea water had completely flattened the latter, and carried enormous quantities of sand and mud inland, and further flooding took place in early April when temporary repairs, consisting of a line of wooden piles backed by sand-bags were washed away by a storm (Mosby, 1939). As a result, parts of the area remained flooded for 3 months, despite the provision of emergency pumps, and the cutting of temporary gaps in the embankments beside Martham North Broad and Somerton Dyke in order to allow the sea water to flow away down the R. Thurne. Eventually, however, the breach was sealed and the dunes re-formed by bulldozers. In addition, lengths of sea wall were constructed where the dune defences were weakest, namely at Horsey (2.0 km) and Eccles (2.4 km); these were built of concrete-filled bags dowelled together with steel rods.

All told, 7469 acres (3024 ha) were flooded with sea water, (see Map 10.1), in some places to a depth of over 2.4 m. Sainty *et al.* (1939) note that of this, 752 acres (304 ha) and 3459 acres (1400 ha) were under arable and grass respectively, whilst a further 1660 acres (672 ha) consisted of marsh which, through neglect, had become overgrown with rushes and reeds. 307 acres (124 ha) of woodland, osier beds, gardens and buildings were also affected, whilst the remaining 1291 acres (523 ha) lay inside the tidal embankments. The total size of the area flooded may be contrasted with the figure of 5800 ha which the National Rivers Authority has recently estimated would be inundated in the event that the sea wall between Happisburgh and Winterton is breached by a major surge.

When the 1938 flood did finally recede, it revealed a scene of desolation, with trees and bushes killed, and the land colonized by glassworts and other halophytes. Buxton (1940–1944), who carefully documented the effects of the flood and the process of recovery, notes that five years elapsed before the worst affected grazing marshes were back in the condition they were in prior to the flood. In contrast, Horsey Mere was recolonized by Fennel-leaved Pondweed, Spiked Water-milfoil and other waterweeds during the summer of 1940.

The dune defences were breached again during the great surge of 31 January 1953, this time at Sea Palling, but although seven lives were lost, and much damage caused to property in the village (Harland & Harland, 1980), most of the water found its way into the dyke system of the Brograve Level, and only about 490 ha were flooded.

During the next few years, the remaining lengths of dune between Happisburgh and Winterton were protected with reinforced concrete walling, having a total length of 7.8 km. However, parts of the Horsey and Eccles bag-walls collapsed during the 1960s and 1970s and had to be repaired, and inspections showed that other sections had been seriously weakened as a result of the corrosion of the dowels holding the bags together. In the circumstances, the Norfolk and Suffolk Local Land Drainage Committee agreed in 1978 that all the remaining legnths of bag-wall should be replaced, and work on the Eccles section was completed in 1984. Meantime, serious erosion had been occurring south of Winterton Ness (the dune frontage here had retreated by 70 m in places since 1974, and a mean loss of 15 m was recorded during the winter of 1980/1), and the Committee decided that the southern end of the Horsey sea wall should be extended for a distance of 1068 m in order to reduce the risk of a further disastrous incursion of the sea.

Cuts in AWA's grant-earning investment allocation, together with a reduction in the rate of grant available for sea (and tidal river) defences from 85 to 50 per cent (recently restored to 65 per cent) seriously hampered its work programme from 1984/5 onwards. The Authority's inability to replace the remaining length of bag-wall at Horsey (1.7 km) caused particular concern, and in a Press Statement issued in March 1986, AWA drew attention to the catastrophic damage which Broadland would suffer in the event that the sea defences were breached here during a major surge. Fortunately, the Authority's pleas were heeded by Government, and the grant ceiling of its Norwich Division was increased from £1.31 million to £1.56 million, thus enabling it to place a contract for the necessary works. These commenced in January 1987, and were completed early in 1988, at an estimated cost of just under £2.7 million.

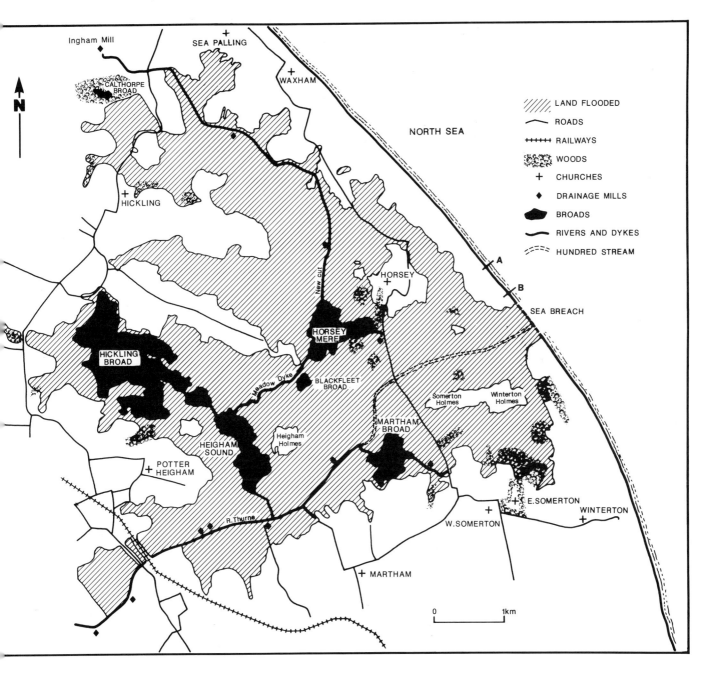

The area subject to sea flooding in 1938. The map by Sainty *et al.* (1939) from which this is derived was inaccurately scaled and probably as a result of this, the breach in the dunes was shown to be of width *c.* 430 m, instead of the 642 m referred to in the accompanying text. In addition, the outfall of the Hundred Stream (which is assumed to have been on the alignment of the present district council boundary) was drawn too far north. Although these imperfections have been rectified, some uncertainty remains about the exact location of the edges of the breach. The letters AB mark the position of the low-resistance strata encountered by Anglian Water during the construction of a new section of concrete sea wall in 1987.

Map 10.1

During the course of the work, measurements were made by AWA of the depths to which the cased piles supporting the structure were driven into the underlying beach deposits. These indicated that the latter have a very low resistance to loads for a distance of some 550 m; indeed, in order to reduce the risk of the new defences being undermined, extra long supporting piles were used in this area. The southern end of this low-resistance section of beach deposits is located *c.* 625 m north of the boundary between the districts of North Norfolk and Great Yarmouth which, as explained in Chapter 3, is thought to mark the position of the former outfall of the Hundred Stream. The load-bearing resistance of the strata in this latter area was neither less nor more than the norm, this despite the fact that the beach deposits here are known to have been washed out to a considerable depth during the 1938 sea flood. In the circumstances, it seems unlikely that the low-resistance strata encountered to the north (whose location is shown on Map 10.1) mark the position of a former breach in the dunes. An alternative, and perhaps more likely explanation is that they occupy the site of a much earlier outfall of the R. Thurne, and that this subsequently shifted southwards to take up the position marked today by the eastern end of the district council boundary. Further stratigraphical research needs to be carried out before this hypothesis can be put to the test.

The replacement of the remaining section of bag-wall should, in theory, have rendered Broadland more secure against breakthroughs by the sea between Happisburgh and Winterton than at any time in its history. But soon after the work had been completed, the National Rivers Authority (which inherited the AWA's flood defence responsibilities in 1989) began to be concerned about the rate at which the beach fronting the sea wall was eroding, and these fears were confirmed in 1990, when over a metre of beach material was scoured away from this section of coast within a few months. The situation just south of Happisburgh was particularly grave, since it was not just the sand and shingle which was washed away here, but about a metre of the underlying clay into which the toe-piles of the wall had been driven. Engineering studies showed that if this erosion was allowed to continue, there was a real risk that sections of the sea wall would topple over backwards during a major surge, so producing a disastrous sea flood. To reduce the likelihood of this happening, it was decided to protect the toe-piling with imported rock for a distance of several hundred metres. This emergency work (which will cost about three-quarters of a million pounds) was carried out early in 1991. As a more permanent measure, it is planned to construct a series of off-shore breakwaters between Happisburg and Winterton. These will, it is hoped, provide conditions favouring the accretion of sand and shingle on the beach, thus protecting the sea wall on this stretch of coast from further erosion.

Riverine floods

Although Broadland is currently fairly well protected against marine incursions, the Drained Marshland Area is still very much at risk from flooding caused by the overtopping or breaching of the tidal embankments. This can occur during a storm surge, or in a period of high fluvial flows following heavy and prolonged rainfall in the catchment, or as a result of a combination of these events.

The amount of damage caused by a flood varies according to its duration, the salinity of the water, and the use being made of the affected marshland. But in general, provided the flooding does not last for more than a few days, grass marshland with a high water-table will recover quite quickly, even when covered by brackish water, and a normal 'bite' can be expected the following year. Salt-flooded arable land, on the other hand, requires expensive and time-consuming remedial measures designed to restore the calcium-sodium balance in the soil to the normal level (MAFF, 1962), and five years or more can elapse before normal yields can once again be obtained from such land, especially if it does not have an under-drainage system.

Major floods are known to have occurred in 1287 and 1290, and it was perhaps one of these that deposited the layer of freshwater silt encountered during the excavation of the site of the former port of Norwich near Whitefriars Bridge (Ayers & Murphy, 1983; Ayers, 1985; Ayers, 1987). The surface of this silt lies at 1.08 m OD in the Norman building excavated here in 1981, and which is now incorporated in the basement of the new Courthouse.

Fluvial flooding took place in 1519, and in 1565 a sudden thaw resulted in much

Table 10a   Flooding in Broadland – 1954 to 1989

Date	Cause	Areas flooded	Valley	Water levels attained (above OD)	
December '54	Surge	Parts of Yarmouth, the Raveningham Marshes and *c.* 12 025 ha elsewhere in the Yare and Bure valleys	Yare and Bure	Yarmouth	2.36 m
January '59	Heavy fluvial flows and high tides	Horning Grove Level and riverside properties in Wroxham and Horning	Bure	–	
February '62	Surge	Langley Marshes, and the Oulton, Carleton Colville, Barnby, Blundeston and Flixton Marshes	Yare and Waveney	–	
February '65	Surge and heavy fluvial flows	Herringfleet, St. Olaves and Geldeston marshes and Strumpshaw marshes	Waveney and Yare	Yarmouth	1.98 m
March '68	Surge	Cantley and Monks Levels Long and Short Dam Levels	Yare and Waveney	Yarmouth Haddiscoe Rockland	1.90 m 1.64 m 1.16 m
September '68	Heavy fluvial flows (over 7.5 cm of rain fell in much of the R. Waveney's catchment on 15.9.68)	Extensive areas between Ellingham and Castle Mill	Waveney	—	
November '71	Surge	Geldeston Level, Strumpshaw Level and part of Postwick Level	Waveney and Yare	Yarmouth Haddiscoe	2.32 m 1.60 m
November & December '73	Surge	Share Mill and Geldeston Levels	Waveney	–	
January '76	Surge	Marshes near the Breydon North Wall, and Cantley and Monks Levels and the Blundeston, Somerleyton and Burgh Marshes } *c.* 1500 ha	Yare and Waveney	Yarmouth Haddiscoe	2.69 m 1.76 m
January '78	Surge	Some overtopping and slight damage at Somerleyton and Gillingham, and beside the R. Chet	Waveney and Chet	Yarmouth Haddiscoe Rockland Beccles	2.19 m 1.62 m 1.10 m 1.31 m
February '79	Heavy fluvial flows and spring tides	10 houses at Geldeston, and a substantial area of Waveney valley marshland. The embankment near Barsham was breached	Waveney	–	
December '80	Heavy fluvial flows	The Gillingham Level, Geldeston Marshes and low-lying parts of Beccles.	Waveney	–	
April '81	Heavy fluvial flows	The Gillingham and Barsham Levels were flooded, and some overtopping occurred elsewhere, for instance above Ludham Bridge	Waveney and Bure	–	
February '83	Surge	Both banks of the R.Yare near Beauchamp Arms, and 300 m of embankment beside the New Cut were overtopped, and the Breydon North Wall seriously damaged	Yare	Yarmouth Haddiscoe Rockland	2.59 m 1.70 m 1.13 m
January '85	Heavy fluvial flows due to rapid snow-melt	Gillingham wall overtopped. A considerable amount of marshland, and some houses, flooded	Waveney	–	
February '88	Surge, followed by prolonged high water levels	*c.* 1200 ha of marsh flooded (see page 67)	Yare & Waveney mainly	Yarmouth Haddiscoe	1.8 m 1.6 m
February '89	Surge (fortunately at low tide during a period of neaps)	Bank overtopping at Cantley, Hardley & in the Waveney valley	Yare & Waveney	Yarmouth Haddiscoe Rockland Beccles	2.01 m 1.6 m 1.23 m 1.31 m

Notes:
1. The Yarmouth tide records were taken at the South Denes Power station and not at the harbour entrance.
2. Minor floods have occurred at several other occasions since the early 1950s, notably in the upper tidal reaches of the R. Waveney. In addition, boatyards and other riverside properties in the Bure, Ant, Thurne and Yare valleys are very susceptible to flooding, following minor surges, and/ or periods of heavy rainfall.
3. It will be seen that water levels at Haddiscoe have on several occasions exceeded those encountered here in 1953 (1.53 OD), even though the surge level at Yarmouth has been significantly less each time. This is due to the widespread 'relief' flooding which occurred in 1953 as a result of the numerous breaches in the embankments, particularly in the vicinity of Breydon Water and the New Cut.

Sources: Annual reports of the ESNRB and ESNRA, and the Norfolk and Suffolk Local Land Drainage Committee.

damage being caused to "mills, bridges, and banks in most places" (Blomefield, 1805–1810). Woodward (1881) lists eleven other such events between 1570 and 1795, whilst in 1809, the water covering the marshes was so deep that it was impossible to sail wherries downriver safely (Clark, 1961). According to Woodward, the R. Wensum rose 10 feet (*c.*3 m) above its normal level following prolonged rainfall in November 1878, and between three and six thousand houses in Norwich were flooded.

The largest fluvial event this century was in 1912, following the exceptional rainfall over the catchments of the rivers on 25 and 26 August that year (see page 30). The

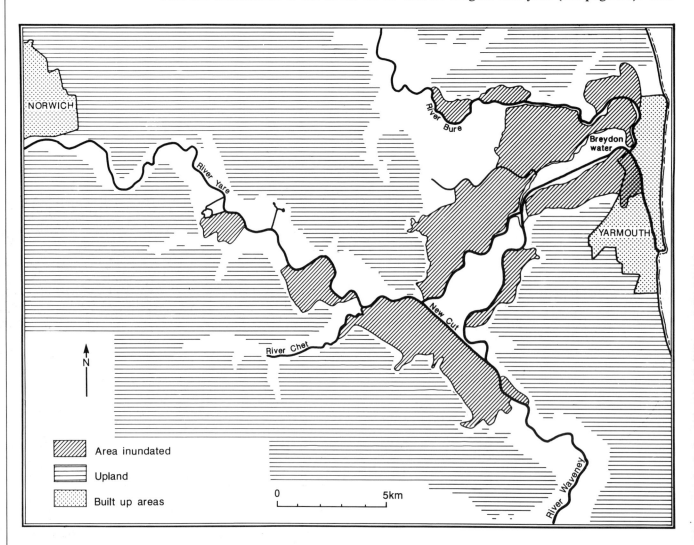

Map 10.2

Areas flooded by the 1953 surge.

Source: Ministry of Agriculture, Fisheries & Food (1962)

Wensum rose to 2.345 m above OD (or 2.12 m above its present mean level), and large parts of Norwich were flooded (signs recording the water levels attained can be seen at several points in the city). Over 100 bridges and culverts in the county were washed away, and large parts of the Drained Marshland Area were inundated. Numerous sluices and windpumps were destroyed, and at some places, for example Strumpshaw and Horning, so much damage was caused to the drainage system, that repairs were not considered worthwhile, and marshes were allowed to revert to fen.

The Broadland valleys were again subject to severe fluvial flooding in 1947, and various areas have been flooded from time to time since then, the Beccles, Gillingham and Geldeston Marshes being particularly susceptible (see Table 10a). But on each of these occasions, the damage caused was small compared with that resulting from the surge-induced events of 1905, 1921, 1943, and above all January 1953, when water levels rose to 3.25 m OD at the mouth of the Haven, 1.53 m OD at Haddiscoe, and 1.28 m OD at Rockland. Enormous damage was caused to the embankments protecting the lower reaches of the rivers, five separate breaches being torn in the south wall of the New Cut, while one of the three breaks in the Breydon North Wall was nearly 40 m wide (EEN, 1953). As a result, some 5950 ha were flooded (MAFF, 1962) (Map. 10.2). Worse still, the breaching of Breydon's South Wall led to *c.*250 ha being flooded

Sandbagging a breach in the embankment beside the New Cut – 1953.

Plate XXXIV

This photograph was taken from a point about a kilometre north-west of the bridge carrying the A143 Beccles to Yarmouth road over the New Cut. The Thurlton Marshes to the left are flooded, and the Reedham to Lowestoft railway line has been left unsupported. This line was again cut by surge tide flooding in December 1990, this time near Somerleyton.

Photo: Courtesy of the Eastern Daily Press

Plate XXXV

Preparing to fill a breach in the left (north) bank of the R. Yare at Seven Mile House – 1953.

The longer a breach like this remains unfilled, the greater the depth to which it is liable to be scoured by the inrush of water, and the more difficult it becomes to repair. All the sandbags would have had to be brought to this site by water, as there was no road down to it in the 1950s.

The photographer would have been standing about 200 m upstream of the diesel-driven pumps which featured so prominently in the Halvergate controversy. These were installed in 1937 as a replacement for the steam-powered pumping station, whose chimney stack can be seen on the right. This subsequently collapsed, but was re-built to about half its previous height in the mid-1980s. Polkey's Mill, to the left of the stack, is due to be restored shortly.

Photo: Courtesy of the Eastern Daily Press

in the Cobholm district of Yarmouth, in some places to a depth of over 2 m. 9 lives were lost, 3500 houses and 100 industrial premises flooded, and a week elapsed before all the 10 000 people who had had to be evacuated could return to their homes (Rendel, Palmer & Tritton, 1977).

In most cases the flood defences were breached as a result of being overtopped by a considerable depth of water. As this flowed over onto the marshland behind, the steeply sloping rear walls of the embankments were progressively washed out to base level, the process being hastened in exposed situations (e.g. Breydon Water) by wave action (Cotton, 1953).

Not unexpectedly, the salinity of the flood water on the marshes was much greater nearest the sea than further up-valley. Measurements taken four days after the surge showed that Haddiscoe Island was flooded with water containing $c.52\,000$ mg Cl$^-$ l^{-1} (85.6 per cent seawater), whilst figures of 21 505 mg l^{-1} and 1580 mg l^{-1} were recorded from the Claxton and Geldeston Levels respectively (MAFF, 1962). Fortunately, most of the marshes flooded were under grass, rather than arable, but even so, the sward was completely destroyed in many places, particularly where the land was subject to pro-longed flooding by high-salinity water. The rate at which the marshland returned to its former level of productivity was dependent on a number of factors, notably the soil type. In addition, recovery was greatly assisted by improved drainage, the provision of foot drains being particularly beneficial.

The cost of repairing the tidal embankments (see Plates XXXIV, XXXV & XXXVI) was estimated to be about £198 000 (c. £2.35 million at 1990 prices), of which £152 000 was spent on the Breydon walls (RPT, 1977). These sums do not include the cost of improvement works carried out subsequently, nor the substantial expenses in-curred by bodies such as Yarmouth Corporation, the Port and Haven Commissioners and British Rail.

The Lord Mayor of Norwich launched a Flood Relief Appeal, and much of the money raised from this was used to compensate uninsured farmers for losses of livestock and damage to property; acreage payments were also made for land which had been flooded. All told, about £216 000 (c. £2.56 million at 1990 prices) was paid out to farmers after the flood, but the true cost of the disaster to agriculture would have been considerably higher than this.

Total Identifiable Costs of the 1953 Flood (£'000)

Cost Item	1953 Prices	1990 Prices
Public Bodies	305.6	3629
Industries	57.4	681
Housing	859.4	10 204
Agriculture	215.9	2563
Total	**1438.3**	**17 077**

NB. These figures are almost certainly under-estimates.

Source: Report compiled in 1963 for the East Suffolk and Norfolk River Authority and published by Rendel, Palmer and Tritton (1977).

Although no subsequent event has produced damage on the scale of that caused in 1953, surges have continued to occur every few years, and have been responsible for much of the flooding which has occurred in the region during the past 30 years (Table 10a). The most recent event was at the end of February 1988, when some 1800 ha of marshland was inundated. The surge responsible only attained a height of 1.8 m OD at Yarmouth, substantially less than in 1953, but very high water levels were maintained in the river system for several days afterwards, owing to the strong north-westerly winds, and this weakened the defences. Breaches were created in the embankments protecting the Castle, Share, Herringfleet and Belton marshes in the Waveney valley, and the flood banks beside the Yare at Strumpshaw and the Chet at Hardley were also severely damaged. Partial breaching occurred at 15 other localities, and overtopping was also widespread. Most of the marshland flooded was located in the valleys of the Yare and Waveney, the area between Barnby and Somerleyton being particularly badly affected,

Plate XXXVI

Short Dyke, Rockland, soon after two breaches in its embankment had been temporarily repaired with sand bags – 1953.

This is one of two navigable dykes connecting Rockland Broad with the R. Yare, which is just visible in the middle distance. Note that a motorized wherry is being used as a lighter.

The flooded grazing marshland on the right forms part of the Claxton Level. The pump responsible for draining this could not be started until all the breaches in the Level's protective embankments had been repaired.

Photo: Courtesy of the Eastern Daily Press

but above-average salinities were maintained for longer in the Bure and its tributaries than in the southern rivers, owing to the greater fluvial discharge rates of the latter.

Perhaps the most alarming aspect of this event was that the National Rivers Authority calculated that the water levels attained in the tidal sections of the rivers had a return period of only 1 in 7. When taken in conjunction with the extensive amount of flooding which occurred, this is a clear indication of the deplorable state the region's tidal embankments are now in.

The Yare Basin Flood Control Scheme

The idea of constructing a barrage at Great Yarmouth, so as to exclude tidal influence from Broadland, and thus eliminate the risk of flooding due to embankment failures, has been mooted by land-drainage engineers for at least a century. In 1937, for example, the Great Yarmouth Port and Haven Commissioners received a report pointing out that a barrage had been talked about "time and again", and referring to the reasons why the idea had been "resuscitated". Because of strong opposition from the Commissioners and boating interests and the high cost of a barrage, nothing was done, but the enormous damage caused by the 1953 surge tide, kindled renewed interest in the suggestion, and in June that year, the East Suffolk and Norfolk River Board asked Rendel, Palmer and Tritton (RPT), a firm of consultant engineers, to advise on the ways in which abnormal tides could be excluded from the river system. The firm's report, dated March 1956, recommended that a lifting barrier, costing some £700 000 (*c.* £7.57 million at 1990 prices) should be built near Gorleston Lower Ferry in the Haven. Subsequent discussions between representatives of the River Board, the Great Yarmouth Borough Council and the Port and Haven Commissioners led to a suggestion that the barrier should be combined with a new road bridge, and this proposal was duly submitted to the Ministry of Agriculture, Fisheries and Food for consideration. Nothing further was done until January 1959, when fluvial flooding took place in the Wroxham and Horning areas. Investigations by RPT for the River Board showed that a barrier of the type they had proposed would not, on its own, be suited to the control of such floods, and the firm was therefore invited to assess by means of computer modelling techniques the amount of river bank raising which would be required to withstand fluvial flooding, both with and without a barrier. RPT's report was completed in August 1961, but during subsequent investigations by River Board staff, it became apparent that if a barrier in the Haven had to be closed when the rivers Yare and Waveney were carrying heavy fluvial flows, large volumes of water would be backed up the R. Bure, greatly increasing the risk of flooding in this valley. Accordingly, yet another report was commissioned from RPT, this time about the possibility of providing a separate surge-control structure across the R. Bure. The consultants were also asked to examine the feasibility of by-passing the lowermost reaches of the river by creating a new channel for it between Scare Gap and Breydon Water.

After discussing the various options, the River Board decided in 1963 to ask the Ministry of Agriculture to indicate whether grant aid for a barrier across the Haven, plus associated bank-raising works would be eligible for grant assistance. But despite periodic meetings between staff of the Ministry, and the Board's successor, the East Suffolk and Norfolk River Authority, the only decision taken was to raise the flood defences in the Haven to the 1953 surge level. Official reports of this period carefully refrain from giving the reason why no headway was made with the barrier project, but this was undoubtedly due to the implacable, and long-sustained hostility shown by the Great Yarmouth Port and Haven Commissioners towards any scheme which might impede navigation in the Haven or the lowermost reaches of the rivers.

Renewed interest was taken in the flood-control problem in the 1970s as a result of the increasing amount of marshland being put under the plough, the understandable desire of farmers to ensure that the land they had newly converted was not damaged by flooding, and by evidence that the incidence of surge-induced flooding was increasing (see Table 10a). In addition, staff taking up their appointments with the recently formed Norfolk and Suffolk Rivers Division of the Anglian Water Authority were dismayed to discover that despite the not inconsiderable sums spent on flood protection since 1952 (see Table 10b) the tidal embankments were in a parlous condition. The majority

Table 10b. Grant-aided capital expenditure on riverine flood protection in Broadland – 1952/3 to 1989/90

Year	Actual spend	Expenditure at 1990 prices	Year	Actual spend	Expenditure at 1990 prices
1952/3	41 475	500 821	1971/2	99 730	620 196
1953/4	238 768*	2 835 013	1972/3	125 883	730 768
1954/5	83 932*	980 191	1973/4	197 176	1 049 145
1955/6	53 113	599 177	1974/5	156 022	715 400
1956/7	47 839	517 839	1975/6	276 071	1 018 882
1957/8	59 525	623 446	1976/7	204 943	649 008
1958/9	59 209	603 616	1977/8	169 994	464 681
1959/60	58 711	594 882	1978/9	249 344	629 369
1960/1	76 400	766 310	1979/80	175 296	390 200
1961/2	89 224	870 371	1980/1	325 602	614 285
1962/3	86 819	814 952	1981/2	453 427**	764 678
1963/4	112 606	1 037 435	1982/3	425 273	702 265
1964/5	122 745	1 094 366	1983/4	627 976	932 313
1965/6	73 918	629 695	1984/5	924 715†	1 307 691
1966/7	92 746	760 150	1985/6	126 368	168 457
1967/8	128 882	1 029 194	1986/7	647 409	834 636
1968/9	112 190	856 051	1987/8	566 027	700 668
1969/70	88 041	637 560	1988/9	614 587	725 230
1970/1	113 976	775 692	1989/90	359 230	393 217

* Figures inflated by the cost of repairing damage caused by the 1953 floods.
** Includes £114 777 for the protection of Geldeston village.
† Includes £397 757 for the protection of Gillingham and Beccles.

NB. these figures exclude the cost of works carried out on the flood walls of the Haven, and the Bure downstream of Yarmouth Yacht Station; very substantial sums have been spent in this part of the region since the mid-1980s. The figures in the Table also represent a considerable under-statement of the funds spent on Broadland's riverine flood defences, as they do not include the cost of maintenance works; these are financed from revenue, and annual breakdowns of this account are not usually available (though some £239 000 was spent on maintaining Broadland's tidal embankments in 1988/9). In addition, in most years, particularly since 1985/6, one or more capital projects are carried out in the region which are not eligible for grant, usually because the Norwich Division's grant-earning allocation has been used up on other schemes. The piling in 1988/9 of a section of the R. Yare at Langley at a cost of £102 878 provides an example of such a project.

Sources:
1952/3 to 1964/5 – Annual Reports of the East Suffolk & Norfolk River Board
1965/6 to 1973/4 – Annual Reports of the East Suffolk & Norfolk River Authority
1974/5 to 1982/3 – Annual Reports of the Norfolk & Suffolk River Division of the AWA (Norwich).
1983/4 to 1988/9 – Annual Reports of the Norfolk & Suffolk Local Land Drainage Committee (Anglian Water, Norwich).
    1989/90 – Annual Report of the Norfolk & Suffolk Local Flood Defence Committee

appeared to be settling [at a mean rate subsequently estimated by Brooke and Turner (1989) at 30 mm per year] and were consequently of insufficient height to withstand a surge; in addition, their crests were often only about a metre wide. To make matters worse, many embankments were found to be structurally weakened by the presence of a soke dyke only a few metres to the rear, and by the fact that they were being undermined at the water's edge, following the loss of the ronds through tidal scouring and wave action. In view of these findings, the Norfolk and Suffolk Local Land Drainage Committee was advised that unless a comprehensive protection scheme was put into effect very soon, there was likely to be very serious flooding in the region the next time there was a major surge.

In 1974 the AWA decided, in response to representations from this Committee, to invite Dr David Wallace of the Department of Rural Land Economy of Cambridge University to assess the benefits to agriculture which would result if such a scheme was carried out. His report has never been published, but he is believed to have taken the view that a barrage or barrier was not strictly necessary, in that the amount of damage likely to be caused by flooding would, judging from past events, be less than the additional value that farmers would obtain from ploughing up their marshes. But he felt that the psychological value of a barrage, and in particular the feeling that it would afford farmers real security against flooding, would be vital if significant numbers of them were to be persuaded to invest the large sums of money required to convert their marsh holdings to arable.

The need for a greater measure of protection was again forcibly demonstrated in January 1976, when a surge breached the embankments in several places, and flooded some 1500 ha of marshland in the Yare and Waveney valleys. The Breydon North Wall was particularly badly affected, being breached in six places, with the result that both the A47, and the Yarmouth to Norwich railway line were temporarily cut.

The 1976 Surge reinforced the Land Drainage Committee's determination to commission a comprehensive study of the ways in which the Drained Marshland Area could be afforded improved protection against flooding, and the advantages and disadvantages which would accrue if this was done, and Rendel, Palmer and Tritton successfully tendered for the task. At the insistence of the Ministry of Agriculture, the AWA set up a Steering Committee, consisting of a wide range of interested parties, to receive and comment upon the progress reports produced by the consultants and, on completion of the contract, advise the Land Drainage Committee as to what action it should take. The Steering Committee duly fulfilled these functions, but was dissolved by the Drainage Committee when the latter received the final report of the consultants in April 1978.

During the first phase of their study RPT investigated three ways of providing additional protection against flooding; a permanent barrage with one or more locks; a barrier to exclude surge tides, and the raising and strengthening of the existing tidal embankments. It was soon realized that it would be impossible to construct a barrage downstream of the Haven Bridge without severely disrupting traffic in the port, and although three possible upriver locations were considered, each scheme would have had a high capital cost, for example, £14.5 million (1976 prices) for barrages and locks across the R. Bure near its outfall and the R. Yare at Breydon Viaduct. The recurrent expenditure would also be very heavy. Phytoplankton blooms would probably develop upstream of a barrage owing to the reduced flushing rate, and this would increase the cost of treating water abstracted from Horning and elsewhere. Although additional quantities of water would become available for domestic and industrial use and for spray irrigation once a barrage had been constructed, it would be cheaper to meet the extra demand by means of river regulation schemes such as that already in train on the R. Dove, a tributary of the R. Waveney. In addition, the proposal to reorganize Yarmouth's sewerage system would have to be brought forward, as untreated effluent could not continue to be discharged direct to the rivers Bure and Yare once tidal action had been excluded from them. Dredging costs, too, would be increased, owing to reduced tidal scouring in the Haven and the lower reaches of the rivers, and consequent siltation.

RPT concluded on the basis of evidence put forward by the NCC, that by eliminating tidal influence from the rivers, a barrage would have very damaging effects on the ecology of Broadland. In the light of this, and the fact that such a scheme would not, in any event, be viable economically it recommended that it should be eliminated from further consideration, and this was subsequently accepted by the Land Drainage Committee.

RPT investigated the possibility of locating a surge barrier at two sites downstream of the Haven Bridge. The first of these was at Queens Road, a site then under consideration for a possible second river crossing, and the second was at a point some 220 m upstream of the Lower Ferry, where it would have provided much of Yarmouth and Gorleston, as well as Broadland, with protection against flooding. RPT suggested that the barrier at Queens Road need only reduce the navigable width of the river there from 75 m to 70 m, and at the Lower Ferry site from 95 m to 80 m, and that a headroom of 22 m at mean high water spring tides could be provided at both locations. But in the face of a resolute refusal by the Port and Haven Commissioners to cooperate (even to the extent that for several months they declined to provide RPT with data which the firm needed), a decision was taken not to pursue the investigation of the sites downstream of the Haven Bridge any further. Another, more widely publicized reason why this conclusion was reached, was the relatively high cost of these structures. RPT estimated that barriers on the Queens Road and Lower Ferry sites would require outlays of £8.6 million and £10.27 million respectively, whereas a similar structure could be built 300 m upstream of the Haven Bridge (see Map 10.3a) for only £5.01 million (a figure subsequently revised during the Phase II studies to £7.39 million).

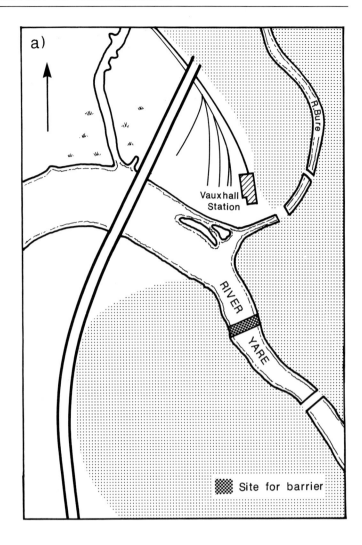

Map 10.3

Locations for a barrier under consideration in the mid-1970s, and their relationship to the site chosen for the bridge to carry the then projected Yarmouth Inner Relief Road across Breydon Water:

(a) Barrier to be located *c*. 300 m upstream of the Haven Bridge; relief road bridge to be built on site of former Breydon railway viaduct;

(b) Combined road bridge and Yare Barrier to be constructed on site of former railway viaduct; separate barrier to be provided for the R. Bure just upstream of its confluence with the R. Yare;

(c) Combined road bridge and barrier to be constructed on site of former railway viaduct; a new channel to be created for the R. Bure so that it discharged upstream of bridge/barrier structure, thus obviating the need for a separate Bure barrier.

Source: Great Yarmouth District Council (1981)

The principal reason for the Port and Haven Commissioners' aversion to a barrier downstream of the Haven Bridge was that when closed it would prevent ships entering and leaving the port. Moreover, the Commissioners considered that there was a real risk that the AWA would find it increasingly difficult to finance as much work on Broadland's tidal embankments as was required, and that in order to reduce the likelihood of agricultural land being flooded, would start lowering the barrier during high spring tides, rather than just prior to a major surge, as planned. In these circumstances there would, of course, be far more disruption of shipping movements in the Haven than envisaged by RPT. The Commissioners had particularly strong objections to a barrier on the Lower Ferry site, as they took the view that once this had been lowered, there would be insufficient space downstream of it to accommodate ships seeking shelter in stormy weather.

In addition to the Haven Bridge site, RPT investigated two other possible upriver locations for a barrier. The first of these was on the alignment of the former railway viaduct at the seaward end of Breydon Water (see Map 10.3b), while the other was at the western end of the latter, just downstream of the Yare-Waveney confluence. This was rejected on the grounds that a barrier here would do nothing to reduce the risk of Breydon's North and South Walls being breached or overtopped during a surge. Such a scheme would also be expensive, as a separate barrier would have to be provided near the outfall of the R. Bure.

In the circumstances, RPT concluded that only two possible locations for a barrier warranted further investigation, the Haven Bridge and Breydon Viaduct sites. Since a barrier on the latter could, if necessary, be combined with a bridge for the projected new relief road for Yarmouth, RPT recommended that the economic arguments for and against this should be examined during the second phase of the investigations. It also urged that the merits of a Selective Bank-raising Scheme should be assessed. This would involve varying the standard of flood protection afforded different blocks of marsh

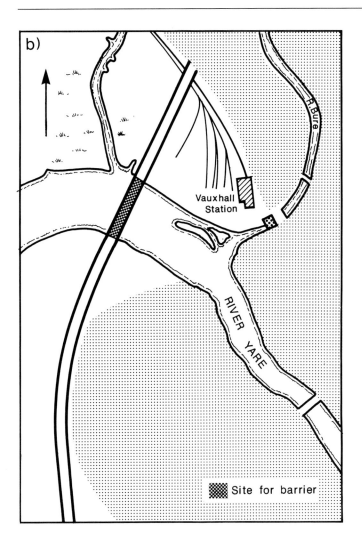

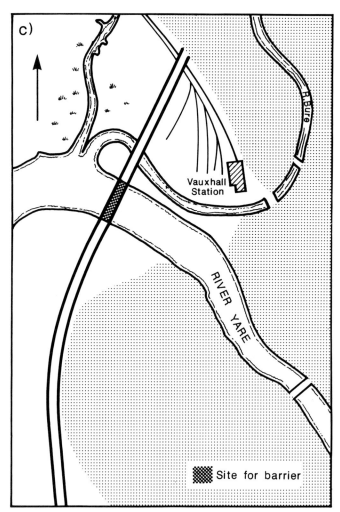

according to what could be justified on economic grounds, rather than giving the whole of the Drained Marshland Area a uniform level of protection. But this recommendation was rejected by the Land Drainage Committee which instructed that RPT should instead assess the cost of carrying out a Full Embankment Scheme over a period of eight to ten years, instead of four, as originally proposed. The Committee accepted RPT's other recommendations for the Phase II Study, including the need for an assessment of the rate of agricultural improvement which would occur in the event that a Flood Protection Scheme was implemented. In addition, RPT was asked to examine the possibility of providing one or more washlands for the temporary storage of flood water, an idea canvassed by the author which was later to become known as the Partial Embankment Scheme.

An analysis of the water levels attained during previous surges and their incidence, fluvial discharge rates from upriver, and the heights of the existing tidal defences, was commenced at an early stage of the investigation, and the resulting data were incorporated in a multi-branch computer programme developed by RPT during their earlier work in the region. This was proved during the Phase I study by reference to measured fluvial flows, and records taken simultaneously at tide-gauging stations operated by the AWA on the three main rivers.

The computer model enabled RPT to simulate different combinations of surge and fluvial flows, and thus predict which sections of the tidal defences would be overtopped under existing conditions, the amount they would need to be raised to give varying levels of protection, and the extent to which down and up-river water levels would be affected by a flood control structure installed at different sites near Yarmouth.

Further refinements were made to the model for the Phase II studies and it was then used to discover which combinations of surge and fluvial flow having a joint return period of either 25 or 100 years produced maximum water levels in the rivers, and how these would be affected in the event that new washlands were provided in the vicinity of

Breydon Water. In assessing these joint probabilities, RPT made allowances for the most likely state of the tide at Yarmouth when a surge took place (0.9 m OD) and the mean water level of the broads (taken to be 0.45 m OD); the firm also assumed that surges of sufficient height would only occur between September and April, and that each surge would most probably extend over three complete tide cycles (just over 36 hours).

The following combination of surge tide and fluvial flood were found by RPT to have a joint probability of return of 100 years:

Surge return period	Rainflood return period
100 years	4 days
25 years	16 days
5 years	80 days
80 days	5 years
16 days	25 years
4 days	100 years

NB. The 'days' are within a surge year (= 240 days)

It was found that maximum water levels would be attained almost everywhere when a 1 in 100 year surge took place when the rivers were carrying a fluvial flow having a nominal return period of 4 days. RPT was able to show that if, as it recommended, these levels were adopted for design purposes, this would be sufficient to prevent marshes in the Bure and Yare valleys being flooded following a very heavy (1 in 100 year) rainstorm but that there would, in these circumstances, be some overtopping of the banks of the R. Waveney upstream of Geldeston.

The computer runs provided ample confirmation of the parlous condition of the embankments. For instance, during a joint event involving a 1 in 5 year surge and a rainflood with a return period of 80 days, the freeboard of the rivers Yare and Waveney would vary from about 0.5 m in some places to zero in others, whilst those of the R. Bure, though slightly higher, would probably not withstand a surge having a return period greater than about 1 in 20 years. These and other figures served to confirm the worst fears of farmers and drainage engineers, especially as RPT demonstrated by separate calculations that a surge similar to that of 1976 was likely to recur every 13 years. The 1953 surge, on the other hand, was estimated to have a return period of about 175 years.

When RPT examined the practicability of a full-scale bank-raising scheme, it identified a number of formidable problems. To safeguard the marshes against a 1 in 100 year surge-dominated event, it would be necessary to raise and strengthen over 200 km of the existing embankments, including 47 km beside the R. Bure, 50 km beside the Yare and 68 km beside the Waveney. In addition many of the soke dykes are located so close to the bank that they would have to be filled in and re-sited 30 m or so to the rear. Because of the poor quality of the materials available at many of the sites, RPT thought that clay would often have to be imported from elsewhere, greatly inflating the cost of the work. However, somewhat surprisingly, the firm had little to say about the inadequate foundations of the existing embankments, and the very real risk that some sections would collapse altogether if any attempt was made to raise them to the required height. But this point was subsequently made forcibly by staff of the AWA, and caused the Land Drainage Committee to rule out a Full Embankment Scheme on the grounds of impracticability, as well as prohibitive cost (about £17.7 million at 1976 prices).

RPT concluded from its computer runs that if a Partial Embankment Scheme was put into effect, Haddiscoe Island (744 ha) would be a more suitable site for a washland, than the 602 ha of marshland behind the Breydon South Wall, which formed the other site tentatively identified for this purpose. RPT predicted that if the crest level of the Island's embankments were lowered to 1.5 m OD, it would, on average, be flooded once a year. During a 1 in 100 year surge-dominated event, it would reduce water levels in the Waveney by about 0.7 m, whilst those of the R. Yare would fall by *c.* 0.8 m in the vicinity of Berney Arms, declining to *c.* 0.25 m two kilometres upstream of Cantley; water levels in the Bure would not be lowered significantly by such a wash. Although the banks of the Yare and Waveney would not need to be raised and strengthened as much as with a Full Embankment Scheme, it was estimated that £8.5 million would have to be spent on flood protection upstream of the Haven Bridge (£3.88 million, £2.56 million and £2.06 million on the embankments of the rivers Bure, Yare and Waveney respectively) and a further £310 000 on improving Yarmouth's defences.

A major advantage of a Partial Embankment Scheme was that the washland would prove highly attractive to birdlife, especially if, as the NCC later suggested, it was sub-divided by cross-walls and subjected to different flooding regimes, so that saline lagoons, reedbeds and other habitats developed in the different sub-compartments.

RPT decided on the basis of its computer runs, that if a barrier was provided, it would be best to close it on those occasions when water levels in the Haven were likely to attain a height of 1.8 m OD or more. This is 0.3 m lower than the present danger mark, and 0.85 m above the mean level of high water spring tides. The consultants calculated that if this operational threshold was selected, the barrier would, on average, have to be closed between seven and ten times a year, allowing for tests and maintenance runs.

In carrying out their cost-benefit analysis, RPT concluded, on the basis of information provided by the IDBs and a series of interviews, that its 21 336 ha Phase II Study Area could be categorized as follows:

	ha
Land already improved	4048
Land likely to be improved without enhanced flood protection	810
Unimprovable land (mainly alder woodlands near the valley margins)	1417
Farm buildings, roads etc.	202
Area potentially benefiting from enhanced flood protection	14 859

RPT estimated that 45 per cent of the marshland which had already been 'improved' (a word used synonymously in its report with 'converted' and 'developed') was under wheat, and that this was yielding 6.2 tonnes per hectare (although yields of 8 tonnes/ha have been recorded from certain sites), while the remainder was being used to grow barley (5 per cent), sugar beet and other root crops (6 per cent), peas and other vegetables (4 per cent) and improved grass (40 per cent).

Estimates by RPT of the rate and extent to which the potentially improvable area would be developed were based on a two-stage interview programme, designed to establish the degree of interest in the conversion of grassland to arable and relate this to farm size, and cropping and stocking patterns. The initial interviews were conducted by telephone with a sample of 81 farmers owning holdings of more than 10 ha. Later, the 36 individuals who expressed a positive interest were personally interviewed.

From the results obtained and from these and other interviews, and an evaluation of flood protection schemes elsewhere, the following forecasts were made of the most likely, optimistic and pessimistic rates of development once the area had been afforded protection with a barrier.

Years After completion of Scheme	←———	*Hectarage "improved"*	——→
	Pessimistic	*Most Likely*	*Optimistic*
1	73	109	146
5	2174	3243	4348
10	2470	4595	8138
15	4538	6891	11 976
20	5105	8976	14 020

RPT predicted that any areas left unimproved twenty years after the Flood Protection Scheme had been completed, would be converted during the following twenty years. This would bring the total area improved up to 14 859 ha, by which time the net agricultural benefits would, according to RPT, be £3.7 million per year.

Farmers were much more uncertain about the efficacy of a bank-raising scheme, and the consultants therefore suggested that if this method of flood protection was adopted, the conversion of grassland to arable would be delayed by about five years, and would then take place more slowly than with a barrier.

Although the benefits accruing from a Flood Protection Scheme would be primarily agricultural, it would also remove the risk of isolated cottages on the marshes being inundated. But the position over boatyards, riverside bungalows such as those at Potter Heigham and Brundall, and the low-lying parts of Loddon, Chedgrave and other villages, was less clear-cut, since these are at risk not so much from surges, as from fluvial floods following periods of heavy rainfall. In the circumstances RPT assessed the benefits from a barrier in respect of residential and commercial property at only £5600 per year.

On the supposition that the conversion of grass marshland to arable was inhibited primarily by the fear of flooding, the consultants then calculated the likely rate of return for each possible scheme, in terms of its agricultural and other benefits, and its costs. Their conclusions can be summarized as follows:

Type of scheme (to give protection during a 1:100 year surge)	Cost (1976 prices)	Likely internal rate of return
Full Embankment Scheme (implemented over 10 years)	£17.7 million	6%
Partial Embankment Scheme (using Haddiscoe Is. as the washland area)	£ 8.8 million*	8%
Haven Br. Barrier	£ 7.4 million	12% (11%–14%)**
Breydon Viaduct Barrier (including subsidiary structure on R. Bure)	£ 9.2 million	11% (10%–13%)**
Breydon Viaduct Barrier and road bridge – combined structure, (Inc. subsidiary structure on R. Bure)	£11.3 million	–

* According to the AWA, the cost of a Partial Embankment Scheme would have been *c.* £12 million if land purchase (estimated at £2 million), evacuation sluices, design fees and supervision had been included.

** These figures relate respectively to pessimistic and optimistic rates of marsh improvement.

On the assumption that the bridge for the proposed new relief road for Yarmouth would cost £3.2 million, RPT pointed out that £1.1 million would be saved if a combined barrier and bridge was built on the Breydon Viaduct site, rather than separate structures. On the other hand, the cost of providing a barrier upstream of the Haven Bridge, and a separate road bridge on the Breydon alignment would be £0.7 million less than a combined structure. Accordingly, the firm adopted this as its preferred solution, at the same time recommending that the barrier should be of the high level, drop-gate type, providing a headroom clearance of 22 m at mean high water spring tides, and a mean span navigable width of 50 m.

It was estimated that the barrier itself would cost £5.68 million, but that raising and strengthening the flood defences downstream and upstream of it would cost a further £460 000 and £1.25 million respectively. The AWA subsequently disclosed that £559 000 of this latter sum would have to be spent on the R. Yare, £658 000 on the Waveney, and £27 000 on the Bure, whose banks are, in general, more robust than those of the other rivers. RPT claimed that once these works had been carried out, no further capital expenditure would need to be incurred on the embankments, though bank maintenance, estimated at £300 000 per annum would have to continue indefinitely, whether or not a barrier was built.

When members of the Land Drainage Committee considered RPT's recommendations at their meeting in April 1978, they agreed that a barrier upstream of the Haven Bridge would be their preferred option, and instructed that consultations should take place with a wide range of different interests.

During the ensuing months, RPT's work came under attack from several quarters. Conservationists, for example, pointed out that although the firm's terms of reference required it to examine . . . "the effects on the environmental and amenity aspects of the area, with particular regard to the need for the preservation of the existing character of

Broadland, and the conservation of the area's unique ecological habitats", it had included in its report only a brief initial appraisal by the NCC of the ecological effects of a flood protection scheme, together with a supplementary note summarizing the conservation advantages of a Partial Embankment Scheme. Virtually nothing was said by the consultants about the changes in the landscape which took place when grass marshland was converted to arable, despite the fact that an acceleration in the rate at which this was occurring was quoted as being the principal justification for providing the Drained Marshland Area with an enhanced degree of protection against flooding.

The NCC and the Countryside Commission were particularly vexed by the Land Drainage Committee's failure to insist that the consultants carry out a proper appraisal of the environmental implications of their proposals, since this breached the convention that an organization wishing to initiate a new project should seek to satisfy those likely to be affected that it would not jeopardize their interests. Feelings on the subject were further ruffled in September 1978, when the Chairman of the AWA's Broads Committee ruled that members should confine their comments on the Flood Protection Scheme to the Authority's statutory functions of water conservation, sewage disposal, effluent quality control and fisheries management, and not debate its wider, environmental effects.

Despite its aversion to commissioning a study which it considered should have been produced and paid for by the Land Drainage Committee, the Countryside Commission decided to invite a specialist firm, Land Use Consultants Ltd., to carry out a rapid appraisal of the Broadland landscape, and advise how this was likely to be affected by a comprehensive flood protection scheme. In their report, dated November 1978, the consultants pointed out that the marshscape, though subject to slow and long-continued changes, has strong cultural and artistic associations, and forms an excellent foil to the rivers and broads. Five distinct types of scenery were identified, ranging from fully enclosed valleys such as those of the upper Bure, Ant and Yare, to the open landscape of the Halvergate marshes. A full-scale flood protection scheme would, by hastening the conversion of grassland to arable, cause the loss of some of the components of Broadland's landscape, and introduce new ones, thus substantially altering the scenic character of the region. It was thought that opportunities for ameliorating these changes would be very limited, but it was recommended that the extent of the areas likely to be converted to arable, and the practicablity and cost of maintaining adequate examples of the existing landscape types, should be investigated.

In a memorandum prepared by members of Faculty of the School of Environmental Sciences of the UEA, and presented at a seminar about the proposed Flood Protection Scheme in November 1978 (Norfolk CC, 1979), the view was expressed that it was unfortunate that RPT had not assessed the cost and environmental effects of continuing the present AWA policy of raising and strengthening the flood banks as the need arose. RPT was also criticized for not producing a series of cost-benefit analyses assuming different wheat prices, and varying rates of marsh improvement in the absence of a barrier. It was claimed that the consultants should have produced such a 'Sensitivity Analysis' in order to meet the terms of reference laid down for the Study.

RPT was also taken to task for assessing the benefits of a flood protection scheme by extrapolating from the answers given by an unbalanced sample of farmers. 26 out of the 28 individuals known to own more than 3000 acres (1215 ha) had been contacted by telephone and over half of these were subsequently interviewed personally. But of 134 farmers who owned between 25 and 50 acres (10–20 ha) only 14 were telephoned, and only 4 of these expressed any direct interest in such a scheme. It was also pointed out that some of the questions posed during the interviews – for example, "if a flood control scheme was successfully introduced, effectively minimizing the risk of flooding, salinity or drainage problems, what improvements would you undertake?" – were phrased in such a way as to produce a very biased response.

RPT enlarged its study area from 18 218 ha to 21 336 ha for the Stage II investigations (an increase of 17 per cent) following, as the firm put it . . . "a detailed examination of the records of the 18 IDBs". But why, it was asked, was this done, when most of the additional land, particularly that in the Hickling-Horsey area was too far up-valley to benefit from any protection afforded against surge tides at or near Yarmouth? Similarly, why did RPT revise its estimates of the amount of land which had already been improved from 4858 ha to 4048 ha, and at the same time claim that if no flood protection was provided, only 810 ha more would be converted, instead of the 1215 ha it had previously suggested?

The critics pointed out that the net result of these changes was that the amount of land classed as 'potentially improvable' was increased by 4333 ha, thus making it much more likely that a barrier near the Haven Bridge would be viable at a 10 per cent discount rate, when it had marginally failed this test when the Phase I figures were used.

The apparent benefits accruing from a barrier scheme were also increased as a result of RPT's decision to reduce the time-scale used in its cost-benefit analysis from 25 to 20 years, and to base its economic analysis on the assumption that 75 per cent of the newly drained land would be put down to wheat and other arable crops, and the remaining 25 per cent to improved grass, instead of the 60 to 40 ratio used in Phase I.

More fundamentally, John Bowers, an economist at Leeds University, suggested that it was wrong in principle to determine the level of protection to be afforded against flooding, and then seek to justify this by the application of cost-benefit techniques. Bowers argued that the maximum level of flood protection which is justified is that which yields farmers a normal rate of return on investment in land improvement. Only when this level has been determined, should schemes be appraised by means of cost-benefit analyses (Bowers, 1978).

The formal consultations which took place during the second half of 1978 demonstrated that the National Farmers Union, the Country Landowners Association and the Internal Drainage Boards were, as had been widely predicted, very much in favour of the proposed Barrier. They were equally unanimous in their opposition to the Partial Embankment Scheme, partly because this would lead to the loss of valuable agricultural land, and partly because like the Full Embankment Scheme, it would not give farmers the security which a barrier would afford them. In view of its responsibility for Haddiscoe Island, the area provisionally selected by RPT as being most suitable for a washland, the Langley, Chedgrave and Toft Monks Drainage Board not surprisingly objected particularly vehemently to the partial Embankment Scheme. AWA staff, too, were unhappy with it on the grounds that RPT had not allowed for the cost of providing evacuation sluices and other works on the Island, and that if a second surge occurred before the water from the first had been fully discharged (incidentally a most improbable event), a disastrous flood was inevitable. But whilst farmers and land-drainage engineers were strongly in favour of the Barrier Scheme, there was widespread anxiety and, in some cases, outright opposition to it in other quarters. For example, when Yarmouth councillors learnt that water levels in the upper reaches of the Haven would rise about half a metre higher when the barrier was closed, than they would otherwise, they decided to oppose it on the grounds that the barrier would actually increase, rather than reduce, the risk of property in the borough being flooded. They also considered that the cost and difficulty of raising the flood defences downstream of the barrier to the required level had been grossly under-estimated by RPT. The Great Yarmouth Port and Haven Commissioners, too, had reservations about any scheme which would impede the use of the Haven and the rivers for navigation, though they indicated their willingness to have further discussions with the AWA. The boat-hiring associations, on the other hand, stated that they would accept a barrier near the Haven Bridge, but would strongly oppose one on the Breydon Viaduct site.

The NCC objected to the Barrier Scheme on the grounds that it would accelerate the rate at which marshland was being put under the plough, to the detriment of wildlife, and in particular the aquatic fauna and flora of the marsh dykes. Like the Port and Haven Commissioners, it was also concerned lest the threshold water level at which it was planned that the barrier should be closed (1.8 m OD) should at some time in the future be lowered in order to keep out high spring tides as well as major surges, and thus reduce the cost of maintaining the tidal embankments upriver. It was stressed that such a change would be extremely damaging to the ecology of the region, and yet might be very difficult to resist in view of the high capital cost of the barrier, and the mounting problems already being encountered by the AWA in maintaining the embankments in the face of the erosion produced by boat wash.

In an attempt to find a compromise acceptable to both conservation and farming interests, the NCC urged the Land Drainage Committee to reconsider the possibility of carrying out a Selective Bank-raising Scheme. This would, the NCC argued, be a logical extension of the present system of maintaining the embankments, which does, in effect, afford certain areas a better degree of protection against flooding than others. Moreover, such a scheme would recognize the fact that the agricultural productivity of some parts of the Drained Marshland Area is much greater than others. But in subsequent discussions, the NCC's suggestion was rejected outright by the Land Drainage Committee on the grounds that if certain areas were given an above-average degree of protection, this would automatically increase the susceptibility of the remainder to flooding. It was also argued that it would be unfair to give some farmers a greater measure of security against flooding than others, and that it might even lead to charges of misfeasance being made against the AWA.

The Countryside Commission objected to the barrier because of the extent and nature of the changes which it would bring about in a region which it considered merited national park status; the Commission also reiterated its demand that the Land Drainage Committee should commission a proper assessment of the environmental effects of its proposals, a view echoed by the Suffolk County Council. Members of the Norfolk County Council, too, had considerable reservations about the scheme, and after several debates and considerable internal dissension, decided that the whole issue was so complex and contentious that it should be subject to detailed scrutiny at a public inquiry. In contrast, the barrier scheme was supported by the Broadland, Waveney and North Norfolk District Councils.

In March 1979, the Land Drainage Committee decided, after considering the views expressed, that another attempt should be made to allay the fears of those opposed to the barrier scheme. In particular, it urged conservationists to accept that it would reduce the risk of the aquatic plant and animal life of the grazing marsh ditches being destroyed by salt-water flooding, and would therefore be beneficial, rather than inimical to their interests. This was a legitimate point. But as far as conservationists were concerned, its importance was overridden by the fact that one of the primary purposes of the barrier was to increase the rate at which grass marshland was converted to arable – a process much more detrimental to the scenery and wildlife of the region, than the occasional flooding of dykes by seawater.

Despite a further round of meetings with the principal objectors, little progress was made, and in October, the Committee reiterated its view that a barrier on the Haven Bridge site remained its preferred course of action. It did, however, decide to commission a study of the practicability of constructing a combined bridge and barrier on the alignment of the former Breydon Viaduct, and also called for a report on a proposal put forward by the Chairman of the Port and Haven Commissioners, which would involve the diversion of the lowermost reaches of the R. Bure so that the latter discharged immediately upstream of a combined bridge and barrier (see Map 10.3c.) The major advantage of this proposal was that the movements of pleasure craft would not be impeded at times when the barrier was closed: the inter-connection between the rivers Bure and Yare would also be made less hazardous for navigation.

Conscious that it had only been established a short while previously, the Broads Authority decided in November 1979, to accept in principle that the region must be safeguarded against salt-water flooding, but to reserve judgement on the barrier scheme until it had been able to consider its environmental implications. To assist it do this, the Authority commissioned a preliminary Environmental Impact Assessment from two firms of consultants, Environmental Resource Management Ltd. and Trans Econ Ltd. Published in 1980, this dealt with the hydrological, ecological and economic implications of the barrier scheme, and the ways in which the region's special environmental importance might be safeguarded if it was implemented. The authors of the Assessment also identified a number of research projects which would have to be carried out if the effects of a flood protection scheme were to be fully assessed. They recommended, for example, that the soils in the region should be mapped so that the boundaries of the areas liable to become acidic when drained, and which were therefore unsuitable for arable cropping, could be identified. A survey was also needed to determine whether the grass marshland unlikely to be converted by its owners coincided with that classified as being of special amenity value (see page 3), and whether this would provide an adequate refuge for the aquatic plant and animal life characteristic of the region. It was also suggested that since a great deal of marshland was likely to be put under the plough during the next ten years or so, whether or not a barrier was provided, ways should be sought of ensuring that the dyke systems of such areas could be managed so as to maximize their ecological interest. Finally, the authors of the Assessment concluded that the measures available to conservationists for safeguarding land of special ecological and landscape significance were deficient in certain respects, and that special efforts should be made to tap the funds available from the EEC for environmental projects.

Following detailed discussion of the Impact Assessment, the Broads Authority decided in May 1980 that a Plan for safeguarding the nature conservation and amenity interest likely to be affected by the flood protection proposals should be developed by its officers in conjunction with other interested parties. This would take the form of Rural Land Use Strategy, a concept previously canvassed by the NCC but rejected by the Land Drainage Committee. The Authority also decided that the cost of implementing its Plan should be regarded as an essential component of the flood protection scheme, and that if agreement on this principle could not be reached with the AWA and the two ministries concerned (DoE and MAFF), it would be obliged to regard the proposals as unacceptable.

To provide the information required for the Safeguarding Plan, the Authority agreed to fund several research projects. One of these was a more detailed examination of the ecology and water chemistry of marsh dykes, the factors responsible for determining which aquatic plants occurred in them, and the way they were affected when the water-table was lowered to enable the adjoining land to be put under the plough (see page 266). The Authority also decided to commission an investigation of the distribution of acid sulphate soils in the region, and the effect they had on farm economics, since the claim made in the Impact Assessment that some of the soils of the Drained Mashland Area were unsuitable for arable use owing to their high pyrite content had not been accepted by the farming community.

While these additional surveys were in progress, members of the Land Drainage Committee had been advised that if the R. Bure was diverted so that it discharged upstream of a barrier and bridge on the site of the former Breydon viaduct (see Map 10.3c), the flood protection scheme would cost an extra £1.7 million at 1979 prices, or, if its junction with the R. Yare was diverted for another 500 m to the west as the Port and Haven Commissioners would have preferred, a further £3.5 million. Desirable as these proposals were from the navigational point of view, there seemed no prospect of the necessary funds being available, and the Committee therefore decided not to consider them further. However with an eye on Parliament, and the obvious political advantages of going for a unified structure, its members decided in July 1980 that they favoured a combined barrier and road bridge on the Breydon Water alignment, rather than a barrier on its own just upstream of the Haven Bridge. This proposal was duly supported by the Anglian (Regional) Drainage Committee in September and two months later, the Anglian Water Authority agreed that the necessary Bill should be drafted, and laid before Parliament by November 1981.

But it was not to be! Talks showed that it would take much longer to obtain the legal and financial clearances required for a barrier, than for a bridge, and rather than risk the political furore which would occur if there was the smallest delay in making a start on the latter, the Local Land Drainage Committee decided in December 1980 to revert to its original preference for a barrier just upstream of the Haven Bridge (see Plate 31). Hardly had this decision been endorsed by the Anglian Drainage Committee, than the Port and Haven Commissioners announced that they were "totally and irrevocably" opposed to any barrier in the region, thus confirming what O'Riordan (1982) and many others had suspected from the beginning, namely that there was no possibility of reaching agreement among the principal interested parties over such a contentious scheme. Clearly, it was now time for the MAFF to decide what was to be done, and after several months it told the AWA that it would like the cost-benefit analysis for the Scheme reworked to take account of the land use changes which had occurred since RPT published its report. This decision can be related to the realization that the firm had seriously under-estimated the rate at which marshland would be put under the plough in the absence of a barrier or some other form of comprehensive protection against flooding. Their claim that in these circumstances only a further 810 ha would be converted had been received with much scepticism by farmers as well as conservationists, and it came as no surprise when air photographs taken in January 1980, and subsequently interpreted for the Broads Authority by the Institute of Terrestrial Ecology, showed that a total of some 5600 ha had by then been put under the plough, an increase of 1552 ha over the figure estimated by RPT to have been improved by 1976. Further areas of grass marsh were converted during the ensuing months, and by 1982, it was estimated that *c.* 694 ha, or *c.* 35 per cent of the Authority's Executive Area, was in arable cultivation (Fuller, 1984; Fuller, 1986; Fuller, Brown and Mountford, 1986).

AWA originally intended to re-work the cost-benefit analysis for the MAFF on an in-house basis, but delays were occasioned by staff shortages, by uncertainties concerning the outcome of the long-running Halvergate controversy, and by the need to hold discussions with the Broads Authority and other key agencies about the Marsh Safeguarding Plan. Accordingly, the Land Drainage Committee decided in February 1983, to invite RPT to produce a revised estimate of the cost of building a barrier on the Haven Bridge site, and raising and strengthening the flood defences upstream and downstream of it. RPT was also asked to reassess (a) the agricultural benefits which would accrue if such a scheme was implemented, making allowance for the presence of acid sulphate soils, and the need to safeguard the wetland areas scheduled by the NCC as SSSIs, or designated in the Broads Authority's draft Strategy and Management Plan as being of particular ecological and/or scenic importance, and (b) the potential benefits arising from the enhanced degree of flood protection afforded to residential and commercial premises at Yarmouth and elsewhere. In carrying out this re-appraisal, the consultants would be required to take account of the fact that the Test Discount had been lowered by the Treasury from 10 to 5 per cent since their earlier report was produced – a decision which had been heavily criticized by many economists (e.g. O'Riordan, 1980).

In its report, RPT concluded that the capital and operational costs of a barrier and its associated works, discounted at 5 per cent, would be £15.8 million (*c.* 23.5 million at 1990 prices). In reassessing the agricultural benefits of the scheme, RPT noted that some 4906 ha were already under the plough, and that of the remaining area of unimproved marsh, only 4125 ha were not subject to some form of constraint, arising from the acidity of the soil, or because the land had been categorized as being of environmental importance. Given the doubts expressed previously about whether the provision of a barrier would significantly affect the rate of marsh conversion, RPT decided to examine two 'scenarios', the first of these assumed that the 4125 ha would be subject to improvement, and that this could be ascribed, and therefore credited, to the scheme, whilst the other assumed that they would be improved whether or not a barrier was provided. The agricultural benefits of these scenarios were assessed at £13.6 million and £6.8 million respectively at a 5 per cent discount rate (RPT, 1983).

After taking into account the other benefits of a barrier, including an allowance for the fact that it would prevent environmentally sensitive areas of marsh being flooded by salt water, to the detriment of the aquatic fauna and flora of their dykes, RPT concluded that the scheme would have a positive Net Present Value (NPV) of £4.5 million under the first scenario, but that under the second the NPV would be negative at £2.4 million.

RPT's report was received by the Land Drainage Committee in July 1983, and forwarded to the MAFF, with a renewed request that grant be made available for the scheme. While this was under consideration, the Broads Authority arranged for RPT's report to be assessed by Dr. K. Turner, an economist on the staff of the School of Environmental Sciences of the University of East Anglia. He concluded, *inter alia*, that their analysis . . . "is seriously flawed at the technical level", the effect being that the firm had over-estimated . . . "the project's benefits, [particularly the agricultural benefits] and under-estimated its costs".

Although Turner's appraisal was not submitted formally to the MAFF, there is reason to believe that its staff were aware of his findings and they were subsequently published in an amended and extended form (Turner, 1983). In any event, few were surprised when the Ministry and the AWA announced in February 1984 that . . . "the economic evidence has made it difficult to justify building the Yare Barrier at the present time", and that the AWA would instead . . . "investigate alternative solutions that can achieve a degree of (flood) protection for Broadland".

The Norwich Division of the AWA reacted to this decision by commencing an in-house survey of the state of the embankments in the region, the aim being to ensure that the limited funds available for repairs and maintenance were spent to the best advantage. As a result of this investigation, it became painfully apparent that large parts of Broadland were, as a consequence of bank settlement, slumping and erosion, at even greater risk of flooding than they had been in the mid-1970s when RPT compiled its Report. To make matters worse, 1984/5 saw the introduction of major changes in the way flood protection works were financed. In the past, virtually all capital schemes of this type had been funded by a combination of grant aid, and borrowing. However, the Government made it clear that not only would the Authority's grant-earning ceiling be reduced, but that much stricter borrowing limits would be imposed upon it. In addition, flood defence works which, until the end of 1983/4 had been eligible for MAFF grant at the rate of 85 per cent if located in the middle and lower reaches of the rivers*, and at 70 per cent for the remainder of the region, would in future only attract grants of 50 and 35 per cent respectively†. Many such capital projects would therefore have to be funded from the revenue account, thus making it necessary for AWA to reduce its expenditure on routine maintenance tasks. In the face of these changes, the Land Drainage Committee decided that it would have to increase by some 12 per cent its annual precepts on the Norfolk and Suffolk County Councils, and the internal drainage boards in its area of responsibility. In the event, the Norwich Division's grant-earning ceiling was only £1.15 million in 1985/6, compared with a mean figure of £3 272 427 for the period 1980/1 to 1983/4, if the allocations for these years are converted to 1986 prices. As a result, only £126 368 was spent on grant-aided capital projects in Broadland in 1985/6, compared with £924 715 the previous year. Even if the cost of protecting Gillingham and Beccles against flooding is excluded from this latter figure, capital expenditure was less than a quarter of that in 1984/5. Piling and other works carried out in 1985/6 in the vicinity of Runham did not attract grant, and a further £210 000, drawn from the revenue account, had to be spent on other urgent projects in the region.

The Norwich Division's grant-earning investment allocation was slightly increased in 1986/7 (although the average rate of grant paid out for works carried out that year fell from 43 to 37 per cent) and, as indicated on page 317, the Government later made available additional funds as a result of the representations made by AWA in March 1986. But most of the money available for capital works that year had to be spent on the sea defences at Horsey, and on the walls of the Haven, which were in such a state of disrepair as to make it likely that much of Yarmouth, Gorleston and Caister would be flooded in the event that there was a major surge. The Breydon South Wall was also in a parlous state as a result of wave erosion, and a start was made on strengthening this, and re-piling the left bank of the R. Yare near Five Mile House, part of which had collapsed in February 1986. Expenditure on these works in 1986/7 amounted to £510 391, and a further £137 018 was spent on the Beccles-Gillingham flood protection scheme.

Confronted with the changed economic situation, and the alarming, and almost unchecked, deterioration in the condition of the region's riverine flood defences, the Land Drainage Committee decided that rather than rely on the *ad hoc* and piecemeal approach towards bank-protection works which until then had been pursued by the AWA and its predecessors, it would be essential to develop a comprehensive flood alleviation strategy for the region, based on economics. A preliminary study, aimed at assessing the data requirements for such a project, developing a methodology in terms of a cost-benefit analysis, and testing the feasibility of the approach on selected areas, was commissioned by the AWA from members of the School of Environmental Sciences, UEA, in October 1985, and it was arranged that this work would be part-funded by the Broads Authority, in view of its environmental implications.

The appraisal took account of the ecological damage which would be caused by saline flooding, as well as the economic losses, and showed that a 1 in 25 year standard of protection could be justified for the Halvergate triangle – one of the areas chosen for the preliminary analysis – but that increased levels of protection were not warranted for the second area examined, the Hardley Marshes (Turner, Brooke & Hey, 1986). After reviewing the various methods used to strengthen flood defences (e.g. piling, revetment and geo-textile techniques), Turner *et al.* recommended AWA to carry out experiments aimed at finding out whether the resistance of tidal embankments to slumping could be increased if drains were installed in them. They also pointed out, as RPT had done in

---

* These are defined for this purpose as being downstream of Beccles Bridge on the R. Waveney, Rockland Dyke on the Yare, Wroxham Broad on the Bure, Barton Broad on the Ant, and Candle Dyke on the Thurne.

† These figures were increased for projects in the Norwich Division to 60 and 45 per cent respectively in 1987/8, and to 65 and 45 per cent in 1990/1.

the 1970s, that washlands could fulfil a useful role in flood alleviation, and that this aspect merited further investigation. On the basis of these recommendations, the AWA and the Broads Authority decided to invite the consultants to extend the scope of their studies to cover the whole of Broadland, and their report was submitted to the National Rivers Authority in September 1989 (Brooke & Turner, 1989).

The future

Although it would be unwise to prejudge the results of the comprehensive review which has been carried out by Brooke and Turner, it would seem inevitable that the shortage of funds, combined with the Government's insistence on the rigorous use of cost-benefit analyses, will force the National Rivers Authority (which inherited the AWA's flood-defence responsibilities in September 1989) to stop maintaining the embankments fronting various areas of low productivity marshland. As a result, they will ultimately become permanently flooded, an unfortunate development from the nature conservation point of view, since such areas will often consist of species-rich grass marshland on peat. Experience elsewhere, for instance on the marshes adjoining the Whitlingham sewage treatment works, has shown that when such terrain is subject to freshwater flooding, it is colonized by a floristically rather dull community referable to the FILIPEN-DULION Alliance (see Chapter 7). The adoption of such a policy will therefore reduce, rather than increase, the wildlife interest of the region. This situation may be contrasted with that in the Blyth valley in East Suffolk, where the flooding of the Bulcamp, Sandpit Covert and Angel Marshes by saline water during the 1920s and 1930s resulted in the conversion of large expanses of grassland to intertidal mudflats of prime ornithological importance.

The prognosis for Broadland in the longer term is very uncertain. Recent research by bodies such as the United States Department of Energy and the Climatic Research Unit of the University of East Anglia on the 'Greenhouse Effect' (the rise in world temperatures caused by the increasing quantities of carbon dioxide, methane, chlorofluorocarbons and other gases in the atmosphere) suggests that the sea level will rise much more rapidly during the next 50 to 100 years than it has done during recent historical times. Opinions on this vary widely, but the most likely figure is a rise of relative sea level of between 15 and 30 cm by the year 2030, mainly as a consequence of thermal expansion in the oceans, and the melting of mid- and high-altitude glaciers (Warrick, 1989). This, plus the increased likelihood of a major surge occurring (see page 65), greatly magnifies the risk of high-quality agricultural land being flooded, unless the region is protected by a tidal barrier*. It is one of the great ironies that such a proposal would probably now be supported, rather than opposed, by organizations such as the Broads Authority and the NCC, on the grounds that in view of the weakened state of the tidal embankments, and the near-impossibility of raising these sufficiently to keep pace with the rising sea level, a barrier is the only realistic way of preventing large parts of the Drained Marshland Area becoming permanently flooded. While it would be easy in such circumstances for land drainage engineers to accuse such bodies of being illogical, given their resolute hostility to RPT's barrier proposals in the 1970s, one needs to bear in mind that the principal justification put forward for the latter in this period, was the need to allow – or even actively encourage – farmers to convert their grass marshland to arable. Fortunately, from the nature conservation and scenic points-of-view, this is no longer the case. Indeed, confronted with falling grain prices, and the subsidies available to them under the ESA scheme, landowners will in future be more likely to put their marshes back to grass, than the other way about.

However desirable on farming and environmental grounds, it is doubtful whether a barrier could be justified economically, unless it was designed to safeguard, not only Broadland, but the town of Great Yarmouth. To achieve this, the barrier would, in the author's opinion, have to be sited as near as possible to the mouth of the Haven, preferably well downriver from the site near the Lower Ferry, first proposed by RPT in 1956, but rejected then, and again in the mid-1970s. In fact, by the early 1980s, the

---

* In 1991, after the above was written, the NRA appointed Binnie and Partners to develop a comprehensive flood alleviation strategy for Broadland. Six options have been identified for in-depth studies (Binnie & Partners, 1991), one of these being the provision of a tidal barrier across the R. Yare. Binnies are due to complete their investigations and report to the NRA in May 1992.

town had become so vulnerable to riverine flooding during a major surge that the AWA was obliged to start raising the height of the quays in the Haven, and the walls of the lower reaches of the R. Bure. Almost three-quarters of a million pounds was spent on these between 1980/1 and 1985/6, and a report produced by consultant engineers in December 1985 indicated that a further £6.72 million would have to be spent during the next few years if the town's defences were to be brought up to a standard sufficient to prevent flooding on the 1953 scale. Most of the necessary work (which involved raising the defences in the Haven by about 50 cm) had been carried out by the spring of 1990, and when the project has been completed, the immediate advantages accruing to the town from a barrier will have been reduced. In addition, even if the Yarmouth Port Authority* is successful in its bid to raise the funds needed to construct an outer harbour for the town, it will undoubtedly still oppose a barrier being built across the lower reaches of the Haven, on the grounds that this would constitute an impediment to navigation.

One way to counter the Port Authority's objections would be to construct a rising-sector gate barrier in the Haven, similar to the one on the R. Thames at Woolwich. A structure of this sort would be much more costly than the drop-gate barrier which RPT recommended in the mid 1970s should be built upstream of the Haven Bridge. On the other hand, the extra cost could perhaps be justified on the basis that such a barrier would be capable of affording long-term security, not just to agricultural land and the Broadland environment, but to residential and industrial premises in Yarmouth, and most important of all, human lives.

What the future holds for Broadland in the very long term is anyone's guess. There is very little agreement amongst scientists about what is likely to happen during the next 50 years or so, never mind the coming centuries. But if, as has been predicted in a recent Dutch study cited by Boorman *et al.* (1989), sea levels rise by a metre during the next 100 years (instead of *c.*10 to 15 cm per century during historic times), and by 5 m during the ensuing 200 years, it would seem likely that Broadland will once again be subject to a marine transgression, perhaps not dissimilar in its ecological effects to the events of this nature which have been described in Chapter 2.

---

* The Great Yarmouth Port and Haven Commissioners were re-constituted as a Port Authority in September 1989 (see page 389).

Chapter 11
The Use and Management of the Waterways

Early history

For centuries the rivers formed the main lines of communication in East Norfolk, and many settlements were founded where there was easy access to the water. The Romans may have had this in mind in about 70 AD, when they established their first garrison town in Norfolk – *Venta Icenorum* – on the east bank of the Tas, a tributary of the R. Yare, and the remains of what is thought to have been a quay have been found at Trowse Eye, the confluence of the rivers Yare and Wensum. This is believed to have been in use from about AD 50 to 150 (Green, 1972).

A small settlement was founded at Caister-by-Yarmouth in about AD 125, but although this is thought to have been a port, investigations have failed to reveal evidence for a harbour (Murphy, pers. comm.). The Roman fortress of *Garionnonum*, situated at Burgh Castle on the opposite side of what was at this time an open estuary, was founded towards the end of the third century AD, and would have provided trading vessels with protection against pirates.

Little is known about the use made of Broadland's rivers during the ensuing Saxon period, but by the tenth century, a series of hamlets beside the R. Wensum had been unified under the name of Northwic, and in 1004 this was described in the Anglo-Saxon Chronicle as a borough. There is evidence that considerable trading took place between here and Europe during the eleventh century (Carter, 1978), and recent archaeological excavations have confirmed what had been suspected for a long time, namely that a commercial waterfront existed in the vicinity of Whitefriars Bridge in late Saxon times (Ayers & Murphy, 1983; Ayers, 1985). This site would have been chosen because of its proximity to areas known to have been occupied at this time. In addition, the right (south) bank of the river is bordered here by a raised spur of gravel, now occupied by St. Martin-at-Palace Plain, and this would have provided a much more convenient berthing and beaching place for vessels than the soft marshy terrain which at this time bordered the river further downstream.

By the time of the Norman Conquest, the Anglo-Danish population of the city had risen to about 5500, making it one of the largest settlements in England. Much trading took place during the eleventh century, both with France – Caen stone, pottery, millstones and other goods being imported – and with other parts of England (Green, 1972). During this period, sea-going vessels were able to reach Norwich direct. However, the strong tidal currents in the Haven, combined with its awkward, ever-changing entrance (which would have been carried further and further south as the

Yarmouth shingle spit lengthened), would have made it difficult, if not dangerous, to navigate, and this, together with the increasing size of the craft in use, meant that by about 1300, most cargoes bound to and from the hinterland were being transhipped to river craft, either in the Haven, or in Yarmouth Roads. The town itself had initially developed as a small fisherman's settlement, and had become a free borough in 1209. Its protective walls with their ten gates and sixteen towers, were started in 1285, but not completed until the end of the fourteenth century (Manship, 1619). Last to be finished (in 1396 according to Nail, 1866), was the magnificent North-west Tower, which today stands alone on the North Quay, incongruously near the Yarmouth Yacht Station.

Yarmouth's development as an entrepôt brought it increasing affluence, but at the same time led to conflicts with Norwich which were to last for the next six centuries. Blomefield (1805–1810) records that as early as 1249 the citizens of Norwich sued the people of Yarmouth . . . "for not permitting their keels to come laden with goods and merchandise to the city, as they always did in the past, and detaining them there".

Further difficulties arose in 1331, following a decision by King Edward III that the sale of wool, sheepskins and other commodities should in future only take place in Norwich. The burgesses of Yarmouth showed their displeasure at this by preventing vessels bound for Norwich sailing upriver, but the resulting lawsuit led the King to issue a writ ordering Yarmouth to desist (Armstrong, 1781).

Although jetties were provided in Yarmouth Haven to cater for the needs of sea-going vessels, their comings and goings were constantly handicapped by the tendency for the mouth of the river to silt up and, according to Ecclestone and Ecclestone (1959), this became unusable in about 1337. In an attempt to overcome this difficulty, a channel was dug through the shingle bank between Hopton and Corton in 1347 (see Fig. 11A) and when this became choked, another new cut was dug, this time just south of the town walls. This too quickly silted up, and a third attempt was made in 1408, almost opposite Newton Cross. This channel was in use for about 100 years, but new ones had to be dug in 1508, *c.* 1529 and 1549. Work on the present entrance to the Haven was begun in 1559, and for the first time, pilings were used to prevent the river breaking back into its natural channel to the south.

That efforts to maintain a navigable channel between the Haven and the sea continued over such a long period, despite the heavy drain this must have placed on local resources, shows how dependent Yarmouth people were on water-borne trading. Nevertheless they were well aware that the easier the entrance to the Haven, the greater their vulnerability to seaborne invasion. Periodic efforts were therefore made to renovate or improve the town's defences, particularly during troubled times. In 1588 a boom was put across the Haven, two men being employed to open it at convenient times, and ensure that it was always in place at night.

Norwich, which in 1004 had been sacked by a riverborne raiding party under the leadership of Sweyn, King of Denmark, had taken similar precautions nearly three centuries earlier; its masonry walls, started in 1297, and completed in 1334, included boom towers at Conesford, the remains of which can be seen beside Carrow Bridge.

Although the port of Norwich was located near Whitefriars Bridge in the eleventh century (and perhaps earlier), the centre of activity had shifted to the vicinity of King Street, a kilometre further downstream, by the beginning of the twelfth century (Ayers, 1985). Consequently, as Norwich grew in size and prosperity, it was the facilities here, rather than at Whitefriars, which were improved to cope with the increasing volume of commercial traffic on the R. Yare. Bromefield records that the 'common staithe' was provided with a crane in 1404, while another was installed here during the reign of Edward VI. However, sea-going vessels seldom, if ever, visited Norwich because of the difficulty of getting into and out of the Haven, and the shallowness of the channel across Breydon Water. That the city archives refer to the arrival of a 'ship' at Conesford Towers in 1675 is perhaps indicative of the novelty of the event. Imports from the fourteenth to the seventeenth centuries included timber, herrings, furs, cloths, salt, sugar, wine and Caen stone for building, whilst wool, hides, dairy produce, grain and, from 1350 onwards, worsted cloth, were exported from the city during this period (Wren, 1976).

Norwich people undoubtedly resented having to pay tolls on merchandise transhipped at Yarmouth, but they would have known that it was much cheaper to transport goods by water, than by road. For instance, Manship reported that in 1607, when the

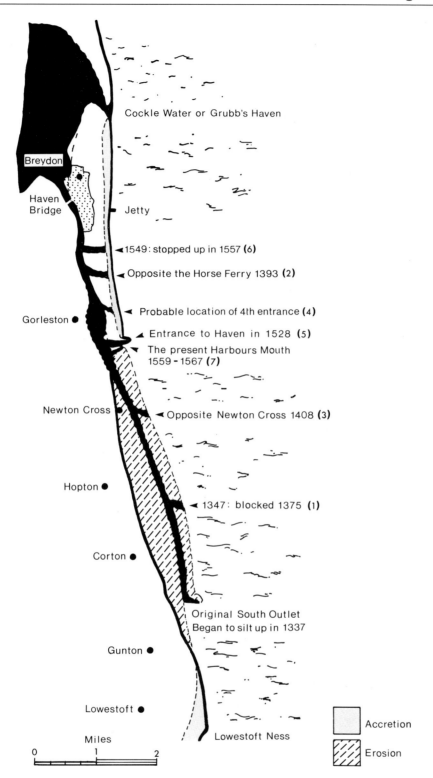

Cockle Water or Grubb's Haven

Breydon

Haven Bridge

Jetty

◄ 1549: stopped up in 1557 **(6)**

◄ Opposite the Horse Ferry 1393 **(2)**

◄ Probable location of 4th entrance **(4)**

Gorleston ●

◄ Entrance to Haven in 1528 **(5)**

◄ The present Harbours Mouth 1559 - 1567 **(7)**

Newton Cross

◄ Opposite Newton Cross 1408 **(3)**

Hopton ●

◄ 1347: blocked 1375 **(1)**

Corton ●

Original South Outlet
Began to silt up in 1337

Gunton ●

Lowestoft ●

Miles

0   1   2

Lowestoft Ness

Accretion

Erosion

Fig. 11A

The locations of the seven attempts made to create a navigable entrance to the Haven through the Yarmouth shingle spit.

Source: Ecclestone and Ecclestone (1959), who based their figure on the writings of Manship (1619) and other historians

R. Yare froze over, . . . "men pay more than 24 shillings for carriage of that by land from Yarmouth to Norwich which by water . . . would have been carried . . . for less than one shilling and fourpence."

Yarmouth spent over £31 000 on its Haven between 1549 and 1613, and despite its efforts to raise money, both by petitions to the King, and by selling off its assets, the town was in debt to the tune of £9400 by 1667. Things obviously could not be allowed to continue, and the Yarmouth Haven and Pier Commission, the predecessor of the Great Yarmouth Port and Haven Commission, was established by an Act of 1670. The eight commissioners were appointed by Norwich, Yarmouth, Norfolk and Suffolk, while the town clerk of Yarmouth handled the Commission's day to day affairs.

The Act laid down a scale of charges to be levied on all incoming goods, except fish, and decreed that the money should be spent on . . . "Yarmouth Haven and Peers [*sic*] and nothing else whatsoever". The Commission was able to raise loans on the strength of this power, and soon after its formation gave Yarmouth Corporation £12 000 towards the cost of improving the Haven and its jetties. The formative Act expired in 1677, but the Commission continued to operate under a series of Acts passed during the late seventeenth and early eighteenth centuries.

The Commission was a funding, rather than a managerial organization, and its terms

Table 11a   Coal and Goods imported through Yarmouth on Norwich's Account: 1787–1800 and 1814–21

Date	Coal (chaldrons)	% of total Yarmouth import	Goods (tons)	% of total Yarmouth import
1787	28 740	50	8111	57
1788	29 086	48	9284	70
1789	27 531	44	8138	48
1790	28 101	48	9040	61
1791	28 544	52	10 743	64
1792	31 179	51	9299	49
1793	30 677	49	10 415	55
1794	24 460	42	9181	46
1795	27 775	43	7922	38
1796	24 977	41	9083	35
1797	27 995	42	5772	32
1798	26 817	39	7010	47
1799	22 114	38	5767	36
1800	23 492	33	7107	33
1814	36 149	43	11 008	61
1815	37 366	43	13 609	56
1816	38 478	46	10 963	64
1817	32 717	39	13 519	63
1818	45 062	51	16 287	48
1819	43 458	51	18 947	48
1820	50 046	50	18 135	53
1821	44 568	48	17 600	59

Source: Murphy (1979)

of reference would have precluded it from spending money on the rivers. In any event, jurisdiction over the Yare, Bure and Waveney as far upstream as Hardley Cross, Acle Bridge and St. Olaves Bridge respectively had by long tradition been exercised by Yarmouth Corporation. Until 1748, the town bailiffs used to visit these points in August each year, and after checking *en route* that the fishermen were using nets which conformed to the regulations, would issue a proclamation re-affirming their jurisdiction. A similar ceremony was performed by Norwich dignitaries each year at Hardley Cross, which from time immemorial has marked the downstream limit of the city's jurisdiction over the R. Yare (Southwell, 1888); indeed this stretch of the river is still included within the Corporation's boundary.

Very little information is available about the way the rivers were managed between the fourteenth and seventeenth centuries, nor do we know when the channels linking Ranworth, Cockshoot, South Walsham and other by-passed broads with the river were dug, except that this must have been after these medieval peat pits became flooded in the early fourteenth century. An indication of the importance of riverborne trading to settlements in the hinterland is afforded by Bungay, which in 1670, obtained parliamentary powers to carry out works on the Waveney. The preamble to the Act notes that the river above Beccles had . . . "become clogged and landed up so that keeles (*sic*), lighters and other boates (*sic*) cannot pass", and this would suggest that this section of the river was navigable prior to the seventeenth century. Locks were constructed at Geldeston,

Ellingham and Wainford, and following the opening of the waterway to boat traffic in *c.* 1673, the prosperity of Bungay increased considerably. Despite various vicissitudes, income from the canalized section of the river amounted to £550 in *c.* 1810, but a proposal to extend the navigation to Harleston, Eye and Diss was abandoned in 1818 as a result of strong opposition from commercial interests in Bungay (Ridgard, 1982).

Specific arrangements for managing the rivers, as well as the Haven, were laid down in the *Yarmouth Haven and Pier Act* of 1722. This decreed that of every 12 pence obtained from the tolls levied on coal, grain and other merchandise unloaded at Yarmouth, sixpence should be spent on the Haven. Of the remainder, a penny halfpenny was to be paid to the Chamberlain of Norwich and used for dredging and cleansing the R. Yare between New Mills and Hardley Cross, whilst persons appointed to care for the R. Bure (including the R. Ant upstream to Dilham), the R. Waveney, and the bridge and quays at Yarmouth, were to receive a halfpenny share each. The Act specified that the remaining threepence could, if a majority of the Commission agreed, be used to dredge the channel through Breydon Water.

Yarmouth, Norwich, Norfolk and Suffolk each appointed three of the 12 members of the Commission, but although this was made accountable for the toll monies, Yarmouth Corporation remained responsible for collecting the latter, and for managing the Haven and Breydon Water.

The provisions of the 1722 Act were re-enacted with minor amendments in 1749, 1756 and 1772, but the deepening of the channel through Breydon Water was on each occasion left as a permissive power of the Commission, rather than an obligation. Dredging and other works led to a gradual improvement in the navigability of the Haven and its approaches, but Yarmouth people were understandably reluctant to jeopardize the jobs, revenue and influence which resulted from the town's entrepôt trade (Table 11a) by enabling sea-going ships to gain direct access to Norwich. The channel through Breydon was therefore left undredged, despite periodic protests from Norwich merchants about the high tolls they had to pay, and the delays which occurred as a result of the need to transfer cargoes from ship to river craft, and vice versa.

It is not clear how the arrangements laid down in the Act for managing the rivers worked out in practice. However, Norwich Corporation seems to have done its best with that part of the Yare within its jurisdiction, as an official notice, issued in 1741, refers to the need for the owners of land adjoining the river between Norwich and Hardley Cross to . . . "cut their banks, and draw their hoves* and weeds, and remove all other impediments from the river and its adjoining creeks". The Bure too, seems to have been kept deep enough to allow river craft to reach its navigable limits, since the *John and Joseph*, a hatch keel of 50 tons burthen was advertised for sale at Coltishall in 1749 (Malster, 1971). That the rivers were being regularly maintained during the eighteenth century is also suggested by the fact that moves were made to extend the navigation further upstream, as the prosperity of towns in the hinterland increased. The Bure was canalized from Horstead to Aylsham between 1774 and 1779, locks being constructed at Horstead, Buxton, Lamas, Oxnead, Burgh and Aylsham. The southward loop of the river around Ward Marsh, opposite St. Benet's, was probably by-passed at the same time. In contrast, proposals to make the R. Wensum navigable as far upstream as Fakenham (Armstrong, 1781) had, according to Bacon (1844), been made "on more than one occasion", but had had to be abandoned as a result of objections from the riparian owners. The same writer notes that proposals to re-open (*sic*) the Muckfleet River so as to allow boats to reach the Ormesby-Rollesby-Filby group of broads were abandoned in 1843, the inference being that this tributary of the Bure was at one time navigable.

Keels and wherries

For many centuries, the main type of craft in use on Broadland's waterways was the keel. This had a mast mounted amidships on a tabernacle, and a single square sail, and probably evolved from the Viking longboat (Clark, 1961). In 1912, a keel which had last been used as a lighter in the 1890s, and which had subsequently been sunk in a dyke on

---

* Floating masses of reedswamp known today as 'hovers'.

the south side of the R. Yare just downstream of Postwick Grove, was partially excavated and measured. She was found to have been about 55 feet (16.8 m) long with a maximum beam of 13 feet 8 inches (4.2 m), and a depth amidships of about 4 feet (1.2 m), rising to 4 feet 10 inches (1.5 m) near the stern; she would probably have been capable of carrying about 30 tons of cargo (WAD, 1931). In 1985, this vessel was salvaged by a team working under the direction of Ms Douglas-Sherwood, and moved

Plate XXXVII

The *Albion* on the R. Bure – 1987.

Although this is the only trading wherry currently afloat, her owners – the Norfolk Wherry Trust – have acquired a second vessel, the *Lord Roberts*, and hope, when funds permit, to raise this from her watery grave and restore her. A third trading wherry, the *Maud*, is owned privately, and is at present being rebuilt at Upton.

The cost of maintaining the *Albion* and similar large sailing craft in good repair is extremely high; for instance, the new 1200 sq ft (279 sq m) sail which had to be made for her in 1988, cost some £3000. Fortunately, generous grants for this and other essential work on these traditional Broadland craft have been forthcoming from boat-hiring interests and the Broads Authority.

Oby Mill dates from 1753, and is the oldest drainage mill of known age in the region. It is one of eleven mills which the Norfolk Windmills Trust is currently 'protecting', prior to restoration.

Photo: R.N. Flowers

to Hales Hall, near Loddon, where she was placed under a plastic cover (EDP, 1985). She was transferred to Cannon Wharf, Norwich, in 1988 so that members of the Norfolk Keel Trust could commence the not-inconsiderable task of restoring her. Sadly, the necessary funds have not been forthcoming, and although the vessel is protected from the weather, her timbers are drying out and deteriorating.

Keels continued in use until well into the nineteenth century, but their inability to sail close-hauled constituted a major handicap on Broadland's twisting rivers, and in the late sixteenth century a new type of vessel, the wherry, began to come into service. This is thought to have developed by adapting the hull of a keel to take the type of mast and rigging then being used by small vessels on the Dutch waterways (Clark, 1961). The earliest known written reference to the new type of vessel appears in 1604, when 7 shillings was paid for "two wherries rowing down to Whitlingham", whilst in a will of 1610, a half-share in a wherry called the 'Spred Eagle' (*sic*) was bequeathed by J. Smythe of Yarmouth to John Cornelis (Clark, 1961).

Early wherries were probably incapable of carrying more than about 5 tons of cargo, but their fore and aft rig enabled them to sail much closer to the wind than a keel. Their consequent ability to make faster passages rendered them better suited to carrying passengers, mail and other urgent goods. During the ensuing 50 years, the numbers of wherries in use, and their size, increased rapidly, and by the end of the eighteenth century, they had attained their definitive appearance. The tarred hull was double-ended, with a single hold protected by a hatch cover, whilst the cabin, large enough for the crew of two, was situated near the stern. Aft of this, there was a small well, from which the tiller and mainsheet could be tended. The stout mast was counterbalanced, and could be raised and lowered by the forestay, whilst the black, high-peaked, loose-footed sail was controlled by a single halyard. Trading wherries were traditionally clinker-built, as are the *Maud*, which is currently being restored at Upton by Mr and Mrs Pargeter after lying submerged in Ranworth Inner Broad for several years (EDP, 1985), and the *Lord Roberts* which has been acquired by the Norfolk Wherry Trust for restoration if and when funds permit. In contrast, the 40 ton *Albion*, which was built at Oulton Broad in 1898, and used for many years by a firm of malsters at Bungay before being bought for preservation by the Wherry Trust in 1949, is a carvel vessel (see Plate XXXVII). Several steel wherries were also built (including the *Uranus* now lying sunk in Bargate Broad), but these were unpopular with their crews, because they handled poorly, and their cabins were very hot in summer and cold in the winter.

By 1798, no fewer than 120 wherries were registered for use on the rivers compared with only 36 keels. The average tonnage of the wherries on the R. Yare was 30, on the Waveney 27.7 and on the Bure 23.9, whilst the corresponding figures for the keels were 66.4, 58 and 29.3 tons (Clark, 1961).

By the mid-nineteenth century, when commercial traffic on the waterways was at its height, about 300 wherries were plying for trade. A typical vessel of about 30 tons would be about 52 feet (15.8 m) long, with a beam of about 13 feet (4.0 m) and a draught when laden of only about 2 feet 6 inches. The 110 wherries registered with the Bure Commissioners in 1868 had a total burthen of 1985 tons, and therefore averaged about 18 tons each. The largest wherry ever built was the *Wonder* of about 80 tons, which used to take coal out to steamers lying in Yarmouth Roads. At the opposite end of the scale was the *Wasp*, a 12-tonner, and the *Cabbage*, which appropriately enough took garden produce from Ludham to Yarmouth.

An enormous range of goods and merchandise was transported by wherry, but the most important cargoes in the eighteenth and nineteenth centuries were corn, coal, and chalk for making into lime. Passengers and mail were also carried, as the roads across the marshes were often impassable, particularly during the winter.

The Norwich-Yarmouth controversy

The relationship between Yarmouth and Norwich had long been an uneasy one as a consequence of the latter's entrepôt role, and from the 1740s onwards, a number of events conspired to exacerbate the difficulties. In 1762, for instance, there was a dispute leading to court action over whether the measure used in Yarmouth to weigh coal conformed to the legal Winchester bushel (Murphy, 1979). Friction also occurred in

1786, when a small sea-going collier, the *Endeavour* of Castleford, managed to navigate the shoals in Breydon and reach Norwich, only to be refused permission to unload by the Customs authorities, on the grounds that the cargoes carried by such vessels must be measured and assessed for duty in Yarmouth. To make matters worse, Norwich became increasingly convinced during this period that the tolls levied on coal in Yarmouth were largely responsible for the worsted industry's financial difficulties, and that if sea-going colliers could reach Norwich direct, coal prices could be reduced, so enabling the woollen firms concerned to compete more successfully with the increasing numbers of mechanized firms operating in the West Riding. According to Murphy, this feeling of resentment was probably misplaced, as the sixpence per chaldron duty levied at this time by Yarmouth Corporation was very small compared with the dues imposed by law on sea-borne coal, which by 1785 stood at seven shillings per chaldron.

Just how envious Norwich was of the revenue Yarmouth derived from the tolls it levied on imports can be gauged from the fact that these amounted to about £10 000 a year in the early nineteenth century, whereas the fourpence per ton toll levied on cargoes arriving in Norwich between 1821 and 1836 only generated a mean annual income for the Corporation of £1068 (Bacon, 1844). In the circumstances, it is hardly surprising that as traffic on the R. Yare grew – a regular steamer service was commenced on it in 1813 – tension between Norwich and Yarmouth mounted as a result of the latter's resolute refusal to improve the channel across Breydon Water, and thus enable sea-going vessels to gain direct access to the city.

The idea of by-passing the Breydon shoals with a new deep-water channel capable of taking sea-going vessels seems to have first been put forward in 1814 by Alderman Crisp Brown, a Norwich maltster and coal importer. Murphy (1979) believes that he did so in the knowledge that steam power was increasingly coming into use for the propulsion of ships, thus making it feasible to use tugs to bring strings of large craft up to Norwich. Less certainly, his idea may have been linked with the ending of the East India Company's monopoly of trade with India (though not China) in 1813, and the consequent possibility that the worsted merchants of Norwich could send their goods direct to that country. In any event, Crisp Brown's idea attracted considerable interest locally, and led to a 'Norwich-a-port' campaign being launched. Soon afterwards a committee of Norwich Corporation commissioned a consultant engineer, William Cubitt, to advise as to how and where such a new channel could be created.

Cubitt's first proposal, costed at some £36 000, was to dredge the middle reaches of the Yare where necessary, build a dam across the top of Breydon Water, and dig a new channel through the marshes south of the latter. But this idea was dropped in 1818 in the face of outraged protests from Yarmouth and, acting on a suggestion by Cubitt, the Committee almost immediately asked him to carry out a second investigation, this time into the possibility of creating a new navigation between Norwich and the sea at Lowestoft, thus by-passing Yarmouth altogether. His report, completed in 1820, costed this scheme at £87 500 (Cubitt, 1822). It involved dredging the middle and upper reaches of the R. Yare (£15 745), digging a new cut between the Yare at Reedham and the Waveney at Haddiscoe (£8200), providing a new swing-bridge at Haddiscoe (£3000), deepening and widening Oulton Dyke (£4000), constructing a lock, new bridge and embankments at Mutford (£12 000), the excavation of a new channel through Lake Lothing to the sea (£5000), and the construction at Lowestoft of a bridge and flood gates (£11 500) and two training walls (£10 000). The remaining £18 055 was set aside for 'engines and implements', and contingencies. Most of these works were within the scope of contemporary engineering to accomplish successfully. However, Cubitt seriously under-estimated the difficulty of preventing the navigation silting up at its seaward outlet, and his idea of periodically flushing away accumulations of sediment with water temporarily impounded in Lake Lothing, was later to prove quite impracticable.

In 1821, a prospectus was issued by Crisp Brown, calling for the formation of a company to obtain the necessary Act of Parliament, and build the Norwich to Lowestoft navigation in accordance with Cubitt's plans. This, plus his idea that corn exports should be subject to a levy so as to reduce the rate imposed on imported coal, generated a lot of interest amongst Norwich merchants. However his scheme did not attract as much financial support as its proponents hoped; indeed, by 1825 they had still only raised £27 000 towards the company's proposed capitalization of £100 000. According to Murphy, the main object of issuing the prospectus was to persuade Yarmouth to accept the first and cheaper scheme as the lesser of two evils, and some confirmation of this is provided by Norwich's decision in 1822 to ask the renowned engineer, Thomas Telford, to assess the practicability of the two proposals. Although he considered both technically feasible, he clearly favoured the Breydon scheme, on the grounds that it would cost £48 740, compared with £95 760 for the Lowestoft project (Telford, 1822). He also concluded his report by pointing out that it was in the best interests of all concerned to agree a scheme whereby ships drawing up to 10 feet could reach Norwich via Yarmouth.

Unfortunately, Yarmouth flatly refused to discuss either scheme with Norwich, and as a result, both sides indulged in an outburst of polemical pamphleteering and letter writing, during the course of which centuries of distrust rose to the surface. Particularly strong views in support of Yarmouth's desire to maintain the *status quo* were expressed by the Customs and Excise Authority which feared that unhindered smuggling would occur in the event that sea-going craft could sail direct to Norwich via either Yarmouth or Lowestoft.

In the light of Yarmouth's continued intransigence, a new company was launched in 1825 to promote the Norwich–Lowestoft navigation, and this turn of events worried the Haven and Pier Commissioners sufficiently to cause them to invite a consultant engineer, James Walker, to consider the practicality of the scheme, and the effect which it would have on Yarmouth Haven in the event that it was implemented. In his report, Walker concluded that Cubitt's method of keeping the sea outlet of Lake Lothing free of silt would prove unworkable and, like Telford, strongly urged Yarmouth to seek a compromise with Norwich. Walker also pointed out that if the Commissioners were genuinely anxious to stimulate trading with Norwich, they should resort to the use of steam . . . "both as the means of dispatch (i.e. tugs) and of cleansing the rivers".

Meantime, the promoters of the scheme had arranged for the necessary Bill to be introduced into Parliament. However, the evidence presented on their behalf by Cubitt and others was ill prepared, and the Bill was lost in Committee by 25 votes to 20.

Anxious to be seen to be accommodating, the Commissioners authorized an initial expenditure of £8000 on dredging the Breydon shoals. They also asked Walker to advise on the practicability of . . . "making Braydon [*sic*] navigable for vessels drawing up to 10 ft [3.0 m]". In his report (YPH* 106), dated September 1826, Walker pointed out that much of the preliminary work had already been done by the Commission's own staff, and that the remaining shoals, particularly those just downstream of the confluence of the rivers Yare and Waveney (the Burgh Flats) could be removed to give a 100-foot wide channel at a cost of £3000. He suggested that the necessary 300 000 cubic yards of mud could probably be removed in two or three years with the 'engine' which the Commissioners had recently ordered. This was a steam dredger which in 1828, its first full year of operation, raised some 60 000 tons, at an average cost of £1 per 60 tons (Norfolk & Norwich Record Office C 28/3). The Commissioners' archives indicate that during this period they were also operating a 'dydling engine', the eight scoops of which were geared to a whim made to revolve by two horses. In 1828, this raised 14 325 tons, at an average cost similar to that of the steam dredger. Both machines would have spent most of the time deepening the Haven, rather than the rivers, and it is interesting that Arthur Young, in his 1804 account of Norfolk agriculture, records that a Coltishall farmer had found that the calcareous mud derived from the Haven greatly improved the productivity of his land.

Despite the paltry cost of adopting Walker's suggestions, the Haven and Piers Commissioners took no action on them. Instead, following an acrimonious meeting with a deputation from Norwich, and in the light of the hard line being adopted by Yarmouth Corporation, they decided to object outright to both the proposals put forward by the city – the Breydon lateral cut, and the Norwich to Lowestoft scheme. In adopting such an intransigent attitude, any hope of finding a commonsense and face-saving solution, involving the part-funding by Norwich of the dredging and other improvement works so obviously needed in the Breydon area, was lost. Moreover, as Murphy points out, the wave of anger generated in the city by the Commissioners' response, resulted in the rejuvenation of the navigation company, and a decision being taken to apply again for

---

* This and other 'YPH' references relate to the indexed archives of the Yarmouth Port and Haven Commission and its predecessors. They are held at the Norfolk Record Office.

the necessary parliamentary sanction. This time the proponents of the scheme were successful, and the enabling Bill was given the Royal Assent in May 1827.

Thomas Bayliss, who had contracted to create the navigation for £98 000, started work at once, and during the course of the next six years, Cubitt's plans were implemented. Two of the principal tasks involved dredging a channel from Lake Lothing to the sea through Kirkley Ham, the shingle bank which had formed south of Lowestoft since 1730, and the construction of Mutford Lock (see Plate XXXVIII). In recognition of the fact that the latter was to link two water bodies – Oulton Broad and Lake Lothing – which are subject to differing tidal regimes, it was equipped with double gates at each end so that ships could use it regardless of whether the water level in the Broad happened to be above or below that in the Lake. But although unique in this respect, the lock's physical dimensions were such that it could only take vessels up to 86 feet (26 m)

Plate XXXVIII

Mutford Lock and Oulton Broad – 1989.

Constructed in the late 1820s as part of the ill-fated Norwich to Lowestoft navigation, this lock is unique in Britain in that it has double gates at either end. This enables sea-going vessels to move between Oulton Broad and Lake Lothing, regardless of the state of the tide. The lock is owned and operated by Associated British Ports, but the latter is currently (1990) engaged in discussions with the Broads Authority regarding its future management.

Oulton Broad is unusual in that it is largely surrounded by urban development. Moreover, no account of its stratigraphy has yet been published. It is therefore not yet certain that, like virtually all the other broads, it owes its origin to the activities of medieval peat diggers.

Photo: Richard Denyer

long, with a beam of 21 feet (6.4 m) and draught 8 feet (2.4 m). Meantime, Oulton Dyke had been temporarily dammed off at both ends, so that it could be widened, and the curves at its south-eastern end straightened; Slutton's Dyke, part of the former channel, can still be seen near the western end of the Broad.

Cubitt had planned that the 2.75 mile (4.4 km) long New Cut (see Plate 16) should be 80 feet (24.4 m) wide, but to save money, this was reduced to 70 feet (21.3 m). According to Maltster (1982) work on it started in July 1832 and, almost unbelievably, was completed six months later. Other projects, including the provision of a new swing-bridge at Carrow, and the dredging of various shoals in the R. Yare, were finished the same year. But the proposal to dig new channels to by-pass the bends at Whitlingham, Surlingham Ferry and Brundall, had to be abandoned since the promoters had by this time already had to borrow an additional £50 000 from the Exchequer Bill Loan Commissioners, with whom the new Navigation was mortgaged.

For a year or so, the Navigation was well used. The first sea-going vessels were towed up to Norwich in September 1833 and the following year, no fewer than 94 ships carrying coal, and another 79 with general goods, arrived in Norwich. 105 vessels passed through Lowestoft in the other direction, 87 of them with cargoes of grain, flour and malt for London (Wren, 1976). But all was far from well on the financial front. The company responsible for the Navigation went bankrupt in October 1834, and a year later, when its assets were auctioned lock, stock and barrel, no bids were forthcoming. Prospective purchasers were doubtless put off by the fact that the Navigation's total income at that time amounted to a mere £6000, especially as this had only been earned by the expedient of lowering the rates to attract custom.

The Navigation remained more or less in limbo until 1844, when it was purchased from the Exchequer Bill Commission by the Victorian entrepreneur S. M. Peto, for £4935 (Murphy, in litt.). It was Peto who, a year later, promoted a Bill for making a railway between Lowestoft and Reedham, and improving the harbour at Lowestoft, both projects being greatly facilitated by his ownership of the former company's assets.

Several factors contributed to the collapse of the Lowestoft Navigation. Its principal *raison d'être* was eliminated when the duties on sea-borne coal were repealed in 1830. In addition, an application by Norwich for bonded warehouses and other customs facilities, such as those which had long existed in Yarmouth, was turned down in 1833. To make matters worse, the Haven and Piers Commissioners reduced the tolls payable by vessels transhipping their cargoes at Yarmouth, so attracting some of the Norwich-bound trade which might otherwise have gone via Lowestoft. The Navigation also suffered from several serious physical defects. Mutford Lock was too small for many sea-going craft, and those vessels which did use it often had to be towed to and from Norwich on account of the difficulties involved in navigating the numerous bends on the Yare. The draught of the ships using the waterway was also limited to 8 feet because the Company had been forced to save money by specifying this depth for the New Cut, instead of the 10 feet proposed by Cubitt. Last but not least, it proved impossible, as Walker and others had predicted, to prevent the channel from Lake Lothing to the sea silting up. Indeed, Joseph Hume reported in 1946 that the bar at the entrance to Lowestoft harbour prevented vessels drawing more than 5 to 6 feet entering or leaving, whereas ships with a draught of 14 to 15 feet could pass over the bar at Yarmouth (Tidal Harbour Commission, 1846).

The demise of the Norwich-Lowestoft Navigation was a disappointment to many, not least Beccles Corporation, which perhaps rather ambitiously, had obtained powers in 1831 to deepen the R. Waveney, and create a new channel between Share Mill and the southern end of Oulton Dyke, so that ships bound to and from the town could more easily take advantage of the seaward end of the new waterway. It soon became apparent that this scheme would never be viable, and most vessels bound to and from Beccles continued to use the Yarmouth route.

Relationships between Norwich and Yarmouth remained tense, despite a re-definition of the roles of the two corporations *vis-à-vis* that of the navigation authority in the *Great Yarmouth Haven, Bridge and Navigation Act* 1835. Under this, it was arranged that Yarmouth Corporation should hand over responsibility for collecting the port dues to the Commissioners. The new Act also decreed that the latter should pay Norwich Corporation up to £600 per annum towards the cost of maintaining the R. Yare in a navigable condition as far downstream as Hardley Cross, and the individuals appointed to look after the Bure and Waveney should be allowed to spend up to £200 on each of these rivers. But although the skippers of wherries and keels had for years found it difficult and often dangerous to navigate the upper part of Breydon Water, owing to the shoals in the vicinity of Burgh Flats, the new Act did not, as one might have expected, make it mandatory for the Commissioners to deal with this problem. Instead it decreed that a majority of them must agree before the Breydon channel was dredged, even if this were to be for the benefit of river craft only. If the Commissioners wanted to provide a channel deep enough for sea-going vessels, they were required under the Act to employ an engineer to advise as to whether the tidal embankments beside the rivers would thereby be weakened and, if necessary, pay compensation to the marsh owners for any damage caused. The inclusion of such a provision reveals an early recognition of the conflicts which can arise between the interests of land drainage and navigation.

In 1845 the Commissioners refused by a majority vote to agree to a channel for sea-going vessels being provided, although the following year they somewhat reluctantly authorized the Burgh shoals to be dredged to give an additional 12 to 18 inches of water. But for Norwich Corporation this was quite insufficient. It had already spent a great deal of money dredging a channel for sea-going vessels between Hardley Cross and Whitlingham, and between 1846 and 1848 it had had the remaining upriver sections deepened to a similar standard. In addition, a new 50 chain (1009 m) long bypass had been cut for the river at Whitlingham, during the construction of the Norwich-Reedham-Yarmouth railway in 1843. Rather than put up with further procrastination from the Commissioners, the Corporation had a Bill drafted which, if enacted, would have severed responsibility for the Wensum, Yare and part of the Haven from the former and transferred it to . . ."the Mayor, Aldermen and citizens of Norwich", thus divesting the Commissioners of a considerable part of their revenue. In making this move, the Corporation was undoubtedly encouraged by the Second Report of the Tidal Harbour Commissioners (1846) which had strongly criticized the Haven and Pier Commission for not maintaining the channel across Breydon in a navigable condition. Interestingly enough, they had also made the point that it was no part of the navigation authority's job to safeguard the flood banks of the river which had, as their report put it, . . . "been embanked by private parties for their own advantage".

When the Haven and Pier Commissioners considered the draft of the Norwich and Yarmouth Navigation Bill, they voted that they would not even discuss the matter with Norwich. However, under the *Great Yarmouth Haven, Bridge, and Navigation Improvement Act* of 1849, the Commissioners' borrowing limit was raised from the £20000 allowed under the 1835 Act to £60000. This enabled them to complete the reconstruction of the Haven Bridge, a structure which had long been an impediment to navigation owing to its semi-derelict condition. The old bridge had, in fact, been pulled down by the Commissioners under the powers conferred upon them by the 1835 Act, but they had had temporarily to halt work on its replacement because of the restriction which this legislation placed on their borrowing powers. The 1849 Act also enabled the Commissioners to increase the sums payable for managing the rivers Yare and Bure to £800 and £300 respectively. But the clause in the 1835 Act laying down the conditions which had to be met before the Commissioners could create a passage for sea-going vessels through Breydon Water, was retained in the new Act. Indeed, a proposal that the Breydon channel should be deepened to 10 feet was rejected on a majority vote only a few months after the 1849 Act came into force.

The minutes of the Commissioners (YPH 1–21) show that five years later the same proposal was made yet again, this time by a working party which they themselves had set up. This group also recommended that to increase tidal scour, and thus prevent the dredged channel silting up again, a training wall should be provided near the junction of the rivers Yare and Waveney. But the Group's advice went unheeded, and although £400 was spent on dredging the Burgh shoals in 1855, the rate of siltation was so high that in 1858 the Commissioners were told that the channel through the upper part of Breydon was barely 30 feet wide, and that for a distance of 4500 feet it was only about 3 feet 9 inches deep at low tide. Although the Commissioners instructed that a dredger should be used to create a channel 60 feet wide and 6 feet deep at low water, little seems to have been done until 1862, when they received yet another working group report on the subject. At long last action was taken, and by 1864 Messrs. Hoborough, precursors of the well-known contractors May Gurney Ltd, had dredged a 6.5 feet deep channel across Burgh Flats, at a cost of £757 10s.* This would have enabled coasting vessels typical of the period to have reached Norwich at high tide; ketch-rigged barges, for instance, carrying about 200 tons, only drew about 7.5 feet (Malster, 1971). Hoboroughs also dredged the Haven between the Bridge and the Lower Ferry (£1261 18s.), and built a training wall, popularly known as the Dickey Works, to help scour out the channel across the Burgh Flats (£405 2s.). These works were completed by 1864, and seem to have solved once and for all, the siltation problem which had existed for so long in this area.

The Commissioners were again reorganized in 1866, under the terms of the *Great Yarmouth Port and Haven Act*. Separate committees were formed for the Yare, Bure and Waveney, and although each had to operate under the general supervision of the Commissioners, it had to fund its activities by levying tolls on vessels using its river and the cargoes they carried. For their part, the Commissioners remained responsible for Breydon Water as well as the Haven, but no longer had to pay for the management of the rivers out of the tolls they levied at Yarmouth. Simultaneously, the *Tonnage Act* of 1726, which had empowered Norwich to levy tolls on incoming goods, and use these for repairing the city's walls, gates and roads, as well as its bridges, wharves and staithes, was repealed on the grounds that it was wrong for toll monies to be used for purposes unconnected with the management of the port.

Guided by their consultant, William Cubitt, the Commissioners almost at once embarked on a massive programme of improvement works at Yarmouth. These were designed to widen the Haven to 270 feet (86.6 m), and increase its sectional area from 2424 square feet (225 sq m) to 3253 square feet (302 sq m). New quay headings were also constructed, and training walls provided to increase tidal scour at the Harbour mouth. The Commissioners' minutes show that the net result of these works was that in 1868 there was between 10 and 12 feet (3.1 to 3.7 m) of water over the bar at neap tides.

The commercial use of the waterways from the nineteenth century onwards

Apart from the Thurne, which formerly had an outfall to the sea between Horsey and Winterton, the Ant is the most extensively altered of the Broadland rivers, most of the modifications to its course having been prompted by a desire to improve its navigability (see page 40). Nevertheless, the full benefits of these alterations would not have been felt until 1825, when the North Walsham and Dilham Canal was opened. Originally, this had six locks, and extended to Antingham, where there was a bone mill. However, the section upstream of Swafield was little used, and had become derelict by the turn of the century; navigation rights over it were extinguished by a Ministry of Transport Order in 1927. The canal was capable of accommodating wherries of up to 20 tons, and according to Bacon (1844), a toll of 3 pence per ton per mile was levied on cargoes of corn, flour or coal, and a penny halfpenny, on manure, marl and other goods. Total receipts amounted to £382 in 1827, £263 in 1830, £336 in 1834 and 1838, and £486 in 1842.

The amount of navigable water in Broadland was probably at a maximum in the nineteenth century. Few of the broads were yet shallow enough to have been overgrown by emergent vegetation, and recreational pressure had not developed sufficiently to make it necessary for owners to close off some sites from the river to deter trespassers and vandals. Bungay, Aylsham and North Walsham could all be reached by boat, whilst Waxham Cut was still navigable as far upstream as Lound Bridge where there was a brick works. Other waterways in active use in Victorian times were those linking 'Little Switzerland' with the River Bure, Colmans Dyke (sometimes known as the Flushing Channel) at Whitlingham, and another small cut off the R. Yare near Thorpe Old Hall. These channels were dug to enable wherries to be loaded with chalk from the extensive quarries nearby, for conveyance to limekilns (see page 6), or to the cement works at Burgh Castle (opened in about 1858) and Berney Arms. But some of the chalk and clay mixture required by these factories was dredged from the rivers and broads, most of which were still in a Phase I condition during this period (see Chapter 5).

The Enclosure Acts, too, had resulted in an increase in the amount of navigable

---

* See footnote on page 88 for information about the old currency.

water, since these frequently decreed that a boat dyke should be provided to enable vessels to reach the land allotted for use as a public staithe, the local name for a landing place. Examples of villages where boat dykes as well as staithes were provided by this means include Upton, Thurne and Hickling. Responsibility for having these boat dykes dug lay with the Enclosure Commissioners who in their Awards, usually then allotted both dyke and staithe to the Drainage Commissioners appointed under the latter. In a few cases, notably at Reedham and Horning, the parish staithe was allotted to the Surveyor of Highways, and in this event the land is now vested in the local authority (Kemp, 1986a; Ellis, 1967).

In some parishes, several staithes were established at the time of Enclosure. Of three mentioned in the Ludham Award, one was at the head of Womack Water (which was defined as a 'boat-dyke'), another at Ludham Bridge and the third at How Hill.

The exact legal status of some staithes has been a contentious issue locally for years (e.g. EDP, 1975), but it would seem that those allotted to the Drainage Commissioners at the time of Enclosure remain in the ownership of their direct successors, the internal drainage boards, unless they happen to be located beside a main river. In this event they will have been inherited by the East Norfolk Rivers Catchment Board, following the passing of the *Land Drainage Act*, 1930, and will thus now be owned by its eventual successor, the National Rivers Authority. The staithes at Martham (3), Ludham (3), West Somerton, Potter Heigham, Repps, Thurne, Upton and Horsey are of this type. But the position is complicated by the fact that some staithes were established by landowners for their own private use, and were either not used by the public at all, or only with the consent of the owner.

It is likely that many staithes existed long before Enclosure (Kemp, 1968); the *Horsey Enclosure Act*, for example, refers to the need to . . . "repair the common dyke leading to the staithe now used". Some staithes may even date from the time when the broad beside which they are located was first made navigable by the creation of breaches, both in the peaty baulks left by the medieval diggers, and in the 'rond' separating the excavation from the river. Possible support for this comes from the likelihood that the word 'staithe' is derived from 'steath', the Anglo-Saxon name for a landing place.

Whatever their origin, many staithes fell into disuse as the amount of commercial traffic on the waterways declined, and the existence of many of them is now largely forgotten (Kemp, 1984). De Salis (1904) records 27 staithes beside the rivers Bure, Ant and Thurne and their associated broads, and a further 10 and 9 in the Yare and Waveney valleys respectively. But these are certainly under-estimates since the 1838 Ordnance Survey map shows that in the Yare valley alone, there were at least eight more staithes than he identified. In a report commissioned by the Broads Authority on the status of staithes and their management, Kemp (1986b) identifies 56, of which 16 are in the Ant valley, 12 each in the valleys of the Bure and Thurne, 10 are beside the Waveney, and 6 are in the Yare valley.

Staithes fulfilled a vital role in the local economy, and the ability freely to make use of them was, like other public 'rights', jealously guarded. A hint of this is afforded by a sketch in the Port and Haven Commissioners' archives of the channel leading to Cantley staithe, the inscription of which notes that this had been "arbitrarily" stopped up by a Mr Gilbert (YPH 1787). Similarly in 1853, during a tour of inspection, the Commissioners were vexed to find that the upstream entrance to Wroxham Broad had been closed off from the river, and that the owner, Mr Trafford, was in the habit of charging for admission to water frolics (YPH 81).

In both these cases the navigation authority was presented with a *fait accompli*, and no action seems to have been taken. It was a different story in 1866, when a Drainage Commission sought powers to dig a new dyke between the R. Waveney and Oulton Broad across Share Marsh, and remove the embankments beside Mutford Lock, thus enabling water levels to be lowered in the whole valley. The preamble to the Bill also proposed that all the Acts relating to Yarmouth Haven should be repealed. This goaded the Commissioners into petitioning Parliament, and the Act passed in 1866 was concerned solely with improving the drainage of the Waveney valley between Hoxne and Beccles.

The 1835 *Haven and Pier Act* decreed that the Commissioners should regularly inspect the rivers, and the reports which have survived provide a valuable insight into what Broadland was like in the Victorian era. Generally speaking, the uppermost reaches of the rivers were much the same depth as they are today. For instance, the 1843 inspection, made at a time when there was little water coming downstream, revealed that the R. Bure was 3 feet 8 inches (1.1 m) deep at Coltishall, while the Thurne had 3.5 to 4 feet of water in it at 'Dungeon Dyke' (YPH 80). Corresponding 'low water' figures today are 4.5 feet at the Rising Sun, and 4 feet at Dungeon Corner (Hart, pers. comm.). Further downstream, the differences become more marked. The Ant in 1843 was only about 3 feet deep and 24 feet (*c.* 7 m) wide downstream of Ludham Bridge, whereas these reaches are a foot deeper and over 65 feet (20 m) wide today. The same year, the R. Waveney was only 8 to 9 feet (2.4 to 2.7 m) deep at Stanley Staithe, whereas there is 12 feet (3.6 m) of water at this point today. The differences were even greater in the lowermost reaches of the R. Bure. The 1857 report notes that in the 'Common Reach' off Caister . . . " the best of the water in the channel is five feet, and very narrow, not more than thirty feet (*c.* 9 m) wide; at low water the depth will be reduced one foot" (YPH 82). Today, Caister Reach (by the airfield) is 12 feet deep over much of its present width (*c.* 43 m).

At low tide, this stretch of the Bure would have been barely navigable by loaded wherries, and following a survey in 1871, it was estimated that to deepen it by some 3 feet, it would be necessary to remove some 62 000 tons of mud, at a likely cost of £2066 (YPH 1237). Clearly, it would have been essential to use a mechanical dredger to tackle a task of this magnitude. However, the traditional way of countering the effects of natural siltation was by dydling. Walter White, writing in 1865, gives a description of this arduous task:

> Standing on the bank, with a scoop or dredge fixed to the end of a long pole, he plunges it into the stream as far as he can lean forward with safety, then resting the pole on his shoulder, which is protected by a thick pad as a fulcrum, he drags up the scoop by a bodily effort, and drops the muddy contents upon the bank. Thus by one process the bottom is deepened and the bank heightened . . . To reach the middle of the stream he works from a barge moored to the shore.

White records that a dydler was expected to clean out eight roods (about 40 m) a day, for which he would be paid 4 shillings.

The Commissioners' archives reveal that Works Superintendents were employed on each river and that these individuals were in attendance during the inspections. Doubtless on their advice, the Commission members made on-the-spot decisions as to which stretches of waterway were to be dredged, dydled, or cleared of overhanging trees. Instructions were also given regarding the repair of staithes and other waterside structures, and the removal of obstructions. For example, in 1843, the Commissioners discovered that the flow in the R. Waveney upstream of Beccles was being impeded by weeds "cut above the locks and suffered to pass down". They accordingly agreed that the dyke reeves of Mettingham and Shipmeadow (who would have been employed by the Commission of Sewers for this river) should be instructed . . . "to discontinue such practice and draw on shore the cut weeds". But the Commissioners would have been powerless to do anything about Ludham 'Old' Bridge, the arch of which was so low and narrow as to limit the size of the vessels able to trade on the Ant. This bridge was washed away by the 1912 floods, but even when reconstructed remained an impediment to navigation until it was finally demolished and re-built in 1960. Irstead Shoals, situated just south of Barton Broad on one of the artificial stretches of this river (see page 40), was another notorious bottleneck, and as late as 1884, Walter Rye noted that wherries were liable to get stuck here.

The rearrangements brought about by the 1866 Act resulted in the rivers being managed more intensively, at least initially. Over £357 was spent by the Bure Commissioners in 1868, while in 1874, the Yare and Waveney Commissioners spent £622 and £112 on dredging their respective rivers (YPH 220). Although these sums may appear derisory, much could have been achieved with them. For instance, a contractor was paid £31 1s. 9d. for dredging some 1650 tons of mud from the R. Bure in 1865. Similarly, the cost of removing 300 tons of sediment from the Thurne between Heigham Sound and Potter Heigham bridge was estimated to be 4 pence per ton the following year (YPH 978 – 979).

Despite the Yare Commissioners' efforts to maintain their river in a navigable condition, few sea-going vessels were visiting Norwich by the turn of the century, and the revenue from such craft amounted to a paltry £44 in 1905, and £65 in 1913 (Stratton,

1958). Most of the vessels were Thames sailing barges bringing barley for malting, cement, tiles, rice and wheat, and taking away mustard cake, and 'Wincarnis' tonic wine from Colman's factor.

Photographs by Emerson and others in the late Victorian era show that many, if not all, the waterways contained a luxuriant growth of submerged aquatic vegetation in the summer months. This must have represented a considerable impediment to navigation, and to supplement the work of the men hired by the Rivers Commissioners to cut and remove the weed ("drawing the rivers"), some wherry skippers rigged a pair of submerged scythe blades at the stern of their vessels so that they carved a channel through the weeds as they went. Skippers were also well aware how difficult it was to sail up a river bordered by trees, and it was not unknown for them to put their crew ashore to cut down saplings growing near the bank.

The opening of the railways between Norwich and Yarmouth via Reedham in 1844, from Reedham to Lowestoft in 1847, from Whitlingham to North Walsham via Wroxham in 1847, and from Brundall to Yarmouth via Acle in 1883, brought about a profound change in the economy of the region, and the life-style of its inhabitants. Owing to the parlous state of the roads, many of the latter had been dependent on passenger-carrying vessels on the rivers when they wished to visit Norwich or Yarmouth. But the railways provided direct links between many outlying villages and the larger settlements. Moreover, the railway companies went to considerable lengths to enable persons not directly served by a station to gain access to one. For instance, they laid out new roads across the marshes so that people who lived in Claxton, Rockland, Surlingham and other villages to the south of the R. Yare could gain access to the stations at Buckenham and Brundall to the north of it by way of the ferries at Buckenham and Coldham Hall (see Plate XXXIX).

Inevitably, the amount of passenger traffic on the rivers rapidly declined with the arrival of the railways. More seriously, the latter started to carry goods which until then had always been conveyed by water. Although the wherry owners put up a stout resistance in the face of the increasing competition, only about 100 trading vessels were left by the 1880s, and the last wherry to be built, the *Ella*, was launched in 1912. Some of the surviving vessels were fitted with engines to reduce their dependence on the wind, but despite the fillip to trade which resulted from the opening of a coal-fired power station at Duke Street, Norwich at the beginning of the present century, very few wherries were left by the 1920s, owing to the competition being exerted by then by road hauliers as well as the railway companies. The relative unimportance of trading wherries, compared with pleasure vessels as a source of revenue for the Rivers Commissioners in the mid-1920s is illustrated by the following figures (YPH 223–224):

	1925			1926		
Bure Commissioners	£	s	d	£	s	d
Commercial wherries	40	9	5	133	1	2
Passenger vessels	13	14	11	19	4	6
Yachts and rowboats	873	1	6	957	13	6
Yare Commissioners						
'Local trading vessels' (wherries)	149	18	0	164	8	6
'Pleasure vessels' (Undifferentiated)	1058	4	11	1128	19	9

Note: The figures for 1925 & 1926 can be converted to approximate 1990 prices by multiplying by 25.4 and 26 respectively.

Reedham Ferry – 1985.

Plate XXXIX

There were originally three vehicle ferries in the Yare valley – at Surlingham, Buckenham and Reedham – each of which could be hand-wound across the river on hawsers or chains. The first two went out of use in the 1940s, but the one at Reedham was fitted with a small motor in 1951. The vessel shown in the photo was launched in 1983, and is well used, particularly during the summer months. Charges in 1991 for a car were £1.60, a lorry £3 and for a pedestrian 40p.

Until the 1960s, a 'request' ferry service for pedestrians wishing to cross the R. Yare at Brundall was operated by the publican at Coldham Hall, and there was a 'pull-yourself-across-on-a-chain' pontoon at Horning. However, in 1967 this was removed for safety reasons by Steward and Patteson, the brewery company which at that time owned the Ferry Inn. The only other ferry on the R. Bure – at Stokesby – went out of use following the construction in 1911 of a new road linking that village with the A1064 near Acle Bridge.

Photo: R.N. Flowers

Inevitably, too, as trading activity declined, parts of the waterway system fell into a derelict condition, and were closed to navigation. For example, when locks on the canalized sections of the Upper Bure and Waveney were damaged by the fluvial floods of 1912, it was not considered worthwhile repairing them, and navigation rights on the former were extinguished in 1928 by a Ministry of Transport Order made under Section 45 of the *Railway and Canal Act* 1888. Six years later, the navigation upstream of Geldeston was, at the request of the Catchment Board, terminated by an Order made by the Minister of Agriculture under section 41 of the *Land Drainage Act* 1930.

To avoid the expense of maintaining long lengths of embankment, land-drainage interests were keen to dam off from the main river small waterways no longer used by boat traffic; indeed following the 1947 floods, a member of the East Norfolk Rivers Catchment Board went so far as to suggest that the R. Chet should be closed to navigation. This idea was dropped as a result of vehement protests from private boat owners and the late Nat Bircham, a wherryman, who at that time was still trading on the river. But in 1953, following a reorganization of the Brograve Level drainage system, the East Suffolk and Norfolk River Board had little difficulty in persuading the Minister of Agriculture to close off Waxham Cut upstream of Bridge Farm, Waxham, despite objections from local people and the Inland Waterways Association.

It is significant that in both these cases it was left to independent interests to champion the cause of navigation. This is symptomatic of the fact that during the 1930s, 1940s and early 1950s, the Great Yarmouth Port and Haven Commissioners were primarily interested in the commercial use of the Haven and the R. Yare, and showed little real concern as to what was happening on the other Broadland rivers. Indeed until 1953, the river inspectors were the only staff to have any responsibilities outside the confines of the Haven. From then on a more positive attitude was adopted by the Commission towards safeguarding navigational interests. For instance, although it acceded to a request from the River Board in 1960 that Tunstall Dyke should be dammed off from the R. Bure and provided with a tidal flap-sluice, it indicated that these obstructions would have to be removed if boats ever needed to use this waterway again.

The North Walsham and Dilham Canal lay outside the Commission's jurisdiction, and its history, and the vicissitudes to which it has been subject, are described by Walker (1973) and Griston (1981). The floods of 1912 damaged its bank at Bacton Wood, and also washed part of a road into the canal below Ebridge Mill. As six different wherries were still plying between Dilham and Swafield at this time, carrying cargoes totalling some 2300 tons per annum (including corn, feeding stuffs, fertilizers and oak billets for smoking herrings at Yarmouth), the flood damage was repaired by the Company owning the navigation. Indeed, during the next ten to fifteen years the canal continued to be fairly heavily used, and in 1924, it was cleaned out with a paraffin-engined grab dredger mounted on a double pontoon; until a year or so ago the derelict hulk of this could still be seen in the turning basin above Ebridge Mill. But by 1931 only one motorized wherry, the *Ella*, was using the canal, and although she made 83 separate trips, carrying 1600 tons altogether, the end was obviously in sight; she last used the waterway with Nat Bircham at the helm in 1935. In the early 1950s, the River Board considered the possibility of obtaining from the Ministry of Agriculture a Closure Order over the canal, but decided that the compensation it would have to pay the Company owning it would make this uneconomic. The canal is therefore still subject to a statutory right of navigation, even though it is in a completely derelict state upstream of Honing Lock.

Apart from a few auxiliary-engined Thames sailing barges, which brought grain to the maltings at Beccles before the Second World War, and again during the 1950s (EDP, 1954a), commercial traffic on the Bure and Waveney had virtually ceased by about 1930. In contrast, the R. Yare carried increasing numbers of freighters from the First World War onwards. In part, this can be attributed to the opening in 1912 of the Cantley sugar beet factory, which initially received both coal and beet by water, and which exported pulp and molasses. But most of the traffic on the Yare during the early 1920s was bound to and from Norwich, and resulted from the establishment by Boulton and Paul Ltd. during the war of their Riverside Works, and the transfer there of their foundry, wire-weaving, structural steel and other departments shortly afterwards. Many of the 101 sea-going vessels which visited the city in 1923, and which together generated a revenue for the Yare Commissioners of £204, were steamers bringing wire, glass and spelter to the factory from Antwerp, and departing with wire netting and other goods

(Stratton, 1958). The next year, the river was used by half as many coasters again, carrying 50043 tons of cargo. The opening of a power station at Thorpe in 1927, as a replacement for the Duke Street installations, boosted traffic on the river still further, and many of the vessels which visited Norwich in 1932, were colliers. The port became even busier following the rebuilding of the Corporation Quay, the provision of a turning bay for ships downriver from Foundry Bridge, and the construction in 1933 of new silos beside the river at Colman's factory, and at Read's flour mill.

The growth of commercial traffic on the R. Yare was actively encouraged by the toll rebates offered by both the Great Yarmouth Port and Haven Commissioners, and the Yare Commissioners (Anon., 1934). The former reduced their tolls by a third in 1920, and took a further 33.3 per cent off ten years later, whilst the Yare Commissioners offered a rebate of 10 per cent in 1931, 20 per cent in 1932 and 30 per cent from 1933 onwards. The net effect of these measures can be seen from the following figures:

Year	No. of vessels	Reg'd tonnage	Cargo (dwt)
1930/1	375	27447	50043
1931/2	451	50991	105697
1932/3	576	63831	134125

Traffic peaked in 1936, when 753 vessels, together carrying some 375000 tons of cargo, used the river, and this level of activity continued for the next three years. Imports of coal continued to predominate, and in 1938, no fewer than 58 per cent of the ships using the port were colliers. 18 per cent of the remaining vessels carried grain, whilst the other principal cargoes were cement, tiles, petrol, oil cake and timber (James *et al.*, 1945).

Sea-going vessels continued to visit Norwich during the Second World War, and in the 1950s and 1960s, the port was used by about 500 freighters a year, the main cargoes being timber and grain, and coal for the gasworks and the power station at Thorpe (see Plate 33). The last collier arrived at the latter in 1970, shortly before the closure of the coal-fired plant, and since then the number of ships plying to and from Norwich has undergone a marked decrease (see Table 11b).

Table 11b   Commercial traffic on the R. Yare: 1971 – 1988

| Year | Norwich | | Cantley | |
	No. of vessels	Cargo tonnage (DWT)	No. of vessels	Cargo tonnage (DWT)
1971	176	70400	15	11500
1972	195	65500	12	9600
1973	192	81500	17	13900
1974	156	60800	14	11000
1975	137	47300	10	8200
1976	144	47800	6	4900
1977	82	29000	8	7400
1978	99	36000	17	16500
1979	145	50600	21	20100
1980	134	50500	25	23300
1981	109	39200	31	29000
1982	64	20000	36	34500
1983	57	16900	27	25200
1984	58	18700	20	18000
1985	43	16300	28	26100
1986	38	15600	20	15600
1987	29	10568	23	24153
1988	7	2796	15	14961

Source: Great Yarmouth Port and Haven Commissioners' Records

One of the principal reasons for this decline lies in the physical constraints to which Norwich-bound ships are subject. They must have a beam of less than 10.6 m in order to pass through the Haven Bridge, and they must not draw more than 2.8 m if they are safely to navigate the river upstream of Surlingham. Vessels up to 47 m long can be swung in the turning bay just downstream of Foundry Bridge, but if they are longer than this, they must be moved stern-first down to Trowse Eye, where the confluence of the rivers Yare and Wensum provides more room for manoeuvre.

The vessels using the port in 1975/6 were, on average, 40.5 m in length, with a maximum of about 53 m; their mean tonnage was 380 dwt, the largest vessel carrying 596 dwt (Rendel, Palmer & Tritton, 1977). The principal cargoes at this time were honey and grain for Colman's of Norwich and Read Woodrow Ltd. respectively, but although scrap-iron destined for the Continent was being exported in considerable quantities, this trade ceased in the early 1980s.

According to a report published by the East Anglia Economic Council in 1977, the total tonnage carried on the river declined by 80 per cent between 1966 and 1976, and because of this, doubt was cast on the long-term viability of Norwich as a port. However, a more optimistic view was taken in a report compiled the following year for the Inland Waterways Association (IWA). In commenting on this, the Port and Haven Commissioners indicated that because of the constraints on port expansion in Norwich, and the difficulty and expense of having lifting bridges on roads crossing the navigation, there was a need to look for alternative sites for future development. Of the five areas suggested in the IWA report, the one favoured by the Commissioners is situated beside the Whitlingham sewage treatment works. It has a mile-long river frontage, and when the southern by-pass for Norwich is built, would have excellent access to this, and other nearby main roads. This, and other options for the future, were subject to an in-depth study by a Working Group set up at the request of the Planning and Transportation Committee of the Norfolk County Council, and those interested are recommended to refer to this Group's report (Norfolk County Council, 1978).

It will be seen from Table 11b that the IWA's optimism about the port's future has not been borne out in practice. In 1982, for instance, there were no exports, and imports only amounted to *c.* 20 000 tonnes, the principal cargoes being fertilizer, grain and soya meal. In 1985 a little grain was exported, but imported cargoes totalled only 13 915 tonnes, made up of fertilizer (8677 t) grain (2881 t) and meal (2537 t) (Hart, pers. comm.). Corresponding tonnages for 1987 were fertilizer 5190, grain 335 (plus 698 exported), meal 1469, beet pellets 1825, potatoes 438, salt 467 and sundries 146. By the following year, Read Woodrow Ltd. had become almost wholly dependent on home-grown cereals for its milling business, thus making it unnecessary to continue importing grain. Partly as a result of this, only 7 ships visited the city in 1988, bringing 1272 tonnes of fertilizer, 1258 t of meal and 276 t of beet pellets, the dues payable on these cargoes amounting to a paltry £1128.

Although trading to and from Norwich shows signs of petering out altogether, Cantley continues to generate some commercial traffic on the river. Beet pellets are still sometimes exported (1255 tonnes in 1985 and 1511 t in 1987), but the great majority of the vessels using the factory's quays are fuel-oil tankers, which in the 1970s averaged *c.* 750 dwt, and drew up to 3.2 m when laden (Rendel, Palmer & Tritton, 1976). The number of ship-loads involved has fluctuated considerably over the past 20 years or so (see Table 11b); for instance, 33 586 tonnes of oil were delivered in 1982, 15 600 t in 1986, and 22 642 t in 1987, the latter generating an income for the Commissioners of almost £8200 (Hart, pers. comm.).

Continuing a practice not dissimilar to the one which caused the citizens of Norwich so much anguish during the seventeenth, eighteenth and early nineteenth centuries, the Great Yarmouth Port and Haven Commission, and its successor from 1989 onwards, the Great Yarmouth Port Authority, levies tolls on city-bound ships and their cargoes. The dues on these sea-going vessels form a contribution towards the cost of maintaining the navigation, and are levied on a tonnage basis on entry to the Haven, plus a 50 per cent supplement for the use of the R. Yare. This extra, upriver toll goes to the organization responsible for managing the latter, which until the end of 1988/9 was the Rivers Commission. The toll on upriver commodities consists of a tonnage payment made to the body responsible for the quays in the city, again formerly the Rivers Commission, but from April 1989 onwards the 'new' Broads Authority, plus a 50 per cent supplement levied by the Haven Commissioners, now the Port Authority. The justification for this extra commodity charge is not clear, given the fact that city-bound ships do not normally use the quays and other facilities at Yarmouth.

Ship dues in 1988 were levied at a rate of £0.254 per tonne on a general cargo vessel, and £0.216 per tonne on a tanker, whilst cargo dues ranged from £0.831 per dead-weight tonne on light oils to £0.487 per tonne on commodities such as grain, soya and beet pellets. Thus the dues payable that year on a ship with a gross registered tonnage of 400, with a cargo of 550 tonnes of bulk soya bound for Norwich would have been as follows:

Ship entry tolls to the Haven at £.0.254/tonne	= £101.60
Upriver supplement at £0.127/tonne	= £ 50.80
Commodity toll at £0.487/tonne	= £267.85
Haven toll on upriver commodity at £0.244/tonne	= £134.20
Total	= £554.45

A 20 per cent discount on the up-river toll would have been allowable had the cargo been off-loaded at one of the private wharves in the city, such as those owned by Read Woodrow Ltd. and Colman's of Norwich.

The revenue from cargo and ship dues on the R. Yare amounted to £16 322 in 1984, and £20 195 in 1986, but declined to £7815 in 1988. The total gross registered tonnage of the 22 ships using the river that year was 13 417, and they carried a total of 17 757 tonnes of cargo. In comparison, the cargoes handled in the port of Great Yarmouth in 1988 amounted to almost two million tonnes, of which just over half resulted from the roll-on, roll-off trade. The vessels entering the Haven that year had a gross registered tonnage of about 5 million tonnes, and generated an income for the Port Authority of *c*. £2.7 million.

The use of the waterways for boat-borne holidays and recreation

The waterways have been used for pleasure, as well as trading, for at least 200 years, and probably much longer. Wherries were regularly raced, not only at sites such as Barton, Oulton and Wroxham Broads but, between about 1882 and 1902, on the sea at Yarmouth, Gorleston and Lowestoft (Clark, 1961). Races for other types of sailing craft also took place from very early days (see Plate XL) and in about 1800, the lateener, an open vessel with a lateen sail carried on a foremast stepped near the bows, was developed specially for competitive events. By 1830, about 20 of these craft had been built, but from about 1847 they were gradually superseded by cutters – gaff-rigged yachts with a jib as well as a foresail, and often a top-sail. The *Maria*, a lateener of length 23 feet (7 m), beam 8 feet (2.4 m) and draught 3 feet, which was built in about 1934 (Preston, 1984) and last sailed in 1913, was given to the Yarmouth Maritime Museum by the late Arthur Thrower in 1961, and is now preserved by the Norfolk Museums Service.

Water frolics, or what would today be called regattas, were held annually at Thorpe and Burgh Castle from the early nineteenth century onwards, and the custom spread during Victorian times. Fawcett (1977) notes that the Thorpe frolic attracted 10 000 spectators in 1823, and twice as many the following year, when the scene was delightfully captured by Joseph Stannard in a painting now in the Castle Museum, Norwich. Frolics were also held now and then at Hickling, Barton and elsewhere and, in 1859, the Norfolk and Suffolk Yacht Club was formed to . . . "assist in the organisation of such events, and generally promote the interest of pleasure boating". In its first year it organized frolics at Cantley, Wroxham and Oulton.

Walter White (1865) gives a vivid description of a frolic held on Wroxham Broad about this time: . . . "And still sail after sail, and bright pennons appear beyond the trees, and lively music sounds; and so the preparation goes on until a hundred yachts and wherries, to say nothing of small boats, are congregated on the Broad." White observed this scene as a holidaymaker, since a few days previously, he had boarded a friend's 30-ton, skippered yacht at Coltishall. After the regatta they went on to explore the R. Bure and its tributaries before finally leaving the vessel at Stalham.

Pleasure steamers, later to give way to today's diesel-powered craft, started taking out groups of day trippers on the rivers and broads in Victorian times, Wroxham, Norwich

Plate XL

'Broads One-designs' under sail at Coldham Hall – *c.* 1980.

The class to which these 'Brown Boats' belong was founded in 1900, and several of the 33 vessels within it were launched eighty or more years ago. Each has an overall length of 24 feet (7.3 m), and a sail area of 252 square feet (23.4 sq m).

There are several other classes of sailing craft special to the region, the most famous being the Yare and Bure One-designs (the 'White Boats'), of which there are 116, the Norfolk Punts (78), the Waveney One-designs (26) and the Norfolk 14 ft One-designs (86). Numerous races are held for each class during the season, the competition for places being extremely keen.

Founded in 1908, the fleet of White Boats is almost as old as that of the Brown Boats. But because of the very high cost of good quality hardwoods, the numbers of boats in both these fleets, and also in the Norfolk Punt class, are now being augmented by vessels fabricated out of Glass Reinforced Plastic.

Photo: Johnny Marr/Eastern Counties Newspapers

and Yarmouth having always been the principal centres from which such craft operated. In about 1930, Arthur Patterson wrote a guide for Yarmouth holidaymakers who, at a cost of 3 shillings a head, had decided to take a day trip from Southtown to Brundall Gardens on the steamship *Victorious*. These Gardens, which comprised several acres of landscaped grounds, a lake, tea rooms and other facilities were, like Bramerton Woods End, a rather similar site on the other side of the river, very popular with day visitors, since they could be reached both by land and by water (Patterson, *c.* 1930: Levine, 1977).

The first person known to have made a living out of hiring out boats to individuals wanting to take a holiday afloat was John Loynes (Goodey, 1978). He founded his business in Norwich, but in 1878 acquired a plot of land beside Wroxham Bridge, from which the firm of Faircraft Loynes continues to operate to this day. John Loynes was also the first to advertise regularly, and Davies's guide of 1882 carries an announcement that he had vessels ranging in size from 13 feet to 20 feet for hire at both Norwich and Wroxham. According to Goodey these boats cost from 3 to 4 guineas (£3 3s. to £4 4s.) a week with a crew, or from £1 5s. to £2 without. Loynes's pioneer efforts were soon copied and by 1887, when the second edition of Suffling's *Land of the Broads* was published, no fewer than 39 boatyards were advertising craft for hire; however, many of these would have been day-boats, rather then cruising vessels.

Although the railways caused a rapid decline in the amount of trading on the rivers, they provided a major stimulus to their use for tourism. Besides extolling the pleasures of a holiday afloat, early guidebooks pointed out how easy it was to reach places like Wroxham, Oulton, Potter Heigham and Brundall by train and, in 1891, the Great Eastern Railway boasted that it could convey passengers from London to Yarmouth in three and a quarter hours (for £1 first-class and half that third-class) and that intermediate stations in Broadland were well served by stopping trains.

Not the least of the region's attractions for the sailing enthusiast was, and indeed still is, the ability to sail for miles without having to lower one's mast to pass under a bridge. The Bure is only bridged once (at Acle) in the 25 miles between Wroxham and Yarmouth whilst, provided the swing bridges at Reedham and Somerleyton are open, one can sail unimpeded from Trowse Eye to Beccles, a distance (via the New Cut) of over 30 miles.

Broadland's attractions for the self-catering holidaymaker in the late nineteenth and early twentieth centuries would undoubtedly have been freedom, independence and relaxation, just as they are today (Hoseason, 1977). Low cost might also have been quoted, had a visitor survey been carried out, but this would, as now, have been given a lower rating of importance than the other three factors.

As the demand for hire yachts grew, and more and more boatyards were founded to meet it, some of the more enterprising wherry owners decided to follow suit. At first, ordinary trading vessels were tidied up, provided with simple furniture and let to parties of visitors during the summer months, before being taken back into service for the rest of the year. But the idea proved so popular that some vessels were permanently converted for recreational use. Later, specially built 'pleasure wherries' and 'wherry yachts' (which combined the rig of a wherry with the hull of a yacht) were developed. According to Clark (1961), there were originally 35 of the former, and of these, two – the *Solace* (built in 1903) and the *Hathor* (built at Reedham in 1905, and re-launched in April 1989) – have been restored and are in regular use (see Plate XLI). The wherry yacht *Olive* (built in 1909) was listed in the hire catalogues until 1958, but after a spell as a houseboat was restored so that, like the *Hathor*, she could be used by charter parties (Bower, 1989). Another wherry yacht, the *Norada* (built in 1912 and known for many years as the *Lady Edith* until she was given back her original name in 1987), is used in the same way, whilst a third vessel of the same type, the *White Moth* (launched in 1915) has been available for hire since July 1990, following restoration. Rebuilding such vessels is extremely time-consuming and expensive (a new mast, for instance, costs at least £1500), and several of the restorations mentioned above (and also the recovery of the Norfolk Keel and the trading wherry *Maud*) were grant-aided by the 'old' Broads Authority, whose members rightly believed that these vessels form an important element in Broadland's cultural heritage. By April 1988 the Authority had made available a total of £7900 for such work, and had strongly recommended its successor, the 'new' Broads Authority, to adopt a similarly supportive policy.

As the popularity of Broadland grew, more and more boatyards found it onerous to have to deal direct with potential customers, as well as cope with the practical aspects of their business. Blakes Norfolk Broads Holidays Ltd. was therefore founded in 1908 to handle bookings on behalf of such firms. They acted for 13 yards in 1909, the craft listed in their catalogue for that year including 24 pleasure wherries and similar vessels (one of which was fitted with an auxiliary engine), 93 yachts, 1 auxiliary-engined yacht and 2 motor vessels provided with sleeping accomodation. Most of these craft were based at Wroxham, where there were 3 largish firms – Ernest Collins, Alfred Collins, and the Norfolk Broads Yachting Station – but George Applegate of Potter Heigham had 10 boats, Smith & Powley of Horning 4, A.R.Brown of St. Olaves 11 and Millers of Oulton Broad 7, whilst smaller numbers were hired out from another yard at Oulton, and from Stalham and Yarmouth. Hart & Sons of Wroxham offered to hire out their three vessels from Thorpe, rather than from their home base, whilst the Norfolk Broads

Yachting Station was prepared to allow holidaymakers to collect its boats from Potter Heigham instead of Wroxham.

All the wherries and 21 of the yachts listed in the catalogue came with a crew, and professional assistance was available on request for several other vessels, usually for an extra £1 per week. In most of these boats, the crew consisted of a skipper and a steward, but a third man was carried by one of the wherries.

About six hundred holidaymakers could, in theory, have been accommodated in the vessels listed by Blakes in 1909, the most expensive being the wherry *Gaviota*, which cost 16 guineas (£16 16s.) per week in the main holiday season, reducing to 12 guineas (£12 12s.) per week at other times. Ten of the yachts were over 40 feet (12 m) in length and, on average, cost £7 per week at off-peak times, rising to £10 at the height of the season. A further 20 yachts were between 30 and 39 feet overall, whilst 41 were between 25 and 29 feet long. Some of the remaining 22 vessels did not have cabins, their occupants being expected to sleep under awnings. Forty-one of the yachts belonged to 11 classes, suggesting that hire operators could already see the advantages of standardization.

Plate XLI

The pleasure wherry *Hathor* on the R. Yare at Reedham – 1989.

This vessel, one of only two surviving pleasure wherries, was re-launched following an extensive refit, shortly before this photograph was taken.

She is professionally skippered, and like the wherry yachts *Olive*, *Norada* and *White Moth*, is capable of accommodating parties of 10 to 12 persons.

Although fitted with an auxiliary engine, those hiring her are expected to be able to quant her when, as in the photo, there is insufficient wind to give her steerage way. Her rig, only part of which is shown here, is very similar to that of the *Albion* (Plate XXXVII).

Photo: Richard Denyer

Although Blakes acted for some of the larger firms, Loynes and numerous smaller operators continued to handle their own bookings. For this reason, it is impossible to say exactly how many vessels were being hired out during this period. Nor is it known how many privately owned boats were kept on the waterways, since the Commissioner's records are incomplete. However, tolls levied in 1909 on pleasure craft produced an income of £164 for the Yare Commissioners and £96 for the Bure Commissioners. Of the 277 boats licensed by the latter 146 were sailing craft, 105 were rowing boats and punts, 20 were motorized and 6 were steam-powered (YPH 257). Ten years later the Bure Commissioners raised £116 12s. from privately owned boats, £78 18s. 6d. from hire craft, and £90 11s. 6d. from commercial vessels, mainly wherries (YPH 222). According to the Commissioner's minutes, the pleasure craft comprised 322 yachts and dinghies, 64 motor craft, 62 pleasure wherries and houseboats and 244 rowing boats (YPH 73).

These figures are of special interest, because they not only show the relative proportions of sail and powered craft during this period, but provide an indication of the pressures being exerted on the waterways by the differing types of boat traffic. Unfortunately, a breakdown of this sort is not normally given in the Commissioner's records, probably because until 1964 the tolls levied on pleasure craft were the same, regardless of whether the boat was being used for private purposes or for hire.

The holiday trade suffered a severe setback as a result of the 1914–1918 War, but some hire craft remained in service throughout, and the industry recovered fairly quickly once hostilities had ceased. Blakes' catalogue for 1920 lists 165 vessels, including 144 yachts (23 of which came with a professional crew), 17 wherries (all attended) and 4 motor cruisers; about 750 persons could have been accommodated on these vessels at any one time. Hire charges were significantly less than they are today. For instance, a two berth 20 foot (6 m) yacht could have been hired through Blakes for between £3 15s. and £5 (*c.* £50–£67 at 1985 prices) a week, depending on the time of year, whereas in 1985 the weekly charge for a vessel of similar size and type was between £95 and £135. Moreover, at the height of the season it would have been possible to hire a 43 foot, skippered yacht for only £16 per week (*c.* £216 at 1985 prices).

Table 11c shows that 98 of the boats booked in 1920 by Blakes were based at Wroxham, the only other centre of any size being Oulton with 25 vessels. Given the number of firms who were still handling their own bookings at this time, it would be rash to draw any firm conclusions from these figures. However, the fact that only three of the Blakes boats were based at Horning and eight at Potter Heigham shows that these centres were still at an early stage in their development. Of the 426 vessels listed in Blake's catalogue for 1929, 247 were yachts (22 of which were attended), 13 were wherries (6 of which had been fitted with auxiliary engines) and, most significantly of all, 155 were motor cruisers. It was still possible to hire a 40-foot yacht, complete with crew, for between £10 and £15 per week (*c.* £273–£410 at 1990 prices) though the wherries and wherry yachts were relatively expensive. For instance, the wherry yacht *White Heather* could have been hired with a crew of two for between £12 12s. and £14 14s. in 1909, but cost between £17 10s. and £25 15s. in 1929 (*c.* £478 and £703 at 1990 prices). A typical 4-berth, auxiliary-engined sailing cruiser cost between £7 10s. and £10 per week (*c.* £166 and £221 at 1987 prices), whereas the weekly hire charges for a vessel of similar size and type in 1987 would have been rather more than this, especially at the height of the season. However, the cost of hiring a 6-berth motor cruiser in 1929 was between £12 and £17 per week; these figures are equivalent to £265 and £375 at 1987 prices, and are therefore in line with the prices which were being charged for the cheaper 6-berth cruisers that year.

Of the 1772 persons who could, in theory, have been accomodated at any one time in Blakes' 1929 hire fleet, 942 would have been in yachts, 672 in motor cruisers, 115 in wherries and wherry yachts, and 43 in auxiliary yachts. Table 11c shows that almost twice as many of these boats were being hired out from yards in the northern river valleys than in the south, and that whilst Wroxham and Oulton, with 168 and 81 vessels respectively, remained the largest centres, Horning (56), Potter Heigham (30) and Thorpe (32) had expanded greatly since 1920 (see Map 11.1).

Blakes' catalogues suggest that the number of yachts for hire remained more or less static during the 1930s; however, the rising popularity of motor cruisers is indicated by the inclusion of 310 such vessels in the firm's 1939 list. Since this is less than half the

Table 11c   The numbers and location of vessels for hire in the region: 1920 – 1988

| | 1920 | | | | | 1929 | | | | | 1939 | | | | | 1949 | | | | |
	W	*Y*	*A*	*M*	*T*	*W*	*Y*	*A*	*M*	*T*	*W*	*Y*	*A*	*M*	*T*	*W*	*Y*	*A*	*M*	*T*
Coltishall	–	–	–	–	–	–	–	–	2	2	–	–	–	–	–	–	–	–	6	6
Belaugh	–	–	–	–	–	–	–	–	–	–	–	–	–	–	–	–	–	–	–	–
Wroxham	13	85	–	–	98	9	122	–	37	168	3	127	2	78	210	3	112	5	69	189
Horning	–	2	–	1	3	1	22	1	32	56	–	35	6	47	88	–	39	2	32	73
S. Walsham	–	–	–	–	–	–	–	–	–	–	–	–	–	–	–	–	–	–	–	–
Upton	–	–	–	–	–	–	–	–	–	–	–	–	–	–	–	–	–	–	–	–
Acle	1	5	–	–	6	1	10	–	–	11	–	8	1	16	25	–	6	1	14	21
Stracey Arms	–	–	–	–	–	–	–	–	–	–	–	–	–	–	–	–	–	–	–	–
Wayford Bridge	–	–	–	–	–	–	4	–	–	4	–	6	–	–	6	–	6	–	–	6
Stalham	–	5	–	–	5	–	10	–	1	11	–	10	1	–	11	–	–	–	9	9
Sutton	–	–	–	–	–	–	–	–	–	–	–	–	–	–	–	–	–	–	–	–
Barton Turf	–	–	–	–	–	–	–	–	–	–	–	–	–	–	–	–	–	–	–	–
Neatishead	–	–	–	–	–	–	–	–	–	–	–	–	–	–	–	–	–	–	–	–
Hickling	–	–	–	–	–	–	–	–	–	–	–	–	–	–	–	–	–	–	–	–
Waxham	–	–	–	–	–	–	–	–	–	–	–	–	–	–	–	–	–	–	–	–
Martham	–	–	–	–	–	–	–	–	–	–	–	–	–	–	–	–	–	–	–	–
Potter Heigham	–	8	–	–	8	–	19	–	11	30	–	23	–	48	71	–	35	–	54	89
Ludham	–	–	–	–	–	–	–	–	–	–	–	11	–	–	11	–	12	–	–	12
Total N Rivers	14	105	–	1	120	11	187	1	83	282	3	220	10	189	422	3	210	8	184	405
Norwich	–	–	–	–	–	–	–	–	5	5	–	–	–	–	–	–	–	–	–	–
Thorpe	–	10	–	1	11	–	8	1	23	32	–	–	–	23	23	–	–	–	22	22
Brundall	1	3	–	–	4	–	4	–	11	15	–	–	–	17	17	–	–	–	24	24
Buckenham Ferry	–	–	–	–	–	–	–	–	–	–	–	–	–	–	–	–	–	–	–	–
Langley	–	–	–	–	–	–	–	–	–	–	–	–	–	–	–	–	–	–	–	–
Loddon/Chedgrave	–	–	–	–	–	–	–	–	–	–	–	–	–	–	–	–	–	–	–	–
Reedham	–	–	–	–	1	–	–	–	1	1	–	–	–	4	4	–	–	–	9	9
Berney Arms	–	–	–	–	–	–	–	–	–	–	–	–	–	–	–	–	–	–	–	–
Gt. Yarmouth	–	–	–	–	–	–	–	–	–	–	–	–	–	–	–	–	–	–	–	–
Geldeston	–	–	–	–	–	–	–	–	–	–	–	–	–	–	–	–	–	–	–	–
Beccles	–	2	–	1	3	–	2	–	5	7	–	2	–	9	11	–	–	–	–	–
Oulton Broad	2	22	–	1	25	2	46	9	24	81	2	29	9	63	103	2	14	8	57	81
Somerleyton	–	–	–	–	–	–	–	–	–	–	–	–	–	–	–	–	–	–	–	–
Burgh St. Peter	–	–	–	–	–	–	–	–	–	–	–	–	–	–	–	–	–	–	–	–
St. Olaves	–	1	–	–	1	–	–	–	3	3	–	2	–	5	7	–	1	–	5	6
Burgh Castle	–	–	–	–	–	–	–	–	–	–	–	–	–	–	–	–	–	–	–	–
Totals S Rivers	3	39	–	3	45	2	60	10	72	144	2	33	9	121	165	2	15	8	117	142
Grand Totals	17	144	–	4	165	13	247	11	155	426	5	253	19	310	587	5	225	16	301	547

Definitions:
W – Wherries & Wherry yachts (all were motorized from 1939 onwards). No such vessels were available for hire in the years 1962, 1969, 1979 and 1983.
Y – Yachts; i.e. sailing cruisers without an engine, or with an outboard motor only. The latter are classed as 'Motorized Sailing Craft' by the Navigation Authority.
Aux. – 'Auxiliary' sailing cruisers, i.e. sailing cruisers fitted with an inboard engine.
M – Motor cruisers
T – Totals

Sources:
The figures given for 1920, 1929 and 1939 were obtained from the catalogues issued by Blakes – the only booking agency operating in the region in these years. They will, however, understate the numbers of craft available for hire, since some yards were still handling their own bookings in these years (indeed a few small firms have continued to do so up to the present time).

The figures for 1949 were extracted from the catalogues produced by Blakes and Hoseasons, the latter firm having been founded three years previously.

	1955				1962				1969				1979				1983				1988				
W	Y	A	M	T	Y	A	M	T	Y	A	M	T	Y	A	M	T	Y	A	M	T	W	Y	A	M	T
–	–	1	10	11	–	1	10	11	–	1	10	11	–	–	–	–	–	–	–	–	–	–	–	–	–
–	–	–	3	3	–	–	7	7	–	–	12	12	–	–	15	15	–	–	16	16	–	–	–	16	16
2	84	32	122	240	46	44	219	309	4	38	250	292	–	1	417	418	–	1	448	449	–	–	–	327	327
–	49	7	56	112	36	17	110	163	16	15	165	196	–	4	281	285	–	3	180	183	1	–	7	175	183
–	–	–	2	2	–	–	10	10	–	–	17	17	–	–	22	22	–	–	18	18	–	–	–	16	16
–	–	–	–	–	10	1	–	11	11	4	–	15	3	10	–	13	2	11	–	13	–	–	15	–	15
–	4	5	25	34	–	4	38	42	–	–	38	38	–	2	51	53	–	10	84	94	–	–	9	99	108
–	–	–	–	–	–	–	9	9	–	–	–	–	–	–	–	–	–	–	–	–	–	–	–	–	–
–	7	3	3	13	4	3	6	13	–	3	15	18	2	12	14	28	2	10	13	25	–	–	–	6	6
–	3	1	17	21	–	3	81	84	–	–	210	210	–	–	338	338	–	1	190	191	–	–	2	222	224
–	–	–	2	2	–	–	5	5	–	–	–	–	–	–	16	16	–	–	12	12	–	–	–	11	11
–	–	–	2	2	–	–	1	1	–	–	–	–	–	–	–	–	–	–	–	–	–	–	–	–	–
–	–	–	–	–	–	–	10	10	–	–	–	–	–	–	–	–	–	–	16	16	–	–	–	–	–
–	–	–	–	–	–	–	1	1	–	–	7	7	–	–	13	13	–	–	10	10	–	–	–	10	10
–	–	–	–	–	–	–	2	2	–	–	3	3	–	–	–	–	–	–	–	–	–	–	–	–	–
–	5	–	30	35	1	10	42	53	2	23	49	74	1	37	50	88	1	38	48	87	–	1	11	6	18
–	40	12	63	115	33	17	68	118	35	26	92	153	4	22	165	191	1	25	159	185	–	–	30	104	134
–	14	–	3	17	14	–	2	16	–	–	9	9	–	–	20	20	–	–	21	21	–	–	–	16	16
2	206	61	338	607	144	100	621	865	68	110	877	1055	10	88	1422	1500	6	99	1215	1320	1	1	74	1008	1084
–	–	–	–	–	–	–	–	–	–	–	–	–	–	–	–	–	–	–	–	–	–	–	–	–	–
–	–	1	49	50	1	3	62	66	–	–	267	267	–	–	78	78	–	–	85	85	–	–	–	79	79
1	–	–	31	32	1	2	74	77	–	–	156	156	–	–	214	241	–	–	255	255	–	1	–	219	220
–	–	–	–	–	–	–	3	3	–	–	–	–	–	–	–	–	–	–	–	–	–	–	–	–	–
–	–	–	5	5	–	–	–	–	–	–	–	–	–	–	–	–	–	–	–	–	–	–	–	–	–
–	–	–	–	–	–	–	23	23	–	–	48	48	–	–	117	117	–	–	111	111	–	–	–	66	66
–	–	–	11	11	–	–	14	14	–	–	34	34	–	1	23	24	–	1	21	22	–	–	1	20	21
–	–	–	–	–	–	–	4	4	–	–	–	–	–	–	–	–	–	–	–	–	–	–	–	–	–
–	–	–	12	12	–	–	12	12	–	–	15	15	–	–	–	–	–	–	–	–	–	–	–	–	–
–	–	–	–	–	–	–	8	8	–	–	7	7	–	–	9	9	–	–	–	–	–	–	–	–	–
–	–	3	15	18	–	1	41	42	–	1	60	61	–	1	62	63	–	–	62	62	–	–	–	48	48
1	13	23	106	143	10	26	131	167	–	20	122	142	–	7	79	86	–	4	62	66	–	–	1	36	37
–	1	–	7	8	–	–	13	13	–	–	17	17	–	–	20	20	–	–	28	28	–	–	–	16	16
–	–	–	3	3	–	–	–	–	–	–	–	–	–	–	–	–	–	–	–	–	–	–	–	–	–
–	3	–	24	27	–	4	20	24	–	2	40	42	–	–	91	91	–	–	80	80	–	–	–	55	55
–	1	1	1	3	–	2	3	5	–	–	13	13	–	–	28	28	–	–	27	27	–	–	–	–	–
2	18	28	264	312	12	38	408	458	–	23	779	802	–	9	748	757	–	5	731	736	–	1	2	539	542
4	224	89	602	919	156	138	1029	1323	68	133	1686	1857	10	97	2150	2257	6	104	1946	2056	1	2	76	1547	1626

The 1955 figures were derived from the catalogues issued by the four booking agencies then trading – Blakes, Hoseasons, Bradbeers and Broads Holidays Ltd.

The figures for 1962 were obtained from the catalogues issued by Blakes, Hoseasons and Bradbeers, and by two boat hire firms (Moore's of Wroxham and Robinsons of Oulton Broad) which were handling their own bookings that year. The number of vessels being handled by Broads Holidays Ltd. that year is not known, but is unlikely to have exceeded 35.

The 1969 figures are for Blakes' and Hoseason's fleets only.

The figures for 1979 and 1983 were obtained from the catalogues issued by Blakes, Hoseasons and Freshfield Holidays for these years, supplemented by additional data provided by these firms, whilst the figures for 1988 relate to the vessels being handled that year by Blakes, Hoseasons and Pennant Holidays.

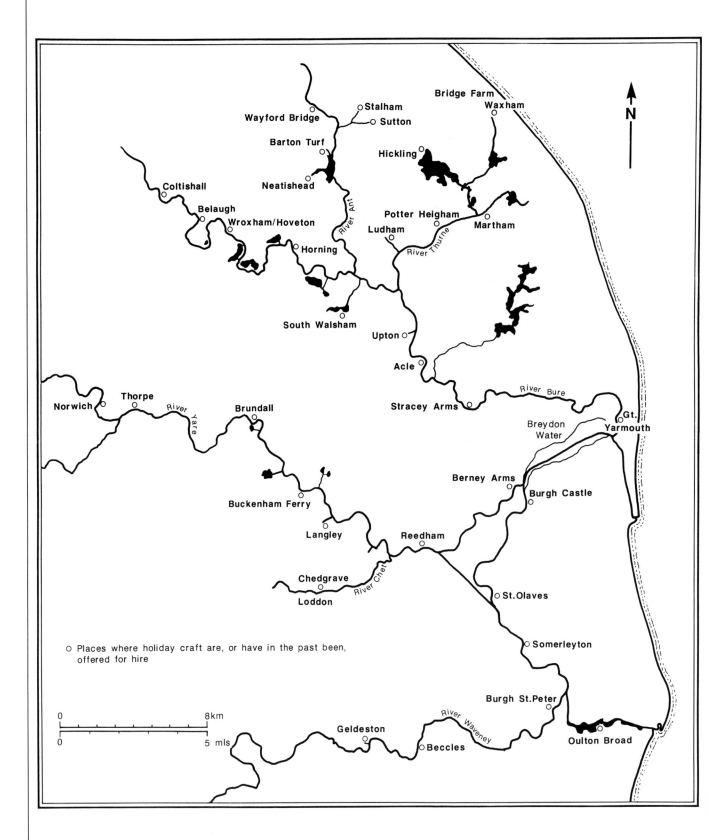

Map 11.1   The locations of boatyards which are, or have been engaged in hiring out holiday craft in Broadland.
Their relative importance at different times between 1920 and 1988 can be gauged from the figures
presented in Table 11c. (© Crown Copyright)

number of hire motor cruisers included in the following 'rough estimates' produced by the Rivers Commissioners in 1946 for the Broads Conference Report, it would seem that numerous boatyards were still handling their own bookings.

Approximate numbers of motor craft registered by the Rivers Commissioners in 1939

	Private	*Hire*	*Total*
R. Bure	634	421	1055
R. Yare	270	96	366
R. Waveney	364	146	510
Totals	1268	663	1931

Holiday boating ceased completely during the War and steps were taken to prevent enemy sea-planes landing on the Broads (in contrast to the situation in 1917, when part of Hickling Broad was requisitioned for use by our own sea-planes as an alternative to their base off Yarmouth –YPH 73). Stakes were driven in, or boats sunk, at most sites, whilst mines were laid in Barton, Rockland, Surlingham and Oulton Broads, and perhaps elsewhere. After the War, these were removed, or in the case of the latter site, detonated *in situ* by the Royal Navy, and vessels which had been requisitioned were handed back to their owners. But many craft were in a semi-derelict condition, and it is surprising that 3405 were registered with the Commissioners for the three rivers in 1946. This total was made up as follows:

	Private			**Hire**			
	Motor	*Sailing*	*Rowing*	*Motor*	*Sailing*	*Rowing*	*Total*
R.Bure	497	379	386	351	503	94	2210
R. Yare	150	106	160	63	24	37	540
R. Waveney	200	131	95	97	59	73	655
Totals	847	616	641	511	586	204	3405

Source: Statement produced in 1947 by the Great Yarmouth Port and Haven Commissioners for the Broads Conference Report.

The same year it was reported to the Broads Conference Investigation Committee that the hirers of motor cruisers had an understanding amongst themselves that none of their vessels would be capable of exceeding 8.5 mph. Although cynics will claim that this arrangement was prompted mainly by the need to limit wear and tear on the craft and their engines, it is charitable to believe that hirers were already aware of the erosion and nuisance to others which their boats could cause when inexpertly handled.

In 1945, a second boat-letting agency was established in the region by W.B. Hoseason, and four years later, the catalogues for this firm, and Blakes, listed 5 wherries, 225 yachts (none of which was attended), 16 auxiliary yachts and 301 motor cruisers; the slight decrease in the numbers of vessels compared with 1939 can probably be attributed to the effects of the War. Two other agencies, R.B. Bradbeer Ltd. and Broads Holidays, were founded in the early 1950s and the 1955 catalogues for the four firms together list 4 motorized wherries, 224 yachts, 89 auxiliaries and 602 motor cruisers. These figures undoubtedly understate the total number of hire vessels in use at this time, because firms such as Robinsons of Oulton (about 25 vessels), the Martham Boat Development Company (about 35) and Moores of Wroxham (about 25) were still handling their own bookings. It will be seen from Table 11c that there was still a marked imbalance between the number of vessels hired out from yards on the northern and southern rivers, most of the yachts and auxiliaries on the booking agents' lists being based on the former.

The 1962 catalogues issued by Blakes, Hoseasons, Bradbeers, Moores and Robinsons listed 156 yachts, 138 auxiliaries and 1029 motor cruisers. A further 75 vessels, mostly motorized, are likely to have been operated by independent companies and by Broads Holidays, giving a grand total of some 1400 vessels available for hire that year; of these, about 1080 would have been motor cruisers.

Table 11d   The numbers of hire and privately-owned craft: 1964 and 1967–1970

	1964		1967		1968		1969		1970	
	H	*P*	*H*	*P*	*H*	*P*	*H*	*P*	*H*	*P*
Motor craft	2739	2377	2945	3057	3131	2912	3157	3057	3062	3142
Sailing craft	1278	1178	864	1425	829	1351	804	1411	753	1407
Row boats and canoes	670	923	490	999	485	914	498	856	468	911
Houseboats	53	29	35	36	49	30	48	31	46	29

H = Hire Craft   P = Privately-owned craft

Source: Rivers Yare, Bure and Waveney Commissioners — summary records.

Table 11e   The numbers of hire craft registered with the Rivers Commissioners (1971–1988) and the 'new' Broads Authority (1989–1990)

	1971	*1972*	*1973*	*1974*	*1975*	*1976*	*1977*
Motor Cruisers	1942	1894	1868	1910	2051	2000	1991
Motorized Sailing Craft*	143	139	139	131	128	131	133
Day Launches	512	518	524	509	514	510	488
Outboard Dinghies	240	232	218	201	189	162	148
Passenger Vessels	20	22	22	26	26	30	31
Workboats	1	3	1	4	1	3	6
Patrol Launches	–	–	–	–	–	–	–
Total Motors:	2858	2808	2772	2781	2909	2836	2813
Sailing Craft	693	680	680	688	728	647	648
Rowing Craft	474	490	485	457	447	431	423
Houseboats	42	41	40	37	38	37	35
Total	4067	4019	3977	3963	4122	3951	3919

* These have been defined by the Rivers Commissioners, and from 1989 onwards, the 'new' Broads Authority, as sailing vessels having a block area of 6 sq m or more, which have an inboard or outboard engine of 10 brake horsepower or less.

** The inconsistencies between these figures and those given in Table 11c for 1979 cannot be satisfactorily explained.

*** Included in the total of motor cruisers

Table 11f   The numbers of privately-owned vessels registered with the Rivers Commissioners (1971–1987) and the 'new' Broads Authority (1989–1990)*

	1971	*1972*	*1973*	*1974*	*1975*	*1976*	*1977*
Motor Cruisers	1246	1544	1710	1844	1982	1953	1987
Motorized Sailing Craft	492	433	640	673	676	719	705
Day Launches	725	741	778	781	807	828	807
Outboard Dinghies	972	1075	1222	1244	1324	1199	1163
Passenger Vessels	–	–	–	–	–	–	–
Workboats	15	16	17	26	17	33	56
Patrol Launches	13	14	15	14	14	16	17
Total Motors:	3463	3823	4382	4581	4820	4748	4736
Sailing Craft	1603	1639	1752	1761	1833	1761	1681
Rowing Craft	1011	1104	1100	1211	1270	1268	1294
Houseboats	33	32	23	23	27	26	24
Total	6110	6598	7257	7577	7950	7805	7735

* These figures do not include visiting boats and vessels used exclusively on waters such as Wroxham and Filby Broads which are outside the Commissioners' jurisdiction. The latter do not have to be licensed.

** These have been defined by the Rivers Commissioners, and from 1989 onwards, the 'new' Broads Authority, as sailing vessels having a block area of 6 sq m or more, which have an inboard or outboard engine of 10 brake horsepower or less.

*** Patrol launches were classed as day launches from 1984 onwards.

The Rivers Commissioners' records prior to 1964 rarely distinguish between privately-owned and hire craft and it is therefore impossible to determine their relative proportions. However the total number of motor vessels registered rose from 3146 in 1957 to 3646 in 1959 and 4688 in 1962. Comparison of the latter figure with that based on the boat-letting agencies' catalogues, suggests that there were some 3608 privately-owned motor vessels on the waterways that year. The numbers of craft in the hire and private categories are given in Table 11d for the years 1964, and 1967–1970, and for 1971–1990 in Tables 11e and 11f.

1978	1979	1980	1981	1982	1983	1984	1985	1986	1987	1988	1989	1990
2071	2137*	2187	2208	2113	2017	1810†	1660†	1627	1592	2001	1975	1955
112	113*	111	108	109	106	103	109	93	94	93	91	89
461	452	446	413	370	310	290	405	381	397	††	††	††
142	123	103	56	43	29	30	28	25	22	1	6	21
30	29	30	30	30	***	***	***	***	27	††	–	–
–	–	–	–	1	–	–	–	–	–	–	–	–
–	–	–	–	–	–	–	–	–	–	–	–	–
2816	2854	2877	2815	2666	2462	2233	2202	2126	2132	2095	2072	2065
623	607	578	507	427	410	404	399	360	360	353	335	348
420	452	394	419	387	375	337	343	315	321	304	292	271
36	34	31	32	31	26	26	20	19	19	21	23	22
3895	3947	3880	3773	3511	3273	3000	2964	2820	2832	2773	2722	2706

† Part of the decline in numbers between 1984 and 1985 resulted from a decision by the Commissioners that some vessels previously categorized as motor cruisers should in future be classed as day launches.

†† Day launches and passenger vessels were classed as 'motor cruisers' from 1988 onwards.

1978	1979	1980	1981	1982	1983	1984	1985	1986	1987	1988	1989	1990
2047	2113	2279	2344	2363	3024	3297†	1727†	1818	1918	4331	4454	4404
750	822	851	832	922	896	962	1041	1130	1203	1274	1347	1384
766	785	813	793	760	720	715†	2208†	2415	2343	††	††	††
1145	1160	1256	1094	1093	666	712	685	618	712	829	946	950
–	–	–	–	–	–	–	–	–	–	–	–	–
71	61	89	80	82	100	109	105	130	126	130	114	123
21	24	25	30	32	30	***	***	***	***	***	***	***
4800	4965	5313	5173	5252	5436	5795	5766	6111	6302	6564	6861	6861
1613	1599	1651	1597	1615	1648	1773	1785	1815	1875	1874	1938	1855
1275	1299	1320	1287	1330	1374	1408	1371	1372	1244	1257	1215	1193
27	29	41	33	33	26	25	21	21	22	23	20	20
7715	7892	8325	8090	8230	8484	9001	8943	9319	9443	9718	10034	9929

† The abrupt differences between the figures for 1984 and 1985 resulted from a decision by the Commissioners that some vessels previously categorized as motor cruisers should in future be classed as day launches.

†† Day launches were classed as 'motor cruisers' in 1988.

It will be seen from Table 11c that the total number of sailing cruisers available for hire almost halved between 1962 and 1979. This can be related to the countrywide upsurge in small sailing boat ownership which has taken place during the past 30 years and which has made a holiday in Broadland much less of a novelty for sailing enthusiasts than it was in the past. But several other factors have contributed to the decline, not least the fact that although the modern 'sail cruisers' now being hired out from some yards offer a standard of accommodation at least as good as that of the average motor cruiser, many of the older sailing vessels possess facilities which are somewhat spartan in comparison. Furthermore, the cost of maintaining, and ultimately replacing, a yacht is greater than for a motor vessel of comparable size. As a result, most of the firms which have been set up since the War have concentrated on hiring out motor cruisers rather than sailing craft, whilst those which have acquired old-established companies have often been reluctant to continue to operate yachts, when it was easier and cheaper to manage a fleet of motor vessels. In addition, the increasing volume of traffic on the rivers has made them less suitable for sailing on than in the past. The tree-lined middle and upper reaches of the Bure and Ant are specially frustrating to yachtsmen in light airs, as the pitching produced by the wash of passing motor vessels, is constantly knocking what wind there is out of the sails. Indeed, during the 1950s and 1960s, when numerous sailing cruisers were still being hired out from Wroxham, the Blakes firms concerned clubbed together to offer their clients a free, end-of-the-week, tow-you-back-to-base service from Woodbastwick Staithe.

One or two of the motor cruisers launched during the 1930s were still in use fifty years later (for instance, the *Prince of Light* was advertised for hire by Herbert Woods Ltd. of Potter Heigham in 1989), but most vessels only remain in service for about 12 years before being sold off, often for private use on the region's waterways. Boats which prove expensive to maintain, or more difficult to let, tend to be phased out of service more quickly than the remainder. In general, the yachts and auxiliaries available for hire have more extended lives than the motor cruisers, and quite a number of pre-war vessels are still in use.

The numbers of hire motor cruisers registered with the Commissioners showed an overall increase between 1971 and 1981, but since then have declined (Table 11e). This trend is confirmed by the records of the boat-letting agencies (Table 11c) which show that they handled only 1946 such vessels in 1983, compared with 2150 in 1979, a 9 per cent reduction. These decreases can be related to the onset of the economic recession, and a consequent reduction in the demand for holidays in the region. The Broads Hire Boat Federation (1983) has pointed out that the number of bookings made with its members decreased in 1982 by 40 per cent compared with the previous year. In addition a survey commissioned by the Federation showed that local shopkeepers at Loddon, Potter Heigham and Horning experienced a reduction in turnover of between 17 and 30 per cent between 1979 and 1982.

The increased economic pressure made it necessary for most yards to reduce the size of their fleets, in some cases drastically. For instance, the number of motor cruisers operated by Richardsons, the largest firm at Stalham, declined from 294 in 1979, to *c.* 128 in 1983. Similarly, Herbert Woods' fleet at Potter Heigham, which comprised 320 vessels in 1976, had fallen to 245 craft by 1981, and consisted of only 98 motor cruisers and 30 auxiliary yachts in 1988. Perhaps inevitably, some of the weaker companies went out of business altogether. The boat-letting agencies' catalogues show that there were 102 firms trading in 1979, 99 in 1983, 85 in 1986, and only 80 in 1988. In some cases, the land formerly occupied by the boatyard has been redeveloped for housing, whilst other firms have turned their attention to servicing, repairing and providing moorings for privately-owned craft.

Another symptom of the increased economic pressure to which the hire boat industry was subject in the early 1980s was the formation of two new booking agencies. Freshfields Holidays was established in 1982 by Richardsons (though following a company reorganization five years later, responsibility for handling the firm's bookings was assumed by Hoseasons), whilst in 1986, a consortium of five firms, previously affiliated to Blakes, formed their own boat-letting agency, Pennant Holidays.

Following the 1983 season, both Blakes and Hoseasons predicted that the number of craft available for hire in Broadland would continue to decline for the next few years, and the fact that only 1592 hire motor cruisers were licensed for use in 1987 (Table

11e) confirms the accuracy of this forecast. Although the number of such vessels appears likely to stabilize at this figure for the time being – a point seemingly confirmed by the fact that only 1547 motor cruisers were advertised in the hire firms' catalogues for 1988 (see Table 11c) – there could be a slight resurgence in the event that changes in the exchange rate, and other factors, increase the cost of a holiday abroad compared with that in Broadland.

Unlike the hire sector, the numbers of privately-owned craft have increased fairly steadily since the 1970s (Table 11f). This is almost certainly a reflection, not only of a general rise in the standard of living, but of the burgeoning population of East Anglia. According to Anglia 2000 (1989), the latter increased by 1.1 per cent per annum between 1983 and 1987 (with a corresponding increase in output of 5.5 per cent), and given the likelihood that a significant proportion of these immigrants live within easy travelling distance of Broadland, it is significant that the total number of privately-owned craft rose by over 10 per cent during the same period.

Over 40 per cent of the vessels in the private sector are sailing or rowing craft, or small (up to 12 feet) outboard dinghies which cause minimal damage to the environment. On the other hand, such vessels occupy physical space on the rivers and broads when in use, and contribute to their congestion at busy times. Those connected with the hire industry also point to the fact that many of the larger private craft are kept on riverside moorings, thus detracting from the natural appearance of the waterways. The validity of this claim was confirmed in 1987/8 when the Broads Authority carried out a survey of the number of mooring spaces in the region occupied by privately-owned craft. It was estimated that there were a total of 4884 spaces, and that although 2295 of these were in boatyards, the remaining 2589 were located either beside the river itself (frontage moorings), or in off-river cuts, dykes or basins. The distribution of the 78 sites where these 2589 vessels were moored was as follows: R. Waveney 23 (of which 13 were frontage sites); R. Yare 15(7); R. Bure 18 (9); R. Thurne 12 (2); R. Ant 10 (1).

Broadland's continued popularity among sailing enthusiasts is indicated by the fact that the numbers of private yachts fitted with inboard or outboard engines (and therefore classed as 'auxiliaries' in Table 11f) almost tripled between 1971 and 1990 (see Plate 32). The numbers of half-deckers, racing dinghies and other non-engined sailing craft also increased during this period, though apparently not to the same extent as the larger vessels. In fact, the numbers of such craft registered with the Rivers Commissioners (and since 1989 the Broads Authority) are not a true reflection of the total numbers in use in the region, since some small sailing boats are used exclusively on sites such as Filby, Rollesby and Wroxham Broads which lie outside the jurisdiction of the Navigation Authority.

A further indication of the region's continued popularity with sailors is the fact that regular races are organized on the rivers and broads by no fewer than 14 yacht and sailing clubs, many with lengthy waiting lists. These, plus a further 11 clubs and committees concerned, either with arranging regattas (such as those held each year at Acle, Barton Broad and Thurne Mouth), or long distance races for cruisers (such as the Yare Navigation Race organized each September by the Coldham Hall Sailing Club) are affiliated to the Norfolk and Suffolk Yachting Association. Founded in 1894, this is the local arm of the Royal Yachting Association, its objectives being . . . "to serve and protect the interests of those who use the broads, whether they are rowing, canoeing, windsurfing, sailing or motor boating". Each year the Association publishes a 'Green Book' which not only lists the innumerable events for sailing enthusiasts which are due to take place in the region, but contains tidal predictions and other useful data.

Waterborne holidays and recreation – the economic implications

Christopher Groves, one-time Chief Inspector of the Rivers Commissioners, estimated in the late 1970s that about a quarter of a million persons were spending a holiday afloat in the region each year. A similar number were making use of the fleet of motor launches available for hire by the hour or day, while a further quarter of a million were thought to be taking a trip on one of the large, passenger-carrying vessels ('water buses') operated from Hoveton, Horning, Hickling, Oulton and Great

Yarmouth (Groves, pers. comm.). Although the numbers of craft available for day or weekly hire has declined since these estimates were made (see Table 11c), Groves probably under-estimated the number of people carried on 'water buses'. Indeed, the Honorary Secretary of the Norfolk and Suffolk Pleasure Boat Owners Association (which was formed in 1988 to represent the interests of 'water bus' operators) claims that some 400 000 people are carried on such craft each year (see Plates 34 & XLII). In the circumstances, Groves' overall estimate of about three quarters of a million waterborne visitors a year probably holds true for the mid to late-1980s. To this figure must be added the number of persons – estimated at between 100 000 and 150 000 – who seek relaxation and pleasure on privately-owned vessels, plus countless anglers, picnickers and other casual visitors. Thus the rivers and broads are probably seen and used by at least a million people a year.

The two associations which represented the boat hirers in the 1970s claimed that in 1979 they brought into the region more than £12 million worth of direct benefit in the shape of public spending, and that this had increased to £16 million by 1981, and to about £25 million by 1990, if Pennants' fleet is included (Court, pers. comm.). Much

Plate XLII

The *Southern Comfort* on the R. Bure near Horning – 1989.

When launched at Wroxham in the winter of 1975/6, this vessel caused something of a stir. However, she creates noticeably less wash than most motor cruisers, and has proved very popular, both with those on board, and onlookers. She has been based at Horning since 1978.

The *Southern Comfort* and other 'double-deckers', such as the *Vintage Broadsman* and the *Cordon Rouge* operated by Broads Tours of Wroxham, afford much better views over the fens and drained marshland adjoining the rivers and broads than can be obtained from a water bus of the traditional type.

Photo: Richard Denyer

of this money finds its way into the local economy via shops and pubs, whose turnover is greatly increased by the influx of visitors.

The actual earnings of the companies involved in letting out holiday craft are not known, but probably amounted to about £14 million in 1990. Between 10 and 12 per cent of this comes from overseas as an 'invisible export', following determined efforts by the boat-letting agencies to publicize the attractions of Broadland abroad, particularly in France, Germany and Holland. Of the £1 million earned by Blakes Holidays Ltd. in overseas revenue in 1984, about half came from boatyards and holiday homes in and around Broadland (Court, pers. comm.). Similarly, some 11 per cent of the bookings made by Blakes in Broadland during the financial year 1988/9 went to overseas customers.

The holiday and recreational industry provides many local people with a living. According to the Broads Hire Boat Federation (1979), about 800 full-time workers were employed at boatyards in the region in the late 1970s, and at the height of the season, a further 1200 part-timers were engaged in servicing each cruiser on 'change-over' days, and making it ready for collection by the incoming hirers. The latter figure may have been an over-estimate, since a Broads Authority census revealed that the numbers of full-time, part-time and seasonal boatyard employees in 1986 were 756, 153 and 662 respectively.

The size of the firms concerned varies greatly, but the Broads Authority's 1986 survey showed that 62 of the 95 yards which answered a questionnaire were letting out fewer than 20 boats. Of the remaining firms, 23 had between 20 and 50 vessels, and 8 between 50 and 100, whilst only 2 concerns had more than 100 craft on their books. Some yards undertake the repair and maintenance of privately-owned boats, as well as their own hire craft, but other firms in the region prefer to specialize in one sector or the other.

In the past, many firms built their own boats in their entirety, and a few continue to do so. More usually however, prefabricated hulls of glass-reinforced plastic or other materials are bought in from specialist firms, and fitted out by the yards to their own requirements. Many of the new vessels are absorbed into the hire fleet as replacements for older craft, or are purchased by local people, but some are destined for use on waterways elsewhere in Britain, or abroad. In the late 1970s, there were two firms at Brundall and three at Wroxham, specializing in the construction of large, sea-going pleasure craft, but since then one of the Wroxham concerns has transferred this part of its business elsewhere, and one of the Brundall firms has ceased trading.

Fishing

Broadland's fish populations (see page 147) have been exploited for centuries, both by commercial interests, and by anglers. Eels were formerly caught in traps and sets (nets strung across a river, and provided with one or more bow-nets, each expanded on wooden hoops, and ending in a 'poke' from which the trapped eels can be removed when the tide has turned), or by spearing the fish with eel-picks, or by 'babbing' – dangling in the water a weighted bunch of earthworms threaded on worsted. The importance of the eel fishery to the local economy in the past is indicated by the fact that there were 38 sets downstream of Acle Bridge, Hardley Cross and St. Olave's Bridge during the reign of King Henry VII (and probably many others upriver of these points), and numerous sets were still in use in the mid-nineteenth century (Dutt, 1906). Dutch Fyke nets (see Plates XLII & XLIV) were first licensed for use in 1955, and have become very popular since 1959, most of the eels caught in Broadland now being taken in them (Wortley, pers. comm.). 778 fyke-net licences were issued by the AWA's Norfolk and Suffolk Rivers Division in 1981, but this fell to 343 in 1982, following a fourfold increase in the fee to £6 per 'instrument', and only 282 licences were issued in 1985. But this decline in the trade was short-lived, since 43 individuals purchased from the National Rivers Authority a total of 488 licences to use eel-fishing 'instruments' in Norfolk and Suffolk in 1990. Most of these will have been exercised in Broadland, rather than in other parts of East Anglia (Wortley, *in litt.*).

Three sets were in operation in the region in 1984, but only one – located at the southern end of Candle Dyke – has been in use since 1985, and then only spas-

Plate XLIII

A fyke net set out to show its system of internal, netted cones – 1989.

These traps can be used singly (as shown), but are more usually set in pairs, the plain netting visible on the right of the photograph being attached to a similar trap, out of view on the right. When used in this way, an eel encountering the central netting will tend to enter a trap whether it swims to the right, or the left.

Photo: National Rivers Authority

modically. The eel fishing season usually starts in April and lasts until November, the nets being set at night, and raised early in the morning before any holiday craft get under way. The AWA was one of the few water authorities not to impose by-laws making it an offence to operate a fyke net without an entrance guard to prevent non-target species becoming entrapped within, and at least one otter is known to have died in this way during the past few years (see page 229). It is suspected, though not proved, that large bream sometimes suffer the same fate, and news that the National Rivers Authority intends shortly to introduce by-laws making it mandatory to use a guard on a fyke net was therefore welcomed by anglers, as well as nature conservationists.

No statistics are available about the number of eels caught in the region, since licencees have not been required to provide the AWA, or its successor, the National Rivers Authority, with data about their catches. However, many of the fish are exported to Holland, and the buyer for the firm concerned collected 20.5 tons in 1981. Although this was claimed to represent about 70 per cent of the total catch in the region, suggesting that about 30 tons were caught that year, the real total may have been 10 or 20 tons more than this (Wortley, *in litt.*). Very little is known about the recruitment rate, but this is thought to be good, or very good in most years. Nevertheless, the average size of the

An eel-fisherman, Tom Boddington, using a fyke net at Womack Water – 1988.   Plate XLIV

Eels are still abundant in the rivers and broads, and several individuals make a living out of them. Statistics are hard to come by, but the catches are reputedly good, many of the fish being exported to Holland.

Fishing in Broadland is regulated by by-laws made in 1976 under the *Salmon and Freshwater Fisheries Act* 1975. Under these regulations it is obligatory for eel fishermen to tag each 'instrument' they use.

Photo: Richard Denyer

eels caught has been declining since the late 1970s, suggesting that the population is now being over-exploited.

The Smelt is another species which has been fished commercially in Broadland for centuries (Southwell, 1887). Originally, there was no close season, but the *Norfolk and Suffolk Fisheries Act* of 1877 made it illegal to catch this species on Breydon between May and August, whilst at other times of the year, nets with a mesh size of five-eighths of an inch (1.59 cm) or less could not be used. It was also decreed that Smelt must not be caught on their annual 'run' upriver to spawn except at certain defined places between 10 March and 12 May; even then, a cast or drop net with a diameter of 16 feet or less had to be used.

Although these types of net and the draw (seine) nets traditionally employed on Breydon, have not been used by commercial fishermen in Broadland for many years, between 4 and 6 tons of Smelt, representing some twenty-two to twenty-three thousand fish, have since the late 1970s been caught in fyke nets set near Haddiscoe during the spring 'run' up the R. Waveney. Each year, the catch is sold to the Otter Trust, since the two fishermen concerned, have been unable to find a reliable alternative market. There is still an annual run of Smelt up to the tidal limits of the Wensum and Yare, as well as the Waveney, and the fact that many adult fish die after spawning results in complaints being made each spring that there has been a fish 'kill'. The species also occurs in the other rivers, notably the Thurne, where it has been recorded as far upstream as Hickling Broad.

One of Broadland's principal attractions is its coarse fishing, and of 620 boat hirers who completed a questionaire about their holiday, 28 per cent of those who had visited the region before, and 22 per cent of the first timers, mentioned fishing as one of the reasons why they had come to Broadland (Walker, 1981). The rivers and broads are also fished by large numbers of local people, and by parties of anglers from further afield, particularly when fishing matches are being held. Separate figures relating to the number of fishermen who use the region are not available, but in the area covered by the East Suffolk and Norfolk River Board (and later the East Suffolk and Norfolk River Authority), about 50 000 licences were sold in 1962, 75 000 in 1968 and 55 000 in 1973.

The total numbers of rod and line licences issued by the AWA in its Norfolk and Suffolk Rivers Division (latterly the Norwich Division) were as follows:

1976 – 74 270	1983 – 53 000
1977 – 74 238	1984 – 51 572
1978 – 73 414	1985 – 50 089
1979 – 68 932	1986 – 49 566
1980 – 64 148	1987 – 52 086
1981 – 63 733	1988 – 55 608
1982 – 56 380	

It is thought that a majority of these licence holders fished in Broadland, at least occasionally. But comparable figures for 1989 and 1990 are not available, as the National Rivers Authority does not keep a separate record of the number of licences issued in the Norwich area, rather than elsewhere in its Eastern Region.

The downward trend in the number of licences issued between 1976 and 1986 may in part reflect the decision taken by the AWA in 1975 that licence fees would in future have to match the Authority's expenditure on fishery work. In line with this policy, the cost of a regional licence was increased from £2.75 to £3.80 at the beginning of 1979, and to £6.00 in 1982, whilst divisional licence fees were raised fom £2.00 to £3.00 in 1982, and to £4.00 in 1986. Concessionary rates are available for old age pensioners and children aged between 12 and 15, and seven-day licences (costing £1.50) are also popular, over 20 000 being issued each year, mainly to holidaymakers.

Provided an angler has a licence, he has a statutory right to fish in tidal water. However, access is not always possible, and it was therefore the policy of the Norfolk Fisheries Board, and later the River Board and River Authority, to purchase or hire the banks of rivers and broads so as to enable anglers to gain access to tidal water. The AWA did not renew the leases of certain areas, for example Hickling Broad, when they expired, but in 1981 the Authority still owned some 30 000 m of river bank, and hired a further 14 263 m. The rentals payable that year on the latter only amounted to about £600, but despite this, it was suggested that the river bank leases should not be renewed, in accordance with the Authority's policy of not retaining direct responsibility for the provision of facilities for anglers. This proposal was unanimously rejected by members of the Broads Committee, on the grounds that the region's waterways are of national importance for tourism and recreation, and should therefore be regarded by the AWA as a special case.

Angling from banks owned or hired by the National Rivers Authority, as the successor to the AWA, is free, but at other sites, for example, Wroxham Broad, the owners levy a small fee on those wishing to fish. Elsewhere, for instance at Decoy, Ranworth and Alderfen Broads, the fishing rights are leased by angling clubs.

Although very large numbers of people continue to derive pleasure from angling in the Broadland waterways, the quality of the sport available has undoubtedly deteriorated during the past 25 years. In part this can be attributed to a decline in the size and diversity of the fish populations present. However, many anglers experience frustration and aggravation when fishing in a waterway being used by numerous boats, often somewhat thoughtlessly handled (Owens, 1977, 1978 & 1983). Many anglers consider that the R. Ant and other heavily used rivers are no longer worth fishing during the summer months, and the AWA's surveys (see page 147) suggest that in such waters, the fish take refuge in off-river dykes and mooring basins during the daytime.

These problems have been exacerbated in the larger Thurne broads by the *Prymnesium*-induced fish kills which have occurred in them since 1969 (see page 134). Few fish were caught in these waters during the 1970s, though shoals of Bream which had swum back down the R. Thurne after outbreaks of the disease have afforded the angler good sport on occasions. Pike in the upper Thurne, too, have tended to increase, both in number and size, and those specializing in this species have enjoyed something of a bonanza. During a visit to Hickling Broad in 1982, D. Amies took 8 Pike, for a total of 159 lbs (72.3 kg), and later caught five more, together weighing 108 lbs (49.1 kg). Many of the fish turned the scales at over 20 lbs, and one was of 36 lbs 6 oz (16.5 kg) (Knights, 1982). In February 1985, the British record which had been held by a 40 lb (18.2 kg) pike caught in Horsey Mere by P. Hancock in 1967, was broken by a fish of 41 lb 8 oz (18.9 kg) taken from an unidentified locality in the upper Thurne (Dyson, 1985), and by January 1986, the same fish had been captured by specimen hunters on at least three other occasions; indeed, the fish was given the nickname 'Big Dora'!

The management of the rivers from 1900 onwards

The Commissioners appointed under the *Great Yarmouth Port and Haven Act* of 1866 were at first unable to obtain any revenue from the developing holiday industry since the Act specifically exempted pleasure craft from tolls. However, this anomaly was rectified by an Act of 1900, which laid down a scale of charges to be levied on such vessels, and the extra income thus generated encouraged the Commissioners for the R. Bure to embark on a major programme of maintenance dredging. A hydrographic survey in 1908 showed that the river was only 2 to 4 feet deep between Horstead Mill and Coltishall Manor House, whilst minimum figures of 18 inches, 2 feet and 3 feet 3 inches were recorded at points downstream of the latter, Wroxham Bridge and Horning Ferry respectively (YPH 1734). Between 1910 and 1920 nearly 29 km of the main river and its tributaries were dredged, and although the lengths of waterway dealt with varied from year to year, over 3000 m of the main river were deepened in 1910, 1915 and 1918, whilst in 1913, no less than 6611 m were cleaned out (YPH 1757–1759). Unfortunately, neither the depth of water aimed at, nor the cost of the works, is given in the Commission's records. However, in 1911 they spent £384 on dredging 1092 m of the Thurne between Potter Heigham and Candle Dyke.

In addition to dredging the rivers, the Commissioners provided quay headings at busy landing places so as to prevent the river banks collapsing into the river, and thereby forming an obstruction to navigation. However, old photographs show that relatively few places had had to be piled in this way around the turn of the century, and confirmation of this is provided by the fact that although the Yare Commissioners spent £2254 on maintenance works in 1911, only £17 of this went on quay headings. In contrast, £1773 was expended on dredging (YPH 219).

The 1866 Act enabled the Commissioners to regulate, *inter alia*, the speed at which vessels were navigated on the rivers, and by-laws enacted for the R. Yare in 1882, and for the other two rivers in 1890, ordained that . . . "every steam vessel navigating the river . . . shall be navigated with care and caution, and at a speed, and in a manner which shall not endanger the safety of other vessels or moorings, or cause damage thereto, or to the banks of the river". The appearance of petrol-engined craft made it necessary to amend the by-laws in 1909 so that this clause covered all powered vessels, but it is indicative of its special relevance to the Rivers Commissioners' duties that in slightly amended form, it featured in their regulations right up to the end of March 1989, when they were disbanded in favour of the 'new' Broads Authority.

As pleasure boating increased, complaints began to be made about the behaviour of visitors, despite the by-laws. Three men were fined for using obscene language at Fishley on the R. Bure in 1916, and in 1924, the Waveney Commissioners were asked by Beccles Corporation to erect notices on Town Reach following allegations of damage caused by speeding motor boats; six years later they issued a summons against a boat owner following a complaint by Lord Somerleyton (YPH 76).

As time went on, it became apparent that in certain places it was not sufficient to rely solely on the 'care and caution' by-law, but that a specific speed limit was needed. The minutes of the Bure Commissioners (YPH 73) show that this was discussed as early as 1914, but it was not until 1931, that a 5 mph limit was imposed on the river at Wroxham and Horning, the maximum penalty for an infringement being £5 (c. £122 at 1987 prices). In the years following, by-laws were made which extended the list of controlled areas to include Potter Heigham (1932), Beccles (1936), Ludham Bridge (1937), Coltishall, Acle Bridge, Irstead, and Womack Water (1964), whilst the R. Chet, Malthouse and South Walsham Inner and Outer Broads, Ranworth Dam, Fleet Dyke and the R. Ant as far upstream as the Commissioners' limit of jurisdiction (350 yards upstream of Wayford Bridge) were added in 1966. Further controls were imposed in 1970 following a public inquiry. These extended the 5 mph limit to some 60 miles of waterway, and imposed a 7 mph restriction on a further 20 miles.

Evidence that the Bure Commissioners were employing an inspector to patrol the river, and regulate public behaviour before the First World War is provided by a minute dated October 1914, which gave instructions that the inspector's launch, purchased the previous year, should be laid up for the winter. Inspectors were also employed on the Yare and Waveney during the 1920s and 1930s and by 1946, there were two on the R. Yare, and one each on the Bure and Waveney. The police started to patrol the rivers in the late 1930s, but although they had two launches in use during the 1960s and 1970s, these were withdrawn from service in the early 1980s.

Difficulties had been experienced at Oulton Broad and Dyke after the First World War, because these popular and much frequented waterways lay outside the formal jurisdiction of the Rivers Commissioners. To resolve this anomaly, a separate navigation authority for these waterways, known as the Oulton Broad Joint Committee, was established under the *Pier and Harbour Orders Confirmation Act* 1922 (confirming the *Lowestoft (Oulton Broad) Order* of 1922). This had powers to provide moorings and other facilities for vessels, to collect fees from those who moored their boats in these waters, and regulate their use by means of by-laws. The Act also enabled the Great Yarmouth Port and Haven Commissioners, through their Waveney Commission, to levy tolls on pleasure craft using Oulton Broad and Dyke, the Joint Committee receiving a small grant in lieu.

The Joint Committee was supposed to use any surplus revenue to improve its area of responsibility, but in practice the funds available were so limited that very little could be achieved. In addition, virtually no dredging was carried out, even in the main navigable channel, because this remained the job of the London and North-Eastern Railway, as owners of the assets of the ill-fated Norwich to Lowestoft Navigation.

By-laws, including an enjoiner to use 'care and caution' were promulgated by the Joint Committee in 1923, and in 1934, it was made an offence to drive a speedboat on the Broad at more than 10 mph without written consent. These regulations were amended, and extended to Oulton Dyke, in 1952.

Meantime, the revenue derived by the Commissions responsible for the three main rivers was rising as a result of the increasing number of pleasure craft using them. Thus whilst commercial traffic on the Bure and Yare yielded only £40 and £150 respectively in tolls in 1925, £873 was raised by the Bure Commissioners that year from pleasure craft: this increased the following year to £958 (c. £20 158 at 1987 prices) (YPH 223–224). Tolls received by the Yare Commissioners from such vessels amounted to £1058 and £1129 for these years. But these figures must not be taken to mean that more pleasure craft were being used on the R. Yare than on the R. Bure, as until 1971, it was the custom to allow people to register their vessels with the Yare Commissioners even though they kept them on the Bure, and vice versa. A further complication was that between 1912 and 1935, the Yare Commissioners leased from the Waveney Commissioners the right to levy tolls on the vessels using the latter's river, the annual rent payable in 1931 being £400 (YPH 76).

Local people were keenly aware of the need to keep the waterways in good condition, and in a letter to the *Eastern Daily Press* in 1921, the Hickling Regatta Committee complained that as a result of neglect, the channels to Hickling, Catfield, Palling and Waxham were almost choked with aquatic vegetation, and that "pleasure sailing above Potter Heigham bridge is nearly killed" (Bygrave *et al.*, 1921). Although this implied a lack of interest on the part of the Bure Commissioners, the minutes of their meetings between 1916 and 1922 contain numerous references to the parlous state of this and other parts of the navigation, and their inability to carry out the necessary works owing to the diminution of their toll receipts during the War. In 1919, in a bid to overcome these difficulties, the Bure Commissioners increased their tolls on vessels, and the goods carried on commercial craft, by 50 per cent; the same year they were offered a grant of £300 from the Port and Haven Commissioners, on condition that they spent £190 on a new engine for their inspector's launch (YPH 73). Tolls and charges were raised by a further 75 per cent on all three rivers the following year, the Board of Trade decreeing that powered vessels should be charged an annual toll of seven shillings and sixpence (37.5p) per ton (with a maximum charge of £7 10s. per boat) and five shillings (25p) per ton for a vessel propelled in any other way (maximum charge £5, or £89.90 at 1990 prices).

It was probably in response to their improved financial position that the Commissioners arranged in 1920 that a centrifugal pump mounted on a wherry should be employed to try and clear the weed from Heigham Sound and Deep-go dyke, and from the river Thurne between Martham Staithe and Somerton (YPH 1759). Although 2400 yards (2193 m) were dealt with at a cost of £334, the results were obviously unsatisfactory, since they agreed in 1922 that they would contribute up to £200 to match the funds raised by a public subscription organized by the Hickling Regatta Committee. In December the same year it was announced that as a result of this local initiative, 3470 tons of weed had been removed from the channel across Heigham Sound and Hickling Broad, thus enabling yachts and trading wherries to reach the Pleasure Boat staithe for the first time since 1913 (EDP, 1922b).

According to Turrill (1923), the weed in Hickling Broad at that time consisted almost entirely of *Cladophora Sauteri*, and was best removed with a long-handled net, equipped with a hoe-like cutting edge. He reports that in 1923 nine men in five boats were engaged in the task, and two years later it was announced that nearly £1400 had been spent on the project (EDP, 1925). By present-day standards, the work must have been laborious in the extreme. Nevertheless two men were able to collect four cart-loads a day, the material being sold to farmers as a manure for two shillings a ton (Gurney, 1922).

The weed problem was not confined to the Thurne waterways. Boating interests had long experienced difficulty in navigating the Waveney, for example, and in 1932, the Commissioners for this river agreed after a trial that it would save money if they purchased a mechanical weed-cutter rather than continue to rely on hand-clearance methods.

Only fragmentary information is available about the maintenance works carried out by the Rivers Commissioners during the 1920s and 1930s, but the following figures for 1925 and 1926 are probably fairly typical (YPH 223–224).

	Dredging (£)		Weed Clearance (£)		Total (£)	
	1925	1926	1925	1926	1925	1926
R. Bure	992	1142	251	311	1565	1637
R. Waveney	152	Nil	69	68	247	84
R. Yare	5704*	3236†	152	182	8084	4917

* including £5234 on 'dipper' dredging and £466 on 'grab' dredging
† including £57 for 'bag and spoon' dredging (i.e. dydling)

Little, if anything, was done during the Second World War to maintain the Bure and Waveney in a navigable condition, and afterwards the Great Yarmouth Port and Haven Commissioners were far more interested in stimulating the growth of Yarmouth as a port by restoring the Haven [which, it was estimated, needed £809 000 spent on it as a consequence of wartime neglect – EDP, (1952a], than assisting the Commissioners for the rivers carry out their responsibilities, this despite the fact that pleasure boat traffic soon began to exceed the levels encountered before the War. Not the least of the problems was that although boat tolls were doubled in the late 1940s, the funds available to the Commissioners for the Bure and Waveney were nothing like large enough to enable them to tackle the backlog of management tasks which had developed during the previous 20 years or so. To make matters worse, the Commissioners' system of collecting tolls was somewhat lackadaisical, and they displayed a curious reluctance to prosecute evaders (Collier, pers. comm.). Neither were the Port and Haven Commissioners particularly zealous in the defence of their interests in the rivers during this period. In 1949, for instance, their then Clerk indicated in response to a proposal that the bridge carrying the A47 over Tunstall Dyke should be lowered, that the public had no rights

Table 11g   Rivers Yare, Bure and Waveney Commissioners – Summary of Toll Revenue: 1971/2 to 1989

	1971/2 £	1972/3 £	1973/4 £	1974/5 £	1975/6 £	1976/7 £	1977/8 £	1978/9 £
Commercial Tolls								
Ships	978	1036	760	518	1291	1717	2058	2104
Cargo (= tonnage dues)	6017	9439	6290	4766	5740	3206	6142	9519
Workboats, trading vessels etc.	104	66	66	195	99	80	80	80
Pleasure Craft								
Hire	55801	56754	56587	77537	82851	142220	161879	197472
Private	33331	36483	41812	57778	61362	84321	84268	102793
Short visits (up to 14 days)	3724	4194	5086	6835	6741	10011	9320	10376
Tolls levied on nos. carried in passenger craft	2232	2008	2552	2750	3126	3794	3878	4054
Less Refunds	–275	–177	–220	–	–	–	–	–
Totals	101732	109803	112933	150379	161210	245349	267625	326398

over this waterway, this despite the fact that it was at that time still tidal and therefore subject to a Common Law right of navigation.

Changes were obviously needed, and new appointments, both at member and officer level, helped to bring these about. For instance, in 1952 a proposal that tolls be raised to a level 150 per cent above the pre-War figure was agreed by the recreational interests after some initial opposition, on condition that both the private and the hire sectors were in future represented on the Port and Haven Commission.

Further improvements were brought about in 1953, when the Bure and the Waveney Commissions were amalgamated, thus streamlining the way in which these rivers were managed. After an initial period, when plant and staff were engaged in helping to make good the damage caused by the 1953 floods, the new Commission embarked on an extensive programme of dredging and other works. The Bowes Committee (1958) was told that £11000 (c. £112150 at 1990 prices) was spent on the Bure and Waveney in 1957/8, and the vigour with which the Commissioners pursued their objectives can be gauged from the fact that over a million tons of spoil were removed from the waterways within their jurisdiction between 1954 and 1971 (Groves, *in litt.*). Special attention was given to deepening and removing shoals from the main rivers, but several broads were also dredged, including Malthouse Broad (118220 tons), South Walsham Outer Broad and Fleet Dyke (172820 tons), Horsey Mere (123800 tons) and Womack Water (25000 tons).

Unlike the Bure and Waveney Commissions, the Yare Commission continued to receive a toll revenue throughout the War, and very soon after the end of hostilities, it embarked on a programme of works designed to improve the navigability of the Yare, and thus ensure the continued prosperity of the port of Norwich. However, initially at least, the Commissioners evinced little interest in improving facilities for the boat-borne holidaymaker, and the clearance in 1952 of the reeds and waterweeds which had rendered Rockland Broad virtually unnavigable since the War was carried out on the initiative of the Norfolk and Suffolk Broads Yacht Owners Association (EDP, 1952b). Similarly, it was the East Suffolk and Norfolk River Board, and not the Yare Commissioners, which operated an Acrow Suction-dredger on this site in 1959. This was a blatant attempt by the Board to substantiate its claim, made as a response to the report of the Bowes Committee, that it was "the ideal authority" to assume responsibility for navigation in Broadland. In the event, the machine proved unsuitable for use in the region, and did little more than create some large depressions in the floor of the former

1979/80 £	1980/1 £	1981/2 £	1982/3 £	1983 (9 months)	1984 £	1985 £	1986 £	1987 £	1988 £	1989 (3 months)
2880	3634	3281	3760	2417	5027	5541	7176	4237	2720	844
12119	12745	12083	16333	10136	11295	13520	13019	12696	6323	1427
251	251	261	–	–	–	–	–	–	–	–
203942	317132	350287	348379	246468	322425	319754	335847	361476	380612	96324
106623	112685	138925	144874	115881	168196	180536	201982	228443	249786	64637
9622	9144	10361	12262	10890	10925	11052	12455	12954	12812	–
4310	4696	–	–	–	–	–	–	–	–	–
–	–	–	–	–	–	–	–	–	–	–
399747	460287	515198	525608	385792	517863	530403	570479	619806	652253	163232

Source: Gt. Yarmouth Port & Haven Commissioners records

peat pit, the sand and gravel derived therefrom being deposited beside the flood bank on the south side of the Broad.

In fairness, it should be recorded that the Yare Commission funded no less than 77 separate dredging projects between 1950 and 1971 (Groves, *in litt.*), and that although most of these were concerned with improving the navigability of the Yare, Bargate Broad, the R. Chet (see page 73), and later, the channels across Rockland Broad, were also deepened. Records of the amounts of material removed were only kept for 45 of these schemes, but these alone accounted for over 328 000 tons. In 1958, 1962 and again in 1966/7, the Yare Commission also dredged Haddiscoe Cut, a waterway whose future had been subject to a prolonged and acrimonious wrangle after the Second World War. A relic of the ill-fated Norwich to Lowestoft Navigation, the Cut had been owned successively by the Norfolk, Eastern Counties, Great Eastern and London and North-Eastern Railway companies, none of which had, for obvious reasons, been exactly enthusiastic about maintaining it in a navigable condition. In 1945, the District Manager of the LNER had asked that the Broads Conference Investigation Committee consider closing the waterway on the grounds that it was costly to maintain and that . . . "it added little to the amenities of the neighbourhood". He also pointed out that if a dam was built across it, the A143 Haddiscoe to Great Yarmouth road could be routed on this, thus avoiding the expense of reconstructing the inadequate, hump-backed bridge which at that time carried this road across the Cut.

Although this suggestion was rejected in the Committee's report, the issue was raised again in 1953, this time by the River Board's Northern Area Drainage Committee. Members of this had not been satisfied that breaches in the southern bank of the Cut made by the surge that year had been properly repaired, and after discussions with various interested parties, the British Transport Commission (BTC) announced in 1954 that it would seek powers to close the waterway to navigation (EDP, 1954b). This produced a public outcry, and after much debate, it was agreed in 1957 that the River Board would assume responsibility for repairing and maintaining the banks of the Cut, but would permit it to be used for navigation for a further ten years at least (EDP, 1957a). In return for these undertakings (which were formalized in the *British Transport Commission Act* 1958), the BTC agreed to continue to contribute £10 000 towards the cost of the 1957 maintenance programme, and to make a further lump sum payment of £10 000 to the Board, whilst the Yare Commission indicated its willingness to maintain the waterway in a navigable condition, and to contribute £1000 a year towards the cost

Table 11h   Rivers Yare, Bure and Waveney Commissioners – Summary of Income and Expenditure: 1971/2 to 1989

	1971/2 £	1972/3 £	1973/4 £	1974/5 £	1975/6 £	1976/7 £	1977/8 £	1978/9 £
Income								
Tolls on goods, sea going vessels, passengers and pleasure craft (private and hire)	101 732	109 803	112 933	150 379	161 210	245 349	267 625	326 398
Interest, profits on sales of assets and investments etc	3846	4471	3584	6836	3170	11 178	8964	10 578
Total	105 578	114 274	116 517	157 210	164 380	256 527	276 589	336 976
Expenditure								
Administration, Repair Yard and miscellaneous expenses	24 219	24 400	29 927	43 882	43 594	62 349	64 625	94 222
Inspectorate	21 199	25 236	30 368	41 836	53 916	65 847	75 269	82 477
River works (inc. Haddiscoe Cut payments)	60 608	64 286	62 175	86 227	68 703	109 961	125 883	144 592
Total	106 026	113 922	122 470	171 945	166 213	238 157	265 777	321 291
Profit (Loss) before Tax	(448)	352	(5953)	(14 735)	(1833)	18 370	10 812	15 685
Corporation Tax (Credit)	–	–	–	–	–	2000	2668	3438
Net Surplus (Deficiency)	(448)	352	(5953)	(14 735)	(1833)	16 370	8144	12 247

of repairing its banks (EDP, 1957b). The agreement was renewed in 1968 (when it was decided that the Commissioners' payments would henceforward be £2000 per year, subsequently increased to £5000 pa in 1977), and re-negotiated in 1979, when it was arranged that the Commissioners would in future contribute two-thirds of the annual costs incurred by the AWA in keeping the Cut open for navigation. Payments since then have increased from £7500 in 1979/80, to £13 839 in 1984/5 and £19 218 in 1987/8.

In 1971, the Yare Commission amalgamated with the Bure and Waveney Commission to form the Rivers Committee of the Great Yarmouth Port and Haven Commissioners, or more formally, the Rivers Yare, Bure and Waveney Commission. Apart from Breydon Water and the lowermost reaches of the R. Bure, which historically form part of the port of Yarmouth, and which therefore came within the purview of the Haven Committee of the Port and Haven Commission, and Oulton Broad, which had been managed by the Waveney District Council since 1975, this Committee was responsible for the rivers, and those broads having recognized rights of public navigation over them*, until it was disbanded in 1989 following the creation of the 'new' Broads Authority (see Chapter 12).

The Rivers Commissioners raised the funds for their management projects, and also for their administrative and other expenses, by levying tolls on the vessels using the

---

* In effect, this included all the broads listed in Table 3g as being 'open to general navigation', apart from Wroxham, Salhouse and Hoveton Little Broads.

waterways, and the goods and passengers they carried. The contributions made to their revenue by hire and privately-owned craft, and commercial traffic on the R. Yare, are given in Table 11g, whilst the Commissioners' total income and expenditure for the period between 1971/2 and 1989 is summarized in Table 11h.

Originally, the Rivers Commission had twelve members, eight of whom were appointed by local authorities, while two represented the private yacht-owners, and two the hire craft operators. However, under a Harbour Revision Order approved by the Minister of Transport in 1984, the local authority representation on the Commission was reduced to five. Private yachting interests and the boat-letters continued to be represented by two members each, while the Chairman and Chief Executive of the Port

1979/80 £	1980/1 £	1981/2 £	1982/3 £	1983 (9 months)	1984 £	1985 £	1986 £	1987 £	1988 £	1989 (3 months)
339747	460287	515918	525608	385792	517868	530403	570479	619806	652253	163232
20103	58229	31944	25367	16546	35425	23700	27287	113951	37323	3222
359850	518516	547142	550975	402338	553293	554103	597766	733757	689576	166454
107858	134088	126521	124942	106734	133674	162683	187758	235390	194301	48152
102672	107806	139262	168380	129297	188791	194578	206359	238116	255272	80091
166905	228958	236292	246708	166942	207097	199980	187507	194515	242059	41559
377435	470852	502075	540030	402973	529562	557241	581604	668021	691632	169802
(17585)	47664	45067	10945	(635)	23731	(3138)	16142	65736	(2056)	(3348)
(21)	14960	19492	5255	(7492)	6676	(942)	5758	N/A	N/A	N/A
(17564)	32704	25575	5720	6857	17055	(2196)	10384	N/A	N/A	N/A

Source: Gt. Yarmouth Port & Haven Commissioners.

and Haven Commissioners attended meetings in an *ex officio* capacity.

From 1971 onwards the Rivers Commissioners continued the programmes of work started by their predecessors. The channels across Heigham Sound and Hickling Broad and, more recently, the southern part of Barton Broad, were dredged, as well as numerous stretches of river. Of particular note was the widening in 1974 of the reach of the Bure just upstream of St. Benet's, which had originally been dug two centuries or so previously to by-pass a natural meander around Ward Marsh. Another project for which the commissioners received widespread acclaim was the dredging of the north-western section of Bridge Broad, near Wroxham, in 1980. This involved the removal of some 12920 cu m of sediment, at a cost of *c.* £35000, and resulted in the creation of just over a hectare of navigable water in one of the most heavily used parts of the region.

The Oulton Broad Joint Committee remained in existence until 1975, when responsibility for managing Oulton Dyke was transferred to the Great Yarmouth Port and Haven Commissioners under the *Oulton Broad Revision Order* 1975. This also conferred the Committee's responsibilities for the Broad upon the Waveney District Council, which by this time had acquired the freehold of most of the site, together with the adjoining yacht station. The Order also empowered the Council to dredge the Broad, enter into an arrangement with Associated British Ports for the operation and maintenance of Mutford Lock, and if it so wished, conclude agency arrangements with the Port and Haven Commissioners for any or all of its duties as a navigation authority. This latter clause enabled the District Council a few years later to arrange for the Commissioners to carry out some much-needed dredging in the northern part of the Broad.

When open waters such as Oulton, Malthouse and Hickling Broads are being dredged, it is rarely possible to dump all the spoil on the margin of the site, and much of it therefore has to be taken away on motorized lighters, and unloaded onto waste ground elsewhere. The same, double-handling technique has to be used when a stretch of river is being dredged, unless this happens to be bordered by fen vegetation when the spoil can often be dumped on the bank; occasionally, some of the material can be used to raise and strengthen the ronds or embankments or, as at Postwick, infill a piece of waste ground prior to redevelopment.

Although suction dredgers have, for the reasons outlined in Chapters 5 and 13 been used during the past 10 years or so on a number of non-navigable broads, the Commissioners did not employ them, partly because the outlet pipe could form an obstruction to navigation, and partly because of the difficulties involved in finding a suitable site to serve as a settlement lagoon, and obtaining the landowner's consent to use it as such. It has also been argued that the costs of using a mud pump are higher than employing a conventional grab-dredger or hydraulic excavator. On the other hand, the environmental benefits – in terms of removing the phosphorus-rich sediments near the surface – are very considerable, and it is likely that increased attention will be given to the possibility of using suction dredgers on publicly navigable broads now that the new Broads Authority has taken up its duties. Forseeing this, its predecessor invited the Soil Survey of England and Wales to analyse the sediments from four sites (Barton and Hoveton Little Broads, and the lagoons created to receive the mud removed from Cockshoot and Belaugh Broads) to determine whether they contained chemical con-taminants which could preclude their use as a soil conditioner, or for some other purpose. The results, presented to the Authority in October 1988, indicate that the sediments from all four sites contain certain potentially toxic elements, the lead and zinc levels in particular being significantly higher than expected.

The proportion of the Rivers Commissioners' outgoings spent on dredging varied considerably during the 1970s and early 1980s, ranging from about 36 per cent in 1971/2, to only 17 per cent in 1982/3. In 1986, the last year for which itemized figures are available, £132179 was deployed on work of this type, representing about 23 per cent of the Commissioners' total expenditure.

In addition to dredging the rivers and broads, the Commissioners allocated funds each year for the provision of piled moorings, such as those at Hoveton, Sutton, Herringfleet, Rockland, Somerleyton and Thorpe. Between 9 and 12 per cent of their annual expenditure was spent on such work during the 1970s and early 1980s, though in 1985, this proportion rose to 17 per cent, mainly because of the extensive piling work carried out that year in the vicinity of Salhouse Broad. Other tasks performed by the Commissioners included the erection and maintenance of warning and speed limit signs, and the removal when necessary, of underwater obstructions. They were also responsible for weed cutting, a job which their predecessors, the Bure Commissioners, had found specially daunting. Particular problems had been encountered as a result of the dense growths of *Cladophora Sauteri* which grew in the larger Thurne Broads, and in about 1954, Desmond Truman (who had recently become a Commissioner), designed a machine capable of collecting up this alga, and dumping it in a motorized lighter alongside (see Plate 35). The Commissioners' records show that the number of 8-ton loads removed from Hickling Broad and Heigham Sound with this equipment averaged 228 between 1960 and 1968. However, these figures fell to 183, 90, 135, 119, 30 and zero in the ensuing years owing to the effects of nutrient enrichment (see page 127), and the machine was not used again after 1975; it was towed away and broken up in 1986.

Water-lilies, Fennel-leaved Pondweed and other waterweeds started to re-appear in the larger Thurne broads from the late 1970s onwards, and because of this, and the increasingly vigorous growth of such plants in the upper reaches of the rivers, the Commissioners found it necessary to purchase a new weed-cutting machine in 1982. As a result their expenditure on weed clearance, which had declined from £4181 in 1971/2 (or about 4 per cent of their total outgoings) to only £159 in 1981/2, latterly amounted to between 1 and 2 per cent of their annual expenditure.

As traffic on the waterways increased, the Commissioners took on further inspectors, and during the 1970s and 1980s they operated four launches on the northern rivers, and four on the southern (see Plate 36). £21199 was spent on the inspectorate in 1971/2, representing about 20 per cent of the Commissioners' total expenditure, but this proportion rose during the ensuing years, and amounted to about 35 per cent of their outgoings in 1984, 1985 and 1986.

The Commissioners employed three extra inspectors to serve as 'reliefs', and the men were not expected to sleep on board, as they were in the past. But their main task remained the same: to patrol the rivers and broads, and provide any necessary advice and assistance to those using them. The inspectors were, and will doubtless continue to be, responsible for checking that each boat has been licensed, and for enforcing the by-laws, particularly those relating to the speed of vessels, and the behaviour of their occupants. In many cases, a verbal warning suffices, but each year between 10 and 40 individuals are prosecuted for causing excessive wash, moving after sunset without lights, using firearms and so on. In 1987, for example, 13 helmsmen were successfully prosecuted for such offences, resulting in a total of £2340 being levied by magistrates in fines and costs. A further 19 individuals were fined for licence evasion.

1979 saw the introduction of new by-laws relating to speeding, restrictions being imposed on all the waterways within the Commissioners' jurisdiction. Vessels would not be allowed to exceed 5 mph (*c*. 8 kph) in built-up areas and on some sections of the river system (e.g. the R. Ant), while a 7 mph (*c*. 11 kph) limit was to be enforced everywhere else, apart form certain particularly narrow waterways such as the upper reaches of the R. Chet, Waxham Cut and the dykes leading to Surlingham and Rockland Broads, where a 3 mph limit would be introduced. The testing of powered craft would be allowed on eight defined lengths of river, but only at certain times, whilst speedboats (whose owners would have to apply for special exemption from the general regulations) would be confined to five places on the R. Yare, and five on the R. Waveney, again at specified times only. Various conditions governing the use of such craft were also introduced, notably that their wash must not be more than 12 inches high when it hits the bank.

In general, these by-laws proved satisfactory, albeit difficult to enforce effectively. However, the regulations governing the use and licencing of speedboats proved defective in several respects. Alarmed by the increasing number of such vessels (423 had to be granted exemption from the general limits in 1987), and anxious to alleviate this and other problems connected with speedboating before they handed over responsibility for navigation on the rivers to the 'new' Broads Authority in 1989, the Commissioners decided in 1988 to seek amendments to their by-laws, the effect of which would be to prevent the use of such boats anywhere on the river system, save in connection with water-skiing. In addition, the new regulations would make it obligatory for each boat (whose 'block area'* would be limited to 13 sq m) to be crewed by two persons, additional to the water-skier. A public inquiry to consider objections to the proposed new regulations took place in June 1988, and a few months later it was announced that the new by-laws had been approved, and would come into force in February 1989.†

Welcome as these measures are, it is widely felt that the confined and heavily used waters of Broadland are unsuitable for water-skiing, and that it is essential that alternative sites are made available for those wishing to practise the sport; indeed, many conservationists will not be satisfied until water-skiing is totally banned on the rivers and broads. The skiers' use of Train Reach, a section of the R. Yare just downstream of Brundall, causes particular concern, as it is bordered on both sides by the RSPB's Strumpshaw, Rockland and Surlingham Marshes nature reserve. This is visited by very large numbers of birdwatchers, many of whom are surprised and annoyed by the noise and disturbance which takes place when the adjoining river is being used by water-skiers at the times prescribed by the Navigation Authority, which include Saturday mornings and Sunday afternoons after 4 pm.

The concepts of 'zonation of use', and 'time zoning' are frequently cited by those concerned with water-based recreation as ways of reconciling and harmonizing competing uses, but are clearly not working well at Train Reach. Oulton Broad, in contrast, provides a good example of a site where 'multi-purpose use' (a phrase fashionable in the 1960s!) is being quite successfully practised. Unlike the other broads, Oulton is urbanized, and part-bordered by a public park, but despite this, is heavily used, both by

---

* 'Block area' is defined on page 393
† As a result of these measures only *c*. 250 sports boats were licensed for use in 1989.

yachting buffs and broads holidaymakers. There is much windsurfing as well, but for most water sports enthusiasts, and innumerable holidaymakers from Lowestoft and Yarmouth, the site's principal attraction is that it forms the venue for speed-boat racing during the summer months. This has been organized for many years by the Lowestoft and Oulton Broad Motor Boat Club, which holds about 19 or 20 events each year, usually on Thursday evenings (see Plate XLV).

In an attempt to reduce speeding on the rivers and broads, the Commissioners started using an electronic speed-measurer in 1962, and introduced new, and more sensitive equipment in 1985. But the enforcement of the speed limits is made difficult in Broadland, not only by the very large numbers of boats in use, but by the absence of locks. On

Plate XLV

Speedboat racing on Oulton Broad – 1989.

Races are held regularly on this site during the summer months, good views being obtained from the adjoining Nicholas Everitt Park.

The old maltings in the background are listed by the Department of the Environment as being of Grade II Architectural and Historic interest; they were converted to residential accommodation in the mid-1970s.

Photo: Richard Denyer

other navigable waterways, such as the R. Thames, the lock-keepers can keep a look-out for those breaking the speed limits, issue warnings, and if necessary, pass on details of suspected miscreants to their colleagues up or down-river. On the other hand, the delays which are apt to occur at locks probably encourage more overtaking than on Broadland's unfettered system of waterways.

In the face of growing complaints about bank erosion, and other environmental problems, the boat-hire operators decided in 1980 to install engine-governors so that their vessels could not be driven at speeds in excess of the 7 mph limit. This initiative was welcomed by environmentalists who were not aware until the publication of May and Waters' report in 1986 (see page 395) that most hire craft are physically incapable of going faster than this. Nevertheless, the limitation placed on the faster vessels has probably alleviated the bank erosion problem to some extent, even if the occasional hirer, more mechanically minded than the rest, manages to alter the governor's setting on his boat so as to make faster progress.

A much more serious drawback to these voluntary arrangements for speed regulation is that they have not yet been emulated by the owners of private motor cruisers and day-craft. When invited to explain why they had not yet brought pressure to bear on such individuals, the Commissioners argued that privately-owned craft are liable to be taken out to sea, and that it would therefore be unreasonable to ask that they be fitted with engine governors. In fact, this argument is spurious, as most private motor vessels are used exclusively on the rivers.

Although it is generally agreed that hire craft, being in use day in and day out during much of the holiday season, tend to exert a greater pressure on the Broadland environment than privately-owned vessels, the Commissioners did not take account of this factor in their toll charges until 1964. In that year, they introduced a differential system, whereby a hire operator had to pay a quarter as much again as a private owner for a similar vessel. Toll differentials were increased to 75 per cent for the 1976 season, and the following year, hire operators had to pay twice as much as a private owner for a vessel of comparable size. A 3 to 1 differential was introduced for the 1980 season.

The effect of these changes was to increase the percentage of the Commissioners' income derived from the hire sector from about 50 per cent in the period 1971/2 to 1975/6, to a maximum of 64 per cent in 1981/2. Thereafter, the proportion gradually declined, and was 56 per cent in 1986. Conversely, the proportion of the Commissioners' income contributed by privately-owned vessels (including those visiting the region for up to 14 days) rose from 35 per cent in 1971/2, to 41 per cent in 1974/5 and 1975/6 as a result of the increasing numbers of such craft using the waterways. During the next five years, it declined as a consequence of the introduction of the 3 to 1 differential, and the increasing numbers of hire craft (see Table 11e), reaching a nadir of 23 per cent in 1980/1. Thereafter, the private sector's contribution once again rose, attaining 36 per cent of the Commissioners' total income in 1986. This can be attributed to the continuing increase in the numbers of private vessels (see Table 11f), and the simultaneous reduction in the size of the hire fleet.

The decision by Government that the Rivers Commissioners' responsibilities should be assumed by a 'new' Broads Authority, and the passing of the *Norfolk and Suffolk Broads Act* 1988 giving effect to this (see Chapter 12), made it necessary to adjust the provisions of various Great Yarmouth Port and Haven Acts and Orders made between 1866 and 1986. This was done by means of a Statutory Instrument (No. 1737), entitled the *Great Yarmouth Port Authority Harbour Revision Order*, which, following a public inquiry, came into force in September 1989. This formally disbanded the Rivers Commissioners, and re-constituted the Great Yarmouth Port and Haven Commissioners as a Port Authority. However, it needs to be remembered that the former was never responsible for Breydon Water and the lowermost reaches of the R. Bure, which have, for centuries, been regarded as part of the 'Haven' for administrative purposes; thus, the newly created Port Authority will exercise jurisdiction over these waterways. Close liaison between the latter body, and the 'new' Broads Authority (through its Navigation Committee) will therefore be required to avoid conflicts of interest, and ensure that vessels can pass unhindered from one part of the navigation to the other. The fact that the Port Authority is entitled to appoint two members of the Broads Authority (one of whom must serve on the latter's Navigation Committee) should help to ensure that this objective is achieved.

The environmental effects of recreational usage

In assessing the environmental effects of boat traffic on a waterway it is customary, albeit somewhat misleading, to consider the size of the vessels, and the proportion of the time they are in use. Table 11i shows that in 1975, over 500 of the motor craft licensed by the Commissioners had a net registered tonnage of 15 tons or more, whilst 88 were in the 20 ton plus category. Many of these were water buses operated by firms such as Broads Tours Ltd. of Wroxham, and would therefore have been in very frequent use during the main holiday season. Moreover, the average size of these passenger-carrying vessels has tended to increase since 1975, because with ever-increasing labour costs, it is

Table 11i   The size distribution of motor cruisers in 1975

Net Registered Tonnage	Hire craft nos.	Private craft nos.
Less than 2	11	63
2	18	515
3	20	325
4	46	252
5	71	172
6	190	145
7	216	123
8	135	78
9	155	64
10	201	54
11	115	26
12	180	41
13	168	37
14	67	28
15	145	15
16	98	7
17	48	13
18	78	6
19	6	5
20	80	8
	2048	1977
Total NRT:	22007	9979
Average NRT:	10.75	5.05

Source: Data supplied by the Rivers Commissioners.

more economical for a skipper and his crew to take out a large vessel than a small one. Of the 30 water buses registered with the Commissioners in 1981, the numbers of passengers allowed under Board of Trade regulations, varied from 12 to 222, with an average of 72 (Groves, pers. comm.).

The total net registered tonnage of the hire craft in use in the region in 1975 was more than twice that of the privately-owned vessels (Table 11i); furthermore, the tonnage of the former increased more quickly during the 1970s than that of the latter – the figures being 9.33 tons and 5.11 tons in 1971, and 11.17 tons and 5.44 tons in 1980 (Groves, pers. comm.). Against this must be set the fact that booking agencies have found that cruisers with 10 or 11 berths are more difficult to let than those with accommodation for 6 or 8 persons. It is because of this that broatively few such vessels are now being introduced into the fleet; moreover, many of the largest hire craft are being replaced with smaller vessels once they have completed a reasonable period of service (usually about 10 to 12 years).

It would be unwise to place too much reliance on these statistics, because the net registered tonnage of a vessel cannot be used on its own as a measure of the environmental damage it causes. Boats are notoriously variable in the amount of wash they produce, and many lightly-built craft appear to generate more wave action at a given speed, than much heavier boats. Day launches, in particular, often produce more wash than quite large cruisers, especially when their passengers are congregated in the stern, thus causing the boat to 'squat'. Much also depends on the way a vessel is handled. About 40 to 50 large, twin-engined, sea-going craft, manufactured by firms such as JCL Marine and Broom Boats Ltd. are in use in the region (most of them being kept at Brundall), and these can produce a great deal of wash if driven irresponsibly in Broadland's confined waters.

As far as the other physical dimensions of the boats are concerned, Table 11j shows

Table 11j   Average dimensions of hire motor cruisers: 1939–1979

	4-berth			6-berth			8-berth		
	L	*B*	*N*	*L*	*B*	*N*	*L*	*B*	*N*
1939	29.2	8.8	103	35.9	9.6	47	41.5	10.75	16
1955	30.1	9.2	166	35.8	9.9	49	40.2	10.6	22
1962	29.3	9.5	334	36.3	10.3	100	40.9	10.9	37
1979*	31.4	10.3	290	36.6	11.2	178	40.5	11.6	55

L = Length (ft) : B = Beam (ft) : N = Number in sample
* Blakes fleet only

Source: Brochures produced by the boat-letting agencies for the years 1939, 1955, 1962 and 1979.

that between 1939 and 1979, the average beam of the hire motor cruisers increased more than their length. This trend resulted from the desire of boat-letters to develop minimum cost hulls, capable of series production, and of providing comfortable accommodation. These objectives have been made easier to attain since the early 1960s by the increasing use of reinforced plastic, and to a lesser extent concrete or steel, for hull construction, instead of timber. But owing to the high cost of making moulds, there has been a tendency to produce a limited number of hull designs, each capable of being fitted out to individual requirements.

Conscious of the need to discourage the development and use of over-wide craft, the Commissioners introduced Beam Restriction By-laws in 1974. These made it an offence to use a vessel whose beam exceeds 12 feet 6 inches (3.81 m) on the R. Ant, R. Chet, Meadow Dyke and various other narrow waterways unless it was registered with the Commissioners prior to 1974. These regulations were extended in 1981, when it became an offence to use a pleasure craft with a beam of over 20 feet (6.1 m) on the R. Yare, 18 feet (5.49 m) on the lower Waveney and Haddiscoe Cut, and 14 feet (4.27 m) on the rivers Bure and Thurne, S. Walsham Fleet Dyke, Ranworth Dam and the R. Waveney upstream of Beccles, unless it was registered with the Commissioners prior to March 1980.

The length measurements of the sailing and power-driven craft in use in the region in 1988 are given in Table 11k.

The vessels in use today are not only beamier, but have more powerful engines than in the past. During the 1930s, the average motor cruiser was fitted with a small side-valve petrol engine, and even in the mid-1950s most power units had an RAC rating of between 8 and 12 hp. Since then, it has become customary to install the marine equivalents of engines designed for use in commercial vehicles. Many of these generate 60 hp or more, and thus have a power output twice, or even three times as great as that of the engines employed twenty-five years ago, particularly at low revs.

Prior to the Second World War, virtually all Broadland's motor craft were powered by petrol engines and, even in 1955, less than 5 per cent of the fleet of 602 cruisers were diesels. By 1962, however, this proportion had risen to about 29 per cent and by 1971, over 65 per cent of Blake's fleet of 961 motor cruisers were diesels. By 1979, out of 1273 vessels in this fleet, only 49 were petrol-driven; of this number only 5 were four-berth vessels, the remainder having only 2 or 3 berths.

The changeover to diesel was prompted partly in the interests of safety – a spate of serious fires occurred in the 1960s as a result of petrol vapour in the bilges being accidentally ignited – and partly because of the greater reliability of diesels. Running costs, too, are lower for the latter since diesel fuel for use in boats is cheaper than for road vehicles, owing to a tax anomaly.

From an environmental point of view, diesel-engined craft suffer from certain disadvantages compared with those powered by petrol. The latter evaporates more quickly if accidentally spilt, for instance during refuelling, and its odour is much less persistent than that of diesel fuel. In addition, the exhaust from diesel-engined craft can leave a thin film of unburnt fuel on the water surface, especially if the injectors have not been regularly serviced. Most motor cruisers are now fitted with an engine undertray, to prevent fuel and lubricant leaks from finding their way into the bilges, and thus into the river. But in practice, the trays tend to get flooded, sometimes as a result of careless servicing.

The presence of a thin film of oil on the water is offensive to many people. However, this form of pollution is normally confined to narrow, heavily used stretches of river and, ecologically, is of little significance compared with nutrient enrichment.

Table 11k   The lengths of the power-driven and sailing craft in use in 1988 (outboard dinghies excluded)

Length (ft)	Motor cruisers		Aux. sailing craft		Day launches		Passenger vessels (hire only)	Sailing craft	
	Hire	Private	Hire	Private	Hire	Private		Hire	Private
up to 12	–	–	–	2	4	277	–	314	874
12–16	–	–	–	86	72	949	–	15	691
16–21	–	–	3	570	321	1117	–	17	251
21–25	74	607	9	344	–	–	–	10	41
25–30	519	682	58	155	–	–	–	4	10
30–35	494	379	22	44	–	–	–	–	3
35–40	315	183	–	2	–	–	–	–	2
40–55	190*	67	2	–	–	–	18	–	3
over 55	–	–	–	–	–	–	9†	–	–
Totals	1592	1918	94	1203	397	2343	27	360	1875

* All but about 15 of these vessels were 42 feet or less; no cruiser was longer than 45 feet.
† Eight of these boats were between 55 and 69 feet long; one had a length of 105 feet.

Source: Rivers Commissioners' 1988 register.

Most craft are now fitted with sound-proofed engine compartments, but the noise and reverberation produced by some of the vessels in use can be very annoying, both to their occupants and bystanders. The Commissioners acquired a noise metre in the late 1970s with the intention of instituting proceedings against the owners of craft whose vessels are inadequately silenced (Groves, pers. comm.), but this did not prove possible in practice.

Electrically-powered vessels have a major advantage over diesel and petrol-driven craft in that they are virtually silent. A few such vessels are already in use on the waterways, and it seems likely that their numbers will increase greatly during the next few years. The main drawback of electrically-powered boats is their limited range, and it is encouraging that plans are currently being drawn up to provide facilities at selected boatyards where the batteries of such vessels can be recharged.

Although it is frequently claimed that the modern, beamy cruiser with its high-powered diesel engine, produces more wash and underwater 'draw' than its counterpart of 30 to 40 years ago, there is no factual evidence to prove or disprove this. Indeed, such assertions are a gross over-simplification, as the amount of wash produced by a vessel is dependent, not just on its dimensions and the power of its engine, but on a host of variables, including the distribution of weight within the vessel, its underwater profile in relation to the depth of the water (the 'blockage factor'), the angle of its propeller shaft relative to the horizontal, the distance between the vessel and the bank, and last but not least, its speed through the water. Most watermen believe that there are, in fact, 'good' and 'bad' hulls today, just as there were in the past. Indeed, what is disquieting to the environmentalist is that the underwater configuration of the vessels now in use in the region has been dictated primarily by the need to provide comfortable and spacious accommodation aboard, and that the designer has had little incentive to produce hulls generating minimum amounts of wash when moving at the speeds appropriate for the confined waters of Broadland. An incidental advantage of such vessels would be that they would not need such high-powered engines; thus, their capital and running costs would be less. It might also be possible to power them electrically, so reducing noise and eliminating any risk of the waterways being polluted by oil or petrol.

Another way in which financial incentives could be used to encourage the design of craft having a minimal effect on the environment would be to calculate the toll payable on a boat according to the wash it generates. Each vessel would be tested, and given a handicap rating, so that a higher toll could be levied on craft producing a disproportionate amount of wash, than on those generating less than average. In theory, this would be an admirable system, but in practice it would be difficult and costly to administer. Another defect is that it fails to recognize that boat tolls form an insignificant part of the cost of operating and maintaining a boat in the region.

Although the Commissioners were not prepared to consider introducing a handicap system of assessing boat tolls, they decided that from 1981 onwards, these should be based on the vessel's 'block area' – i.e. its length times its beam in square metres – rather than on its net registered tonnage as in the past. The latter was related, not to the weight of the vessel, but to its capacity, and when applied to pleasure craft suffered from the serious environmental defect that the larger the engine of the vessel, the smaller the toll payable on it. The block-area formula (which was adopted by the 'new' Broads Authority when it took over its navigation functions from the Rivers Commissioners in 1989) overcomes this problem, and at the same time is easier to apply. It also avoids the large (55 per cent) difference in tolls payable under the old system for the minimum category, and that for 2 tons and over.

In 1990, the toll levied by the Broads Authority on a privately-owned motor launch with a block area of 5 square metres or less was £25.15, whilst the owners of powered craft with block areas of 10, 15, 20, 30 and 40 square metres were required to pay £33.33, £42.68, £52.03, £70.73 and £89.43 respectively. The toll on a sailing dinghy was £16.65, whilst the charge on a yacht with a block area of 10 square metres or more was set at half the figure payable on a motor boat of comparable size. Tolls levied on motorized sailing craft were intermediate between those on motor vessels and yachts, whilst £12.35 was payable on rowing boats, punts and canoes. Given the one to three differential between private and hire craft of comparable dimensions, a firm which let out a four-berth motor cruiser of length 3.14 feet (9.56 m) and beam 10.3 feet (3.14 m) – the mean dimensions of such vessels in 1979 (see Table 11k) – would have had to pay a toll of £212.19 in 1990, whilst the corresponding figures for average-sized six and eight-berth motor cruisers would have been £257.07 and £290.73 respectively. In contrast, the toll on a hire yacht of length 22 feet and beam 8 feet which did not have either an inboard or an outboard motor would have been only £66.69, whilst £128.85 would have been payable on a motorized hire sailing cruiser of length 27.9 feet (8.48 m) and beam 8.9 feet (2.69 m).

During the course of his studies on riverine erosion (see page 77), Stephen Payne tested at various speeds and distances from the bank seven different craft, including a day launch and hire cruisers ranging in length from 24 feet to 42 feet. However, he concluded that the wash each generated was not significantly different from that produced by the University's 3.9 ton, 6.4 m long research vessel *Envoy*. Consequently, in a report compiled for the Broads Authority, he and his supervisor presented data for the amount of wash produced by *Envoy* at varying speeds and distances from the bank, and used this to support their assertion that the boats in use in Broadland do not generate excessive amounts of wash unless they are driven at speeds in excess of 7 mph (Payne & Hey, 1982).

Payne and Hey's results cannot easily be reconciled with those of Bonham (1980), who found that there was considerable variation in the amounts of wash generated by vessels on the R. Thames at Wallingford. Moreover, their measurements of wash were taken from single craft, moving at different speeds, and they did not attempt to quantify the complex wave movements produced when vessels are overtaking one another, or passing in opposite directions, this despite the likelihood that the rate of bank erosion is increased under these circumstances. In view of these uncertainties, and the very great

Plate XLVI

Measuring the wash produced by a day launch at Salhouse Broad – 1986.

The wash characteristics of 20 vessels of varying dimensions were tested both on Salhouse Broad and on an adjoining section of the R. Bure, the object being to determine whether a significant reduction in the rate of bank erosion would result if the speed limits applied to virtually all the waterways in the region were reduced. The staff of the Hydraulics Research Station (who carried out the research for the Broads Authority) concluded that such reductions would be justified. They also suggested that their results be used to encourage hire-boat operators to renew their fleets with hulls which generate the minimum amount of wash.

Photo: R.N. Flowers

importance attached to the bank erosion problem by the Broads Authority, it decided on the recommendation of its Research Advisory Panel to commission a further series of tests, aimed at measuring the wash characteristics of a range of hire motor cruisers and day launches. The bid for this contract by the Hydraulics Research Station (HRS) proved successful, and it was arranged that it would be funded jointly by the Broads Authority and the Port and Haven Commissioners (£12500 each), the Countryside Commission (£10000) and the Broads Hire Boat Federation (£1000).

Salhouse Great Broad and the adjoining reaches of the R. Bure were selected for the trials, which were carried out by the HRS team on 20 vessels of varying dimensions (see Plate XLVI). One of these was an experimental craft, with a ducted propulsion system designed by Mr Czerniak of Nottingham, but the remainder consisted of 16 conventional hire cruisers, ranging in length from 7.8 to 13.6 m, and three day launches. From the data obtained, each boat was ascribed a wash index, representing the cumulative energy of the waves it generated, modified to take account of the depression of the water surface which occurs close to and travelling with, the boat. No attempt was made to measure the amount of bank erosion caused by each boat at different speeds, but it was considered reasonable to assume that this is approximately proportional to the vessel's wash index (May & Waters, 1986).

The wash indices of the boats tested varied considerably, those of the day launches being particularly high. At 6 mph the wash index of the worst craft exceeded that of the best boat by a factor of 5.3, and it was found that over the speed range tested, 3.8 to 7 mph, an increase of 1 mph caused the wash index to rise on average by a factor of 2.9. Not all the boats were capable of attaining 7 mph, especially in the relatively shallow water of Salhouse Broad, but it was concluded that the wash index, (and therefore by inference, the rate of bank erosion) would be reduced by a factor of 2, if the general speed limit was lowered from 7 to 6 mph. The belief of local watermen that there are 'good' and 'bad' hulls, as far as wash generation is concerned, was confirmed, and May and Waters argued that the data from the trials could be used to encourage boat operators to renew their fleets from those products which generated least wave action, pending the introduction of new, low-wash designs.

May and Waters completed their report in November 1986, but representatives of the organizations which had funded their study had some reservations about their data and findings, and following an assessment by a panel of naval architects, three further investigations were commissioned by the Broads Authority.

The first of these involved a re-appraisal of May and Waters' conclusions by P.L. Ashford, the Authority's consultant hydrologist, and R. M. Martins, a naval architect responsible for the design of several of the holiday craft currently in use in the region. Their report (Ashford and Martins, 1988) corroborates and amplifies many of the HRS team's findings. In particular, they confirmed that speed is the principal determinant of boat wash. However, by using a more sophisticated mathematical relationship between the two factors, they demonstrated that in the speed range 4 to 7 mph, an increase of 1 mph increases the boat-wave energy arriving at a unit length of bank by, on average, a factor of 3.4 (a slight increase on the figure advanced by May and Waters). They also pointed out that as the speed of a boat rises, the length of bank passed per hour of use increases. Taking this factor into account, they concluded that each 1 mph increase in speed, causes a fourfold rise in the amount of boat-wave energy arriving at the river banks.

Although May and Waters had demonstrated that there was a relationship between the fore and aft trim of the boats tested, and their wash characteristics, they had concluded from experiments that bow-heaviness increased the wash by an average of 20 per cent, whilst this was increased by 4 per cent if the vessels were stern heavy. Ashford and Martins pointed out that these figures are averages, and that the wash characteristics of twelve of the boats tested could be improved, if they were re-ballasted so that they were slightly stern-heavy. This finding raises the possibility that the amount of wash, and therefore the rate of bank erosion, could be reduced if the boats using the waterways were re-ballasted so that they were slightly stern-heavy. However, in many vessels, any reduction in wash achievable in this way is offset, or even cancelled out, by their additional displacement, which causes them to generate more wash than would otherwise be the case. Furthermore, stern ballasting would actually increase, rather than reduce, the wash produced by some boats. It would thus be necessary to test every class of boat to determine whether its wash characteristics would be improved, or worsened, by re-ballasting. Ashford (*in litt.*) considers that even if the necessary resources could be found to achieve such a monumental task, the reduction in bank erosion which would result would probably be less than 10 per cent, equivalent to a decrease in the general speed limit of about 0.1 mph.

Ashford and Martins endorsed the view that it would be possible to design low-wash hulls, and recommended that those responsible should pay special attention to the need to select suitable longitudinal curves for below-waterline areas, and optimum prismatic coefficients. This is particularly necessary in the forward half of the hull, since the contours here largely dictate the amount of wash generated. In essence, therefore, hulls should be planned on the premise that wash generation and turbulence will be minimized if they are designed for the least possible residual resistance, and in accordance with currently accepted principles.

Ashford and Martins also concluded that any review of speed limits should not only take into account the considerable reductions in wave energies which result from even quite small reductions in speed, but also the fact, demonstrated by May and Waters, that wash declines with increasing waterline length, but increases with displacement. In the circumstances, they suggested that consideration should be given to applying a lower speed limit on boats with a waterline length less than about 6 m, than on larger vessels.

The second investigation commissioned by the Broads Authority following the submission of May and Waters' report was a comparative study of wind and boat-generated waves in the region (Vincent, 1988). This involved using measurements taken at the Meteorological Station at RAF Coltishall between 1978 and 1987 to calculate the wind-wave energy generated in twelve reaches of the rivers Bure and Yare. These were chosen to represent a range of different orientations and lengths, and the sheltering effect of flood banks, waterside trees and other vegetation was also taken into account.

Although one of the factors prompting this study was the belief, widely held amongst boating interests, that wind waves are a more important determinant of the rate of bank erosion than the wash produced by passing vessels, no attempt was made to measure the erosive effect of waves of either sort, in view of the formidable complexities and cost of carrying out such a study.

Dr Vincent demonstrated that in terms of the total annual wave energy incident on the banks, wind-generated wave energy exceeds that due to boats travelling at 7 mph by various amounts up to an order of magnitude. But most of this energy is due to waves of small amplitude and of height less than 50 mm. Larger wind waves are comparatively rare, and at these larger wave heights, the amount of energy contributed by boat wash predominates. This finding presented Dr Vincent with something of a quandary, since it is by no means clear whether short periods of large waves are more, or less, efficient in causing bank erosion, than prolonged periods of smaller waves. If energy conversion to erosion is more efficient in respect of large waves, then boat wash is the major factor. If, on the other hand, smaller waves are equally efficient, wash is the lesser factor, though still very significant in sections of river carrying heavy boat traffic.

In an 'in-house' appraisal of the reports produced by Vincent, Ashford and Martins, and May and Waters, Paul Ashford calculated that if large and small waves convert the same proportion of their respective energies into erosion, the rate at which this takes place on the Bure would be reduced by 24 per cent if the speed limit on it was reduced from 7 mph to 6 mph. The corresponding figure for the R. Yare would be 8 per cent. If, however, larger waves are more erosive than small ones, the rate of erosion on the Bure would be reduced, on average, by 67 per cent, and on the Yare by 40 per cent, if the speed limit was reduced in this way. In general, it was considered that an intermediate result was more likely than these two extremes, and Ashford therefore concluded that the erosion rate would be reduced by between 35 and 55 per cent on the Bure, and by between 15 and 30 per cent on the Yare. A further reduction in the rate of bank erosion would occur if the speed limit was reduced to 5 mph, but this would probably not be worthwhile, except on sections of river carrying particularly heavy traffic.

The third study carried out for the Broads Authority involved measurements by the Port and Haven Commissioners of the current velocity in the vicinity of Breydon Bridge, Cobholm and Yarmouth Yacht Station at varying states of the tide. This investigation was triggered by claims by boating interests that the general speed limit could not safely be reduced as it is essential that boats can travel at 7 mph in order that they can be taken through Breydon Water and the lowermost reaches of the Bure at all states of the tide. In the event, the assertions that currents in this area frequently exceed 4 mph were shown to be unfounded, the maximum current speed recorded on the flood tide of 4 August 1988 being 2.94 mph at Cobholm. Measurements at Yarmouth Yacht Station of the ebb of 27 September – one of the biggest spring tides that year – gave a maximum fugure of 3.05 mph, but it is likely that this figure would have been marginally exceeded at Cobholm, where the current tends to run slightly more strongly. Nevertheless, it would seem that even if boats were speed-governed to 6 mph, they could still be taken safely through the lowermost reaches of the Bure and Yare at all states of the tide.

The studies by May and Waters and Ashford and Martins, demonstrated that the wash produced by vessels comprises not only a train of waves, whose energy, when transmitted to the banks, is one of the main factors responsible for erosion, but also eddies and propeller scour. Both these phenomena, and also reverse flow – the rearward movement of water displaced in front of a boat to fill the space behind it – can stir up sediment, particularly in shallow, confined and heavily used waters. Vessels which are stern-heavy are especially prone to do this, since the extra power which is needed to drive them through the water at a given speed, is dissipated in the form of increased eddying, and a more intense propeller jet (Ashford & Martins, 1988).

The extent to which stirred-up sediment, rather than the presence of large standing crops of phytoplankton is responsible for the high turbidity of Broadland's waterways (see Chapter 5) has recently been investigated by Garrad and Hey (1987). By collecting samples at hourly intervals from the Bure both upstream and downstream of the navigable limit, they demonstrated that there are distinct diurnal variations in the amount of sediment in heavily used sections of the river. The inorganic fraction, in particular, rises to a maximum in mid-afternoon and falls to a minimum in the early morning, the very pattern which one would expect if boats were at least partly responsible for the observed turbidity. It was also significant that these diurnal variations are absent at Horstead, upstream of the navigable limit, and also from Ranworth Inner Broad, from which power boats are excluded (Fig. 11B).

Garrad and Hey demonstrated, as did Ashford and Martins, that different types of boat stir up sediment to varying degrees. Some craft cause sediment entrainment at velocities of less than 2 mph, whilst others only cause this to happen at speeds in excess of 4 mph. All seven of the vessels tested by Garrad and Hey stirred up the sediment when driven at or near 7 mph. These findings provide an interesting parallel with those of Ashford and Martins, who point out that the speed of the propeller jet is very high in many Broadland craft. Indeed, they suggest that boat designers should, subject to other constraints, aim to use large-diameter propellers, driven through reduction gearing, rather than small, directly-driven propellers. The angle of the propeller shaft is also important; the closer this is to the horizontal the better, since the longer the jet takes to reach the bottom, the less will be its erosive effect on the sediment.

The extent to which the waterways are, or are not, overcrowded has been debated for years. As long ago as 1886 Walter Rye complained of the difficulty of finding a mooring place at Wroxham "since there were 80 yachts within hailing distance of the bridge", and he would undoubtedly be horrified by the situation which exists today (see Plate 37). One of the difficulties is that people tend to use the word 'overcrowding' when they mean 'congestion', and vice versa.

Congestion is best used to denote what happens when the free flow of vessels is impeded, usually in the vicinity of a narrow bridge, or when boats ahead are man-oeuvring in an attempt to find a mooring. Yachts can also produce congestion when several of them are tacking out of sequence on a heavily used or narrow river, or during a regatta.

Overcrowding may be defined as that intensity of use which affects peoples' ability to utilize the waterspace in the way they want, thus reducing their enjoyment. But in a review of the literature on the subject, Owens (1985) has pointed out that there is an element of subjectivity in this as some individuals are content to wait patiently until the way ahead is clear, while others are infuriated by even the smallest delay. Similarly, some do not mind taking their place in an almost uninterrupted line of vessels moving up or down river, while others feel aggrieved even if one or two other boats are in sight. Walker (1978 & 1981), who studied the boat users' perception of these issues, found that few holidaymakers mentioned overcrowding as a problem, though about 20 per cent of hirers who completed questionnaires claimed to have had difficulty finding a mooring on at least five occasions per week, and over half admitted to being bothered by the wash of other vessels – both symptoms of the congested state of the waterways. Private owners, on the other hand, were generally less satisfied with their recreational experience, and about a fifth of those who filled in a questionnaire felt that the waterways were 'overcrowded', or that they had 'too many cruisers' on them. But rather than

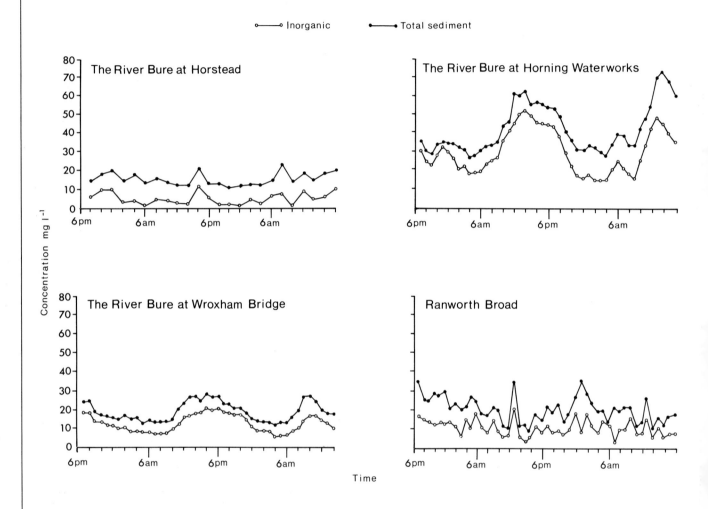

Fig. 11B — Daily variations in the total amount of suspended sediment, and the inorganic material therein, at non-navigable (the R. Bure at Horstead and Ranworth Broad) and navigable sites – September 1980.

Source: Garrad and Hey (1987)

give up keeping a boat, they tended to use it at times when they knew from experience that few other vessels would be encountered. Saturdays, which are 'change-over' days for many hire craft, are particularly popular with private owners.

The amount of boat traffic at different places was measured on two days in August 1967 (Broads Consortium, 1971), and on three days in August in both 1976 (Broads Authority, 1982c & 1986*). Boat movements at Horning were also recorded on each Tuesday during the 1976 season, and in one complete week in August; information about daily traffic flows was also collected that year at Irstead and Thurne Mouth.

---

* A summary of this census was presented to the Strategy Committee of the Broads Authority in December 1986. The author is grateful for the opportunity to study a full set of the data obtained.

An aerial view of the Bure-Yare confluence – 1988.

Plate 31

Rendel, Palmer and Tritton recommended that a Surge Barrier be built across the R. Yare just north of a point midway between the Haven Bridge (visible on the right) and the Bure-Yare confluence. The mudflats to the north of the lifting bridge carrying the Yarmouth Relief Road across the lower end of Breydon Water are accreting rapidly, and are being colonized by saltmarsh plants. The blue-roofed Asda store to the right was still under construction when the photograph was taken.

Cobholm, the urban area between the Relief Road and the northern end of the Haven, is very low-lying, and several lives were lost here during the 1953 surge flood.

Photo: BKS Surveys / Norfolk County Council

Plate 32   **The yacht *Bryony* on the R. Ant near How Hill – 1990.**

Built by Alfred Pegg of Wroxham, *Bryony* cost £300 (*c.* £8070 at 1990 prices) when launched in 1928. Her overall length is 27 ft. (8.2 m), her beam 7 ft. 10 in (2.4 m), and she draws 2 ft 9in (0.84 m). Her top-sail rig stands her in good stead, particularly when, as here, she is negotiating confined, tree-lined waters.

Bryony is one of many pre-Second World War vessels in the River Cruiser Class. To belong to this, a yacht must conform to various criteria, not least the fact that she was designed specifically and exclusively for use on the Broadland waterways. Numerous races are organized for the Class during the season, and some of these cover considerable distances. The longest – the Yare Navigation Race – involves sailing from Coldham Hall (opposite Brundall) to Breydon Water and back, a round trip of some 50 km.

Many of the vessels in the River Cruiser Class were acquired for private use after they had been engaged in the hire trade. But *Bryony* has been owned privately since new.

Photo: Martin George

Plate 33

The Port of Norwich – 1962.

Norwich was still being visited by quite large numbers of coasters in the early 1960s, though trading activity had declined since the Port's heyday in the mid-1930s. Cargoes of grain were regularly arriving at Read Woodrow's flour mills (seen here in the left foreground), whilst timber ships were unloaded at a yard on the site now occupied by the Hotel Nelson. Shipments of scrap steel, destined for the Continent, were still being made from a wharf just upstream of the flour mill, while the river was also being used by colliers bound for the Thorpe coal-fired power station, a short distance downstream of Carrow Bridge, from which this photo was taken.

Trading in timber, scrap steel and coal ended during the late 1960s and early 1970s, and Read Woodrows stopped importing grain in 1988. As a result, only a very small number of ships used the Port in 1989 and 1990.

Photo: Martin George

A single-decker 'water bus' on the R. Bure near Decoy Staithe – 1981.

Plate 34

Broads Tours of Wroxham were operating 18 vessels of this type in the late 1960s and 1970s, their passenger-carrying capacity ranging from 30 to 100. But with rising labour costs, the firm found the smaller craft increasingly uneconomic, and although it still had 14 vessels of this type in 1984, it now only has 4, all of which are capable of carrying between 90 and 100 passengers. Similar vessels, or their modern glass-fibre counterparts, are operated from Norwich, Potter Heigham and Oulton Broad, as well as by another firm in Wroxham.

The Rivers Commissioners cut back the alders growing at the water's-edge in this section of the R. Bure during the early 1950s, and applied an arboricide to the stumps. But unfortunately, many of the trees subsequently recovered, and although they have been periodically cut back again, their presence, plus the wash generated by large numbers of motor cruisers and day launches, has rendered the R. Bure upstream of Ant Mouth much less suitable for sailing craft than it was prior to the Second World War.

Photo: Martin George

Plate 35

The Hickling weed-collecting machine in use – 1968.

This machine, though rather 'Heath Robinson' in appearance, proved remarkably efficient in collecting up *Cladophora* and other filamentous algae from the marked boating channels across Hickling Broad and Heigham Sound. It was in use from the mid-1950s onwards, but because of the 'switch' from Phase II to Phase III which occurred in the late 1960s and early 1970s, it was not employed after 1975; it was broken up in 1986.

Photo: Martin George

Plate 36   **A river inspector's launch at Wroxham – 1990.**

Inspectors have patrolled the R. Bure since 1913, and by the 1930s, if not before, there were launches on the Yare and Waveney as well, each man reporting direct to one of the Commissioners responsible for his river.

The Rivers Commissioners managed the inspectorate until 1989, when its functions on the main river system were taken over by the 'new' Broads Authority. The latter currently operates 7 launches (4 on the northern rivers, and 3 on the southern); an eighth vessel is maintained by the Yarmouth Port Authority, and used to patrol those sections of the waterway system for which it is responsible, namely Breydon Water and the lowermost reaches of the R. Bure. All the launches are radio-controlled, and this enables the inspectors to respond to calls for assistance quite quickly, despite the substantial lengths of river which each individual is expected to patrol.

The helmsman of the cruiser on the left has decided to turn round, rather than try and negotiate Wroxham Bridge. According to Gowen (1990), this dates from 1614, though rebuilt in 1897. Unlike Potter Heigham Bridge (see Plate VII), it is structurally unsound, and had to be covered by a Bailey-type bridge in 1968.

Photo: Martin George

Plate 37

Ranworth Staithe in high summer – 1981.

Opinions vary greatly as to what constitutes 'overcrowding' and 'congestion', and some people would do almost anything to avoid being embroiled in the sort of scene portrayed in this photograph. Many others, however, would regard it as an indication of just how popular Broadland still is, despite all the environmental problems, and what a lot of pleasure and fun is derived from the region each year.

Photo: Martin George

A hired motor launch and sailing cruiser near Horning Church – 1981.

Plate 38

Day launches often generate almost as much wash as quite large motor cruisers, and they are frequently driven by persons who know little about the region. Since vessels of this type are normally hired out by the hour or the day, those taking them out tend to be motivated by a desire to cover the maximum possible mileage in the limited time available. In the circumstances, it is perhaps fortunate from the environmental point of view that the number of such launches has declined by about a fifth over the past 20 years.

The number of yachts for hire (such as the one in the photograph) has also declined, one of the factors responsible being the ever-increasing number of persons who own small sailing craft, and who can use them on lakes, rivers and reservoirs near their own homes. This trend is regrettable, since many visitors to Broadland derive pleasure from seeing sailing craft in action, even if they themselves do not wish to participate.

Photo: Martin George

Plate 39

**An aerial view of the R. Thurne, looking north-eastwards towards Herbert Woods'
boatyard at Potter Heigham and, in the far distance, the dune-clad coast between
Winterton and Horsey – 1973.**

Although the region's waterscape remains largely undeveloped, the banks of the R. Thurne upstream and
downstream of Potter Heigham bridge provide an exception to this. There are 210 chalets and huts in this
area, many having been erected in the 1920s, when planning control as we know it today was non-existent.

A major controversy arose in the early 1980s, when it became known that the Broads Authority was
considering taking steps to clear away some, or even all, of this ribbon development, much of which is self-
built and unsightly. In the face of strong objections from the Thurne Tenants' Association, a compromise
plan was worked out wherein several sections of river bank will ultimately be cleared of development, so
that they come to resemble the area shown in the right foreground. Although only 32 chalets will be
removed under this plan, steps have been taken to ensure the quality of the remainder will, in the course
of time, be upgraded.

Photo: John Hubbard/Nature Conservancy Council

A party of Conservation Corps volunteers hand-pulling scrub at Woodbastwick Fen – 1967.

Plate 40

The Conservation Corps (as it was then called) was formed by the Council for Nature in 1959, and a party organized by the new body was first used on the Woodbastwick part of the Bure Marshes National Nature Reserve in 1964. Since then, numerous other groups of volunteer workers have been established, and they now form a most important source of labour on the region's nature reserves.

The Conservation Corps itself, now reorganized as the British Trust for Conservation Volunteers, has become a highly professional body, and although many tasks are still carried out, literally, by hand, its leaders are qualified to use chain saws and other mechanical aids. The productivity of its work parties has, as a result, been immeasurably increased compared with the early days, when only bow saws, axes and spades could be used for jobs such as tree and bush clearance.

Photo: Martin George

Plate 41

A hired tracked hydraulic excavator in difficulties at Woodbastwick Fen – 1966.

When the Bure Marshes National Nature Reserve was established by the Nature Conservancy in the late 1950s, three of the five broads within it were, for reasons not then understood, already showing signs of ecological deterioration. Consequently, a high priority was given to restoring the only other open-water bodies in the site, namely the dykes. Many of these were almost completely filled with sediment, and efforts were therefore concentrated on finding a way of removing this. The Conservancy's early endeavours were not always successful, as the photograph shows, and it was not until a suction dredger was developed (see Plate LIV) that real progress was made.

Photo: Martin George

Plate 42

**Looking north-westwards from the tree hide on the Hickling Broad
National Nature Reserve – 1970.**

This is one of six really outstanding viewpoints in the region, the others being the mills at Berney Arms and Horsey, the tower of Ranworth Church, the tower hide on the RSPB's Strumpshaw reserve, and How Hill. It was built, at the Conservancy's insistence, when the Norfolk Naturalists' Trust was laying out its 'Water Trail' on the Hickling reserve in 1970, and has been an immensely popular attraction ever since.

In addition to providing panoramic views over the reserve, the visitor who clambers up the ladders to the *c.* 20 m high tower, should be able to make out on a clear day the dunes between Horsey and Winterton, Horsey Mere, Sea Palling Church tower and, in the extreme north-west, the radio towers used in connection with the Bacton Gas Terminal. Close-ups of the canopy fauna of an oak tree can also be obtained, one of the highlights being the Purple Hairstreak butterflies which are on the wing here in late July and August.

Photo: Martin George

Plate 43

**The Ranworth Conservation Centre
under construction beside Malthouse
Broad – 1976.**

This much admired building was designed for the Norfolk Naturalists' Trust by A. Maufe of Fielden & Mawson Ltd. It floats on pontoons fabricated by Windboats Marine Ltd. of Wroxham, and when completed, was floated round to its moorings overlooking Ranworth (Inner) Broad. It is approached by a walkway traversing the triangular-shaped area of Swamp Carr which for the past 100 years or so has separated Ranworth and Malthouse Broads.

Photo: Martin George

All three censuses showed that the middle Bure is the most crowded stretch of river, with a mean of over 900 boat movements a day at Horning in August each year. It is not unusual for over a thousand boats to pass this point each day during this month, especially on Sundays, and the mean number of vessels recorded here on Tuesdays during the summer of 1976 ranged from 798 in June, to 872 in July and 710 in September; even in October, there were, on average, 324 vessels passing to and fro daily. The Thurne is another busy river, the average number of boats using it on the three days sampled in August 1976 and 1986 being 786 and 656 respectively. The Ant is noticeably less crowded, with a mean of 478 vessels passing Irstead in August 1976 and 437 in 1986.

The southern rivers are generally less busy. The mean number of vessels passing Brundall in August 1976 was 369 (367 in 1986), while the Waveney at Beccles was even quieter, with a mean of 261 boats in 1976 (245 in 1986). In contrast, traffic on Oulton Dyke averaged 653 vessels per day over the same three-day period in 1976, though this figure had declined to 454 ten years later.

Although there were nearly twice as many privately-owned vessels as hire craft in use in 1976, it will be seen from Map 11.2 that the traffic on the rivers that year was made up largely of the latter. The proportion of hire cruisers at Horning did not fall below 40 per cent on any of the days censused that year, and reached 60 per cent on Sundays. If hired day launches are added to these figures, the proportion never fell below 70 per cent, and rose to 80 per cent of the total flow on two days.

By amalgamating some of the categories of boats used in the more detailed 1976 survey to form the six classes employed in 1967, and using the nine census points used on each occasion, it is possible to show that total boat traffic did not increase significantly between 1967 and 1976. There was, however, a shift in the distribution of the traffic as boat movements on the southern rivers increased by 10 per cent and declined by 4 per cent on the northern, this despite the fact that following the closure of a large hire yard at Thorpe, the vessels formerly based there were acquired by establishments in the northern river system.

The decrease in the number of hire craft since 1979 is reflected in a 12 per cent reduction in the total amount of boat traffic on the rivers in 1986 compared with 1976, the decline being slightly greater in the southern rivers (14.4 per cent), than the northern (10.7 per cent). The mean number of hire motor cruisers passing Horning Ferry during the three days censused in August 1986 was 464, compared with 502 during the corresponding period in 1976, whilst the number of hire motor launches in use on this stretch of river showed an even more marked decrease, from 267 to 209. In contrast, the mean number of privately-owned motor cruisers and day launches rose from 67 to 77, the difference being particularly marked when the two Sundays are compared: 247 boat movements in 1986, and only 140 in 1976.

Several important points need to be borne in mind in connection with these census results. Firstly, when considering the environmental effects of river traffic, it is misleading to think only in terms of total boat numbers, since these reveal little about the impact different types of vessel have on the waterways. Sailing dinghies, for instance, produce a negligible amount of bank erosion, but can add very considerably to the problem of congestion when being raced in confined waters. Conversely, hired day launches cause a disproportionate amount of wash, partly because of the configuration of their hulls, and partly because they are all too often driven by novices whose main aim is to cover the maximum possible distance in the time available (see Plate 38).

Any discussion confined to boat numbers conceals the fact that hired vessels exert a more continuous form of pressure on the environment than privately-owned craft, most of which are only used occasionally (see Map 11.2). But the 1976 census showed that even hire motor cruisers are only on the move for about 4 hours a day, the rest of the time being spent on moorings, preferably near a pub or at a holiday centre such as Wroxham, Great Yarmouth or Oulton.

Bordered by large expanses of fen and woodland, and with numerous broads nearby, the northern rivers are regarded by most people as being more attractive scenically than the Yare and Waveney, which have fewer broads, and which for much of their length are embanked, or worse still, piled. It was because of the scenic attractions of the Bure and its tributaries that Wroxham, Horning and Potter Heigham were established as the main centres of the tourist industry in the late nineteenth century, and why hire operators continued to favour these sites during the first half of the present century, rather than places in the south. The resultant imbalance between the number of vessels available for hire in the north and south is clearly shown in Table 11c. More recently, the difference in numbers has tended to narrow, not least because one of the policies set out in the Broads Consortium's 1971 Study and Plan was to discourage further boatyard expansion in the north and, conversely, permit such development at selected sites in the south.

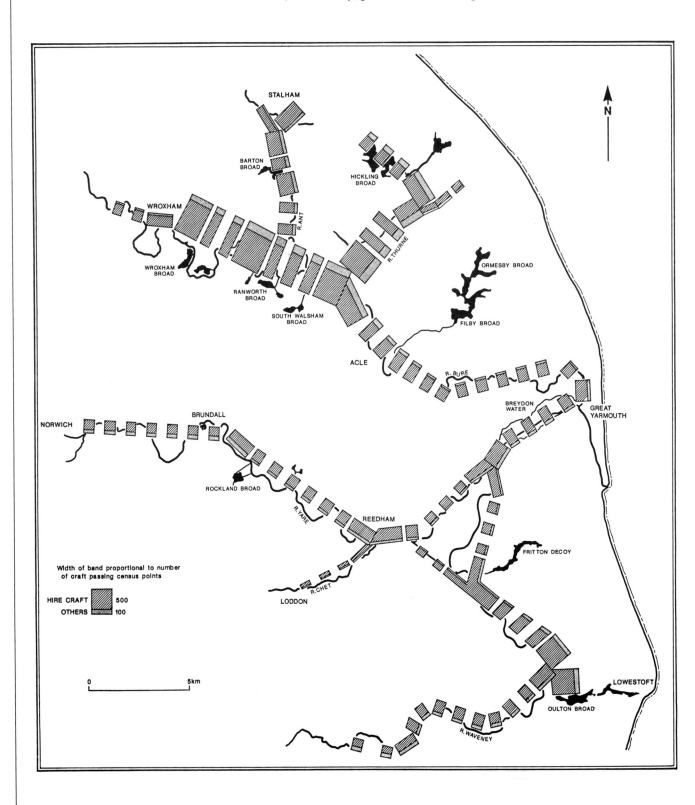

Map 11.2   The distribution of hire and privately-owned craft on the Broadland waterways on Tuesday, 10 August 1976.

Source: Traffic census carried out by the Gt. Yarmouth Port and Haven Commissioners.

Brundall, for example, which had only 8 hire yards in 1962, had 18 by 1979, together with two large marinas for privately-owned vessels. A similar expansion in boat hiring took place at Chedgrave and Loddon during the same period (see page 443). But although there were only 51 boat-hire yards beside the Bure and its tributaries in 1979, compared with 55 in the southern rivers (50 and 50 respectively in 1983), most of the larger firms are located beside the northern rivers. It is for this reason that the number of

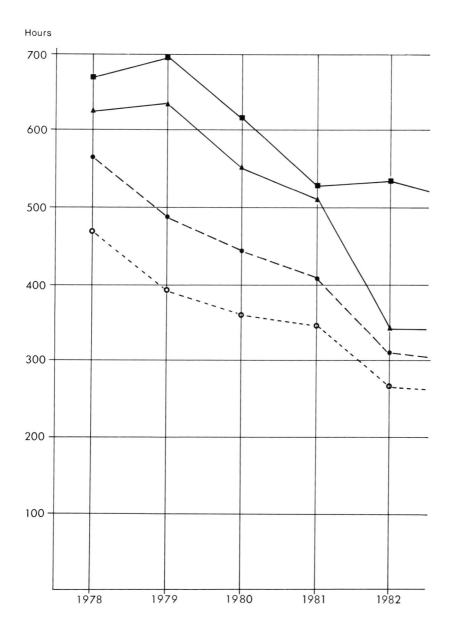

Fig. 11c

Engine hours per season for four (unnamed) classes of motor cruisers in use during the period 1978 to 1982.

Source: Broads Hire Boat Federation (1983)

hire vessels in the north has, for the past 20 years, remained almost twice that in the south (see Table 11c).

Although the increase in the number of boats being hired out in the southern part of the region generated more traffic on the Yare and Waveney during the 1970s, surveys have shown that most people hiring a vessel at a southern yard wish to visit the northern rivers and broads. This would explain why traffic through Yarmouth appears from the census results to have increased by 54 per cent between 1967 and 1976.

The rivers and broads are at their busiest in July and August, but the booking agencies operate a sliding scale of charges so as to encourage the use of hire craft during off-peak periods, and extend the season, which lasts from early March until mid-November. Easter week is traditionally popular with sailing enthusiasts and school parties, and there is a similar, though smaller, increase in the number of bookings during the autumn half-term. Relatively few boatyards are prepared to hire out their craft during the winter, because this interferes with their arrangements for servicing the vessels, and because breakdowns tend to occur owing to the heavy demands put on the batteries for heating purposes. Despite these limitations, a few vessels are on the move every week of the year, and about 30 boats were booked out to hardy souls for the Christmas holidays in 1979 and 1985.

In Hoseason's fleet, the average number of weeks booked per cruiser was just over 23 between 1961 and 1970 (Hoseason, 1970), and is likely to have remained at, or slightly above this level until about 1978. Thereafter, bookings declined, mainly as a result of the depression, and this trend is revealed in Figure 11c, which shows the amount of time which four different classes of motor cruiser spent on the move between 1978 and 1982. Since then, the average number of weeks booked per cruiser has tended to increase, a trend influenced by the decline in the number of boats available for hire (see Table 11e), and the steps taken by the industry to ensure that their prices are competitive with those charged for other types of holiday, notably package tours to the Mediterranean.

In pursuit of this objective, the prospective holidaymaker is offered a wide range of prices to choose from. In 1989, for example, a couple wishing to hire a 2-berth motor cruiser for a week in the off-peak season could have selected one costing as little as £141, or as much as £228. But if they had opted to take their holiday between the third weeks of July and August, they would have had to pay £222 or £370 for the same vessels. Because of the wide range of different boats available, and their varying size, age and quality, average figures mean little, but in 1989, most 2-berth motor cruisers cost between £160 and £200 in off-peak times, and between £270 and £320 in high summer.

Corresponding figures for a 'typical' 6-berth cruiser ranged from about £325 in the early spring and autumn, to £540 during the peak summer weeks, but some boats are considerably cheaper, and others more expensive, than this. It will be noted that the cost per head of hiring such a vessel is somewhat less than would be incurred by a couple on a 2-berth cruiser, and this difference is even greater for larger vessels.

Prices for a 4-berth auxiliary-engined sailing cruiser in 1989 ranged from about £225 to £305 for those prepared to take their holiday in an off-peak week, but the cost of such vessels increased to between £310 and £420 over Easter, at the end of May, and in mid-summer.

In a description of Broadland's tourist industry, the Owners Associations (1979) point out that about 30 per cent of the bookings made between 1976 and 1979 were by people who had had a holiday afloat in the region before, and use this fact to illustrate its continuing popularity. The incidence of repeat booking was examined in greater detail by Walker (1981), who found that out of 620 hire parties who completed a questionnaire, 18 per cent contained a member who had been to the region once before, and 27 per cent individuals who had visited it between 2 and 5 times. Nine per cent of the parties contained someone who had been between 6 and 10 times previously, and 8 per cent a person who, astonishingly, had visited it even more often. These results are of interest to the boat-letter, as well as the environmentalist, because individuals making a return visit are more likely to treat the vessel they have hired, and Broadland itself, with care and consideration, than those who have never been to the area before, and do not intend to do so again.

The decline in the number of yachts for hire during the past 30 years (see Table 11c) is widely regretted. Visually, they form a most attractive feature of the waterways (see Plate 38), and most holidaymakers seem to enjoy seeing them, even though two of them tacking up a narrow river can cause a considerable tail-back of other craft. Environmentally, of course, a yacht is preferable to a motor cruiser of comparable size, as it causes far less bank erosion, and it is therefore encouraging that several boatyards are prepared to retain such craft in their fleets; indeed a few firms have introduced new vessels.

Litter is a perennial problem in Broadland as elswhere, and despite the disposal facilities provided by local authorities near many popular mooring places, it continues to be dumped by boat users and anglers in seemingly endless quantites, either in full view on the river banks, where it attracts rats, carrion crows and other undesirable species, or out of sight in the rivers and broads themselves. Each spring a river-bank clean-up campaign is organized by the Broads Authority, with the help of the appropriate district councils and, until 1989, the Rivers Commisioners. In 1981, 710 bagfuls of litter were collected (550 from the northern rivers, and 160 from the south) at a cost of nearly £4000. Between 750 and 850 bagfuls were taken away in each subsequent year, and the total rose to 1063 in 1985.

Litter is not the only problem. Anti-social behaviour was frequently mentioned by boat users completing questionnaires about their experiences (Walker, 1978). Vessels are driven at excessive speed, or with a lack of consideration for others, and there is rowdyism and vandalism, particularly when the pubs close at night. All these are

Windsurfing on Hickling Broad – 1987.

This site has proved very popular with those wishing to practice this fast-growing sport, and the Hickling Windsurfing Club was formed in 1984.

Windsurfers tend to congregate in the north-west corner of the Broad, where there is a hard-standing from which they can launch their craft and land, and this sometimes leads to friction between them and other water users, particularly dinghy sailors.

Photo: R.N. Flowers

Plate XLVII

offences under the by-laws, and the river inspectors, and the police, keep a sharp look-out for the troublemaker, and will institute proceedings when necessary. But much of the damage is not wanton, but is born of simple ignorance. How can a holidaymaker know that if he drives his motor cruiser or day boat too close to the river bank, he is helping to trigger a chain of events which will ultimately lead to increased erosion, and a higher rate of sedimentation in the broads?

Ignorance, allied to a disregard for the interests of others, is responsible for many of the user conflicts which occur in Broadland, notably those between anglers and boat users. These are most frequent on the narrower rivers, and occur from mid-June (the end of the close season for fishing) onwards; incidents rarely occur after the end of October as most boats have by then been laid up for the winter. Owens (1978), who investigated the phenomenon, found that most (72.8 per cent) anglers believed that their chance of catching fish had diminished during the previous five years, most of them blaming "the amount of boat traffic" (44.6 per cent), "an increased number of boats", or "pollution from boats" (13.0 per cent). Conversely, nearly half the private boat owners interviewed, reported that they had been inconvenienced by anglers, usually as a result of their occupation of mooring spaces, or because of their slowness in reeling in when their line was across a waterway. Owens points out that an angry exchange, for instance at a mooring, is long-remembered, and that a seemingly trivial event, such as having to reel in, can become deeply frustrating if experienced repeatedly.

In an attempt to improve the relationship between boat users and anglers, the Commissioners agreed in 1976 to ask owners and hirers not to use their motor vessels on certain stretches of the rivers Bure and Thurne (totalling 13 km) before 9 am on Sundays between mid-June and the end of October. Owen's survey revealed that this request was viewed sympathetically by many boat users, and that it was strongly backed by anglers. However, 87 per cent of the latter felt that the areas covered by the experiment should be extended, and 66 per cent of these felt that the restrictions on motor boat usage should be on a compulsory, rather than a voluntary basis.

Conflicts occur, not only between boating interests and anglers, but among different types of boat user. Hirers unfamiliar with the tense atmosphere which often prevails during sailing races are taken aback when they are shouted at for getting in the way, and in light weather, yachtsmen are aggrieved when the wind is constantly knocked out of their sails by the wash of passing motor vessels.

Friction has also occurred on Hickling Broad between windsurfers and dinghy-sailing members of the Hickling Sailing Club and, in 1984, following meetings between the various interested parties, the Hickling Windsurfing Club was formed (see Plate XLVII). Although this has done much to alleviate the problems, there is no obligation on board-sailors to join the club, and occasional conflicts of interest continue to occur between non-members and others. In addition, some board-sailors like to practise their sport throughout the winter, and are thus liable to disturb the birdlife of the reserve. But a proposal that wind-surfers be asked not to use the site between the beginning of December and the end of March had to be abandoned as a result of objections from those concerned.

Conscious both of the need for improved understanding between different user interests, and of the success of the Broads Consortium's Code of Behaviour (published and widely circulated in the late 1960s), both Blakes and Hoseasons produced for the 1981 season leaflets setting out for the people who hire boats through them, a series of 'dos and don'ts', explaining why these are necessary, and suggesting ways in which holidaymakers can help to safeguard the environment. The 'old' Broads Authority, too, was well aware of the need to provide more information and interpretive facilities in the region, and during its period in office, implemented many of the recommendations made in a report which it commissioned on the subject (Broads Authority, 1982d) (see Chapter 13).

Another widely acclaimed initiative by this Authority was the establishment in March 1982 of the Broadland Partnership. This is a consortium of local commercial interests which aims to encourage by means of annual awards and other incentives, the provision of higher standards of boat and shore-based accommodation for visitors, and ensure that local shops, pubs and other premises not only offer a warm welcome and good value for money, but are maintained in a visually attractive condition. Information about the Partnership's activities was published in a newsletter produced twice yearly, an arrangement which has been continued since 1989 by the 'new' Broads Authority.

Chapter 12
Planning and Administering the Region

The period up to 1961

Accustomed as we now are to Structure and Local Plans, and the exercise of tight planning control and building regulations, it is salutary to remember that prior to the 1930s, the only constraints on development in Broadland, as elsewhere, were those laid down in the Public Health Acts. Enforcement even of these regulations was lax by present-day standards, and the ribbon-like development to be seen beside the rivers at Potter Heigham, Brundall and elsewhere is a legacy of the lack of effective control after the First World War.

The passing of the *Town Planning Act* in 1925 and the *Local Government Act* in 1929, paved the way for a more structured approach, and by 1931, when the Addison Committee compiled its report, there were 42 Joint Town Planning Committees in England and Wales with powers to prepare planning schemes, and a further 61 joint committees with advisory functions (Financial Secretary to the Treasury, 1931). The first body to be established in rural East Anglia to consider and advise upon planning issues was the Norfolk (East Central) Joint Planning Committee. Formed in 1930, this had jurisdiction over the area between the rivers Bure and Yare. Responsibility for the area north of the Bure, including the Ant and Thurne valleys, lay with the Norfolk (North and East) Joint Planning Committee, set up four years later, whilst the remaining parts of Broadland came within the purview of the East Suffolk (North Area) and South Norfolk Joint Planning Committees, established in 1935 and 1936 respectively.

The principal function of these committees, as formalized by the *Town and Country Planning Act* 1932, was to draw up planning schemes for their areas of responsibility, and advise the relevant rural and urban district councils on the control of development. In general, the guidelines produced by the committees laid stress on the need to direct industrial and commercial development to the most suitable area, and safeguard the natural characteristics and amenities of the region. The principal points laid down in the Zoning Plan produced by the Norfolk (North and East) Joint Committee were as follows:

1. River banks and land in the immediate vicinity of broads to be preserved as far as possible in their natural state;
2. Keypoints of scenery and areas of special landscape value to be preserved and building around these reservations to be of a very sparse character;
3. Places to be selected for development with a view to amenity and convenience and economy in public services;

4. A restriction to be placed on building in areas where by reason of the level or nature of the land the provision of sewers or other public services would be likely to give rise to difficulties or be unduly costly;

5. All buildings except private boathouses to be kept sufficiently far back from the edge of rivers and broads so as not to disfigure, impair or alter the natural beauty of the locality;

6. Strict control of the design and external appearance of all buildings and advertisements.

The schemes differentiated between Development Zones, usually centred on existing towns and villages, and Agricultural (or low-lying) Zones, where residential and commercial building would be restricted unless required in connection with farming, horticultural or other rural activities.

The outbreak of the Second World War brought Broadland holiday-making to an abrupt end, and work on the planning schemes slowed in the face of shortages of trained staff, and more pressing needs. Thought was given, however, to the selection of sites of particular importance for nature conservation, and at the Government's request, the Society for the Promotion of Nature Reserves established a Nature Reserves Investigation Committee (NRIC) to draw up a list of sites deemed worthy of preservation (see page 452). In its report (SPNR, 1945), the NRIC raised an issue which was to come up again and again during the ensuing 40 years, namely the legal status to be afforded the region. The Committee's suggestion was that Broadland should be established as a 'Scheduled Area', rather than as a national park as proposed by the Addison Committee in 1931, and the Scott Committee in 1942. Such a 'Scheduled Area' was defined by the NRIC as one in which further development would be prohibited or drastically restricted. Additional or special facilities (such as those which might be provided in a national park) would not be made available, although the public's existing rights over land and water would not be interfered with.

In the light of the views expressed by the NRIC and its Norfolk sub-committee, and the realization that the region would quickly come under renewed commercial and developmental pressures with the cessation of hostilities, the Joint Planning Committees decided that a number of large landowners should be invited to conclude 'Open Space' agreements under Section 34 of the 1932 Act. These would commit them to maintaining their land in its existing, undeveloped state, whilst in return the local authority would undertake to include in its definitive Planning Scheme conditions aimed at attaining this objective. By February 1946, forty landowners in the region had agreed in principle to their property being scheduled as 'private open space', or included within 'wildlife reservations'. Laudable as this initiative was, it subsequently became clear that designations of this type would not be viewed favourably by the Ministry of Town and Country Planning unless it could be shown that the objective of the agreement could not be attained by means of a Planning Scheme and orthodox development control methods. The Ministry also made it clear that compensation would be payable in the event that an owner subsequently felt himself to be disadvantaged by the conditions laid down in such a Scheme. In the circumstances, no Section 34 agreements were, as far as can be ascertained, actually negotiated.

Meantime, the future of Broadland had been under discussion in Whitehall. This can be attributed, partly to the comments made in the NRIC report, and partly to an inter-departmental debate which had taken place during the drafting of a section on national parks which was to have been included in a White Paper on the control of land use (Ministry of Town and Country Planning, 1944). In addition, pressure had been exerted on the Government of the day by the Standing Committee on National Parks, a body which had been formed in the mid-1930s by the Council for the Protection of Rural England (CPRE) and its counterpart in Wales, and which had endorsed a list of 21 proposed national parks (one of which comprised the Norfolk Broads) drawn up for it in 1935 (Sheail, 1976). In July 1944, the Ministry of Town and Country Planning wrote to the Norfolk County Council indicating that . . . "the time is ripe for an investigation into the problems connected with the preservation, control and improvement" of Broadland, and asking the Council to arrange a conference, to be attended by representatives of the numerous bodies having responsibilities or interests in the region. The Council agreed to this request, and the first Broads Conference took place in April 1945 in Norwich.

During the course of this it was agreed that an Investigation Committee should be established to make an in-depth study of the problems, and the ways in which these could best be dealt with, and three sub-committees – Water, Land, Natural Life and Sporting Interests – were formed to help the Committee achieve these objectives.

In a paper produced for the Committee in October 1945, William Stubbs, the planning officer responsible for those parts of Broadland located in Norfolk, identified the following factors . . . "which tend to destroy or cause injury to the amenities of the area".

1. Pollution of the rivers by the discharge of sewage from river craft;
2. Defilement of the river banks and the spoilation of riverside areas by the throwing away of waste materials and rubbish by holiday makers;
3. Unrestrained multiplication in the size and number of the various types of craft using the waters;
4. Short-term plot-letting by the Catchment Board and riparian owners of river banks for the erection of bungalows and shacks;
5. Alterations in the contour of river banks by heaping instead of spreading to prearranged levels, drainage excavations and spoil;
6. Contraction of broads and waterways due to reed growth, possibly accelerated by drainage operations;
7. Curtailment of sailing facilities due to unrestricted growing of trees on the river banks;
8. Decay and destruction of old pumping windmills, riverside inns and other buildings characteristic of Broadland's scenery;

It is indicative of Stubbs' powers of perception that not only are most of these factors just as germane to Broadland today as they were in the 1940s, but that he concluded that the remedy for them . . . "would be in the integration of the powers and responsibilities of the various bodies exercising control".

A second Broads Conference was held in May 1947, and afterwards the Investigation Committee's Report, together with a summary statement, was submitted formally to Lewis Silkin, the then Minister of Town and Country Planning (Norfolk County Council, 1947). It consisted of an account of the geography and land use of the region, the organizations having interests and responsibilities in it, and the problems to which it was subject; a description of the natural history of Broadland compiled by Ted Ellis was annexed to it. The Report made a large number of recommendations, including the need to control pollution, police the waterways more effectively, and strengthen the powers of the Catchment Board, the Great Yarmouth Port and Haven Commissioners, and the planning authorities. Prophetically, the Report also urged that . . . "any projects for the erection of dams or barrages should be the subject of very full enquiry and consultation with all the interests concerned". But the Investigation Committee's principal recommendation was that a Broads Committee should be formed.

> . . . This should be more than consultative; its purpose will be to get things done in the interests of the users of the Broads. The character and value of these waters are in danger from three sources – the violence of the sea, the growth of vegetation and the actions of man. The weakness of the defence against these dangers lies in the great number of Authorities involved.
>
> The Broads Committee would co-ordinate these Authorities – it would work to secure co-operation and a common policy – it would give advice when sought and stimulation when necessary. We believe this Committee could be made a potent instrument determining the future welfare and development of our unique heritage.

The need for such a committee had been identified as a result of the Investigation Committee's belief that . . . "the term National Park as we understand it does not fit an area like the Broads, but the question should be considered further in the light of more definite legislative proposals".

The recommendation also reflected the prolonged discussions which the members of the Committee had had about the practicability of establishing an overall authority for the region, and their reluctant conclusion that however desirable this was, the goal was unattainable in view of the likelihood that some at least of the existing authorities would oppose the idea.

It is symptomatic of one of the main problems which was to characterize the administration of Broadland for the next 30 years, namely the emphasis placed on the planning function in the region, rather than on the identification and implementation of measures aimed at remedying, through management, the environmental problems to which it is subject, that the only action taken to put into effect these various recommendations was the formation of the Broads Joint Advisory Committee in 1949. As a statutory joint committee of the four planning authorities which had assumed responsibilities in Broadland as a consequence of the *Town and Country Planning Act*, 1947 (The Norfolk and East Suffolk County Councils, and the Norwich and Great Yarmouth County Borough Councils), this was concerned primarily with advising these authorities on development control, and its members displayed a lamentable reluctance to tackle the environmental problems so clearly identified in the Investigation Committee's Report, this despite the fact that they were supposed to consider . . . "matters of mutual interest generally relating to the development, planning and use of the Broads Area". This deficiency is the more surprising in that the membership of the Committee was drawn from many of the organizations which managed and used Broadland, including the navigation, river and water supply authorities, the boat-hire operators, the Norfolk Agricultural Executive Committee, the Country Landowners' Association and the Norfolk Naturalists' Trust, as well as from the county, borough and rural district councils.

Useful as the Committee may have been as a planning advisory body, it is doubtful whether its most ardent supporters would claim that it acted as a stimulant to anyone (other than the hapless Norfolk County Council officials who had to service it), let alone that it was, in the words of the Broads Conference Report . . . "a potent instrument determining the future . . . of our unique heritage". Moreover, it failed to prevent what most environmentalists today would regard as major planning blunders at Stalham, Brundall, Chedgrave and elsewhere (see page 440).

The discussions in Whitehall which had resulted in the convening of the first Broads Conference, and the subsequent establishment of the Investigation Committee, also led to John Dower being commissioned by the then Minister of Town and Country Planning, Mr. W. S. Morrison, to review the purposes and requirements of national parks, and the means by which they could be set up.

Dower identified ten areas which he thought should be established as national parks as soon as possible, but relegated the Broads to a reserve list of a further 12 sites, because:

> . . . there are many complications, both of drainage, navigation etc., and of existing misuses and disfigurements; and the requirements differ materially from those of a regular National Park. It may prove better to deal with the area on some *ad hoc* scheme of combined national and local action, which should include the protection of substantial areas of mere and marsh as strict Nature Reserves.

Owing to differences of opinion between the departments concerned (Cherry, 1975), Dower's findings were not endorsed by the Government as had originally been intended, but were published in May 1945, as a consultant's report (Ministry of Town & Country Planning, 1945). Almost immediately afterwards, Morrison appointed a committee, under the chairmanship of Sir Arthur Hobhouse, to review Dower's proposals, and make recommendations as to which areas should be established as national parks, and how this could best be done. The formation of the Hobhouse Committee coincided with a change of government, and it soon became clear that the new Minister, Lewis Silkin, was prepared to argue the case for establishing national parks more forcibly than his predecessor had been.

Members of the Hobhouse Committee met on no less than eighty occasions, and made 17 survey tours, including one to Broadland, during the course of which they had discussions with the Investigation Committee set up as a result of the Broads Conference, and received a copy of its draft findings. Their own Report, published in 1947, listed the Broads as one of twelve areas in England and Wales which they felt should be established as national parks. The recommended area (see Map 12.1) covered about 181 square miles, but they were careful to point out that the boundary of this, and the other proposed parks, would need to be examined in more detail later (Ministry of Town and Country Planning, 1947a).

Hobhouse, like Dower, recognized that . . . "the Broads have a special claim to selection as a National Park quite apart from their natural beauty, by reason of their

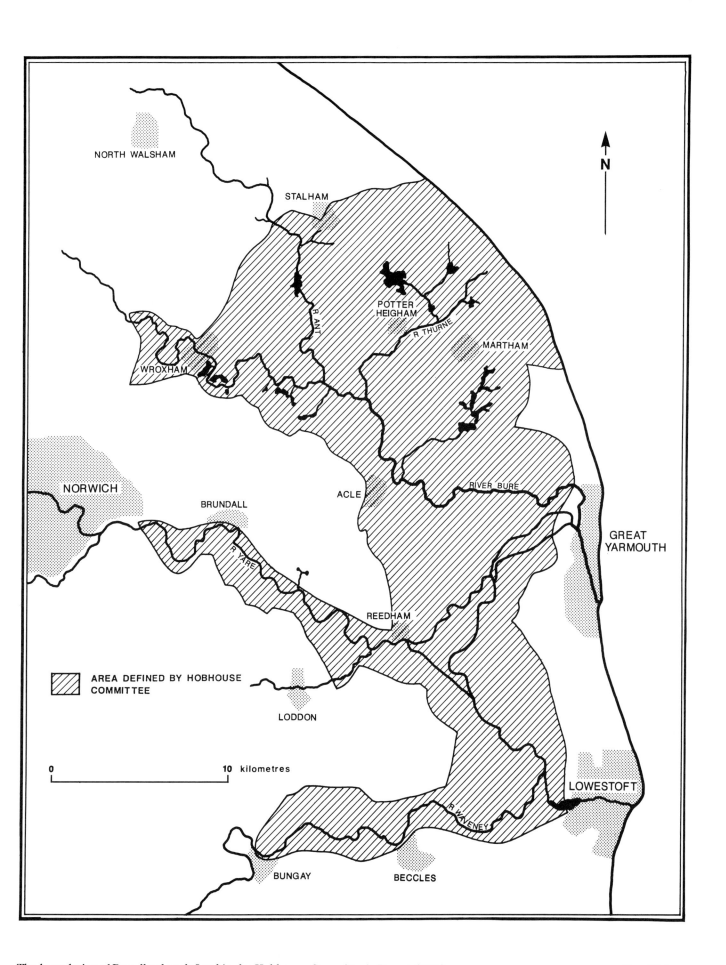

The boundaries of Broadland as defined in the Hobhouse Committee's Report (1947).

Map 12.1

holiday and recreational value and the interest of their plant and animal life". His committee also showed itself aware of the many and varied problems which would have to be faced if the area was to be effectively safeguarded. Those mentioned in the Report include the infilling and overgrowth of the broads, the vulnerability of the area to flooding by extreme tides, rights of access, conflicting water uses, pollution from organic material and salt water, the need to protect wildlife, the intensity of water usage for supply purposes and recreation, the noise from waterborne activity, the maintenance of landing places and the preservation of windpumps. The Committee noted that:

> . . . the many and formidable problems which will face the National Parks Commission in the Broads will undoubtedly entail expenditure on a larger scale than will be needed in other parks, both in direct action by the Commission and assisting the efforts of local authorities and bodies.

Despite its apprehensions on this score, the Committee concluded that:

> . . . this expenditure will be fully justified by the contribution which will be made to the nation's holiday and tourist services, by ensuring the preservation and increased public enjoyment of what are undoubtedly the finest inland sailing waters in the country.

Many of the recommendations made in the Hobhouse Committee's Report were given effect in the *National Parks and Access to the Countryside Act* 1949, including the formation of a National Parks Commission, and by September 1955, ten national parks had been established in England and Wales. However, for two reasons, no action was taken over the Broads. The multiplicity of different authorities responsible for planning and managing the area, and the strong commercial pressures to which it was already subject, made it potentially more difficult to deal with than the other proposed parks. But even more worrying for the National Parks Commission was the belief, widely held in the early 1950s and referred to in the Hobhouse Report, that the region would be extremely costly to manage.

Several references had been made in the Broads Conference Report to the fact that the broads were filling up with sediment and being overgrown with vegetation, and the idea seems to have gained ground during the late 1940s that it was essential that they should be restored to the condition they were in during the 1920s. In 1948, the Chief Engineer to the East Norfolk Rivers Catchment Board, S.W. Mobbs, advised the Ministry of Town and Country Planning that it would cost about £965 000 (c. £13.5 million at 1990 prices) to achieve this objective (EDP, 1948), and at the request of the Broads Joint Advisory Committee the issue was examined in more detail in 1950. After seeking advice from Mobbs, and from representatives of the Rivers Commissioners and the four rural district councils involved, R. Hopkins (the then County Planning Officer for Norfolk) concluded (quite rightly) that it would be prohibitively costly to restore all the broads to their former condition, and as a compromise he suggested that the effects of long-continued neglect should be counteracted by a 10-year programme of works. £66 000 (c. £922 000 at 1990 prices) would be spent on renovating the 18 broads which had been subject to particularly severe sedimentation and overgrowth, and a further £10 000 (c. £140 000 at 1990 prices) per annum on maintenance dredging and tree clearance. Maintaining the navigable channels would cost about £20 000 per year, whilst the provision of more mooring places would require a further £4500 (c. £63 800 at 1990 prices) a year. It was thought that additional drainage works costing c. £15 000 would be needed, and that setting up, and subsequently running, a warden service would cost £6600 and £1600 per annum respectively.

In 1951, another report was produced about the cost of remedial management, this time by A. A. Lane, an engineering inspector on the staff of the Ministry of Transport. Lane concluded that at least four million tons of sediment would have to be removed if the job was to be done thoroughly, and that this would cost £750 000 (c. £9.6 million at 1990 prices), and possibly as much as £890 000 if the work was spread over 20 years. A year or so later K. Cotton, then Chief Engineer to the East Suffolk and Norfolk River Board suggested that £250 000 would be a more reasonable estimate, but despite this, and attempts by Charles Collier, the then Chief Inspector for the Bure and Waveney Commissioners, to introduce a note of greater realism into the debate, the cost of restoring the broads to their former condition continued to cause concern both nationally and locally. These fears were seemingly confirmed in 1951, when Dr Joyce Lambert pointed out that, as a result of sedimentation, many broads contained only 3 to

4 feet of water, and were thus likely to be rapidly overgrown by marginal reedswamp, and later, fen vegetation.

Confronted as we are today with broads which have either lost, or are fast losing their marginal reedswamp, it is ironic that in the early 1950s it was the high cost of preventing this vegetation overgrowing them which perhaps more than any other factor, inhibited action on the national park proposal. As early as 1953, the National Parks Commission had been told by the Ministry of Transport that work on the scale suggested by Lane was "out of the question for the time being", and in winding up a debate in the House of Commons in March 1955, when many MPs had pressed for action to be taken, Mr Hugh Molson, Joint Parliamentary Secretary, Ministry of Transport, reiterated the Government's concern about the high cost of managing the area. When asked whether it would not be possible to restore one of the broads as an experiment, Molson provided a good example of ministerial stone-walling by replying that he would refer the idea to the National Parks Commission, but that it was . . . "really a matter that might be tried by the local authorities or by the landowners concerned".

To their credit, members of the National Parks Commission seem to have been unconvinced by the figures being bandied about, and in June 1955, they asked the Nature Conservancy to investigate . . . "what work would have to be done, and at what cost, to stabilise some at least of the existing broads for recreational purposes, and perhaps to improve them". Although the Conservancy agreed in principle to carry out the necessary scientific survey, this was made conditional on more funds being made available by the Treasury. In the event these were not forthcoming, and the project was shelved.

In 1956, the Ministry of Transport and Civil Aviation appointed a committee under the chairmanship of H. L. Bowes, . . . "to consider and report on the future of the country's system of inland waterways . . . and the present law relating to the closing of waterways to navigation, and to make recommendations". Chapter X of the Committee's Report, which was published in June 1958, is devoted to an account of Broadland's physical features, and the way in which the region was administered. After noting in this that opinions differed . . . "widely and vehemently both on the extent of the (infilling) problem, and on the means of its solution", the Committee expressed its conviction . . . "that, to begin with, any idea of spending enormous sums immediately would be a totally wrong approach" (Ministry of Transport and Civil Aviation, 1958).

As with others before it, the Bowes Committee felt obliged to consider what status should be afforded the region, and after assessing the pros and cons for establishing it as a national park, decided that the only real justification for this was that it would enable government funds to be spent in the region. The Committee pointed out that this objective could be more easily achieved if the Rivers Commissioners were empowered to receive grants from central government towards the cost of capital improvements and precept on local authorities. After making a number of other suggestions aimed at improving the Commission's ability to manage the region's waterways, they urged that . . . "Legislation to give effect to [our] recommendations should not be deferred pending further research and investigations concerning the Broads, but should be introduced as soon as possible as a government measure".

Unfortunately these admirable sentiments were not reciprocated in Whitehall, and the White Paper issued in February 1959, in response to the Bowes Committee Report blandly remarked that . . . "the Government agreed with the view that proposals for very costly schemes of improvement are not justified in present circumstances, and that instead there should be a gradual extension of the work which has already been carried out. The proposals for new administrative arrangements would involve adjustment of responsibilities among a number of authorities operating in the area, and it is, in the Government's view, essential that the proposals should be thoroughly explored between the interests concerned before any decision is taken. Discussions between representatives of the bodies concerned, including the National Parks Commission, have already begun, and when the discussions have been concluded, the Government will consider what course of action to adopt" (Ministry of Transport and Civil Aviation, 1959).

During the ensuing consultations, the East Suffolk and Norfolk River Board created a furore locally by claiming that it was the "ideal authority" to assume responsibility for maintaining the rivers and broads in a navigable state, and that the activities of the Great Yarmouth Port and Haven Commissioners should be confined to Yarmouth Haven.

The Board adopted this attitude because of its dissatisfaction over the Commissioners' continued refusal to contribute towards the cost of maintaining the river banks, this despite the fact that it was the Commissioners and not the Board which levied tolls on boats, and which therefore benefited financially from the traffic on the waterways. The Board felt that since it was the boats which were increasing the rate at which the embankments were eroding and, on the Yare, damaging the protective piling, it was inequitable that the cost of the necessary repairs should be borne wholly by land-drainage interests.

The Port and Haven Commissioners had already pointed out in their comments on the Bowes Committee's Report that the River Board's bid to assume responsibility for navigation was totally unacceptable, and that such a step would be a direct contradiction of what the Committee had concluded (Great Yarmouth Port and Haven Commissioners, 1959). The proposal also caused a great deal of unease amongst boating interests, who suspected that if the Board was given the necessary powers, it would at once increase the tolls levied on their craft to help pay for bank maintenance, or worse still, close off navigable waterways such as the New Cut on the grounds that it was not economic to keep them open to boat traffic because of the damage caused to the banks.

The Bowes Committee's comments on the future status to be afforded the Region also generated a response from those for and against national park designation. Members of a working group set up by the CPRE's Standing Committee on National Parks decided, albeit with some reluctance, that . . . "collectively the disadvantages of designation are very strong". In arriving at this conclusion, they referred to the likelihood . . . "that the two counties would bitterly resist the establishment of a Joint Board (such as exists for the Peak District National Park), and that the Minister of Housing would concede in its place a Joint Advisory Committee and two planning committees for the Park Area – one for each county". In an oblique reference to the undue attention already being given to planning the region, rather than managing it, they also considered . . . "There would be a grave risk of any National Park administration being cluttered up with the details of planning applications for the lands between the Broads and failing to handle the crucial issue of navigation, already partly in the hands of an existing statutory authority."

The Youth Hostels Association, on the other hand, in a submission to the National Parks Commission dated June 1958, urged that a Park should be established in the region as soon as possible, preferably by the formation of a planning board, rather than a joint advisory committee. Support for national park designation also came in July 1960 from the Inland Waterways Association who, after castigating the Broads Society for . . . "failing to offer any constructive views despite the elapse of two years", referred to . . . "the rumblings in Broadland caused by the consistent failure of anyone to agree on what action should be taken."

Early in 1960, the National Parks Commission held officer level discussions with the principal bodies concerned, and some of its members toured the region in the summer. It later advised the Minister of Housing and Local Government:

> . . . that in the view of the Commission the unique character of the Broads makes them in no way comparable in type with the other areas which, in conformity with general requirements laid down in the *National Parks and Access to the Countryside Act* 1949, it has selected and designated as national parks. It has therefore come to the conclusion that designation under the Act would not be appropriate.

Baldwin (1975), who reviewed the reasons for this decision, believes that the Commission was not only concerned about the high cost of managing the waterways, but was doubtful whether parts of the region, and in particular the Drained Marshland Area, were of national scenic significance. The Commission may also have had reservations about the wisdom of designating such a heavily commercialized area as a national park, although it is unlikely that his view would prevail today, given the commercialism apparent in parts of the Lake District, the Pembrokeshire Coast and other parks.

A less charitable explanation of the decision is that the Commission was, as the Inland Waterways Association claimed at the time, "a pitifully negative body", which was reluctant to take on the strong vested interests which existed in the region. Either way, the Government of the day had no option but to accept the Commission's recommendation. However, in announcing this in the Commons in August 1961, the Minister of Housing and Local Government indicated that:

. . . In these circumstances I have agreed with my right hon. Friend, the Minister of Transport, that he will now, in consultation with my right hon. Friend the Minister of Agriculture, Fisheries and Food and myself, proceed to consider the views of the Great Yarmouth Port and Haven Commissioners, the East Suffolk and Norfolk River Board, and other local bodies about the future of the Broads.

The Report on Broadland, the Consortium Committee and the Study and Plan

During the course of the discussions which took place following the Minister's announcement, it was agreed that what was needed was a factual survey of the problems, along the lines of that suggested by the National Parks Commission in 1955, and the Nature Conservancy undertook to carry this out.

Work started at once, and a consultation document, entitled 'A draft survey of the Broads and their current problems' was published in March 1963. This stimulated much debate, and a certain amount of controversy locally, and a Working Group, consisting of nominees from the principal interested parties was set up to assist Conservancy staff produce a definitive version of the Survey. This was published as the *Report on Broadland* in July 1965.

After describing the physical features and ecology of the region, the Report gives an account of the recreational and other uses to which the waterways are put; the environmental effects of these activities are summarized as an appendix, entitled 'a Chart of Human Impacts on Broadland'. The Report also makes predictions concerning the future use of the region, and suggests ways in which the increasing pressures on it could be accommodated, for instance by providing new broads and waterways.

After stressing the need to adopt as a basic policy the conservation and enhancement of the Broadland environment, the Report recommends that . . . "The major authorities directly concerned should pool their resources to prepare, as a matter of urgency, a Plan for the unification and extension of powers, policies and practices relating to the future planning, management and development of Broadland".

The Report also draws attention to various measures, including improved pollution control, the regulation of boat numbers, speed and design and the provision of mooring facilities, which needed to be investigated by expert groups. It also recommends that discussions should take place concerning the possibility of creating new waterways, and making better use of the existing ones.

Repeated references are made to the region's susceptibility to ecological change, and a poignant warning is given that . . . "Time is not on the side of Broadland. To do nothing is to abandon the region to erosion, conflict and decay."

A Supplement to the Report, signed by all the members of the Working group other than the Conservancy's officers, points out that . . . "no organisation appears at present to possess powers to raise and apportion money on the scale necessary to carry out the substantial programmes of work which are required to meet the growing pressures on the region".

After referring to the need to designate Broadland as a National Recreational Area, a concept which at that time was under consideration in government circles, the Group suggested that . . . "in order to prepare for the necessary changes, a Consortium of the Planning, River and Navigation Authorities, under the chairmanship of a person of standing appointed by the Government should be set up as soon as possible". This should:

(a) Implement the proposals (in the Report) falling within the powers of the Authorities comprising the Consortium;
(b) Encourage and facilitate appropriate action by bodies other than those on the Consortium;
(c) Develop support among other bodies and the general public for the policies and measures proposed;
(d) Maintain close working liaison between the interests concerned;
(e) Create new facilities for the public enjoyment of Broadland within the strategy of the Conservancy's Report;

413

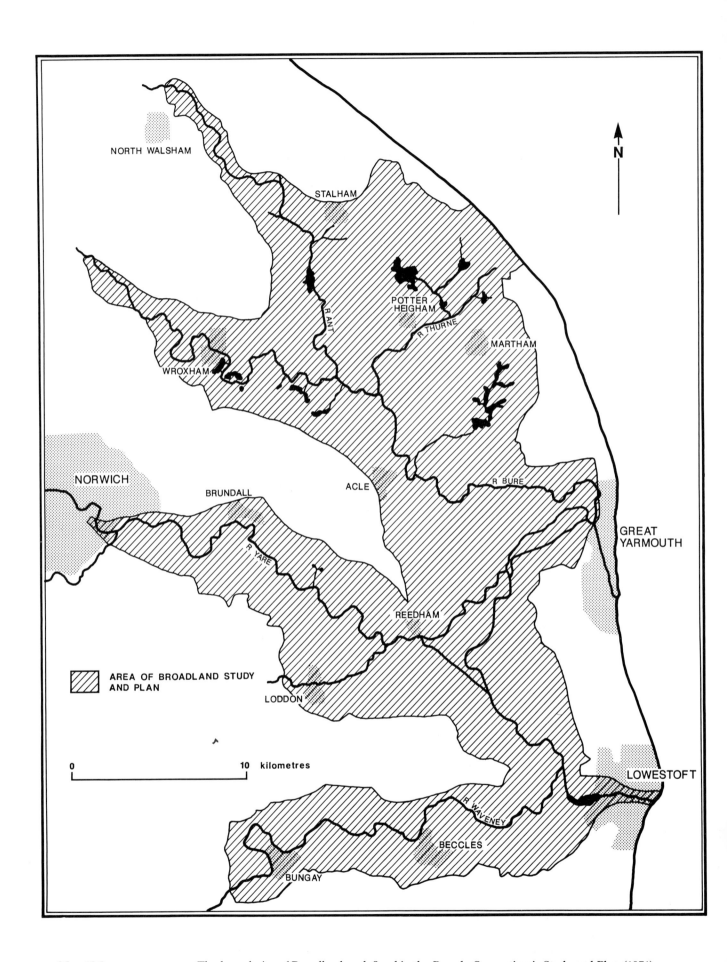

Map 12.2   The boundaries of Broadland as defined in the Broads Consortium's Study and Plan (1971).

(f) Maintain a constant review of trends and developments in the area and initiate action to obtain data on them;

(g) Detect and appraise gaps in the powers necesary to implement fully the agreed policies;

(h) Advise on the economic implications of their proposals and on ways and means of financing them;

(i) Recommend any necessary statutory changes.

A decision to establish a Consortium was taken by the organizations principally concerned in January 1966, and a Committee, under the chairmanship of Major-General A. H. Dowson, was formed soon afterwards. The Norfolk County Council, East Suffolk and Norfolk River Authority and the Great Yarmouth Port and Haven Commissioners each appointed four representatives to this committee, and it was later joined by a member of the East Suffolk County Council.

The Consortium Committee published an illustrated *Broadland Code* in 1968, but it rightly considered that the most urgent task was to prepare a management plan for the region. To this end the Committee decided in September 1966 to invite R. I. Maxwell, then County Planning Officer for Norfolk, to . . . "Carry out a detailed survey of all the factors affecting Broadland and prepare a draft plan for its future management and development up to the year 2000, in accordance with the broad policy directive laid down by the Committee".

The policy document referred to (which was published in 1966, and again in 1971 as an appendix to Maxwell's report) set out the principles which had been agreed by the Consortium Committee. The most important of these were the need:

(1) To restore and preserve the natural environment, which constitutes the chief attraction and value of the area. The appearance of isolation and remoteness at present still apparent from the water must be kept inviolable.

(2) To accept that the factors of increasing pollution, leisure, mobility, and affluence are bound gradually to increase the demand for facilities for recreation and holidays, and that these must be reasonably satisfied as part of a scheme of national provision, provided schemes are assured of economic viability and unlikely to cause damage to the policy set out above or to essential other interests.

Assisted by staff from his planning department, and from various other organizations, Maxwell started work in April 1967. But although his report was completed in August 1969, the Consortium Committee carried out extensive consultations before formulating its own conclusions, and the *c.* 61 000 word, copiously illustrated *Broadland Study and Plan* was not published until October 1971. The boundary of the area defined as Broadland in this document is shown in Map 12.2.

The *Study and Plan* falls into two parts: the first comprises Maxwell's report, while the second, much shorter section consists of the Committee's comments on this, and the conclusions and recommendations which it reached following its consultations with outside parties.

After an introductory chapter, outlining the origins of the Consortium, and the responsibilities of its constituent authorities, the next three chapters of Maxwell's report are descriptive, and deal in turn with the landscape, ecology and physical features of the region; its population, agriculture, industry, communications, public services and buildings, and the holiday and recreational use to which it is subject. These descriptive chapters were accepted without amendment by the Consortium Committee.

Maxwell's fifth chapter contains an analysis of the two principal problems which he identified:

(1) the confict between the expansion of holiday and recreational activities, and the concept of a natural Broadland character and culture; and

(2) the conflicting demands of the various holiday and recreational uses for a limited amount of water space.

After discussing these, he concluded that . . . "the projected increase in the number of boats of all kinds clearly indicates that the problems will become progressively more serious, and an assessment of the physical capacity of the waterway system is necessary".

The appraisal which follows was one of the most controversial sections of the Report, since the conclusion is reached that on the basis of three moving craft per acre of water, the . . . "theoretical physical capacity of the rivers and broads which are at present navigable is about 9200 evenly-moving craft". Maxwell himself realized that densities as high as this would be excessive, and he therefore arbitrarily halved the total figure to give an 'acceptable physical capacity' of about 4600 moving craft. He then went on to argue that on the basis of a census carried out in 1967, which had shown that some 3000 vessels were likely to be on the move during busy periods, the waterways were together capable of taking an additional 1600 moving craft.

Although Maxwell admitted that the 'acceptable capacity' of the middle Bure, Ant and Thurne (which he estimated to be about 1600 moving vessels) was being almost attained, or even slightly exceeded, at certain times, he considered that the rivers Yare, Waveney and lower Bure could readily accommodate extra traffic. On the assumption that the existing proportions of different types of vessel would be maintained, he calculated that an additional 700 to 800 hire cruisers, and 260 day launches, could be permitted on these rivers.

Although he dismissed the widely-held view that much of the waterway system was already heavily overcrowded, Maxwell admitted, almost as an afterthought, that:

> Factors which might impose environmental limits on the number of moving boats in certain parts of Broadland include the need to avoid erosion of banks and the consequent cost of dredging and piling, the desire to conserve wildlife and features of ecologial interest, the desire to retain the character of a particular area where it would be prejudiced by an increase in boating activity, and the desire to avoid conflict with anglers and other users. The 'environmental capacity' of the waterways may therefore be less than the 'acceptable physical capacity', it may vary in different parts of the area, and it will be conditioned by the roles defined for those parts.

The last section of the 'Analysis' is entitled 'Possibilities for Physical Development'. Here, Maxwell and his team gave full rein to their imagination by indicating on maps, a host of places where they thought new broads and waterways could be provided. The great majority of these are no more than planners' pipe-dreams, and are discarded later on the grounds of impracticability and excessive cost. Nevertheless, their inclusion as 'possible starters' in the Study and Plan caused considerable confusion when it was published. In addition, at least two of Maxwell's ideas, namely the creation of a channel between South Walsham and Malthouse Broads, and the excavation of a new cut across the Halvergate marshes, linking the Bure at Runham Swim with the R. Yare at Reedham (a proposal subsequently shown by the AWA to be totally impracticable, as well as environmentally very damaging) were subsequently adopted by the Broads Hire Boat Federation, and actively canvassed in their 1979 and 1988 Reports.

In his 'Conclusion' chapter Maxwell recognized the need to cater for:

(a) the preservation of Broadland's character;
(b) the conservation of unique ecological habitats;
(c) the development and management of Broadland as a holiday area;
(d) the development and management of the area for recreation on land and water.

Since the Consortium Committee had recognized the need to cater for increased recreational and holiday use, and since conflicts seemed certain to occur between (a) and (b), and (c) and (d), Maxwell decided to identify those parts of the region which are better suited to particular roles than others. Given the popularity and nature conservation value of the northern rivers and their flood plains, he proposed that the primary objective here should be to safeguard their existing character and prevent any expansion of recreational activity. He did, however, recommend that additional moorings and holiday accommodation be provided at Acle and Stokesby, and that the Hundred Dyke should be made navigable in order to relieve congestion on the lower reaches of the rivers Ant and Thurne.

Because the southern rivers were, in Maxwell's opinion, generally under-used, he proposed a strategy designed to obtain a better balance of use between the northern and southern parts of the region. This was to be attained by establishing major new holiday and recreational centres at Great Yarmouth, Reedham, Brundall, Oulton Broad, St. Olaves and Beccles, and more limited expansion at Burgh St. Peter, Somerleyton and Belton. Maxwell linked these proposals with the suggestion that new navigable broads should be provided at Strumphaw, Surlingham and Fritton, and that large areas of open water, primarily for recreation, should be created at Whitlingham, Postwick, Oulton Broad, Somerleyton and Beccles. He also proposed that new mooring basins should be established at Brundall, Reedham, Belton, St. Olaves, Burgh St. Peter and Beccles, and that a new cut should be dug across Share Marsh to link the R. Waveney with Oulton Broad, a waterway which, it will be recalled, Beccles Corporation had wanted to create as long ago as 1831.

Maxwell estimated that these new areas of open water would cost some £3.6 million, (*c.* £26 million at 1990 prices) and that other works, including the establishment of a co-ordinated network of footpaths, landscaping, windpump restoration, and the establishment of country parks in the Trowse/Whitlingham/Postwick/Bramerton, and Fritton/Herringfleet areas would bring the total sum required up to *c.* £4.4 million (*c.* £31.9 million at 1990 prices); if spread over a period of, say, 15 years, this would represent an expenditure of *c.* £300 000 per annum (*c.* £2.17 million per annum at 1990 prices).

He proposed that this sum should be raised by drastically increasing the tolls levied on boats using the waterways, and by obtaining, perhaps by means of rate precepts, an increased revenue from commercial and other properties which benefit from their proximity to the water.

Maxwell claimed that if all his proposals were carried out, it would be possible to accommodate about 23 000 vessels on Broadland's waterways, rather than the *c.* 10 000 licensed to use them in 1967. Most of the increase would be accommodated on the waterways in the south of the region, including of course the new broads and channels which Maxwell had recommended should be created in this area to help meet the demand. But he overlooked, or chose to ignore, the fact that even with the existing levels of usage, the banks of the rivers were being severely eroded, and that the problem would become even more acute if they had to carry the amount of boat traffic which he had in mind.

The consultations carried out by the Consortium Committee revealed that almost everyone disagreed with Maxwell's predictions concerning the levels of boat usage which could be accommodated in the region. The Committee itself was obviously unhappy with them, and decided that . . . "any expansion in the growth in the numbers of commercial (hire) motor cruisers must be discouraged", and that there was also a need to prevent the numbers of day launches increasing, and curb the launching of trailer-borne craft.

Although it endorsed Maxwell's proposal that steps should be taken to achieve a more uniform distribution of holiday and recreational pressure between the north and the south, the Committee decided that it would be quite wrong to allow a substantial increase in commercial development in the south since this would in time create a situation comparable to the congestion already existing in the north. Accordingly the Committee agreed that although the attractions of the south should be increased, this could be achieved only by the creation of new areas of open water, and by the provision of limited additional boat hiring and holiday accommodation at Acle, Yarmouth, Brundall, Reedham and Oulton Broad. Even this policy was fiercely criticized subsequently, on the grounds that if more craft were allowed on the southern rivers, this would inevitably increase pressure on the north, in view of the presence here of most of the places which the average holidaymaker wishes to visit (e.g. Wroxham, Ranworth, Barton and Hickling Broads).

The Consortium Committee accepted in broad principle Maxwell's suggestions for zoning the use of Broadland's waterways, and the land adjoining them, and the Zoning Table which forms Appendix 4 to the Study and Plan, constituted the main guide to development control in the region until the early 1980s. The Committee also endorsed his proposal that the feasibility of retaining the Port of Norwich should be investigated by the city and county planning authorities, and agreed, albeit with the Norfolk County Council representatives dissenting, that a study should be carried out of the pros and cons of constructing a fixed tidal barrage, with locks, at Great Yarmouth (see Chapter 10).

The Committee felt that Maxwell's definition of what he called Broadland's 'functions' (i.e. to support the continuing economic and social life of the area; to provide areas of special character . . . for scientific and general study; to meet a national and local holiday need etc.) were far too 'demand-orientated', and decided instead that the policy for the region should be:

(a) to recognize and accept that for the future the overriding consideration must be to ensure that the unique character and charm of the area as a whole is preserved, and wherever possible enhanced, and that in particular, the nature reserves and sites of special scientific interest are adequately protected;
(b) to ensure the protection of important local enterprises, especially water conservation, and the growing of food and other natural products;
(c) to facilitate the pursuit of scientific, educational and nature study;
(d) to enable the Broads area to be used for recreational and holiday purposes, whether water-borne or land-based, to such extent as is compatible with the requirements of (a) and (b) and generally in such a way and subject to any necessary controls as will achieve a maximum of enjoyment with a minimum of conflict.

This is a very conservation-orientated policy statement, as implicit within it there is a recognition that Broadland must be regarded as a resource which, because of its vulnerability to over-exploitation, needs to be planned with care, and managed wisely, if it is to be available for the enjoyment and use of future generations. In Maxwell's version, on the other hand, the main emphasis is on demand, and the belief that the region can, and indeed must, be 'developed' in response to this, regardless of the environmental consequences. Indeed, though never overtly stated in his Report, Maxwell seems to have been much more conscious of the need to generate additional jobs and rateable value in the region, than safeguard it as a unique national asset.

Maxwell's suggestion that a new Broads Authority should be created, which would take over the functions of the Rivers Commissioners, and also have powers to make by-laws, acquire land, secure the removal of caravans and other forms of development detrimental to the area, precept on the rating authorities, and contribute towards the cost of works carried out by other organizations, was rejected by the Committee on the grounds that it would not unify the powers, responsibilities and management of the region as Maxwell claimed. Planning control, for instance, would remain vested in the existing planning authorities, while the River Authority would continue to be responsible for land drainage, water conservation and the control of pollution.

Members of the Committee concluded, like others before them, that desirable as an overall authority was, this was not a practicable proposition. The River Authority, for example, could not be divested of its responsibilities in Broadland, as this would run counter to the concept of integrated river management prescribed in the *Water Resources Act* 1963 (and subsequently taken even further in the *Water Act* 1973). Similarly, the Committee felt that the region could not be planned in isolation from the rest of Norfolk and Suffolk.

The Committee eventually decided by a majority vote that the best solution would be for the River Authority to assume the responsibilities of the Rivers Commissioners. Given the intention, current at the time as a consequence of the Maud Commission's recommendations, that local government would be reorganized in such a way that Broadland came within the purview of a single planning authority, the Committee argued that its proposal would, if adopted, lead to the region being planned and managed by two, rather than six authorities.

On the vexed question of finance, the Committee noted from their consultations that there was a general consensus that Maxwell's proposals were too narrowly based, and thus unacceptable, especially to the boat-hiring interests. Obviously nonplussed, the Committee decided to side-step the issue altogether by suggesting:

. . . that the implications of the finance proposals are such that the whole matter is one which must of necessity be left for further consideration by whatever new Authority is eventually established to manage and control the affairs of Broadland.

To compound the Committee's problems, the Great Yarmouth Port and Haven Commissioners predictably disagreed strongly with the suggestion that they should hand over their responsibilities for the rivers, and insisted on issuing a memorandum of dissent at the same time as the Study and Plan was published. This made the case for the establishment of a new organization in Broadland, similiar to the Lea Valley Regional Park Authority. As a short-term measure, the Commissioners suggested that they should hold liaison meetings with the River Authority regularly, rather than spasmodically.

The interim years, 1971–1978

To the surprise of the Nature Conservancy, which had suggested in its 1965 Report that the Consortium should carry out a number of other on-going tasks, besides drafting a Plan for the region, the Committee was disbanded by the organizations represented on it immediately after the Study and Plan was published in 1971. The Conservancy's disappointment was shared by those who felt that in view of the numerous organizations with responsibilities in the region, and their past reluctance to co-ordinate their endeavours, it would have been useful if the Consortium and its Committee had remained in existence. The need for an element of continuity in the way Broadland was administered was also accentuated by the steps being taken in the early 1970s to reorganize local government and set up a series of regional water authorities.

The latter proposal caused particular unease locally, and several organizations made representations, urging the Government to modify its proposals so that the management of Broadland's rivers remained under local control. In May 1973, Mr (now Sir) Eldon Griffiths, the Minister responsible for piloting the Water Bill through Parliament, met a delegation of local interests at Horning and agreed, in the light of the views expressed, that when the new regional water authority was established, it would be asked to form a special committee for the Broads area. The Minister subsequently announced in Parliament that he was satisfied:

> . . . that it will be quite practicable to establish such a committee consisting of people with the necessary local knowledge and experience of the Broads, and at the same time complying with the Water Bill's requirements that two-thirds of the members of such a committee must also be members of the authority . . . These arrangements should ensure that the special position of Broadland is recognised and safeguarded within the regional water authority.

The Broads Committee of the Anglian Water Authority as it subsequently became known, met for the first time in March 1974, and decided that the remaining third of its membership should consist of persons nominated by the Rivers Commissioners, the NCC, the Anglers Consultative Council, the Broads Society and the private and commercial boating interests. The Committee was given executive responsibility for all AWA's functions, both in Broadland itself, and in the catchments of its rivers, apart from land drainage and flood control which were vested in the Norfolk and Suffolk Local Land Drainage Committee. This became the Norfolk and Suffolk Local Flood Defence Committee in 1989.

One of the Committee's earliest, and most important, decisions was to agree in December 1974, that "no action be taken at the present time" regarding the draft order which had, in accordance with the majority recommendation made by the Consortium Committee, been submitted to the Secretary of State for the Environment and the Minister of Agriculture by the River Authority in 1973, and which would have transferred to the latter (and its successor, the AWA) the functions of the Rivers Commissioners. This decision was prompted largely by the new Committee's anxiety not to awaken the old antagonisms between navigation and land-drainage interests; however, these continued to erupt from time to time.

The other major administrative change which occurred in Broadland in the early 1970s resulted from the Government's rejection of the Maud Commission's report (1969) which had, *inter alia*, suggested that all the services concerned with the physical environment in a region (planning, transportation and major development) should be in the hands of a single authority. Instead, the Government announced its intention of introducing a Bill which would provide for the creation of a pattern of local government based on two levels of operational authorities (counties and districts), plus metropolitan counties in certain conurbations (DoE, 1971). Draft proposals for the new district councils in Norfolk were subject to considerable criticism at a Boundary Commission hearing in Norwich in September 1972, several of the local authorities concerned arguing that Broadland should be administered by a single district council. But other considerations prevailed, and when the new arrangements came into force in April 1974, those concerned with the welfare of the region were dismayed to find that it came within the ambit of no less than six district councils, plus the Norfolk and Suffolk County Councils. Bearing in mind the separate roles of the AWA and the Rivers Commissioners, this meant that there would in future be ten organizations with major statutory responsibilities in the region, rather than the four which had existed previously.

To ensure that each of the local authorities received advice on planning control and other matters, the Norfolk County Council decided that a non-statutory 'Broads Consultative Committee' should be set up in place of the Joint Advisory Committee which had gone out of existence at the end of March 1974, as a consequence of the reform of local government. The terms of reference of the new Committee were:

(a) To consider and advise upon all plans, schemes, or proposals of any of the constituent authorities relating to, or likely to affect the use of the whole or any part of the Broads area for recreational or holiday purposes, or the character or amenities of the area . . .

(b) To consider all planning applications relating to development in the Broads area which . . . [are] likely to affect the character of the Broads area, and to advise the constituent planning authorities thereon.

In addition to representatives from each of the six local authorities, the AWA, the Great Yarmouth Port and Haven Commissioners, conservation, angling, landowning, farming, and private and commercial boating interests were each invited to appoint nominees to the Committee.

Although some of the organizations with planning and managerial functions in Broadland communicated with one another more regularly, and with greater effect during the 1970s than they had done in the past, the plethora of committees which existed during this period did little to resolve the problem of divided responsibility which had bedevilled the region's affairs for so long. Moreover, each committee had its shortcomings. The Local Land Drainage Committee, for example, did not have any environmental agencies represented on it, despite the profound effect which drainage works can have on conservation interests. Similarly, the Broads Committee was unable for constitutional reasons to deal with matters coming within the purview of any organization other than the AWA. In addition, despite the Ministerial assurance that this Committee would consist of people with a "knowledge and experience of the Broads", its AWA members did not always possess these attributes initially, although once appointed, they invariably proved interested and anxious to learn about the region and its problems. Some of the senior, Huntingdon-based officials of the AWA never seem to have been convinced of the need for a special committee for Broadland, especially one with executive powers, and it doubtless came as a relief to them when it was disbanded in 1983. This resulted from the comprehensive reorganization of the Authority, consequent upon the passing of the *Water Act* that year, and in recognition of the belief that the creation of the Broads Authority had reduced the need for a special AWA committee for the region. The AWA itself underwent a marked change in character as a result of the passing of the 1983 Act, as local authority representation on it (and other regional water authorities) was largely eliminated, and control was vested in a small executive Board, whose members were appointed by Ministers.

The membership of the Consultative Committee was much more widely representative than that of the Broads Committee or the Local Land Drainage Committee, but like its predecessor, the Joint Advisory Committee, it devoted relatively little time to discussing the management of the region, preferring instead to concentrate on its planning and advisory role. This it did assiduously, and although environmentalists could, and did, find much to criticize in the Study and Plan, particularly in regard to its failure to take adequate account of the ecological fragility of the region, the Consultative Committee could hardly be blamed for these deficiencies. Indeed, when in January 1978, it became apparent that the proposal in the Plan to allow additional boat hiring and other facilities in the Yare and Waveney valleys would increase boating pressure elsewhere, the Committee passed a resolution indicating that . . . "it was generally opposed to any development, whether on the northern or the southern rivers which would be likely to increase cruiser traffic on the northern rivers".

Most of the other provisions relating to development control which had been agreed by the Consortium Committee were adhered to by the appropriate planning authorities on the advice of the Consultative Committee, and to this extent, the Study and Plan was implemented. However, the same cannot be said of the management recommendations contained in the Plan, very few of which were acted upon. For instance, although a small (*c.* 7 ha), but very popular Picnic Site was opened by the South Norfolk District Council at Whitlingham in 1978, the proposal in the Plan that country parks and new 'broads' should be established in the Trowse/Whitlingham/Postwick/Bramerton, and Fritton/Herringfleet areas received scant attention until the Broads Authority came into existence. Fortunately, Fritton Lake and its surroundings, which have been open to the public since 1906, and which are visited by between one hundred and twenty, and one hundred and fifty thousand persons a year, were formally designated in 1976 as a Country Park, covering some 94 ha. However, this resulted from the initiative of its owner, Lord Somerleyton, rather than a local authority. Indeed, until 1981, when Salhouse Broad was leased by the Broads Authority for use as a public recreational area, only one other facility of this type existed in the region – a very small (0.6 ha) Picnic Site established by the East Anglian Water Company beside Rollesby Broad in 1978.

Proposals in the Study and Plan for new or extended waterways were also dealt with very cursorily. The AWA's Broads Committee, for instance, having been advised in 1975 that the £400 000 (*c.* £1.48 million at 1990 prices) which would be required to make the Hundred Dyke navigable would not attract MAFF grant, decided not to proceed with the project. Similarly, no action was taken to implement the recommendation that the North Walsham and Dilham Canal, the river Bure upstream of Coltishall and the Waveney above Geldeston be reopened for casual boating and recreation.

Many people believed that the principal reason why so few of the management proposals in the Study and Plan were being implemented lay in the multiplicity of different organizations having interests in the region, and the fact that no single person was responsible for initiating the necessary action. With this latter point in mind, the author suggested at a meeting of the Consultative Committee in March 1977, that a Broads Officer should be appointed to fulfil this role, and after some discussion, it was agreed that the views of the constituent organizations on this proposal should be sought.

In the meantime, public concern about the environmental degradation taking place in the region was mounting rapidly. Not only had waterweeds disappeared from most of the broads, but there had been outbreaks of avian botulism, fish kills in the Thurne water-ways, and losses of marginal reedswamp from both the rivers and the broads. Several of these problems were by now under investigation as a result of a plea made by the Norfolk Naturalists' Trust in 1975 that a major programme of ecological research should be carried out in the region (see page 489). But as the full complexity of the changes taking place, and the difficulty of resolving them became apparent, more and more people became convinced that the administration of the region needed to be drastically over-hauled. Support for this came from the apparent impossibility of preventing further increases in the numbers of vessels using the waterways, the conflicts arising from the Rivers Commissioners' inability to contribute towards the cost of making good the bank erosion caused by boat wash, the increasingly strident demands by farmers that the standard of protection afforded the region against flooding should be improved, thus enabling them to convert their grass marshland to arable, and the growing antagonisms between different users of the waterways, notably anglers and the hirers of motor craft.

In the face of these mounting pressures, it was suggested, not for the first time, that a more harmonious and cohesive administration would be achieved if the region was designated as a national park. The Countryside Commission's response to this was to issue a Consultation Paper in November 1976, outlining the purposes of such a park, and the way in which one could be set up, planned and administered in Broadland. Although the Commission made it clear that it was merely testing public opinion on the issue, it obviously had in mind that the Government had recently endorsed (DoE, 1976) the Sanford Committee's recommendation (DoE, 1974) that:

> . . . in considering possible new national parks, the Commission should examine more diverse types of landscape, provided that they are of the highest quality, than the rugged

uplands which dominate our existing parks . . . and should seek . . . to redress to some extent at least, the existing uneven geographical distribution of the national parks, none of which is close to the large populations of the south and south-east of England.

The Discussion Paper provoked a lively debate about the future of the region, and in August 1977, the Commission issued a second consultation document (CCP 104). In this, it outlined four possible courses of action, Option A being the designation of a national park using existing legislation, whilst Option B would involve delaying the establishment of a park until amending legislation had been passed by Parliament. This would need to ensure that the national park authority was empowered to exercise control over navigation and water quality, a point considered essential by the Norfolk and Suffolk County Councils. Under Option C, an entirely new authority specifically designed to deal with Broadland's problems would be established, while Option D was related to the possibility that a national Inland Navigation Authority, then under consideration, might be set up. This could result in a new authority being created in the region, or the taking over by the AWA of the Rivers Commissioners navigational functions, as proposed by the Consortium Committee in 1971. Two short-term measures were also canvassed, one being a broadening of the Consultative Committee's role, and the other the appointment of a Broads Officer. Neither of these proposals was particularly favoured by the Commission, doubtless because if it had supported such temporary expedients, it would weaken the case for the adoption of one or other of its four, long-term options.

Although still not committed to any particular course of action, the Commission indicated its belief:

> . . . that the best pragmatic approach is to pursue Option B, recognizing that it may well disappoint many people who would have preferred to see established an authority which would more exactly meet what, in their view, are the special requirements of the Broads.

While awaiting comments on its second Consultation Paper, members of the Commission and its senior staff visited Broadland in November 1977, and discussed its future with a wide range of local people and organizations. A public meeting was also held.

As was foreseen, none of the options received universal support (Countryside Commission, 1979). Option A was rejected by most people, partly because they considered, rightly or wrongly, that a national park authority set up under the existing legislation would not cure Broadland's ills, and also because it would take at least four years to establish. Option D was unanimously opposed, and although Option C received much support, the Commission subsequently expressed the view that . . . "it was unrealistic to believe that Government would agree to create a special authority for the Broads, giving it national finance and powers taken from the existing statutory agencies in the area".

Option B was backed by most conservation and amenity organizations, either as their preferred course of action, or as the next best alternative to a one-off authority. Two distinct variants of this option were suggested:

(1) The proposed national park authority to have statutory control of standards over water, including quality and levels, which would then be binding on the Anglian Water Authority, and over boats, including number, size, design and speed, the Port and Haven Commissioners continuing to administer the navigation within these constraints.

(2) The Anglian Water Authority and Port and Haven Commissioners to be statutorily bound to operate "in general accord with" a national park plan, and the Port and Haven Commissioners to seek powers to control the number of boats through a licencing system.

The Norfolk County Council was arguably the most influential of the organizations whose views had been canvassed by the Countryside Commission, and it must have come as a severe blow to the latter, and indeed many others, when the Council decided in January 1978 that it was opposed to a national park. Indeed, its attitude was labelled as 'deplorable' in an *Eastern Daily Press* editorial (EDP, 1978a), a view quickly endorsed by representatives of the Broads Society, Ludham Society, Norfolk Naturalists' Trust,

Norfolk Society, Ramblers Association and the Suffolk Preservation Society (Kemp *et al.*, 1978). Particular surprise was expressed that the County Council had not awaited the outcome of a new initiative taken a few days previously by the Norfolk Branch of the Association of District Councils. Members of this had decided to intervene because, apart from Norwich City Council which was in favour of a national park, none of the other five district councils with responsibilities in Broadland was particularly happy with the options identified by the Commission, not least because there was no guarantee that each of them would be represented on any new authority established in the region. But rather than adopt a negative stance, the Association had set up a Working Group to study the proposals which had been put foward.

The members of this Group were opposed to a national park because they considered that the existing authorities (including the AWA and the Rivers Commissioners) already possessed, or could easily obtain, the powers and expertise required to solve the region's problems. Nevertheless, the Group accepted that there was a need for greater co-ordination of effort in the region, and after much discussion it was suggested that a Consortium of local organizations should be formed. The original idea was that this should be an advisory body, but it was later decided that it would be better if the eight local authorities concerned delegated to it their executive powers in respect of a defined area, and that it assumed an advisory role over a much larger area, subsequently identified as consisting of those parts of the catchments of the Broadland rivers located within the Districts of Great Yarmouth, Norwich, Broadland, North and South Norfolk and Waveney.

The Group agreed that the Norfolk County Council should be represented on the Consortium by five of its members, and that the Suffolk County Council, the Broadland, North Norfolk, South Norfolk and Waveney District Councils, the Norwich City Council, the Great Yarmouth Borough Council, the AWA and the Great Yarmouth Port and Haven Commissioners should nominate two each. A Broads Officer would be appointed to service the Consortium and ensure that its policies were implemented. On the crucial question of finance, it was proposed that £190000 per annum should be made available by the local authorities for the first two years (£50000 from the Norfolk County Council and £20000 from each of the remainder), rising to £285000 per annum for the following three years, with the AWA and the Great Yarmouth Port and Haven Commissioners contributing in the form of capital works, plus a share of the Authority's administrative expenses.

The Working Group's recommendations were endorsed by the full Association and publicized in early March (EDP, 1978b), the proponents of the scheme being quick to point out that it had two principal advantages over the Commission's proposals: the Consortium could be set up much more quickly than could a national park authority, and equally important, at least for some organizations, Broadland would remain under the control of local people.

Although the Commission accepted the logic behind the first of these arguments, it had grave reservations about the desirability of allowing local organizations to retain full responsibility for administering the region. Accordingly, it formally resolved at its meeting in April 1978, that . . . "the area commonly known as the Norfolk Broads has such special environmental quality and character, and is of such significance for recreation as to merit the distinction of designation as a national park, and the benefit of the associated special powers and Treasury support".

Nevertheless, in view of the steps being taken locally to establish the Consortium (which soon became known as the Broads Authority), the Commission decided temporarily to defer commencing the designation process, and to support the new organization with grant aid and advice, provided certain conditions were met. These included the need for the Commission to agree the boundary of the Executive Area, and be allowed to nominate three persons to serve on it. The Commission indicated that it would review the effectiveness of the new authority at the end of 1980, and that it would reconsider its policy regarding the designation of a national park in Broadland in 1983.

Many people were initially somewhat sceptical about the Broads Authority, on the grounds that it had been set up by the very organizations which in the past had so signally failed to work together to solve the region's problems. On the whole, however, there was a feeling of relief that a body with such wide-ranging responsibilities had at last been established, and a general desire to help it in every way possible.

The Broads Authority

As initially conceived, the 'old' Broads Authority was a Joint Local Authority Committee, established under Sections 101 and 102 of the *Local Government Act* 1972, and its constitution, area of operation, and terms of reference were set out in an Agreement, signed on behalf of the participating organizations in March 1980. The objectives of the Authority were formally defined as follows:

> Recognising the national importance of the area for its landscape, nature conservation and recreational value, the overriding consideration is to conserve and enhance the natural beauty of the area as a whole, including its wildlife, while protecting the economic and social interests of those who live and work in the area, and preserving its natural resources and (having regard to these interests and resources) facilitating the use of the Broads for recreation and holiday purposes both waterborne and land-based, and for the pursuit of scientific research, education and nature study.

The Agreement also defined the way the Authority should be managed and financed, and the relationships between it, and the bodies which set it up. None of the constituent parties could withdraw its membership unless it had given all the other parties at least two years written warning of its intention to do so. However, the Authority could be disbanded if a majority of the county and district councils represented on it agreed on this course of action, after consultation with the other parties.

Under the Agreement, the Authority was empowered to carry forward from year to year unspent parts of its annual income. But although the sums to be made available by the constituent authorities were prescribed for the first five years (1978/9–1982/3 inclusive) the amounts to be allocated for subsequent years were not specified, the Agreement merely indicating that these . . . "shall be determined by agreement between all the Councils not later than two years and two months before the commencement of the financial year to which these contributions relate".

The Authority's terms of reference mentioned the need to define Broadland's problems, and devise and implement solutions for them, both by the exercise of its own executive functions, and by making recommendations to other parties. In addition, the Authority was required to prepare, periodically revise, and put into effect a management plan for the region, to coordinate the activities of other organizations, and to act as a forum of communication between interested parties about all matters relating to Broadland. It was responsible for a full range of local authority functions in its Executive Area, including the planning and provision of recreational facilities, nature conservation, the planting of trees, the preservation of ancient monuments and buildings of outstanding architectural or historic interest, and the creation, diversion and closure of public footpaths and bridleways.

To assist it achieve these objectives, the Countryside Commission agreed to grant-aid the salaries of the Authority's staff and its administrative expenses (including the cost of preparing a management plan for the region), and also those projects which fell within the ambit of the Commission's overall policies. This undertaking, which was periodically renewed, proved of immense benefit to the Authority, the Commission's total annual commitments under these headings, being as follows:

Year	Countryside Commission's grant	Percentage of funds disbursed by the Authority
1978/9	2450	45
1979/80	14780	7
1980/1	45300	16
1981/2	108363	22
1982/3	163373	31
1983/4	180115	25
1984/5	273783	39
1985/6	221206	35
1986/7	259963	33
1987/8	219778	28
1988/9	436936	46

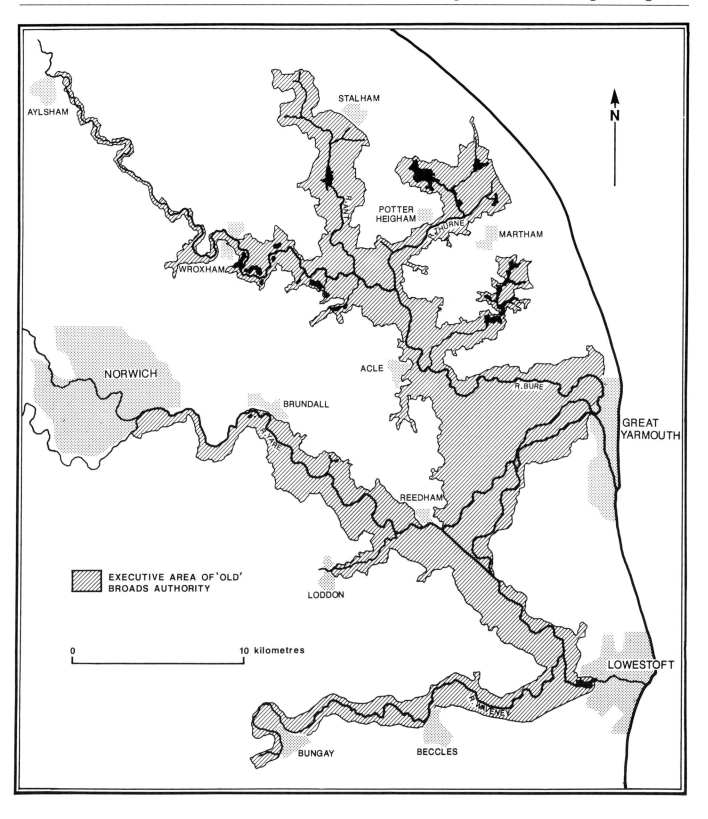

Map 12.3

The boundaries of the 'Executive Area' of the 'old' Broads Authority (1978 – 1989).

The Broads Authority met formally for the first time in September 1978, the late Guy Richards, one of the Norfolk County Council's nominees, being elected Chairman. It was decided that Broadland District Council's offer of office accommodation should be accepted, and that the late Philip Taylor, then that Council's Chief Executive, should act as secretary to the Authority until a Broads Officer was appointed. It was also agreed that meetings should be held each month, and that a Finance Committee should be appointed. Among many items discussed during the ensuing months were the appointment of officers from other organizations to provide the Authority with advice on planning, legal, conservation, scientific, financial and other matters, and the boundary of the Executive Area. This is reproduced as Map 12.3, and it will be noted that much of the catchment of the Upper Thurne, including Calthorpe Broad, is excluded. This decision, which was taken in the light of views expressed by the North Norfolk District Council, caused the NCC and other conservation agencies much concern, given the very poor quality of the water reaching Horsey Mere from the drained marshland in this part of Broadland, and the consequent desirability of having this area within the ambit of the Broads Authority.

The new organization assumed its planning functions in April 1979, and at first all major issues were dealt with by the full Authority. However, this soon proved impracticable, and from November 1979, these were delegated to a Planning Committee. The need for such a committee can be gauged from the fact that it determined no less than 310 applications in 1987–8. Although 140 of these were concerned with minor issues, and were therefore dealt with by officers under delegated powers, site visits had to be held in respect of several difficult or controversial cases. The Committee was also consulted about a further 8 planning applications affecting the Authority's Advisory Area.

The post of Broads Officer, or more formally, the Authority's Principal Adviser and Chief Executive, was advertised in July 1978, but although 1400 applications were received, a great deal of difficulty was encountered in filling the vacancy. However, Aitken Clark, Professor of Regional Planning at Clemson University, South Carolina, was appointed in May 1979, and took up his duties four months later.

In April 1979, the Authority received a report from its technical advisers which identified a number of environmentally-desirable projects which could be carried out immediately, and which were in accordance with the provisions of the 1971 Study and Plan. Included in this 'Interim Action Programme', and given special priority by the Authority, were four schemes of direct relevance to nature conservation: contributing £7500 towards the purchase by the Suffolk Trust of its Carlton Colville reserve; commissioning an Environmental Impact Analysis of the Yare Basin Flood Control Scheme (see page 325); funding a research programme into the causes of reedswamp regression (see page 185), and the experimental mud-pumping of a broad (see page 502). The Interim Action Programme also embraced an investigation of the problems involved in creating new broads (the conclusion reached being that this would have to be combined with the commercial extraction of sand and gravel, as had been done by the University of East Anglia), the identification of areas where waterborne congestion could be relieved by providing more overnight mooring places, and several landscape improvement projects, including the restoration of selected drainage mills.

As part of its conditional support for the new Authority, the Countryside Commission was insistent that it should give high priority to the production of a new management plan for the region. In adopting this stance, the Commission was in effect endorsing the belief of many local people that the 1971 Study and Plan was seriously out-of-date. Several of the concepts on which it was based, notably the assumption that more holiday and recreational facilities could be provided beside the lower Bure and the Yare and Waveney without increasing the pressure on the rest of the waterway system, had proved to be fallacious. More seriously, the Study and Plan failed to take adequately into account the water quality, bank erosion and other environmental problems to which the region had become subject.

Rather than establish a single working party to supervise the preparation of the new plan, as had been done when the 'Report on Broadland' was being drafted, Aitken Clark set up separate groups concerned with Ecology, Landscape and Recreation, and invited each to consider the needs of its specialist interest, and make recommendations. The final reports of the three groups were published in February 1982 (Broads Authority, 1982a, b & c), and were then integrated by the Authority's staff into a draft Strategy and Management Plan for the region. This was discussed, and in due course approved by the Strategy Committee (which had been established primarily for this purpose in June 1980), and after it had been endorsed by the full Authority, was issued in December 1982 as a Consultation Document under the title 'What Future for Broadland?' (Broads Authority, 1982e).

Extensive discussions with interested parties took place during the ensuing four years, and the Authority also arranged a number of public meetings so that views on the provisions of the draft plan could be expressed. Not unexpectedly, some of the heaviest criticisms were voiced by boating interests who felt that some of the policies set out in the document placed too much emphasis on the needs of environmental conservation, and not enough on those of the holiday industry. To assist it deal with the comments made by these and other interested parties, the Strategy Committee set up a small Implementation Sub-Committee, and after much discussion, and not a little wrangling, this agreed a revised version of the plan. Following further debate, this was accepted by the Strategy Committee, and after the definitive version had been formally endorsed by the full Authority, it was published as a copiously illustrated, 128-page document in 1987 (Broads Authority, 1987a).

The production of the *Broads Plan* with its 104 clearly set-out policies was far from being the only planning initiative taken by the Authority during the early 1980s. For example, it commissioned consultants to produce a series of 'Design Guides' for the region (Owers & Lumley Associates, 1985–1986). These are helping to ensure that new developments in the region are of a better quality than has sometimes been the case in the past. In addition, they are assisting in the mammoth task of up-grading those areas which, through a combination of poor design, and under-investment, often extending over a period of 80 years or so, are now in a thoroughly run-down state. In this connection, a Local Plan has been prepared for the area around Potter Heigham Bridge (Owers & Lumley Associates, 1985), and pilot 'environmental improvement schemes' have been produced for a number of sites, including Ranworth and Upton Staithes.

In contrast to the system practised in the national parks, the Authority made use of specialists employed by other organizations, thus saving money, and avoiding duplication of effort. For instance, planning applications were processed by staff of the appropriate district council planning departments, who prepared and presented reports to the Authority's Planning Committee. Norfolk County Council's Director of Property and Planning co-ordinated these arrangements, ensured that there was consistency in the interpretation of policy, and acted as lead adviser to the Committee. Similarly, the Authority was provided with advice on legal matters by Norfolk County Council's Solicitor. These arrangements worked well; nevertheless, as its commitments increased, the Authority was obliged to appoint more staff, this despite some opposition from certain members who, particularly at first, seemed to interpret any request from their Chief Executive for more assistants as indicative of 'empire-building'. By April 1986, Aitken Clark was being supported by four individuals with managerial qualifications, seven wardens and estate staff, two interpretive officers, seven administrative and support staff and eight part-timers, most of whom were working in the Authority's Tourist and Information Centres. Three years later, the full-time establishment consisted of 22 permanent posts, plus 4 individuals on short-term contracts.

The membership of the Consultative Committee was much more widely representative than was that of the Broads Authority, and when the latter was set up, many believed that the Committee could act as a useful 'sounding board' of local opinion for it. At first, the Committee continued to be serviced by staff of the Norfolk County Council, but it was generally accepted that this was anomalous, and in December 1981, the Authority agreed to assume responsibility for it. At the same time, it resolved that in future the Committee would:

> Advise the Broads Authority upon such matters seen to raise questions of major policy relating to the functions of the Authority within its executive and advisory areas as may be referred to the Committee by the Authority or as may be identified by the Committee as warranting their attention.

To avoid duplication of effort, the Authority decided that the county and district councils, the AWA and the Great Yarmouth Port and Haven Commissioners would not in future be represented on the Committee at member level, but that the Chairman and Vice-Chairman of the Authority should attend its meetings in a non-voting capacity. It was also agreed that the Committee's membership should be broadened to include the Royal Yachting Association, the RSPB, the Suffolk Trust for Nature Conservation, the Eastern Council for Sport and Recreation, the East Anglian Tourist Board, the Friends of the Earth and the Norfolk Society. The Committee met for the first time in its new guise in February 1982.

In addition to the working groups set up in connection with the drafting of a management plan for the region, several sub-committees and advisory panels were established by the Authority to assist its main committees with their work. The inter-relationships between these are illustrated in Fig. 12A.

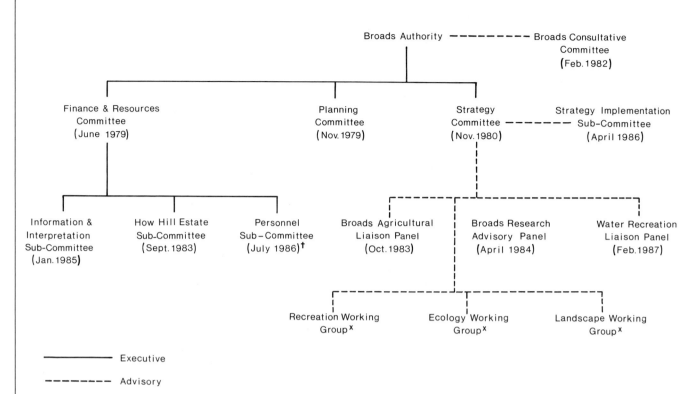

Executive

-------- Advisory

ˣ These 3 Working Groups did not meet again after they had finalised their Reports.

† Prior to July 1986, this sub-committee had met on an ad hoc basis.

Fig. 12ᴀ   The committee structure of the Broads Authority – September 1978 to March 1989.

Source: Minutes of the Broads Authority

Table 12a   Broads Authority – Income & Expenditure – 1978/9 to 1988/9

Income	1978/9	1979/80	1980/1	1981/2	1982/3
Countryside Commission grants for administration and Strategy & Management Plan (Note 1)	2450	13780	33612	67763	106759
Constituent Authorities	2919	190000	190000	285000	285000
Participating bodies					
(a) AWA	–	1573	3376	5253	6481
(b) Gt. Yarmouth Port & Haven Commission	–	1573	3376	5253	6481
Transfer from Special Fund	–		–	–	–
Interest on miscellaneous income	1	15990	16663	19704	17081
	5370	222916	247027	383013	421802
Expenditure					
Managerial and administrative (Note 2)	5438	46004	75989	146881	213426
Projects (net) – see table 12b	Nil	7500	47079	147391	141658
	5438	53504	123068	294272	355084

Notes:
1. The Commission's contributions for projects are additional to these sums and are included in the 'Grants and Income' columns of Table 12b.
2. This includes salaries, travelling and subsistence, office accommodation, supplies and services, agencies and contractual services, Strategy and Management Plan costs and sales and, up to 1981/2, miscellaneous 'operational expenses'.

The Authority's income and expenditure since its formation are summarized in Table 12a, and its outlay on projects in Table 12b. The latter provides an insight into the balance of effort given by the Authority to different aspects of its work, and some of its activities in relation to nature conservation, interpretation, research and experimental management are described in the next chapter. But the Authority also carried out numerous other environmentally beneficial projects. Many of these are listed in the Annual Report it produced for the year 1986/7 (Broads Authority, 1987b), and it will suffice here to say that they covered topics as diverse as improvements to the staithes and associated car parks at Ranworth, Upton and Horsey, helping to fund the renovation of selected drainage mills (see page 249), establishing a number of circular walks in the region (those needing to be regularly mown extended to 22 miles by 1989, a sizeable maintenance commitment), studying how best to tackle the litter-clearance problem, restoring a derelict barn at Tunstall so that it could be used by campers, and funding projects to enable the disabled to make better use of the region's waterways. The Authority also assisted the Rivers Commissioners financially with numerous environmentally-desirable works, such as piling Sutton Staithe and the rond separating Salhouse Broad from the R. Bure, and gave grants to private individuals for repairing buildings of vernacular interest (e.g. thatched cottages in Ludham, a pub beside the river at Coltishall, and a boathouse beside Horsey Mere), or historic value (e.g. Thorpe Old Hall and Langley Abbey). The sums disbursed for this purpose amounted to £5636 in 1982/3, £7399 in 1983/4, £15 499 in 1984/5, £10 760 in 1985/6, £10 845 in 1986/7, £12 300 in 1987/8 and £6511 in 1988/9. Grant-aid expenditure for nature reserve acquisition, conservation management and interpretive projects is given in Tables 12c, 12d and 12e, while the costs incurred by the Authority in respect of various research and experimental management projects are set out in Table 12f.

Given the difficulties faced by the Authority in its early years, and the delays always encountered in setting up new projects from scratch, it was inevitable that its income should at first exceed its expenditure. As a result, substantial funds had to be transferred each year to a reserve or 'special' fund; by March 1983 this stood at £400 000. Although several of the constituent local authorities found it disquieting that such a large sum had been allowed to accumulate (not least because of the cut-backs in expenditure which they themselves were having to make in the early 1980s), most observers were favourably impressed by the way in which the Authority was setting about its task. Thus in February 1981, when the Countryside Commission fulfilled its commitment to review the Authority's activities, there was near-universal support for its conclusion that . . . "[the Authority] is to be congratulated on the speed with which it has established itself

1983/4	1984/5	1985/6	1986/7	1987/8	1988/9
127 463	170 103	161 310	172 280	177 409	425 790
285 000	303 000	318 150	325 900	332 150	346 750
8503	8786	9282	11 364	12 419	14 282
8503	8786	9282	11 364	12 419	14 282
184 350	25 506	30 389	76 109	100 000	70 016
15 022	20 691	1373	34 697	23 101	–
628 841	536 872	529 786	631 714	657 498	871 120
288 456	331 040	276 631	[324 683] (Note 4)	[354 819] (Note 4)	[408 068] (Note 4)
289 111 (Note 3)	241 377	253 155	631 714	657 498	871 120
577 567	572 417	529 786	631 714	657 498	871 120

3. Includes the net cost of purchasing the How Hill estate.
4. These sums were re-charged to project expenditure in these years (see Table 12b).
5. The following monies were transferred to the reserve (or 'special') fund: 1979/80–£150 000; 1980/1–£100 000; 1981/2–£20 000; 1982/3–£27 598.

Table 12b   Broads Authority Project expenditure — 1979/80 to 1988/9

	1979/80 (Note 1)			1980/1 (Note 1)			1981/2 (Note 1)			1982/3			1983/4		
	Exp	Grants & Income	Net	Exp	Grants & Income	Net	Exp	Grants & Income	Net	Exp	Grants & Income	Net	Exp	Grants & Income	Net
Conservation															
(a) Rivers & broads	–	–	–	24754	10088	14666	84929	18243	66686	86075	31790	54285	53826	15625	38201
(b) Fens & woodlands	7500 (Note 2)	–	7500 (Note 2)	–	–	–	–	–	–	1846	–	1846	1942	–	1942
(c) Drained marshland	–	–	–	15500 (Note 3)	750	14750 (Note 3)	14181	2700	11481	25914	6782	19132	23359	5061	18298
													11274	2400	8874
													122922	22500	100422
													(Note 4)		(Note 4)
(d) How Hill	–	–	–	–	–	–	–	–	–	–	–	–	–	–	–
(e) Conservation Management (inc. grants for management works by other bodies) (Note 5)	–	–	–	–	–	–	–	–	–	–	–	–			
Planning and Design															
(a) Buildings & Settlements; ancient monuments etc.	–	–	–	12125	–	12125	35096	5974	29122	20774	750	20024	19533	700	18833
(b) Local studies & plans	–	–	–	–	–	–	–	–	–	17482	8741	8741	8521	1756	6765
Recreation															
(a) Projects	–	–	–	5432	1394	4038	19412	7118	12294	9053	3100	5953	25664	19509	6155
(b) Recreation Management	–	–	–	–	–	–	34231	13650	20581	23897	6075	17822	59850	39471	20379
Information & Tourism															
(a) Centres	–	–	–	1500	–	1500	8249	1250	6999	18644	8956	9688	61514	3950	57564
(b) General	–	–	–	–	–	–	2658	2430	228	4987	820	4167	22670	10992	11678
Totals	7500	–	7500	59311	12232	47079	198756	51365	147391	208672	67014	141658	411075	121964	289111

as a strong, independent voice in the Broads; no mean task in the present uncertain climate". The Commission also believed that . . . "the Authority has proved through its initial actions and approach that it has the potential of achieving substantial environmental improvement in the Broads and is the agency best fitted to address the landscape conservation and recreational management problems of the area", and concluded that . . ." there is no case, at present, for designating a national park in the Broads", but that it . . . "will review the position finally at the end of 1983" (Countryside Commission, 1981).

In the meantime, the Authority would continue to receive the Commission's wholehearted support and, subject to the Government's approval, provide grant aid for 'appropriate activities'. There is a certain irony in the fact that Mr Michael Heseltine, then Secretary of State for the Environment, chose to announce that he approved this arrangement, when he addressed the delegates to the annual national park conference during their visit to Broadland in September 1981.

Table 12c   Broads Authority Grants for nature reserve acquisition

Year	Name of site	Approx Cost (£)	Grant (£)	Recipient
1980/1	Carlton Colville Marshes	45000	14000	Suffolk Trust for Nat. Cons.
1980/1	Upton Fen	N/A	7500	NNT
1984/5	Upton Grazing Marsh	7520	1875	NNT
1986/7	Berney Marshes	400000	20000	RSPB
1986/7	Heigham Holmes	550000	20000	National Trust
1987/8	Ted Ellis Memorial Reserve (Wheatfen)	120000	10000 (over 2 yrs)	Ted Ellis Trust
1987/8	Castle Marshes (Barnby)	23500	3000	Suffolk Wildlife Trust
1988/9	Castle Marshes	105000	17000	Suffolk Wildlife Trust

	1984/5			1985/6			1986/7			1987/8			1988/9	
Exp	*Grants & Income*	*Net*	*Exp*	*Grants & Income*	*Net*	*Exp (Note 6)*	*Grants & Income*	*Net*	*Exp (Note 6)*	*Grants & Income*	*Net*	*Exp (Note 6)*	*Grants & Income*	*Net*
53243	18793	34450	40403	14608	25795	143187	63599	79588	108512	37463	71049	108284	4424	103860
1496	–	1496	10639	583	10056	35073	2421	32652	42359	417	41942	71359	–	71359
108008	57037	50971	48296	33064	15232	116724	29050	87674	65906	8967	56939	82299	8396	73903
22933	7444	15489	26769	9920	16849	48009	7462	40547	46156	10332	35824	29070	8951	20119
–	–	–	66211	19529	46682	95371	25129	70242	102203	18670	85533	97285	15665	81620
22474	1568	22316	42001	13242	28759	45229	1480	43749	53693	9248	44445	51622	–	51622
3107	3955	848	2075	489	1586	36975	–	36975	24180	–	24180	56767	–	56767
23297	8887	14410	53594	2656	50938	70390	7740	62650	115754	4063	111691	154380	3750	150630
22126	10411	11715	26615	1388	25227	54554	6962	47592	48045	8377	39668	54886	10493	44393
107942	36127	71815	25526	19296	6230	67682	21767	45915	72254	24906	47348	96363	31454	64909
21770	2207	19563	30249	4448	25801	94175	10045	84130	106214	5335	100879	153292	1354	151938
386396	145019	241377	372378	119223	253155	807369	175655	631714	785276	127778	657498	955607	84487	871120

Notes: 1. The figures for 1979/80 to 1981/2 do not include the cost of various surveys, minor projects and other operational expenses.

2. This represents a grant to the Norfolk Naturalists' Trust towards the cost of purchasing Upton Fen.

3. Includes a grant of £14 000 to the Suffolk Trust for Nature Conservation towards the cost of purchasing the Carlton Colville nature reserve.

4. These figures relate to the capital cost of purchasing the How Hill estate. The NCC's grant amounted to £22 500.

5. This was classed as managerial and administrative expenditure until 1985/6 (see Table 12a).

6. Including apportioned managerial and administrative costs.

Table 12d   Broads Authority grants for Interpretive and Educative Projects — 1980/1 to 1988/9

Year	Site	Project	Total cost	Grant	Recipient
1980/1	Ranworth Cons. Centre	Walkway	4050	1500	Norfolk Naturalists' Trust (NNT)
1980/1	–	Code of Behaviour	7000	875	Blakes
1980/1	–	Code of Behaviour	4700	588	Hoseasons
1980/1	Strumpshaw Fen	Visitor Centre etc.	4700	2350	Royal Society for the Protection of Birds (RSPB)
1980/1	Ranworth Cons. Centre	Summer Warden	2500	2500	NNT
1981/2	Various sites	Interpretive Panels (maintenance)	2060	750	Norfolk Heritage Trust (NHT)
1980/1	Ranworth Cons. Centre	Re-designing Displays	6000	1000	NNT
1982/3	–	Code of behaviour for anglers	546	273	Norfolk & Suffolk Anglers Consultative Committee
1982/3	Various sites	Interpretive Panels (maintenance)	7500	3700	NHT
1984/5	Strumpshaw Fen	Bird Hide	2000	500	RSPB
1985/6	Loddon Staithe	Interpretive Sign	220	110	Loddon PC
1985/6	Beccles Marsh	Nature Trail	1317	500	Suffolk Trust for Nat. Cons. (STNC)
1985/6	–	Slide/Tape Sequence	N/A	600	NHT
1986/7	Horsey Staithe	'Talking Post'	600	200	Nat. Trust
1986/7	Carlton Colville	Interpretive Centre	58 600	1300	STNC
1986/7	How Hill Centre	Facilities for day visits by schools & seasonal warden	3176	1588	How Hill Trust
1986/7	–	Cons. of films of the 1920s & 1930s	440	220	E. Anglian Film Archive
1986/7	–	Poster about nature reserves	278	100	NNT
1987/8	Ranworth Cons. Centre	Improvement of interpretive facilities	10 600	3300	NNT
1987/8	Ranworth Cons. Centre	Improvement of interpretive facilities	10 600	3300	NNT
1987/8	Carlton Marshes Centre	Interpretive displays	N/A	10 000	Suffolk Wildlife Trust (SWT)
1988/9	Carlton Marshes Centre	Interpretive displays	15 000	3500	SWT

Table 12e   Broads Authority Grants for Conservation Management Projects — 1980/1 to 1988/9

Year	Site	Project	Total cost	Grant	Recipient
1980/1	Ranworth Broad	Piling	5756	2650	Norfolk Naturalists' Trust (NNT)
1980/1	Alderfen Broad	Dyke restoration	2000	750	NNT
1981/2	Brayden Marshes	Dyke restoration	3000	1500	J. Buxton
1982/3	Mallow Marsh (N. of Barton Broad)	Dyke restoration	600	250	P. Joiner
1982/3	Upton Fen	Dyke restoration & walkway	7000	2340	NNT
1982/3	Martham Broad & Starch Grass	Dyke restoration	2468	823	NNT
1983/4	Strumpshaw Broad	Suction-dredging	20000	5000	Royal Society for the Protection of Birds (RSPB)
1983/4	Upton Fen	Dyke restoration	2780	640	NNT
1983/4	Mallow & Mill Marshes (Barton Broad)	Dyke restoration	1346	673	P. Joiner & A. Macdonald
1984/5	Broadside '84	Misc. activities	–	900	British Trust for Conservation Volunteers (BTCV)
1984/5	Horning Hall Marshes	Dyke restoration	800	400	Church Commissioners
1984/5	Broadland Nature Reserves (NRs)	Wardening	8445	4000	NNT
1984/5	Brayden Marshes	Dyke restoration	2070	1035	J. Buxton
1984/5	Mill Marsh (N. of Barton Broad)	Water level control	300	150	A. Macdonald
1984/5	Smallburgh Fen	Dyke restoration	350	175	NNT
1985/6	North Cove (Nr. Barnby)	Dyke clearance & water level control	1300	600	B. Blower
1985/6	Broadland NRs	Wardening	7600	3810	NNT
1985/6	Mallow Marsh	Dyke restoration	984	328	P. Joiner
1985/6	Upton Fen	Dyke restoration	1183	394	NNT
1985/6	Barton Turf NR	Dyke restoration	2100	700	Herts County Council
1985/6	Strumpshaw Fen	Dyke creation	6000	2000	RSPB
1985/6	Catfield Fen	Dyke restoration	452	226	M.B. High
1986/7	Broadland NRs	Wardening	22635	4527	NNT
1986/7	Mill Marsh	Dyke restoration	500	250	A. Macdonald
1986/7	Berney Arms NR	Purchase of boat	8000	2000	RSPB
1987/8	Broadside '87	Misc. activities	3400	1200	BTCV
1987/8	Sharp St. Fen	Dyke restoration	550	275	M. Boardman
1987/8	Broadland NRs	Wardening	12800	3200	NNT
1987/8	Ronds at Mautby	Dredging foot-drains	750	375	Van Poortvliet
1987/8	Brayden Marshes	Dyke restoration (Gibbs Outlet)	2750	1375	J. Buxton
1988/9	Broadland NRs	Wardening	17500	7000	NNT
1988/9	Broadside '88	Misc. activities	19086	1500	BTCV
1988/9	Mallow Marsh	Dyke restoration	900	400	A. Macdonald

Members of the Countryside Commission visited the region in May 1983, and discussed its future administration with various interested parties. At a subsequent meeting, the Commission reaffirmed its view that . . . "the Broads are of national importance for their landscape, wildlife and opportunities for recreation", and in July 1983, it issued a Consultation Document (CCP 158) identifying three options for the future:

(a) a continuation of the Broads Authority, possibly with some minor changes in the way it is administered and financed;

(b) a national park authority, either a Committee or a Board, established either under the existing legislation, or amended legislation;

(c) a special statutory authority established under a private Act of Parliament.

The Commission received formal reponses from over 70 organizations and individuals, and in September 1983, it issued a Statement, giving its 'in principle' support to the establishment of a Special Authority (Countryside Commission, 1983b). Its reasons for reaching this conclusion, together with a summary of responses made to the consultation document, and a review of the progress made to date by the Broads Authority, were set out in a Report (CCP 163) published in March 1984. This concluded that the

Special Authority should, as a minimum requirement, have all the powers presently enjoyed by the Broads Authority, but that its executive area should be designated as a Special Area under Section 41 of the *Wildlife and Countryside Act* 1981. The Commission also felt that the proportion of members representing the national interest should be increased, and that central Government should find 75 per cent of the cost of its expenditure, with higher rates for management agreements. Although responsibility for water quality control would remain with Anglian Water, the new agency should be empowered to undertake innovative and experimental projects in this sphere (Countryside Commission, 1984).

By far the most contentious recommendation made by the Commission was that the new agency should become the navigation authority for the rivers, thus divesting the Great Yarmouth Port and Haven Commission of a function which its predecessor, the Yarmouth Haven and Pier Commission first acquired in 1722 (see Chapter 10). The main argument advanced in favour of this take-over was that the Broads Authority and the Rivers Commissioners had not established a cohesive working relationship, and that it would be unsatisfactory for the special authority to have to rely on the Commissioners to implement its policies, insofar as these related to the rivers and navigable broads.

Following discussions between the interested parties, it was agreed that a Private Bill setting up a special authority would be promoted jointly by the six local authorities with

Table 12f Expenditure by the Broads Authority and others on research (R) and experimental management (EM) projects between 1980/1 and 1988/9

Topic	Period of funding	Broads Auth. Expenditure (£)	Total Expenditure (£)	Other funding bodies
Rivers and Broads				
1. Reedswamp regression (R)	1980/1–1985/6	49371	91809	CC
2. Riverbank protection (EM)	1981/2–1988/9	28998	N/A	AWA
3. Riverbank erosion rates (R)	1980/1–1982/3	3458	3891	CC & GYPHC
4. Nature of riverbank material (R)	1981/2	810	3060	CC & AWA
5. Regulatory mechanisms (R)	1982/3–1984/5	48720	78720	SDIA
6. Deterioration and restoration of freshwater ecosystems (R)	1985/6–1987/8	33000	88000	SDIA, NCC & AWA
7. Restoration of broads (EM)				
(a) Cockshoot Broad	1980/1–1983/4	65377	67877	NCC
(b) Belaugh Broad	1986/7–1988/9	90794	120794	NCC, CC & WWF
8. Monitoring the R. Bure and Ant phosphorus reduction programme (R)	1986/7–1988/9*	60418	N/A	NCC & AWA
Fens & carr woodlands				
9. Hydrology of wetlands (R)	1986/7–1988/9*	15856	95158	NCC & AWA
10. Quality of thatching reed (R)	1987/8–1988/9*	22295	87530	NCC, MAFF, DoE & RDC
Drained Marshland Area				
11. Dyke survey (R)	1980/1–1981/2	2200	2250	NFU
12. Dyke management (R)	1981/2–1984/5	25401	34033	CC
13. Acid sulphate soils (R)	1980/1–1982/3	3203	6003	CC
Miscellaneous projects				
14. Vegetation mapping & survey (R)	1981/2–1988/9*	36750	43500	CC
15. Flood alleviation Strategy (R)	1986/7–1988/9*	16924	47400	AWA
16. Boat hull design/wash (R)	1986/7–1988/9	45531	48600	GYPHC

* Projects which were continued in 1989/90 under the auspices of the 'new' Broads Authority

Key:
AWA – Anglian Water Authority
CC – Countryside Commission
DoE – Department of the Environment
GYPHC – Great Yarmouth Port and Haven Commission

MAFF – Ministry of Agriculture, Fisheries and Food
NFU – National Farmers' Union
RDC – Rural Development Commission
SDIA – Soap and Detergent Industries Association
WWF – World Wildlife Fund

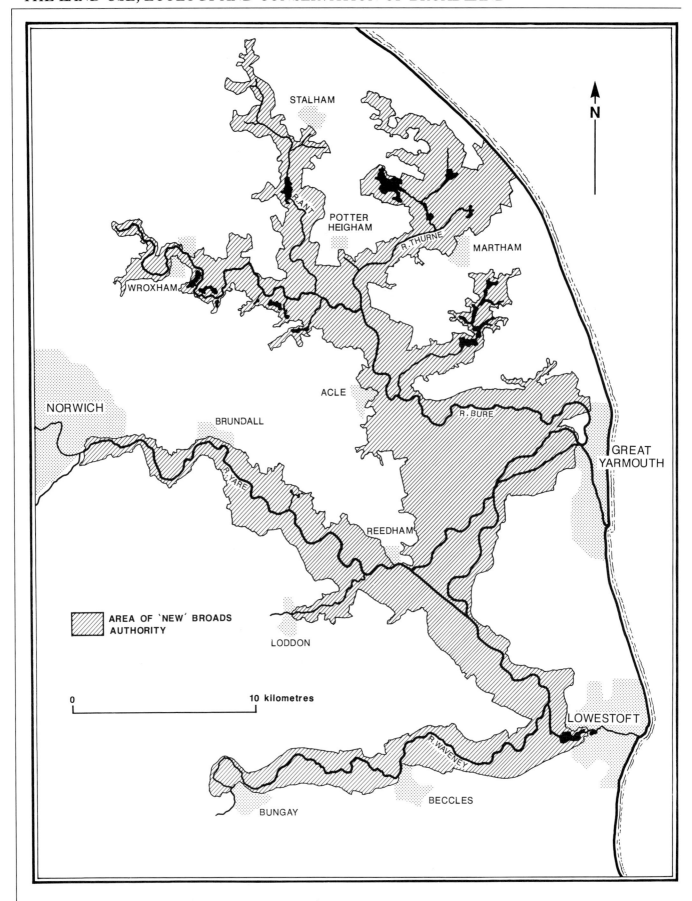

Map 12.4   The area of responsibility of the 'new' Broads Authority (1989 onwards).

direct interests in the region, that the Norfolk County Council should act as the lead agency for this, and that the aim should be to deposit the draft Bill with Parliament in November 1985. It was also arranged that the Countryside Commission would meet half the cost of promoting the Bill, estimated to be £115 000, and that Parliamentary Agents should be engaged to act for the co-promoters. Separate officers' and members' working groups were set up, and these began the task of drafting the Bill in the spring of 1984.

Not the least of the problems was to agree a boundary for the new authority, and after considerable discussion, it was decided that this should:

(a) include those sections of the flood plains (as defined by the IDBs) bordering the navigable sections of the rivers;
(b) encompass Broads-related development, and avoid sub-divided small settlements whenever possible;
(c) include areas of particular visual importance.

The first of these criteria led to the exclusion of the once-canalized section of the R. Bure between Coltishall and Aylsham, even though this had been included within the Executive Area of the 'old' Authority. It was also agreed, despite some initial opposition from the North Norfolk District Council, that the boundary of the new organization should encompass the area north of Hickling and Horsey which had previously been omitted (see Maps 12.3 and 12.4). Various other, less important, boundary anomalies were resolved satisfactorily during the course of consultations with the local authorities concerned and other interested parties, but despite pleas from conservation interests, and the landowner involved, Lord Somerleyton, Fritton Lake was excluded. This decision was taken following objections from Great Yarmouth Borough Council, whose representatives drew attention to what they termed "the commercial activities taking place on the site", and the difficulties which the new authority might encounter when trying to reconcile these with its overall policies. Quite how the delegates from Yarmouth distinguished between what was happening at Fritton Lake, and the much more intensive commercial interests operating elsewhere in the region, was not clear.

Another of the decisions taken by the Working Groups was to abandon the concept of an 'Advisory Area' for the new Authority on the grounds that this had served little useful purpose, other than to enable the existing Authority to comment on proposals to abstract more water from the Broadland rivers, or discharge effluent into them from new or enlarged sewage treatment works*.

Meantime, Whitehall had been kept closely informed of what was afoot, and in July 1984 Mr William Waldegrave, then Under-Secretary of State for the Environment, announced during an adjournment debate in the Commons that the Government had endorsed in principle the proposal to establish a Special Statutory Authority in the region. He also indicated that in order to maintain the momentum gained since 1978, the Government had agreed that the Countryside Commission should continue to grant-aid the existing Authority, until the new one had been set up.

The draft Broads Bill was issued for public comment in April 1985 (Norfolk County Council, 1985a), and generated a lot of interest, and not a little controversy, responses being received from no fewer than 97 organizations (including 41 navigational and recreational interests), and 43 private individuals (Norfolk County Council, 1985b). As expected, the most contentious issue by far proved to be the proposal that the new Authority should assume responsibility for navigation, and despite numerous meetings, the Rivers Commissioners and their supporters (which included commercial shipping and boat-hire interests, the Inland Waterways Association, and the Royal Yachting Association) remained resolute in their determination to resist this take-over. Even a compromise proposal which would allow the Commissioners to exercise their existing functions in the region on an agency basis for the new authority was rejected in September on a majority vote. Although the Commissioners reluctantly agreed this arrangement 'in principle' at a meeting later that month chaired by Mr Waldegrave, subsequent

---

* It was later decided that in place of an Advisory Area, the Bill should make it obligatory for the Authority to be consulted about any proposals likely to affect the quality of the water in the Broadland rivers. This requirement was in due course carried forward into the *Norfolk and Suffolk Broads Act* 1988 as Clause 35 of Schedule 3.

more detailed discussions between the parties concerned showed that numerous problems would need to be resolved before a mutually acceptable scheme could be worked out.

Meantime, the draft Bill had been amended in the light of the other comments received during the consultation exercise, and after it had been formally approved by the co-promoting authorities, it was, in accordance with customary practice, submitted by the latter's parliamentary agents to Counsel for the Speaker for his endorsement. To the consternation of the co-promoters and other interested parties, it became known in early November that the proposed legislation was considered to be 'hybrid' (i.e. that its provisions lay partly in the private, and partly in the public domain), and that it would not, therefore be eligible for submission as a Private Bill as intended. Eleventh-hour efforts to modify the Bill's financial provisions so as to meet the Speaker's Counsel's objections proved of no avail, and the Bill was not laid before Parliament by 27 November, the deadline for receipt of such measures in that parliamentary session. In a subsequent statement, Mr Waldegrave indicated that there were two reasons for the hybridity ruling: the wide issues of public policy which would be raised by the transfer to the new Authority of many of the functions of existing statutory bodies and secondly, the substantial Exchequer funding which the authority would require if it was to operate effectively (Hansard (HC) 9.12.85).

Attempts to introduce the proposed legislation to Parliament as a Private Members Bill proved abortive, as none of the MPs successful in the ballot was prepared to take on the onerous task of steering it through Parliament. In the circumstances, there was widespread, though not universal, relief locally when the Secretary of State for the Environment announced in March 1986 that the Government intended to introduce, as soon as possible, a Bill setting up a new Statutory Authority for the region. This would have the same status as a national park authority, and would assume responsibility for navigation, as well as taking over the powers of the present Broads Authority. The Minister also expressed the hope that the new body would, subject to parliamentary approval, come formally into existence on 1 April 1988 (Hansard (HC) 7.3.86 Col. 288).

The Norfolk and Suffolk Broads Bill was introduced into Parliament in November 1986, and after a three-hour debate, was given an unopposed second reading on 1 December (Hansard (HC) Col. 663–710). The Commons Select Committee hearing occupied nine days; its members visited the region on 26 March and reported on their findings five days later. The Bill's subsequent progress was delayed by the General Election in May. However, as a hybrid Bill, it was not 'lost' as a result of this, but was adopted by the incoming (Conservative) Government and re-introduced into Parliament the following month. Its subsequent progress can be summarized as follows:

House of Commons Standing Committee B – 14, 16 & 21 July 1987
House of Commons Third Reading – 4 November 1987 (Hansard (HC) Col. 1018–1038)
House of Lords Second Reading – 16 November 1987 (Hansard (HL) Col. 10–21 & 25–36)
House of Lords Select Committee – 8 & 9 December 1987
House of Lords in Committee – 1 February 1988(Hansard (HL) Col. 899–928)
House of Lords, Report Stage – 15 February 1988 (Hansard (HL) Col. 469)
House of Lords, Third Reading – 22 February 1988 (Hansard (HL) Col. 940)
House of Commons, Consideration of Lords Amendments – 29 February 1988 (Hansard (HC) Col. 755–765)
Royal Assent – 15 March 1988.

The Government decided to adopt, with minor amendments, the same boundary for the new authority as had been agreed previously, following discussions between the district and county councils. However, the Government's Bill differed from the Private Bill in that many of the detailed provisions within the latter were consigned to seven lengthy schedules. As a result, it ran to only 26 clauses instead of the 102 clauses of the Private Bill. Much more importantly, its definition of the general duties of the new Authority, as set out in Clause 2(1) was subtly different. Instead of indicating that this should . . . "develop, conserve and manage the Broads for the purposes of navigation, recreation, wildlife conservation and enhancing the natural beauty and amenity of the area'', the Government's Bill (as originally laid before Parliament) stated that the authority should . . .

develop, conserve and manage the Broads for the purpose of:

(a) navigation;
(b) preserving and enhancing the natural beauty of the Broads; and
(c) promoting the enjoyment of the Broads by the public.

Another important difference between the Private and the Government's Bills was that the latter would enable the NCC to nominate a member of the new Authority, the Countryside Commission's nominees being correspondingly reduced from three to two. The Government's Bill also afforded boating and navigational interests more and better safeguards, and additional representation on the authority, than had the Private Bill. Despite this, the Great Yarmouth Port and Haven Commissioners put in a petition which, *inter alia*, opposed the transfer to the new Authority of the navigation between Norwich and Yarmouth. In the event, the Select Committee decided that this offended against the principle of the Bill, as endorsed by the House of Commons at the Second Reading. Since, in these circumstances, the Bill would have to be regarded as 're-hybridized', thus necessitating its reintroduction into Parliament as a new piece of legislation, the Committee rejected the proposal.

Much of the evidence presented to the Select Committee was, as might be expected, concerned with the composition of the new Authority. The Government resisted a suggestion by the voluntary bodies that the NCC and the Countryside Commission should each have two nominees on it, on the grounds that this would upset the balance which had been struck between the various interested parties. Similarly, the Select Committee refused to accede to a request by the Friends of the Earth that the Secretary of State should be obliged, when appointing members of the Authority, to ensure that some at least of these could represent conservation and angling interests. This may be contrasted with the Committee's decision, made in response to representations by the National Farmers' Union, that two of the Secretary of State's appointments to the Authority should be capable of representing farming and landowning interests.

The wording of Clause 2(1) caused more controversy than any other, as strenuous efforts were made by the voluntary conservation bodies, including the RSPB, the Norfolk Naturalists' Trust, the Suffolk Trust for Nature Conservation, the Council for the Protection of Rural England and the Council for National Parks, to persuade the Commons Select Committee to give conservation primacy over the other objectives. This proposal was strongly resisted by the Government on the grounds that it would not only upset the balance which it had struck in the Bill between navigation and conservation, but would represent such a fundamental shift in policy, that the Bill would have to be regarded as 're-hybridized'. In the event, the Committee decided that this clause should be amended to read as follows:

It shall be the general duty of the Authority to manage the Broads for the purposes of

(a) conserving and enhancing the natural beauty of the Broads;
(b) promoting the enjoyment of the Broads by the public; and
(c) protecting the interests of navigation.

The Committee made a number of other alterations to the Bill in the light of the evidence presented to it. For instance, it instructed that the phrase ''conserving the natural beauty of an area'' should be defined as covering the conservation of its flora, fauna, and geological and physiographical features [cf. Clause 25(2)]. It also altered Schedule 5 of the Bill to facilitate the temporary closure of waterways for research and conservation purposes.

In its formal Report, the Committee expressed its belief that the Bill, as amended, represented a fair balance between the conflicting interests, and hoped that it would . . . ''encourage co-operation and goodwill – the only way in which the Broads will flourish''.

Although the revised version of Clause 2(1) was endorsed by the Commons Standing

Committee, the voluntary bodies were still not satisfied, and at the House of Lords Select Committee hearing in December, they pleaded that an additional sentence be added at its end making it obligatory for the new authority to carry out its duties . . . "in such a way as to ensure their [the Broads] long-term conservation". It was argued on their behalf that this amendment would be in accord with the recommendation of the National Park Policies Review Committee (the Sandford Report) to the effect that if an irreconcilable conflict of interest occurs within a national park, priority should be given to the conservation of natural beauty, a policy subsequently accepted by Government (DoE, 1976). In presenting evidence on behalf of the Government, Mr David Walley gave a broad hint that the Minister responsible was considering making a statement about the application of the Sanford principle to the Broads, when the Bill was being given its Third Reading in the Lords. However, he strongly opposed the inclusion in the Bill of the supplementary clause put forward by the voluntary conservation bodies. This was also resisted by the local authorities and by the boating interests, both of whom put in counter-petitions, and in his closing speech, Counsel for the Government expressed the view that it represented a 'back-door' way of giving conservation primacy over the authority's other two objectives. In the event, the proposal was rejected by the Committee.

Two of the fourteen amendments considered when the Bill returned to the House of Lords were of particular interest to conservationists; both were tabled by Baroness Nicol. The first was that the NCC should have two nominees on the authority, rather than one, and that the Secretary of State's appointments should be correspondingly reduced from nine to eight. Although this suggestion was supported by a number of peers, it was firmly resisted by Lord Hesketh on behalf of the Government, on the grounds that it would upset the balance which had been achieved in the Bill. The second amendment of special interest was that a new clause should be added to the Bill introducing the Sanford principle, and making it obligatory for the Secretary of State to issue guidance as to how this was to be implemented by the Authority. This amendment received little support, even from Lord Sanford himself, when it became clear that it would almost certainly result in the Bill being re-hybridized. Nevertheless, several members certainly pressed the Government to make a verbal statement indicating that the Sanford principle should apply to the Broads, just as it did to the national parks. Strong behind-the-scenes pressure to make such an announcement had been put on the Government by the Countryside Commission during the preceding two or three weeks, and it is understood that it had been decided to respond positively. Curiously, the opportunity to make such a statement was not taken, either at the later stages in the Lords, or when the latter's amendments to the Bill were being considered by the Commons. Nevertheless, during the course of a speech at How Hill in June 1988, three months after the Act had been given the Royal Assent, Mr Colin Moynihan, then Parliamentary Under-Secretary in the Department of the Environment, indicated that the Government accepted that the future of Broadland was wholly dependent on the adoption of environmentally-benign policies in it.

It was originally hoped that the new Authority would take up its formal duties (thus supplanting the 'old' Broads Authority) in October 1988, but Lord Hesketh announced during the Lords Committee's discussion of the Bill on 1 February that this would not be possible in view of the large amount of preparatory work needed beforehand, and that the target date would be 1 April 1989.

The new Authority met on a number of occasions prior to assuming its formal responsibilities, and amongst the items discussed included the appointment of a Chief Executive, Mr Aitken Clark being invited to occupy this post, at least for the first few years. Consideration was also given to arrangements for taking over from the Great Yarmouth Port and Haven Commission the collection of boat tolls, and the assets and staff of its Rivers Committee, as prescribed in an Order (No. 27) which came into effect on 1 April 1989. The membership and terms of reference of the Authority's committees were also subject to much debate, and it was eventually decided that in addition to a Navigation Commitee (which the Authority is obliged to have under the terms of its formative Act) there should be Planning, Policy and Resources, and Environment Committees.

The establishment of the new Authority, and the way it assumed responsibility for the *c.* 288 square kilometres designated in the Act (see Map 12.4), received widespread approbation. Environmentalists were also delighted to learn that the Government had agreed that its budget for 1989/90 would be set at £1.1 million, an increase of some £229 000 over the 'old' Authority's expenditure the previous year. However, just before the Authority took up its formal responsibilities, the Treasury announced that unlike national park authorities, it would not qualify for exemption under Section 20 of the *VAT Act* 1983. This decision meant, in effect, that the Authority would not be able to reclaim VAT expenditure on its non-business activities. In the face of strong representations, the Department of the Environment subsequently indicated that in recognition of the Treasury's decision, the Authority's budget would be increased from the planned figure of £1.1 million to £1 143 316. However, much to the Navigation Committee's annoyance (one of whose members likened the Treasury's ruling to a 'kick-in-the-teeth') a similar undertaking could not be made in respect of the navigation account, as tolls form the only source of funds for this. In the circumstances, the Committee was obliged to raise its charges for the 1990/1 boating season by 12.5 per cent.

Subsequent discussions led to a decision being taken that the 1989/90 allocation would be divided up as follows:

Conservation	–	£357 188	(£243 987)*
Planning	–	£65 176	(£64 739)*
Information & Interpretation	–	£225 980	(£164 079)*
Recreation	–	£155 140	(£175 247)*
Management & Administration	–	£339 832	(£223 068)*

* Expenditure by the 'old' Authority in 1988/9.

In the event net expenditure differed somewhat from these figures; details are included in the Authority's Statement of Accounts for 1989/90 (Broads Authority, 1991).

The Authority receives three-quarters of its budget in the form of grants from the Department of the Environment, while in 1989/90 the remainder came from the Norfolk County Council (£82 500), and £27 500 from each of the other seven participating authorities. These figures are separate from the Authority's income and expenditure in respect of its navigation function, which balanced out at £748 230 in the year 1989/90.

The Authority's budget for 1990/1 remained largely unaltered at £1.1 million, the intention being that a third of this sum would be spent on conservation projects, research and management schemes, and slightly more than this on information and facilities for public access. In 1991/2, the Authority's budget increased to £1.5 million, the proportion to be spent on conservation being set to rise to 36 per cent, with slight reductions in the quotas available for information, interpretation and public access, and management and administration.

Encouraging as it is that such large sums of money are now being spent each year in this environmentally most important region, it is salutary to reflect that it took almost exactly 58 years to afford it the national park status which the Addison Committee considered it deserved. As will have become apparent, the blame for this can be ascribed, not so much to governmental prevarication – though this certainly played a part at various times – but to the activities of local vested interests.

It would be naïve in the extreme to think that these disparate interests will cease to operate just because of the establishment of a new and more powerful administrative authority for the region. This was well illustrated by a controversy which arose in 1990 concerning the alignment of the proposed Wroxham/Hoveton by-pass. The Navigation Committee of the Authority understandably (and rightly) took the view that it would be less damaging to boating interests if the bridge carrying this road over the R. Bure was sited upstream of Wroxham, since this section of the river only carries about a tenth of the boat traffic using the Bure downstream of the town. Members of the Committee also considered that a new downriver bridge would cause increased congestion, and form a hazard to navigation. With these points in mind, they urged the Authority to support one or other of the routes for the proposed by-pass which were aligned to the west of Wroxham and Hoveton. These views were not shared by the Planning and Environment Committees, members of which pointed out that the Authority had a year or so previously expressed its opposition to a western route for a by-pass, on the grounds that this would have to cross an area (the Belaugh 'peninsular') of very great scenic and nature conservation interest. A new road to the east of Wroxham and Hoveton would, in contrast, have a much less disturbing impact on the Broadland environment. Prolonged, and sometimes acrimonious, discussions failed to break the deadlock, and in November 1990, the full Authority decided by 17 votes to 6 formally to oppose a western alignment for the new road. Members of the Navigation Committee were far from happy about this, and they sought, and received an assurance from Aitken Clark that they could express their views at the public inquiry held about the by-pass proposals in the autumn of 1990.

Although controversies such as this will doubtless continue to arise from time to time, the 'new' Broads Authority is, like its predecessor, firmly committed to reconciling as far as possible the conflicting interests which exist in the region, and this must remain one of its most important roles in the coming years.

Planning control in Broadland between 1930 and 1989 – an environmental assessment

Given the time and effort spent since the last War on devising planning policies for the region, and exercising development control, it is instructive to consider how effective the planning process has been from the environmental point of view. Prominent amongst the successes may be numbered the fact that commercial and residential development has been confined to existing towns and villages, and that the planning control and enforcement measures taken to prevent unsuitable, low-lying sites such as Crabbett's Marsh, Horning, being built over have been generally successful, if administratively time-consuming and laborious. The result has been that Broadland's chief attraction – its waterscape – has been largely safeguarded. There are, of course, some exceptions, not least the houseboats just upriver from Weyford Bridge (see Plate XLVIII) and the chalets and bungalows which line many kilometres of river frontage near Brundall and Potter Heigham (see Plate 39). But whilst it can be argued that most of these are a legacy of uncontrolled development during the 1920s and 1930s for which planning officials and their committees can hardly be blamed, they have been slow to tackle some of the 'blackspots'. For example, although the Norfolk County Council encouraged the development of the 'Riverside Estate' at Brundall after the War (despite the high susceptibility of this area to flooding, and its very indifferent access) it did little to exercise effective control over the resultant agglomeration of houseboats, caravans, chalets, and boatyards until 1969, when it issued 12 enforcement notices in respect of the area. Nine of these were subsequently confirmed on appeal by the Minister of Housing and Local Government, but developments in this area were not finally brought under control until 1979, when the Broadland District Council approved a Local Plan for Brundall, and set about enforcing its provisions. Similarly, the possibility of improving the appearance of Potter Heigham, or more controversially, eliminating some, or even all, of the 202 chalets built on the ronds of the River Thurne nearby, only started to receive serious attention in 1983, when a Draft Plan for Consultation was produced for the area. After much discussion, and not a little controversy, a definitive Plan for it was formally endorsed by the Broads Authority two years later (Broads Authority, 1985).

Under the provisions of this Plan, it was arranged that the majority of the riverside plot land would be long-leased by the AWA (who had inherited the problem from their predecessors, the East Norfolk Rivers Catchment Board, the East Suffolk and Norfolk River Board, and the East Suffolk and Norfolk River Authority) to a specially-formed body, the Thurne Bungalows Management Company. The sub-leases issued by this would contain convenants designed to ensure, first, that the quality of the chalets and huts on the individual plots would, in the course of time, be upgraded, and second, that any extensions to the properties would be on a small scale, and in conformity with the Building Control Regulations. The remaining parts of the plot land, consisting of several discrete sections of river bank both up and downriver from Potter Heigham Bridge, would be long-leased to the Broads Authority by the AWA. Sub-leases extending beyond the end of the century will not be entered into by the latter, and as these, and the existing leases from the AWA expire, the buildings will be removed, thus creating a series of open spaces along this section of the R. Thurne.

With the benefit of hindsight, some of the decisions taken by the planning authorities in the 1950s can now be seen to have been very environmentally damaging. Perhaps the most glaring examples concern the allowance of boatyard development at, or near, the

Houseboats on the R. Ant, just upstream of Wayford Bridge – 1978.

Plate XLVIII

These vessels, and similar ones moored at various other locations, including Hickling and Bridge Broad East, are let out during the holiday season. When they first appeared in the early 1960s, much concern was expressed by amenity interests about their effect on the waterscape. However, following a public inquiry, it was ruled that such craft are, contrary to what their owners had claimed, susceptible to planning control. This is probably one of the reasons why their numbers have remained fairly static during the past 20 years or so. In addition, though cheaper to hire than a motor cruiser of comparable size, many people prefer to be mobile when having a holiday afloat.

Photo: Peter Wakely/Nature Conservancy Council

upstream limits of navigation. Stalham Dyke, for example, was a secluded backwater before the Second World War, and even in 1955, only 21 vessels were being hired out from a yard beside the staithe at its northern end. However, in 1959 a second firm [R. Richardson (Pleasure Craft) Ltd.] was given planning permission to erect boatsheds, workshops and toilets on a site nearby, those responsible for this decision ignoring the fact that each time a boat is hired out at Stalham, it has to make a double journey across the Barton Broad nature reserve, and along the narrow, and winding River Ant.

The number of motor cruisers available for hire at the new yard had increased to 54 by 1961, and the following year (when it was offering an additional 29 vessels) permission was granted for the erection of another boatshed, together with a store and office. Yet more buildings and an enlarged mooring basin were authorized in 1966, and in 1967, the hire fleet operated by Richardsons consisted of 175 motor vessels. This had increased to 248 by 1972, and after a temporary decline, reached a maximum of 294 in 1979. By then, the business occupied a site of 10 ha, including nearly 2.5 ha of open water moorings.

Given the numbers of vessels available for hire at Stalham by the early 1960s, it is surprising that planning permission was granted for two further yards here – one in 1964 and the other in 1966. As a result, some 300 motor cruisers were being hired out from the four yards at the head of Stalham Dyke by the mid-1970s. The amount of boat traffic which this generated on the waterways linking Stalham with the main river system was revealed by the 1976 census, which showed that nearly 400 vessels per day were passing up and down Stalham Dyke in August that year.

Fortunately from the environmental point of view, the numbers of vessels available for hire at Stalham declined from 338 in 1979 to 190 in 1983, mainly as a result of the depression, and the consequent decline in the demand for holidays afloat. The hire fleet operated by Richardsons was reduced from 294 to 128 over this period, partly because some of the vessels were taken over by another firm at Stalham under a leasing arrangement, and partly through the withdrawal of obsolete and unprofitable craft. In addition, substantial numbers of vessels were transferred to the River Thames, and the French waterways, where the hire trade was faring better than in Broadland. To offset the reduction in the size of their hire fleet, Richardsons provided more mooring spaces for privately-owned craft; however, as explained in Chapter 11, these do not exert as much pressure on the rivers and broads as do comparable numbers of hire craft.

The saga over Catfield Dyke, a waterway at the extreme western end of Hickling Broad, provides another illustration of the concern felt by conservationists over boatyard developments in the headwaters of the river system. There was formerly a staithe at the distal end of the Dyke, but this had long been disused, and in 1964 its owners, the Catfield Parish Council, decided to invite tenders for its lease. A bid by the Norfolk Naturalists' Trust (which manages the adjoining nature reserve) was unsuccessful, and the area was leased by a local river-contractor, P. E. Thain, who wished to keep his wherries there. Soon after Mr Thain's death a year or so later, the lease was taken over by L. R. J. Buck, who established a small boatyard on the staithe, and the land immediately adjoining it. This caused the Trust, the Nature Conservancy and the Broads Society much concern, as the regular passage of boats up and down the Dyke soon destroyed the luxuriant growth of Water Soldier and other aquatic plants which had formerly occurred therein. It also ran counter to their declared aim of ensuring that recreational developments beside the Hickling Broad nature reserve were confined to the area around the Pleasure Boat inn.

After considerable lobbying, the Norfolk County Council agreed to issue an enforcement notice, and following an appeal by Mr Buck, a public inquiry was held in 1970. The Minister's decision given the following year, was that planning permission would be granted for five years for the building, repair and storage of a limited number of boats, but that the hiring of vessels would not be permitted. Planning permission has subsequently been renewed at five-year intervals by the local authority, though on each occasion this has been done despite objections by the NCC and the Norfolk Naturalists' Trust.

The R. Chet provides a classic example of the failure of planners in the past to take adequate account of the environmental consequences of their policy decisions. The river is very narrow and winding, and for almost the whole of its length is bounded by tidal embankments protecting drained marshland. But despite this, planning permission was given between 1958 and 1961 for four new boatyards at Chedgrave, the result being that by 1962, 25 hire vessels, plus several privately-owned craft, were making regular journeys up and down the river. Although surveys by the River Authority demonstrated that a serious bank erosion problem was developing as a consequence of this traffic (see page 73), planning consents continued to be given, so that by 1979, there were eight boatyards in Loddon and Chedgrave, together hiring out 117 vessels (111 in 1983). As a result, long sections of this river have had to be piled, at very considerable cost, and it seems likely that the remaining reaches will have to be 'canalized' in this way during the next few years.

For the environmentalist, one of the most depressing features about Broadland is the indifferent quality of much of the development in its towns and villages. Some of the shoddiest examples, such as are to be seen in parts of Wroxham, Hoveton and Potter Heigham, date from the inter-War years, when planning control as we know it today was weak or non-existent. But post-War standards were not much better, and one gains the impression that some of the buildings put up between 1948 and 1978 were the cheapest the developer could persuade the planners to agree to, rather than the most attractive for the particular conditions. In fairness, it has to be pointed out that when local authorities refused permission for unsightly, or unsuitable development, the applicants often won their cases on appeal. For instance, a proposal to create a new mooring basin at Potter Heigham, capable of accommodating up to 200 vessels, was turned down by the North Norfolk District Council in 1975, but allowed on appeal by the Secretary of State for the Environment in 1982, provided no hire craft were operated from it. Ministerial decisions of this nature tend to discourage local authorities from pursuing their goal of improving standards, and responsibility for some of the misguided planning decisions made since the last War must therefore be laid at the door of central, rather than local, government.

Fortunately, things improved soon after the establishment of the Broads Authority, and the Government's determination to support the latter's bid to raise environmental standards is reflected in the fact that out of 21 appeals in 1986/7 against enforcement action taken by the Authority, or its refusal to grant planning permission, only 7 were upheld by the Secretary of State. Although the corresponding figures for 1987/8 were 16 and 4, the Government's resolve appeared to weaken somewhat the following year, since 11 of the 21 appeals against the Authority's refusal to grant planning permission were allowed that year. Fortunately, most of these were of a technical nature (e.g. traffic-related items), and the majority of the cases involving strategic issues, such as applications affecting land outside villages, were dismissed.

Not the least of the problems confronting both the new and the old Broads Authority has been the need to exercise a greater measure of control over the design and siting of agricultural buildings. These can appear very obtrusive in the open landscapes characteristic of the Drained Marshland Area, and during the early 1980s members of the Authority were much vexed to learn that some landowners within the latter were taking advantage of the fact that such buildings are classed as 'permitted development' (i.e. they can be erected without planning permission) if they have a floor area of less than 465 m, are less than 12 m tall, are not located within 25 m of a classified road, and are erected on land in agricultural use.

Following the designation in April 1985 of Broadland as a 'Special Area' under Section 41 of the *Wildlife and Countryside Act* 1981, farmers have been required to obtain the consent of the Authority before undertaking any operations (including building works) for which they intend to seek grant assistance from the MAFF. However, it was considered desirable to make arrangements to ensure that the Authority was consulted about the design and siting of all farm buildings, whether or not the individual concerned was proposing to apply for a grant. This objective could, in theory, be achieved if the Secretary of State for the Environment applied an Article 4 Direction to the Authority's area of responsibility under the *Town and Country Planning Act 1971**. However, such directions are normally used in respect of sites, rather than areas, and it was considered most unlikely that he would agree to use his powers to encompass the whole of Broadland. Accordingly, the Authority decided in March 1986 to invite him to make the region subject to a Landscape Area Special Development Order (LASDO), a

---

* Now superseded by the *Town and Country Planning Act* 1990.

type of designation devised in 1980 (and subsequently extended by the *Agriculture and Forestry Development in National Parks etc. Special Development Order* 1986) which can, and has been used to define 'permitted development' in national parks and other conservation areas. In the event it was decided that this designation should not be applied to Broadland at that time, but the Department of the Environment indicated that the region would be made subject to such an Order when the new Authority came into existence.

Another initiative which came under scrutiny during the mid-1980s concerned the possibility that the Broads Authority should, in common with national park authorities, be empowered to designate key areas, within which Landscape Conservation Orders (LCO) could be made (DoE, 1986). Owners and occupiers in these areas would be encouraged to notify the Authority of their intention to carry out operations likely to be damaging to the landscape, and if it proved impossible to negotiate a management agreement voluntarily, it could, as a last resort, impose an LCO prohibiting specified operations being undertaken in a defined area. Compensation, either in the form of annual payments, or a lump sum, could be claimed from the Authority, and owners and occupiers who were aggrieved by the Order, would have a right of appeal to the Secretary of State.

Although the Government's proposals were generally welcomed by conservation agencies, farming and landowning interests viewed them with concern, on the grounds that they would, if implemented, represent a further restriction on their ability to farm their land in the way they consider best. In the light of these objections, the junior Environment Minister, Mrs Virginia Bottomley, announced in September 1988 (ironically at the annual conference of national park authorities) that the Government had decided to defer any further consideration of LCOs for the time being.

One of the most important planning issues discussed by the 'old' Broads Authority during its period of office concerned the provision of new recreational lakes in the Yare valley, just downstream of Norwich. Investigations carried out when the Interim Action Programme was under discussion in 1978/9 had revealed that the cost of creating new 'broads' would be prohibitive unless this could be combined with the commercial exploitation of sand and gravel resources in the chosen area. No reserves of sufficient size appear to exist in the Herringfleet/Fritton area, thus ruling out the possibility of providing new waterways and broads in this part of Broadland, as had been suggested in the 1971 Study and Plan. However, it was known that large quantities of sand and gravel underlie the Trowse, Thorpe, Whitlingham and Postwick marshes, another of the areas where additional open water was considered desirable, and in 1986, consultants acting for the Crown Point Estate, as owners of the Trowse and Thorpe marshes, produced a Feasibility Study setting out how these mineral reserves could be exploited. Suggestions were also made as to how the 'broads' thus created, together with the surrounding area, could be used for various forms of waterborne and land-based recreation (Land Use Consultants, 1986).

After discussions with interested parties, the consultants hardened up their proposals, and in the summer of 1988 a formal planning application was made for sand and gravel extraction, the establishment of a 24 ha Country Park (as an enlargement of the existing Picnic Site at Whitlingham), and the provision of car parks and other facilities for visitors. Formal permission for these activities was granted by the Norfolk County Council[†], following detailed, and wide-ranging consultations with interested parties. Separate planning applications will be made later for other recreational facilities in the vicinity of Trowse; these will probably include a new golf course, a visitor centre, extensions to the ski club, and a cross-country course for horse riders.

Preliminary work on the Scheme for which planning permission has been granted commenced in 1990, and will ultimately involve the processing each year of some 220 000 tonnes of sand and gravel. Extraction has started near Trowse, where the washing and grading plant is located, and will gradually be extended down-valley, so

---

* LASDOs (and also 'Special Areas' designated under S 41(3) of the *Wildlife and Countryside Act* 1981) are now categorized as Article 1(5) land in the *Town and Country Planning General Development Order* 1988. This came into force in December 1988.

† This application was determined by the County Council, rather than the Broads Authority, because under the planning legislation, proposals in respect of mineral working have to be dealt with by a county, rather than and district planning authority.

that after about 20 years, some 47 ha of open water will have been created, as a consequence of the removal of about 4.3 million tonnes of sand and gravel.

The open water facilities to be provided will comprise:

(a) A 4.6 ha Training Lake near Trowse, to be used for instruction in sailing, wind-surfing and sub-aqua.

(b) Trowse Broad (35.2 ha). This is due to be completed by 2005, by which time it will accommodate a 1500 m rowing course and open water usable by dinghy sailors, canoeists and wind surfers. Parts of the site will be set aside as a nature reserve, and for fishing, and there will be a footpath around the periphery of the lake. Limited use of part of the site should be possible by 1996.

(c) Thorpe Broad (7.1 ha) – due to be completed by 2010. In the Feasibility Study, and also in the original planning application (made in June 1988), it was proposed that this site should be used for water-skiing. However, as a result of strong objections from conservationists and residents of Thorpe St. Andrew, this suggestion was withdrawn in a revised application submitted in November 1989, and it was agreed that once completed, this Broad, and the adjoining grazing marshes, should be set aside as a nature reserve. This decision was greeted with considerable dismay by water-sports enthusiasts, on the grounds that there is an urgent need to provide more water space in the region for this increasingly popular activity.

(d) The Flushing Channel will be dredged so as to provide short-stay moorings for pleasure craft using the R. Yare.

The relationship between land drainage and navigation

The unsuccessful attempts made by the East Suffolk and Norfolk River Board, and its successor, the East Suffolk and Norfolk River Authority, to take over the functions of the Rivers Commissioners (see pages 411 and 419) provide a good illustration of the conflict of interest between land drainage and navigation which has existed in Broadland – as elsewhere – for at least 150 years. In its simplest form, this results from the anxiety of drainage interests to minimize the risk of agricultural land being flooded, an objective which can, in certain circumstances, lead them to propose that certain little-used water-ways are dammed off. Boating interests are usually reluctant to allow this to happen, since they know from experience that once a waterway has been closed to navigation, it is virtually impossible to reopen it. The fact that Waxham Cut upstream of Bridge Farm is now dry for much of the year, following its closure to boat traffic in the early 1950s, provides a good example of this. But the issue is much more complex than this. For instance, the dredging work carried out by a navigation authority to enable larger vessels to use a river can cause increased tidal scouring, and thus jeopardize its flood banks. In addition, since it levies tolls on vessels, a navigation authority has a vested interest in ensuring that the waterways for which it is responsible are well used, whilst the organiza-tions responsible for land drainage and flood control have to pay for any repairs made necessary as a consequence of the increased boat traffic.

The resentment which this can engender was voiced at a conference in 1933, which was arranged following the receipt of a large number of complaints by the East Norfolk Rivers Catchment Board (formed 2 years previously) about the damage caused to the banks of the R. Yare by ships bound to and from Norwich and Cantley. At this meeting, it was proposed, either that the size of the ships using this river should be limited, or that their speed should be rigorously controlled. However, neither of these suggestions proved practicable, since in the first case, it was claimed that the Commissioners did not possess the necessary powers (although they could probably have promulgated by-laws, if they had so wished), and in the second, it was pointed out that the ships needed to proceed at a reasonable speed if they were to maintain steerage way. In effect, the conference achieved little, except to demonstrate that there was a basic incompatibility between the policy of the Commissioners, who were anxious to encourage the growth of river-borne trading, and thus maximize their toll revenue, and that of the Catchment Board, which was statutorily responsible for remedying, often at not inconsiderable cost, any damage caused thereby. Still dissatisfied, and undaunted by its failure to achieve a solution through direct negotiation, the Catchment Board sent a deputation to

London in 1934 to make representations to the Ministry of Agriculture and the Board of Trade (Anon, 1934). However, the two departments seem to have prevaricated, and no action was taken to alleviate the conflict of interest.

The Commissioners' reluctance to help meet the cost of piling works made necessary by the erosion caused by the wash of passing boats continued to receive adverse comment locally from time to time, and was discussed again formally by the parties principally concerned in 1976. However, the Commissioners claimed, not for the first time, that they were not empowered to make such contributions unless they were satisfied that the works proposed would have a beneficial effect on navigational interests, and that each case would therefore have to be considered on its merits.

Soon after this meeting the Commissioners offered to meet 15 per cent of the cost of some 250 m of piling required on the left bank of the River Ant just upstream of Ludham Bridge, on condition that when the work had been completed, boats would be allowed to moor for up to 24 hours beside this length of river bank. The condition was unacceptable to the Norfolk and Suffolk Fisheries Advisory Committee, which felt that the official recognition of moorings would increase the difficulty of angling from this stretch of river bank, whilst the Norfolk and Suffolk Local Land Drainage Committee decided that since the offer had only been made because the scheme was of benefit to navigation, it should, on a point of principle, be rejected. No one was particularly happy about the resultant impasse, not least because the stretch of bank in question had long been one of the most popular mooring places in Broadland. Nevertheless, despite further meetings, the Land Drainage Committee refused to alter its decision. Instead, it proposed that the Commissioners should make a contribution of, say, £5000 per annum, towards the cost of the AWA's piling programme in Broadland. However, this suggestion was turned down by the Commissioners on the grounds that they would be acting *ultra vires* if they made general payments of this nature.

Fortunately, a more flexible attitude was adopted by the two parties in 1980, when it was agreed that the Commissioners would meet half the £6000 that it cost to pile some 31 m of bank at the head of Rockland Dyke, the remainder being found by the AWA (7.5 per cent), grant-aided by the MAFF (42.5 per cent).

Despite this example of co-operation between drainage and navigational interests, and a generally improved relationship betwen the AWA and the Rivers Commissioners, IDBs continued to complain that the wash produced by pleasure craft was weakening the tidal embankments, and making them more susceptible to leakage, especially when water levels in the rivers and broads were high. They pointed out that the extra pumping required was greatly increasing their costs, and were particularly aggrieved that this was occurring at a time when the payments they had to make to AWA towards the cost of bank maintenance were rising rapidly. They also felt it was wrong in principle that the Commissioners would only made a financial contribution towards the cost of such works if boating interests would thereby benefit.

In January 1981, the Clerk to a Consortium of the four IDBs in north-east Broadland wrote formally to the Minister of Agriculture alleging that the Commissioners did, in fact, possess the power to make contributions, even if boating interests did not directly benefit, and claiming that these . . . "are either not being used at all, or certainly not sufficiently to protect Land Drainage from the depredations of a very lucrative leisure industry". To rectify the situation, the Minister was urged to use his powers under Section 27 of the *Land Drainage Act* 1976, to amend the legislation under which the Commissioners operate so that a special toll could be levied on all boat users to help meet the cost of maintaining the river banks.

It is understood that this proposal was sympathetically received, and although it did not elicit any immediate action because of uncertainties about the future of the Yare Barrier Flood Control Scheme, it would be surprising if land-drainage interests did not raise the issue again at some future date. Such an approach would now need to be made in the first instance to the 'new' Broads Authority in view of the fact that this assumed the Rivers Commissioners' functions in April 1989. It would, however, present the Authority with a dilemma, since the *Norfolk and Suffolk Broads Act* 1988, does not specify whether financial contributions can or cannot be made from its navigation account to help meet the costs of bank maintenance incurred by the AWA's successor, the National Rivers Authority. It would seem that those responsible for drafting this legislation shied away from tackling this potentially very contentious issue.

If the National Rivers Authority or the IDBs do decide to raise this issue again, they are likely to argue that now that it has been demonstrated that the wash generated by powered craft is at least partly responsible for the increased rates of bank erosion currently being experienced in the region, it is only fair that the tolls payable on such vessels should reflect this fact. If this was done by applying a percentage supplement to the tolls levied on motor craft, this would, because of the 3:1 differential applicable to vessels in the hire and private sectors, automatically take account of the much greater environmental pressure exercised on the region's waterways by hired vessels, than by privately-owned boats of comparable size.

The boat number issue

Repeated assertions have been made since the early 1950s that a limit will sooner or later have to be imposed on the numbers of craft licensed to use Broadland's waterways, and concern has frequently been expressed on account of the fact that neither the Rivers Commission, nor its successor, the 'new' Broads Authority possess the powers necessary to achieve this objective. Soon after the publication of the Study and Plan, and in response to the adverse comments made by land-drainage interests about the expansionist policies advocated in it, the Rivers Commissioners issued a Consultation Document setting out the pros and cons for imposing a limit on the number of pleasure craft allowed to use the waterways. They also established a small working group to examine the problem in detail, and sought advice from their Parliamentary Agents as to whether the necessary legislation would be likely to receive support at Westminster. The advice given was unequivocal; Parliament would never agree to such a proposal as it would conflict with the public's Common Law right to navigate on tidal water; indeed it would be analogous to imposing a limit on the number of vehicles licensed to use the roads. Although the validity of this argument was questioned in some quarters, the Commissioners considered that there was a real risk that boat owners would try to forestall any anticipated restrictions by taking out licences for additional vessels, thus increasing still further the pressure on the waterways. In view of this, the Commissioners announced in June 1975 that they would not be seeking powers to restrict the number of craft, but would instead pursue a variety of other measures, including closer liaison with boat-letting interests, particularly in regard to the number of day launches (of which there were, by general consent, too many at that time), improved control on boat mooring, and better enforcement of the regulations governing speed and wash. They would also encourage local authorities to ensure that better shore-based facilities were provided, especially near public mooring places.

The Commissioners' reluctance to tackle the boat number issue, together with their obvious inability to enforce the speed restrictions which they had imposed (and which they extended in 1979 to cover virtually the entire waterway system), prompted planning authorities to take an increasingly restrictive attitude towards the boat-hire industry from the mid-1970s onwards. In some cases, permission was refused outright for new, or extended boatyards, whilst elsewhere the applicants were invited to enter into agreements negotiated under Section 52 of the *Town and Country Planning Act* 1971, whereby they undertook not to keep or hire out more than a given number of vessels from their premises.

Although such agreements can be negotiated at any time, regardless of whether a planning application has or has not been submitted, experience has shown that they are not an ideal way of limiting boat numbers. They cannot be imposed on an individual by the planning authority, but must be concluded voluntarily. Moreover, because of the commercial pressures to which they are subject, boatyard operators often exhibit a marked, if understandable, reluctance to enter into them. In addition if, as is normally the case, the agreements contain restrictive covenants, these can only be enforced against the signatories, and their successors in title. Thus, to be effective, an agreement must be with the freeholder of the land, rather than a leaseholder or a prospective purchaser and developer.

These factors are reflected in the relatively small numbers of Section 52 agreements negotiated within the 'old' Broads Authority's Executive Area; in May 1980, there were eight, and there were still only about two dozen in 1986.

The great majority of Broadland's boatyards are covered by planning consents granted long before 1971, when local authorities were first empowered to negotiate Section 52 agreements. The number of vessels which can be kept at each yard is therefore usually limited by the fact that the planning permission given for it was made conditional on the buildings and their associated 'wet berths', not exceeding a given size. However, few yards are operated at their maximum theoretical capacity, and a survey by staff of the Norfolk County Council's Planning Department in the late 1970s showed that a substantial number of additional vessels could be kept at, or hired out from, the existing yards without any additional planning consents being granted. Thus, the exercise of development control will not of itself be capable of preventing further increases in the number of vessels kept on the waterways, in the event that socio-economic circumstances became conducive to this. In fact, and perhaps fortunately from the environmental point of view, this is likely to apply only to the private sector. As a result of a combination of factors, notably the recession of the early 1980s, the high cost of maintaining hire craft and building replacements of the quality now expected by holidaymakers, and the strong competition provided by firms offering package holidays abroad, the number of motor cruisers available for hire in the region has, as we have seen in Chapter 11, decreased very significantly during the past 10 years (see Table 11d). Furthermore, the general consensus in the trade is that the figures reached in the late 1970s are most unlikely to be attained again. This downward trend is reflected in the fact that 15 water-frontage sites occupied by firms engaged in hiring out boats prior to 1970 had been re-developed for housing by 1988, and that a further 24 companies had either gone over to industrial work, or were engaged in servicing privately-owned craft and providing moorings for them (Broads Boat Hire Federation, 1988).

Chapter 13
Nature Conservation

Early history

Early conservation legislation in Broadland, as in Britain as a whole, was enacted to safeguard fish, birds and mammals for resource management reasons, rather than as a means of protecting rare or endangered species. Southwell (1887), who reviewed the regulations which formerly governed the use of the region's fisheries, points out that under a Charter of 1461, Norwich Corporation was given powers to prevent the destruction of young fish, and control the use of nets, wears and other 'engines' between Sheep Wash (just downstream of New Mills) and Hardley Cross, whilst in 1556 it was made an offence to fish at night and use various catching devices. Eel fishing too, was controlled from very early days. In 1576, there were 38 setts in the lower reaches of the rivers Bure, Yare and Waveney, each hired out by Yarmouth Corporation for a penny a year, and checked when the town dignitaries carried out their annual inspection of the sections of river within their jurisdiction.

Wildfowl, too, were protected, at least in theory. An Act of 1534 made it illegal to destroy, except with a long bow, "dukkes, mallardes, wygeons, teales, wyldgeese, and dyverse other kyndes of wyldfowle" between the end of May, and the end of August (Dutt, 1906). The same legislation provided that between the first of March and the thirtieth of June, the eggs of "byttour, heroune, shoverlard, malarde, tele" and other wildfowl should not be taken. It is doubtful whether this Act was ever enforced and it was repealed in 1550 on the grounds that . . . "Benefytt was therebye taken awaye from the poore people that were wont to live by their skill in taking of the sayde fowle, wherby they were wont at that time to susteyne themselves with their poor households, to the great savinge of other kynds of vyttaile, of which ayde they are now destitute to their great and extreame ympoverishinge".

In 1770, another Act was passed, this time making it illegal to net, drive or take Teal, Wigeon, and other waterfowl between July and August inclusive. A preamble to this refers to "the great damage and decay of the breed of wildfowl" which was resulting from the use of such techniques during the moulting season. But both this Act, and the regulations governing Broadland's fisheries were widely flouted, and in 1857 the Norwich and Norfolk Anglers' Society was established in response to the growing threat to fish stocks posed by poachers and commercial interests. Pressure from the Society led in 1877 to Frank Buckland being commissioned by the Home Secretary to report on the problem, and during his investigations he found ample evidence, both of the enormous numbers of fish which were being caught – it was not unknown for 7 to 8 tons (7005 to 8120 kg) to be dispatched to London by overnight train – and of the decline in catches which had occurred as a result of the over-exploitation (Dutt, 1906).

Meantime, the indiscriminate slaughtering of birds continued, both for the pot and to satisfy the Victorian's mania for collecting, the position being made even worse with the passing of the *Game Act* 1831, since this repealed most of the older protective statutes. Black Terns, for instance, which Lubbock noted were nesting "in myriads" near Upton Broad in 1818, and which were quite common elsewhere in the region at this time, were progressively reduced in number, the last known attempt at breeding being made at Sutton Broad in 1858. But not only were the eggs of this pair collected, but the birds themselves were shot (Lubbock, 1897).

The growing realization that species were becoming extinct as a consequence of such excesses led Parliament to enact legislation in 1869, 1872 and again in 1876, affording various species a close season. A more comprehensive measure, the *Wild Birds Protection Act* 1880, afforded all birds a close season, and rendered the killing and taking of certain species subject to special penalties (Sheail, 1976). This, and further Acts passed in 1894 and 1896, also enabled the Home Secretary, on the application of a county, or borough council, to extend or vary the close season, add or remove a species from the specially-protected list, and afford certain birds or their eggs protection in defined areas. The Society for the Protection of Birds (formed in 1889 and given royal recognition in 1904) can take much of the credit for persuading Parliament to pass these later Acts; indeed, the Society was originally established to discourage the use of birds' feathers in millinery, and it did not broaden its species-protective functions to encompass the acquisition and management of nature reserves until the early 1930s.

Unfortunately, the new regulations suffered from numerous defects, not least the fact that owners and occupiers, and persons authorized by them, could kill on their property any bird not on the specially-protected list. In addition, no general protection was extended to the eggs of wild birds, and although the 1894 Act enabled the Home Secretary to issue an order banning the taking or destruction of the eggs of defined species, it was not an offence to have eggs in one's possession, or sell them. Consequently, it was virtually impossible to prosecute egg thieves successfully, unless they were caught red-handed. And even if an offender was apprehended, the penalties which could be imposed were derisory, being £1 for each scheduled bird or egg taken.

Partly because of this, and the complexity of the new regulations, their provisions were widely flouted, and local enforcement societies were therefore established to prevent the legislation becoming a dead-letter. The first such body in Norfolk, and perhaps in Britain, was the Breydon Wild Birds Protection Society. This was formed in 1888 to care for a site which, despite being very heavily shot over, was widely regarded as one of the best areas for birds in the country (WGC, 1921). The Society appointed Samuel 'Ducker' Chambers to act as a watcher between April and August each year, and provided him with a punt and a houseboat, subsequently moored in Ship Creek. Another individual, R. J. Buddery, was asked by the Society to ensure that the game dealers in Yarmouth did not trade in protected species. On the basis of evidence provided by its watchers, the Society instituted several successful prosecutions; for instance, Albert Beckett, landlord of the Lord Nelson, was fined 40 shillings for shooting two spoonbills in June 1888 (Allard, 1988).

In response to pressure from the Norfolk and Norwich Naturalists' Society (which had been founded in 1869), the Norfolk County Council, through its newly formed Wild Birds Protection Acts Committee, persuaded the Home Secretary to issue an Order in 1895 making it an offence to take or destroy the eggs of any wild bird in two parts of Broadland. One of these included Hickling Broad, Horsey Mere, Martham Broad and the adjoining fens and marshes, while the other took in the Ormesby-Rollesby-Filby group of broads. The Order also conferred special protection on Bearded Tits in the county, and on the eggs of several other species characteristic of Broadland, including Ruffs, Great Crested Grebes and all wild duck (Southwell, 1896).

During the ensuing fifty years, the County Council successfully sought renewals of this Order, at first annually, and later at four to five-year intervals. On almost every occasion, amendments were made to the list of species protected; Kingfishers and Bitterns, for example, were protected under the 1880 Act, but it was not until 1898 and 1905 respectively that it became an offence to collect their eggs in those parts of Norfolk not listed as special protection areas. In 1899, Sunday shooting was banned between the beginning of September and the end of March in the two designated parts of Broadland,

and two years later, following complaints about the amount of shooting elsewhere, the ban was extended to include the rivers Bure and Yare and their tributaries, and the adjoining fens and broads. The same Order, and a similar one obtained by the Norwich City Council in respect of those parts of the Wensum and Yare valleys over which it exercised jurisdiction, made it illegal to collect birds' eggs anywhere in Broadland, apart from the Waveney valley.

Although these, and other amendments to the orders made subsequently by the Home Secretary, improved and extended the protection afforded to different birds and their eggs, this was only achieved at the expense of simplicity, and despite periodic attempts by members of the Norfolk and Norwich Naturalists' Society to clarify which species were and were not protected (e.g. Long, 1929), the situation became increasingly confused. The Montagu Committee (1919) concluded from evidence presented to it just prior to the First World War that . . . "as long as the law remains as varied and as difficult to understand as at present, it can hardly be expected to secure any satisfactory degree of observance." Furthermore, the police were presented with an almost impossible task because, as the Committee remarked, . . . "the average constable has no great knowledge of birds, and probably would not know a protected bird when he saw it".

Despite these problems, there gradually developed a greater respect for the legislation, particularly at Breydon Water, thanks to the efforts of Chambers, and his successor, George Jary (1900–1927). But subscriptions to the Protection Society, which had amounted to over £40 in the first year, tailed off, and the newly formed RSPB had to assist it financially several times during the next 20 years to enable it to pay Jary's wages. In 1921, it became apparent that the existing, somewhat *ad hoc*, arrangements could not be allowed to continue, and it was decided that a sub-committee of the Norfolk and Norwich Naturalists' Society, to be known as the Norfolk Wild Birds Protection Committee, should assume the functions of the Breydon Society, and of similar bodies formed later for Blakeney Point and the Wells and Wolferton areas. Funds to enable the new committee to employ watchers at Breydon and elsewhere were raised, and endeavours to enforce the legislation were pursued with renewed vigour. In 1922, for example, an individual was successfully prosecuted for shooting a Ringed Plover on Breydon Water, while in 1928, three persons were each fined the maximum penalty of £1 for shooting Great Crested Grebes at Potter Heigham (Long, 1928).

The first of several Wild Birds Advisory Committees was established by the Government in 1921 to help enhance and extend the legislation, and an Act was passed in 1933 which improved the regulations governing the sale of wild birds. However, little was done to implement the other recommendations made by the Montagu Committee, and in a joint statement issued by the County Councils' Association and the RSPB in 1938, attention was drawn to the unsatisfactory situation. The issue was shelved during the War, but afterwards the proposals of a resuscitated Wild Birds Advisory Committee led, through a private member's Bill, to the passing of the *Protection of Birds Act* in 1954. This greatly simplified the regulations, since apart from certain quarry and pest species it afforded all birds year-round protection. The three species particularly characteristic of Broadland – the Marsh Harrier, Bittern and Bearded Tit – were afforded special (Schedule 1) protection under the Act, and various other rarities, including Savi's and Cetti's Warblers, were added to this schedule later.

The legislation relating to wild birds and their eggs was further improved by the *Protection of Birds Act* 1967, which made it unlawful for an unauthorized person to ring or mark any wild bird. It also became an offence wilfully to disturb a Schedule 1 bird while it is on or near its nest, and the police were given powers to stop and search persons (and their cars and boats) suspected of having taken or destroyed the egg of such a bird. In addition, Section 7 of the Act gave the Secretary of State the power temporarily to ban wildfowling for up to 14 days during periods of unusually cold weather. An appeal to desist from shooting had been issued by the Wildfowlers' Association of Great Britain and Ireland during the exceptionally hard winter of 1962/3, and although most sportsmen complied, a hard core of marsh cowboys had refused to do so, thus making it necessary to include an enabling clause in the 1967 Act. After some initial confusion, an NCC Working Group drew up criteria for deciding when a temporary ban on wildfowling was justified (see Swift, 1982), and the system has been successfully used on a number of occasions since 1981. It has undoubtedly had a beneficial effect in Broadland, since prior to 1963 a lamentably large number of weak and emaciated birds were shot on Breydon Water and elsewhere during periods of hard weather.

The regulations governing fishing were never as complex as those relating to birds, but they were strengthened, and made more readily enforceable in 1940, when the Ministry of Agriculture, Fisheries and Food established the Norfolk Fishery Board, under the *Salmon and Freshwater Fisheries Act* 1923. Twelve years later, the functions of the Board were assumed by the East Suffolk and Norfolk River Board, and responsibility for the region's fisheries was later taken over by the latter's successor, the East Suffolk and Norfolk River Authority. The AWA became responsible for fishery management in 1973, and this function was inherited by the National Rivers Authority in 1989.

The role of the Norfolk Naturalists' Trust and other voluntary bodies

The exemplary prosecutions brought from time to time against those who shot, or stole the eggs of birds afforded protection, together with a gradual increase, in the public's appreciation of nature, undoubtedly helped to ensure that some of the rarer species characteristic of Broadland returned to their former haunts. Nor must we overlook the enlightened attitude of certain landowners, the two outstanding examples in the region being Lord Desborough and Anthony Buxton, who at Hickling and Horsey respectively demonstrated during the 1930s how large estates could be managed for nature conservation, as well as for sporting purposes. However, it became increasingly clear to local naturalists that if the wildlife of areas such as Broadland was to be afforded adequate protection, it would be essential for land to be acquired specifically for this purpose. This approach had been pioneered by Charles Rothschild, who had founded the Society for the Promotion of Nature Reserves (the forerunner of the Royal Society for Nature Conservation) in 1912, and which was responsible for the first lists of sites in England, Wales and Scotland considered "worthy of preservation" (SPNR, 1915). Broadland was one of eight localities considered by the Society to be of "primary importance", the areas around Horning, Barton, Hickling and Upton being singled out for a grade 1 star listing on account of their animal, bird, plant and insect life.

Although Charles Rothschild died in 1923, his pioneering efforts bore further fruit three years later when Sydney Long and a small group of friends decided to found the Norfolk Naturalists' Trust (NNT). The Trust's first Broadland reserve, a 10.5 ha area of reed and sedge beds known as Starch Grass, situated to the north-west of Martham Broad, was purchased in 1928 for £140 (c. £3765 at 1990 prices), and two years later, it acquired the freehold of a second site – Alderfen Broad and its adjoining fens – for £2200 (£62 200 at 1990 prices). But given the limited resources of the Trust in its early years (the minutes of its Council show that its annual turnover only exceeded £1500 twice between 1926 and 1944), it is not altogether surprising that it did not establish another reserve in Broadland until the late 1940s. Nevertheless, it continued its endeavours to safeguard wildlife during this period. In 1933, for example, it relieved the Naturalists' Society of responsibility for the measures being taken at Breydon Water and elsewhere to enforce the legislation relating to the protection of birds.

During the War, local naturalists turned their attention to drawing up lists of sites which needed to be safeguarded. The initiative for this came from the Society for the Promotion of Nature Reserves (SPNR) which, realizing that the pressures on the countryside would increase after the War, and that the Government was therefore likely to take a greater interest in rural land-use planning, had convened a conference in 1941 on 'Nature preservation in post-war reconstruction'. Copies of the conclusions reached were sent to the Government, which responded by suggesting that a committee be formed to advise it on matters relating to nature reserves. This was done in 1942 in the guise of the Nature Reserves Investigation Committee (NRIC) which was invited, *inter alia*, "to report on the types and approximate areas of reserves and sanctuaries which should be provided and the localities where they should be situated". The Committee, which was chaired by Sir Lawrence Chubb, worked closely with John Dower who, the same year, had been asked by the Minister of Works and Planning to undertake a survey of potential national parks, later widened to include other 'amenity areas'. To assist the NRIC in its task, regional sub-committees were formed, the one for Norfolk being chaired by Anthony Buxton, and including in its membership such well-known naturalists as B. B. Riviere, E. A. Ellis, J. E. Sainty and E. L. Swann.

The Norfolk Committee's report, which is dated August 1943, recommended that the valley of the Bure below Wroxham, together with its broads and tributaries, and the Ant and Thurne, and the Yare valley below Norwich, also with its associated broads, should all be 'scheduled areas'. The Committee also decided that the most suitable area for a nature reserve was the Hickling-Horsey district, to include some 6000 acres (2429 ha) between the northern end of the Brayden Marshes and the R. Thurne, and encompassing Starch Grass. The other sites which the Committee considered should be established as reserves were:

> Calthorpe Broad,
> Decoy and Cockshoot Broads and the Woodbastwick fens,
> Ranworth Broad and the fens to the north,
> Upton Great and Little Broads, and the 'Doles',
> Sutton Broad,
> Barton Broad,
> Wheatfen and the adjoining fens,
> Buckenham Broad and its adjoining fens.

In a summary to the Report, the Committee recommended that three areas, Hickling-Horsey, Ranworth-Woodbastwick and Wheatfen, should be given a priority rating.

During the ensuing months, the NRIC compared the lists of proposed nature reserves submitted by its regional sub-committees, with those produced previously. These included a submission made to the Board of Agriculture by the SPNR in 1915, and a list of sites compiled by the British Correlating Committee for the Protection of Nature (founded in 1924) which had been included as an Annexe to the Report of the Addison Committee (Financial Secretary to the Treasury, 1931). The NRIC also considered wartime submissions by the Royal Entomological Society, the Royal Society for the Protection of Birds and the British Ecological Society, the latter having identified in its 1943 Report – 'Nature Conservation and Nature Reserves' – two sites in Broadland, namely Heron's Carr (Barton) and Surlingham Broad. Of the 47 sites in England and Wales which the NRIC finally decided were of national significance two, namely the Hickling-Horsey-Winterton area, and Barton Broad, were in Broadland. Both were given a category 'A' rating to indicate that the Committee considered that they were of outstanding importance, and that they must therefore be safeguarded as reserves. The northern part of Broadland (excluding the Waveney valley) was included in the list of 25 'Conservation Areas' identified by the NRIC, and several sites in the Bure, Ant, Thurne and Yare valleys, including Cockshoot, Decoy, Ranworth, Upton, Alderfen, Sutton, Calthorpe, Surlingham and Rockland Broads, were singled out as being of 'special importance' (SPNR, 1945).

These recommendations were broadly accepted by the Wildlife Conservation Special Committee set up by the Government in 1945 under the chairmanship of Dr Julian Huxley. However Winterton Dunes was separated from the proposed Hickling-Horsey reserve, and the Committee applied the term 'Scientific Areas' to the 'Conservation Areas' listed by the NRIC (Ministry of Town and Country Planning, 1947b).

The Hickling–Horsey area identified by the Huxley Committee as being of national nature conservation importance included the Whiteslea Estate at Hickling, which had been established as a sporting estate-cum-bird sanctuary by Lord Lucas in about 1909. In 1917 the 97 ha which he owned were inherited by the Hon. Ivor Grenfell, but because he was a minor, his father, Lord Desborough, assumed responsibility for managing the area. Following Grenfell's death in a road accident in 1926, the estate passed to Lord Desborough who continued to extend it as opportunities arose so that by the mid-1940s he owned 256 ha, and leased a further 208 ha from Col. John Mills, a neighbouring landowner. Lord Desborough entered into negotiations for the sale of the estate to Mr Christopher Cadbury in 1944, but he died the following year, and it passed to his daughter, Lady Gage. With Mr Cadbury's agreement, and with the help of grants from him, the RSPB, the Pilgrim Trust and the Society for the Promotion of Nature Reserves, it was then acquired from her by the Norfolk Naturalists' Trust for £8972 (c. £152 000 at 1990 prices).

The Horsey Estate was purchased by Lady Lucas in 1912, and has long been run on similar lines to the Whiteslea Estate. In 1930, it was purchased by the late Anthony Buxton, who donated it to the National Trust in 1948 on a lease-back arrangement. Since then, the Mere and the marshes and fens which adjoin it have been managed as a reserve, at first by Mr Buxton and since 1970 by his son, John.

Other reserves established in the region just after the War include Barton Broad, which was purchased by the Norfolk Naturalists' Trust in 1946, and Bargate Island, opposite Brundall in the Yare valley, which was given to it in 1948. The following year, Ranworth and Cockshoot Broads were donated to the Trust by the late Col. H. J. Cator, whilst Surlingham Broad was purchased in 1952 for £1112 (c. £13 400 at 1990 prices). Like Hickling, all these reserves included substantial areas of fen vegetation, as well as open water.

The Norfolk Naturalists' Trust remained a fairly small organization throughout the 1950s, and this restricted its ability to establish further reserves. However, thanks to the growing interest in conservation, its membership and financial resources increased rapidly from the mid-1960s onwards (see Table 13a), and this enabled it to acquire

Table 13a   The Norfolk Naturalists' Trust

	1952	1962	1972	1982
Nos. of members	786	900	4104	7170
Income (excl. donations, legacies & sales of assets – (£)	4949 (59 670)	5884 (55 231)	24 378 (141 518)	147 906 (229 660)
Expenditure on nature reserve management – (£)*	3872 (46 755)	4614 (43 311)	17 221 (99 702)	119 404** (185 404)

Notes:
The figures in brackets relate to 1990 prices.
* This covers all the Trust's reserves – figures for the Broadland sites only are not available.
** Including wages, rents etc.

further sites as reserves. Those in Broadland comprise Firs Marsh, near Burgh St. Peter (leased in 1964), Martham North and South Broads (leased in 1971), Hardley Flood and Smallburgh Fen (leased in 1972), part of Ranworth Fen (made subject to a management agreement in 1979, and five years later leased to the Trust by the owner, Mr. I. V. B. Mills), 65 ha of Upton Fen (purchased in 1979 with the help of grants from the Broads Authority, NCC and World Wildlife Fund*), and a small grazing marsh nearby (purchased in 1984). In the early 1980s, the Trust extended its nearby Barton Broad reserve eastwards by leasing parts of Catfield Fen, and by May 1986 it was safeguarding 11 sites in the region, with a combined hectarage of 1155, representing nearly half of its total land holding (NNT, 1986).

The Suffolk Trust for Nature Conservation (renamed the Suffolk Wildlife Trust in 1988) has had fewer opportunities to establish reserves in Broadland than the Norfolk Trust, as it was not founded until 1961; in addition, the only part of the region within its county is the southern side of the Waveney valley. Nevertheless, it leased two sites near Carlton Colville in 1975. The first of these comprises some unreclaimed fen and flooded peat workings known as Sprat's Water (6 ha), while the other is a 16 ha reed-bed, Whitecast Marsh. Both areas, together with some 19 ha of grazing marsh nearby, were bought by the Trust in 1980, and incorporated in a unified reserve known as the Carlton Marshes. The purchase price (£45 000), plus some £20 000 for the future management of the site, was raised by public appeal, to which the Broads Authority contributed £14 000, the NCC £11 000, the Suffolk County Council £10 000, the World Wildlife Fund £8500 and the National Heritage Memorial Fund £5000. Soon after this land had been acquired, the Trust negotiated a management agreement over some 17 ha of

* This organization renamed itself the World Wide Fund for Nature in 1988.

wet woodland and rough marsh at North Cove (Barnby), a mile or so up-valley from the Carlton Marshes reserve.

The RSPB acquired a direct managerial interest in Broadland in 1975, when it leased from Mr. W. S. Key and the other trustees of the Holmes Estate, Strumpshaw Broad and the adjoining fens and grazing marshes, together covering 127 ha. It subsequently purchased the freehold of a further 53 ha of fen, and leased two other small areas, so that by 1989, the Strumpshaw reserve extended to some 183 ha. The Society acquired the freehold of *c.* 108 ha at Surlingham, on the south side of the river Yare, in the late 1970s, and the combined areas became known as the Strumpshaw Fen and Surlingham Marshes reserve. Shooting rights were also leased near Rockland Broad, and although the latter is not yet formally incorporated in the reserve, talks about its future have taken place between the Society, the Rockland St. Mary and Hellington Parish Council and wildfowling interests. Steps have also been taken to regulate the 'free-for-all' shooting which took place over this Broad until recently.

Although the Hickling and Horsey reserves and one or two other sites afforded protection during the two decades after the War include grazing marshland, as well as

1986	1987	1988	1989(August)	1990	
8498	*c.*8100	8443	10442	11708	Nos. of members
210871	212475	253825	300923	312875	Income (excl. donations, legacies
(271854)	(263016)	(299521)	(329393)	–	& sales of assets) – £
153295**	170920**	200467**	251079**	301079**	Expenditure on nature reserve
(197627)	(211577)	(236557)	(274833)	–	management – £

Source: Annual Reports of the NNT, apart from the membership figures for 1987, 1989 and 1990 which were provided by Trust Staff.

open water and fen, conservationists initially tended to concentrate their attention on the two latter habitat types as it was thought that these supported a greater wealth of plant and animal life. However, surveys commissioned by the NCC in the 1970s showed that grass marshland not only has its own intrinsic interest, but that the dyke system associated with it provides a refuge for most of the aquatic plants and animals formerly found in the rivers and broads, but now largely eliminated as a consequence of nutrient enrichment (see Chapter 8). In addition, it is now realized that Broadland's fens, open waters and grass marshes are ecologically interdependent. Marsh Harriers, for instance, breed in the former, but range widely over the adjoining countryside, obtaining much of their food in the Drained Marshland Area. In view of this, and the likelihood that more and more grass marsh would be put under the plough, conservationists increased their efforts during the 1980s to safeguard such terrain. The RSPB, for example, bought *c.* 37 ha near Berney Arms in 1985, and a further *c.* 112 ha in the same area the following year. Similarly, the Suffolk Trust acquired an interest in *c.* 14 ha of grass marshland to the north of Oulton Dyke in 1982, and during 1988/9 purchased holdings of *c.* 18 and *c.* 51 ha in the Castle Marshes, just up-valley from the area it already owned near Carlton Colville. The total cost of these acquisitions was £136180, but one third of this sum was made available by the NCC in grants. Meantime, the National Trust had succeeded in buying, with the help of financial assistance from the National Heritage Fund (£300000), NCC (£75000) and Broads Authority (£20000) the area known as Heigham Holmes. This consists of some 186 ha of marsh (of which *c.* 97 ha is under grass), situated in close proximity to the Hickling, Horsey and Martham Broads reserves, and is to be managed in close conjunction with them.

The Otter Trust established its headquarters at Earsham, just up-valley from Bungay, in 1975, and has always taken a close interest in what is happening in Broadland. The Trust acquired *c*. 13 ha of Stanley Carr near Beccles, in 1980, and manages this site as a nature reserve. It also reintroduced otters into a fen beside one of the northern rivers in 1988 (see page 229).

No account of the voluntary bodies operating in the region would be complete without a mention of the Broads Society. This was formed in 1956 to consider all Broadland issues, with a view to conserving the region's beauty and environmental quality, preserving and enlarging its navigational facilities, and encouraging the maximum use of the area, consistent with these aims. It currently has a membership of about 2000, and takes a keen interest in all developmental and other proposals likely to affect the region. Recent issues in which the Society has adopted a particularly active role have included the future of How Hill (see page 479), the contents of the Broads Bill and the controversy over the proposed Wroxham/Hoveton by-pass (see Chapter 12).

The National Parks and Access to the Countryside Act, 1949

The formation in March 1949 of the Nature Conservancy as a Corporation incorporated by Royal Charter, and the passing of the *National Parks and Access to the Countryside Act* a few months later, gave a new dimension to the steps being taken to safeguard the ecology of Broadland. One of the Conservancy's first tasks was to review the recommendations which had been made in the Report of the Wildlife Conservation Special Committee (Ministry of Town and Country Planning, 1947b). Two sites in the region, namely Barton Broad and the Hickling-Horsey area, had been included in the list of proposed national nature reserves compiled by this Committee, but this recommendation had been made before Joyce Lambert and her fellow workers had completed their research on the ecology of the fens, and the origin of the broads. In 1954, the Conservancy decided in the light of advice proffered by Dr Lambert that some of the fens and broads in the middle Bure valley, subsequently (but somewhat illogically) known as the Bure Marshes, should be substituted for Barton Broad. This decision was taken in the belief, then current, that there was a wider range of fen communities here than in the Ant valley*, and because the four broads selected for inclusion in the proposed reserve (Ranworth, Cockshoot, Decoy and Hoveton Great) were not subject to disturbance by boat traffic, as was Barton Broad. Dr Lambert also argued that since Ranworth Broad occupied a deeper basin than the latter, it would grow over more slowly, and therefore be easier to maintain as open water.

Although Barton Broad and its adjoining fens was dropped from the list of proposed national nature reserves, two sites were added. The natural history of the first of these – the Surlingham-Wheatfen-Rockland area – had been subject to prolonged study by Ted Ellis and others, and was in consequence better known than any other part of the region. The second addition was Calthorpe Broad which in 1953 had been given to the Conservancy by Mrs. S. G. Gurney, widow of the well known naturalist, Robert Gurney.

Soon after these decisions had been made, discussions started between the Conservancy, the NNT and Major J. M. Mills (who had assumed responsibility for his father's estate in 1947), concerning the possibility of establishing Hickling Broad and its adjoining fens and grazing marshes, as a national nature reserve (NNR). The negotiations were fairly protracted, but were brought to a successful conclusion in 1957, with the coming into force of nature reserve agreements covering 487 ha; the site was formally declared in June 1958. Additional areas acquired by the Trust subsequently were made subject to supplementary agreements with the Conservancy in 1974 and 1975.

Under the agreements, the Trust remains responsible for the day-to-day management and staffing of the site, overall policy being determined by a management committee consisting of four representatives of the Trust and three of the Conservancy. The latter provides the Trust with a substantial annual grant towards the cost of running the reserve, whilst in return the Conservancy is able to use the site for research and other purposes, provided of course these are acceptable to the Trust. It was agreed between

---

* As a result of the work of Dr Bryan Wheeler and his colleagues, it is now known that the fens of the Ant valley are, in fact much more ecologically diverse than those of the Bure valley (see Chapter 7).

the parties at the outset that no shooting would be permitted over the south-west corner of the reserve. However, a sporting syndicate continued to operate over the remainder of the site until 1965, when the Trust decided that it could afford to forgo the not-inconsiderable revenue which it derived from this source. The coot shoots, which had taken place once or twice annually over the Broad for as long as anyone could remember, ceased in 1963*.

Whilst the discussions over Hickling Broad were in train, the Conservancy negotiated nature reserve agreements with the NNT over Ranworth and Cockshoot Broads and their adjoining fens, and with Mr John Cator over Decoy Broad and the Woodbastwick fens; the two areas, together covering 297 ha, were declared as the Bure Marshes NNR in June 1958. Three months later the Hoveton Great Broad area (115 ha) was added to the reserve by agreement with the late Mr. T. R. C. Blofeld, and in 1981 it was again extended, this time by the inclusion of Ranworth Flood (see page 212) which the Conservancy leased from Mr. F. Cator. The reserve now covers 451 ha.

During the 1960s, the deficiencies in the list of proposed national nature reserves in the 1947 Huxley Committee's report became increasingly apparent and, in 1965, the Conservancy embarked on a major survey, aimed at identifying all those sites which are of national ecological interest. This Domesday-like work was finally published in 1977 as the Nature Conservation Review, and it contains a detailed rationale for site selection, as well as descriptions of 735 areas in Britain considered to be of Grade 1 or 2 national importance (Ratcliffe, 1977).

Seven of the Grade 1 sites listed in the Review are located in Broadland, and three of these were afforded an asterisk to indicate that they are of international, as well as national significance (see Table 13b). One further site, Smallburgh Fen, was given a Grade 2 rating, though in practice this is of no significance, since the Conservancy decided, after the Review was published, that all the sites listed in it should be regarded as being of key importance for nature conservation.

In his introduction to the Nature Conservation Review, Dr Ratcliffe pointed out that it would be necessary to amend the lists of key sites from time to time to take account of new and improved data, and in the event, numerous additions and boundary amendments have been made. Indeed, by 1988, the number of sites in Britain recognized as being of national ecological importance totalled 937, of which 498, with a combined hectarage of 451 749, are in England. It will be seen from the notes to Table 13b that this trend is reflected in Broadland, the total size of the area now assessed as being of prime importance – 3482 ha – being substantially greater than the total estimated hectarage of the sites listed in the Review – 2442.

The international importance of the Bure Marshes NNR and the Hickling-Horsey-Martham complex was formally recognized by the Government in 1976 when these sites were included in the initial list of 13 wetlands in the United Kingdom to be afforded protection under the Ramsar Convention. This is an international initiative, devised at a conference in Ramsar, Iran, in 1971, which is aimed at stemming the progressive loss of wetlands, particularly those of importance for waterfowl. The Convention was signed by the UK Government in 1973, and formally ratified three years later. The qualifying criteria used in the selection of sites, and the administrative arrangements employed in the designation process, are described in a Conservancy leaflet (NCC, 1988).

In addition to empowering the Nature Conservancy (and from 1973 onwards, the Nature Conservancy Council), to acquire and manage nature reserves, the *National Parks and Access to the Countryside Act* made it possible for local authorities to safeguard sites of nature conservation importance. The first, and until 1984 the only, such local nature reserve in Norfolk was established at Breydon Water in 1967 (see page 473). The Act also made it obligatory for the Conservancy to notify local authorities of sites which it considered to be of special scientific interest (SSSIs). The first lists of such sites in Norfolk and East Suffolk were produced in 1954, and although they only included eight biological sites in Broadland, six more were added in 1958. Further additions and deletions were made in subsequent years, and by 1979, 21 ecologically important sites, with a combined hectarage of 2304, together with three geological sites in the region, were scheduled.

---

* A more detailed description of the history and wildlife of the Hickling reserve – regarded by many as the 'jewel in the Norfolk Trust's crown' – has been compiled by Stewart Linsell, and was published in 1990.

The SSSI system was originally conceived as a way of ensuring that the Conservancy was afforded an opportunity to comment upon planning proposals made in respect of sites of particular scientific importance, local authorities being obliged, under a General Development Order to take these views into account when determining the issue. In general, these arrangements worked fairly well in Broadland and few sites were damaged as a result of a failure by a planning authority to heed the advice proffered it by the Conservancy. On the other hand, the latter was not necessarily consulted about developments proposed outside the boundary of a scheduled site, and which, if permitted, could affect it adversely. For example, the decisions made during the late 1950s and 1960s by the Norfolk County Council, and on one occasion, following an appeal, by the

Table 13b   List of key sites in Broadland

Name	Ref. No. in Review	Grading in Review	Ha (approx.)
Bure Marshes	P7 & W 38	1*	450 – see note 1
Hickling Broad & Horsey Mere (inc. Martham Broad)	OW12 & P6	1*	851 – see note 2
Surlingham Marshes, Wheatfen & Rockland Broad	P8	1*	315 – see note 3
Ant Marshes (inc. Barton Broad)	P20	1	500 – see note 4
Calthorpe Broad	OW16 & P10	1	44
Sutton Broad	P9	1	170 – see note 4
Upton Broad	OW15 & P108	1	105 – see note 5
Smallburgh Fen	P15	2	7
Ludham Marshes	–	–	73 – see note 6

Notes:

1. In 1989 this site was extended to form the 'Bure Broads and Marshes', with a hectarage of *c.* 769.

2. In 1989 this site was extended to form the 'Upper Thurne Broads and Marshes', with a hectarage of 1159.

3. In 1988 this site was extended to encompass the fens and marshes on the north (Strumpshaw) side of the R. Yare, to form the 'Yare Broads and Marshes'. This has a hectarage of 726.

4. These two sites were amalgamated in 1989 to form the 'Ant Valley Broads and Marshes'; this has a hectarage of 735.

5. The hectarage of this site was increased to 228 after the Review was published as a result of the inclusion of 123 ha of the adjoining grazing marshland.

6. This site was recognized as being of prime ecological importance after the Review was published. It was purchased by the NCC during 1983 and 1984, and declared a national nature reserve in 1987.

* Indicates that site is considered to be of international importance.

Minister of Housing and Local Government, to allow the expansion of boat-hiring yards at Stalham (see page 442), led to a substantial increase in the number of powered craft passing to and fro across Barton Broad, an SSSI and Norfolk Naturalists' Trust reserve. Similarly, the Minister's decision in 1971 to allow a boatyard established in the mid-1960s at the end of Catfield Dyke to continue to build and repair private craft (see page 442) increased the recreational pressure on the adjoining Hickling Broad NNR.

In the mid-1950s, it was arranged that the scope of the consultations over SSSIs should be extended to cover grant applications made to the MAFF and Forestry Commission. However, these arrangements never proved wholly satisfactory, especially in connection with farm improvement schemes. The Ministry took the view that its principal obligation was to stimulate increased agricultural productivity, and in some cases, it offered farmers grants, despite the Conservancy's objections. Moreover, even when grants were withheld, the owners and occupiers of SSSIs felt themselves disadvantaged as a result of their inability to obtain financial redress from the Conservancy; indeed, in these circumstances, they sometimes proceeded to plough up and drain their land without grant. Difficulties were also experienced with the River Authority and the Internal Drainage Boards, none of which was required to consult the Conservancy about its activities even if these were likely to alter the water regime of an NNR or SSSI. Nor did they take much account of Section 11 of the *Countryside Act* 1968, even though this enjoined them, as public bodies, to have regard to "the desirability of conserving the natural beauty and amenity of the countryside" when carrying out their duties.

Reference has been made in the previous Chapter to the organizational changes to which local government and the water industry have been subject since the Second World War, and the nation's nature conservation service has been similarly affected. In response to the recommendations made by the Committee of Enquiry into the Organization of the Civil Service (the Trend Report), the Government decided in 1965 that the Nature Conservancy should become a component body of the Natural Environment Research Council (NERC) set up under the *Science and Technology Act* 1965. However,

Table 13c   NCC grants for projects in Broadland – 1974/5 to 1988/9

Year	Recipient	Project	Grant (£)
1975/6	Norfolk Nat. Trust	Establishing Ranworth Cons. Centre	2500
1975/6	Norfolk Nat. Trust	Bank reinforcement – Martham Broad	800
1975/6	Norfolk Nat. Trust	Rotary slasher (Barton & Hickling Broads)	375
1976/7	Norfolk Nat. Trust	Dyke restoration – Barton Broad	50
1976/7	RSPB	Secondhand tractor – Strumpshaw Fen	300
1976/7	RSPB	Observation hide – Buckenham marshes	200
1978/9	Peter Boardman	Excavating new broad (*c.* 0.5 ha) nr. How Hill	5595
1978/9	Norfolk Nat. Trust	Diverting nutrient-rich inflow stream – Alderfen Broad	702
1981/2	Broads Authority	Transplanting waterweeds & fencing – Barton Broad	168
1982/3	Norfolk Nat. Trust	Access control – Martham Broad	373
1982/3	Norfolk Nat. Trust	Dyke restoration – Upton Fen	269
1982/3	Broads Authority	Mud-pumping Cockshoot Broad	2500
1983/4	Anglian Water Auth.	Enlarging Hundred Stream as part of scheme to prevent polluted land drainage water reaching Martham Broad	1967
1983/4	Happisburgh to Winterton IDB	Re-locating land drainage pump away from Martham Broad (1st. instalment)	5000
1983/4	Norfolk Nat. Trust	Dyke restoration – fens beside Martham Broad	450
1983/4	Norfolk Nat. Trust	Dyke restoration – Upton Fen	245
1985/6	Norfolk Nat. Trust	Dyke restoration – Upton Fen	327
1985/6	Norfolk Nat. Trust	Dyke restoration – fens beside Martham Broad	1000
1985/6	Happisburgh to Winterton IDB	Re-locating land drainage pump away from Martham Broad (2nd. instalment)	3500
1985/6	Suffolk Trust for Nat. Cons.	Suction-dredging Round Water – Carlton Marshes NR	390
1986/7	RSPB	Employing warden – Surlingham NR	3839
1986/7	RSPB	Employing warden – Berney Arms NR	4930
1986/7	Norfolk Nat. Trust (on behalf of Ted Ellis Trust)	Bridge building – Wheatfen	438
1986/7	Suffolk Trust for Nat. Cons.	Dyke renovation – Carlton Colville NR	200
1987/8	Hertfordshire CC	Extend pond at Barton Turf Educ. NR.	468
1987/8	Norfolk Nat. Trust	Dyke restoration – fens beside Martham Broad	450
1987/8	Norfolk Nat. Trust	New interpretive panels – Ranworth Cons. Centre (1st instalment)	1900
1988/9	Norfolk Nat. Trust	New interpretive panels – Ranworth Cons. Centre (2nd instalment)	1400
1988/9	Suffolk Wildlife Trust	Materials for sluices – Castle Marshes	2128
1988/9	Suffolk Wildlife Trust	Footpath reinforcement – Sprat's Water	144

its terms of reference, as defined in the 1949 Royal Charter (which were . . . "to provide scientific advice on the conservation and control of the natural flora and fauna of Great Britain; to establish, maintain and manage nature reserves in Great Britain, including the maintenance of physical features of scientific interest; and to organise and develop the research and scientific services related thereto"), remained much the same. A further, and in practical terms, more important organizational change took place in 1973, when it was decided that the conservation and advisory activities of the Nature Conservancy Committee of NERC (but not its research functions, which remained vested in the latter) should be assumed by a new body, the Nature Conservancy Council (NCC). Like its predecessors this is responsible* under the terms of the *Nature Conservancy Council Act* 1973, for establishing, maintaining and managing nature reserves, providing advice and disseminating knowledge about nature conservation, and supporting and conducting research relevant to these functions. The Council's policies, and the means by which they were to be accomplished, were published in 1974 (NCC, 1975).

Table 13d   NCC grants for land purchase in Broadland – 1978/9 to 1988/9

Year	Recipient	Site	Area (ha)	Cost (£)	Grant (£)
1980/1	Suffolk Trust for Nat. Cons.	Sprat's Water & Carlton Marshes	25.1	45 000	11 000
1983/4	Norfolk Nat. Trust	Upton grazing marsh	1.3	5 250	1 750
1983/4	Broads Auth.	How Hill Estate (pt.)	124.3	90 000	22 500
1986/7	National Trust	Heigham Holmes (pt.)	97.2	225 000	75 000
1986/7	RSPB	Fens nr. Coldham Hall (Surlingham)	3.6	9 000	1 100
1988/9	Ted Ellis Trust	Wheatfen	41.3	36 000	18 000
1988/9	Suffolk Wildlife Trust	Castle Marshes	18.2	23 500	7 833
1988/9	Suffolk Wildlife Trust	Castle Marshes	41.3	36 000	18 000

The Act gave the new Council certain powers which its predecessors did not possess, and of these the most important, as far as Broadland is concerned, is its ability to give grants. Initially, the funds available were used solely to assist voluntary bodies and private individuals carry out land management and interpretive projects beneficial to nature conservation. However, in 1978/9, following an increase in the NCC's Grant-in-Aid from the Department of the Environment, it was decided to make available funds towards the cost of acquiring SSSI-quality land which was to be designated as a nature reserve, and also for helping voluntary bodies increase their capacity to undertake conservation management works, and interpretive projects. The NNT received one of these three-year 'capacity' grants in 1978/9, thus enabling it to appoint Richard Hobbs as its Field Officer, and this, plus the Suffolk Trust's receipt of a grant towards the cost of employing a Development Officer in 1983/4 and 1984/5, undoubtedly enabled these organizations to accomplish more in Broadland than would otherwise have been possible.

The grants made available by the NCC for projects and land acquisition in Broadland between 1974/5 and 1988/9 are listed in Tables 13c and 13d respectively.

The Wildlife and Countryside Act 1981

During the late 1970s it became apparent that increasing numbers of SSSIs were being destroyed or damaged each year, and a countrywide survey indicated that about 13 per cent suffered significant damage to their wildlife interest in 1980, mainly as a result of

---

* Following the Government's decision, announced in July 1989, that three independent country agencies should be set up in place of the NCC, the latter's functions in England were taken over by 'English Nature' in April 1991. This and the bodies with responsibilities in Scotland and Wales were set up under the terms of Sections 128–139 of the *Environmental Protection Act* 1990.

agricultural operations (Nature Conservancy Council, 1982a). The widespread concern felt about this reflected the growing interest which the public had been taking in environmental conservation since the early 1970s, and this, plus the increasingly obvious deficiencies in the existing legislation prompted the Government to introduce its Wildlife and Countryside Bill to the House of Lords in November 1980. Eleven months later, and after much debate and controversy, the Bill received the Royal Assent as the most comprehensive piece of wildlife legislation ever enacted at Westminster.

The provisions of the *Wildlife and Countryside Act* 1981 have been described elsewhere, for instance by the NCC (1983) and Denyer-Green (1983). However, its main benefits in Broadland have been firstly, to strengthen the legislation relating to SSSIs (Sections 28-33), secondly, to enable the Broads Authority to take steps to safeguard land of high amenity and landscape value within the region [(Sections 39 and 41(3)], thirdly, to make it obligatory for internal drainage boards and the AWA (and its successor, the National Rivers Authority) to take more account of the needs of nature conservation (Section 48), and fourthly, to improve the protection afforded to the rare plants and animals which occur in the region (Sections 1 - 27). Section 38 of the Act also broadened the remit of the NCC's grant-giving powers to cover any activity beneficial to nature conservation. Previously, its grants to outside bodies had been limited (under Section 3 of the *Nature Conservancy Act* 1973) to projects which the Council itself had the power to carry out.

Another provision of the Act which has proved helpful in Broadland is Section 3(1), which enables the Secretary of State to designate sites of particular ornithological importance as 'Areas of Special Protection' (AOSP). These are equivalent to the statutory Bird Sanctuaries which could be established by Orders made under Section 3 of the *Protection of Birds Act* 1954, and should not be confused with the similarly-named 'Special Protection Areas', which are designated by the Government to fulfil its commitments in respect of an EEC Directive, dated April 1979, on the Conservation of Wild Birds (see NCC, 1986). Part of the National Trust's Horsey Estate, including the Brayden Marshes, Horsey Mere, and the marshland to the south, was made an AOSP in 1988, the effect being that any person who enters the designated area without authority, or who kills, takes the egg of, or disturbs any bird within it, is liable to a special penalty, as prescribed under the Act.

One of the key principles enshrined in the new Act was that conflicts over the management of SSSIs should in future be resolved by co-operation and compromise, rather than by diktat. It also contained clauses making it obligatory for the NCC and other relevant authorities to offer compensation to owners who were proposing to alter the management of their land in a way considered harmful to conservation interests. The likelihood – subsequently amply realized – that the NCC would have to deal with large numbers of such 'profits-forgone' claims in respect of its SSSIs, made it essential for it to review the procedures relating to the selection of such sites (Moore, 1982). This involved rationalizing and strengthening the criteria used to decide whether a particular site was, or was not, of sufficient merit to warrant being notified (NCC, 1982b)*, and also making a check to ensure that the existing SSSIs met the new criteria, and that no areas of special biological, geological or physiographical interest had been overlooked.

The necessary surveys were carried out in Broadland in 1982 and 1983, and led to decisions being taken that eight new SSSIs should be notified in the region, but that six of the existing ones – Billockby Sand Pit, Burgh St. Peter Fen, Burntfen Broad, Crown Point Pit, Fritton Lake and Wigg's Carr – did not meet the qualifying criteria, and would therefore have to be de-notified. It was also decided that significant amendments would have to be made to the boundaries of several sites, whilst others could be amalgamated. These changes took some time to implement in view of the NCC's obligation under the new Act to contact all the individuals who own or occupy land within each SSSI, and ensure that they are aware of the reasons why it is about to re-notified (if it had been scheduled under Secion 23 of the 1949 Act), or, in the case of a new site, forewarn them that steps were being taken to notify it under Section 28 of the new legislation. Lists of 'Potentially Damaging Operations' (PDOs) also had to be drawn up, and formal 'consents' issued by the NCC for management works which had been agreed

---

* Revised guidelines for use in connection with the selection of SSSIs were published in full by the NCC in 1989.

as a result of discussions between the parties concerned. Despite these and other administrative complications, all 25 SSSIs in Broadland (as defined in the Introduction) plus six other sites located just outside its boundaries, had been formally re-notified or notified under the new Act by January 1991 (see Table 13e).

One of the 25 sites, Bramerton Pits, has been notified on account of its geological importance, but the remaining 24 encompass 5144 ha of prime ecological interest. Of this, 581 ha is open water, 1727 ha is fen, 1195 is woodland and scrub, 1170 is grassland, whilst just under 400 ha consists of saltmarsh and intertidal mudflats. The remaining hectarage is made up of fragments of other habitats, a little arable and one or two unmapped areas.

The agreements whereby the NCC can compensate owners and occcupiers for not

Table 13e Sites in and near Broadland which have been, or are about to be, notified as SSSIs under S.28 of the *Wildlife and Countryside Act* 1981

Name of site	*Status*	*NGR*	*Ha*	*Comments*
Alderfen Broad	E	TG 355195	20.6	NNT reserve
Ant Broads and Marshes†	A**	TG 362213	735.1	Pts. estd. as reserves by NNT
Barnby Broad and Marshes	N	TM 480910	189.6	
Bramerton Pits	E	TG 295060 & TG 298061	0.5	Geological site
Breydon Water	N	TG 500075	506.5	Local Nature Reserve
Broad Fen, Dilham	E	TG 343255	36.9	
Bure Broads and Marshes	A**	TG 346160	768.6	Inc. the Bure Marshes NNR
Burgh Common & Muckfleet Marshes	E	TG 445127	118.0	
Caistor St. Edmund Chalk Pit*	E	TG 239048	23.8	Geological site
Calthorpe Broad	E	TG 412258	43.5	Owned by NCC
Catton Grove Chalk Pit (Norwich)*	E	TG 239048	23.8	Geological site
Decoy Carr, Acle†	E	TG 405090	55.4	
Ducan's Marsh, Claxton†*	N	TG 339027	3.6	
East Ruston Common*	E	TG 340280	38.3	
Geldeston Meadows†	N	TM 396916	13.4	
Hall Farm Fen, Hemsby†	N	TG 481170	10.5	
Halvergate Marshes†	E	TG 435060	162.3	
Hardley Flood	N	TG 380997	48.1	NNT reserve
Limpenhoe Meadows†	N	TG 399031	11.6	
Ludham to Potter Heigham Marshes†	E	TG 402177	101.3	Inc. Ludham Marshes NNR
Poplar Farm Meadows, Langley†	E	TG 370021	7.2	
Priory Meadows, Hickling†	N	TG 417254	24.0	
Shallam Dyke Marshes, Thurne†	N	TG 399165	71.7	
Smallburgh Fen	E	TG 327246	7.3	NNT reserve
Sprat's Water & Marshes	E	TM 507921	55.5	SWT reserve
Stanley & Alder Carrs, Aldeby	E	TG 434928	43.5	Pt. Otter Trust reserve
Sweetbriar Road Meadows*	N	TG 208097	9.5	Local Nature Reserve
Upper Thurne Broads & Marshes†	A**	TG 430210	1159.2	Inc. Hickling Broad NNR (NNT/NCC) & areas owned by National Trust
Upton Broad & Marshes†	E	TG 390137	227.6	Pt. NNT reserve
Winterton-Horsey Dunes*	E	TG 490210	472.2	Inc. Winterton Dunes NNR
Yare Broads & Marshes†	A**	TG 330063	726.4	Inc. RSPB & NNT reserves

Key:
E   Existing SSSI, previously notified under the 1949 Act (sometimes with minor boundary changes)
A   Aggregate site (including two or more 1949 Act sites)
N   New SSSI, not scheduled under the 1949 Act
*   SSSIs located just outside the boundaries of Broadland, as defined in the Introduction.
** The NCC is minded to recommend the Government to designate these four sites as a unified Special Protection Area (see page 461). It also believes that their combined importance in an international context is sufficient to warrant their designation as a Ramsar site. Parts of them were afforded this status in 1976 (see page 457).
†   Sites which either wholly or in part, are, or have been, subject to profits-forgone agreements negotiated under Section 15 of the *Countryside Act*, 1968.

damaging the scientific interest of scheduled sites proved to be complex and time-consuming to negotiate. Nevertheless, by January 1990 no fewer than 35 profits-forgone agreements had been concluded under Section 15 of the *Countryside Act* 1968. These together covered 575 ha, and were made in respect of 14 of the sites listed in Table 13e. They enabled the NCC to make annual payments to the owners or part-owners of the sites concerned and in two cases their tenants. One other agreement (covering 16 ha) was negotiated whereby the owner received a once-and-for-all payment, as allowed under the Financial Guidelines issued by the Government following the passing of the *Wildlife and Countryside Act*. 19 of the annual agreements were allowed to elapse following the designation of Broadland as an Environmentally Sensitive Area (see page 486), as the owners concerned opted to join this Scheme, rather than continue to receive compensation from the NCC. The remaining 16 agreements in force in January 1990 covered an area of 394 ha, their average cost being £160.50 per hectare.

The NCC's powers in relation to the wider countryside, under both its formative Act (1973) and the *Wildlife and Countryside Act*, are very limited, and the main burden of safeguarding non-SSSI land within the region therefore had to be assumed by the Broads Authority on its formation in the late 1970s. The complex background to the latter's endeavours to protect the 9287 ha in the Drained Marshland Area which it deemed in 1980 to be of special scenic importance have been described in Chapter 9. Suffice here to say that in 1983 the Authority concluded under Section 39 of the 1981 Act a 10-year management agreement with the owner of 94 ha of marshland at Oby, and that a similar deal was subsequently negotiated over *c.* 11 ha near Barnby. In both cases, the compensation payable is, thanks to the generosity of the individuals concerned, less than the profits they have forgone. The Authority also concluded a number of holding agreements to ensure that marshland of high scenic importance was maintained under grass until it could be safeguarded in other ways, for instance under the Broads Grazing Marshes Conservation Scheme (see page 304). By December 1985, about 450 ha had been temporarily protected in this way, though not all the agreements were in force simultaneously. Some were negotiated by the Authority as a result of the informal notification scheme put into effect early in 1983 (see page 300), whilst others stemmed form the Secretary of State's decision (implemented in April 1985) to designate Broadland as a 'Special Area' under Section 41 (3) of the Act (see Chapter 9).

Despite the inordinate amount of time and effort which the Authority had to devote to safeguarding the Drained Marshland Area, it acquired a direct managerial interest in several important fenland sites. Apart from the How Hill estate (148 ha) which it purchased in 1983 (see page 479), and Broad Fen, Dilham (37 ha), over which it negotiated an informal, 5-year agreement in 1982 (subsequently extended), this was achieved by means of S. 39 agreements. By 1989, these had been concluded over the following sites:

Site	Owner	Ha
Horning Marsh	East Anglian Water Co.	40.5
The Trinity Broads	East Anglian Water Co.	N/A
North Cove (Barnby)	Mr. B. Blower	10
Sharp Street Fens	Mr. M. Boardman	12
Hall Fen, Irstead	Dr. J. Russell-Wells	16
Catfield Fen	Mr. M. High	8
Hands Marsh (Sutton)	Mr. J. Withers	6

All these sites have, in effect, been managed as nature reserves during the past few years, and it is confidently expected that they will continue to be run in this way by the 'new' Authority.

Section 48 of the Act, which requires regional water authorities* and internal drainage boards to further the cause of conservation insofar as this is consistent with their responsibilities under the Land Drainage Acts, has proved useful on several occasions.

---

* This commitment was inherited by the National Rivers Authority following the passing of the *Water Act* 1988.

It was, for example, quoted by conservationists during the negotiations over the proposal to relocate the second pump for the Somerton Level (see page 310). It also made it much easier for the AWA to justify spending funds on extending its experimental phosphorus-reduction programme to the R. Bure (see page 515).

Local Authority by-laws, making it an offence to uproot certain wild plants, had been in force in various parts of Britain for many years. But their provisions differed from county to county, and they were seldom utilized. The inclusion in the new Act of Section 13(1)(a), making it an offence for anyone not duly authorized 'intentionally' to uproot any wild plant, was therefore welcomed by conservationists. The new regulations were used for the first time in May 1984, when two individuals were fined £250 each for removing Water Soldier plants from dykes within the Ludham Marshes NNR, and another successful prosecution, involving the unauthorized collection of the same species from dykes within the Upton Marshes SSSI, took place in August 1990.

Lastly, the new legislation re-enacted with amendments the *Protection of Birds Acts* 1954-1967, and the *Conservation of Wild Creatures and Wild Plants Act* 1975, to the benefit of several of Broadland's 'specials'. For instance, the new Act made it illegal to collect, or have in one's possession, Swallowtail butterflies and Norfolk Aeshna dragonflies without a licence, while the protection which Otters had been given in 1978 under the *Conservation of Wild Creatures and Rare Plants Act* was extended to their holts, so as to prevent these animals being disturbed when lying up or rearing young.

One of Broadland's rarest species, the Fen Orchid, was included on Schedule 8, the list of plants afforded special protection under the Act, and on the advice of the NCC, the Government added the Holly-leaved Naiad to this in March 1988. Both these plants have been given a 'vulnerable' rating by the International Union for Nature Conservation and, with the Crested Buckler Fern – another species commoner in Broadland than anywhere else in Britain – are given a mention in the Red Data Book (Perring & Farrell, 1983).

The Act also strengthened the safeguards applied to birds. Two species particularly characteristic of Broadland, Bewick's Swan and Garganey, were added to the list of those protected by special penalties, and several others, including the Bean Goose and the Redshank, were removed from the list of quarry species. Members of local wildfowling clubs had, in fact, avoided shooting Bean Geese for many years on account of their rarity in Britain, but occasional specimens had been killed by 'marsh cowboys'.

The management of Broadland's nature reserves

a) Introduction

The problems encountered by those managing wetlands are often complex, and this is specially true in Broadland, where many of the reserves are susceptible to external influences over which conservation agencies can exercise little direct control. Nutrient enrichment, for instance, though having very damaging effects on the aquatic flora and fauna of protected sites, lies within the purview of the National Rivers Authority, in view of its statutory responsibility for water quality control. But unless this organization is prepared to insist that water companies, farmers and industrial concerns reduce phosphorus inputs to the main rivers, conservationists can do little to restore to good ecological condition those reserves which are fed by water from the latter. Similarly, neither the Norfolk Naturalists' Trust, nor the NCC can do much about the heavy boating pressure being exerted on reserves such as Barton and Hickling Broads, over which the public have long been accustomed to exercise a right of navigation, other than try to persuade the 'new' Broads Authority, as the body responsible for boat-licensing, to reduce the damage by more rigorously enforcing its by-laws, or by designating areas from which boats are to be temporarily excluded.

'Open' (unbushed) fen communities are of particular nature conservation importance in the region on account of their ecological diversity, and the occurence in them of rarities such as the Swallowtail butterfly, Bearded Tit and Marsh Harrier (see Chapter 7). But if such communities are left untended, they quickly revert to scrub and woodland, and the Norfolk Naturalists' Trust has sometimes been criticized on the grounds that parts of its Broadland reserves, and in some cases, whole sites, show all too clearly the effects of long-continued lack of management. In part, this is a reflection of the fact that many of them were purchased at knock-down prices, and at a time, when the Trust felt, probably rightly, that the main object should be to acquire the freehold of sites of prime natural history interest, rather than worry too much about how they were to be managed in future. In addition, few realized how difficult it would be to muster the resources to cut the reed and saw-sedge, slub out the dykes, remove invading bushes, and carry out the host of other tasks necessary to maintain a fenland reserve in the desired condition. For instance, whereas Lord Desborough employed on his Whiteslea Estate – a smaller area than the present Hickling reserve – a head keeper, 4 assistant keepers and 7 marshmen (Cadbury, 1966), the Trust has for many years had to manage this showpiece site with a labour force of only 4 (which in 1989 comprised a warden, assistant warden, foreman marshman and fenman). Had it not been for the substantial annual grants it has received from the Nature Conservancy since 1958, the Trust would probably have found it impossible to maintain even this level of staffing.

In view of its limited financial resources, the Trust was forced to adopt a *laissez-faire* policy for most of the other sites it acquired in the region during the 1930s, 1940s and 1950s, and although a limited amount of scrub clearance and other work was carried out on various sites during the next two decades, it was not until 1979, when the Trust received a 3-year 'capacity' grant from the NCC to enable it to employ a Field Officer, that a regular programme of work was embarked upon. This was given a further fillip in 1981 with the appointment of a warden-cum-estate worker for its reserves in the Bure and Ant valleys. But even now, some of the Trust's sites, for example, Surlingham Broad, receive relatively little attention.

Other organizations, because of the smaller number of Broadland reserves for which they are responsible, have found it easier than has the Norfolk Naturalists' Trust to allocate the funds needed to manage them. The Woodbastwick part of the Bure Marshes NNR, for example, has been actively managed by the Conservancy since 1966, when an estate-worker post was allotted to it. Part-time assistants were employed from 1971 onwards in view of the dangers inherent in having one man working alone in the soft and often treacherous terrain, and a second full-time post was allocated to the reserve in 1978. Estate workers have also been employed on the How Hill estate for many years, and when this was acquired by the Broads Authority, it was arranged that two men should continue to work there.

Volunteers have been successfully employed on many reserves. The Norfolk Naturalists' Trust, for example, regularly receives help on its reserves from Gorleston Grammar and other schools, as well as various conservation corps, including that based at the University of East Anglia. Similarly, literally hundreds of volunteers from these and other organizations, and from the RSPB's Norwich and Lowestoft Members' Groups assist on the Strumpshaw reserve each year. These efforts were given a welcome boost in May 1985, when the Broads Authority, the Norfolk County Council, the Norwich City Council and the Countryside Commission agreed to fund for three years, the appointment by the British Trust for Conservation Volunteers (BTCV) of a Field Officer for Norfolk.

The Broads Authority has major fenland management commitments. Not only does it look after its own reserve at How Hill and the sites over which it has negotiated management agreements, but it assists landowners by supplying labour, loaning them specialist equipment, such as its suction-dredger, and providing grant aid (see Table 12e). Altogether some 21 fenland sites, together covering some 890 ha, were being managed in this way by 1990.

Like the Norfolk Naturalists' Trust and the RSPB, the Authority receives much assistance from schools, colleges, the Norfolk Conservation Corps, Toc H, and various other bodies. However, in 1982, it decided to form its own group of volunteers, the Beavers, and since then this has carried out over 2000 person-days of work. A further 800 person-days resulted from the operation of a Youth Opportunities Scheme in 1982, and the following year, the Authority and the British Trust for Conservation Volunteers jointly launched a new initiative, the Broadland Campaign. Each year, about 10 week-long residential tasks are organized under the auspices of this, and by 1989, some 3500 person-days of work had been carried out on a variety of fenland sites. Practical, on-site training is provided for all these groups by the staff of the Authority, and tuition and work experience is also available for the unemployed, as part of a Volunteer Projects Programme scheme.

The Authority sponsored its first Community Programme (CP) scheme in 1983. This operated in association with the North Norfolk District Council, and developed from a ten-person team operating for 6 months in 1983, to five teams, involving a total of 47 persons, in 1988. Altogether, some 36000 person-days were worked under the Community Programme, but unfortunately it was replaced by the Government's Employment Training (ET) scheme in 1988. Bodies such as the Broads Authority, the RSPB and the Norfolk Naturalists' Trust which had been using CP teams, quickly found that ET was not nearly so well-suited to their needs, and as a result, the number of persons working on conservation projects in the region has undergone a dramatic decline. Nevertheless, the Authority's staff can take much credit for having organized some 50000 person-days of work between 1982 and 1988, as this represents the equivalent of a workforce of 26 individuals employed full-time on the region's fens.

The NCC has employed a peripatetic warden to look after its interests in Broadland since 1969, but the number of field staff working full-time in the region rose rapidly during the 1980s in concert with the Broads Authority's increasing commitments. By 1988, it had in its employ two countryside wardens and four assistant wardens, in addition to the two How Hill estate workers already mentioned. Two large reserves, namely Hickling and Strumpshaw/Surlingham, have two or more full-time wardens apiece, and part-time or seasonal watchers are used elsewhere, for instance at Horsey, Breydon Water and Buckenham Marshes (to safeguard the flock of Bean Geese). However, day-to-day responsibility for most other reserves in the region lies with their honorary wardens. Their job is to keep an eye on the site, carry out routine management tasks, and in some cases help organize and supervise work parties.

Management plans have been prepared for most of the reserves in the region. The 'objectives' sections of such plans typically refer to the intention to safeguard the mosaic of plant communities which has developed as a result of natural processes, modified by long-continued human usage. Other objectives include the conservation of the rare and local species which occur on the site, and the promotion of research on its ecology, stratigraphy and land use history, particularly where this will improve the conservationist's ability to manage the site, and others like it.

Drafting the prescriptive sections of a plan provides a good opportunity for deciding what priority should be given to the various tasks which need to be carried out, and estimating the resources which will be required. The use of the reserve by others also has to be reviewed. If it has been established by means of a lease or agreement, the landowner may have retained the shooting or fishing rights, and his permission may be required before certain works can be embarked upon. The plan must also take into account the use of the site by the public. There may, for example, be rights of way over it, or it may be traversed by navigable channels, as at Barton, Hickling and Surlingham Broads, and Breydon Water. In the case of the national nature reserves, a work programme based on the provisions of the plan, is agreed each year by the scientists, land agent and field staff primarily concerned. Event Record Cards are kept for almost all the reserves in the region, and print-outs of the data from these, and the Project Recording System which has been used on NCC-managed sites since 1987 in place of Event Record Cards, provides a valuable summary of what has been achieved over the years.

b) The management of the fens

Experience has shown that the best way of safeguarding the plant and animal life of fenland reserves, and at the same time generating an income to defray the cost of managing them, is to exploit them as a source of reed, saw-sedge and other traditional produce. But this objective is often not easy to achieve. For instance, much of the reed harvested on the Hickling reserve during the 1950s was obtained from the reedswamp fringing the Broad. But when water levels rose above the norm, this could only be done from a boat, a slow and laborious process; in addition, Allen scythes, introduced following the 1953 trials (see page 215) could not be used at all in such situations. It was therefore decided in 1968 that it would be more efficient to concentrate reed production at sites where the water level could be controlled. This would cut out the delays occasioned when the water in the broad was too high for easy cutting, avoid the need to 'boat out' the crop to a place where it could be stacked ready for collection by lorry, minimize the risk of Marsh Harriers and Bitterns being disturbed by the reed-cutters, and enable the latter to take full advantage of a productivity bonus scheme introduced by the Trust. Profiting from the experience gained during the creation of the Ranworth and Horsey 'floods', the Hickling Management Committee decided that Bygrave's and Lino's marshes, together totalling *c.* 16 ha, should be embanked. At the same time, permission was obtained from the River Authority to insert a pipe through the tidal embankment surrounding the Broad, so that the new flood could be irrigated when required.

These measures proved very successful, and the Hickling reed harvest continues to provide the Trust with a substantial income. The mean number of bundles cut annually between 1964/5 and 1987/8 was 19378 (maximum 27750 in 1967/8, and minimum 10050 in 1987/8), the average prices charged per bundle ranging from one shilling and sixpence (7.5p) in 1964/5 to £1 in 1987/8, and £1.30 in 1990/1.

The sedge-beds on the Hickling reserve were decimated by coypus during the 1950s, and for many years only two areas were considered worth cutting. These usually yielded between two and four thousand bunches per year, though no sedge at all was harvested on the reserve in 1982 and 1984, and only 1000 bunches in 1983; these were sold for 28p per bunch. 3500 bunches were cut by the reserve staff in 1988 (and sold for 60p per bunch), and a further 4000 bunches were removed by a contractor from sedge-beds near Swim Coots which had not been harvested for many years.

Saw-sedge is harvested in sufficient quantities from the Brayden Marshes at Horsey, and from the fens beside Martham South Broad, to make a significant contribution towards the cost of managing these sites. However, in the interests of breeding birds and invertebrate conservation, sizeable areas are left uncut in order that a deep mattress of litter may accumulate. On other reserves, such as Ranworth and Upton Fens, most of the sedge-beds have, through long neglect, become heavily overgrown with trees and bushes. These are being removed so as to bring the fens back into productive use, and at the same time re-create the habitat favoured by such insects as the Swallowtail butterfly. But few private landowners can afford the large outlay required to achieve these objectives, and the NCC has therefore negotiated management agreements under Section 15 of the *Countryside Act* 1968, over two areas of fen (totalling *c.* 75 ha) in the Ant valley, and with John Buxton in respect of Horsey Mere and its adjoining fens and marshes (332 ha). These agreements enable the NCC to provide those concerned with financial assistance, and thus ensure that more is done for nature conservation than would otherwise be possible. They are thus very different from the 'profits-forgone' agreements which the NCC negotiates (also under S.15 of the *Countryside Act*) with SSSI owners proposing to alter the management of their land in a way inimical to the interests of conservation.

Tree and bush clearance is, at best, a labour-intensive task (see Plate 40), and during the winter cannot be carried out at all for long periods owing to the fens being flooded. The bird-breeding season has to be avoided, and working conditions during the summer months are unpleasant, due to the uneven, tussocky terrain, the waist-high vegetation, the numerous horseflies and mosquitoes, and the high relative humidity. Given the difficulties, it is surprising how much fen is now being cleared, the technique commonly used being to chain-saw off the bushes and trees at ground level, pile them up and burn when dry, and treat the regrowth from the cut stumps with an arboricide, care being taken that this does not find its way into any adjoining waterways in view of the toxicity of such chemicals to aquatic plants. Until fairly recently 2:4:5-T was widely used, and proved very effective when applied to birch and alder, though less so on sallow. Since the dioxin (TCDD) scare, Krenite or Garlon have been successfully used on many sites.

On the basis of the RSPB's experience of managing its fenland reserves, both in Broadland and elsewhere, Burgess and Evans (1989) conclude that it takes professionals about 100 man-days to clear a hectare of dense carr, and volunteers about three times as long. Corresponding figures for clearing compartments invaded by varying amounts of scrub range from 50 to 70 professional man-days, to 100 to 150 volunteer man-days. In neither case do these figures include the time which has to be spent applying herbicides to the cut stumps, which can take a further 1 to 3 man-days per hectare.

On most fens, the high water-table, and ultra-soft terrain precludes the use of conventional tractors, which rut the surface and, in the case of a reed-bed, damage the crop (see page 215), even if they do not actually become bogged down. To avoid such damage, a 'Platypus' wide-tracked 'Bogmaster' crawler was used at Ranworth Flood during the 1950s and 1960s to tow sleds laden with bundles of reed off the site. This machine was later acquired by the Conservancy, and fitted with a Wolesley swipe so that fens at Woodbastwick which had been colonized by Bog Myrtle, young sallows and other scrub species could be cleared. In 1974, the Platypus was replaced with a County Ford, adapted to take an additional set of wheels, and fitted with a self-retrieval winch at the front and a Ransome heavy duty rotary cutter at the back, and in 1985, this in turn gave way to a Ford 1910 tractor equipped with Trelleborg tyres, and a Gallagher roto-slasher.

The main objection to using a swipe or rotary cutter for fenland management, is that a mulch of dead vegetation is left on the surface. This eventually becomes incorporated in the peat, thus re-cycling nutrients back into the system. This favours the continued growth of coarse, nutrient-demanding plants such as Great Hairy Willow-herb, Yellow Loosestrife and Meadowsweet which tend to suppress smaller, more delicate species.

To overcome this problem, three of the compartments at Woodbastwick (totalling *c.* 3.5 ha) which have been cleared of scrub, are motor-scythed each summer, the cut material being raked up, and removed. Ultimately, it is hoped to sell this as 'litter' or marsh hay. But the main benefit has been greatly to increase the floristic diversity of the compartments concerned. Bog Pimpernel, Lesser Spearwort, Early Marsh Orchid (*Dactylorhiza incarnata*), Marsh Helleborine, Adder's-tongue and various other species not previously recorded from them have appeared, as have several others (including Ragged Robin, Meadow Thistle, Common Skull-cap (*Scutellaria galericulata*) and the sedges *Carex lepidocarpa* and *C. panicea* which were previously confined to regularly-mown rides. At the same time, most of the taller, nutrient-demanding species have been suppressed or eliminated. However, it is not known whether these changes are attributable to a reduction in nutrient levels in the soil (consequent upon the annual removal of fresh-cut material), the inability of the coarser species to tolerate regular cutting, or a combination of both these factors.

When fenmen wish to clear a compartment which has been neglected for several years, they will burn it off, and this technique occasionally has to be employed on nature reserves (see Plate XLIX). But fen fires are disliked by conservationists, not least because they are extremely difficult to control, owing to the large quantities of highly combustible litter usually present. Uncontrolled fires almost certainly have a devastating effect on invertebrates and small mammal populations, though recent, and as yet unpublished work carried out on the Hickling reserve by Dr. R. James of the School of Biological Sciences of UEA, suggests that provided only small areas are burnt at a time, the effect on invertebrates is no greater than on similar areas where the reed has been cut, rather than burnt off. There is also anecdotal evidence that the effect on invertebrates and other forms of wildlife depends on the wind direction and the height of the water-table at the time of the fire. If the site is burnt down-wind, or if there is standing water present, much of the litter is left, and a lot of invertebrates survive therein. Conversely, if a dry compartment is burnt against the wind, combustion is much more complete, and the losses of wildlife will be correspondingly greater. It has also been found that numerous sallow seedlings will often germinate in the open ground conditions which result from a fen fire. The moral is clear: burning off a compartment already colonized by sallow bushes may make the scrub encroachment problem worse, rather than better.

The aspect of fen management which seems to cause more debate amongst conservationists than any other, both in Broadland and elsewhere (e.g. on the North Norfolk coast) concerns the management of reed-beds. The basic problem is that the objectives of the three groups of people primarily interested, namely plant and animal ecologists, reed-cutters and ornithologists, do not wholly coincide. The former are, as was pointed out in Chapter 7, anxious to encourage the continuation of reed harvesting, as they regard this as a way of checking natural succession, and thus ensuring that the fens remain in an open, unbushed condition. On the other hand, the reed being cut on a few of these sites is now of very poor quality, and there is a real danger that thatchers will, quite wrongly, assume that all the reed being produced in the region is sub-standard, and either obtain the material they need from abroad, or from other parts of the United Kingdom. Faced with such a threat, local reed-cutters might decide to abandon the older 'traditional' sites and turn their attention to 'floods' created from parts of the

Drained Marshland Area newly taken out of agricultural use. Provided the necessary ecological information was available, it might even be possible to grow biotypes of reed on such areas which had been specially selected for high productivity and durability when used for thatching. But changes of this nature would be viewed with dismay by conservationists since the older reed-fens would quickly revert to scrub and alder woodland, and the new reed-beds would, in comparison with the old, have a very restricted invertebrate fauna. Ornithologists, on the other hand, would quite like to see new reed-

Burning off a fen near Horning – 1989.　　　　　　　　　　　　　　　　　　　Plate XLIX

Much litter accumulates in a fen which has been neglected for some years, and it may be necessary to burn this off in order to get the site back into a state when it can once again be regularly mown for marsh hay, saw-sedge, reed or some other crop.

This particular fen had only just been fired when the photograph was taken, and a few minutes later the flames were 5 m or more high. The damaging effects of this form of management on the invertebrates of a site can be minimized if only small parts of it are burnt off at any one time.

Photo: R.N. Flowers

beds created since these would probably be quickly colonized by Broadland's avian 'specials', notably Marsh Harriers, Bearded Tits, Savi's Warblers and (hopefully) Bitterns, provided substantial areas were left uncut each year. In this connection, Burgess and Evans (1989) suggest that to maximize bird populations, no more than 10 per cent of a large reed-bed should be cut in any one year. Such a proviso, plus the fact that ornithologists would, because of the disturbance factor, like to see the harvesting of reeds cease by mid-March at the latest, is most unlikely to be acceptable to those responsible for creating such floods.

Wheeler (1978: 1980a, b & c): Wheeler & Giller (1982a & c) and Giller & Wheeler (1986) have demonstrated at Catfield that some of the rarest, and therefore to a conservationist, most important fen communities in the region occur in abandoned peat cuttings. Since the infilling and consequent terrestrialization of these turf ponds is an on-going hydroseral process, these communities, and in particular the *Peucedano-Phragmitetum Caricetosum* (see page 205) have a finite life, and Wheeler (1983) has pointed out that the only way of ensuring their continued survival is to rejuvenate the hydrosere by creating new peat-cuts.

Following an investigation of a number of sites, Wheeler concluded that the locations for these artificial scrapes would have to be very carefully chosen if the full conservation benefits were to be obtained. In particular, they must overlie pure peat, rather than peat and estuarine clay, and their water supply must not be too enriched, brackish or acidic. In addition, colonization by the species (e.g. the Fen Orchid) and communities which conservationists are specially anxious to safeguard would probably be quicker if the peat-cuts were located close to existing, species-rich vegetation.

The original intention was that the Broads Authority would pay for the creation of an experimental turf pond on the NNT's Upton Fen reserve. However, on investigation, it was found that much of this site is underlain by estuarine clay, rather than pure peat, and it was feared that any excavations here would be colonized by *Phragmites* and *Typha* rather than species-rich fen communities. The initial experiments were therefore carried out at Broad Fen, Dilham, where five turf ponds, each between 30 and 100 cm deep, and with a total surface area of *c.* 1600 sq m, were dug between 1982 and 1987. Additional scrapes were created in 1985 at Hands Marsh near Horning (surface area *c.* 80 sq m) and Reedham Marsh near How Hill (*c.* 130 sq m).

Gary Kennison, who records the flora of these excavations for the Broads Authority each year (a most commendable initiative – management experiments of this type are all too often inadequately monitored by conservationists), has pointed out that although they are still at an early stage in the succession, numerous interesting plants have already appeared. Fen species present include Marsh Cinquefoil, Greater Spearwort, Marsh Lousewort, Bog Pimpernel and Lesser Water-Plantain, whilst *Chara hispida*, *C. globularis*, *C. vulgaris*, *Potamogeton coloratus*, *Utricularia intermedia* and several other aquatics have been recorded from the deeper water areas (Kennison, 1985b, 1986 a & b, & 1987).

These turf ponds, and other excavations, such as the new 'broads' created on Strumpshaw Fen by the RSPB between 1980 and 1982, have helped to offset the substantial losses of open water which have occurred in Broadland during the past century or so (see page 45), a problem compounded by the fact that most broads in the

Plate L   **The Nature Conservancy's mud pump in action on the Woodbastwick part of the Bure Marshes National Nature Reserve – 1975.**

Attempts to develop a suction dredger capable of removing deep accumulations of phosphorus-rich sediment from fen dykes were initiated by regional staff of the Nature Conservancy in the late 1960s. Welcome advice and assistance were received from May Gurney Ltd. and Messrs Sykes Ltd., and following the development of several prototypes, the 'Univac' based machine shown in the photograph came into use on the reserve in 1970.

The nozzle through which the mud and water mixture is discharged can be turned through 180°, thus making it possible to deposit the dredgings on either side of the dyke.

Much was learnt from this machine, and a more sophisticated version was built for the Broads Authority in the mid-1980s. Instead of using muscle power (as in the photo) to move the underwater suction intake from one side of the dyke to the other, this utilizes hydraulic rams. The Authority's machine is also more readily transportable than the NCC's, and it has been successfully employed on a number of different sites in the region.

Photo: Brian Grimes/Nature Conservancy Council

Bure, Ant and Yare valleys were virtually devoid of waterweeds, and the invertebrates associated with them, by the late 1950s. At many sites, the only areas of aquatic habitat left are the fen dykes, and these are often in a near-derelict condition as a consequence of long-continued neglect. In view of this, the Nature Conservancy carried out a series of trials at Woodbastwick during the 1960s aimed at discovering how best to restore such water bodies to an ecologically satisfactory condition. The first step was to cut back the trees and bushes which had grown up beside them, and thus reduce the effects of shading and leaf-fall. Efforts were then concentrated on finding ways of removing the sediment which had accumulated as a result of lack of management. Hydraulic excavators were tried, but did not prove entirely successful, because they could not readily remove the watery material near the surface; in addition, their great weight made it impossible to use them on some parts of the reserve, even when they were on 'mats' (see Plate 41). Such machines are, however, used occasionally, either to create new waterways, or to remove fallen trees and other debris from dykes which have become completely derelict. A double diaphragm pump was also tried out but, although it proved capable of removing mud of the consistency of toothpaste, its output was so limited that progress along the dyke being cleaned out was painfully slow. Attention then turned to the possibility of using a suction dredger. An experimental venturi-based system devised by May Gurney Ltd. failed to give satisfactory results, but trials showed that 'Univac' pumps were eminently suitable for the task. With the assistance of Messrs. Sykes Ltd., several different-sized machines were tested, and it was eventually decided to mount a 127 mm pump of this type on a steel pontoon (see Plate L). The machine was first used in 1970, and proved capable of removing a metre-deep layer of sediment from up to 30 m of dyke per hour.

It was soon found that mud-pumped dykes near the landward margin of the reserve were rapidly colonized by aquatic wildlife. Hornwort and Greater Bladderwort were usually the first plants to reappear, but at some sites, ten or more different species were recorded after two or three years. Water Soldier, a notable absentee from the list of re-colonizers, was experimentally reintroduced in 1972, and proceeded to reproduce vegetatively so rapidly that for a time surplus plants had to be removed periodically so as to prevent the dyke becoming completely choked (see Plate XXIII).

Much was learnt from these mud-pumping experiments. For example, it was discovered that cleaned-out dykes which passed through, or close to, the edges of a former turf pond tend to re-fill with sediment very quickly, almost certainly because the mud which had formed in the flooded working prior to its overgrowth by peat-forming plants is squeezed out laterally into the dyke as a result of the increasing weight, both of the peat itself, and the trees and bushes growing thereon.

Another point to emerge from the Woodbastwick experiments which was to assume great importance later, was that dykes which had been suction-dredged, and which because of their location received little water from the river, developed a much more varied waterweed flora than those subject to regular, tide-induced flushing. The hypothesis advanced in the mid-1970s was that the flora was being adversely affected by the high nitrogen and phosphorus content of the river water, and when in 1977 it became clear from the research at Brundall Broad and elsewhere that this explanation, though simplistic, was broadly correct, it was decided to dam off the dyke system of Woodbastwick Fen so that it was hydrologically isolated from the river for much of the year. It was realized that water would continue to get into the dykes during the winter when the site is flooded, but it was felt that this would not invalidate the experiment as nutrient concentrations in the river are relatively low then. In the event, the quantity and diversity of the dyke flora increased dramatically as soon as the dams were installed. They have also had the incidental advantage of reducing the rate at which the dyke system of the reserve is filling up with river-borne sediment.

For some reason not understood (though possibly linked with the installation of the dams, and a consequent decrease in the amount of nutrient-rich water entering the dyke system), the vigour with which waterweeds grew in mud-pumped dykes during the 1970s has not been sustained. Several species, including Water Soldier, virtually disappeared during the 1980s, and attempts to re-introduce the latter have proved largely abortive. Research on the causes of this phenomenon, which was totally unexpected, is urgently required, given the desirability of maintaining an ecologically diverse community of aquatic plants and animals on this, and other fenland reserves.

Technically successful as the Woodbastwick mud-pump has been, it suffers from a number of drawbacks, notably the absence of a hydraulic system capable of moving the suction head to and fro across the dyke being cleaned out. This and other deficiencies were taken into account in the early 1980s when the Broads Authority decided to purchase its own suction dredger. This machine has been successfully employed on a number of open water sites, notably Crome's Broad and Round Water (part of the Suffolk Wildlife Trust's Sprat's Water reserve). It has also been used to mud-pump fen dykes at Ranworth extending to some 3 km, How Hill (*c.* 3 km), Hickling (*c.* 1 km) and Catfield (*c.* 1 km). It is because of the Authority's policy of making this machine available for work on privately-owned land that the number of grants which it gave for dyke restoration declined from the mid-1980s onwards (see Table 12e).

No account of the conservation management of the Broadland fens would be complete without a brief mention of the attempts made to introduce into them the Large Copper butterfly (*Lycaena dispar*). It had long been suspected that the British race of this insect, *L. dispar dispar*, once occurred in the region, as Stephens (1827) mentions that it had been recorded from Norfolk and Suffolk, as well as the fens around Cambridge and Huntingdon, while Winter (1858) reports having seen four specimens at Ranworth in 1858. Evidence to substantiate Winter's claim was forthcoming in 1980 when Tony Irwin of the Castle Museum was able to examine two specimens sold at an auction at Aylsham. The first of these was a male, labelled Ranworth 1860, and the second a female, with a label indicating that it was caught at Woodbastwick in 1864 (Irwin, 1984). The latter may well have been one of the last specimens of *L. dispar dispar* to have been caught anywhere in Britain as this sub-species is believed to have become extinct in its former stronghold in the Fens in about 1851 (Howarth, 1973).

A colony of the continental race of the butterfly, *L. dispar rutilus*, had been successfully established by E. B. Purefoy at Greenfield, Co. Tipperary (Eire) in 1913, and over 550 pupae from there were brought over in 1926 and, on hatching, released onto Woodbastwick Fen in July that year (Gurney, 1926). Unfortunately, this introduction proved unsuccessful (Gurney, 1927), and a subsequent attempt to establish a colony of the Dutch race of this insect, *L. dispar batavus*, at Wheatfen in 1949 also proved abortive (Ellis, 1951 & 1965a).

The NCC is currently experiencing considerable difficulty in maintaining a viable colony of *L. dispar batavus* at Woodwalton Fen (into which it was introduced by Purefoy in 1927), and in the author's opinion, any further attempts to get this species established in Broadland are doomed to failure, unless those responsible are prepared to plant up large expanses of fen with the larval food-plant, Great Water Dock. It would also be essential to follow the Woodwalton practice of maintaining a stock in captivity so that the 'wild' colony can be augmented or re-instated when necessary.

c) The management of the Breydon Water Local Nature Reserve

Following the take-over of the functions of the Norfolk Wild Birds Protection Committee by the Norfolk Naturalists' Trust in 1933, the latter employed Walter Bulldeath (who had become seasonal warden of Breydon Water in 1928) until the outbreak of the Second World War. His duties were assumed by the late Robin Harrison in 1945, but there were increasing complaints about the amount of irresponsible shooting taking place on the site, and in 1959, negotiations aimed at establishing a sanctuary in the area were opened on the personal initiative of Michael Seago, a member of the Trust's Council. Although about 100 ha of marshland near the Breydon North Wall had been covered by informal, no-shooting agreements by 1962, numerous 'marsh cowboys' continued to operate over Breydon Water itself, and in 1962, the Honorary Secretary of the Great Yarmouth and District Wildfowlers' Association wrote to the Home Secretary asking that shooting over the relict estuary should in future be regulated by a permit system. This approach was misunderstood at the Home Office, and in September 1963, the Great Yarmouth Borough Council was asked whether it would agree to Breydon Water being designated as a statutory bird sanctuary under Section 3 of the *Protection of Birds Act* 1954. This idea was supported by Norfolk County Council's Wild Birds Protection Committee and by naturalist organizations, but was greeted with consternation by local wildfowlers, who believed, not necessarily correctly, that if such a sanctuary was created, they would be prohibited from practising their sport over most, if not all, the site. Ill feelings were generated between the naturalists and sportsmen, but the dispute was successfully resolved at a meeting convened by the Nature Conservancy in 1964, when it was agreed that the local authorities concerned should be asked to use the powers conferred upon them by Section 21 of the *National Parks and Access to the Countryside Act* 1949 to designate Breydon Water as a Local Nature Reserve (LNR). This request was in due course accepted, and it was arranged that the Norfolk and East Suffolk County Councils would lease from the Crown Estates Commissioners the intertidal flats which lie respectively to the north and south of the navigable channel. The Borough Council already owned the north-east corner of the relict estuary, and the three areas, together totalling 383 ha, were formally declared a Local Nature Reserve in March 1968. By-laws regulating shooting and other activities on the reserve were enacted a few months later, but attempts to persuade the owners of grazing marshland adjoining the reserve to enter into nature reserve agreements proved unsuccessful.

It was arranged that responsibility for advising the local authorities on the management policies for the Reserve would rest with an Advisory Committee on which there would be three representatives from both the naturalist and wildfowling interests, and one each from the Nature Conservancy, the Great Yarmouth Port and Haven Commissioners, the East Suffolk and Norfolk River Authority (later the AWA), the Breydon Preservation Society, and the three local authorities. Day-to-day problems would be dealt with by a subordinate management committee, and it was agreed that this and the Advisory Committee would be serviced by staff of the Borough Council.

These arrangements continued virtually unaltered for the next 20 years, the only significant change being made in 1974, when the southern half of the reserve was taken into Norfolk as a result of the reform of local government, and the newly formed Suffolk County Council decided, not unnaturally, that it need not be represented on the Advisory Committee.

Breydon Water differs from other Broadland reserves in that the management problems encountered here are more to do with vandalism and illicit shooting than habitat change. A key role is therefore played by the honorary wardens who patrol the site so as to ensure compliance with the by-laws, and organize routine tasks, such as the clearance of tideline refuse. An observation hut was erected for these individuals on the North Wall in 1973, and three years later a hide overlooking the north-east corner of the site was provided for visitors.

Emulating a technique first used at Ranworth Broad in 1961, and subsequently employed successfully at a number of other sites, including Hardley Flood, and Hoveton Great, Martham South and Barton Broads, rafts for Common Terns to nest on have been put out on Breydon Water each year since 1977. By 1987, no fewer than 452 Common Tern chicks had reached the free-flying stage, the best year up to then being 1986 when 62 pairs raised 77 young (Allard, 1987). In 1987, 1988 and 1989, the number of pairs breeding on the rafts rose to 63, 82 and 93, with 101, *c.* 90 and 75 chicks fledged respectively (Street, pers. comm.).

Although habitat manipulation, as practised on most other Broadland reserves, is not called for at Breydon, an exception has had to be made in respect of the Common Cordgrass, *Spartina anglica*. This alien species first appeared in the north-west corner of the site in 1961, and started to spread rapidly, thus endangering the status of *Enteromorpha* sp. and the Eelgrasses *Zostera marina* and *Z. noltii*, all three of which form a food source for Wigeon and Brent Geese. A decision to eliminate the *Spartina* was taken by the Advisory Committee in 1971, and this objective has been actively pursued by a variety of techniques, including treating the plants with Fenuron (a pelleted substituted urea herbicide), smothering them with plastic sacks weighted down at the edges, and up-rooting.

Until the mid-1980s, the organizations concerned with the reserve appeared to be reasonably content with the way it was being managed, and their approval in principle of a management plan drafted for the site by Tony Laws of the British Association for Shooting and Conservation, with some assistance from Richard Hobbs of the Norfolk Naturalists' Trust, seemed to augur well for the future. However, in November 1986, when the Advisory Committee was considering a revised version of this plan, a major controversy erupted as a result of a suggestion by the RSPB's representatives that in view of the establishment by their Society of a new reserve at Berney Arms, adjoining the LNR, it would be logical for it to assume responsibility for managing those parts of the latter which the Norfolk County Council leased from the Crown Estates Commissioners. This proposal was sympathetically received by the County Council, on the grounds that it would no longer have to meet its share of the cost of administering the LNR (which in 1986 amounted to just over £2000), and that these funds could therefore be used for conservation projects elsewhere in the county. In contrast, wildfowling interests were strenuously opposed to the suggestion since they felt that the Society would, as elsewhere, wish to curtail shooting on the site, or even ban it altogether (Anon, 1986b).

In presenting its proposals formally to the Advisory Committee in January 1987, the RSPB stressed the desirability of managing the reserve as an entity, and expressed the hope that the Great Yarmouth Borough Council, as well as the Norfolk County Council, would enter into some form of agreement with it. The Society promised that it would greatly increase the amount of research and survey carried out on the reserve and encourage more visitor use; it would, in addition, wish to liaise closely with other organizations interested in the site, probably under the aegis of an advisory committee. On the vexed issue of wildfowling, the Society admitted that it would like to establish large no-shooting zones to the north and the south of the main channel, but indicated that the size and location of these would be negotiated with wildfowlers, and not imposed upon them.

Although the naturalists' organizations represented on the Committee were in favour of the RSPB's proposals, the wildfowlers remained implacably opposed. In the light of this, the Society indicated its willingness to manage the LNR for the two local authorities on an agency basis, rather than lease it from them as it had originally hoped, and after a lengthy debate, this proposal was formally accepted by the Advisory Committee. However, although the Libraries and Recreation Committee of the Norfolk County Council decided in December 1987 to take up this offer, and hand over to the RSPB those parts of the reserve which the Council leased from the Crown Estates Commissioners, the Borough Council rejected the Society's proposals. Instead, it negotiated a deal with the Great Yarmouth Naturalists' Society and the Great Yarmouth and District Wildfowlers' Association, whereby these organizations took over joint responsibility for managing that part of the site owned by the Borough Council. The effect of these decisions by the two local authorities was to terminate the arrangements negotiated in the 1960s, and the Advisory and Management Committees established at that time were disbanded in February 1988. In their place, the RSPB has set up a new advisory panel so that other conservation agencies interested in the management of Breydon can make their views known to the Society.

It remains to be seen how these arrangements will work out in practice, given the very hostile feelings (as expressed by Foyster, 1988) which many local wildfowlers currently feel towards the RSPB.

A further, and very different complication regarding the future management of Breydon Water resulted from the decision to reconstitute the Great Yarmouth Port and Haven Commissioners as a Port Authority (see page 389). The Statutory Instrument which was used to achieve this objective makes no mention of nature conservation, and following objections from the NCC and the RSPB it was decided that the Port Authority would negotiate agreements with these bodies. These will be worded in such a way as to ensure that they are consulted before the Authority carries out any works which could affect the ecological interest of the Breydon Water SSSI.

d) The management of the drained marshland reserves

Unimproved grass marshland is well represented on the Hickling, Strumpshaw, Ludham, How Hill, Horsey and Carlton Colville reserves and is normally cattle-grazed under licence, the animals being used in effect as a management tool to maintain the sward in the desired condition. To help produce a species-rich sward, particularly on acidic or peaty soils, liming is not permitted and the use of herbicides is confined to the spot-treatment of thistles, nettles and other coarse species. Applications of nitrogen, if allowed at all, are usually limited to about 170 units per hectare.

Green (1986) has demonstrated that a high water-table must be maintained during the bird-breeding season to enable Snipe (and Black-tailed Godwit if present) to probe for food, and that depressions on the marsh need to be water-filled, if Redshank are to rear their young successfully. The same worker has also shown that marshes being used by breeding waders should not be grazed until late May or early June, in order to minimize the risk of the nests being trampled by livestock. These findings are borne in mind by those responsible for managing drained marshland reserves, special efforts being made to ensure that a high water-table is maintained during the early summer on sites known to be favoured by breeding waders.

Partly because of the management constraints imposed on graziers in the interests of nature conservation, and partly because of the growing shortage of livestock in the region (particularly beef animals), marshes sometimes have to be cut for hay, rather than cattle grazed. However, in the interests of breeding birds, the grass is not cut until the beginning of July.

Drained marshland is often included in nature reserves primarily because of the biological interest of its dyke system, rather than because the marshes themselves possess any special floristic or ornithological value. At such sites, it is doubly important to ensure that the water in the dykes is maintained at a high level during the summer months, and that it is not polluted, for instance by slurry from an adjoining livestock unit. In addition, the dykes are slubbed out in rotation so that as many stages in the hydrosere as possible are present at any one time.

e) Providing for the visitor

The attitude adopted by conservationists towards those wishing to visit their reserves to see and study wildlife has changed out of all recognition during the past 30 years or so. It is salutary to reflect that apart from Hickling, where the headkeeper would, by appointment, take up to 4 birdwatchers on a conducted tour of the site, no reserve in Broadland was provided with facilities for even the dedicated ornithologist, let alone the casual sightseer, until the 1960s. The first visitor scheme for the Hickling reserve was devised in 1958, but although hides overlooking Rush Hills and Swim Coots were provided the following year, the numbers of people taking advantage of them remained pitifully small by today's standards; in 1960, for example, the Management Committee was told by the headkeeper, Ted Piggin (1945–1965) that 40 to 50 individuals had visited the hides that year. Nevertheless, despite the slow start, the Trust and the Conservancy had embarked on a policy which was to have very far-reaching consequences. Symptomatic of the changed attitude was the decision taken in 1963 that the keepers at Hickling should in future be known as wardens, and since then, George Bishop (1965–1968), Bob Sankey (1968–1974), Stewart Linsell (1974–1987) and the present warden, Francis Russell, have, at the behest of the Committee responsible for the reserve, developed a wide range of facilities for the visitor. Shallow lagoons and Minsmere-like 'scrapes' have been created, and in most of these, the water level can be varied seasonally in order to provide the conditions favoured by different species of waterfowl. New and larger hides overlooking these pools have also been built, and from these the visitor (of whom there were 2638 in 1988) can observe an astonishing variety of species. For instance, one or more pairs of Common Terns have nested on islands on Rush Hills in most years since 1953, with a maximum of 18 pairs in 1986. But while it is not unusual for this species to breed inland – as witnessed by the success of the tern rafts mentioned earlier – ornithologists were surprised and delighted in 1973 when Little Terns, possibly displaced from their colonies on the beach between Horsey and Winterton, started to nest on shingle-covered 'islands' at Rush Hills, and later, Deary's Scrape. A large extension to the latter, known as Cadbury's Pool after Mr Christopher Cadbury – Chairman of the Hickling Management Committee since its formation in 1958 and a major benefactor to the Trust – was completed early in 1982, with the objective of enabling visitors to see this and other species without the need for Trust staff to have to ferry parties to and from Rush Hills by boat. Work on the new pool had hardly been completed, when a pair of Avocets settled down beside it and nested, rearing one young bird successfully.

In 1968 an attractive, thatched observation room was built for use in connection with the various self-guiding walks which were by then being established on the reserve, and two years later, a 'Water Trail' was opened. This, the first of its kind in Europe, enables visitors to inspect the reserve by boat, and land at selected points. There is a tree-top platform at one of these, and superb views of the reserve can be obtained from this (see Plate 42). The water trail won a 'Countryside in 1970' Award, and has always been popular, particularly with school parties; for instance, of the 1635 persons who went on it in 1981, 672 were children. This, and the other visitor facilities on this reserve generated an income of £1983 for the Trust in 1979, and this rose to £5570 in 1986 and to £12162 in 1989. Sales of souvenirs and other goods in the two latter years contributed a further £2303 and £2877 respectively.

Hickling is not the only site where facilities have been made available for the bird-watcher and naturalist. In 1976, the East Anglian Real Property Company gave the RSPB permission to erect a hut near the Buckenham Level land drainage pump to enable visitors to see the Bean geese (see page 264) and other wildfowl which overwinter in this area without disturbing them or trespassing. In some years this has been used by as many as 3000 persons. Hides have also been provided at Hardley Flood and Breydon Water, whilst at Strumpshaw, the RSPB has built a combined visitor centre and look-out beside one of the broads, as well as a 'tower hide' overlooking some of the newly excavated pools.

The first attempt to interpret Broadland, as distinct from providing facilities for the visiting birdwatcher, was made on the Bure Marshes NNR in 1968, when the Nature Conservancy laid out a double line of railway sleepers through the fens adjoining Hoveton Great Broad, to form a walkway, or 'nature trail'. This location was chosen, partly because it is close to a very busy stretch of the R. Bure, and was therefore likely to be well used, and partly because some particularly fine examples of tussock fen, swamp carr and alder woodland occur in this part of the reserve (see Plates XXII, XXIV and XXV). These communities are so wet, treacherous and jungle-like that they were pre-viously seldom, if ever, seen by the holiday-maker. But the trail enables people to visit them in safety, and at the same time see a broad which is not open to boat traffic, but which is of great scenic beauty. The trail is looked after by an attendant, who also helps visitors moor their boats and answers enquiries.

In a study of the reactions of visitors to the trail, Charter (1975) found that it met the expectations of 78 per cent of the people interviewed. Adults were particularly inter-ested in the history of the region (16 per cent), the swamp and jungle-like woodland (14 per cent) and in the views across the broad (10 per cent), but children were more preoccupied with the birdlife (or the lack of it!), and this formed the main topic of conversation in family parties. The survey showed that many visitors would have wel-comed further information, and the NCC has therefore provided illustrated panels at many of the stopping points on the trail to supplement the descriptive leaflet. Since 1968, the trail has been open each day from early May until mid-September and by the end of the 1989 season had been seen by over 150000 persons.

In order to focus attention on the growing environmental problems in the region, and at the same time enlist support for its activities, the Norfolk Naturists' Trust decided in 1972 to establish a nature conservation centre. A public appeal with this as one of its principal objectives was therefore launched the following year. After several possible locations had been examined, a site on the edge of the Swamp Carr separating Ran-worth and Malthouse Broads was selected. This had the advantage of being on the edge of a Trust-owned nature reserve, and of being approachable by water as well as from the land. However, since the chosen site lay near the middle of what was until the early nineteenth century a continuous sheet of open water, it soon became apparent that a conventional building would have to be supported on long, and therefore very expen-sive, piles. To overcome this difficulty the Trust decided that the Centre should be founded on two floating caissons, fabricated in ferro-concrete by Windboats Marine Ltd. of Wroxham. The building itself (see Plate 43) is of timber, and after it had been constructed beside Malthouse Broad, was towed round to its moorings at the eastern end of Ranworth Broad. A short length of quay-heading was provided so that water-borne visitors could berth their boats beside the Centre, and a 500 m long walkway was constructed to give access to the Centre from Ranworth village, and at the same time enable visitors to study the tussock fen and other communities which occur on the peninsular between the two broads.

The Centre and its walkway cost just over £50000, but the Trust received grants totalling £42250, the main contrbutors being the Countryside Commission (£25000), the Ernest Cook Trust and the Norfolk County Council (£5000 each), and the Car-negie (UK) Trust and the NCC (£2500 each).

The Centre, which is manned by a seasonal warden, assisted by a team of volunteers, was officially opened by HM the Queen in November 1976, and ten years later had been visited by over 140000 persons. Between 17000 and 18000 visitors have been to the Centre each year since then, and many more will have used the walkway, thus seeing the desciptive panels which have been provided along its route.

A survey carried out for the Trust in August 1977 (O'Riordan & Sinclair, 1977) showed that about 40 per cent of the visitors to the Centre came from Norfolk, 11 per cent from elsewhere in East Anglia, 18 per cent from London and the South-East, 10 per cent from the South and South-West, and 9 per cent from the Midlands, and that the great majority arrived by car (66 per cent) or boat (31 per cent). When asked what they had learnt most from their visit to the Centre, 25 per cent of the respondents to the questionnaire mentioned the history of the region, and 14 per cent its general conservation problems. About a third claimed that they had an improved understanding of the environmental management issues facing the Trust as a result of their visit, whilst 41 per cent admitted that they had learnt something new, usually about the history or ecology of the region (see Plate LI).

A major increase in the public's awareness of the environmental problems being faced in the region resulted from the screening by Anglia Television of a film entitled 'No

Plate LI **An interior view of part of the Ranworth Conservation Centre – 1985.**

John Allwood was responsible for designing the original interpretive displays in this Centre, the Area Museums Service providing advice, and a grant of £2000 towards their cost.

The Centre, which is owned and managed by the Norfolk Naturalists' Trust, is visited each year by some 17 to 18 thousand persons, and has undoubtedly done much to focus public attention on the environmental problems currently being encountered in the region, and the ways in which these are being tackled.

Superb views over Ranworth Broad can be obtained from the gallery, the ornithological interest being centred on the large number of Cormorants which roost on trees on the north side of the Broad, and the colony of Common Terns which nest on specially-made rafts placed near the western end of the latter.

Photo: Richard Denyer

Lullaby for the Broads'. This was directed by Geoffrey Weaver, and was a hard-hitting account of the major issues, not least the conversion of grass marshland to arable, the proposed Yare Barrier, nutrient enrichment, and what it termed the over-exploitation of the waterways by recreation and tourist interests. The film was first shown by Anglia Television on 20 November 1979, and since it was put out in the evening at peak viewing time, and was 'networked' by 13 other independent television companies, it was seen by almost nine million persons (Weaver, pers. comm.). Its strictures on what was happening in the region caused considerable concern in some quarters, notably among local boatyards and the boat-letting agencies, several of whose customers cancelled their reservations on account of the scenes of pollution and overcrowding shown in the film.

A more dispassionate attempt to interpret Broadland was made by Norfolk Heritage, an experimental project operating as a Department of the County's Museum Service, which, in 1977, published the first of what was to have been a series of interpretive guides. Several of the 32 places chosen to illustrate the theme 'Water transport in Norfolk' are located in Broadland, including the New Cut, Pull's Ferry (Norwich), Loddon, Langley and Horsey Staithes, St. Benet's Abbey, Geldeston Lock, Stokesby, Reedham Ferry and Berney Arms Mill. At each site an interpretive panel was provided, explaining the historical features of interest of the site, and the way these related to the 'story' told in the booklet.

Unfortunately, the Norfolk County Council decided in 1979 that it would be unable to continue to support the Heritage project financially, and it was therefore wound up. However 2 years later, with monetary assistance from the Carnegie (UK) Trust, which had supported a Pilot Interpretive Scheme in Norfolk between 1973 and 1976, the project was resurrected by an independent committee, and in August 1982, a charitable Trust, Norfolk Heritage, was formed to run it. Although this has received annual grants from the Broads Authority, its ability to take on new commitments has up to now been curtailed by an acute shortage of resources.

Interpretive facilities have also been provided at How Hill (see Plate LII), which, with its 148 ha estate, was acquired by the Norfolk Education Committee from the Boardman family in 1966, and opened as a Residential Centre two years later. It has accommodation for 44, a lecture room capable of seating 100, and although it was initially used mainly for teachers' in-service training and adult education, courses for children soon began to predominate. Most of these were concerned with the geography and natural history of Broadland, and the nature trail laid out around Crome's Broad and through the adjoining fens and marshes was heavily used, both by participants on these courses, and by large numbers of school parties on day visits.

The cost of running the Centre (*c.* £100 000 in 1981/2) greatly exceeded the income which it generated (estimated by the warden to be about £42 000 that year); moreover, the revenue produced from the sales of reed and sedge, and from the fees levied on anglers and campers, (which together amounted to *c.* £8000 in 1981/2), was small in relation to the labour and other costs incurred in managing the estate and gardens (*c.* £34 000 per annum). It was widely believed that the Centre could have been run more economically, and because of this and its popularity with teachers and environmentalists, there was much adverse comment when it became known in 1982 that the Education Committee was considering selling it off. For instance, the West Norfolk Association of the National Union of Teachers passed a resolution "viewing with disgust" the proposal, whilst the Broads Authority issued a Press Release expressing its "shock and dismay".

Protracted discussions took place between the interested parties during the ensuing months, and it was eventually arranged that the house itself plus its curtilage would be purchased by the Norwich Union Insurance Group, which would lease it for a peppercorn rent to a Charitable Trust for use as a Day and Residential Field Centre. It was also agreed that the Broads Authority would, with the help of a grant of £22 500 from the NCC, purchase the Estate for use as a nature reserve, part of the deal being that parties of students from the Centre would be allowed to visit this, and so learn about its natural history interest, and the ways in which this was being safeguarded. The Authority also agreed to long-lease to the How Hill Trust the playing fields, campsite and water gardens on the Estate.

The How Hill Trust launched a major appeal for funds in March 1985, the main objective being to improve and extend the existing accommodation in the Centre so as to make it financially self-supporting. The Trustees also expressed a wish to establish a new Nature Centre, self-guiding walks, a picnic site and other facilities for day visitors. An ambitious target of £400 000 was set for the Appeal, and by March 1989 about half this sum had been raised.

Although the Broads Authority was unwilling to assume responsibility for running the How Hill Centre – its members thought this would be seen as duplicating the functions of the Norfolk Education Committee – it actively pursued the policies advocated in the Report of its Information and Interpretation Working Group (Broads Authority, 1982d). Symptomatic of this is that the Authority's net expenditure under this heading

Plate LII

How Hill – 1988.

This beautiful house, set on high ground overlooking the Ant valley, was designed and built for Edward T. Boardman in 1904. It was his family's home until 1966 when, with its 148 ha estate, it was acquired by the Norfolk Education Committee for use as a residential centre. Despite being well used and very popular, the Committee decided in 1982 that it could no longer afford to run it as such, and after much local debate, the house was purchased by the Norwich Union Insurance Group. They then leased it for a peppercorn rent to a specially-created charitable body, the How Hill Trust, for use as a day and residential field centre.

The Education Committee sold the estate to the Broads Authority, which leases those parts of it nearest the house to the Trust, for use in connection with the field centre.

Photo: Richard Denyer

rose from £7227 in 1981/2 to £91378 in 1984/5; this was nearly 38 per cent of its total net outlay on projects that year. These sums include contributions from the Authority towards the cost of providing an Information Centre on the RSPB's Strumpshaw reserve, making a film about the region, and compiling Codes of Behaviour for anglers and holidaymakers. The Norfolk Naturalists' Trust also received grants towards the cost of running its Ranworth Conservation Centre, and redesigning the displays therein (see Table 12d).

The Authority also carried out numerous 'in-house' projects. For example, it produced a series of 'Fact Packs' about the region, set up a mobile display about its work, established a water-borne nature trail on its estate at How Hill, and renovated and opened to the public an eel-catcher's house beside the R. Ant, known as Toad Hole Cottage. The latter was visited by 10109 persons in 1987, 18658 in 1988, and no fewer than 35549 in 1989 (generating an income for the Authority of £14786), while the 6409 visitors who went on the water trail in 1989 (compared with 2260 in 1987 and 4376 in 1988) produced a revenue of £7624.

The Authority established visitor centres at Hoveton, Ranworth and Beccles in 1984, and these too have proved very popular. The numbers of persons visiting them in 1987, 1988 and 1989 were respectively: Hoveton 37264, 32791 and 35967; Ranworth 27075, 30686 and 28903; Beccles 19525, 19572 and 23907. Sales at the three centres together generated an income for the Authority of £13984 in 1987, £17741 in 1988 and £19333 in 1989.

The 'new' Broads Authority continues to run these facilities, and like its predecessor, also organizes each year a series of workshops, guided walks, pond-dipping sessions and other events, collectively known as 'Fun in the Broads'. These too have proved very popular, and with the other interpretive facilities now provided in the region, are undoubtedly helping to explain to visitors and local residents alike why Broadland is so special, what the problems are, and how these are being tackled.

These activities would have been strongly supported by Dr Ted Ellis, who during his lifetime (1909–1986) went to great lengths to instill in young people an awareness of the joys and fascination of natural history. He was always ready to take parties of schoolchildren around the c. 50 ha of fen and woodland which he purchased at Wheatfen, following his move there in the 1940s, and on his death in July 1986, his widow, Phyllis, and a group of well-wishers decided to set up a charitable trust to perpetuate Ted's memory in the form of an educational nature reserve.

Even before the Trust's appeal was formally launched (by Dr David Bellamy in November 1987), £80000 had been raised, and although part of this was in the form of grants from organizations such as the NCC (£18000), Broads Authority, Norfolk County Council and Eastern Counties Newspapers, much of it came from private individuals who had loved and respected Ted, and what he stood for.

The Ted Ellis Trust has already made a start on creating footpaths through the fens, and clearing some of the bushes which have colonized the latter, and in June 1989 it was granted planning permission for a Study Centre on the site.

The Broads Grazing Marshes Conservation Scheme and Environmentally Sensitive Area

Although most of the Drained Marshland Area was formerly under grass, an increasing hectarage was, for the reasons set out in Chapter 9, put down to arable from the mid-1960s onwards, and the process accelerated rapidly during the ensuing ten years. The NCC reacted to this threat by safeguarding more grass marshes; the hectarage included in NNRs and SSSIs rose from c. 120 in 1972 to c. 580 in 1981, in concert with the improved knowledge about the location of sites of particular value for wildlife accruing from the surveys carried out during the 1970s by the NCC and RSPB. But virtually nothing could be done to prevent changes in land use in the remainder of the Drained Marshland Area, and its future as one of the largest tracts of predominantly grass marshland left in Britain looked bleak indeed until the Broads Authority was formed in 1978.

Members of the new body were quick to appreciate that a good working knowledge of the ecology and birdlife of the marshes already existed. However, although general descriptions of the landscape of the region had been given by the Broads Consortium

(1971) and Land Use Consultants (1978), no attempt had been made to grade the scenic importance of the river valleys. One of the Authority's first tasks was therefore to commission such a survey, and link the resultant information with the ecological data already existing so that the whole area could be graded according to its value for landscape and wildlife. Only when this had been done, was the Authority in a position to tackle the not-inconsiderable problem of ensuring that the 9287 ha which it had recognized as being of prime (Grade 1 and 2) importance were safeguarded against adverse changes in land use.

The long drawn-out saga which ensued has been described in Chapter 9, and it will suffice here to say that it was centred on the future of the Halvergate 'triangle', and that it led to the launching in March 1985, of the Broads Grazing Marshes Conservation Scheme (BGMCS) under Secion 40 of the *Wildlife and Countryside Act*. The aim of this experimental project was to demonstrate how livestock farming and landscape preservation could be integrated, its specific objectives being defined as follows:

a) to keep permanent grassland with grazing livestock on the central Broads marshes;
b) to encourage the management of the grazing marshes in ways which would support both farming and conservation (conservation was not defined, but was subsequently stated to be primarily concerned with the preservation of the landscape);
c) to re-establish permanent grassland in some areas formerly grazed but now arable.

It was arranged that the Scheme would be administered by a small Unit, headed by Keith Turner of the Countryside Commission, and based at MAFF's Divisional Office in Norwich. SSSIs would not be included within the area covered since responsibility for safeguarding such sites was vested in the NCC. The subsidy for marshes which had been registered would be £50 per acre (£123.55/ha), rather than the £40/acre originally suggested, and for the sake of convenience, land being grazed by dairy cows would be eligible, despite MAFF's concern lest this be regarded as being inconsistent with its recent ruling that milk production should in future be subject to quotas. Since these decisions had not been matched by a corresponding increase in the funds which the Government had agreed to make available for the 3-year experiment (£1.7 million), it was estimated that allowing for administrative and monitoring costs, it would be possible to pay a subsidy in respect of *c.* 3800 ha only. On the assumption that there would be a take-up of between 70 and 80 per cent, the experimental area for the first year was defined as the Halvergate 'triangle'. Haddiscoe Island, and the Belton, Fritton and Limpenhoe marshes, together totalling *c.* 4854 ha* (see Map 13.1). Apart from *c.* 862 ha which was under the plough, and *c.* 204 ha being managed as intensive grassland with high nitrogen usage, this area consisted of unimproved pasture, much of it of Grade 1 or 2 landscape importance, and owned by some 150 individuals (Turner & Pritchard, 1985).

It was decided at the outset that the criteria for eligibility should be kept as simple as possible in order to minimize the cost of administering the Scheme, and encourage farmers to opt into it. Accordingly, it was arranged that owner occupiers and tenants who registered would merely be required to agree to graze the land for the period of the experiment with cattle, sheep or horses, and maintain a stocking rate during the season of between 1.2 and 3.6 Livestock Units† per hectare. They would be required to consult the Unit before:

a) removing any landscape or archaeological feature ;
b) erecting any buildings or constructing roads;
c) underdraining, levelling or direct-seeding the land;
d) applying more than 100 units of nitrogen per acre (240 units/ha);
e) applying herbicides, other than to control thistles, docks or ragwort.

---

* Note that this and other hectarage figures given in respect of this Scheme have been calculated from the acreages quoted in Turner and Pritchard's reports. The hectarages in the latter are erroneous (Pritchard, pers. comm.).

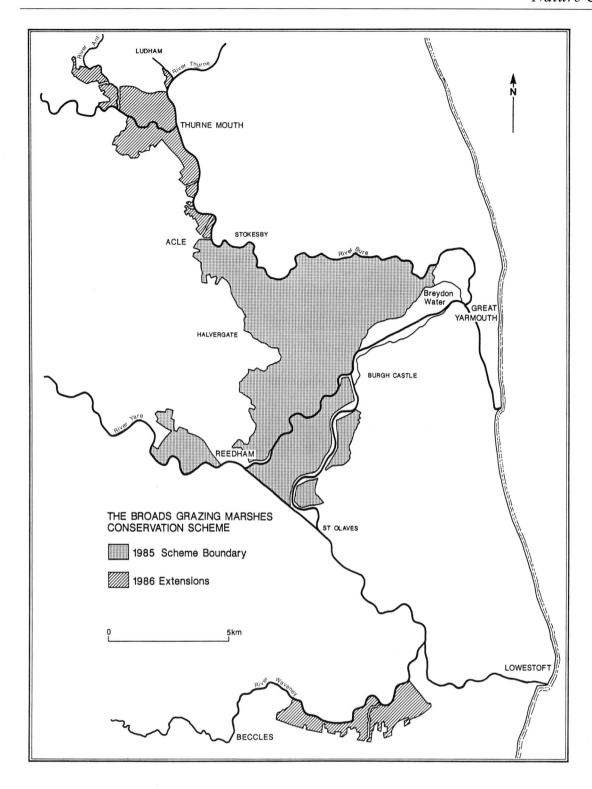

The boundaries of the Broads Grazing Marshes Conservation Scheme.

Source: Turner and Pritchard (1986)

Map 13.1

† Livestock Units were defined as follows: mature cattle and horses – 1 LU; young cattle (6 months to 2 years old) – 0.6 LU; sheep – 0.15 LU. This is a simplified version of the definition set out in the footnote on page 257.

The Scheme proved popular with farmers and by the end of the season, 102 applications had been accepted for payment; these covered 3387 ha, or 89.4 per cent of the eligible area (Turner & Pritchard, 1985). Of the remaining unimproved grassland within the area covered by the Scheme, 37 ha had been recently acquired by the RSPB, and were deemed ineligible for funding on account of the substantial grant which the Countryside Commission had made available towards the purchase cost, whilst a further 185 ha were excluded, on the grounds that they were subject to one-year holding agreements negotiated by the Broads Authority before the Scheme came into effect.

The Scheme was operated in the same way in 1986, but 113 ha in the Halvergate triangle previously subject to S. 39 agreements with the Broads Authority, were included. The coverage of the Scheme was also extended to encompass *c.* 866 ha in the Upton, South Walsham and St. Benet's Levels (of which *c.* 563 ha were eligible), and some 518 ha in the Waveney valley east of Beccles, all but 132 ha of which consisted of unimproved grass, and which were therefore eligible for the subsidy (see Map 13.1). In the event, payments were made in respect of 159 claims, covering *c.* 4397 ha, or 90.7 per cent of the eligible marshland (Turner & Pritchard, 1986).

The same number of payments was made in 1987, though over a slightly reduced hectarage. As a result, the amount of subsidy paid out that year totalled £526 003, compared with £543 007 in 1986, and £418 349 in 1985. Administrative costs over the three years were kept commendably low, at only about £71 000, and total expenditure on the Scheme was therefore within the overall allocation of £1.7 million (Countryside Commission & MAFF, 1988).

It is difficult to assess the Scheme objectively because it was put into effect at a time when the economics of farming were altering rapidly. For the reasons set out in Chapter 9 (notably the availability of substantial drainage grants, and a reduction in the profitability of cattle raising, compared with cereal production), the rate of arable conversion in the Drained Marshland Area averaged 276 ha per year between 1980 and 1982, and rose to 366 ha in 1983, and 554 ha in 1984 (Brewster, pers. comm.). It was partly on this basis, and partly on account of his familiarity with the attitudes of local farmers, that Brewster (who at that time was the Broads Authority's Assistant Broads Officer, Conservation) believes that between 800 and 1200 ha in the Halvergate area would have been put under the plough had not the BGMC Scheme been put into effect. Against this must be set the fact that from the mid-1980s onwards, farmers were confronted with a rapidly changing scenario. Drainage grant rates had been reduced, grain prices were tending to fall, there was a general squeeze on capital and, most worrying of all for the industry, the growing awareness of the cereal surplus problem was making it increasingly likely that major changes in the agricultural support system would have to be introduced shortly. It was probably because of these factors that arable conversion in the Drained Marshland Area fell to 374 ha in 1985, and to only 20 ha in 1986.

In the light of the substantial cost of the BGMC Scheme, its experimental nature, and the uncertainties about farm economics which prevailed at the time it was launched, the Countryside Commission decided to commission from the Faculty of Economic and Social Studies of Manchester University, a full-scale economic evaluation of it. The following are the principal conclusions from this Study (Colman *et al.*, 1988).

(a) The annual rate of grassland loss would have been between 2.5 and 4.5 per cent of the area covered by the Scheme, had not the latter been in operation. However, this forecast is based on the conditions prevailing in 1985, and the authors believe that the annual rate of conversion would, in practice, have been at the lower end of this range, or even less than 2.5 per cent, as a result of the increasing uncertainties felt by farmers during the period covered by the Scheme about the wisdom of putting their grass marshland down to cereals.

(b) A comparison of the direct budgetary costs of the Scheme with the cost of achieving the same result by concluding 'proven-loss' management agreements with those wishing to put their land under the plough, showed that the latter method would have been more cost effective. Similarly, the discounted net cost of purchasing marshes threatened with conversion would have been less than the total payments made under the Scheme.

(c) The net budgetary cost of the Scheme was significantly reduced as a consequence of indirect savings resulting from the fact that land remaining under had it been used for cereal production. On the other hand, Colman *et al.* point out that if management agreements or land purchase had been used to achieve the same results as the BGMC Scheme, the indirect savings would have been even greater.

In a subsequent comment on the Report (EDP, 1988b), Professor Colman noted that with hindsight, the flat rate payment of £50 per acre created difficulties, since it was not set high enough for owners who genuinely wished to put their land under the plough. On the other hand, it provided an over-generous subsidy for those who had no intention of putting their grassland down to arable, or who possessed land unsuitable for conversion.

Whatever its economic merits or otherwise, the Scheme undoubtedly fulfilled the valuable 'political' function of taking the heat out of the Halvergate controversy, and bringing about a much better working relationship between farming and conservation interests than had existed previously. Indeed, surveys of owners and occupiers within the Scheme area, and various local organizations, including county, district and parish councils, and naturalist and environmental agencies, showed that 93 per cent supported the broad objectives of the Scheme (Colman *et al.*, 1988). It can certainly be adjudged a success in terms of landscape preservation, because only *c.* 5 ha of grassland within the area of the Scheme was ploughed up during the time it was in operation; moreover, this loss was counterbalanced by the fact that *c.* 5.4 ha of arable within the area was put down to permanent grassland during the same period (Countryside Commission & MAFF, 1988).

The ecological merits of the Scheme were less clear cut. Obviously, the fauna and flora of the marshes, and their dykes, were not impoverished as a consequence of conversion. However, it would have been helpful if the eligibility criteria drawn up for the Scheme had taken rather more account of the needs of nature conservation. For instance, no distinction was drawn between cattle, sheep and horses, this despite the differences in grazing effect which these animals have on grass marshes. Horses are very selective in their feeding, and are therefore liable to cause the sward to deteriorate through a combination of under and over-grazing. Similarly, sheep produce a very close-grazed turf, and unless they are removed by September, the grass will not have time to produce the autumn 'flush' of growth so attractive to Bean geese and other wintering wildfowl. In addition, unless the stocking density is quite high, sheep tend to leave the dyke edges ungrazed, so allowing *Phragmites* and other coarse species to grow up and shade out the aquatic flora of the dyke. It follows that from the nature conservation point of view, sheep should not be grazed on the same marsh for season after season, but should be alternated with cattle, which provide a structured sward, and a much better degree of control over the dyke-edge vegetation.

The criteria adopted for the Scheme allowed a farmer to apply rather more nitrogen to his marshland than is ecologically desirable, and did not restrict his use of potash, phosphates or lime. They also failed to mention the need to graze the aftermath once a marsh had been cut for hay, and even more suprisingly, the necessity of maintaining a high water level in the dykes during the summer months. It would also have been helpful if the payment of subsidy had been made conditional on an individual's willingness to slub out his dykes on a rotational basis.

The most controversial aspect of the Scheme, both for landscape preservation and nature conservation, was the decision to allow those who had registered to take a single cut of silage from their marshes each year. Farmers argued that it was illogical to allow only one cut – why not two or three? – and were aggrieved that if they joined the Scheme, they would not be allowed to carry out the prerequisites for successful silage production – marsh-levelling, dyke-infilling, under-draining and heavy applications of nitrogen. For their part, conservationists pointed out that nothing survives under a silage regime since nesting birds and small mammals are chopped out and dyke-edges become overgrown; scenically too, a marsh is very unsightly immediately after it has been cut. In the circumstances they argued that only those farmers prepared to manage their marshland in a traditional manner (e.g. by grazing and haying) should have been eligible for the subsidy.

These deficiencies are important because the BGMCS formed the model for the Environmentally Sensitive Areas (ESAs) which the Government decided to establish under Section 18(1) of the *Agriculture Act* 1986, in accordance with Article 19 of EEC Regulation No. 797/85. The region was one of 14 areas in England and Wales which the Countryside Commission and the NCC agreed should be short-listed for consideration, and the Government subsequently decided, in the light of strong representations from the Broads Authority, to include it in the first *tranche* of five ESAs to be established in England. The necessary Statutory Instrument was laid before Parliament in December 1986, and the Scheme came into operation the following March.

The Broads ESA encompasses the whole of Broadland as defined in the Introduction, plus additional areas in the upper valleys of the Bure, Ant, Thurne and Waveney rivers (see Map 13.2). It differs from the BGMCS area, not only in its much greater size, but in the fact that it includes land scheduled by the NCC as being of special scientific interest. Provisional figures made available by Greg Pritchard, who was the MAFF's Project Officer for the ESA until May 1990, indicates that it embraces 29 870 ha, of which 13 961 ha is currently under grass, while the remainder consists of 6617 ha of arable, 5810 ha of fen and alder-dominated woodland, 885 ha of open water, and 2597 ha of miscellaneous habitats and developed land.

Administratively, the ESA differs from the BGMCS in that a two-tier system of payments is in use. However, the grants and criteria adopted for the first tier are similar to those employed in the earlier scheme, save that those participating are required to maintain the water in their dykes at a 'suitable' level during the grazing season, and ensure that there is at least 30 cm of water in them during the winter.

To qualify for second-tier payments (set at £200 per hectare), the farmer has to adhere to more rigorous criteria. He must not, for example, top or 'hay' his marshland before mid-July, or apply lime or basic slag to combat the acidity of the soil. In addition, the embargo on more than 45 kg of nitrogen being applied per hectare per year (half the amount allowed in Tier 1) effectively prevents the land being used for the production of silage. Those receiving Tier 2 payments are also required to maintain their dyke water levels within 45 cm of the marsh surface, and not dig out the foot drains. These measures are designed to increase the likelihood that the marsh will be subject to surface flooding in the early summer, and thus improve the chances that it will be used by breeding redshank and other birds. Similarly, to qualify for Tier 2 payments, a farmer must undertake to clean out his dykes in rotation, thus increasing the diversity of their aquatic fauna and flora.

Doubtless because of their familiarity with BGMCS, farmers were quick to enrol within the ESA, and 374 agreements were entered into during its first year of operation (1987), at a total cost of £938 600. These covered 5453 ha eligible for Tier 1 payments, and 1281 ha for Tier 2. A further 159 agreements, covering 4259 ha had been concluded under the BGMC Scheme, and thus well over three-quarters of the grassland within the ESA was subject to subsidies payable under one or other scheme. The BGMCS terminated at the end of 1987, but virtually all the participants in it decided to enrol within the ESA for 1988. As a consequence, the total number of agreements negotiated under its provisions that year rose to 599. These covered a total of 11 887 ha, of which 8932 ha were under Tier 1, and 2955 ha under Tier 2 prescriptions. The total cost of the agreements correspondingly rose to just over £1.7 million.

More farmers joined the ESA Scheme in 1989, making it necessary for MAFF to negotiate agreements with no fewer than 666 individuals. More important from the nature conservation point of view, the management of *c.* 942 ha of marsh qualifying for Tier 1 payments in 1988 was altered so as to meet the Tier 2 criteria. 689 ha of this additional land lies within the Halvergate 'triangle', and its conversion to Tier 2 can be attributed to the steps taken by the Lower Bure, Halvergate Fleet and Acle Marshes IDB to raise water levels in some of its arterial drains so that graziers can take full advantage of the ESA's provisions. It is to be hoped that the example set by this IDB will shortly be emulated by other drainage boards, since many graziers elsewhere in the region are at present unable to raise the water-table of their marshland sufficiently to qualify for Tier 2 payments owing to the low water levels still being maintained in their IDB's arterial drains. This is almost always at the behest of marsh owners who have put their land down to arable, but experience elsewhere (see Chapter 8) has demonstrated that given goodwill, it is often possible to manipulate water levels within a drainage district in such a way that the interests of graziers and arable farmers are reconciled.

Total payments made by MAFF in respect of the Broads ESA in 1989 amounted to

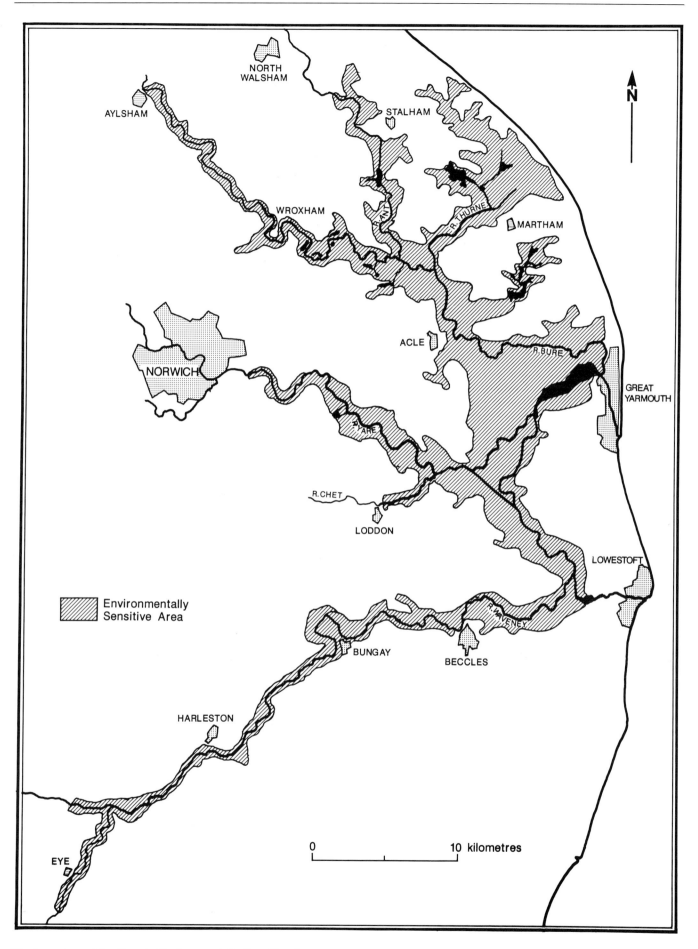

The boundary of the Broads Environmentally Sensitive Area.

Source: MAFF data

Map 13.2

£1 856 390, made up of £1 054 050 for 8432 ha of Tier 1 marsh, and £802 340 for 4011 ha of Tier 2 land. All told, subsidy was paid in respect of *c*. 89 per cent of the eligible grassland left in the region. In addition, about 521 ha of arable marsh within the ESA had been converted back to grassland by the end of 1989.

Anxious to ensure that participants in the Scheme adhere to the regulations, MAFF has set up a system of compliance monitoring, involving the use of air photography, and random ground checks. It has also arranged that the landscape and ecology of areas subject to Tier 1 and 2 payments should be regularly surveyed to check whether any adjustments need to be made to the ESA's prescriptions when these are reviewed in 1992. To this end, the composition of the grassland sward, and the vegetation of the associated dykes, are being regularly monitored at eight localities. In addition, the Broads Authority and the NCC have commissioned reports from the RSPB on the changes taking place in the region's breeding and overwintering bird populations, and the extent to which these are attributable to the ESA's provisions.

Research and the ecological restoration of the rivers and broads

(a) Background

The discussions which took place in the region during the 1940s, and which led, firstly, to the preparation of the report of the Norfolk Nature Reserves Investigation Committee (1943) and, later, to the convening of the first Broads Conference (1945), served to draw attention to the numerous threats to which Broadland was subject. Particular concern was expressed about the drainage of the marshes, the ecological damage which would be caused in the event that dams or barrages were built across the rivers, and the pollution of the latter by sewage, and it became increasingly clear to some of the leading naturalists of the day that research would sooner or later have to be carried out, if the effects of such changes on the ecology of the region were to be properly understood. The late Anthony Buxton was aware that the Council for the Promotion of Field Studies (which re-named itself the Field Studies Council in 1955) was anxious to set up one or more biological field stations in East Anglia, and following correspondence between him and the late Ted Ellis, the latter drafted a lengthy memorandum, dated July 1944, listing some of the projects which could with advantage be investigated in such a centre. The subjects covered ranged from the need for stratigraphical research on the broads and rivers, the causes of bank erosion, the effects of differing forms of management on the fens and marshes, to the ecological impact of recent introductions, such as the Coypu. In his covering letter (a copy of which is in the author's possession), Dr Ellis concluded that . . . "I can think of nothing which can do so much to stimulate interest in natural history in this county", and expressed confidence that . . . "the opportunities for carrying out or giving facilities for work connected with the special problems of the various land-and-water authorities [in the region] would be utilized . . . within a few years".

Sadly, nothing came of this particular initiative. Nevertheless, local naturalists remained aware of the need for a research station cum field study centre in the region, and the concept was given further support when Dr Joyce Lambert embarked on her now classic studies on the ecology of the fens of the Bure and Yare valleys. Prompted by this, and in the knowledge that Broadland was one of the ecologically most important, and yet least understood, wetland systems in Britain, Max Nicholson (Director-General of the Nature Conservancy from 1952 until 1966) opened negotiations in the late 1950s with the late Col. H. J. Cator, aimed at establishing a research station at Ranworth Old Hall. Most unfortunately, it proved impossible to agree on a rental and, with hindsight, there can be little doubt that if this research facility had been established, the nature and extent of Broadland's problems, and the measures needed to combat them, would have been identified more quickly.

In the event, conservationists did not become aware that all was not well with the region's aquatic ecosystem until the early 1960s. In a perceptive account of the multitude of environmental threats to which Broadland was subject at that time, Duffey (1964) refers to . . . "the pollution of the water by petrol and oil, sewage and chemicals", but goes on to point out that no research had been carried out on the effects which such substances were having on aquatic plants and animals. Similarly, the Report on Broadland (Nature Conservancy, 1965) drew attention to the fact that the fauna and flora of the waterways had become impoverished, but failed to identify the reasons why this had happened. Several more years were to elapse before systematic surveys by Nature Conservancy staff (e.g. Morgan, 1972) and others (e.g. Mason & Bryant, 1975b) revealed just how widespread and serious the changes were.

Some of the symptoms of the malaise, notably the algal-induced turbidity of the water, and the replacement of the formerly diverse invertebrate fauna of the broads and rivers by one dominated by tubificid worms and midge larvae, were known from work elsewhere to be symptomatic of nutrient enrichment. In the circumstances, suspicions began to be voiced that the changes which had taken place in Broadland were attributable to the presence in the water of nitrates leached from the river catchments, and either phosphate-based detergents (Ellis, 1970a) or treated sewage effluent (George, 1972). Apparent support for the latter hypothesis came from the fact that Hickling Broad and Horsey Mere, neither of which received significant quantities of sewage, remained in a near-pristine condition throughout the 1960s, whereas waterways in the Yare, Bure and Ant valleys which had had treated sewage discharged into them for half a century or more, were known from anecdotal reports to have lost their waterweeds by the 1950s, if not before. In the circumstances, the catastrophic, *Prymnesium*-induced fish kill which took place in the Thurne broads in 1969, and the near-elimination of their waterweed flora during the ensuing two or three years, served to puzzle, as well as dismay conservationists.

Despite the apparent anomaly presented by the Thurne broads, research by Phillips (1977) and others during the early 1970s strongly supported the nutrient enrichment hypothesis, and in May 1975, the Norfolk Naturalists' Trust, heartened by the way in which the Third Countryside in 1970 Conference had focused attention on the need for environmental conservation (Council for Nature *et al.*, 1970), but alarmed by the ecological degradation which was by then taking place in virtually all the broads it owned, issued a public statement. This called for a major programme of collaborative research focused on the source, movement and fate of the nitrogen and phosphorus in the region's waterways, and the ways in which the effects of enrichment could be mitigated. In view of what it rightly termed "the enormity of the problem", the Trust estimated that up to £250 000 would need to be spent on research, involving several different disciplines (NNT, 1975).

The upsurge in interest generated by the Trust's statement prompted the AWA to extend its routine limnological sampling programme in the region to cover several additional sites; it also increased the number of chemical determinations made on each sample. The statement also led to the commissioning by the NCC, and later by the Broads Authority and other agencies, of several very important investigations directly or indirectly relevant to the nutrient enrichment problem (see Table 5a). Most of these were carried out at the School of Environmental Sciences of the University of East Anglia (UEA) under the direction of Dr (now Professor) Brian Moss, and were funded by the NCC, AWA, Broads Authority, Department of the Environment, the Soap and Detergents Industry Association and the Natural Environment Research Council. An enormous amount of uncosted work has also been carried out on an 'in-house' basis at the University of East Anglia, and by staff of the AWA and its successor, the National Rivers Authority.

A Research Register, listing details of some 86 projects put into effect between 1970 and 1984 has been compiled (Broads Authority, 1984), and this was updated in 1988 (Broads Authority, 1988). In addition abstracts of earlier publications about the fauna, flora, geography, hydrology and land-use history of the region are available (O'Riordan, 1976a).

As will have become apparent from Chapter 5, the research carried out in Broadland since the mid-1970s has greatly improved our understanding of the ways in which an aquatic ecosystem responds to changes in the nutrient regime. But the information gained from the research has also been used by the NCC, Broads Authority, AWA and other organizations to try and restore selected open water sites to the condition they were in 40 years or so ago. The methods used to do this, and the results obtained, are described in the following sections.

(b) The R. Ant and Barton Broad

Research on the nutrient regime of Barton Broad – one of the largest nature reserves in the region – was already in train at UEA when the Norfolk Naturalists' Trust issued its Statement, and those responsible for this work were almost certain that it was in a degraded condition on account of the phosphorus-rich effluents being discharged into the R. Ant by the Stalham and North Walsham sewage treatment works. The prediction by Osborne and Moss (1977) that a reduction of 25 per cent in the phosphorus loadings encountered in the Broad in 1975 would probably be sufficient to allow nutrient-tolerant waterweeds such as Hornwort and Yellow Water-lily to start to re-colonize it, was subsequently shown to be wildly over-optimistic. Nevertheless, at the time it led to very strong pressure being exerted on the AWA by the NCC, Norfolk Naturalists' Trust and other environmental organizations to reduce the amount of phosphorus in the effluents produced by these works. In support of their arguments, conservationists pointed out that phosphate reduction ('stripping') is widely practised in Sweden and the United States, and that in Canada, all new sewage works must by law be provided with such equipment.

Staff of the AWA had considerable reservations about Osborne and Moss' findings; in particular, they felt that 'sediment release' (see page 103), which had been shown to occur at several sites in Broadland, including Alderfen Broad (Osborne & Phillips, 1978), might negate the benefits which would accrue in the event that a phosphorus-reduction programme was put into effect in the catchment of the R. Ant. They also doubted whether Osborne and Moss had made adequate allowance for seasonal variations in the phosphorus concentrations in the river attributable to land drainage and other discharges (Bell & Jones, 1979). Despite these uncertainties, the AWA decided in 1976 to respond to the pressure being exerted on it by conservation interests, and it was agreed, following discussions with Brian Moss, that an attempt should be made to reduce the mean total phosphorus concentration in Barton Broad to 100 μg l^{-1}. This is slightly greater than the mean concentration found in broads still possessing a Phase II flora, and was thought at the time to be the level at which other sites had switched to a Phase III condition. It was decided that to attain this objective, it would be necessary to reduce the mean total phosphorus inputs to Barton Broad from the figure of 10.83 gm^{-2} yr^{-1} calculated by Osborne (1978) to about 3 gm^{-2} yr^{-1}, or c. 7 kg per day.

Phosphate reduction had been practised for several years at various sewage treatment works in the catchment of Lough Neagh (Northern Ireland), but it had not previously been attempted in England, and the AWA therefore decided that initially only one of the works discharging into the R. Ant upstream of Barton Broad should be provided with the necessary equipment, and then on an experimental basis for a three to five-year period.

The relative amounts of phosphorus emanating from the Stalham and North Walsham works could not be determined from the data then available, but it was decided to install the phosphorus-reduction plant at the former, partly because plans for extending and modernizing the North Walsham works were at that time still under discussion, and partly because it was assumed, wrongly as it turned out, that since the effluent from the Stalham works is released into the river only about 3 km upstream of Barton Broad, it would be having a more pronounced effect than that of the North Walsham works, which is discharged some 10.5 km further upriver.

Laboratory experiments were commenced in December 1976, to determine which of a number of different chemicals, including hydrated lime, ferric sulphate and various aluminium compounds, would give the most satisfactory results, and whether it would be best to apply these to the incoming crude sewage, or to the effluent from the biological filters prior to its passage through the humus settlement tanks. Both ferric sulphate and hydrated lime gave good results, but the AWA decided to employ the former because it gave a smaller quantity of sludge and, being a liquid, was easier to apply at varying rates of dosage. In addition, a very alkaline final effluent would have been produced if lime had been employed. The tests also demonstrated that it would be more economical to apply the ferric sulphate to the filter effluent, rather than the incoming sewage.

Field trials started in July 1977 with fixed-rate dosing equipment, but a more sophisticated system, capable of automatically varying the amount of ferric sulphate used

Stalham Sewage Treatment Works, the first such plant in the region to be provided with phosphorus reduction equipment – 1985.

Plate LIII

Phosphoros reduction, using ferric sulphate, has been practised at these Works since 1977, and although there have been various mishaps, a 90% 'strip' has been the norm. Similar equipment was installed in other sewage treatment works discharging to the R. Ant during the late 1970s.

Although the ecological condition of the R. Ant upstream of Barton Broad has improved as a result of these measures, the latter site remains in a Phase III, algal-dominated state. This is now known to be due to the large quantities of phosphorus which have accumulated in the surface sediments of the Broad over the past 40 to 50 years. Under certain conditions, some of the phosphorus is liberated into the water (a process known as 'sediment release'), and this favours the continued presence of large standing crops of phytoplankton in the site, rather than the waterweed-dominated communities which occurred in it until the early 1950s.

Photo: R.N. Flowers

according to the quantity of sewage passing through the Works, was brought into use the following year; this in turn later gave way to a system dependent on the redox potential of the filter effluent (see Plate LIII). After some teething troubles, the plant has proved capable of consistently removing over 90 per cent of the phosphorus from the final effluent, the cost of the chemicals used being approximately 0.8p per cubic metre in 1979 (Bell & Jones, 1979). Since the Stalham Works deal with an average daily flow of about one and a half thousand cubic metres, the chemicals used that year would have

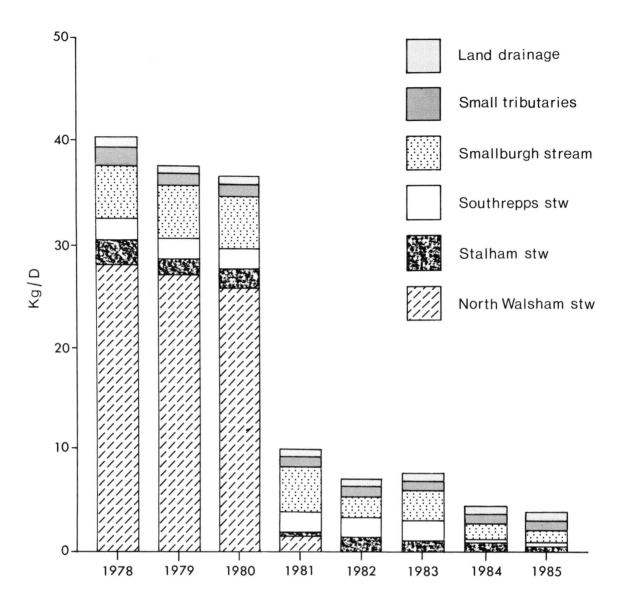

Fig. 13A

Total phosphorus loads received by the R. Ant between 1978 and 1985.

Source: Anglian Water Authority (1986)

cost *c.* £4380. This may be compared with the all-in cost of operating the Stalham plant in 1986/7, which was *c.* £8 per head of the population served, of which between £1.50 and £2 was spent on ferric sulphate (Raymer, pers. comm.).

The results of further work on the nutrient regime of Barton Broad and the R. Ant were published by Moss in 1980 and by Osborne in 1981, and from these studies, and the fortnightly sampling which had been carried out by AWA staff at 18 sites in the Ant catchment from the time the Stalham phosphorus-removal plant was installed, it became clear that about 80 per cent of the phosphorus reaching Barton Broad was emanating from sewage works, with diffuse, mainly agricultural sources making up the remainder, rather than the 40 per cent sewage contribution estimated previously (see Fig. 13A). Moreover, an assessment of the relative amounts of phosphorus coming from the Stalham and North Walsham works during the summer of 1977 suggested that contrary to what had been thought previously, the latter was contributing over twice as much (with 6240 kg yr $^{-1}$) as the Stalham plant (with 2850 kg yr $^{-1}$). Clearly there was no chance of achieving the 100 µg l^{-1} target figure, unless phosphorus inputs from the North Walsham, as well as the Stalham, works were reduced, and this was done in September 1980, when its effluent was diverted to the sea at Mundesley. Discharges still have to be made to the river following periods of heavy rainfall, but in practice this has very rarely proved necessary, and the effluent from the works is, in any event, very dilute on these occasions.

Table 13f   Mean Total Phosphorus concentrations in Barton Broad (μg l⁻¹) – 1975 to 1987

	1975	1976	1977	1978	1979	1980	1981	1982	1983	1984	1985	1986	1987
Spring	219	275	–	307	220	222	112	171	95	152	74	134	91
Summer	407	717	–	356	338	302	193	370	143	205	129	191	161
Winter	166	–	–	290	201	107	121	131	125	76	96	107	–
Annual Mean	–	–	–	310	289	235	153	225	128	164	90	158	116

Source: AWA records.

The phosphorus levels in the river declined still further during 1980 as a result of measures taken at a food-processing factory near Worstead to reduce the amount of phosphorus in the effluent which it discharges to the Smallburgh Stream (a tributary of the Ant) from maxima of about 10 kg d⁻¹ to *c.* 3 kg d⁻¹.

Mean total phosphorus concentrations in Barton Broad (see Table 13f) fell to just above 100 μg l⁻¹ during the winter of 1980 and the early spring of 1981 but then rose rapidly, attaining a figure of 290 μg l⁻¹ in September. Not unexpectedly, large standing crops of phytoplankton developed; indeed, chlorophyll *a* concentrations in the Broad remained similar to those encountered in the 1970s, before the phosphorus reduction programme was commenced (see Fig. 13B). There were two possible explanations; either, phosphorus-rich effluent from the Horning sewage treatment works or some other downstream source was being carried upriver into the Broad by tidal action during the summer months when little fresh water was coming downstream, or phosphorus release was occurring in the Broad as a consequence of the development of anaerobic conditions at the sediment surface. This phenomenon was to be expected, given the large standing crops of phytoplankton in the Broad, and the resultant fall-out of dead and dying algae (Osborne, 1981).

Fig. 13B

Chlorophyll *a* concentrations in Barton Broad – 1977 to 1987.

Source: Anglian Water Authority (1988)

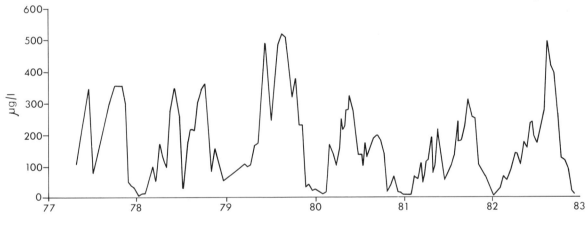

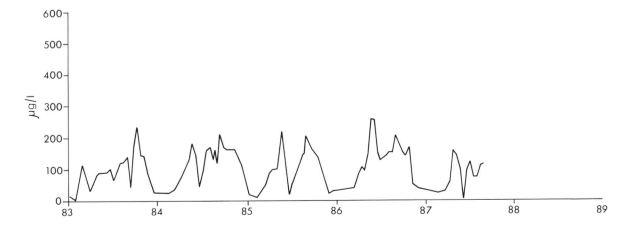

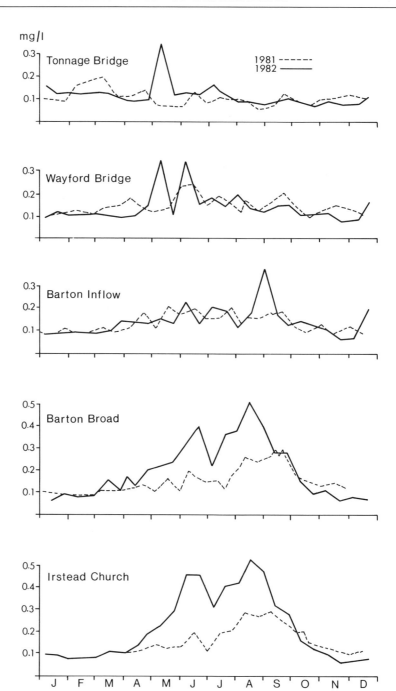

Fig. 13c

Total phosphorus concentrations in the R. Ant and Barton Broad in 1981 and 1982.

Source: Phillips (1984)

Evidence that sediment release was indeed taking place in the Broad was provided by measurements of the phosphorus concentration upstream and downstream of it (Phillips, 1984) (see Fig. 13c), and further confirmation was forthcoming in the summer of 1983, when the mean total phosphorus concentration of the Broad rose to 370 μg l^{-1}, a figure almost four times as large as that recorded in the river above Tonnage Bridge. Dye-tracing experiments downstream of the Broad showed that little water was being backed up into it by tidal action. In any event, the effluent from the Horning sewage treatment works was by this time being treated with ferric sulphate to reduce the likelihood of any phosphorus from downstream reaching the Broad.

During the winter of 1981/2, volunteers organized by the Norfolk Naturalists' Trust and the Broads Authority introduced some 15 000 Water Soldier and Yellow Water-lily plants into a bay at the north-eastern corner of Barton Broad, the idea being that these would utilize some of the phosphorus being carried into the site by the river, and thus reduce the size of the algal crop. Unfortunately, the experiment proved unsuccessful, all but about 40 water-lily plants succumbing the following summer (Brewster, pers. comm.). At the time, it was assumed that the water was so turbid as a result of the amount of phytoplankton in it that the plants had died through lack of light. But some plants were probably lost as a consequence of wave action, because following another, slightly smaller introduction in the spring of 1983, it was found that a larger proportion of the water-lily plants survived in the more sheltered conditions on the western side of the Broad, than in the east.

Phosphorus reduction equipment installed at the Worstead and Southrepps sewage treatment works in the summers of 1982 and 1983 respectively, resulted in a further improvement in the quality of the Ant, as witnessed by the re-appearance in it of Yellow Water-lilies downstream of Wayford Bridge. Also symptomatic of the improved ecological conditions was that Crome's Broad, which each spring is flushed with water drawn from the river, was extensively re-colonized by Hornwort in 1982; indeed, apart from the shallowest bays, this species covered the entire water surface of the southern half of this Broad during the summer of 1983 (Kennison, 1984). But although phosphorus concentrations in Barton Broad remained at, or only just above, the target figure during the winter of 1982/3, they rose to 300 µg l^{-1} the following August, almost certainly as a result of sediment release (Phillips, pers. comm.).

An examination by AWA staff of the water chemistry of the Ant upstream of the Broad has indicated that whereas prior to the installation of phosphorus-reducing equipment in the sewage treatment works, most of the phosphorus in the water was in the soluble reactive form, at least 50 per cent of the load is now particulate. In the winter this is due to the relatively high fluvial flows in the river, which tend to disturb the sediment. However, the particulate fraction increases in the spring as a result of the tendency for rapidly photosynthesizing benthic diatoms and blue-green algae to lift off the sediment surface and float downstream. In addition, by sampling the river early in

Table 13g Loads of total phosphorus discharged annually to the R. Ant (kg d^{-1}) – 1978 to 1987

	1978	*1979*	*1980*	*1981*	*1982*	*1983*	*1984*	*1985*	*1986*	*1987*
N. Walsham STW	28.10	27.17	26.0	1.5	0.0	0.0	0.0	0.0	0.0	0.0
Stalham STW	2.43	1.53	1.73	0.37	1.40*	1.17*	0.63	0.68	0.9	0.8
Southrepps STW	2.00	2.00	2.00	2.00	2.00	1.96	0.38	0.45	0.4	0.7
Smallburgh Tributary	5.00	5.00	5.00	4.39	2.03	2.92	1.86	1.14	1.3	2.3
Other tributaries	1.85	1.16	1.16	1.00	1.00	1.00	1.00	1.00	1.0	1.0
Land Drainage	0.95	0.70	0.77	0.77	0.77	0.77	0.77	0.77	0.8	0.8
Totals	40.33	37.56	36.66	10.03	7.20	7.82	4.64	4.04	4.4	5.6

* Higher than normal figures due to technical difficulties at the Works during the winter of 1982/3.

Sources: AWA (1986) & Phillips (*in litt*) for the year 1986 & 1987.

the morning, and then later on during the day, the AWA has demonstrated that much of the particulate phosphorus in the water just upstream of the Broad is derived from surface sediments which have been re-suspended by boat traffic.

By the end of 1985, mean total phosphorus imputs to the Ant upstream of the Broad were estimated to be about 4 kg d^{-1} (see Table 13g). Chemical dosing equipment had been installed at all the sewage treatment works in the catchment which serve a population of 100 or more, and the food-processing factory in the catchment of the Smallburgh Stream had reduced the phosphorus loading of its effluent to less than a third of what it had been in the 1970s. Since most of the remaining phosphorus reaching the river was coming from background sources, AWA staff concluded that it would not be practicable to reduce phosphorus inputs any further (Phillips, pers. comm.).

Although the Broad continues to be phytoplankton-dominated, chlorophyll *a* concentrations have been significantly lower from 1983 onwards; indeed, these now fall to very low levels each summer (see Figure 13B). Further evidence of the continuing ecological improvement was provided by a fisheries survey carried out in 1985 (AWA, 1986). This indicated that the mean total fish biomass of the open water of the Broad

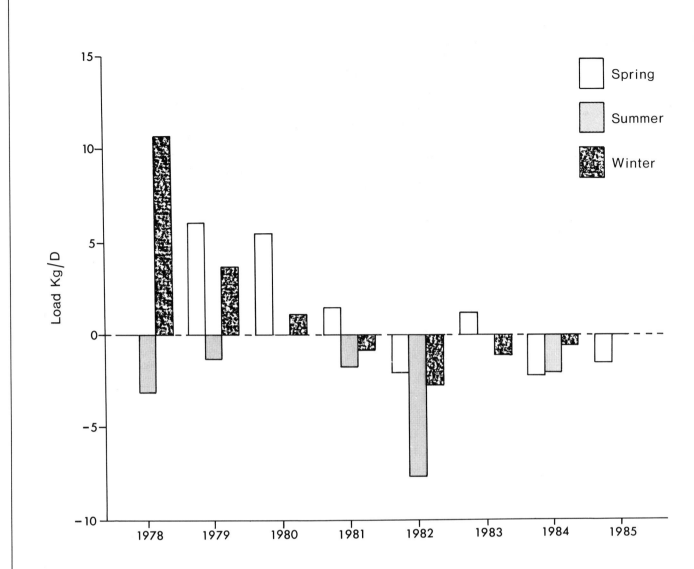

Fig. 13D

Barton Broad: net gains and losses of total phosphorus between 1978 and 1985 in kilograms per day.

Source: Anglian Water Authority (1986)

had risen from 7.8 gm^{-2} in 1979, to 17.8 gm^{-2} in 1985. The small Ruffe, which in 1979 had made up 31 per cent by weight of the total fish population, had declined in number, and now only formed about 0.5 per cent of the total biomass, whereas Roach had increased in number so that they formed 48 per cent of the biomass, compared with only 18.5 per cent in 1979. The growth rates of this, and most other species had also improved considerably.

More phosphorus is now being lost from the Broad each year than enters (see Fig. 13D), and the amount left in the sediment will therefore decrease with time. However, most of the sediment release occurs in the summer when water temperatures are elevated, but when flow rates in the river are at their lowest (Wilkinson, in prep.) Wash-out of sedimentary phosphorus from the Broad is therefore likely to be a slow process, given the very large quantities involved (Osborne & Moss, 1977; Moss, 1980).

Uncertainties remain about the exact mechanisms by which phosphorus is being released from the sediment of the Broad, and research commissioned by the NCC in 1987 is designed to elucidate these (see page 104). But whatever the outcome of these studies, it has become quite obvious that it will take many years, if not decades, for mean total phosphorus concentrations in the site to drop sufficiently to allow a switch from Phase III to Phase II to take place. Increasing attention has therefore been given during the past 3 or 4 years to finding ways of hastening the process. One principle, which had become apparent from research on the Woodbastwick 'ponds' (see page 139), is that if the predation pressure exerted on zooplankton by fish is reduced in an enriched water body, large cladocerans become more numerous, and apply a heavier grazing pressure on the phytoplankton. Evidence for a link between the size of the cladoceran population and phytoplankton production in Barton Broad had already emerged from surveys, which had demonstrated that chlorophyll *a* concentrations are significantly reduced when the population of *Daphnia hyalina* reaches its peak in the early spring, but that as the *Daphnia* population declines, phytoplankton production increases (see Fig. 13E). It was argued that if fish predation on the cladocerans could be artificially reduced, they would graze on the phytoplankton more intensively, and for longer, thus providing the clear-water conditions required by waterweeds. Accordingly, in 1984 a 365 m long netted enclosure was created beside the western (and therefore relatively sheltered) margin of the Broad. The fish population within this was reduced as far as possible by electro-fishing, and *c.* 60 pike were introduced to kill off any survivors, and eliminate small fry entering the enclosure through the netting. About 1350 Yellow Water-lilies, wired in pairs to bricks to anchor them in the sediment, together with some

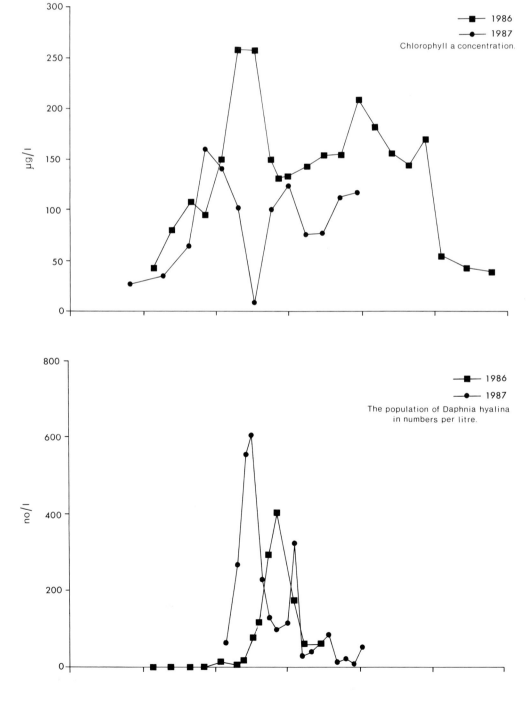

Fig. 13E

The relationship between phytoplankton production (as assessed by the chlorophyll *a* concentration), and the size of the *Daphnia hyalina* population in Barton Broad.

Source: Anglian Water Authority (in litt.)

8000 Water Soldier plants, were then added to provide the underwater 'structure' which cladocerans require. In the event, the experiment proved unsuccessful because of the breaching of the netted enclosure, and the consequent entry of fish. In 1985, a further attempt was made to encourage the development of a large population of cladocerans, this time by introducing into the western enclosure some 50 artefacts fabricated out of chicken wire and lengths of binder twine. For several weeks, the water near these contained a much larger number of cladocerans than control areas nearby (Phillips, pers. comm.). However, the artifacts later sank owing to the weight of periphyton which developed on them, and it was not therefore possible to discover whether such 'refuges' are capable of sustaining a summer population of cladocerans large enough to exert a significant effect on the phytoplankton.

Another technique which has been subject to some discussion locally, and which has been employed experimentally by the AWA at Ardleigh Reservoir (Essex) and elsewhere, would be to apply ferric sulphate to the Broad in the early spring in order to precipitate the soluble reactive phosphorus in the water. This would, in theory, reduce the rate of phytoplankton production, and allow waterweeds, which would have been introduced into the Broad shortly before the chemical was applied to it, to grow in the relatively clear water. Although this technique may eventually be tried out, the general consensus is that repeated applications of ferric sulphate would have to be made, particularly in the summer when sediment release was occurring. Moreover there is so much phosphorus left in the mud, that even if a temporary switch to Phase II occurred, the site would sooner or later revert to Phase III.

Another possible way of restoring Barton Broad to a Phase II condition would be to mud-pump it. However, given the likelihood that this would cost about a million pounds, even if only the upper 30 cm of phosphorus-rich sediment was removed, it was decided, following discussions between the various interested parties, to carry out a pilot project, involving the removal of sediment from a bay on the western side of the Broad. About a quarter of a hectare was suction-dredged to a depth of 1 to 2 m by the Broads Authority during the winter of 1986/7, and the following spring, three pens, constructed of wood and nylon mesh, were placed in the mud-pumped area. Three similar pens were positioned in a nearby area which had not been suction-dredged, and a mixture of 11 different waterweeds, including Hornwort, Canadian Pondweed, Water Soldier and Water Milfoil, was planted in each of the six pens. Similar plantings, to serve as controls to the experiment, were made outside the pens, both in the mud-pumped and the untouched areas.

During the ensuing months, the numbers of *Daphnia hyalina* were, in general, greater inside the pens than in the main body of the Broad, and this was thought to be due to reduced fish predation in the former. Water clarity was also somewhat better in the pens, than outside them, and in the three unpumped enclosures, a dense growth of Hornwort, together with 2 or 3 other waterplant species, had developed by mid-July. In contrast, no waterweeds appeared in the mud-pumped pens, or in the deep and shallow water control areas.

The following tentative conclusions were drawn from these observations:

(i) The sediment in Barton Broad does not contain any substances toxic to waterweeds;

(ii) Suction dredging is likely to decrease the chances of aquatic plants colonizing the Broad, by deepening the water and thus decreasing the amount of light reaching the sediment surface;

(iii) Waterweeds can survive at the chlorophyll *a* concentrations which occurred in Barton Broad in the spring and summer of 1987. Factors other than phytoplankton growth are thus preventing such plants growing in the shallower parts of the site. These might include, firstly, the growth of epiphytic algae which could, if little zooplankton was present, be inhibiting the germination and/or growth of waterweeds, secondly, grazing by waterfowl, and thirdly, the instability of the sediment surface.

The third of these possibilities seems much the most likely; indeed, there is some evidence from previous work at Alderfen Broad that the highly mobile sediments found at this site provides an inhospitable growing medium for waterweeds (Phillips, pers.

comm.). Moreover, preliminary experiments at Barton Broad have demonstrated that the sediment undergoes considerable movement, even in the absence of boat traffic. In the circumstances, it was decided to investigate the possibility of stabilizing the mud surface of the site with finely divided chalk. This technique has been employed with considerable success on lakes and rivers in France over the past ten or fifteen years, the material in question being known as champagne chalk or 'Nautex'. A similar, chalky powder is now being marketed in this country under the trade name 'Siltex', and although the mode of operation of this, and Nautex, has not been fully elucidated, the generally accepted hypothesis is that bacteria attach themselves to the coccoliths of which both materials are composed, and break down organic matter in the sediment. As a result of this bacterial activity, the silt is consolidated, and its surface stabilized, thus making it easier for waterweeds to colonize it.

Despite the scepticism of a number of individuals, notably Brian Moss, 20 tonnes of Siltex were applied by aeroplane to the southern end of Barton Broad (Turkey Broad) in April 1988, at the rate of about 1 tonne per hectare. Crome's Broad was treated in a similar fashion, but neither site exhibited any observable change during the ensuing month, and although a second application of Siltex was made to the former in the autumn of 1988, it was decided not to proceed with the plans to treat Turkey Broad a second time.

(c) Alderfen Broad

A method of rehabilitating an enriched water body which has been successfully practised abroad, notably at Lake Washington, USA (Edmondson, 1970 & 1979; Edmondson & Lehman, 1981) is to divert the nutrient-rich inflows to it so that these no longer pass through the site, but are discharged downstream of it. In 1978, it was decided to employ this technique at Alderfen Broad, a site whose inflow stream was being enriched by discharges from septic tanks, and a small sewage treatment works (see page 127) in its *c.* 15 ha catchment. Accordingly, an existing ditch was widened and deepened to carry the stream around the margin of the Broad, a control sluice being provided to enable water to be channelled through the latter if required. In the event, and despite periodic fish kills during warm weather owing to the temporary de-oxygenation of the water, this has not been done, since the experiment would have been invalidated if enriched water had been allowed to enter the site, even for a short time. The effects of the management trial on the water chemistry and phytoplankton of the Broad, and on its zooplankton and fish populations are described respectively by Moss *et al.*, (1985 & 1986), and Cryer *et al.*, (1986).

The diversion works were completed in February 1979, and by August, the total phosphorus concentrations in the Broad had, as a result of sediment release built up to nearly 900 μg l^{-1} (see Fig 13F), a figure about double that previously recorded at the site by Phillips (1977), and Osborne & Phillips (1978). Moss *et al.* also found that soluble reactive phosphorus levels were correspondingly high (maximum *c.* 120 μg l^{-1}) and chlorophyll *a* concentrations were, at over 200 μg l^{-1}, almost twice that observed in the past. But virtually all the nitrate nitrogen present at the time of closure was quickly used up, and blue-green algae, and in particular *Aphanothece*, predominated during the summer months (Fig. 13G).

Sediment release again occurred during the summer of 1980 as the water temperature rose, but total phosphorus concentrations were only about half those recorded the previous season. Phytoplankton production was less than expected given the amounts of phosphorus, silicon and nitrogen present, and this was probably because of the growing pressure exerted on the algae by the large numbers of cladocerans present (Peirson *et al.*, 1985). Clear water conditions developed on several occasions, and a few sprigs of Hornwort appeared.

Further changes occurred the following year. Total phosphorus concentrations remained relatively low (at less than 100 μg l^{-1} for much of the season), indicating that little sediment release was occurring, whilst significant quantities of nitrate nitrogen were present until August. Chlorophyll *a* levels were less than 50 μg l^{-1} for almost the whole season, and the amount of Hornwort increased until about 10 per cent of the Broad was colonized. This species became so abundant in the summer of 1982 that, as in 1963, it became difficult to row a boat across the Broad. Similar conditions prevailed in 1983, but in July that year, substantial quantities of both phosphorus and silicon

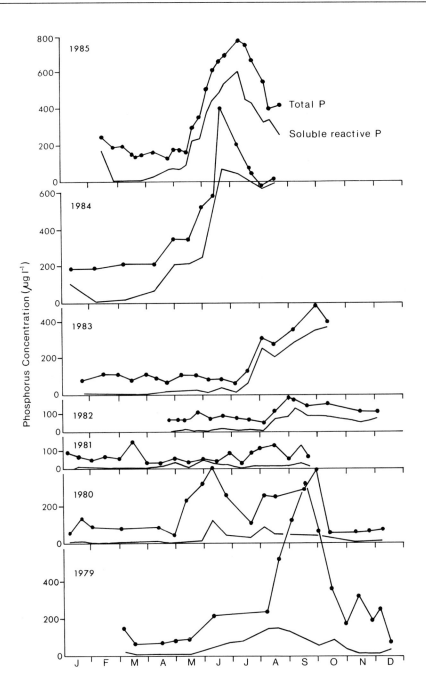

Fig. 13F

Phosphorus concentrations in Alderfen Broad – 1979 to 1985.

Source: Moss et al. *(1986)*

began to be released from the sediment, almost certainly because its surface had become temporarily anoxic under the dense 'canopy' of Hornwort.

Total phosphorus concentrations had risen to 400 µg l⁻¹ by the autumn of 1983, and although these were reduced by half during the next few months, probably as a result of wash-out and sediment re-uptake, sufficient soluble reactive phosphorus remained in February 1984, to support a substantial, albeit short-lived, crop of diatoms (maximum chlorophyll *a* concentration – 200 µg l⁻¹). Hornwort again appeared in early summer, but its growth was markedly less luxuriant than in 1982 and 1983.

Events followed a similar pattern in the early part of 1985, significant quantities of phosphorus being present as a consequence of sediment release. But by June, a large standing crop of *Anabaena* had developed, and this was thought to be fixing atmospheric nitrogen, because very little nitrate nitrogen was present in the water after March that year. *Anabaena* contains little chlorophyll *a*, its place being taken by phycobilin pigments; these made the water in the broad very turbid, even though the concentrations of chlorophyll *a* in it remained fairly low throughout the summer. It was perhaps because of this, that virtually no Hornwort was present in 1985.

Diatom populations in the Broad were noticeably smaller in 1986 than in 1985, but

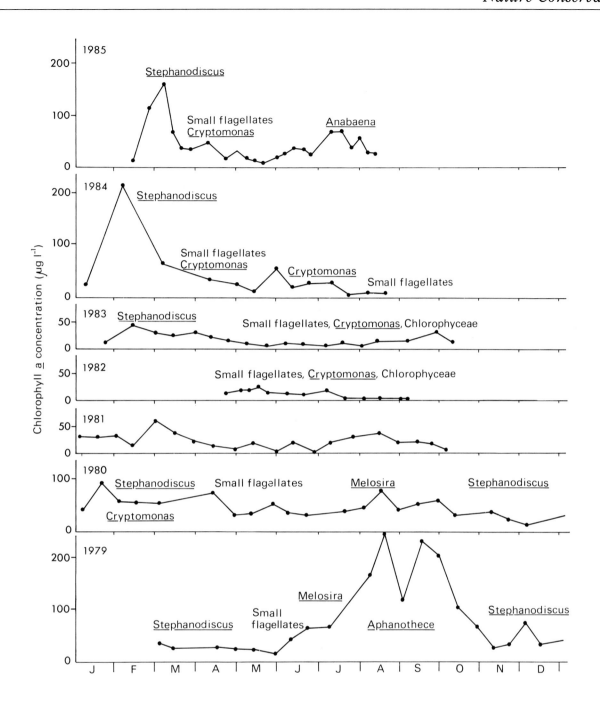

Fig. 13G

Phytoplankton in Alderfen Broad – 1979 to 1985.

Source: Moss et al. *(1986)*

the concentration of soluble reactive phosphorus once again rose above 600 µg l⁻¹ in June as a result of sediment release, and a massive bloom of *Anabaena* developed in August.

Although the Broad was devoid of waterweeds in 1986, Brian Moss suggested on the basis of what had occurred during the past 4 or 5 years that rather than remain permanently in a Phase III condition, with the algae being supplied with phosphorus from the sediment and nitrogen from the atmosphere (possibly supplemented by ammonium from the sediment), the site might revert temporarily to a Phase II state. This would occur if insufficient organic matter reached the sediment surface to prevent it being re-oxidized during the winter, in which event some of the phosphorus in the water could be re-precipitated. In these circumstances, waterweeds (probably dominated by Hornwort in view of the large number of viable propagules likely to be present) might reappear for a few years, only to give way later to another temporary spell of phytoplankton dominance. It was suggested (Moss *et al.*, 1985) that such a cycle might well continue for a long time, since the Broad is only flushed completely about once every two years with the inflow stream diverted; consequently, the overall rate of phosphorus loss from the site is very slow.

Subsequent events suggest that this prediction may well be correct. The maximum and mean concentrations of both chlorophyll *a* and soluble reactive phosphorus were much less in 1987 than in the previous two years, and numerous Hornwort plants appeared. Kennison (1988) estimated that this species covered between 50 and 75 per cent of the Broad in 1988, and that it was almost as abundant as it was in 1982. Unfortunately, the zooplankton population was not monitored in 1988, but it seems likely that the dense growth of Hornwort would have provided a refuge for the larger cladoceran species, and prevented these being decimated by the numerous roach present in the Broad as a result of the 2-year cycle of recruitment known to have occurred in it recently (see page 127).

(d) Cockshoot Broad

One of the projects in the Interim Action Programme approved by the Broads Authority in 1979 (see page 426), was to try and restore a broad to a Phase II condition by removing the nutrient-rich mud which had accumulated in it. Experience with the conventional grab and bucket excavators used by the Rivers Commissioners to dredge sites such as Malthouse Broad and Horsey Mere had shown that although these are reasonably efficient at removing the compacted sediments laid down early on during a broad's history, they leave behind most of the watery muds nearest the surface. Research at Barton Broad and elsewhere during the 1970s had shown that it is these, more recent sediments, which contain most of the nutrients, and it was therefore considered essential to use a suction-dredger on the chosen site, rather than conventional dredging machinery.

The original proposal, put forward jointly by the author and Chris Groves, the Authority's navigation adviser, was to mud-pump Hoveton Little Broad. This site was in a parlous state ecologically, being totally devoid of waterweeds and the invertebrates dependent thereon; in addition, it had been subject to such rapid siltation during the past 30 to 40 years, that it was less than a metre deep in many places. It was planned to suction-dredge the whole site to give a reasonable depth of water, and then dam off Pound End, a lagoon at its western end, so as to exclude enriched, sediment-laden water from this part of the site. The rest of the Broad would have remained open to boat traffic during the holiday season so that navigation, as well as nature conservation, would have benefited from the project. In addition, controlled experiments could have been set up to test the effects of excluding nutrient-rich water and boats from a suction-dredged site.

In the event, this scheme was adjudged too costly, even if phased over a five-year period, and subsequent investigations by Arthur Alsop, the Authority's consultant engineer, showed that a more limited project, involving the restoration of Pound End alone, would also be very expensive, as a lengthy piled dam would have had to be constructed to isolate it from the main part of the Broad*.

At the author's suggestion, attention then turned to Cockshoot Broad, which if anything, was in an even more degraded state than Hoveton Little Broad. In the mid-1950s, this had possessed a good stand of marginal reedswamp, plus several 'islands' of tussock fen and swamp carr. However, the tussocks of *Carex paniculata* on which these communities had been founded had degenerated during the 1960s, and by the early 1970s, the 'islands' consisted only of groups of dead and dying alders. The edges of the Broad were heavily overhung by trees and bushes, whilst so much sediment had been deposited in it as a result of tide-induced flows from the R. Bure (via Cockshoot Dyke and the channel linking Ranworth and Cockshoot Broads), that nowhere was it as much as a metre deep; indeed, wide expanses of bare mud were exposed during the summer months when water levels in the system were low.

On the basis of the experience gained at Woodbastwick Fen and Brundall Inner and Outer Broads, and following an inspection of Buckenham Broad while this was being mud-pumped for its owner, Mr Bruce Giddy, the Broads Authority decided that about

---

* In the autumn of 1989, the 'new' Broads Authority decided, in the light of recommendations made by its predecessor, that both Pound End (5.1 ha) and Black Horse Broad (14.8 ha) should be mud-pumped. In order to achieve the depth of water required for general navigation in the latter site – 1.4 m – and provide about 5 ha of slightly deeper water near its centre, 94 175 cubic metres of sediment will be removed from the Little Broad, while a further 27 175 cubic metres will be taken out of Pound End, with a view to restoring this area to good ecological condition. Work started in November 1989, and is due to be completed in the spring of 1991. In this way the cost of the project will be spread over three financial years.

Suction-dredging Buckenham Broad – 1980.

Plate LIV

Profiting from the experience gained by the late Colin Chapman, who had had Brundall Inner and Outer Broads suction-dredged by B.G. Harris Ltd. in 1975, Mr Bruce Giddy arranged for the same firm to carry out a similar operation at Buckenham Broad in 1980. The 'Mud-cat' which was used at these sites (and later at Strumpshaw, Belaugh and Hoveton Little Broads) pulls itself to and fro on a tautened wire, which is attached to trees or other immovable objects at each end of the broad. This wire (whose reflection can be seen in the left foreground) is shifted bit by bit across the site as work proceeds.

An auger helps to draw sediment into the machine, which then discharges it, together with large volumes of water, through the flexible outfall pipe seen on the right of the machine. This is supported by cylindrical floats where it crosses the broad and, at Buckenham, led to a piece of derelict grazing marsh which had been embanked so that it would serve as a settlement lagoon.

Buckenham Broad received very little inflow water while work was in progress, and as the powerful pump on the 'Mud-cat' lowered the water level, wide expanses of mud (visible on the left) were exposed. The other sites in Broadland which have been mud-pumped have remained in open connection with the river whilst work proceeded, and the water level has not, therefore, been lowered to reveal the progress being made, as happened at Buckenham.

Photo: Martin George

1.3 ha, representing slightly less than half Cockshoot Broad, together with the Dyke leading to it from the R. Bure (0.5 ha) should be suction-dredged by B. G. Harris Ltd with a 'Mud-cat' so as to provide water about a metre deep during the summer months. This would be more than sufficient to remove the phosphorus-rich sediments which had been shown to have accumulated in the site to a depth of *c.* 30 cm since the Second World War (Moss *et al.*, 1981). However, in order to provide additional ecological variety, and obviate the risk of the Broad eventually being completely overgrown by reedswamp species, the NCC paid for a further 0.4 ha of it to be deepened to 1.4 m – a depth of water greater than can be colonized by *Typha angustifilia* or *Phragmites*. It was decided that the remaining parts of the Broad, together totalling *c.* 1.5 ha should be left untouched, partly so that they would serve as a control to the experiment, and partly because they could only have been mud-pumped if the relict swamp carr 'islands' had first been removed. This would have been a very laborious, and therefore costly, undertaking.

It was not possible to dump the sediment derived from Cockshoot Broad and Dyke on to adjoining agricultural land, as Mr Giddy had done when renovating Buckenham Broad, and the *c.* 6750 litres per minute (*c.* 89 000 gallons per hour) output from the 'Mud-cat' (see Plate LIV) was therefore piped to a 4.4 ha block of alder carr to the east, which had been specially embanked to form a settlement lagoon. It was anticipated on the basis of experience in Sweden, that the water draining from this would be highly charged with nutrients, and it was therefore channelled direct to the R. Bure, rather than back into Cockshoot Broad. By March 1982, when the task had been completed, over 25 000 cubic metres of sediment had been deposited in this bunded lagoon, at a cost (including that of creating the latter) of *c.* £1.30 per cubic metre.

It subsequently became apparent that B. G. Harris Ltd had treated the Cockshoot project as something of a 'loss-leader', and that in normal circumstances, the firm would have charged at the rate of approximately £1.50 a cubic metre. A conventional dredger would have been able to remove a similar amount of material for about £1 a cubic metre, this despite the fact that it would have had to be lightered away from the site. However, such a machine would have been incapable of achieving the principal objective of the experiment – the removal of the phosphorus-rich surface sediments from the Broad and Dyke.

At the time the project was carried out, there was no immediate prospect of persuading the AWA to install phosphorus-reduction equipment in the sewage treatment works which discharge effluent into the R. Bure, and dams were therefore built across the river end of Cockshoot Dyke, and the channel connecting Cockshoot and Ranworth Broads. Although these prevent enriched river water entering the site (except for short spells during the winter when the fens are flooded), it continues to receive a supply of freshwater from a small inflow stream; this drains a *c.* 50 ha catchment, in which agricultural land predominates. Some of the trees bordering the Broad were also cut back in the hope that *Phragmites* and other emergent species would recolonize the adjoining fens, and thereafter grow out into the open water to form a stand of marginal reedswamp. If this does not happen during the next few years it is intended to plant Reed, Lesser Reedmace and Bulrushes around the margins of the Broad.

The Authority believed, rightly, that the Cockshoot project would generate a lot of public interest, and it therefore had a hide built overlooking the northern end of the broad. This is linked to the car park at the end of Ferry Road, Woodbastwick, by a walkway running beside the river and Cockshoot Dyke, thus enabling both the car-borne, and the boat-borne visitor to see the site, as well as enjoy a pleasant, water's-edge walk.

At a total cost of £77 207 (of which £9330 was spent on the walkway and hide) (Brewster, *in litt.*), the restoration of Cockshoot Broad must be adjudged expensive. In part this was due to serious technical problems with the dams which proved costly to rectify. However, the project has been very interesting from the ecological point of view. The water cleared very quickly after the site was isolated from the river in April 1982, and phytoplankton production has never attained the levels previously encountered. Phosphorus concentrations in the Broad have also been much lower than they were previously (see Fig. 13H), whilst the total inorganic nitrogen levels only exceeded 1 mg l^{-1} on two occasions between 1982 and 1985, whereas before isolation they were often in excess of 3 mg l^{-1} in the winter and early spring (Moss *et al.*, 1985).

Despite the clarity of the water, the re-colonization of the site by waterweeds has been

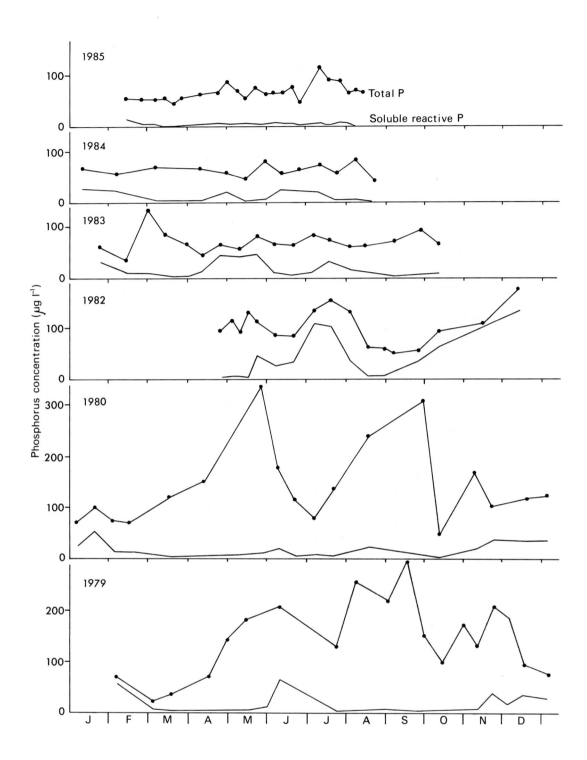

Phosphorus concentrations in Cockshoot Broad – 1979 to 1985.   Fig. 13н

Source: Moss et al. (1985)

much slower than expected. A few Phase II plants appeared in Cockshoot Dyke in the summer of 1982, but hardly any survived, owing to heavy grazing by waterfowl, whilst Jackson (1983) found nothing at all in the Broad itself apart from a few fragments of an unidentified stonewort. The 1983 season proved equally disappointing, and since the slow rate of recolonization was considered to be due to a shortage of viable propagules, the site was restocked the following February, some 8000 Water Soldier plants, 200 Yellow Water-lilies and 120 White Water-lilies being used, plus considerable quantities of Broad-leaved Pondweed, Stiff-leaved Water-Crowfoot, Canadian Pondweed and Ivy-leaved Duckweed. Many of the Water Soldier plants died as a result of bird damage, and a similar fate befell a further 10 000 specimens introduced during the winter of 1984/5. More water-lilies, weighted as before with bricks attached to their rhizomes, were planted in the site in March 1985, and a further introduction of Water Soldier plants was made two months later.

These introductions proved much more successful in Cockshoot Dyke than in the Broad, probably because the latter is more subject to wind and wave action (see Plate LV). Nevertheless, several patches of Yellow and White Water-lilies were growing in the Broad by the end of 1985, and as these spread, they should, by providing more sheltered

Plate LV

Cockshoot Broad – 1987.

Taken five years after this site was suction-dredged and dammed off from the R. Bure, this photograph shows that apart from one or two patches of White Water-lily (the result of deliberate re-introductions), waterweeds are still largely absent.

Lesser Reedmace is well established in the right middle distance and has spread further out into the open water since 1987. But this and other reedswamp species are intolerant of shade, and will not therefore colonize other sectors of the Broad's margins until the alders growing thereon have been cut back.

Photo: Richard Denyer

conditions, make it easier for other plants to re-establish themselves, either from viable propagules left in the sediment (the fragments of *Najas marina* recorded from the site by Kennison in 1984 are thought to fall into this category), or from seeds and turions produced by the species which have recently been reintroduced. The lilies will also provide a refuge for cladocerans, the populations of which have since 1983 been subject to increasing predation by fish (particularly roach), the progeny of individuals trapped in the site when it was isolated from the river. Maximum numbers of daphniids ranged between 100 and 200 per litre in 1983 and 1984, but declined to 39 per litre in 1985.

Electro-fishing in Cockshoot Dyke – 1990.

Plate LVI

This waterway was electro-fished in both 1989 and 1990 in order to reduce the number of fish in it, and therefore the grazing pressure being exerted on the population of *Daphnia pulex* and other large cladocerans. The fish are only stunned by the current, and they were therefore collected up and placed in the adjoining R. Bure.

If, as is hoped, a prolific growth of waterweeds develops in the Dyke (and also in Cockshoot Broad with which it is connected), it should be unnecessary to continue to control the fish population artificially. This is because the cladocerans will be able to avoid being predated by fish by taking shelter amongst the plants during daylight hours. At night, however, when fish find it difficult to see to catch them, they will be able to graze on the phytoplankton with relative impunity. This will maintain the clarity of the water, thus favouring the continued proliferation of waterweeds.

Electro-fishing is one of several biomanipulative techniques currently being used in the region to try to re-create, in selected sites, a balanced Phase II ecosystem.

Photo: Richard Denyer

The increasing predation by fish also brought about a marked change in the composition of the cladoceran population, which was dominated by *Daphnia pulex* in 1982, but which in 1985 and 1986 consisted mainly of *Bosmina longirostris*, a smaller and much less efficient grazer on the phytoplankton. It was because of this that the mean chlorophyll *a* concentration between June and August 1985, rose to 27.2 µg l^{-1}, whereas in the three previous seasons, it had varied between 16 and 17 µg l^{-1} (Moss *et al.*, 1985 and 1986).

An obvious way of reducing the grazing pressure being exerted on the zooplankton would be to remove some or all of the fish from the Broad. The resultant rise in the number of large cladocerans would help to limit phytoplankton production, so improving the clarity of the water, and increasing the rate at which the site is re-colonized by waterweeds. Although there was general agreement that such a measure was likely to prove successful, the consensus amongst ecologists in 1986 and 1987 was that the Broad should be left to its own devices, the main argument for this being that more information about the rate of recovery under natural conditions would thereby be obtained. However, phytoplankton production remained very high during the ensuing summer, and after much discussion amongst those concerned, the Strategy Committee of the Broads Authority decided that as many fish as possible should be removed from the site. It was accordingly netted and electro-fished in the early months of 1989, the catch being transferred to the adjoining R. Bure. Unfortunately, electro-fishing has little effect on small fry, and large shoals of young Roach and other species were observed in Cockshoot Dyke the following summer. These were netted off from the Broad, and the site was again electro-fished in February 1990, the hope being that most of the fish would be large enough by then to be susceptible to this form of control (see Plate LVI).

In the event, these measures (which can be termed 'biomanipulative') were successful, and good water clarity was observed during 1990. But it remains to be seen whether such conditions will persist on this occasion long enough to allow a balanced Phase II community of waterweeds, large cladocerans and fish to develop and coexist in the site, or whether the numbers of zooplanktiverous fish will have to be reduced again in a year or so's time.

(e) Strumpshaw Broad

Soon after establishing its reserve at Strumpshaw, the RSPB concluded, in the light of the experience gained at Brundall, Woodbastwick and elsewhere, that since there was no immediate prospect of the AWA agreeing to reduce nutrient levels in the R. Yare, the only way of restoring the waterways on the site to good ecological condition would be to isolate them from the river. Accordingly, the Society decided in 1978 to dam off the Fleet Dyke which until then had connected the two limbs of Strumpshaw Broad with the river, and embank the main (eastern) part of Strumpshaw Fen so that it was rarely, if ever, flooded by enriched water. This was not difficult, as dredgings have been dumped beside the river for at least 150 years, and it was only necessary to raise and strengthen these piles of spoil in a few places, and arrange that when the AWA next carried out routine maintenance work on Lackford Run (a small tributary of the Yare), the dredgings from this would be dumped on its eastern side to form a cross-wall. This separates the main part of Strumpshaw Fen from the area to the west, which is not embanked and which, like the areas owned by the Society near Rockland Broad, therefore continues to serve as a tidal washland. A sluice has been installed so that surplus water can be drained off the embanked part of the reserve when required, but in normal circumstances as much water as possible is retained following the winter's rains.

In practice, it proved difficult to maintain the fen water-table at the desired level during the summer months, and although river water can be admitted through the sluice, this was seldom done because of the high concentrations of nitrates and phosphates in it. In 1985, it became apparent that the water-table of the reserve was being lowered as a result of the operation by the AWA of their Strumpshaw water-pumping station, and after lengthy discussions, the Authority agreed to sink a borehole from which the Society could obtain compensation water for the fen when required. This borehole, which is sited near Lackford Run, came into operation in 1987.

Although the damming off of the Fleet Dyke prevented enriched, sediment-laden river water reaching Strumpshaw Broad, its east and west limbs (which together

'Water-jetting' at Strumpshaw Broad (East) – 1983.   Plate LVII

Jets of water at high pressure – mounted on a 'Mud-cat' and supplied by a pump mounted on the pontoon visible on the left – being used by the RSPB to break up the raft of peat-forming plants which had reduced the total amount of open water in Strumpshaw Broad (East and West) from 7.6 ha in 1846, to less than 1 ha in the early 1970s. To the right of the machine is the floating mass of rhizomes and other plant remains which it left behind; this debris was subsequently removed from the site with cromes and hand-rakes.

After the jetting equipment had been removed, the Mud-cat was used as a suction dredger to remove the surface layers of sediment which had accumulated in both limbs of the Broad, the aim being to provide a mean water depth of about a metre.

There are now *c.* 2 ha of open water in the eastern part of the site, and a further hectare in the west. As a result, the ornithological interest of the reserve has improved, the number of species frequenting it being greater now than in the mid-1970s.

Photo: R.N. Flowers

extended to less than 1 ha) had become so shallow as a consequence of tide-induced siltation, that the RSPB decided, again in the light of experience gained at Woodbast-wick and elsewhere, that they would have to be mud-pumped if they were to be re-colonized by aquatic plants and animals. Funds were very limited at first, and a 4-inch Sykes Univac pump, and later a Toyo Submersible, were therefore hired for short periods during 1978 and 1979 and operated by groups of volunteers under the super-vision of the warden, Mike Blackburn. In 1983, the Society received grants from the European Economic Community (£10 000) and the World Wildlife Fund (£5000) towards the cost of completing the project, and by dint of much overtime working, and with massive help from volunteers, about a metre of sediment was removed from the east and west limbs of the Broad with a 'Mudcat' hired from B. G. Harris Ltd. In addition, much of the marginal reedswamp which had overgrown the eastern end of the former basin of the Broad (which according to a Tithe Map of 1846 once extended to 7.6 ha) was broken up with high-pressure water jets and removed, so almost doubling the amount of open water in the eastern limb of the Broad (see Plate LVII).

(f) Hickling Broad

Initial thinking, once the principal causes of the ecological malaise affecting Hickling Broad had been identified (see Chapter 5), was to find a way of safeguarding its fish population against further outbreaks of *Prymnesium* poisoning. It was clearly essential to monitor the status of this alga, particularly at times when its population was increasing in size, and the AWA therefore developed a bioassay system capable of detecting *Prym-nesium* toxins in the water at a concentration of one twenty-fifth of the dose which under normal conditions is lethal to fish.

Research in Israel, where *Prymnesium* has caused problems at commercial fish farms, had suggested that fish are able to detect small quantities of toxins in the water and take avoiding action, and it was therefore considered significant that shoals congregate in the lower reaches of the R. Thurne at times when toxins in Hickling Broad reach a lethal concentration. But it was thought that some fish were probably dying when they became trapped in areas from which they could not escape without swimming through water containing toxins. The AWA acted on this principle in 1976, when they sank a series of well-points in the Crag deposits underlying the fens at the western end of Hickling Broad, so that when the *Prymnesium* population in the latter starts to produce ich-thyotoxins, water can be pumped into a specially enlarged tributary of Catfield Dyke. The flow of fresh water prevents toxins extending up these waterways, which thus constitute a refuge for fish trapped at the western end of the Broad.

The Crag-water discharged by the pump is rich in iron (8 to 12 mg Fe l^{-1}), and although it was considered unlikely that the ferric ions would be harmful to fish, there was concern lest the ferrous ions, which are known to be toxic, especially in water with a pH of less than 4.0, should kill the fish which had sought refuge. In the event, these fears have proved groundless, and numerous fish have survived in the refuge during the *Prymnesium* outbreaks which have occurred in the Broad since the mid-1970s.

Although the *Prymnesium* problem had been alleviated by the establishment of the Hickling fish refuge, there was no consensus as to what else could be done to restore the larger Thurne broads to the condition they were in prior to 1969. A small working party, known as the Thurne Study Group, was therefore set up in 1981, and this identified six techniques which might be employed. These were: (i) culling or displacing the gulls roosting on Hickling Broad; (ii) increasing the rate at which this site is flushed in the early spring; (iii) re-stocking the Thurne broads with fish so as to increase the grazing intensity on the *Neomysis* population, thus reducing the pressure on the larger cladocerans, and so enabling them to control the growth of phytoplankton more effec-tively; (iv) treating the broads with ferric sulphate so as to precipitate the phosphorus, thus rendering it unavailable to phytoplankton; (v) applying ammonia to the broads to inhibit the growth of *Prymnesium* in them; and (vi) introducing bundles of brushwood into the broads so as to form an artificial substrate. This would provide the cladocerans with protection against predators (notably *Neomysis* and fish), so increasing the grazing pressure on the phytoplankton. The brushwood would also be colonized by epiphytic algae, so reducing the quantity of nutrients available for phytoplankton production.

None of these options was thought practicable. Bird lovers would undoubtedly object if it became known that large numbers of gulls were to be killed on a national nature reserve, whilst scaring the birds away by broadcasting their alarm calls was of doubtful legality, and would, in any event require elaborate and expensive equipment; in addition, the roost might re-form on Martham Broad or some other ecologically sensitive site nearby. Water of the requisite quality was said not to be available locally in sufficient quantity to increase the flushing rate, and it would be prohibitively expensive to pipe it in from the catchments of the rivers Bure or Ant. Similarly, the effect of a fish restocking programme could be nullified if there was a further outbreak of *Prymnesium*, brushwooding would constitute a hazard to navigation, whilst dosing the nature reserves associated with the upper Thurne with chemicals was thought inappropriate, in view of the uncertainty concerning the long-term effects of this form of treatment.

It was concluded that no new management initiatives should be embarked upon for the time being, but that the limnology of the Thurne broads and the size of the Hickling gull roost should continue to be carefully monitored. In addition, it was felt that since there was a possibility that the mechanical dredging of Horsey Mere and Hickling Broad in the late 1960s and early 1970s might have triggered off an increase in the size of the *Prymnesium* population, and the subsequent release of ichthyotoxins, suction-dredging equipment should be used in future for any necessary deepening of the Thurne broads.

Much concern continued to be expressed during the 1970s and 1980s about the frequent, *Prymnesium*-induced fish kills which were occurring in the larger Thurne broads, and in response to pressure from angling interests, the AWA decided in 1985 to mount some experiments aimed at discovering whether the population of this alga could be controlled chemically. Workers in Israel have demonstrated that free ammonia causes *Pyrmnesium* cells to break down, and can therefore be used as an algicide in fish ponds (Shilo & Shilo, 1955), and following consultations with the Norfolk Naturalists' Trust and the NCC, it was arranged that two small bays beside, but in direct hydrological communication with, Heigham Sound should be used for an experiment involving the use of this chemical. In June 1986, sufficient aqueous ammonia was applied to one of these bays to produce an initial concentration of 2.5 mg l^{-1} assessed as N, and the subsequent fate of this chemical, and the populations of *Prymnesium*, zooplankton and littoral invertebrates were sampled, the other bay being used as a control (AWA, 1987). In addition, cages of fish were placed in both the experimental and the control bays to determine whether the concentrations of ammonia used were sufficiently long-lasting to be toxic to these animals.

In the event, this proved not to be the case, and the zooplankton and the littoral invertebrates were also apparently unaffected. But although the *Prymnesium* cell counts fell from a mean of 9100 cells ml^{-1} to a minimum of 460 cells ml^{-1} during the 8 hours following the dosing, they subsequently showed a steady increase, reaching a mean of 15 000 cells ml^{-1} after 144 hours. The fact that the total *Prymnesium* population was ultimately larger after the dosing than before could have been due to the additional amounts of nitrogen present in the water, once the ammonia concentration had fallen below a toxic level, combined with the tide-induced inflow of 'new' water from the adjoining Heigham Sound.

Although these experiments demonstrated that ammonia could, in theory, be employed for *Prymnesium* control in Hickling Broad, it would be necessary to apply it to the entire site in order to achieve complete success. Indeed, staff of the AWA and its successor, the National Rivers Authority, admit that the treatment would probably fail if any small areas were accidentally left untreated, since the presence of large quantites of residual nitrogen would in this event stimulate a rapid resurgence of the alga.

In the circumstances, the option favoured by both the National Rivers Authority and the NCC is to increase the size, and therefore the effectiveness, of the fish refuge at the western end of the Broad. This will necessitate sinking further boreholes and probably treating the (Crag) water thus obtained to reduce its iron content. In the longer term, and on the assumption that it will not be practicable to augment the supply of low chloride water entering the site, or bring about a permanent reduction in the size of the gull roost, the best solution will probably lie in encouraging the owners of arable marshland in the Thurne catchment, notably the Brograve and Eastfield Levels, to put their land back under grass with a high water-table. This would reduce the amounts of chloride and nitrogen in the land drainage water discharged to the Thurne broads, and thus render the latter less suitable for the growth and proliferation of *Prymnesium*.

However, as noted in Chapter 9, it is most unlikely that the incentives offered under the ESA scheme, will on their own, be sufficient to bring about this change in land use (see page 308) (George, 1990). In the circumstances, the 'new' Broads Authority has reconvened the Thurne Study Group, and invited it to re-examine this and other problems in the upper Thurne catchment, and make recommendations.

(g) Calthorpe Broad

The deep drainage of the marshes within the Brograve Level following the re-organization of its arterial drainage system in the early 1950s, not only increased the nitrogen loading of Horsey Mere (see page 273), but had a major impact on Calthorpe Broad, a site which, somewhat ironically, is owned by the NCC. Between 1966 and 1969, the pH of the Broad ranged from 6.5 to 7.0, but during the summer of 1970, the water level fell dramatically, following the lowering of the water-table of the marshland adjoining the reserve, and damage to a control sluice. Heavy rain fell in November, and almost immediately, the entire fish population died, as did most of the freshwater mussels, *Anodonta cygnea, A. anatina* and *Unio pictorum*, which until then had been present in large numbers. Investigations showed that the pH of the Broad had fallen to 3.0, a remarkable figure for such a water body, and that the fish had died from a breakdown of their gill structure, caused by the acidity of the water.

In an account of this and subsequent events at the site, Gosling and Baker (1980) note that the spawn laid by frogs and toads in the spring of 1971 perished, and that apart from a few swan mussels found that autumn, no benthic invertebrates or zooplankters were present. pH values as low as 3.0 continued to be recorded in the dykes connected with the Broad, and it was not until September 1971, that the pH of the latter started to rise, to reach normality in November.

The site gradually recovered ecologically during 1972 and 1973, and by 1974 most of the plant and animal life found in the 1960s had reappeared, despite the fact that

Fig. 13J

The pH of
(a) Calthorpe Broad,
(b) one of the dykes connected with it, and
(c) the dyke around the edge of the reserve, and therefore some distance away from the Broad.

Source: Gosling and Baker (1980)

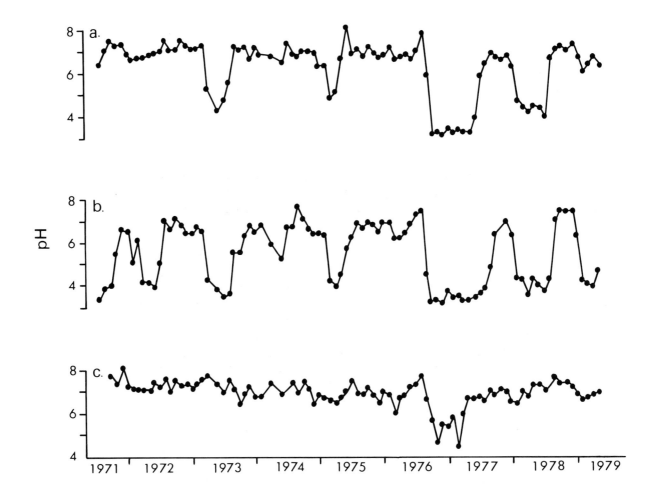

the pH of the Broad and its interconnected dykes fell each year to about 5.5 after the autumnal rains (see Fig 13J).

During the summer of 1976, the Broad almost dried up, and the rains the following autumn caused the pH to drop to about 3.2, where it stayed throughout most of the winter and spring of 1977. In an attempt to reduce the acidity, 1.5 tonnes of ground chalk were applied to the surface of the Broad in May 1977, but this proved to be insufficient to have a long-term effect, and in December 1978, a further 13.5 tonnes were distributed around the margin of the Broad. This restored its pH to near neutrality, though further applications have had to be made now and then to maintain the site in this condition.

The effects of the exceptional acidities encountered in 1971 and 1978 on the water-weed flora are shown in Table 13h. It is of interest that the acid-loving Floating Scirpus

Table 13h   Waterweeds recorded from Calthorpe Broad

	Prior to 1970	1971a	1971b	1974	1977	1979
Callitriche stagnalis	+		+		+	+
Ceratophyllum demersum	+			+		
Eleogeton fluitans						+
Elodea canadensis	+		+	+		
Hippuris vulgaris	+	+	+	+	+	+
Hottonia palustris	+	+	+	+		+
Hydrocharis morsus-ranae	+					
Luronium natans	+					
Myriophyllum sp.	+		+	+		+
Nuphar lutea	+	+	+	+	+	+
Nymphaea alba	+	+	+	+	+	+
Potamogeton spp.	+			+		
Stratiotes aloides	+		+	+		

1971a is a record for the spring, while 1971b is for late summer.
+ indicates presence
Source: Gosling & Baker (1980)

(*Eleogiton fluitans*) which was previously confined to dykes on the reserve, had invaded the Broad itself by 1979. In contrast, Floating Water-Plantain, which is thought to have been introduced to the site in 1949 by its previous owner, the late Robert Gurney, has not been seen since 1974 (Driscoll, 1985a) despite its preference for base-poor conditions.

The late F. J. H. Mackereth (*in litt.*) was the first to attribute the fluctuating acidity of Calthorpe Broad to chemical reactions in the peat. When this is waterlogged, bacterial action causes sulphur compounds in it to be reduced to sulphides, whilst iron salts are converted to the ferrous state. These combine to form the insoluble ferrous di-sulphide ('pyrite') which is stable so long as conditions remain anaerobic. But when water levels in the Broad and its adjoining dykes fall during dry periods, the peat is exposed to atmospheric oxygen, and soluble iron and sulphuric acid are produced. Subsequent heavy rainfall washes the latter out of the peat, and thence into the dykes and Broad. Similar changes can occur in the Drained Marshland Area when the water-table of acid sulphate soils is lowered (see Chapter 9).

A hydrological survey commissioned by the NCC in 1977 showed that it would be prohibitively costly to clay-core or pile Calthorpe Broad and its adjoining fens to reduce water loss (Alsop, 1977). In addition, the site cannot readily be replenished by means of a borehole. The aquifers in the Chalk underlying this part of the region are saline, whilst the water in the Crag deposits immediately underneath the site contains so much ferrous sulphate (*c.* 18 mg l^{-1}) that it would have to be pre-treated with calcium

Plate LVIII

Settlement lagoon near Belaugh Broad – 1987.

A 'Mud-cat' has an output of some 6750 litres per minute (*c.* 89 000 gallons per hour), and it is essential to provide a settlement lagoon where the sediment in the discharge from the machine has time to settle out, before the water in which it is entrained finds its way back to the nearby river or broad. When Buckenham Broad was being mud-pumped in 1980 this problem was solved by creating a bunded lagoon on some adjoining grazing marshes, and a similar plan was adopted by the Broads Authority at Belaugh. The sediment from Brundall, Cockshoot and Hoveton Little Broads was accommodated in lagoons formed on areas of derelict fen near these sites.

Belaugh Old Hall Mill – on the right – is one of the 63 brick-towered drainage mills still standing in the region.

Photo: R.N. Flowers

carbonate before it could be supplied to the Broad. The cost of sinking the necessary well-points, and providing a settling tank and dosing equipment, would be so high that it was decided to continue the palliative treatment of applying chalk to the site periodically in order to control the pH, and to accept, at least for the time being, that the water-table in the Broad and the adjoining fens will often be much lower than is desirable. In short, this is an example of a situation where, perforce, the symptoms of a problem are being tackled, rather than their causes.

(h) The R. Bure and the Belaugh Broad Project

Despite the slow and therefore rather disappointing response obtained from the R. Ant phosphorus reduction experiments, the AWA agreed in 1985, following discussions with the NCC and the Broads Authority, to extend the programme to the Bure. The nutrient budget compiled by Brian Moss and his team for this river (see page 137) had shown that at least 14 sewage works discharge treated effluent into it upstream of Wroxham, but most of these are fairly small, and it was therefore decided that ferric sulphate dosing equipment should only be installed at the four largest – those at Briston (serving a population of 1893), Aylsham (4749), RAF Coltishall (*c.* 1750) and Belaugh (6831). It was considered essential to monitor the effects of this nutrient reduction programme on the ecology and water chemistry of the river and its interconnected broads, and it was arranged that the cost of doing this from 1987 until 1992 should be shared by the AWA, the NCC, the Broads Authority, and through it, the Countryside Commission.

Phosphorus reduction commenced in October 1986, at Briston, Aylsham and Belaugh, but the equipment at the plant serving RAF Coltishall did not become operational until a year later. In addition, teething troubles were experienced, particularly at Belaugh, and in some months, only 60 per cent of the phosphorus reaching the works was removed, instead of the 90 per cent target. Further difficulties were experienced in 1989 and 1990 as a result of the assumption by Anglian Water Services of responsibility for the management of the sewage treatment works previously run by the AWA. In the circumstances, it is too early to judge whether the phosphorus reduction programme will bring about an improvement in the condition of the Bure and its broads. Total phosphorus concentrations in Wroxham Broad were at, or below, 100 µg l^{-1} for much of 1987 (compared with a mean concentration of 168 µg l^{-1} recorded by Moss between 1978 and 1980), and chlorophyll *a* levels were also unusually low, being only 20 µg l^{-1} after the spring flush of diatoms; this was less than half the minima observed by Moss during the summers of 1978, 1979 and 1980. However, these differences were less marked in 1988, and may have resulted from the exceptionally heavy fluvial flows carried by the river during 1987. Moreover, phosphorus released from the sediments seems not to have occurred until July owing to the lower-than-average temperatures.

Determined to derive the maximum possible ecological benefit from the extended phosphorus reduction programme, the Broads Authority decided to mud-pump a second broad in the Bure valley. This would need to be upstream of Swan Bend, Horning, as Moss' nutrient budget studies had demonstrated that there was no realistic chance of getting the broads downstream of this point to switch from a Phase III to a Phase II condition, merely by reducing phosphorus inputs upstream of Wroxham. It was also felt that the chosen site should be left in open communication with the river, thus providing a contrast with Cookshoot Broad which had been hydrologically isolated from the latter once it had been suction-dredged. Two small and heavily-silted sites were identified as being potentially suitable – Belaugh Broad and Snape's Water – but for a variety of reasons, not least the likelihood that the Wroxham and Hoveton bypass might have to be aligned close to the latter, Belaugh Broad was selected for the management experiment.

Surveys showed that the chosen site was dumbell-shaped, with some 11 900 sq m of open water, with a mean depth of *c.* 40 cm, in the north-east, linked by a narrow channel to a smaller bay (of some 5600 sq m) in the south-west. The water in the latter was only about 8 cm deep, and it was calculated that in order to achieve a mean depth of a metre throughout the site, with a slightly deeper area of water near the centre of the main part of the broad, it would be necessary to suction-dredge some 15 270 cubic metres of sediment. Following discussions with the owner, it was decided that this should be dumped on some derelict grazing marsh to the north, rather than on an embanked area of fen, as was done at Cockshoot Broad (see Plate LVIII). To gain access to the site, and improve water circulation, the channel linking it to the river would need to be widened, and several small, tree-covered islands would have to be removed in order to enlarge the link between the two parts of the Broad.

B. G. Harris Ltd successfully tendered for the project, and it was completed in the summer of 1987, at a cost of just over £49 000, the Broads Authority receiving 60 per cent of this in the form of grants from the NCC (£12 500), the Countryside Commission and the World Wildlife Fund. Some 3000 Yellow and White Water-lilies were introduced to the site during the early spring of 1988, in an attempt to speed up its conversion from its existing Phase III condition to Phase II. Several small, fine-gauge netted cages were also installed, and a variety of species placed in these, including Canadian Pondweed, Hornwort and Water Soldier. As anticipated, the plants growing in the open water of the Broad were heavily grazed by Coot and other waterfowl, whereas those in the netted enclosures thrived, thus indicating that conditions in the Broad were suitable for Phase II species, but that their recolonization of the site was, as at Cockshoot Broad, being impeded by the attentions of grazing waterfowl. In recognition of this, four large, bird-proof cages were installed in the Broad early in 1989 (see Plate LIX). These encompass, not only a considerable expanse of open water, but the fine-mesh cages installed the previous year. Numerous Yellow and White Water-lilies have been introduced into these enclosures, as well as into the main part of the Broad, and it is very much hoped that these transplants will be sufficient to trigger the switch from Phase III to Phase II in the whole site.

Changes in the water chemistry and ecology of Belaugh Broad are being carefully monitored. In addition, although the landowner was unwilling to grant a public right of navigation over the site, he has given the Broads Authority permission to take parties of *bona fide* visitors to see it.

Conclusion

As a result of the research and management experiments carried out since the mid-1970s, the nature of the ecological changes which have occurred in Broadland and their causes, are now fairly well understood. In future, therefore, it will be possible to predict the response of different parts of the ecosystem to varying demands being made upon it, and assess the effects of proposed changes of land use management. Sufficient information is also available to check, and hopefully reverse, those processes having an inimical effect on the ecology of the region, and which are, or could become, a constraining influence on the continued use of the region for tourism, recreation and agriculture. Thus although further research is required, for example on the gains and losses of sediment to and from the waterway system, the reasons why *Schoenoplectus* and *Typha* have failed to recolonize the broads and rivers following the elimination of the coypu population, and on the present status and ecological requirements of the invertebrates which occur in the fens (a task now being carried out for the NCC by two zoologists, Andy Foster and Deborah Procter), the main job in the 1990s will be a very challenging one: to apply the knowledge gained to reverse the changes taking place, and restore as much as possible of Broadland's ecosystem to the condition it was in prior to the Second World War.

As far as the broads and rivers are concerned, the most important requirement by far

Plate LIX

Waterfowl exclosures in Belaugh Broad – 1990.

The waterweeds which were introduced to this site soon after it had been suction-dredged in 1987 were, as at Cockshoot Broad, heavily grazed by Coot and other waterfowl, and these exclosures were therefore erected to give the plants therein time thoroughly to establish themselves. When the wire netting is eventually removed, it is hoped that the growth of waterweeds will be sufficiently robust to be self-sustaining, despite the renewed attentions of grazing waterfowl.

This experiment, which is being carefully monitored, is part of the determined efforts being made by the Broads Authority to convert selected open-water sites in the region back to a Phase II, waterweed-dominated, state.

Photo: R.N. Flowers

will be to bring about further improvements in water quality. Phosphorus reduction will need to be practised in additional sewage treatment works, and continuing steps taken to reduce the phosphorus load emanating from other sources, such as livestock units and industrial installations. Increasing the flushing rates of broads adversely affected by nutrient enrichment may be possible in some cases, for instance by widening the channels connecting them with the main river, or augmenting the summer flow rates within the latter with groundwater. But this may not be altogether easy to achieve given the rapidly rising population of East Anglia, and the increased demand for water for domestic and industrial use which will result. The problems may well be exacerbated by Global Warming. If, as has been predicted, the mean rainfall over Eastern England declines, flow rates in the Broadland rivers will be reduced. In addition, the more rapid rises in sea level which are forecast for the coming centuries may well necessitate the provision of a tidal barrier at Yarmouth (see Chapter 10), and this, too, could reduce the flushing rates of broads in direct communication with the main river system, and render them even more susceptible to nutrient enrichment than they are already.

Isolation, combined with the removal of phosphorus-rich sediments, is another option which could be used to bring about a switch from Phase III to Phase II. However, experience at Cockshoot Broad strongly suggests that the removal of zooplanktiverous fish will also be necessary. This is not as easy as it might seem, but the use of poisons, such as Rotenone, though widely practised in America, is probably not acceptable in such an ecologically sensitive area as Broadland, and certainly not in Cockshoot Broad, given its status as a national nature reserve and Ramsar site.

Isolation, and the wholesale removal of fish obviously cannot be practised in the rivers and navigable broads, and in a valuable review of the management options available in such situations, Moss *et al.* (1989) have suggested that cages, enclosing, say, one hectare at a time should be created. The fish within these would be removed, so allowing the development of massive populations of *Daphnia* spp. and other large cladocerans. Waterweeds would, in the near absence of phytoplankton, colonize the cages, and the latter would then be removed, the theory being that the zooplankton/waterweed community would be self-sustaining, despite the presence of fish. This technique, which can be categorized as a form of biomanipulation, is already being tried out at Belaugh Broad, and a similar enclosure has recently (1990) been constructed in Hoveton Great Broad.

Biomanipulative techniques will undoubtedly play an increasing role in the steps being taken to restore the Broadland waterways to the state they were in prior to the Second World War. But the future management of the region's fens presents rather different problems. Regrettably, this has not received anything like as much attention as it deserves, this despite the fact that many fens are, unlike the waterways, still in a near pristine state, as witnessed by the continued occurrence in them of such national rarities as the Fen Orchid, the Crested Buckler Fern and the Swallowtail butterfly. Given the shortages of labour and the consequent lack of management, many fens will not retain their ecological interest much longer, and it is therefore imperative that a management strategy, aimed at identifying the most important sites, and prescribing how these can best be managed, should be formulated as soon as possible. This will need to take account of the experience gained by the Broads Authority from its experimental turf pond project (see page 470), and by the NCC which has dramatically increased the floristic diversity of several fen compartments on the Bure Marshes NNR by regularly removing cut material from them (see page 468). But special attention will have to be given to the needs of the Ant Valley fens, which, by reason of their outstandingly rich flora and fauna, form the most important example of this habitat formation in Broadland, if not in Britain as a whole.

Many other countries have had experience in dealing with the nutrient enrichment and other ecological problems currently being encountered in Broadland, and an increased international dialogue is highly desirable. This is particularly necessary in respect of the Netherlands, many of whose wetland sites originated, like the broads, as peat cuttings, and which are now suffering from a similar *malaise*. In the circumstances, the 'new' Broads Authority decided in 1989 to establish a 'twinning' arrangement with the Dutch in respect of the Weerribben, a proposed national park in the province of Overijessel. Similar arrangements have also been negotiated with the French in regard to the Audomarois Regional Park in the northern part of the Pas de Calais. This park, like Broadland, consists of an extensive system of waterways, many of which are navigable, adjoined by grazing marshland and fen. Exchange visits have already taken place, and it is also encouraging that Dr Ros Boar of the University of East Anglia has, as a separate initiative, established a close working relationship with Dr Van Toorn of the Dutch Instituut voor Oecologisch Onderzoek, since his work on nutrient cycling in reed-beds is of direct relevance to the situation in Broadland.

Another illustration of our new-found willingness to profit from the ecological know-how of other countries was the decision by several regional water authorities, including the AWA, to use specially created reed-beds to purify sewage, a technique originally developed in West Germany, and known variously in this country as the Root-zone Method (Brix, 1987), or the Reed Bed Treatment System (RBTS) (Parr, 1990). The AWA installed an RBTS at the Acle sewage treatment works in 1985, but the reed rhizomes which were employed were slow to become established, and when the Freethorpe works was similarly equipped by the Authority in 1987, reed seedlings were used instead of rhizomes. When the RBTS at Freethorpe becomes fully operational, probably in 1991, it should bring about an improvement in the condition of Halvergate Fleet, which conveys effluent from these works to the Breydon Pump. It would then be possible for the RSPB to use water from the latter to replenish the dyke system of its reserve at Berney Arms, an option which is at present impracticable owing to the polluted condition of the Fleet.

Although nature conservationists will be obliged to concentrate their attention on their reserves and SSSIs, they will need to bear in mind that these only cover a relatively small part of the region, and that the remaining areas constitute a 'matrix', itself of great natural history interest and environmental sensitivity. Equally important, conservationists must not shirk from pointing out that the measures which they advocate will be of benefit not just to nature lovers, but to everyone who lives, visits or works in the region. Thus, the R. Bure phosphorus reduction programme will, if successful, lead to a diminution in the rates of bank erosion and siltation, and improve the appearance of the waterscape and the quality of the fishing, as well as safeguard a host of aquatic plants and animals, many of which are nationally rare and endangered. But to get this message across, conservationists will need, not only to increase their expenditure on nature reserve management, thus demonstrating to other landowners in the region what can be achieved, and how, but continue to ensure by good 'interpretation' that the public's interest and support for conservation, is maintained. The more successful they are in this, the easier it will be for the statutory and commercial organizations concerned, to respond to the 'political' pressures being exercised on them, by extending the scope of the measures they are already taking to enhance the environmental quality of the region. The need for a strong 'green' lobby is increased by the present Government's determination to reduce public expenditure, and its dubious record in relation to environmental issues.

The Broadland scenario has already begun to be affected by the passing of the *Water Act* 1989, and the consequent establishment of the privatized company, known as Anglian Water Services Ltd., and the National Rivers Authority. The new arrangements have resolved a major anomaly created by the *Water Act* 1973, wherein the AWA was expected to regulate water quality despite the fact that its own sewage treatment works were a major source of pollutants. In addition, all three organizations now having responsibilities for water in the region (i.e. the National Rivers Authority, Anglian Water Services and the East Anglian Water Company) are required under Section 8(1) of the new Act to . . . "further the conservation and enhancement of natural beauty and the conservation of flora, fauna and geological and physiological features of special interest" insofar as this objective is consistent with their other duties. The ways in which this conservation clause are to be implemented are set out in a Code of Practice (DoE *et al.*, 1989), and the provisions of this are already beginning to have beneficial results. So, too, are various other clauses in the Act. For instance, although a farmer who is prosecuted for an illicit discharge of farm wastes will be able to plead in mitigation that he adhered to the Code of Good Agricultural Practice on the subject, he will no longer be able to cite this as an absolute defence.

The omens for Broadland are now favourable in many other respects. Evidence for this comes from the general acceptance of the provisions of the Broads Plan (see page 427), the widespread recognition that Broadland is one of the most important wetland complexes in Britain, and the enormously encouraging interest now being taken in

THE LAND USE, ECOLOGY AND CONSERVATION OF BROADLAND

conservation. Symptomatic of this is the rise in the RSPB's adult membership from about 7000 in 1955, to 117950 in 1973 and to 760000 at the beginning of 1991. But perhaps most important of all, the setting up under the *Norfolk and Suffolk Broads Act 1988* of a powerful new authority in the region, provides a basis for much greater optimism now than seemed possible in the early 1970s.

References

Akeroyd, A.V. (1972) Archaeological and historical evidence for subsidence in southern Britain. *Phil. Trans. R. Soc.*, A, **272**, 151–169.

Allard, P.R. (1973) Bewick's Swans in south-east Norfolk. Norfolk Bird Report for 1971. *Trans. Norf. Norw. Nat. Soc.*, **22** (5), 340.

Allard, P.R. (1987) Breydon Water Tern Platforms. Norfolk Bird Report for 1986. *Trans. Norf. Norw. Nat. Soc.*, **27** (6), 408–409.

Allard, P.R. (1988) Breydon Water: a century of protection. Norfolk Bird Report for 1987. *Trans. Norf. Norw. Nat. Soc.*, **28** (2), 87–88.

Allen, A.A. (1984) A fourth locality for *Microvelia umbricola* Wrobl. (Hem. Veliidae). *Entomologist's mon. Mag.*, **120**, p. 183.

Allison, K.J. (1955) *The wool supply and the worsted cloth industry in Norfolk in the sixteenth and seventeenth centuries. Pt.1: Sheep farming and wool production.* Ph.D. thesis, University of Leeds.

Allison, K.J. (1957) The sheep-corn husbandry of Norfolk in the sixteenth and seventeenth centuries. *Agric. Hist. Rev.*, **5**, 12–30.

Allport, G. (1989) Norfolk's Bean Geese and their management. *RSPB Cons. Rev.*, **3**, 59–60.

Alsop, A.G. (1977) *Calthorpe Broad: Report on Water Situation.* 7 pp. report (unpublished) commissioned by the Nature Conservancy Council, Norwich.

Alsop, A.G. (1981) *Brograve and Eastfield Pump Outfalls.* 3 pp. report (unpublished) commissioned by the Broads Authority, Norwich.

Anglia 2000 (1989) *The Anglia Report*, Issue No. 1, Cambridge.

Anglian Water Authority (1979a) *Report on preliminary fisheries surveys carried out in Broadland during the period July 1977 – June 1978.* Report no. NSRD FSR 4/79, Norwich.

Anglian Water Authority (1979b) *Progress report on the Fisheries Survey of the River Ant and Barton Broad – 1979.* Report No. NSRD FSR 5/79, Norwich

Anglian Water Authority (1979–1987) *Reports on fisheries surveys carried out in Broadland*:

> The navigable R. Ant upstream of Barton Broad — June/July 1979. NSRD FSR 1/80.
>
> The R. Ant downstream of Barton Broad — August/October 1979. NSRD FSR 2/80.
>
> Barton Broad — July/October 1979. NSRD FSR 3/80.
>
> Barton Broad and the R. Ant — January 1980. NSRD FSR 4/80.

The R. Thurne — June 1980. NSRD FSR 1/81.

Heigham Sound (R. Thurne catchment) — July 1980. NSRD FSR 2/81.

Hickling Broad (R. Thurne catchment) — August/October 1980. NSRD FSR 3/81.

Horsey Mere (R. Thurne catchment) — September 1980. NSRD FSR 4/81.

R. Thurne catchment — January/February 1981. NSRD FSR 5/81.

Wroxham and Salhouse Broads (R. Bure catchment) — June/July 1981. NSRD FSR 6/81.

Tidal R. Bure (Belaugh to Acle) and Wroxham and Salhouse Broads — February/March 1982. NSRD FSR2/82.

Ranworth Broad — June/July 1984. ND/FSR/12/84.

South Walsham Broad — July 1984. ND/FSR/1/85.

Oulton Broad — July/August 1984. ND/FSR/2/85.

Rockland Broad — August/September 1984. ND/FSR/3/85.

The tidal R. Yare (inc. the tidal sections of the Rivers Wensum and Chet) — September 1984. ND/FSR/4/85.

The tidal R. Waveney — November 1984. ND/FSR/5/85.

The tidal R. Bure — August 1985. ND/FSR/13/85.

Barton Broad and the navigable R. Ant — July 1985. ND/FSR/1/86.

The tidal R. Yare — September 1985. ND/FSR/3/86.

Breydon Water — October 1987. ND/FSR/4/88.

Anglian Water Authority (1981) *Water Resource Planning Working Party No. IV (Norfolk and Suffolk) First Report.* 54 pp. Norwich.

Anglian Water (1985) *Regional Fish Biomass Map.* Fisheries Annual Report No. 2, 1984–85. Huntingdon.

Anglian Water (1986) *River Ant and Barton Broad: Summary of Research 1983–1985.* 10 pp. Norwich Division.

Anglian Water (1987) *Control of Prymnesium in the River Thurne system, Norfolk.* 9 pp. Norwich Division.

Anglian Water (1988) *Research being carried out by Anglian Water.* 7 pp. report (unpublished) prepared for Annual Conservation Liaison Meeting on 25 March, 1988. Norwich Division.

Angus, R.B. (1976) A preliminary note on the British species of *Graphoderus* Sturm, with the additions of *G. bilineatus* Degeer and *G. zonatus* Hoppe to the British list. *Balfour-Browne Newsletter*, **1**, 1–3.

Anon (1934) Confidential Brief for members of a deputation from the East Norfolk Rivers Catchment Board to the Ministry of Agriculture and the Board of Trade concerning the erosion of the banks of the R. Yare by commercial boat traffic. A copy was found amongst the papers of the late L. Hector Read (one-time Chairman of the GYPHC) and made available to the author by his son, Bryan.

Anon (1986a) Net tightens on organotins. *Ends*, No. 142, 6.

Anon (1986b) Wildfowlers may lose shooting if RSPB proposal agreed. News item in *Shooting Times*, 17 December, 1986.

Apling, H. (1984) *Norfolk Corn Windmills.* 377 pp. Norfolk Windmills Trust, Norwich.

Armstrong, M.J. (1781) *The history and antiquities of the county of Norfolk.* Vols. 1 & 4. Crouse, Norwich.

Ashford, P.L. & Martins, R.M. (1988) *A study of the relationship between boat wash and hull form.* Addendum to BARS 12 – Boat Wash Study. BARS 12A. 126 pp. Broads Authority, Norwich.

Ashbourne, T. (1989) The Ice Trade. *Yarmouth Archaeology: 1989*, 16–27.

Ashbourne, T. (1990) The Ice Trade. *Yarmouth Archaeology: 1990*, 53.

Atkin, M. (1983) The chalk tunnels of Norwich. *Norwich Archaeology*, **38** (3), 313–320.

Ayers, B. (1983) *Digging under the Doorstep: Recent excavations in Norwich.* 32 pp. Norfolk Museums Service, Norwich.

Ayers, B. (1985) Fishergate: Norwich, 1985. *NARG News*, **42**, 1–6.

Ayers, B. (1987) Excavations at St. Martin-at-Palace Plain, Norwich, 1981. *East Anglian Archaeology*. Report No. 37. 191 pp.

Ayers, B. & Murphy, P. (1983) A Waterfront Excavation at Whitefriars Street Car Park, Norwich, 1979. *East Anglian Archaeology*, Report No. 17, 1–60.

Babington, G.C. (1890) *Flora of Cambridgeshire*. 327 pp. Van Voorst, London.

Bacon, R.N. (1844) *The report on the agriculture of Norfolk, to which the prize was awarded by the Royal Agricultural Society of England*. 412 pp. Ridgeways, Chapman & Hall, London.

Baker, L. (1983) Breakdown of Swan deaths, 1982. *Swan Rescue Newsletter*, Winter–Spring 1983. Sparham, Norfolk.

Baker, L. & Milsom, R. (1988) *So, you want to go fishing?* 56 pp. Marlon Publications, Shotesham.

Baker, R.E. (1985) Norfolk Duck Decoys. *Trans. Norf. Norw. Nat. Soc.*, **27** (1), 1–8.

Baldwin, M.W. (1975) *The Norfolk Broads: an investigation into national park designation*. 142 pp. M.A. thesis, University of Nottingham.

Balfour-Browne, F. (1905) A study of the aquatic Coleoptera and their surroundings in the Norfolk Broads district. *Trans. Norf. Norw. Nat. Soc.*, **8** (1), 58–82.

Balls, H., Moss, B. & Irvine, K. (1985) The effects of high nutrient loading on interactions between aquatic plants and phytoplankton. *Verh. int. Verein. theor. angew. Limnol.*, **22**, 2912–2915.

Balls, H.R., Moss, B. & Irvine, K.A. (1989) The loss of submerged plants with eutrophication. 1. Experimental design, water chemistry, aquatic plant and phytoplankton biomass in experiments carried out in ponds in the Norfolk Broadland. *Freshwat. Biol.*, **22**, 71–87.

Barfield, A. (1985) Letter in *Farmers' Weekly*, February 1, 1985.

Barringer, J.C. (1971) Hickling: some thoughts upon its topography. *Broads Soc. Bull.*, January 1971, 6–7.

Barringer, J.C. (1973) *An Introduction to Faden's map of Norfolk*. 16 pp. Norfolk Record Society, Norwich.

Barry, D.H. & Jermy, A.C. (1953) Observations on *Najas marina. Trans. Norf. Norw. Nat. Soc.*, **17** (4), 294–297.

Baxter, A.J. (1988) *The abundance and distribution of invertebrates on the north mudflats of Breydon Water and their relevance to the distribution of estuarine birds*. 27 pp. Student dissertation, University of East Anglia, Norwich.

Bell, M.G.W. & Jones, F.H. (1979) *Possible Effects of Phosphorus on Algal Growth in Barton Broad and Related Control Measures*. Institute of Water Pollution Control. Annual Conference, September 1979. Paper No. 2. 16 pp. Maidstone, Kent.

Bennett, A. (1883) On *Najas marina* as a British plant. *J. Bot.*, **21**, 353.

Bennett, A. (1884) Plants new to Norfolk, with notes on other species. *Trans. Norf., Norw. Nat. Soc.*, **3** (5), 633–636.

Bennett, A. (1905) Distribution of *Sonchus palustris*, L., and *Atriplex pedunculata*, L., in England. *Trans. Norf. Norw. Nat. Soc.*, **8** (1), 35–43.

Bennett, A. (1910) *Naias marina*, L. and *Chara stelligera*, Bauer, as Norfolk plants. *Trans. Norf. Norw. Nat. Soc.*, **9** (1), 47–50.

Berge Henegouwen, A.L. van (1988) *Hydrochus megaphallus*, a new and widespread European water beetle described from the Netherlands (Coleoptera: Hydrophilidae). *Balfour-Browne Club Newsletter*, **42**, 18–21.

Bibby, D.J. & Lunn, J. (1982) Conservation of reed beds and their avifauna in England and Wales. *Biol. Cons.*, **23**, 167–186.

Bingham, S.P. (1983) *A guide to the development of grants for Agriculture and Horticulture for England and Wales: 1940–1982*. Economics Division III., MAFF, London.

Binnie & Partners (1991) A flood alleviation strategy for Broadland. Initial Consultation Document. 10 pp. National Rivers Authority, Ipswich.

Bird, M.C.H. (1909) The rural economy, sport and natural history of East Ruston Common. *Trans. Norf. Norw. Nat. Soc.*, **8** (5), 631–666.

Bird, M.C.H. (1919) The hailstorm of July 14, 1917. *Trans. Norf. Norw. Nat. Soc.*, **10** (4), 356–360.

Bird, M.C.H. (1922) The Drought of 1921. *Trans. Norf. Norw. Nat. Soc.*, **11** (3), 241–253.

Birks, H.H. (1976) The history of the flora and fauna of East Anglia. In: *Nature in Norfolk – a heritage in Trust* (ed. Norfolk Naturalists' Trust), pp. 48–61. Jarrold, Norwich.

Bishop, C.T., Aney, E.F.L.J. & Gorham, P.R. (1959) Isolation and identification of the fast death factor in *Microcystis aeruginosa. Can. J. Biochem. Physiol.*, **37**, 453–471.

Blake, J.H. (1890) The geology of the country near Yarmouth and Lowestoft. *Mem. Geol. Surv. U.K.*, 101 pp. HMSO, London.

Blomefield, F. (1805–1810) *An essay towards a topographical history of the County of Norfolk*. Vols. 1–11. Miller, London.

Boar, R.R. & Crook, C.E. (1985) Investigations into the causes of reedswamp regression in the Norfolk Broads. *Verh. int. Verein. theor. angew. Limnol.*, **22**, 2916–2919.

Boar, R.R., Crook, C.E. & Moss, B. (1984) *The decline of reedswamp in the Norfolk Broadland: the importance of rhizome structure*. BARS 10. 70 pp. Broads Authority, Norwich.

Boardman, E.T. (1940) The development of a Broadland estate at How Hill, Ludham, Norfolk. *Trans. Norf. Norw. Nat. Soc.*, **15** (1), 5–21.

Bolingbroke, H. (1965) Native River Craft of the Broads. In: *The Broads* (ed. E.A. Ellis), pp. 260–265. Collins, London.

Bonham, A.J. (1980) *Bank protection using emergent plants against boat wash in rivers and canals*. Report No. IT 206. Hydraulics Research Station, Wallingford.

Bonser, K.J. (1970) *The Drovers*. 256 pp. Macmillan, London.

Boorman, L.A. & Fuller, R.M. (1981) The changing status of reedswamp in the Norfolk Broads. *J. appl. Ecol.*, **18**, 241–269.

Boorman, L.A., Fuller, R.M. & Boar, R.R. (1979) *Recent changes in the distribution of reedswamp in Broadland*. Final Report on Project No. 605. Institute of Terrestrial Ecology, Colney Research Station, Norwich.

Boorman, L.A., Goss-Custard, J.D. & McGrorty, S. (1989) *Climatic change, rising sea level and the British Coast*. Institute of Terrestrial Ecology Research Publication No. 1. 24 pp. HMSO, London.

Boorman, L.A., Sheail, J. & Fuller, R.M. (1977) *The Phragmites die-back problem*. Contract Report to the Nature Conservancy Council. Institute of Terrestrial Ecology, Colney Research Station, Norwich.

Borland, E.D. (1976) Outbreak of botulism in reared East Anglian pheasants. *Vet. Rec.*, **99** (11), 220–221.

Borland, E.D., Moryson, G.R. & Smith, G.R. (1977) Avian botulism and the high prevalence of *Clostridium botulinum* in the Norfolk Broads. *Vet. Rec.*, **100** (6), 106–109.

Bower, P.J.A. (1989) Norfolk Wherries. *The Harnser* (Journal of the Broads Society), Spring, 1989, 15–19.

Bowers, J.K. (1978) *The Yare Basin Flood Control Study*. Report (unpublished) commissioned by the Norfolk Naturalists' Trust, Norwich.

Bowers, J.K. (1983) Cost-benefit analysis of wetland drainage. *Envir. & Plann.* A, **15**, 227–235.

Bowers, J.K. & Cheshire, P. (1983) *Agriculture, the Countryside and Land Use*. 170 pp. Methuen, London.

Bowler, D.C. (1971) *A survey of the Prymnesium problem*. Report No. 1 LR 94. Water Research Association, Medmenham.

Bretherton, R.F. (1951) The early history of the swallow-tail butterfly (*Papilio machaon* L.) in England. *Entomologist's Rec. J. Var.*, **3**, 206–210.

Brix, H. (1987) Treatment of wastewater in the rhizosphere of wetland plants – the root-zone method. *Water Sci. Technol.*, **19**, 107–118.

Broadland Friends of the Earth (1984) *Evidence to the House of Commons Environment Committee on the operation and effectiveness of the Wildlife and Countryside Act 1981*. Norwich.

Broads Authority (1980–1989) Abstracts of Accounts for the financial years ended 31 March 1980 to 31 March 1989. Norwich.

Broads Authority (1982a) *Report of the Ecology Working Group*. BASMP 5. 68 pp. Norwich.

Broads Authority (1982b) *Report of the Landscape Working Group*. BASMP 6. 34 pp. Norwich.

Broads Authority (1982c) *Report of the Recreation Working Group*. BASMP 7. 66 pp. Norwich.

Broads Authority (1982d) *Report of the Information and Interpretation Working Group*. BASMP 8. 38 pp. Norwich.

Broads Authority (1982e) *What future for Broadland? A draft Strategy and Management Plan*. 115 pp. Norwich.

Broads Authority (1984) *Broadland Research Register 1984*. BARS 7. 136 pp. Norwich.

Broads Authority (1985) *Potter Heigham Bridge Local Plan*. BAPD 5. 101 pp. Norwich.

Broads Authority (1987a) *Broads Plan*. 128 pp. Norwich.

Broads Authority (1987b) *Annual Report for 1986–87*. 72 pp. Norwich.

Broads Authority (1988) *Broadland Research Register 1988*. BARS 7a. 83 pp. Norwich.

Broads Authority (1991) *Annual Report for 1989–1990*. 22 pp. Norwich.

Broads Consortium (1971) *Broadland Study and Plan*. 83 pp. Norfolk County Council, Norwich.

Broads Hire Boat Federation (1979) *Boat-hire holidays on the Norfolk Broads: their history, present status and the future*. 20 pp. The Norfolk & Suffolk Broads Yacht Owners' Association, Wroxham, and the Broadland Owners' Association, Oulton Broad.

Broads Hire Boat Federation (1983) *What Future for Broadland? The views of the boat hire business*. 22 pp. The Norfolk & Suffolk Broads Yacht Owners' Association, Wroxham, and the Broadland Owners' Association, Oulton Broad.

Broads Hire Boat Federation (1988) *Boat-hire holidays on the Norfolk Broads: their history, present status and the future*. (A revised and updated version of the 1979 Report.) 24 pp. The Norfolk & Suffolk Broads Yacht Owners' Association, Wroxham, and the Broadland Owners' Association, Oulton Broad.

Brooke, J.S. & Turner, R.K. (1989) *A Flood Alleviation Strategy for Broadland: Final Report to the National Rivers Authority (Anglian Region)*. 5 vols. 309 pp. University of East Anglia, Norwich.

Browne, T. (*c.* 1650) *Notes and letters on the natural history of Norfolk, more especially on the birds and fishes*. Ed. by T. Southwell, 1902. Jarrold, Norwich.

Bruce, C.G. (1962) *List of Lepidoptera recorded from the Bure Marshes NNR in 1962*. Report (unpublished) compiled for the Nature Conservancy, Norwich.

Burgess, N.D. & Evans, C.E. (1989) *Management Case Study: the management of reedbeds for birds*. 78 pp. Royal Society for the Protection of Birds, Sandy.

Buttery, B.R. & Lambert, J.M. (1965) Competition between *Glyceria maxima* and *Phragmites communis* in the region of Surlingham Broad. 1. The competition mechanism *J. Ecol.*, **53**, 163–182.

Buxton, A. (1940) The Norfolk sea floods, February 1938. *Trans. Norf. Norw. Nat. Soc.*, 15 (1), 22–34.

Buxton, A. (1941) The Norfolk sea floods, February 1938. General effects of the flood seen in 1940. *Trans. Norf. Norw. Nat. Soc.*, **15** (2), 150–159.

Buxton, A. (1942) The Norfolk sea floods, February 1938. General effects of the flood seen in 1941. *Trans. Norf. Norw. Nat. Soc.*, **15** (3), 259–267.

Buxton, A. (1943) General effects of the February 1938 flood seen in 1942. *Trans. Norf. Norw. Nat. Soc.*, **15** (4), 332–341.

Buxton, A. (1944) General effects of the February 1938 flood seen in 1943. *Trans. Norf. Norw. Nat. Soc.*, **15** (5), 410–419.

Buxton, Lord (1981a) Letter to *The Times*, 12 August, 1981.

Buxton, Lord (1981b) *Draining Broadland: a recipe for conflict and taxpayers involuntary profligacy*. A record of correspondence between Lord Buxton and various Agriculture Ministers at the height of the Halvergate controversy. Privately printed by Lord Buxton.

Bygrave, J., Barber, H., Crosse, A.A.T., Vincent, J., Riches, W. & Wright, W. (1921) The State of Hickling Broad. Letter to the *Eastern Daily Press*, 21 November, 1921.

W.G.C. (1921) Breydon Water: how the birds are protected. *Eastern Daily Press*. 31 March, 1921.

Cadbury, C.J. (1964) *Pelosia obtusa* Herrich-Schaffer (Lep. Arctiidaes), a species overlooked in Britain? *Entomologist's Rec. J. Var.*, **76**, 181–185.

Cadbury, J.C. (1966) Ted Piggin – Guardian of Hickling Broad. In: *39th. Annual Report of the Norfolk Naturalists' Trust*, 38–39. Norwich.

Caird, J. (1852) *English Agriculture in 1850–51*. 550 pp. Longman, Brown, Green & Longmans, London.

Cambridge, P.G. (1978) Report on a field meeting at Dobb's Plantation, Wroxham. *Bull. geol. Soc. Norfolk*, **30**, 77–78.

Campbell, B.M.S. (1983) Agricultural progress in Medieval England: some evidence from Eastern Norfolk. *Econ. Hist. Rev.* 2 ser., **36** (1), 26–46.

Campbell, L.H., ed., Halliday, J.B. & O'Sullivan, J. (1980) *Wintering birds of the Yare marshes*. Report (unpublished) compiled for the RSPB.

Carill-Worsley, P.E.T. (1932) A fur farm in Norfolk. *Trans. Norf. Norw. Nat. Soc.*, **13** (2), 105–115.

Carr, A.P. (1972) Aspects of spit development and decay: the estuary of the R. Ore, Suffolk. *Fld. Stud.*, **3**, No. 4, 633–653.

Carrodus, C.F., ed. (1949) *Life in a Norfolk village: the story of old Horning*. 162 pp. Soman Wherry, Norwich.

Carter, A. (1978) The Anglo-Saxon origins of Norwich: the problems and approaches. *Anglo-Saxon Engl.*, **7.**, 175–204.

Chanin, P.R.F. & Jefferies, D.J. (1978) The decline of the otter *Lutra lutra* L. in Britain: an analysis of hunting records and discussion of causes. *Biol. J. Linnean Soc. Lond.*, **10** (3), 305–328.

Charter, E. (1975) *Hoveton Great Broad Nature Trail: Visitor Survey*. Report (unpublished) commissioned by the Nature Conservancy Council, Norwich.

Cherry, G.I. (1975) *Environmental Planning 1939–1969: Vol. II, National Parks and Recreation in the countryside*. HMSO, London.

Clapham, A.R., Tutin, T.G. & Moore, D.M. (1989) *Flora of the British Isles*. Third Edition (paperback). 688 pp. Cambridge University Press.

Clark, R. (1961) *Black-sailed Traders*. 264 pp. Putnam, London.

Clarke, K.B. (1989) Marine diatoms at Horning. *The Norfolk Natterjack* (Quarterly bulletin of the Norfolk and Norwich Naturalists' Society), No. 27, 4–5.

Coles, B.P.L. (1977) *The Holocene foraminifera and palaeogeography of Central Broadland*. Ph.D. thesis, University of East Anglia.

Coles, B.P.L. and Funnell, B.M. (1981) Holocene palaeoenvironments of Broadland, England . *Spec. Publs. int. Ass. Sediment*, **5**, 123–131.

Colman, D., Lee, N., Russel, N. & Lee, D. (1988) *Evaluation of the Broads Grazing Marshes Conservation Scheme 1985–88*. Final Report to the Countryside Commission. 220 pp. Department of Agricultural Economics, University of Manchester.

Cooke, G.W. (1976) A Review of the Effects of Agriculture on the Chemical Composition and Quality of Surface and Underground Waters. *Tech. Bull. Minist. Agric. Fish Fd.*, **32**, 5–55. HMSO, London.

Cornford, B. (1979) The Sea Breach Commission in East Norfolk: 1609–1743. *Norfolk Archaeology*, **37** (2), 137–145.

Cornford, B. (1982) Weather and Water Levels in Flegg in the Fourteenth century. *Bull. Norf. Res. Ctte.*, **27**, 10–13.

Cotton, K.E. (1953) Flood Damage in Norfolk and Suffolk. In: *North Sea Floods Conference*, pp. 11–15. Institution of Civil Engineers, London.

Cotton, K.E. (1963) The Coypu. *River Board Assoc. Yb.*, **11**, 31–39.

Cotton, K.E. (1969) Statement made on behalf of the East Suffolk and Norfolk River Authority at the public inquiry held in Norwich in September, 1969, concerning the proposals by the Gt. Yarmouth Port and Haven Commissioners to extend the speed limits on the Broadland waterways.

Council for Nature, Nature Conservancy & Royal Society of Arts (1970) Proceedings of the 'Countryside in 1970' Third Conference. 193 pp. Royal Society of Arts, London.

Countryside Commission (1976) *The Broads: A Consultation paper*. 4 pp. Cheltenham.

Countryside Commission (1977) *The Broads: Possible courses of action*. CCP 104. 26 pp. Cheltenham.

Countryside Commission (1979) *The Broads: comment and decision*. CCP 119. 22 pp. Cheltenham.

Countryside Commission (1981) *The Broads: a statement*. 1 p. Cheltenham.

Countryside Commission (1983a) *The Broads: a review. A Consultation Document*. CCP 158. 38 pp. Cheltenham.

Countryside Commission (1983b) *Broads Review: Policy Statement*. 2 pp. Cheltenham.

Countryside Commission (1984) *The Broads: a review. Conclusions and recommendations*. 68 pp. Cheltenham.

Countryside Commission and Ministry of Agriculture, Fisheries and Food (1988) *Broads Grazing Marshes Conservation Scheme: 1985–1988*. CCD 20. 29 pp. Countryside Commission, Cheltenham.

Cowan & Sons Ltd. (1920) Letter, dated 31 March, 1920, addressed to Professor F.W. Oliver of University College, London. Copies in the possession of the author and in the reference collection, Nature Conservancy Council, Norwich.

Cramp, S. (1963) Toxic chemicals and birds of prey. *Brit. Birds*, **56**, 124–138.

Crompton, G. (1977) *Survey of rare plants in East Anglia: Liparis*. Vol. 6 — Norfolk. Vol. 13 — Suffolk. Reports (unpublished) commissioned by the Nature Conservancy Council, Norwich.

Crook, B. (1988) *Salty death for Broadland fish*. Water Bulletin 15 April, 1988. Anglian Water Authority, Huntingdon.

Crook, C.E., Boar, R.R. & Moss, B. (1983) *The decline of reedswamp in the Norfolk Broadland: causes, consequences and solutions*. BARS 6. 132 pp. Broads Authority, Norwich.

Crook, C.E. & Boar, R.R. (1984) Investigations into the causes of reedswamp decline in Norfolk Broadland. *Norfolk Naturalists' Trust, Annual Report for 1983*, pp. 34–38. Norwich.

Cryer, M., Peirson, G. & Townsend, C.R. (1986) Reciprocal interactions between roach, *Rutilus rutilus*, and zooplankton in a small lake: prey dynamics and fish growth and recruitment. *Limnol. Oceanogr.*, **31** (5), 1022–1038.

Cubitt, W. (1922) Second report to the Committee appointed for taking into consideration the best means of opening a navigable communication from Norwich to the Sea . . . *Norfolk Chronicle and Norwich Gazette*, 26 August, 1822.

W.A.D. (1931) Letter to the *Eastern Evening News*, 10 October, 1931.

Daniels, G.E. (1982) *Amalgamation Schemes*. A statement produced by the Chairman of the Muckfleet and South Flegg IDB. August 1982. Norwich.

Darby, A. (1982) *A study of the water regime of Rockland Broad, Norfolk*. Unpublished thesis: University of Cambridge.

Darby, H.C. (1971) *The Domesday Geography of Eastern England*. 400 pp. Cambridge University Press, London.

Davies, G.C. (1884) *Norfolk Broads and Rivers*. 328 pp. Blackwood, London.

Davies, H.C. (1930) Tides of the River Bure. *Trans. Norf. Norw. Nat. Soc.*, **13** (1), 14–22.

Davis, R.A. (1956) The Coypu. *Agriculture*, **63**, 127–129.

Davis, R.A. (1963) Feral coypus in Britain. *Ann. appl. Biol.*, **5**, 345–348.

Day, J. (1983) The Bittern and Marsh Harrier in Norfolk. *Annual Report of the Norfolk Naturalists' Trust for 1982*, pp. 30–32. Norwich.

Defoe, D. (1722) *A tour through the Eastern Counties*. 135 pp. Republished in 1949 by East Anglian Magazine Ltd., Ipswich.

Dempster, J.P., King, M.L. & Lakhani, K.H. (1976) The status of the swallowtail butterfly in Britain. *Ecol. Entomol.*, **1**, 71–84.

Dent, D.L. (1984) An introduction to acid sulphate soils and their occurrence in East Anglia. In : *Soil Acidification in SE England* (ed. C.P. Burnham & A.J. Moffat). *Seesoil*, **2**, 35–51.

Denyer-Green, B. (1983) *Wildlife and Countryside Act 1981: The Practitioner's Companion*. 265 pp. Surveyor's Publications, London.

Department of the Environment (1971) *Local Government in England. Government proposals for Reorganisation*. White Paper. Cmnd 4584. HMSO, London.

Department of the Environment (1974) *Report of the National Parks Policies Review Committee*. Chairman: Lord Sandford. HMSO, London.

Department of the Environment (1976) *Report of the National Parks Policies Review Committee*. (The Government's conclusions.) Circular 4/76. HMSO, London.

Department of the Environment (1986) *Protecting the Countryside: the Government's consultative proposals for Landscape Conservation Orders*. DoE, London.

Department of the Environment Central Directorate of Environmental Protection (1986) *Nitrate in Water*. Pollution Paper No. 26. 104 pp. HMSO, London.

Department of the Environment, Ministry of Agriculture, Fisheries and Food and the Welsh Office (1989) *The Water Act 1989: Code of Practice on Conservation, Access and Recreation*. 39 pp. DoE, London.

Departmental Committee on the Protection of Birds (1919) *Report and Minutes of Evidence* (Home Office). Cmd. 189 & Cmd. 295. HMSO, London.

De Salis, H.D. (1904) *Bradshaw's Canals and Navigable Rivers of England and Wales.* 480 pp. Blacklock, London.

Doarks, C. (1980) *Botanical survey of marsh dykes in Broadland.* BARS 2. 52 pp. Broads Authority, Norwich.

Doarks, C. (1984) *A study of marsh dykes in Broadland.* BARS 9. 136 pp. Broads Authority, Norwich.

Doarks, C. (1990) *Changes in the flora of grazing marsh dykes in Broadland between 1972–74 and 1988–89.* 24 pp. England Field Unit Report (unpublished). Nature Conservancy Council, Peterborough.

Doarks, C. & Leach, S.J. (1990) *A classification of grazing marsh dyke vegetation in Broadland.* England Field Unit Report. Nature Conservancy Council, Peterborough.

Doarks, C., Leach, S.J., Storer, J., Reid, S.A.J., Newlands, C. & Kennison, G.C.B. (1990) *An atlas of the flora of grazing marsh dykes in Broadland.* England Field Unit Report. Nature Conservancy Council, Peterborough.

Doarks, C. & Storer, J. (1990) *A botanical survey and evaluation of grazing marsh dyke systems in Broadland, 1988–1989.* England Field Unit Report. Natura Conservancy Council, Peterborough.

Drane, A.J. (1979) *A survey of the Coleopteran fauna of Hickling Broad nature reserve.* Report (unpublished) commissioned by the Nature Conservancy Council, Norwich.

Driscoll, R.J. (1975) *Factors affecting the status of aquatic macrophytes in drainage dykes in Broadland, Norfolk.* 4 pp. Report (unpublished) commissioned by the Nature Conservancy Council, Norwich.

Driscoll, R.J. (1976) *Broadland Dyke Survey (maps).* CST Report No. 139. 8 microfiches. Nature Conservancy Council, Norwich.

Driscoll, R.J. (1978) A preliminary report on the distribution of water beetles in Broadland dykes. *Balfour-Browne Club Newsletter,* **8,** 3–14.

Driscoll, R.J. (1981a) *Improvements in land management: their effects on aquatic plants. A preliminary report on the effects of changes in land use and drainage on the diversity and species composition of the dyke flora in the Thurne catchment, 1973–1981.* 7 pp. Report (unpublished) commissioned by the Nature Conservancy Council, Norwich.

Driscoll, R.J. (1981b) *Distribution maps of aquatic macrophytes, bryophytes and algae recorded from drainage dykes in Happisburgh–Winterton IDB sub-areas 1 and 2, Summer 1974.* 73 pp. Report (unpublished) commissioned by the Nature Conservancy Council, Norwich.

Driscoll, R.J. (1981c) *Distribution maps of aquatic macrophytes, bryophytes and algae recorded from drainage dykes in Happisburgh–Winterton IDB sub-areas 1 and 2, Summer 1981.* 69 pp. Report (unpublished) commissioned by the Nature Conservancy Council, Norwich.

Driscoll, R.J. (1981d) *Distribution maps of aquatic vertebrates and invertebrates recorded from drainage dykes in Happisburgh–Winterton IDB sub-areas 1 and 2, Summer 1974.* 95 pp. Report (unpublished) commissioned by the Nature Conservancy Council, Norwich.

Driscoll, R.J. (1982) *Distribution maps of aquatic vertebrates and invertebrates recorded from drainage dykes in Happisburgh–Winterton IDB sub-areas 1 and 2, Summer 1981.* 89 pp. Report (unpublished) commissioned by the Nature Conservancy Council, Norwich.

Driscoll, R.J. (1983a) Improvements in land management: their effects on aquatic plants in Broadland. *Watsonia,* **14** (3), 276–277.

Driscoll, R.J. (1983b) *Land use surveys in Broadland: an inventory of surveys carried out between 1931–1934 and 1982.* Although unpublished, copies are kept at the Castle Museum (Norwich), Nature Conservancy Council (Norwich), Norfolk County Council, University of East Anglia, Broads Authority, Monks Wood Experimental Station and several other places. A supplement was produced in 1984.

Driscoll, R.J. (1983c) *A preliminary classification of Broadland dyke vegetation using TWINSPAN.* CST Notes No. 35. 46 pp. Nature Conservancy Council, Peterborough.

Driscoll, R.J. (1983d) Broadland dykes: the loss of an important wildlife habitat. *Trans. Norf. Norw. Nat. Soc.,* **26**(3), 170–172.

Driscoll, R.J. (1984a) *Chloride ion concentrations in dyke water in the Thurne catchment area in 1974 and 1983.* 62 pp. Report (unpublished) prepared for the Nature Conservancy Council, Norwich.

Driscoll, R.J. (1984b) The dyke vegetation at Oby and Thurne: a comparison of late 19th century and recent records. *Trans. Norf. Norw. Nat. Soc.*, **26** (1), 43–49.

Driscoll, R.J. (1984c) *Aeshna isosceles (Mull.): a survey of some Broadland sites, 8–10 July 1983*. 13 pp. Report (unpublished) produced for the Nature Conservancy Council, Norwich.

Driscoll, R.J. (1984d) Changes in land use in the Thurne catchment area during the period 1931–2 to 1973. *Trans. Norf. Norw. Nat. Soc.*, **26** (5), 282–290.

Driscoll, R.J. (1985a) Floating Water-plaintain, *Luronium natans*, in Norfolk. *Trans. Norf. Norw. Nat. Soc.*, **27** (1), 43–44.

Driscoll, R.J. (1985b) The effect of changes in land management on the dyke flora at Somerton and Winterton. *Trans. Norf. Norw. Nat. Soc.*, **27** (1), 33–41.

Driscoll, R.J. (1985c) *Distribution maps of aquatic invertebrates and aquatic plants recorded from the rivers Bure and Yare, 1982*. Report (subject to limited distribution) commissioned by the Nature Conservancy Council, Norwich.

Driscoll, R.J. (1986) The effect of changes in land management on the dyke fauna at Somerton and Winterton. *Trans Norf. Norw. Nat Soc.*, **27** (3), 215–220.

Driscoll, R.J. & Lees, A.J. (1973) *The Thurne catchment area: a survey of land use, drainage and the flora and fauna of drainage dykes*. 78 pp. Report (unpublished) commissioned by the Nature Conservancy Council, Norwich.

Duffey, E. (1964) The Norfolk Broads. A regional study of wild life conservation in a wetland area with high tourist attraction. *Proceedings of the MAR Conference – November 12/16, 1962*. IUCN Publ., New Ser. 3, Pt 1/C, 290–301. IUCN.

Duffey, E.A.G. (1965) Spiders of the Broads. In: *The Broads* (ed. E.A. Ellis), pp. 171–178. Collins, London.

Dunning, E.D. (1981) 'U' Values — a comparison between conventional roofing and thatching. *Thatching Newsletter*, November 1981, 13. Council for Small Industries in Rural Areas.

Dutt, W.A. (1903) *The Norfolk Broads*. 379 pp. Methuen, London.

Dutt, W.A. (1906) *Wild Life in East Anglia*. 370 pp. Methuen, London.

Dyson, C. (1982) Swans: Anglers' Defence. *Eastern Daily Press*, 22 January, 1982.

Dyson, C. (1985) Secrecy as pike record is broken. *Eastern Daily Press*, 16 February, 1985.

East Anglia Economic Planning Council (1977) *Seaports in East Anglia*. 27 pp. Norwich.

Eastern Daily Press (1908) Report of case heard at Swainsthorpe Petty Sessions concerning fishing rights in Rockland Broad, and its ownership. 9 May, 1908.

Eastern Daily Press (1909) Norwich Sewerage Scheme – the story of an old trouble. 15 July, 1909.

Eastern Daily Press (1922a) East Norfolk Drainage. Report on a conference to consider the setting up of an 'East Norfolk Drainage Board'. 16 September, 1922.

Eastern Daily Press (1922b) Prolific weed checked. 16 December, 1922.

Eastern Daily Press (1924) Report of case heard at the Norwich Shirehall concerning the fishing rights over Wroxham Broad. 15 September, 1924.

Eastern Daily Press (1925) Analysis of Hickling weed. 11 November, 1925.

Eastern Daily Press (1936) Norfolk Reeds for Paper. 14 March, 1936.

Eastern Daily Press (1938) Reports on sea flood at Horsey. 14 & 15 February. 1938.

Eastern Daily Press (1948) Restoring the Broads. 10 July, 1948.

Eastern Daily Press (1952a) Doing Utmost to avoid disaster at Harbour. *29 March, 1952*.

Eastern Daily Press (1952b) Rockland Broad open to river traffic. 6 August, 1952.

Eastern Daily Press (1954a) Cargo vessel at Beccles for first time in 14 years. 16 February, 1954.

Eastern Daily Press (1954b) Proposal to close Haddiscoe Cut. 27 November, 1954.

Eastern Daily Press (1957a) The Cut Reprieved. 26 July, 1957.

Eastern Daily Press (1957b) High Level Bridge for Haddiscoe Cut. 26 November, 1957.

Eastern Daily Press (1975) Sutton Staithe ownership disputed. 25 April, 1975.

Eastern Daily Press (1978a) The Broads. Editorial: 24 January, 1978.

Eastern Daily Press (1978b) Blueprint for Broads Consortium. 4 March, 1978.

Eastern Daily Press (1981) Water Conflict. Editorial: 26 January, 1981.

Eastern Daily Press (1982) Article and photograph. 12 March, 1982.

Eastern Daily Press (1983) Raising of Wherry *Maud.* 27 June, 1983.

Eastern Daily Press (1984) Bankside haul bigger. 18 September, 1984.

Eastern Daily Press (1985) Norfolk keel is pulled from a watery grave. 30 September, 1985.

Eastern Daily Press (1988a) Rockland Broad. Public Notices. 11 July, 1988.

Eastern Daily Press (1988b) Spare-the-plough scheme successful. 21 December, 1988.

Eastern Evening News (1953) Awe-inspiring savagery of Breydon. 6 February, 1953.

East Suffolk and Norfolk River Authority (1971) *First survey of Water Resources and Demands required under the Water Resources Act 1963*, Vol. 1. 126 pp. Norwich.

Ecclestone, A.W. & Ecclestone, J.L. (1959) *The Rise of Great Yarmouth.* 200 pp. Jarrold, Norwich.

Edmondson, W.T. (1970) Phosphorus, nitrogen and algae in Lake Washington after diversion of sewage. *Science, NY,* **169**, 690–691.

Edmondson, W.T. (1979) Lake Washington and the predictability of limnological events. *Arch. Hydrobiol. beih. ergeb. Limnol.,* **13**, 231–241.

Edmondson, W.T. & Lehman, J.T. (1981) The effect of changes in the nutrient income on the condition of Lake Washington. *Limnol. Oceanogr.,* **26**, 1–29.

Edwards, J. (1981) Protecting the Broads' Heritage. Letter to the *Eastern Daily Press,* 6 February, 1981.

Ellis, A.E. (1965) Mollusca, Woodlice and Harvestmen. In: *The Broads* (ed. E.A. Ellis), pp. 164–171. Collins, London.

Ellis, E.A. (1935) Wheatfen Broad, Surlingham. *Trans. Norf. Norw. Nat. Soc.,* **13** (5), 422–451.

Ellis, E.A. (1951) The introduction of the Large Copper Butterfly *Lycaena dispar batavus* (Oberthür) at Wheatfen Broad. *Trans. Norf. Norw. Nat. Soc.,* **17** (2), 84–89.

Ellis, E.A. (1958). In the Countryside. *Eastern Daily Press,* 21 July, 1958.

Ellis, E.A. (1963) Some effects of selective feeding by the Coypu (*Myocastor coypus*) on the vegetation of Broadland. *Trans. Norf. Norw. Nat. Soc.,* **20** (1), 32–35.

Ellis, E.A. (1965a) Freshwater Polyzoa, Leeches and Insects. In: *The Broads* (ed. E.A. Ellis), pp. 161–164, 179–185 and 312–378. Collins, London.

Ellis, E.A. (1965b) Mammals. In: *The Broads* (ed. E.A. Ellis) pp. 221–230. Collins, London.

Ellis, E.A. (1965c) A note on Broadland marshing tools. In: *The Broads* (ed. E.A. Ellis), pp. 379–380. Collins, London.

Ellis, E.A. (1970a) Nuisance of blanket weeds on the Broads. *Eastern Daily Press,* 7 November, 1970.

Ellis, E.A. (1970b) In the countryside. *Eastern Daily Press,* 9 November, 1970.

Ellis, E.A. (1972) Fen Fleabane may again grow in Broadland. Down Nature's byways. *Eastern Daily Press,* 10 June, 1972.

Ellis, E.A. (1977) Water-crickets being ousted by pollution. *Eastern Daily Press,* 29 October, 1977.

Ellis, E.A. (1984). Traps catch a rare visitor (*Perizoma sagittata*). *Eastern Daily Press,* 11 August, 1984.

Ellis, Sir H., ed. (1859) *Chronica Johannis de Oxenedes.* (In latin) 439 pp. Longman, Brown, Green, Longmans & Roberts, London.

Ellis, S.V. (1967) Parish Staithes. *Broads Soc. Bull.,* Autumn 1967. 3 pp.

Emerson, P.H. (1893) *On English Lagoons.* David Nutt, London.

Eminson, D.F. (1978) A comparison of diatom epiphytes, their diversity and density, attached to *Myriophyllum spicatum* L. in Norfolk dykes and Broads. *Br. Phycol. J.,* **13**, 57–64.

Eminson, D.F. & Moss, B. (1980) The composition and ecology of periphyton communities in freshwaters. 1. The influence of host type and external environment on community composition. *Br. Phycol. J.,* **15**, 429–456.

Eminson, D.F. & Phillips, G.L. (1978). A laboratory experiment to examine the effects of nutrient enrichment on macrophyte and epiphyte growth. *Verh. int. Verein. theor. angew. Limnol.,* **20**, 82–87.

Environmental Resource Management Ltd. & Trans Econ Ltd. (1980) *Proposed Yare Basin Flood Control Barrier — Environmental Impact Assessment.* BARS 1. 111 pp. Broads Authority, Norwich.

Environmental Resource Management Ltd. & Trans Econ Ltd. (1981) *Acid Sulphate Soils in Broadland.* BARS 3. 36 pp. Broads Authority, Norwich.

European Inland Fisheries Advisory Commission (1970) *Water Quality Criteria for European Freshwater Fish: Report on Ammonia and Inland Fisheries.* Technical Paper No. 11. 12 pp. FAO, Rome.

European Inland Fisheries Advisory Commission (1973) *Water Quality Criteria for European Freshwater fish: Report on Dissolved Oxygen and Inland Fisheries.* Technical Paper No. 19. 10 pp. FAO, Rome.

European Inland Fisheries Advisory Commission (1984) *Water Quality Criteria for European Freshwater Fish: Report on Nitrite and Freshwater Fish.* Technical Paper No. 46. 19 pp. FAO, Rome.

Farmers' Weekly (1985) Article on Acid Sulphate Soils, 3 May, 1985.

Farmers' Weekly (1987) Beef Supplement. April 17, 1987.

Fawcett, T. (1977) Thorpe Water Frolic. *Norfolk Archaeology*, **36**, pt. 4, 393–398.

Financial Secretary to the Treasury (1931) *Report of the National Park Committee.* Chairman: Lord Addison. Cmnd. 3851. HMSO, London.

Ford, M.J. & Lamb, H.H. (1976) The climate of East Anglia since historical times. In: *Nature in Norfolk – a Heritage in Trust* (ed. Norfolk Naturalists' Trust). Jarrold, Norwich.

Foster, G.N. (1982) Notes on rare Dytiscidae (Coleoptera) in Norfolk. *Trans. Norf. Norw. Nat. Soc.*, **26** (1), 3–10.

Foster, G.N. (1983) Norfolk – the records. *Balfour-Browne Club Newsletter*, **28**, 9.

Foyster, D. (1988) Lament for Breydon. *Shooting Times and Country Magazine.* February 11–17, p. 22.

Freese, S. (1957) *Windmills and Millwrighting.* 168 pp. Cambridge University Press, London.

Fuller, R.M. (1984) *Vegetation mapping of Broadland using aerial photographs.* Report (unpublished) commissioned by the Broads Authority. Institute of Terrestrial Ecology, Abbots Ripton.

Fuller, R.M. (1986) Taking stock of changing Broadland. II. Status of semi-natural and man-made habitats. *J. Biogeogr.*, **13**, 327–337.

Fuller, R.M., Brown, N.J. & Mountford, M.D. (1986) Taking stock of changing Broadland. I. Air photo interpretation and digital cartography. *J. Biogeogr.*, **13**, 313–326.

Funnell, B.M. (1961) The Palaeogene and early Pleistocene of Norfolk. In: The Geology of Norfolk. *Trans. Norf. Norw. Nat. Soc.*, **19** (6), 340–364.

Funnell, B.M. (1976) Past Environments of East Anglia. In: *Nature in Norfolk – a heritage in Trust* (ed. Norfolk Naturalists' Trust), pp. 29–47. Jarrold, Norwich.

Funnell, B.M. (1979) History and prognosis of subsidence and sea-level change in the Lower Yare valley, Norfolk. *Bull. Geol. Soc. Norfolk*, **31**, 35–44.

Funnel, B.M. and West, R.G. (1977) Preglacial Pleistocene deposits of East Anglia. In: *British Quaternary Studies – recent advances* (ed. F.W. Shotton), pp. 247–265. Oxford.

Gane, J.V. (1976a) Barton Broad – then and now. *Barton Turf Parish Magazine*, 23 March, 1976.

Gane, J.V. (1976b) *Insects (Lepidoptera) taken at Irstead between August 1970 and December 1975.* Unpublished, but copies of this report are held at the Castle Museum and the Nature Conservancy Council, Norwich.

Garrad, P.N. (1987) Sediment flux and bank erosion in a tidal recreational waterway. *Proc. National Hydrology Symposium* held at the University of Hull, Sept. 1987, pp. 24.1–24.20.

Garrad, P.N. & Hey, R.D. (1987) Boat traffic, sediment resuspension and turbidity in a Broadland river. *J. Hydrol.*, **95**, 289–297.

Garrad, P.N. & Hey, R.D. (1988a) The effect of boat traffic on river regime. Paper J1, *International Conference on River Regime*, 18–20 May, pp. 395–409. Wiley, Chichester.

Garrad, P.N. & Hey, R.D. (1988b) River Management to Reduce Turbidity in Navigable Broadland Rivers. *J. environ. Management*, **27**, 273–288.

Gaze, J. (undated) *Extracts from the minute book for 1917–1947.* Langley, Chedgrave and Toft Monks Internal Drainage Board, Loddon, Norfolk.

George, M. (1972) The Conservation of Aquatic Wildlife. *Proceedings of the Health Congress* of the Royal Society of Health held at Eastbourne in April 1972. Paper No. 29/72, pp. 138–141. London.

George, M. (1977) The decline in Broadland's aquatic fauna and flora: a review of the present position. *Trans. Norf. Norw. Nat. Soc.*, **24** (2), 41–53.

George, N.J. (1990) *An evaluation of conservation strategies in an area of Broadland.* M.Sc. thesis. University of North Wales, Bangor.

Giller, K.E. & Wheeler, B.D. (1986a) Past peat cutting and present vegetation patterns in an undrained fen in the Norfolk Broadland. *J. Ecol.*, **74**, 219–247.

Giller, K.E. & Wheeler, B.D. (1986b) Peat and peat water chemistry of a flood-plain fen in Broadland, Norfolk, UK. *Freshwat. Biol.*, **16**, 99–114.

Giller, K.E. & Wheeler, B.D. (1988) Acidification and succession in a flood-plain mire in the Norfolk Broadland, UK. *J. Ecol.*, **76**, 849–866.

Goldsmith, J.G. & Banham, P.R., ed. (1970) Section on Chinese Water Deer in the Norfolk Mammal Report for 1968. *Trans. Norf. Norw. Nat. Soc.*, **21** (5), 346–347.

Goldsworthy, B. (1972) *Horsey Mere: a Chemical Investigation in Four Dimensions.* Unpublished B.Sc. dissertation, University of East Anglia.

Goode, D. (1972) Criteria for selection of peatland nature reserves in Britain. *Proc. 4th. International Peat Congress*, I–IV. Helsinki.

Goode, D. & Ratcliffe, D.A. (1977) Peatlands. In: *A Nature Conservation Review* (ed. D.A. Ratcliffe). Vol. 1, pp. 249–287. Vol. 2, pp. 206–244. Cambridge University Press.

Goodey, C. (1978) 100 years of holidays on the Broads. *Eastern Daily Press*, 25 May, 1978.

Gorton, F.A. & Davies, N. (n.d.) *Riverside Intercepting Sewer.* 22 pp. May Gurney Ltd., Norwich.

Gosling, L.M. (1974) The coypu in East Anglia. Norfolk Mammal Report for 1972. *Trans. Norf. Norw. Nat. Soc.*, **23** (1), 49–59.

Gosling, L.M. (1981a) The dynamics and control of a feral coypu population. In: *The Worldwide Furbearer Conference Proceedings* (ed. J.A. Chapman & D. Pursley), pp. 1806–1825.

Gosling, L.M. (1981b) Climatic determinants of spring littering by feral coypus, *Myocastor coypus. J. Zool.*, **195**, 281–288.

Gosling, L.M. (1985) Coypus in East Anglia (1970 to 1984). Norfolk Mammal Report for 1984. *Trans. Norf. Norw. Nat. Soc.*, **27** (2), 151–153.

Gosling, L.M. (1988) A history of coypus in Britain: 1929 to 1988. Norfolk Mammal Report for 1987. *Trans. Norf. Norw. Nat. Soc.*, **28** (2), 154–157.

Gosling, L.M. & Baker, S.J. (1980) Acidity fluctations at a Broadland site in Norfolk. *J. appl. Ecol.*, **17**, 479–490.

Gosling, L.M. & Baker, S.J. (1987) Planning and monitoring an attempt to eradicate coypus from Britain. *Symp. zool. Soc. Lond.*, **58**, 99–113.

Gosling, L.M., Baker, S.J. & Clarke, C.N. (1988) An attempt to remove coypus (*Myocastor coypus*) from a wetland habitat in East Anglia. *J. appl. Ecol.*, **25**, 49–62.

Gosling, L.M., Baker, S.J. & Skinner, J.R. (1983) A simulation approach to investigating the response of a coypu population to climatic variation. *EPPO Bulletin*, **13**, 183–192.

Gosling, L.M., Watt, A.D. & Baker, S.J. (1981) Continuous retrospective census of the East Anglian coypu population between 1970 and 1979. *J. anim. Ecol.*, **50**, 885–901.

Government Statistical Service (1985) *The United Kingdom in figures.* HMSO, London.

Gowen, B. (1990) *The Norfolk Broads: A Portrait in Old Picture Postcards.* 120 pp. S.B. Publications, Market Drayton.

Graff, J. (1981) An investigation of the Frequency Distributions of Annual Sea Level Maxima at Ports around Great Britain. *Estuarine, Coastal and Shelf Science*, **12**, 389–449.

Grantham, R.B. (1869) A description of the Broads. *Q. Jl. geol. Soc. Lond.*, **25**, 258–259.

Great Yarmouth District Council (1981) *Great Yarmouth Port and South Denes District Plan:* Consultation Document. March, 1981.

Great Yarmouth Port and Haven Commissioners (1959) *The Commissioners' Views on the Report of the Committee of Inquiry into Inland Waterways (The Bowes Report): The Broads Area.* 12 pp. Great Yarmouth.

Great Yarmouth Port and Haven Commissioners (1971) *Memorandum on the Report of the Broads Consortium*. 15 pp. Great Yarmouth.

Green, C. (1961) Broadland Fords and Causeways. *Norfolk Archaeology*, **32**, 316–331.

Green, C. & Hutchinson, J.N. (1960) Archaeological evidence. In: *The Making of the Broads*, pp. 113–146. Research Series no. 3. Royal Geographical Society, London.

Green, C. & Hutchinson, J.N. (1965) Relative land and sea levels at Great Yarmouth, Norfolk. *Geogr. J.*, **131**, pt. 1, 86–90.

Green, R.E. (1986) *The management of lowland wet grassland for breeding waders*. CSD Report on Contract No. HF3/03/291. Nature Conservancy Council, Peterborough.

Gregory, J.W. (1892) The physical features of the Norfolk Broads. *Natural Science*, **1**, 347–355.

Grieve, H. (1959) *The Great Tide*. 883 pp. Essex County Council, Chelmsford.

Griston, J. (1981) *The North Walsham–Dilham Canal*. 27 pp. Cowper Press, Mundesley.

Grove, A.T. (1961) Climate. In: *Norwich and its Region*, Ed. F. Briers for the British Association for the Advancement of Science, pp. 42–43. Jarrold, Norwich.

Grove-White, R.B. (1981) Open questions on Broads drainage. Letter to *The Times*, 17 August, 1981.

Gunn, J. (1864) A sketch of the Geology of Norfolk. *History, Gazeteer and Directory of Norfolk* (ed. W. White), pp. 128–131. Simpkin & Marshall, London.

Gurney, Sir E. (1914) Wild Birds Protection in Norfolk: 1914. *Trans. Norf. Norw. Nat. Soc.*, **9** (5), 765–769.

Gurney, E. & Gurney, R. (1908). The Sutton Broad Freshwater Laboratory. *Annls. Biol. lacustre*, **3**, 1–12.

Gurney, G.H. (1926) Introduction of the Large Copper Butterfly *Chrysophanus rutilus* in Norfolk. *Trans. Norf. Norw. Nat. Soc.*, **12** (2), 262–263.

Gurney, G.H. (1927) The Large Copper Butterfly (*Chrysophanus rutilus*). *Trans. Norf. Norw. Nat. Soc.*, **12** (3), 379.

Gurney, J.H. (1901) Coot shooting on Hickling Broad. *Trans. Norf. Norw. Nat. Soc.*, **7** (2), 267–273.

Gurney, J.H. & Southwell, T. (1887) Fauna and Flora of Norfolk. Part XI. Birds: Section 11. *Trans. Norf. Norw. Nat. Soc.*, **4** (3), 397–432.

Gurney, R. (1904) The fresh-and brackish-water Crustacea of East Norfolk. *Trans. Norf. Norw. Nat. Soc.*, **7** (5), 637–660.

Gurney, R. (1907) The Crustacea of the East Norfolk rivers. *Trans. Norf. Norw. Nat. Soc.*, **8** (3), 410–438.

Gurney, R. (1911) The tides of the R. Bure and its tributaries. *Trans. Norf. Norw. Nat. Soc.*, **9** (2), 216–243.

Gurney, R. (1920) Breeding stations of the Black-headed Gull in the British Isles. *Trans. Norf. Norw. Nat. Soc.*, **10** (5), 416–447.

Gurney R. (1922) Report of a visit to Hickling Broad on 27 August. Diary for 1922 held at the Castle Museum, Norwich.

Gurney, R. (1923) Report of a visit to Wicken Fen (Cambridgeshire) on 13 June. Diary for 1923 held at the Castle Museum, Norwich.

Gurney, R. (1929) The freshwater Crustacea of Norfolk. *Trans. Norf. Norw. Nat. Soc.*, **12** (5), 550–581.

Gurney, R. (1965) Life in fresh water, with special reference to the aquatic fauna of the Broads, and an account of the Crustacea. In: *The Broads* (ed. E.A. Ellis), pp. 151–160. Collins, London.

Hamer, M. (1982) Animals still full of pull. *New Scientist*, **96**, No. 1332, 449–452.

Hamilton Publications (1978) *Norfolk and Suffolk Broads Navigation*. Castlemead, Hertford.

Harland, M.G. & Harland, H.J. (1980) *The flooding of Eastern England*. 64 pp. Minimax Books, Peterborough.

Harmer, F.W. (1902) A sketch of the later tertiary history of East Anglia. *Proc. Geol. Ass.*, **17**, 416–479.

Harrison, R.H. (1974) Halvergate without wildfowl. Norfolk Bird Report for 1972. *Trans. Norf. Norw. Nat. Soc.*, **23** (1), 45–46.

Hartley, P.H.T. (1947) The natural history of some British Freshwater Fishes. *Proc. zool. Soc. Lond.*, **117**, 129–206.

Harvey, H.J. & Meredith, T.C. (1981) Ecological studies of *Peucedanum palustre* and their implications for conservation management at Wicken Fen, Cambridgeshire. In: *The Biological Aspects of Rare Plant Conservation* (ed. H. Synge), pp. 365–377. Wiley, Chichester.

Hasan, M.R. & MacIntosh, D.J. (1986) Acute toxicity of ammonia to Common Carp fry. *Aquaculture*, **54**, 97–107.

Haslam, S.M. (1969) The development and emergence of buds in *Phragmites communis* Trin. *Ann. Bot.*, **33**, 289–301.

Haslam, S.M. (1971) Community regulation in *Phragmites communis* Trin. II Mixed stands. *J. Ecol.*, **59**, 75–88.

Haslam, S.M. (1972a) *The Reed ('Norfolk Reed')*. 73 pp. Norfolk Reedgrowers' Association, Norwich.

Haslam, S.M. (1972b) Biological Flora of the British Isles: *Phragmites communis* Trin. *J. Ecol.*, **60**, 585–610.

Haslam, S.M. (1973) Some aspects of the life history and autecology of *Phragmites communis* Trin. *Polskie Archwm. Hydrobiol.*, **20** (1), 79–100.

Hazelden, J., Loveland, P.J. & Sturdy, R.G. (1986) Saline soils in North Kent. *Soil Survey of England and Wales, Special Survey no. 14*. Harpenden.

Henin, S. (1986) Water quality – the French problem. In: *Effects of land use on fresh waters* (ed. J.F. de L.G. Solbé), pp. 210–220. Water Research Centre. Ellis Horwood, Chichester.

Hilton, J. & Phillips, G.L. (1982) The effect of boat activity on turbidity in a shallow Broadland river. *J. appl. Ecol.*, **19**, 143–150.

Hogetsu, K., Okanishi, Y. & Sugawara, H. (1960) Studies on the antagonistic relationship between phytoplankton and aquatic plants. *Jap. J. Limnol.*, **21**, 124–129.

Holdway, P.A. (1979) Influences exerted by salinity on a Norfolk Broads strain of *Prymnesium parvum* (Carter). *Verh. int. Verein. theor. angew. Limnol*, **20**, 2336–2340.

Holdway, P.A., Watson, R.A. & Moss, B. (1978) Aspects of the ecology of *Prymnesium parvum* (Haptophyta) and water chemistry in the Norfolk Broads, England. *Freshwat. Biol.*, **8**, 295–311.

Hollyer, J.N. (1975) The Cetti's Warbler in Kent. *Kent Bird Rep.*, **22**, 84–95.

Hooson, J.E. (1981) Drainage Plans for Norfolk Broads. Letter in *The Times*, June 10, 1981.

Hoseason, J. (1970) Broads' Future. Letter to the *Eastern Daily Press*, August 18, 1970.

Hoseason, J. (1977). *Self-catering holidays in the United Kingdom*. A paper presented to the Annual Convention of the National Federation of Site Operators, Newcastle upon Tyne, 24 March 1977. Reprinted by Hoseasons, Oulton Broad.

House of Lords (1989) *Nitrate in Water*. Select Committee on the European Communities. 16th Report, Session 1988–89. 288 pp. HMSO, London.

Howorth, T.G. (1973) *South's British Butterflies*. 210 pp. Frederick Warne, London.

Humphries, G. (1980) Thatching: new life comes to an old craft. *The Countryman*, Autumn 1980, 148–153.

Hurrell, H.E. (1911) Distribution of the Polyzoa in Norfolk waters. *Trans. Norf. Norw. Nat. Soc.*, **9** (2), 197–205.

Hurrell, H.E. (1927) The ecology of the fresh-water Polyzoa in East Anglia. *Jl. R. microsc. Soc.*, **47**, 135–142.

Hutchinson, G.E. (1975) *A treatise on Limnology. Vol. III: Limnological Botany*. 660 pp. Wiley, New York.

Imperial College of Science and Technology (1987) *Heavy metals in the River Yare, Norfolk, and its associated broads: Survey and Modelling*. Report compiled for Anglian Water by the Department of Civil Engineering. 154 pp. London.

Inland Waterways Association (1978) *The Port of Norwich*: a report prepared for the Great Yarmouth Port & Haven Commissioners by members of the Inland Shipping Group of the Association. 9 pp. Great Yarmouth.

Innes, A.G. (1911) Tidal action in the Bure and its tributaries. *Trans. Norf. Norw. Nat. Soc.*, **9** (2), 244–262.

Irvine, K.A., Moss, B. & Balls, H.R. (1989) The loss of submerged plants with eutrophication. II. Relationships between fish and zooplankton in a set of experimental ponds, and conclusions. *Freshwat. Biol.*, **22**, 89–107.

Irwin, A.G. (1984) The Large Copper, *Lycaena dispar dispar* (Haworth) in the Norfolk Broads. *Ent. Rec. J. var.*, **96**, 212–213.

Irwin, A.G. (1985) *Phytomyza thysselini* Hendel (Diptera: Agromyzidae) a leaf mining fly new to Britain. *Entomologist's Gaz.*, **36**, 103.

Ismay, J. & Wright, P.A. (1976) *Report on the Norfolk Dragonfly Survey 1975*. 6 pp. Confidential report produced for the Nature Conservancy Council, Norwich.

Jackson, M.J. (1978) The changing status of aquatic macrophytes in the Norfolk Broads. *Trans. Norf. Norw. Nat. Soc.*, **24** (4), 137–152.

Jackson, M.J. (1981) *Changes in the ecology of the Norfolk Broads*. Parts 1 & 2. Report (unpublished) commissioned by the Nature Conservancy Council, Norwich.

Jackson, M.J. (1983) *Aquatic macrophyte surveys of the Norfolk Broads, 1977 and 1982*. Report (unpublished) commissioned by the Nature Conservancy Council, Norwich.

Jackson, M.J. & Charter, E. (1978) *A Survey of land use and the aquatic vegetation of drainage dykes in parts of the mid-Yare, Lower Bure and Waveney valleys*. 106 pp. Report (unpublished) commissioned by the Nature Conservancy Council, Norwich.

James, C.H., Rowland Pierce, S. & Rowley, H.C. (1945) *City of Norwich Plan*. 135 pp. Norwich Corporation.

Jefferies, D.J. (1985) An otter casualty from Breydon Water, Norfolk. In: *Otters – Journal of the Otter Trust*, **1** (8), 23–24.

Jefferies, D.J. (1987) The effects of angling interests on otters, with particular reference to disturbance. In: *Angling and Wildlife in Fresh Waters* (ed. P.S. Maitland & A.K. Turner), pp. 23–30. Institute of Terrestrial Ecology, Grange-over-Sands.

Jefferies, D.J., Green, J. & Green, R. (1984) *Commercial fish and crustacean traps: a serious cause of otter Lutra lutra L. mortality in Britain and Europe*. 31 pp. Vincent Wildlife Trust, London.

Jefferies, D.J., Wayre, P. Jessop, R.M. & Mitchell-Jones, A.J. (1986) Reinforcing the native otter (*Lutra lutra*) population in East Anglia: an analysis of the behaviour and range development of the first release group. *Otters – the journal of the Otter Trust*, **1** (9), 65–79.

Jenkins, S.H. & Lockett, W.T. (1943) Loss of phosphorus during sewage purification. *Nature*, **151**, 306–307.

Jennings, J.N. (1952) *The origin of the Broads*. 66 pp. Research Series No. 2, Royal Geographical Society, London.

Jennings, J.N. (1955) Further pollen data from the Norfolk Broads. *New Phytol.*, **54**, 199–207.

Jennings, J.N. and Green, C. (1965) The physiographical evolution of the East Norfolk River Valleys since the Ice Age: In: *The Broads* (ed. E.A. Ellis), pp.13–35. Collins, London.

Jernelov, A. & Asell, B. (1975) The feasibility of restoring mercury-contaminated waters. In: *Heavy Metals in the Aquatic Environment* (ed. P.A. Krenkel). 299 pp. Pergamon Press, Oxford.

John Dossor & Partners (1980) *Land Drainage Improvement Scheme for the Seven Mile and Berney Levels (inc. Manor House Scheme)*. Consultant Engineer's report to the Lower Bure, Halvergate Fleet and Acle Marshes IDB. Norwich.

John Dossor & Partners (1981) *Land Drainage Improvement Scheme for the Tunstall, Acle, Calthorpe and Stracey Levels*. Consultant Engineer's report to the Lower Bure, Halvergate Fleet and Acle Marshes IDB. Norwich.

John Dossor & Partners (1982) *Report on the feasibility of forming washlands along Halvergate Fleet*. Consultant Engineer's Report to the Nature Conservancy Council, Norwich.

Jones, J. & Jones, J. (1977) Limeburning in Norfolk. *J. Norfolk ind. Archaeology Soc.*, **2** (2), 21–31.

Jones, R. (1984) Grey Herons in Norfolk: an exploratory survey. Norfolk Bird Report for 1983. *Trans. Norf. Norw. Nat. Soc.*, **26** (6), 364–365.

Kemp, R. (1968) Staithes. *Broads Soc. Bull.*, December 1968, 3–5.

Kemp, R. (1984) The heritage of parish staithes. *Eastern Daily Press*, 29 October, 1984.

Kemp, R. (1986a) Ownership of parish staithes. *The Harnser* (Magazine of the Broads Society), January 1986, 4–5.

Kemp, R. (1986b) *Staithes: A survey and register*. BAPD 6. 8 pp. Broads Authority, Norwich.

Kemp, R., Walton, M., McLean, A.S., Mott-Radclyffe, C., Le Surf, G. & Paget, H. (1978). Consortium 'not long-term answer'. *Eastern Daily Press*, 2 February, 1978.

Kennison, G.C.B. (1984, 1985a, 1986c & 1988) *Aquatic macrophyte surveys of the Norfolk Broads*. Reports for 1983, 1984, 1985 and 1988. Broads Authority, Norwich.

Kennison, G.C.B. (1985b) *Broadland turf ponds — a monitoring programme*. Report to the Broads Authority, Norwich.

Kennson, G.C.B. (1986a) Preliminary observations on the plant colonisation of experimental turf ponds in a Broadland Fen. *Trans. Norf. Norw. Soc.*, **27** (3), 193–198.

Kennison, G.C.B. (1986b) *Broadland turf ponds — a monitoring programme*. Report to the Broads Authority, Norwich.

Kennison, G.C.B. (1987) *Broadland turf ponds — a monitoring programme*. Report to the Broads Authority, Norwich.

Kerney, M.P., ed. (1976) *Atlas of the non-marine Mollusca of the British Isles*. Conchological Society of Great Britain and the Biological Record Centre, Institute of Terrestrial Sciences, Abbots Ripton.

Klotzli, F. (1973) Conservation of reed beds in Switzerland. *Polskie Archwm. Hydrobiol.*, **20**, 231–237.

Klotzli, F. & Zust, S. (1973) Nitrogen regime in reed beds. *Polskie Archwm. Hydrobiol.*, **20**, 131–136.

Knights, J. (1982) Hickling provides pike record. *Eastern Daily Press*, 19 February, 1982.

Lamb, H.H. (1965) The early medieval warm epoch and its sequel. *Palaeogeogr., Palaeoclim., Palaeoecol.*, **1**, 13–37.

Lamb, H.H. (1977) *Climate: present, past and future. Vol. 2: Climatic History and the Future*. 835 pp. Methuen, London.

Lamb, H.H. (1981) Climatic fluctuations in historical times and their connexion with transgressions of the sea, storm floods and other coastal changes. In: *Transgressies en occupatiegeschiedenis in de kustgebieden van Nederland en Belgie* (ed. A. Verhulst & M.K.E. Gottschalk), pp. 251–290. Rijksuniversiteit, Ghent.

Lamb, H.H. (1982) *Climate, History and the Modern World*. 387 pp. Methuen, London.

Lamb, H.H. & Weiss, I. (1979) *On recent changes of the wind and wave regime of the North Sea and the outlook*. 108 pp. Fachliche Mitteilungen: Herausgeber amt für Wehrgeophysik Nr. 194.

Lambert, J.M. (1946) The distribution and status of *Glyceria maxima* (Hartm.) Holmb. in the region of Surlingham and Rockland Broads. *J. Ecol.*, **33**, 230–267.

Lambert, J.M. (1947) A note on the physiognomy of *Glyceria maxima* reed-swamps in Norfolk. *Trans. Norf. Norw. Nat. Soc.*, **16** (3), 246–249.

Lambert, J.M. (1951) Alluvial stratigraphy and vegetational succession in the region of the Bure valley broads: III – classification, status and distribution of communities. *J. Ecol.*, **39**, 149–170.

Lambert, J.M. (1965) The vegetation of Broadland. In: *The Broads* (ed. E.A. Ellis), pp. 69–92. Collins, London.

Lambert, J.M. & Jennings, J.N. (1951) Alluvial stratigraphy and vegetational succession in the region of the Bure valley Broads: II – detailed vegetational-stratigraphical relationships. *J. Ecol.*, **39**, 120–148.

Lambert, J.M. & Jennings, J.N. (1960) Stratigraphical and associated evidence. In: *The Making of the Broads*, pp. 1–61. Research Series No. 3, Royal Geographical Society, London.

Lambert, J.M., Jennings, J.N. & Smith, C.T. (1965) The Origin of the Broads. In: *The Broads* (ed. E.A. Ellis), pp. 37–65. Collins, London.

Land Use Consultants (1978) *A Landscape Assessment of the Yare Basin Flood Control Study Proposals*. WP 13. 28 pp. Countryside Commission, Cheltenham.

Land Use Consultants (1986) *Crown Point Estate — Pre-Feasibility Study*. 16 pp. London.

Lark, A. (1990) The Havens and marshes of Yarmouth. In: *Yarmouth Archaeology: 1990*, pp. 13–19.

Laurie, E.M.O. (1946) The coypu (*Myocastor coypus*) in Great Britain. *J. anim. Ecol.*, **15**, 22–34.

Leach, S.J. (1988) Rediscovery of *Halimione pedunculata* (L.) Aellen in Britain. *Watsonia*, **17** (2), 170–171.

Leah, R.T., Moss, B. & Forrest, D.E. (1978) Experiments with large enclosures in a fertile, shallow, brackish lake, Hickling Broad, United Kingdom. *Int. Rev. ges. Hydrobiol.*, **63**, 291–310.

Leah, R.T., Moss, B. & Forrest, D.E. (1980) The role of predation in causing major changes in the limnology of a hyper-eutrophic lake. *Int. Rev. ges. Hydrobiol.*, **65**, 223–247.

Lees, A.J. (1982) *A critique of the Halvergate Marshes drainage proposals.* 33 pp. Friends of the Earth, Norwich.

Lees, A.J. (1985) *Industrial mercury pollution in the Broads.* A report produced for the Friends of the Earth. 6 pp. Norwich.

Leutze, C.C.K. (1976) *Social behaviour and dispersion in the water vole, Arvicola terrestris* Lacepede. Ph.D thesis, University of Aberdeen.

Levine, G.J. (1977) *A Concise History of Brundall and Braydeston.* 24 pp. Levine, Brundall.

Linfield, R.S.J. (1980) Ecological changes in a lake fishery and their effects on a stunted roach, *Rutilus rutilus*, population. *J. Fish Biol.*, **16**, 275–298.

Linsell, S. (1990) *Hickling Broad and its wildlife.* 171 pp. Terence Dalton, Lavenham.

Lloyd, C.S., Thomas, G.J., Macdonald, J.W., Borland, E.D., Standring, K. & Smart, J.L. (1976). Wild Bird Mortality caused by botulism in Britain, 1975. *Biol. Cons.*, **10** (2), 119–129.

Long, S.H., ed. (1928). Wild Bird Protection in Norfolk in 1928. *Trans. Norf. Norw. Nat. Soc.*, **12** (4), 482–496.

Long, S.H. ed. (1929) Wild Bird Protection in Norfolk in 1929. *Trans. Norf. Norw. Nat. Soc.*, **12** (5), 677–691.

Long, S.H., ed. (1936) Wild Bird Protection in Norfolk in 1935. *Trans. Norf. Norw. Nat. Soc.*, **14** (1), 86–105.

Lubbock, R. (1845) *Observations on the Fauna of Norfolk and more particularly on the district of the Broads* (ed. T. Southwell, 1879). 239 pp. Jarrold, Norwich.

Mackley, A. (1984) 400 years of water in Norwich. *Anglian News*, July 1984. Anglian Water Authority, Huntingdon.

Maltster, R. (1971) *Wherries and Waterways.* 176 pp. Terence Dalton, Lavenham.

Maltster, R. (1982) *Lowestoft — East Coast Port.* 125 pp. Terence Dalton, Lavenham.

Manship, H. (1619) *History of Yarmouth* (ed. C.J. Palmer). 435 pp. Meall, Great Yarmouth.

Marshall, W. (1787) *The rural economy of Norfolk: comprising the management of landed estates, and the present practice of husbandry in that county.* 2 vols. Cadell, London.

Martin, S. (1970) The study of the Drainage Mills of the Norfolk Broadlands. *Norfolk Archaeology*, **35**, 152–153.

Mason, C.F. & Bryant, R.J. (1974) The structure and diversity of the animal communities in a Broadland reedswamp. *J. Zool.*, **172**, 289–302.

Mason, C.F. & Bryant, R.J. (1975a) Production, nutrient content and decomposition of *Phragmites communis* Trin. and *Typha augustifolia* L. *J. Ecol.*, **63**, 71–95.

Mason, C.F. & Bryant, R.J. (1975b) Changes in the ecology of the Norfolk Broads. *Freshwat. Biol.*, **5**, 257–270.

Mathiasson, S. (1973) A moulting population of non-breeding Mute Swans with special reference to flight feather moult, feeding ecology and habitat selection. *Wildfowl*, **24**, 43–93.

May, J. (1952) *The Norfolk Broads Holiday Book and Pocket Pilot.* 211 pp. Hulton Press, Bristol.

May, R.W.P. & Waters, C.B. (1986) *Boat Wash Study, April–May 1986.* BARS 12. 22 pp. Broads Authority, Norwich.

Merritt, R. (1985) *A survey of some Broadland sites for larvae of Aeshna isosceles (Mull.) 29–30 May 1983 and 9–11 June 1984.* Report (unpublished) produced for the Nature Conservancy Council, Peterborough.

Meteorological Office (1963) Monthly Weather Reports for January, February and March, 1963. **80** (Nos. 1–3). HMSO, London.

Meteorological Office (1987a) Monthly Weather Report for October 1987. **104** (No. 10). HMSO, London

Meteorological Office (1987b) Exceptionally strong winds of 16 October 1987 over the south of England. *Meteorol. Mag.*, **116**, 389–390.

Micklethwait v. Vincent (1892) *The Law Times*, **67**, 225–230.

Middleton, C.S. (1978) *The Broadland Photographers*. Wensum Books, Norwich.

Ministry of Agriculture, Fisheries and Food (1962) *The Effect on Agriculture of the East Coast Floods, 1953*. 243 pp. MAFF, London.

Ministry of Agriculture Fisheries and Food (1975) *Food from our own Resources*. White Paper. Cmnd. 6020. HMSO, London.

Ministry of Agriculture Fisheries and Food (1978) *Report of the Coypu Strategy Group*. 52 pp. HMSO, London.

Ministry of Agriculture Fisheries and Food (1979) *Farming and the Nation*. White Paper. Cmnd. 7458. HMSO, London.

Ministry of Agriculture Fisheries and Food (1981) *Aquatic vegetation of marsh dykes in the Broads Area*. ADAS Technical Note, Norwich.

Ministry of Agriculture Fisheries and Food (1984) Conservation – the Halvergate Story. In: *ADAS Annual Report*: 1983, pp. 73–78. HMSO, London.

Ministry of Agriculture Fisheries and Food (1985) *Financing and Administration of Land Drainage, Flood Prevention and Coast Protection in England and Wales*. Consultation Paper. HMSO, London.

Ministry of Technology (1970) *Phosphates in Sewage and Sewage Effluents*. Notes on Water Pollution No. 49. London.

Ministry of Town and Country Planning (1944) *The Control of Land Use*. White Paper. 15 pp. HMSO, London.

Ministry of Town and Country Planning (1945) *National Parks in England and Wales*. Report by John Dower. Cmnd. 6628. 57 pp. HMSO, London.

Ministry of Town and Country Planning (1947a) *Report of the National Parks Committee (England and Wales)*. Chairman: Sir A. Hobhouse. Cmnd. 7121. 134 pp. HMSO, London.

Ministry of Town and Country Planning (1947b) *Conservation of Nature in England and Wales*. Report of the Wild Life Conservation Special Committee (Chairman: Dr. J.S. Huxley). Cmnd. 7122. 139 pp. HMSO, London.

Ministry of Transport and Civil Aviation (1958) *Report of the Committee of Inquiry into Inland Waterways* (Chairman: H.L. Bowes). Cmnd. 486. 121 pp. HMSO, London.

Ministry of Transport and Civil Aviation (1959) *Government proposals following the Report of the Committee of Inquiry into Inland Waterways*. Cmnd. 676. 8 pp. HMSO, London.

Ministry of Works and Planning (1942) *Report of the Committee on Land Utilization in Rural Areas* (Chairman: Lord Scott). 99 pp. HMSO, London.

Montagu, E.S. (1919) *Report of the Departmental Committee on the Protection of Wild Birds*. Cmnd. 295. HMSO, London.

Mook, J.H. & van der Toorn, J. (1985) Delayed response of Common Reed (*Phragmites australis*) to herbivory as a cause of cyclic fluctuations in the density of the moth *Archanara geminipuncta*. *Oikos*, **44**, 142–148.

Moore, J.A. & Greene, D.M. (1983) *Provisional atlas and catalogue of British Museum (Natural History) specimens of the Characeae*. Institute of Terrestrial Ecology, Abbots Ripton.

Moore, N. (1982) What parts of Britain's countryside must be conserved? *New Scientist*, **93**, No. 1289, 147–149.

Morgan, N.C. (1972) Problems of the conservation of freshwater ecosytems. *Symp. zool. Soc. Lond.*, No. 29, 135–154.

Morgan, N.C. & Britton, R. (1977) Open Waters. In: *A Nature Conservation Review* (ed. D.A. Ratcliffe). Vol. 1, pp. 200–248. Vol. 2, pp. 166–205. Cambridge University Press.

Mosby, J.E.G. (1938) *The Land of Britain – the Report of the Land Utilisation Survey of Britain. Pt. 70, Norfolk*. 256 pp. Geographical Publications, London.

Mosby, J.E.G. (1939) The Horsey Flood, 1938: an example of storm effect on a low coast. In: Recent coastal changes in South-eastern England: a discussion (pp. 399–511). *Geogr. J.*, **93**, 413–418.

Moss, B. (1977) Conservation problems in the Norfolk Broads and rivers of East Anglia — phytoplankton, boats and the causes of turbidity. *Biol. Cons.*, **12**, 95–114.

Moss, B. (1978) The ecological history of a medieval man-made lake. Hickling Broad, Norfolk, United Kingdom. *Hydrobiologia*, **60**, 23–32.

Moss. B. (1979) Algal and other fossil evidence for major changes in Strumpshaw Broad, Norfolk, England in the last two centuries. *Br. Phycol. J.*, **14**, 263–283.

Moss, B. (1980) Further studies on the palaeolimnology and changes in the phosphorus budget of Barton Broad, Norfolk. *Freshwat. Biol.*, **10**, 261–279.

Moss, B. (1981) The composition and ecology of periphyton communities in freshwaters: II. Inter-relationships between water chemistry, phytoplankton populations and periphyton populations in a shallow lake and associated experimental reservoirs ('Lund tubes'). *Br. Phycol. J.*, **16**, 59–76.

Moss, B. (1983) The Norfolk Broadland: experiments in the restoration of a complex wetland. *Biol. Rev.*, **58**, 521–561.

Moss, B. (1984) A good Reed. *The Harnser* (Magazine of the Broads Society), April 1984, 14–15.

Moss, B., Balls, H., Booker, I., Manson, K. & Timms, R.M. (1984) The River Bure, United Kingdom: Patterns of change in chemistry and phytoplankton in a slow-flowing fertile river. *Verh. int. Verein. theor. angew. Limnol.*, **22**, 1959–1964.

Moss, B., Balls, H, & Irvine, K. (1985) *Isolation of Broads as a technique for restoration.* BARS 11. 129 pp. Broads Authority, Norwich.

Moss, B., Balls, H., Irvine, K. & Stansfield, J. (1986) Restoration of two lowland lakes by isolation from nutrient-rich water resources with and without removal of sediment. *J. appl. Ecol.* **23**, 391–414.

Moss, B., Booker, I.R., Manning, H. & Manson, K. (1982) *Study of the River Bure, Norfolk Broads.* Final report (unpublished) to the DoE and the AWA.

Moss, B., Forrest, D.E. & Phillips, G. (1979) Eutrophication and palaeolimnology of two small medieval man-made lakes. *Arch. Hydrobiol.*, **85**, 409–425.

Moss, B., Irvine, K. & Stansfield, J. (1988a) Approaches to the restoration of shallow eutrophicated lakes in England. *Verh. int. Verein, theor. angew. Limnol.*, **23**, 414–418.

Moss, B., Irvine, K. & Stansfield, J. (1988b) *Deterioration and restoration of freshwater ecosystems — a case study of the Norfolk Broads.* Interim Report (unpublished) to the Broads Authority, Soap and Detergent Industry Association, Anglian Water and the Nature Conservancy Council, March 1988.

Moss, B., Irvine, K. & Stansfield, J. (1989) *The restoration of Broadland from hyper-eutrophication.* Final report to the Broads Authority, the Soap and Detergent Industry Association, Anglian Water and the Nature Conservancy Council. The Chief Scientist's Division of the latter subsequently reproduced it as Report Number 939 (Contract No. HF3-03-338). 41 pp. Nature Conservancy Council, Peterborough.

Moss, B. & Leah, R.T. (1980) *Broadland Research.* Contract Report (unpublished) to the Nature Conservancy Council, Norwich.

Moss, B. & Leah, R.T. (1982) Changes in the ecosystem of a guanotrophic and brackish shallow lake in Eastern England: potential problems in its restoration. *Int. Revue ges. Hydrobiol.*, **67**, 625–659.

Moss, B., Leah, R.T. & Clough, B. (1979) Problems of the Norfolk Broads and their impact on freshwater Fisheries. *Proc,. 1st Brit. Freshwat. Fish Conf.*, pp. 67–85. University of Liverpool.

Moss, B., Leah, R.T. & Forrest, D.E. (1978) Ecosystem experimentation in the management of a system of shallow lakes. *Verh. int. Verein. theor. angew. Limnol.*, **20**, 649–653.

Moss, B. & Timms, R.M. (1982) *Studies on Hoveton Great Broad and the limnology of the associated waterway.* Final report (unpublished) to the Nature Conservancy Council on Contract HF3/03/133. Norwich.

Mundy, S.P. (1980) *A key to the British and European Freshwater Bryozoans.* Science Publication, No. 41. 31 pp. Freshwater Biological Association.

Murfitt, R.C. & Weaver, D. J. (1982) *Wet Meadows Survey: Norfolk 1982.* Report commissioned by the Royal Society for the Protection of Birds, Sandy.

Murphy, J. (1979) *The Town and Trade of Great Yarmouth, 1740–1850.* Ph.D. thesis, University of East Anglia.

Murphy, M.C. (1984) *Report of Farming in the Eastern Counties of England: 1982/3.* 155 pp. Dept. of Land Economy, University of Cambridge.

Nail, J.G. (1866) *Great Yarmouth and Lowestoft.* 728 pp. Longmans, Green, Reader & Dyer, London.

Nature Conservancy (1963) *A survey of the Broads and their current problems.* Draft Report. 35 pp. London.

Nature Conservancy (1965) *Report on Broadland.* 98 pp. London.

Nature Conservancy Council (1975) *First Report covering the period 1 November 1973 to 31 March 1975.* 116 pp. London.

Nature Conservancy Council (1976) *Botulism in Waterfowl.* Leaflet. Norwich.

Nature Conservancy Council (1981) *Lead Poisoning in Swans.* Report of the NCC's Working Group. London.

Nature Conservancy Council (1982a) Sites of Special Scientific Interest. In: *Seventh Annual Report covering the period 1 April 1980 to 31 March 1981*, pp. 18–22. Nature Conservancy Council, London.

Nature Conservancy Council (1982b) *The Selection of Sites of Special Scientific Interest.* Explanatory Leaflet. London.

Nature Conservancy Council (1983) *Eighth report covering the period 1 April 1981 to 31 March 1982.* 154 pp. London.

Nature Conservancy Council (1988) *Internationally important wetlands and special protection areas for birds.* Explanatory Leaflet. Peterborough.

Nature Conservancy Council (1989) *Guidelines for the selection of biological SSSIs.* 288 pp. Nature Conservancy Council, Peterborough.

Newbold, C. & Palmer, M.A. (1979) *Trophic adaptations of aquatic plants.* Chief Scientist's Team Notes, No. 18. Nature Conservancy Council, London.

Newson, R.M. (1966) Reproduction in the feral coypu (*Myocastor coypus*). *Symp. zool. Soc. Lond.*, **15**, 323–334.

Newton, I. (1974) Changes attributed to pesticides in the nesting success of the Sparrowhawk in Britain. *J. appl. Ecol.*, **11**, 95–102.

Nicholson, W.A. (1895) Proposal for a freshwater biological station in Norfolk. *Trans. Norf. Norw. Nat. Soc.*, **6** (1), 108–109.

Nicholson, W.A. (1896). High tide on the East Coast. *Trans. Norf. Norw. Nat. Soc.*, **6** (2), 224–225.

Nicholson, W.A. (1900) Sir Thomas Browne as a naturalist. *Trans. Norf. Norw. Nat. Soc.*, **7** (1), 72–89.

Nicholson, W.A. (1904) The Sutton Broad Laboratory. *Trans. Norf. Norw. Nat. Soc.*, **7** (5), 731–732.

Nicholson, W.A. (1914) *A flora of Norfolk.* 214 pp. Richard Clay, London.

Norfolk County Council (1947) *Report of the Broads Conference on the Problems and Requirements of the Broads Area.* 40 pp. + appendix. Norwich.

Norfolk County Council (1978) *Future options for the Port of Norwich.* Report of a Technical Steering Group. 45 pp. Norwich.

Norfolk County Council (1979) *Flood Control and Drainage in the Yare Basin.* Edited proceedings of a seminar held at UEA in November 1978. Norwich.

Norfolk County Council (1985a) *The Broads Bill: draft for consultation.* Norwich.

Norfolk County Council (1985b) *The Broads Bill: Responses to public consultation.* 43 pp. Norwich.

Norfolk Naturalists' Trust (1975) *The decline of wildlife in the Norfolk Broads.* Statement issued by the Trust on 19 May, 1975. Norwich.

Norfolk Naturalists' Trust (1986) *Guide to the Nature Reserves of Norfolk.* Norwich.

Norgate, F. (1884) Appendix on natural history: Mammalia. In: *History of Norfolk* (R.H.M. Mason), p. 12. Wertheimer, Lea & Co., London.

Norgate, T.B. (1973) Weather summary for 1972. *Trans. Norf. Norw. Nat. Soc.*, **22** (6), 432–434.

Norgate, T.B. (1977) Weather 1975/1976. *Trans. Norf. Norw. Nat. Soc.*, **24** (2), 89–93.

Norris, J.D. (1967) A campaign against feral coypus in Great Britain. *J. appl. Ecol.*, **4**, 191–199.

Norwich Corporation (1963) Booklet produced for the opening of the extensions to the *City of Norwich Sewage Purification Works, Whitlingham.* 23 pp. Norwich.

Omernik, J.M. (1976) *The influence of land use on stream nutrient levels.* U.S. Environmental Protection Agency, EPA-600/3-76-014.

O'Riordan, A.M. (1976a) *A Broadland Bibliography.* Unpublished, but copies are kept at, *inter alia,* the Colman & Rye Library, the Castle Museum, the University of East Anglia library, and the offices of the Nature Conservancy Council at Norwich and Peterborough.

O'Riordan, A.M. (1976b) *Review of biological information for the Yare Valley Flood Control Feasibility Study.* Contract report (unpublished) to the Nature Conservancy Council, Norwich.

O'Riordan, T. (1970) Spray Irrigation and the *Water Resources Act,* 1963. *Trans. Inst. Br. Geogr.,* **49,** 33–48.

O'Riordan, T. (1980) *Lessons from the Yare Barrier Controversy.* Text of an inaugural lecture at the School of Environmental Sciences. 38 pp. University of East Anglia, Norwich.

O'Riordan, T. (1982) A case study in the politics of Land Drainage. *Disasters,* **4** (4), 393–410.

O'Riordan, T. (1986) Ploughing into the Halvergate Marshes. In: Lowe *et al., Countryside Conflicts,* pp. 265–300. Gower/Maurice Temple Smith, London.

O'Riordan, T. & Sinclair, H. (1977) *Ranworth Centre Visitor Survey.* 5 pp. Report (unpublished) commissioned by the Norfolk Naturalists' Trust, Norwich. Summarized in the Trust's Annual Report for 1977.

Osborne, P.L. (1978) *Relationships between the phytoplankton and nutrients in the River Ant and Barton, Sutton and Stalham Broads, Norfolk.* Ph.D. thesis, University of East Anglia.

Osborne, P.L. (1981) Phosphorus and nitrogen budgets of Barton Board and predicted effects of a reduction in nutrient loading on phytoplankton biomass in Barton, Sutton and Stalham Broads, Norfolk, United Kingdom. *Int. Revue ges. Hydrobiol.,* **66** (2), 171–202.

Osborne, P.L. & Moss, B. (1977) Palaeolimnology and trends in the phosphorus and iron budgets of an old man-made lake, Barton Broad, Norfolk. *Freshwat. Biol.,* **7,** 213–233.

Osborne, P.L. & Phillips, G.L. (1978) Evidence for nutrient release from the sediments of two shallow and productive lakes. *Verh. int. Verein. theor. angew. Limnol.,* **20,** 654–658.

Otter Trust (1988). *Otters returned to the Norfolk Broads.* Press Release, Earsham, near Bungay.

Owen, J. (1982) *Meotica lohsei* Benick (Col., Staphylinidae) new to Britain. *Entomologist's mon. Mag.,* **118,** 44.

Owen, M., Atkinson-Willes, G.L. & Salmon, D.G. (1986) *Wildfowl in Great Britain.* Second Edition. 613 pp. Cambridge University Press.

Owens, P.L. (1977) Recreational Conflict: the interaction between Norfolk Broads coarse anglers and boat users. In: *Recreational Freshwater Fisheries: their Conservation, Management and Development* (ed. J. Alabaster), pp. 136–152. Water Research Centre, Stevenage.

Owens, P.L. (1978) Conflict between Norfolk Broads coarse anglers and boat users: a managerial issue. In: *Social Issues in Rural Norfolk* (ed. M.J. Moseley), pp. 123–143. University of East Anglia.

Owens, P.L. (1983) *Recreational Conflict and the behaviour of coarse anglers and boat users in the Norfolk Broads.* 536 pp. Ph.D. thesis, University of East Anglia.

Owens, P.L. (1985) Conflict as a social interaction process in environment and behaviour research: the example of leisure and recreation research. *J. environ. Psychology,* **5,** 243–259.

Owers and Lumley Associates (1985) *Potter Heigham Bridge Local Plan.* BAPD 5. Broads Authority, Norwich.

Owers and Lumley Associates (1985 & 1986) *Broads Design Guidance.* Agricultural Buildings (BADG 2). Boatyards & Boatsheds (BADG 3). Waterside Parks & Recreation Areas (BADG 4). Private Boathouses (BADG 6). Broads Authority, Norwich.

Paget, C.J. & Paget, J. (1834) *Sketch of the Natural History of Yarmouth*. 88 pp. Longman Rees & Co. and Simpkin & Marshall, London.

Pallis, M. (1911a) Salinity in the Norfolk Broads. I. On the cause of the salinity of the broads of the River Thurne. *Geogr. J.*, **37**, 284–291.

Pallis, M. (1911b) The river valleys of East Norfolk: their aquatic and fen formations. In: Tansley, A.G., *Types of British Vegetation*, pp. 214–244. Cambridge University Press.

Pallis, M. (1916) The structure and history of Plav; the floating fen of the delta of the Danube. *J. Linn. Soc. Bot.*, **43**, 233–290.

Palmer, M. & Newbold, C. (1983) *Wetland and riparian plants in Britain*. Focus on nature conservation, No. 1. Nature Conservancy Council, London.

Parr, T.S. (1989) Pollution control by *Phragmites*. In: *Annual Report of the Institute of Terrestrial Ecology: 1988–1989*. Huntingdon.

Patterson, A.H. (1905) *Nature in Eastern Norfolk*. 352 pp. Methuen, London.

Patterson, A.H. (*c.* 1930) *Brundall on the Broads*. 14 pp. Brundall Gardens Steamship Co., Yarmouth.

Payne, M. (1986) Agricultural pollution — the farmers' view. In: *Effects of land use on fresh waters* (ed. J.F. de L.G. Solbé), pp. 329–348. Water Research Centre, Ellis Horwood, Chichester.

Payne, S.J. & Hey, R.D. (1982) *River Management to reduce Bank Erosion: Yare and Bure River System*. BARS 4. 35 pp. Broads Authority, Norwich.

Peake, N.B. and Hancock, J.M. (1961) The Upper Cretaceous of Norfolk. In: The Geology of Norfolk. *Trans. Norf. Norw. Nat. Soc.*, **19** (6), 293–339.

Peet, T.N.D. (1963) Notes on the moths of Hickling Broad. *Trans. Norf. Norw. Nat. Soc.*, **20** (1), 36–37.

Peet, T.N.D. (1974) Notes on the moths of Hickling and Wheatfen Broads, with a systematic list of the species. *Trans. Norf. Norw. Nat. Soc.*, **23** (3), 156–166.

Peet, T.N.D. (1978) *Coleophora hydrolapathella* Hering (Lep.: Coleophoridae) a species new to the British Isles. *Entomologist's Rec. J. Var.*, **90**, 15–16.

Peet, T.N.D. (1979) A third specimen of the Small Dotted Footman: *Pelosia obtusa* H.S., in Britain. *Entomologist's Rec. J. Var.*, **91**, 281.

Peirson, G., Cryer, M., Winfield, I.J. & Townsend, C.R. (1984) The impact of reduced nutrient loading on the fish community of a small isolated lake, Alderfen Broad. In: *Proceedings 4th. British Freshwater Fish Conference*, pp. 167–175.

Pentelow, F.T.K. (1937) *Report on the growth of bream and roach in the Norfolk Broads*. Ministry of Agriculture, Fisheries and Food Internal Report. Ref. No. 17593. 22 pp. London.

Perring, F.H. & Farrell, L. (1983) *British Red Data Books. I. Vascular Plants*. 99 pp. Royal Society for Nature Conservation, Lincoln.

Perring, F.H. & Walters, S.M., ed. (1962) *Atlas of the British Flora*. 432 pp. Botanical Society of the British Isles. Nelson, London.

Petch, C.P. & Swann, E.L. (1968) *Flora of Norfolk*. 288 pp. Jarrold, Norwich.

Phillips, B. (1987) *The Review of site changes 1985–1986*. Report (unpublished) commissioned by the Nature Conservancy Council (Peterborough) and the Royal Society for the Protection of Birds (Sandy).

Phillips, G.L. (1976) *An investigation of the distribution and growth of aquatic plants in some of the Norfolk Broads*. Ph.D. thesis, University of East Anglia.

Phillips, G.L. (1977) The mineral nutrient levels in three Norfolk Broads differing in trophic status, and an annual mineral content budget for one of them. *J. Ecol.*, **65**, 447–474.

Phillips, G.L. (1984) A large-scale field experiment in the control of eutrophication in the Norfolk Broads. *Wat. Pollut. Control 1984*, 400–405.

Phillips, G.L., Eminson, D., Moss, B. (1977) A mechanism to account for macrophyte decline in progressively eutrophicated freshwaters. *Aquat. Bot.*, **4**, 103–126.

Phillips, S.P.(1963) A note on the charophytes of Hickling Broad, E. Norfolk. *Proc. Bot. Soc. Br. Isl.*, **5** (1), 23–24.

Poore, M.E.D. (1956) The Ecology of Woodwalton Fen. *J. Ecol.*, **44**, 455–492.

Preston, A.W. (1891) Notes on the great frost of 1890–91. *Trans. Norf. Norw. Nat. Soc.*, **5** (2), 191–196.

Preston, A.W. (1895a) Notes on the great frost of 1894–5. *Trans. Norf. Norw. Nat. Soc.*, **6** (1), 95–98.

Preston, A.W. (1895b) Notes on the great gale of 24th March 1895. *Trans. Norf. Norw. Nat. Soc.*, **6** (1), 99–101.

Preston, A.W. (1913) Notes on the great Norfolk rainstorm of 25th. and 26th. August 1912. *Trans. Norf. Norw. Nat. Soc.*, **9** (4), 551–557.

Preston, A.W. (1922) Meteorological notes, 1921. *Trans. Norf. Norw. Nat. Soc.*, **11** (3), 316–325.

Preston, Sir R. (1984) Maria in 1935. Letter to the *Eastern Daily Press*. 18 May, 1984.

Raghi-Atri, F. & Bornkamm, R. (1980) Über Halmfestigkeit von Schilf (*Phragmites australis* (Cav.) Trin. ex. Steudel) bei unterschiedlicher Nährstoffversorgung. *Arch. Hydrobiol*, **90** (1), 90–105.

Ranson, C.E. (1968) Ice Wedge casts in the Corton Beds. *Geol. Mag.*, **105**, 74–75.

Ranwell, D.S. (1972). *Ecology of Salt Marshes and Sand Dunes*. 258 pp. Chapman & Hall, London.

Ranwell, D.S., Wyer, D.W., Boorman, L.A., Pizzey, J.M. & Waters, R.J. (1974) *Zostera* transplants in Norfolk and Suffolk, Great Britain. *Aquaculture*, **4**, 185–198.

Ratcliffe, D.A. ed. (1977) *A Nature Conservation Review*. Vols. 1 & 2. Cambridge University Press.

Reid, C. (1882) The geology of the country around Cromer. *Mem. Geol. Surv. U.K.*, 143 pp. HMSO, London.

Reid, C. (1913) *Submerged Forests*. 129 pp. Cambridge University Press.

Reid, S.A.J., Newlands, C. & Leach, S.J. (1989) *A new classification of Broadland dyke vegetation*. 11 pp. England Field Unit Report (unpublished). Nature Conservancy Council, Peterborough.

Rendel Palmer & Tritton (1977) *The Yare Basin Flood Control Study*. 3 vols. Report to the Norfolk and Suffolk River Division of the Anglian Water Authority, Norwich.

Rendel Palmer & Tritton (1983) *The Yare Basin Flood Control Study*. Report to the Norwich Division of Anglian Water, Norwich.

Rice, A.A. (1925) Broadland amenities. Letter to the *Eastern Daily Press*, 27 June, 1925.

Richardson, S.J. (1976) Animal Manures as Potential Pollutants. *Tech. Bull. Minist. Agric. Fish Fd.*, **32**, 405–417. HMSO, London.

Ridgard, J. (1982) The Waveney Navigation 1670–1828. *Diss Antiquarian Soc. Newsletter*, No. 21. 4 pp.

Riviere, B.B. (1930) *A History of the birds of Norfolk*. 296 pp. Witherby, London.

Rodwell, J. (1982) *National Vegetation Classification. Mesotrophic Grasslands*. University of Lancaster. Unpublished Report to the Nature Conservancy Council.

Round, P.D. & Campbell, L.H., ed. (1979) *An ornithological survey of the Yare Basin, Spring and Summer, 1979*. Report (unpublished) produced for the Royal Society for the Protection of Birds, Sandy.

Royal Commission on Coast Erosion and the Reclamation of Tidal Lands in the United Kingdom (1907) Vol. I, Pt. II (Minutes of Evidence and Appendices). Cmnd. 3684. 516 pp. HMSO, London.

Royal Commission on Land Drainage in England and Wales (1927) Cmnd. 2993. 60 pp. HMSO, London.

Royal Commission on Local Government in England (1969) *Local Government Reform* (Chairman: Lord Redcliffe-Maud). White Paper. Cmnd. 4040. HMSO, London.

Royal Society for the Protection of Birds (1983) *Land Drainage in England and Wales: an interim report*. 31 pp. Sandy.

Runham Drainage Commission Minutes (1889–1933) Archives of the Muckfleet and South Flegg Internal Drainage Board, Norwich.

Rural Industries Bureau (1961) *The Thatcher's craft*. Rural Industries Bureau Publication No. 69. London.

Russell, E.W. (1973) *Soil Conditions and Plant Growth*, 849 pp. Longmans, London.

Rutledge, P. (1990) Before the walls: the early medieval settlement pattern of Great Yarmouth. *Yarmouth Archaeology: 1990*, 41–48.

Rye, C.G. (*c.* 1962) Midsands Cross, Great Yarmouth. *Norfolk Archaeology*, **33**, 114–118.

Rye, W. (1884) *A month on the Norfolk Broads on board the wherry Zoe, and its tender, the tub, Lotus*. 110 pp. Simpkin & Marshall, London.

Rye, W. (1899) *The rights of fishing, shooting and sailing on the Norfolk Broads.* 113 pp. Jarrold, Norwich.

Ryland, J.S. (1974) A revised key for the identification of intertidal Bryozoa (Polyzoa). *Fld. Std.,* **4** (1), 77–86.

Sainty, J.E. (1949) The origin of the Broads. *Trans. Norf. Norw. Nat. Soc.,* **16** (5), 369–374.

Sainty, J.E., Mosby, J.E.G., Buxton, A. & Ellis, E.A. (1939) The Norfolk sea floods. *Trans. Norf. Norw. Nat. Soc.,* **14** (4), 334–390.

Salmon, D.G. & Moser, M.E. (1975–1987) *Wildfowl and Wader Counts* (with J.S. Kirby for 1985, 1986 & 1987). Wildfowl Trust, Slimbridge.

Salmon, D.G., Prys-Jones, R.P. & Kirby, J.S. (1988) *Wildfowl and Wader Counts 1987–88.* 63 pp. Wildfowl Trust, Slimbridge.

Salmon, D.G., Prys-Jones, R.P. & Kirby, J.S. (1989) *Wildfowl and Wader Counts 1988–89.* 68 pp. Wildfowl and Wetlands Trust, Slimbridge.

Schudel, P. & Moss, B. (In prep.). Potential influence of different agricultural systems on the phosphorus and nitrogen loads of a lowland river.

Seago, M.J. ed. (1954–1988) Norfolk Bird Reports. Published in the *Trans. Norf. Norw. Nat. Soc.,* vols. 18–28.

Seago, M.J. (1967) *Birds of Norfolk.* 148 pp. Jarrold, Norwich.

Sears, J. (1988) Regional and Seasonal Variations in Lead Poisoning in the Mute Swan *Cygnus olor* in relation to the Distribution of Lead and Lead Weights in the Thames area, England. *Biol. Cons.,* **46** (2), 115–134.

Sheail, J. (1976) *Nature in Trust.* 270 pp. Blackie, London.

Shearman, J. (1982) Drainage, Grants and Chemistry Lessons. Letter in *Farmers' Weekly.* 7 May, 1982.

Shennan, I (1989) Holocene crustal movements and sea-level changes in Great Britain. *J. Quaternary Science,* **4,** 77–89.

Shilo, M. & Shilo, M. (1955) Control of the phytoflagellate *Prymnesium parvum. Verh. int. Verein. theor. angew. Limnol.,* **12,** 233–240.

Shirt, D.B., ed. (1987) *British Red Data Books: 2. Insects.* 402 pp. Nature Conservancy Council, Peterborough.

Skinner, B. (1984) *Colour Identification Guide to Moths of the British Isles.* 267 pp. Viking, Harmondsworth.

Smith, A.C. (1978) *Drainage Windmills of the Norfolk Marshes.* 46 pp. Stevenage Museum, Stevenage.

Smith, A.C. (1990) *Drainage Windmills of the Norfolk Marshes* (New edition). 67 pp. Arthur Smith Publications, Stevenage.

Smith, C.T. (1960) Historical Evidence. In: *The Making of the Broads,* p. 63–111. Research Series No. 3, Royal Geographical Society, London.

Smith, C.T. (1966) Dutch peat digging and the origin of the Norfolk Broads. *Geogr. J.,* **132** (1), 69–72.

Smith, G.R. (1975) Recent European outbreaks of botulism in waterfowl. *Bull. int. Waterfowl Res. Bur.,* No. 39/40, 72–74.

Snelling, J.M. (1971) *St. Benet's Abbey, Norfolk.* 20 pp. Guidebook printed by Crowe & Sons, Norwich.

Soar, C.D. (1905) The Hydrachnids of the Norfolk Broads. *Trans. Norf. Norw. Nat. Soc.,* **8** (1), 83–89.

Society for the Promotion of Nature Reserves (1915) *Provisional Schedule of areas in England considered worthy of preservation.* 20 pp. SPNR c/o British Museum (Natural History), London.

Society for the Promotion of Nature Reserves (1945) *National Nature Reserves and Conservation Areas in England and Wales. Memorandum No. 6 of the Conference on Nature Preservation in post-War Reconstruction.* 79 pp. SPNR c/o. British Museum (Natural History), London.

Soil Survey of England and Wales (1987) *Annual Report 1986.* Reprinted from the Rothamsted Annual Report for 1986. Adlard, Dorking.

Southwell, T. (1879) Norfolk Decoys. *Trans. Norf. Norw. Nat. Soc.,* **2** (5), 538–555.

Southwell, T. (1887) On the Smelt (*Osmerus eperlanus*) fishery in the Norfolk waters. *Trans. Norf. Norw. Nat. Soc.,* **4** (3), 338–343.

Southwell, T. (1888) Notes on some ancient customs and regulations with regard to the fresh-water fisheries of the county of Norfolk. *Trans. Norf. Norw. Nat. Soc..*, **4** (4), 433–446.

Southwell, T. (1896) The Wild Birds Protections Acts of 1880 and 1894 as applied to the county of Norfolk. *Trans. Norf. Norw. Nat. Soc.*, **6** (2), 207–214.

Stansfield, J., Moss, B. & Irvine, K. (1989) The loss of submerged plants with eutrophication. III. Potential role of organochlorine pesticides: a palaeoecological study. *Freshwat. Biol.*, **22**, 109–132.

Stearn, W.T. (1986) Marietta Pallis (1882–1963), ecologist and author. *Ann. Musei Goulandris*, 7, 157–173.

Stephens, J.F. (1827) *Illustrations of British Entomology*, Vol. 1: Haustellata. London.

Stephens, N.M. (1957) *The Natural History of the Otter*. 88 pp. Universities Federation for Animal Welfare, London.

Stern, E. (1980) Drainage Scheme puts more Broadland under the plough. *Farmers' Weekly* (Suppl.), 16 May, 1980.

Stevenson, H. (1866, 1870 & 1890) *Birds of Norfolk*. Vols. 1 & 2, Van Voorst, London. Vol. 3, Gurney & Jackson, London.

Stratton, D.C. (1958) *The Ports of Yarmouth and Norwich*. 1800–1957. Geogr. Tripos Essay, University of Cambridge.

Suffling, E.R. (1887) *The Land of the Broads*. 322 pp. Perry, Essex.

Suffling, E.R. (1891) *History and legends of the Broads District*. 217 pp. Jarrold, Norwich.

Sukopp, H., Markstein, B. & Trepl. L. (1975) Röhrichte unter intensiven Grossstadteinfluss. *Beitr. naturk. Forsch. Südwdtl.*, **34**, 371–385.

Swift, J. (1982) Shooting and Severe Weather. *Shooting and Conservation*, Spring and Annual Report Edition, 1982, 13–14.

Tansley, A.G. (1953) *The British Isles and their vegetation*. 2 vols. Cambridge University Press.

Taylor, J.E. (1872) The Norfolk Broads and meres geologically considered. *Trans. Norf. Norw. Nat. Soc.*, **1** (3), 30–40.

Taylor, M. (1984) Mute Swans in Norfolk; the 1983 census results. *BTO News.*, No. 131, 10.

Teasdel, R.H. (1935) The Dutch Inscription in Haddiscoe Church, Norfolk. *Norfolk Archaeology*, **25**, 449–450.

Telford, T. (1822) *The Report of Thomas Telford on the proposed improvement of the navigation to Norwich*. 8 pp. Matchett & Stevenson, Norwich.

Telling, A.E. (1980) The Law relating to public navigation on rivers and suggestions for reform. *The Easterling*, **3** (1), 5–12.

Thompson, P. (1986) *EEC Cereals Policy — What Next?* Paper (7 pp.) given at Power Farming Conference, January 1986. St. Ives, Huntingdon.

Tidal Harbour Commission (1846) *Reports by Joseph Hume on the Port and Haven of Great Yarmouth (No. 12) and Norwich (No. 15)*. HMSO, London.

Timms, R.M. & Moss, B. (1984) Prevention of growth of potentially dense phytoplankton populations by zooplankton grazing, in the presence of zooplanktivorous fish, in a shallow wetland ecosystem. *Limnol. Oceanogr.*, **29** (3), 472–486.

Tooley, M.J. (1978) Interpretation of Holocene sea-level changes. *Geol. För. Stockh. Förh.*, **100**, 203–212.

Turner, E. (1912) The Return of the Bittern. *Trans. Norf. Norw. Nat. Soc.*, **9** (3), 433–436.

Turner, E.L. (1922) The status of birds in Broadland. *Trans. Norf. Norw. Nat. Soc.*, **11** (3), 227–240.

Turner, E.L. (1924) *Broadland Birds*. 172 pp. Country Life, London.

Turner, K. & Pritchard, G. (1985) *Broads Grazing Marshes Conservation Scheme: First Annual Report (1985)*. 6 pp. Broads Unit, MAFF, Norwich.

Turner, K. & Pritchard, G. (1986) *Broads Grazing Marshes Conservation Scheme: Second Annual Report (1986)*. 5 pp. Broads Unit, MAFF, Norwich.

Turner, R.K. (1983) *An Economic Approach to Environmental Management: incorporating a review of Anglian Water's 'Yare Basin Flood Control Study'*. BARS 8. 63 pp. Broads Authority, Norwich.

Turner, R.K., Brooke, J.S. & Hey, R.D. (1986) *A flood alleviation strategy for Broadland*: Interim Report to AWA and the Broads Authority. 136 pp. University of East Anglia.

Turner, R.K., Dent, D. & Hey, R.D. (1983) Evaluation of the environmental impact of wetland flood protection and drainage schemes. *Environ & Plann.*, *A*, **15** (7), 871–888.

Turrill, W.B. (1923) *Report (unpublished) on a visit to the Broads, May 7th to 9th, 1923*. Copies of this report, which is believed to have been commissioned by the Bure Commissioners, are held at the Castle Museum and the Nature Conservancy Council, Norwich.

Underhill-Day, J.C. (1984) Population and breeding biology of Marsh Harriers in Britain since 1900. *J. appl. Ecol.*, **21**, 773–787.

Underhill-Day, J.C. & Wilson, J. (1978) Breeding Bitterns in Britain. *Brit. Birds.*, **71** (7), 285–300.

Valentin, H. (1953) Present vertical movements in the British Isles. *Geogr. J.*, **119**, 299–305.

Vincent, C.E. (1988) *A comparison of Wind-generated Waves and Boat-generated Waves on Broadland Rivers*. Addendum to BARS 12 — Boat Wash Study. BARS 12B. 62 pp. Broads Authority, Norwich.

Vincent, E. (1980) In: *A Season of Birds — A Norfolk Diary 1911*, pp. 7–25. Weidenfeld & Nicolson, London.

Vollenweider, R.A. (1969) Möglicheiten und Grenzen elementarer Modelle der Stoffbilanz von Seen. *Arch. Hydrobiol.*, **66**, 1–36.

Wailes, R. (1956) Norfolk Windmills: Pt.II, Drainage and pumping mills including those of Suffolk. *Newcomen Soc. Trans.*, **30**, 157–177.

Walker, A. (1973) The North Walsham & Dilham Canal. *The Easterling*, **2** (1), 7–14.

Walker, S.E. (1978) A study of boat users of the Norfolk Broads. In: *Social Issues in Rural Norfolk* (ed. M.J. Moseley), pp. 145–16. University of East Anglia.

Walker, S.E. (1981) *Recreational behaviour among boat users on the Norfolk Broads*. Ph.D. thesis, University of East Anglia.

Walton, G.A. (1938) A water-bug new to Great Britain – *Hydrometra gracilenta* Horvath. *Entomologist's mon. Mag.*, **121**, 272–275.

Ward, A.J. (*c.* 1964) *Drainage Pumps*. Unpublished report presented to the Colman & Rye library, Norwich, in 1969.

Warrick, R.A. (1989) Rapid sea-rise threat as greenhouse-world warms. *The Guardian*. 14 April, 1989.

Warwick, T. (1935) Some escapes of coypus (*Myoptamus coypu*) from nutria farms in Great Britain. *J. anim. Ecol.*, **4** (1), 146–147.

Water Resources Board & Scottish Development Department (1968) *Surface Water Year Book*. HMSO, London.

Watson, R.A. (1981) *The Limnology of the Thurne Broads*. Ph.D. thesis, University of East Anglia.

Watson, R.A. & Osborne, P.L. (1979) An algal pigment ratio as an indicator of the nitrogen supply of phytoplankton in three Norfolk Broads. *Freshwat. Biol.* **9**, 585–594.

Weaver, W. (1908) The Bulrush in Commerce. *The Country House: October, 1908*, pp. 326–328. Brook House Publishing Co., London.

Wentworth Day, J. (1967) *Portrait of the Broads*. 239 pp. Robert Hale, London.

West, R.G. (1956) The Quaternary deposits at Hoxne, Suffolk. *Phil. Trans. R. Soc., B.*, **289**, 265–356.

West, R.G. (1961) The glacial and interglacial deposits of Norfolk. In: The Geology of Norfolk. *Trans. Norf. Norw. Nat. Soc.*, **19** (6), 365–375.

West, R.G. (1980) *The pre-glacial Pleistocene of the Norfolk and Suffolk coasts*. 203 pp. Cambridge University Press.

West, R.G. and Donner, J.J. (1956) The Glaciations of East Anglia and the East Midlands: a differentiation based on stone orientation measurements of the tills. *Q. Jl. geol. Soc. Lond.*, **112**, 69–91.

Wetzel, R.G. & Manny, B.A. (1972) Secretion of dissolved organic carbon and nitrogen by aquatic macrophytes. *Verh. int. Verein. theor. angew. Limnol.*, **18**, 162–170.

Wheeler, B.D. (1975) *Phytosociological studies on rich-fen systems in England and Wales.* Ph.D. thesis, University of Durham.

Wheeler, B.D. (1978) The wetland plant communities of the River Ant valley, Norfolk. *Trans. Norf. Norw. Nat. Soc.*, **24** (4), 153–187.

Wheeler, B.D. (1980a) Plant communities of rich-fen systems in England and Wales. I. Introduction: Tall sedge and reed communities. *J. Ecol.*, **68**, 365–395.

Wheeler, B.D. (1980b) Plant communities of rich-fen systems in England and Wales. II. Communities of calcareous mires. *J. Ecol.*, **68**, 405–420.

Wheeler, B.D. (1980c) Plant communities of rich-fen systems in England and Wales. III. Fen meadow, fen grassland and fen woodland communities and contact communities. *J. Ecol.*, **68**, 761–788.

Wheeler, B.D. (1983) *Turf ponds in Broadland.* BARS 5. 56 pp. Broads Authority, Norwich.

Wheeler, B.D. & Giller, K.E. (1982a) Species richness of herbaceous fen vegetation in Broadland, Norfolk, in relationship to the quantity of above-ground plant material. *J. Ecol.*, **70**, 179–200.

Wheeler, B.D. & Giller, K.E. (1982b) Status of aquatic macrophytes in an undrained area of fen in the Norfolk Broads. *Aquat. Bot.*, **12**, 277–296.

Wheeler, B.D. & Giller, K.E. (1982c) *Factors and processes in the development of fen vegetation.* Final Report to the Nature Conservancy Council on Contract HF/03/157, Peterborough.

White, W. (1845) *History, Gazetteer and Directory of Norfolk.* Reprinted in 1969 by David & Charles, Newton Abbot.

White, W. (1865) *Eastern England from the Thames to the Humber.* Vol. 1. 304 pp. Chapman & Hall, London.

Wickstead, T. (1845) *Preliminary report upon a supply of water for the town of Great Yarmouth.* 7 pp. Sloman, Yarmouth.

Wildfowl Trust (1963) *Wildfowl in Great Britain* (ed. G.L. Atkinson-Willes). Monographs of the Nature Conservancy No. 3. 368 pp. HMSO, London.

Willis, J.H. (1948) The weather of January, February and March, 1947. *Trans. Norf. Norw. Nat. Soc.*, **16** (4), 271–273.

Willis, P.D. (1980) *A macro-invertebrate survey of some drainage dykes at Strumpshaw Fen, with particular reference to discovering the effect of dyke managment on macro-invertebrate diversity and density.* Unpublished B.Sc. dissertation, University of East Anglia.

Winfield, I.J., Peirson, G., Cryer, M. & Townsend, C.R. (1983) The behavioural basis of prey selection by under-yearling bream (*Abramis brama* L.) and roach (*Rutilus rutilus* L.) *Freshwat. Biol.*, **13**, 139–149.

Winter, W. (1858) *Lycaena dispar* at Ranworth. *Entomologist's Weekly Intelligentsia*, **4**, 131.

Woodward, H.B. (1881) The geology of the country around Norwich. 215 pp. *Mem. Geol. Surv. U.K.*, HMSO, London.

Woodward, H.B. (1883) The scenery of Norfolk. *Trans. Norf. Norw. Nat. Soc.*, **3** (4), 439–466.

Woodward, S. (1834) *An outline of the geology of Norfolk.* Bound MSS on the Castle Museum, Norwich.

Wren, W.J. (1976) *Ports of the eastern counties: the development of harbours on the coast of the eastern counties from Boston in Lincolnshire to Rochford in Essex.* 207 pp. Terence Dalton, Lavenham.

Yarham, D. (1981) ADAS involvement with premature degradation of thatch. *Thatching Newsletter*, November 1981, 5–7, Council for Small Industries in Rural Areas.

Young, A. (1804) *General view of the Agriculture of the County of Norfolk.* 532 pp. Reprinted in 1967 by David & Charles, Newton Abbot.

Young, C.P. (1986) Nitrate in groundwater and the effects of ploughing on the release of nitrate. In: *Effects of land use on fresh water.* (ed. J.F. de L.G. Solbé), pp. 221–237. Water Research Centre. Ellis Horwood, Chichester.

Yousef, U.A. (1974) *Assessing effects on water quality by boating activity.* U.S. Environmental Protection Agency, EPA 670/2–74–072.

Zijlstra, G. & Van Someren, C.L. (1980) Developments in sub-surface drainage techniques. In: *Land Reclamation and Water Management: Developments, Problems and Challenges.* pp. 171–180. Wageningen.

Index

Page numbers set in bold refer to black and white photographs. Colour photographs are indicated by Plate numbers and in bold.